The United States and Japanese counterpart panels on toxic microorganisms were formed late in 1964 under the United States-Japan Cooperative Program in Natural Resources (UJNR). The panels each currently include eight subject specialists drawn from the four U.S. Departments and two Japanese Ministries most concerned with toxic microorganisms. Charged with exploring and developing bilateral cooperation of benefit to both countries, the panels have focused their efforts on botulism and mycotoxins, subjects of much mutual concern and active research.

The UJNR was started by a proposal made during the Third Cabinet-Level Meeting of the Joint United States-Japan Committee on Trade and Economic Affairs in January 1964. In addition to toxic micro-organisms, current subjects included in the program are desalination of sea water, air pollution, water pollution, energy, forage crops, national park management, mycoplasmosis, wind and seismic effects, protein resources, forestry, and several joint panels and committees in marine resources research, development, and utilization.

Accomplishments include: Increased communications and cooperation among technical specialists; exchanges of information, data, and research findings; some 30 study missions involving over 300 scientists and engineers; four meetings of the Conference, a policy coordinative body; two administrative staff meetings; exchanges of equipment, materials, and samples; several major technical conferences; and beneficial effects on international relations. Because of the importance of natural resources in this cooperation, the Secretary of State asked the Secretary of the Interior to serve as U. S. Coordinator of the UJNR.

Honorable Akira Yoshioka, Counsul-General for Japan to Hawaii, shown addressing the Plenary Session, UJNR Conference on Toxic Microorganisms. Asia Room, East-West Center, University of Hawaii, Honolulu, October 7, 1968.

CONTENTS

MYCOTOXINS

I. The Mycotoxin Problem
Chairman: DR. C. R. BENJAMIN

II. Determination of Mycotoxins
Chairman: DR. S. MATSUURA

Proceedings of the
First U.S.-Japan Conference on

Toxic
Micro-Organisms

MYCOTOXINS · BOTULISM

Under the
U.S.-JAPAN COOPERATIVE PROGRAM IN NATURAL RESOURCES (UJNR)

at Honolulu, Hawaii
October 7–10, 1968

Edited by
MENDEL HERZBERG, Ph. D.
Professor of Microbiology
University of Hawaii

Published by the
UJNR Joint Panels on Toxic Micro-organisms
and the
U.S. Department of the Interior

U.S. DEPARTMENT OF THE INTERIOR
WALTER J. HICKEL, *Secretary*

UNITED STATES-JAPAN COOPERATIVE PROGRAM IN NATURAL RESOURCES (UJNR)

JAMES A. SLATER,
U.S. Coordinator and Chairman
of First UJNR Conference on Toxic Micro-organisms

HIROSHI ANDO, *Japanese Coordinator*

UJNR JOINT PANELS ON TOXIC MICRO-ORGANISMS
CHESTER R. BENJAMIN, *U.S. Panel Chairman*
KOMEI MIYAKI, *Japanese Panel Chairman*

CONVENED at the East-West Center of the University of Hawaii, under the Auspices of the United States-Japan Cooperative Program in Natural Resources (UJNR).

SPONSORED by the counterpart United States and Japanese Panels on Toxic Micro-organisms, UJNR.

FUNDED by a contractual arrangement between the School of Public Health, University of Hawaii, and the U.S. Public Health Service, Department of Health, Education, and Welfare (pursuant to Contract No. PH86-68-101). Contributions were made by the U.S. Department of Health, Education, and Welfare, U.S. Public Health Service, Environmental Control Administration and Food and Drug Administration; the U.S. Department of Agriculture, Agricultural Research Service; the U.S. Department of Defense, Department of the Army, Life Sciences Division; the U.S. Department of the Interior, Fish and Wildlife Service; and the U.S. Department of State, Language Services Division.

Library of Congress Card No. 77-604719

Washington, D.C.: 1970

For sale by the Superintendent of Documents, U.S. Government Printing Office
Washington, D.C. 20402 - Price $5.75
Printed at the U.S. Government Printing Office, Washington, D.C.

BOTULISM

FOREWORD

Scientists and experts in botulism and mycotoxins from Japan and the United States gathered in Honolulu, Hawaii, October 7–10, 1968, at the First UJNR Conference on Toxic Micro-Organisms.

Telegrams expressing best wishes for a most productive conference were received from the Secretary of the Interior, the Secretary of Agriculture, and the Special Assistant to the President for Science and Technology in the United States.

The Conference was held to increase our mutual knowledge and awareness of the technology, methodology, and research progress on botulism and mycotoxins. The specific meeting objectives were:

"1. To focus attention on the problems associated with botulism and mycotoxins.
"2. To organize the recent information on the subject and to point out the deficiencies in our knowledge.
"3. To promote expanded international cooperation and research.
"4. To facilitate an active exchange of technical data and methodology.
"5. To disseminate our research findings and to stimulate the interest of other students."

The meeting was held on the campus of the University of Hawaii at its East-West Center which made many of the arrangements and served as Conference Secretariat. The university joined the UJNR panel on toxic micro-organisms in hosting the Conference. Discussions began in the morning of October 7 and ended in the evening of October 10. On October 11 a joint meeting of the Japanese and United States panels was held to evaluate the Conference, to begin preparation of these proceedings, and to continue the important work of the joint panels.

The Conference consisted of two simultaneously conducted sessions on mycotoxins and botulism. Important research results affecting the production of rice, peanuts, cotton, and soybeans; information on serious potential hazards in certain crops and commercial foods; and accomplishments from such work as assay methods and large-scale feed tests on large animals were exchanged in the sessions on mycotoxins. Production of antitoxin in humans, outbreaks of type E food poisoning, and development of a multiuse toxoid were among the highlights discussed during the botulism sessions.

These proceedings contain presentations made during the bilateral meeting, several associated submissions, and a final joint communique. Lists of the UJNR panel members and of the Conference participants are appended.

JAMES A. SLATER,
Chairman,
First UJNR Conference on Toxic Micro-Organisms.

FOREWORD

EDITOR'S PREFACE

In the interest of expeditious publication of these proceedings, the panel and the authors agreed to allow the editor wide latitude in the editing of their papers. Papers were not resubmitted to the authors for their approval of editorial changes; nor were printers galley proofs submitted to the authors for their final approval. The editor appreciates the confidence which the authors reposed in his judgment. As a consequence of this arrangement, the editor takes full responsibility for any errors of commission or omission which he might have made, albeit with the best of intentions. The editor acknowledges, with thanks, the efforts of Drs. G. Sakaguchi and K. Aibara for their aid in interpreting his queries to Japanese authors and for their advice on the intent of some of the wording in Japanese papers. They contributed valuable suggestions and criticism but, of course, they are in no way responsible for any errors which may appear.

OPENING PLENARY

• • •

OPENING REMARKS

by Dr. James A. Slater,
Chairman of the Conference

Lieutenant Governor Gill, Consul General Yoshioka, Vice President Takasaki, Drs. Amano, Benjamin, and Distinguished Delegates: As U.S. Coordinator of the United States-Japan Cooperative Program in Natural Resources (UJNR), I consider it a high honor to serve as Chairman of this United States-Japan Hawaiian Conference on Toxic Micro-Organisms, and to extend a warm welcome to each of you. My lone regret is that my Japanese counterpart Coordinator, Mr. Hiroshi Ando, was not able to greet you here as cochairman.

This meeting is unique and is a highly significant occasion. It is the first large-scale UJNR Conference and the first major conference bringing together Japanese and U.S. Government scientists working on toxic micro-organisms. From it can flow benefits of many kinds to our two great nations and to the rest of the world.

Our overall objective is well summarized in Secretary of the Interior Stewart Udall's remarks on the UJNR made last year at the United States-Japan Cabinet-level meeting on Trade and Economic Affairs. Secretary Udall said that our program's objective is "to learn what we can from each other so that we can leave to future generations a better environment than this generation has inherited. Rather than each going our separate ways, we are sharing the fruits of our joint efforts."

We are now well along in the UJNR. This is the fifth year of operation. We currently have active panels working, on toxic micro-organisms, desalination of sea water, air pollution, water pollution, energy, forage crops, national parks management, mycoplasmosis, wind and seismic effects, protein resources, and undersea technology.

Five new panels in marine resources will be recommended to the UJNR Conference later this month. These recommendations were developed in response to a joint directive from Prime Minister Sato and President Johnson to seek ways of greatly expanding United States-Japanese cooperation into the dynamic fields of marine resources research, development, and utilization. The panels will deal with marine forecasting, aquaculture, minerals, seabed surveying, and fisheries. Several of our newer UJNR panels, such as Wind and Seismic Effects, Protein Resources, and Undersea Technology, are now underway and are realizing the vast opportunities facing them for applying what we learn from each other to the benefit of domestic programs. For similar reasons and rewards, forestry experts in our two countries met last February and recommended the formation of a UJNR panel on forestry involving forest inventory, protection, mechanization, conservation, and reforestation. Several UJNR panels are now at the point of conducting complementary research, of exchanging equipment and research materials, and of holding joint symposia such as this Conference we are convening today.

But we are not meeting here to marvel at past accomplishments. We are here to compare, gather, and exchange information so man might some day be free from many of the harmful organisms that have plagued him through the ages.

We are concerned less about the facts we know than we are about what we do not know. The minimum accomplishment in this week of talks will be a fruitful exchange of information. In the hours and days ahead, current scientific knowledge will be advanced, research programs will be described, inventories of findings and accomplishments will be given, and future research plans will be defined. The maximum immediate outcome of this Conference will result in identifying and solving grave problems of mutual concern.

Beyond all this, it has been said in many ways and at many times that the key to world peace is now in the hands of scientists, administrators, and technicians. Let us use it! Perhaps this might be the greatest result of our efforts, in this world so torn apart by misunderstanding. On a personal basis, I should like to express here the hope that our efforts will be but a fine beginning for this panel and for the UJNR and that similar meetings will follow. I believe that your work will be exemplary of what can be accomplished as men of good will reason together.

In closing, I should like to thank all of you again for your participation in this international Conference. High officials in our Governments look forward to your constructive findings and sound conclusions.

OPENING REMARKS

by HON. THOMAS P. GILL,
Lieutenant Governor of the State of Hawaii

Those of us who have the pleasurable task of greeting groups visiting our State are often meeting people whose work we don't understand at all. I am quite sure, among the many groups I have had the pleasure of meeting, I probably know as little about your field as any. However, I think you may be able to offer me some assurance, from your studies of micro-organisms, that they behave more predictably than voters! This last election week has been a little trying for some of us.

This UJNR Conference is another way of expressing the useful and understandable concept of cooperation between the United States and Japan. This Conference has many other implications. Certainly, the work that has been done by this group in the past has had important effects on some of the more pressing problems we face in both the Western and Eastern worlds. One of the things that has intrigued me is the problem of how we are going to maintain a human environment on this earth that's worth living in. I think that the United States and Japan may be running a form of competition here. Having been in both places briefly, I came away with the impression it is a very close race between Los Angeles and Tokyo to see which of the two cities can pollute the atmosphere more completely. I don't know whether Tokyo is ahead or Los Angeles is ahead, but I wish to caution you that we are in the middle. We hope that you will solve your air pollution problems before they reach us here in the middle of the Pacific!

Just to prove we are part of the modern world, we are busily creating pollution of our own. We have had the opportunity of knowing that there can be such a thing as clean air and clean water. Pollution control is particularly important to us in this State, not only from the scientific aspect of research in the oceans and in the upper atmosphere, but it is also important to us because we like to have the people who visit and live here enjoy themselves. With the new bigger and faster jets, many hundreds of thousands of people from Los Angeles will fly out for a few days or a weekend just for a breath of fresh air. We hope to keep the air breatheable.

We also, of course, are extremely interested in any work you may have done on the uses and the preservation of the ocean environment. At present, I think our interest in this is primarily recreational, though it is becoming scientific to a growing degree. Some day the ocean may become of greater interest to us from a food production standpoint. Most of you are aware that the largest tonnage of fish caught in Hawaiian waters is caught by Japanese fishermen. Later some are sold back to us. We are glad to share this resource and some day, we may even participate more effectively in harvesting it.

One final thought is of particular interest to me personally: This is the greater role which is going to be played, in the world surrounding the Pacific, by the people of Japan. Those who can understand a little bit more than appears on the front page of the newspapers can see clearly that the future of the Pacific world will depend primarily on the degree of cooperation between the United States and Japan. The future of Asia is, in an ever growing degree, being influenced by the Japanese people. Some of our efforts in the Far East have not been marked by a singular success in recent years; I suspect that in part this may be due to our own lack of understanding of the area. In part, our problems arise from the fact that we have not fully recognized the appropriate power structure for the Far East in the last half of the 1960's.

We look forward to seeing more of you. We hope you will enjoy your stay in our small and water-bound State. We hope you will enjoy our climate, our water and our air, and such facilities as we have been able to make available to you here. Finally, we hope that your meetings will be productive and your conclusions helpful.

Aloha and thank you all for coming.

OPENING REMARKS

by HON. AKIRA YOSHIOKA,
Japanese Consul-General, Hawaii

Mr. Chairman, Distinguished Delegates, and Gentlemen: It is indeed a great honor for me to be able to make a few remarks as a sort of representative of the Japanese Government on this opening session of the Symposium on the Toxic Micro-Organisms of the United States-Japan Cooperative Program in Natural Resources hosted by the U.S. Government.

First of all, I would like to say Aloha to all of you, to the American friends who came from the mainland, as well as to the Japanese friends who have just arrived here from my mother country.

As you know by the introduction of my brief background by Dr. James Slater, I have been in the diplomatic service of the Japanese Government for more than 25 years.

As a diplomat, I am supposed to know everything of something, and something of everything. However, in the field of science in which all of you are specialized and on which you are going to exchange views and information, I must confess utter ignorance. The only thing I know is the significance and importance of the cooperation and collaboration you are going to make in the coming session.

It is also quite significant that this meeting is going to take place at the East-West Center in Hawaii which is located in the center of the Pacific Ocean and just half way from either side and where East and West are going to merge. In Hawaii many ethnic peoples are mixed and mingled. Several decades ago Polynesian, Philippine, Chinese, Japanese, and white Americans well might have had their own communities and it was quite a heterogeneous society. But now racial differences are going to be diluted and Hawaii is, slow as its process may be, now going to be a homogeneous community. It may be proved by the fact that the State of Hawaii is the only State in the United States which is neither molested nor disturbed by the black power.

Hawaii is a model State where the international or interethnic cooperation has been accomplished. In my view, the world of 21st century will take after the State of Hawaii, in the sense that various different nations will mix up and live together and eliminate ethnic traits or characteristics, and form a homogeneous conglomeration. That will be made possible by the development of mass communication media using quite sophisticated instruments. That will be brought to reality by the revolution of transportation, which is symbolized in the transition from the transsonic planes to the supersonic jets.

If you set here an example of cooperation in the field of scientific research between our two countries, that will affect and influence the rest of the world.

If this symposium is instrumental in reducing the peril of the harmful micro-organisms, that will go a long way toward the enhancement of the happiness and welfare not only of our two nations, but also the rest of all the nations of the world.

Your achievements will become the common legacy of mankind. Your accomplishments will be inherited by the coming generations of our two countries and their benefits will be shared by the other peoples of the world as well.

In closing my brief remarks, let me express our sincere thanks to Drs. James Slater, Chester Benjamin, and Theodore Bell and other members of the host country for their marvellous preparation in the procedural as well as in logistic matters.

As I am still a newcomer to Honolulu and your hosts are so capable, I do not think there is much I can do to help the participants of both countries. But if there should be anything I can do to make your stay here enjoyable, the door to my office is always open to all of you.

Thank you.

OPENING REMARKS

by RICHARD S. TAKASAKI,
Vice President, University of Hawaii

May I on behalf of Acting President Hiatt and the University of Hawaii welcome the delegates to this Joint United States-Japan Cooperative Program on Development and Utilization of Natural Resources, Conference on Toxic Micro-Organisms.

We are pleased that you have elected to discuss this important subject on this campus.

Since Hawaii has a very strong cultural tie with Japan, the University of Hawaii is especially pleased to have the privilege of hosting this conference at the East-West Center.

Four years ago the University of Hawaii developed its first Academic Development Plan, which serves as the master plan for guiding the growth and development of the university. The Academic Development Plan recognizes the fact that the University of Hawaii cannot become outstanding in all fields of higher education. It, therefore, assessed the university's potential in relation to Hawaii's location, geography, and people. Based on this analysis, the areas of tropical health, tropical medicine, and tropical agriculture, among others, were selected as areas in which Hawaii will seek to develop real strength and leadership. This Conference on the development and utilization of natural resources concerning toxic micro-organisms, therefore, is of vital interest to us.

May I wish you the best of conferences, and I hope that you thoroughly enjoy your stay at the University of Hawaii.

Please call on us if there is anything we can do to improve our services for this Conference. Aloha.

OPENING REMARKS

by DR. KEISHI AMANO,
Acting Chairman, Japan Toxic Micro-Organisms Panel, UJNR

Mr. Chairman, Distinguished Guests, Participants, and Ladies and Gentlemen: It is my great pleasure to be here to convey the opening remarks to you all from Dr. K. Miyaki, chairman of the Japanese panel, on this occasion of the UJNR Symposium and Panel Meeting on Toxic Micro-Organisms. Dr. Miyaki would have wished to extend his sincere appreciation personally and introduce his panel members to all of you from this platform. However, to our great regret, he is not able to do so, owing to his recent physical difficulty.

OPENING ADDRESS

It was 5 years ago that the cooperative activities between the United States and the Japanese Panels on Toxic Micro-Organisms of the United States-Japan Cooperation on Development and Utilization of Natural Resources was actually started. I believe, during these 5 years, we have come to a much better understanding of our subject by the studies on botulism and myco-toxins that have been made in both countries and this, in turn, has greatly encouraged us to work harder to make the greater advances.

This Hawaiian joint conference will be of utmost significance, not only for reviewing our past cooperation, but also for continuing a closer cooperation between both countries. Presentations of the results of the recent investigations on the two subjects and the full discussions by the attendants here at the East-West Center of the University of Hawaii will, no doubt, contribute a great deal to prevention of the public health hazard arising from the two different toxic micro-organisms and to the advancement of human welfare in the world.

We, the Japanese scientists, all greatly appreciate the efforts of Dr. C. R. Benjamin and other U.S. panel members and Dr. T. L. Bell and his associates of the University of Hawaii for having made arrangements for this Conference. Without the efforts made by the U.S. panel members and the supports by the U.S. Government and the University of Hawaii, we would not have been able to hold such a well-organized conference. We, the Japanese panel members, feel we owe a great deal to the U.S. panel in that we have contributed very little to the making of arrangements for the Conference. I hope, however, that you, the U.S. panel members and other attendants from the United States, will realize our sincerity through the fact that the papers which are going to be presented by the Japanese participants cover nearly all the research activities made in recent years on the two subjects, botulism and mycotoxins, in Japan.

I sincerely hope that all the attendants from both countries will try in cooperation to bring the Conference to a great success.

Thank you very much.

KOMEI MIYAKI,
Chairman,
the Japanese Toxic Micro-Organisms Panel.

May I add some few words myself, Mr. Chairman, Ladies and Gentlemen, on behalf of the Japanese panels and participants gathered in this beautiful conference hall this morning. Firstly, I would like to express our hearty thanks to Dr. Slater, chairman of the Conference, who has been carrying out the important administrative work in order to bring our plan into today's reality. Secondly, I know that Dr. C. R. Benjamin, chairman of American panels, and his colleagues, are now bringing to flower their long cherished dream. Thus, I express my appreciation for the tremendous efforts which they have exerted from the very beginning of our joint symposium program; please allow me to say, "congratulations"!

We are also very much grateful to Dr. Bell, program director of the Conference, and his staff, who have undertaken the various troublesome details in order to arrange the meetings in Honolulu. We are particularly obliged to the American panel for the thoughtful preparation of simultaneous translation. You can hardly imagine how helpful it is to our people to discuss the subjects in a relaxed atmosphere. Most words of my acknowledgments have already been covered by the message sent from our chairman. I realize that, but I also believe that it is worthwhile to repeat them again and over again. Thank you.

OPENING REMARKS

by DR. CHESTER R. BENJAMIN
Chairman, U.S. Toxic Micro-Organisms Panel, UJNR

First, I should like to add a few words of welcome to those already said. Our U.S. Toxic Micro-Organisms Panel is very pleased to be one of the sponsors of the Conference. For some time we have been looking forward to the honor of meeting with you here and are glad to see that so many of you could come. We certainly welcome you to this first UJNR Conference on Toxic Micro-Organisms and hope that you will find the next several days a fruitful and scientifically rewarding experience.

We extend a special welcome to the Japanese participants. Some of you, I know, have worked long and hard to achieve the fine representation shown here. This is particularly true of Dr. Komei Miyaki, your Japanese panel chairman, and we sincerely regret that his health does not permit his personal attendance. Those of you who can come, we cordially invite to the mainland following the Conference to visit our various research laboratories. Some of you may already have completed your arrangements for such visits, but, if not, and if our panel can be of any assistance, please do not hesitate to call upon us.

I next wish to say a few words concerning the background of the Conference, particularly from the viewpoint of our U.S. panel. When our counterpart panels were formed in 1964, it was in recognition of the need for increased scientific cooperation between Japan and the United States on the mutual problems of botulism and mycotoxins. Panel membership was drawn from the four departments and two ministries of our Governments that were most concerned with these problems. Each panel currently has eight members, all of whom are Government scientists chosen on the basis of their subject matter specialties. In the case of our U.S. panel, the members are scattered in six States and the District of Columbia.

In the 4 years of our existence, our panels have participated in a variety of cooperative activities designed to increase our mutual knowledge and awareness of the technology, methodology, and research progress on botulism and mycotoxins. With the notable exception of the present conference, however, our cooperation has been largely a panel-to-panel effort. Conceived as a joint-panel endeavor and planned to bring together 60 or more of the top subject specialists of our two countries, this Conference represents our most ambitious undertaking to date. We have high hopes for its success.

Dr. Slater has given you the overall objective of the UJNR program and has nicely summarized why we are here. I need not belabor the latter point, but would like to augment his remarks by identifying the objectives of the Conference as follows:

(1) To focus attention on the problems associated with botulism and mycotoxins.
(2) To organize the recent information on the subject and point out the deficiencies in our knowledge.
(3) To promote expanded international cooperation and research.
(4) To facilitate an active exchange of technical data and methodology.
(5) To disseminate our research findings and stimulate the interest of other students.

We may or may not achieve all of these objectives and the question of whether we do or do not will not be fully answerable for some years to come. We do know that substantial intellectual and material resources have been devoted to these problems by both countries and the time seems appropriate to assess where we stand. As was pointed out by Dr. Slater, the minimum accomplishment here will be a fruitful exchange of information. How much more will be accomplished is less predictable. The organizers of the Conference, the arrangements committee, the interpreters and language services experts, the University of Hawaii, the East-West Center, and the various agencies and organizations that we represent have all participated in bringing us together and in setting the stage for a productive conference. The rest is up to us.

In closing, let me say on behalf of the U.S. panel that we have deeply appreciated the high spirit of cooperation and the ready assistance that we have received from everyone involved in the Conference. With such cooperative attitudes and the great wealth of talent gathered here, I am confident that this Conference can represent a landmark both in our UJNR program and in our understanding of toxic micro-organisms. May it also serve as a guide to further international cooperation efforts in solving the many complex problems of biology, agriculture, and public health.

COMMUNICATIONS TO THE CONFERENCE

October 3, 1968.

On President Johnson's behalf, I extend greetings and best wishes for a most productive UJNR Conference on Toxic Micro-Organisms and Botulism. You are proving by your efforts that men of science—Men of Good Will—from two great nations can find answers to some of the world's most complex problems.

Dr. DONALD F. HORNIG,
*Special Assistant to the President
for Science and Technology.*

October 4, 1968.

Please pass my warm personal greetings to all participants in UJNR Conference on Toxic Micro-Organisms and Botulism and my sincere hope that this historic Conference will demonstrate that great things can be achieved through cooperation. As cabinet coordinator for the UJNR, I look forward to seeing your accomplishments and the visible results of your fine efforts.

STEWART L. UDALL,
Secretary of the Interior.

October 7, 1968.

Please extend my warm greetings to the representatives of the Joint United States-Japan Cooperation on Development and Utilization of Natural Resources. Your Conference on Toxic Micro-Organisms in Honolulu is an event of special significance as the first comprehensive symposium bringing together the principal authorities of the United States and Japan in this field. Protection of food and feed supplies from toxic contamination is of vital importance. I am sure the various departments and ministries of our two governments cooperating in the meeting will find the extensive exchange of ideas and information most profitable. We have already found many mutual benefits from working together in UJNR. Best wishes for a successful Conference and continuing cooperative actions.

ORVILLE L. FREEMAN,
Secretary of Agriculture.

MYCOTOXINS

• • •

PERSPECTIVES ON THE MYCOTOXIN PROBLEMS IN JAPAN

by KOMEI MIYAKI*
National Institute of Health, Department
of Food Research, Tokyo, Japan

In order to discuss the mycotoxin problems encountered in Japan, it is a prerequisite to understand the climate in Japan and the eating habits of the Japanese people which are very different from those of Western people. For instance, the average yearly temperature in the Tokyo area is 15.5° C. and the average humidity is 71 percent. This climate represents the "high temperature and high humidity" type, which favors the growth of fungi.

The eating habits of the Japanese people are characterized by consumption of rice as the major food. According to the statistics, the average yearly consumption of rice is 130 kg. per capita, in other words, 330 g. per day per capita as polished rice. Starchy food constitutes as high as 65 percent of the total food consumption by the Japanese people. This proportion is approximately 1.5 times higher than the corresponding rate of 40 percent in the Western rations. Even if the living standards of Japanese become much higher in future, people would still consume starchy food as 60 percent of the total diet. This implies that the Japanese people will continue to consume rice in such an amount that would provide about 50 percent of the total calories required.

Another characteristic of the Japanese eating habit is the consumption of fermented foods, such as fermented soybean protein products and, for some people, rice liquor. Our people cannot do without such foodstuffs. Thus, the Japanese people have traditionally been making good use of fungi for more than 1,000 years. On the other hand, how much progress has been made in research on fungi which may be hazardous to human health?

In reviewing the history of mycotoxin research one finds pioneering work was initiated in U.S.S.R. in response to human and animal cases of poisoning, alimentary toxic aloikia (ATA) (1) due to *Fusarium*, and in the United States in animal cases of poisoning due to mold-contaminated feed (2). In Japan, research on mycotoxin was stimulated by the assumption made by Sakaki (3) in 1891 that a notorious human disease, beriberi, must have been caused by moldy rice. I. Miyaki (4) started to work on the molds contaminating rice in 1910. He isolated *Penicillium toxicarium, id est Penicillium citreo-viride*, from stored rice and demonstrated by animal feeding tests that the rice artificially infected with the mold was toxic (5, 6, 7). Hirata (8) and Sakabe et al. (9) demonstrated in 1947 that a toxic metabolite produced by *Penicillium citreo-viride* exhibited neurotoxicity (10).

Tsunoda, a student of I. Miyake, demonstrated that the mice fed on rice experimentally infected with *P. islandicum* developed cirrhosis (11). Further studies were performed on the toxicity of *P. islandicum* and a series of reports were published by Kobayashi et al. (12), M. Miyake et al. (13), Saito (14), Enomoto (15), and Ishiko (16).

In the meantime, as chemical studies on the toxic metabolites were advanced, the chemical structures of luteoskyrin and rubroskyrin were determined by Shibata et al. (17, 18) and structure of islanditoxin was determined by Marumo et al. (19). The toxicities of luteoskyrin and islanditoxin were studied in detail by Uraguchi et al. (20), and it is particularly noteworthy that the carcinogenicity of islanditoxin was proved. Biochemical studies on luteoskyrin are being performed by Morooka et al. (21) and Ueno et al. (22). Recently, Umeda et al. (23) examined the toxic effects of luteoskyrin on the tissue culture of HeLa cells.

An event involving so-called "yellowed rice" occurred in 1953 with the rice imported from Southeast Asia. Although no human cases of poisoning were recorded, such "yellowed rice" was found to be highly contaminated with *P. islandicum*, *P. citreo-viride*, or *P. citrinum* producing a nephrotoxic substance, citrinin (10). Later, scientists in the field of mycotoxin research recommended to the Japanese Government that administrative action should be taken to protect the people against any possible hazards from such "yellowed rice". Consequently the Ministry of Health and Welfare and the Ministry of Agriculture and Forestry dispatched examiners to those countries exporting rice to Japan and, at the same time, started to examine imported rice. The recent advancement in the study of mycotoxin in Japan has been largely stimulated by that event.

In 1953, Hori et al. (24) and Yamamoto (25,) of the Kobe City Institute of Health, investigated an outbreak of poisoning among dairy cows involving

---

*Read by H. Kurata.

more than 100 deaths and demonstrated by experiments on calves that the causative agent was patulin produced by *P. urticae* in the feed (*26*).

In 1955, Iizuka et al. (*27*) found maltorizine, a toxic metabolite produced by *Aspergillus oryzae* var. *microsporus*, to be the cause of the poisoning among dairy cows and also determined its chemical structure. Pathological studies on the poisoned cases were performed by Okubo et al. (*28*). It should be emphasized that *A. oryzae*, a species closely resembling *A. flavus*, had been found to produce this toxic substance before aflatoxin was found in 1960.

Other studies were made on food poisoning due to consumption of noodles and dumplings on which *Fusarium graminearum* had grown. This mold has long been known in Japan as "red mold" of wheat. In 1948, Hirayama et al. (*29*) reported an outbreak of "red mold" poisoning. This disease was spontaneous and acute with such symptoms as fever, chill and vomiting. Takeda et al. (*30*) carried out etiological studies on another outbreak of fusarium-poisoning which occurred in 1951 to 1953 in Hokkaido, the northern-most island of Japan. Tsunoda et al. (*31*) performed similar studies. Both groups failed to isolate the causative substance. In 1958, Uraguchi et al. (*32*) reported pharmacological studies made with *F. roseum*, another species isolated from wheat and barley scab. Attempts were made by Ikeda et al. (*33*) to demonstrate the presence of the toxic substance produced by the strains of *F. graminearum* isolated in 1963 by Kurata et al. (*34*) from specimens of wheat and barley scab prevailing all over Japan. No toxic substance was found in these studies.

Incidentally, Tsunoda (*35*) isolated *Fusarium nivale* in addition to *F. graminearum* from the mold-infested feed that had caused poisoning among cattle. Experimental animals administered a feed artificially inoculated with *F. nivale* showed a very high mortality rate. It appears doubtful that *F. graminearum*, the dominant species commonly isolated from wheat and barley scab, is toxic to animals. Chemical studies on the toxic metabolite of *F. nivale* have been conducted by Tatsuno in cooperation with Morooka, in conjunction with the pathological studies performed by Okubo et al. (*36.*) Biochemical studies on the toxic metabolite have also been performed by Ueno et al. (*57*). The results of these studies will be presented in this Conference. I am sure that a fruitful discussion will take place in this meeting on the species of the causative fungus of the so-called red-mold poisoning.

Extensive mycological studies on the distribution of toxic fungi, especially on stored cereals and imported rice, have been made in Japan by Tsunoda (*37, 38*), Tsuruta (*39*), Iizuka (*40*), and Udagawa (*41*). A mycological study on powdered milk as well as cereal products was performed by Inagaki (*42*). Recently, Kurata et al. (*43*) performed mycological and toxicological studies on various foodstuffs.

Studies on aflatoxin started in Japan in 1964, just after the International Symposium on Oilseed Protein Food held at Mt. Fuji Hotel. At that symposium, the importance of the future studies on aflatoxin was emphasized by many papers concerning mycological, chemical, and biological problems involved and on the practical treatment of agricultural commodities. Aibara and Miyaki (*44*) of the National Institute of Health, realizing the importance of the matter, immediately started to determine the aflatoxin productivity of about 200 strains of industrial koji mold including *A. oryzae*, *A. flavus* and *A. tamarii*. Ten strains of dairy molds were also examined. The standard aflatoxin producing strain, *A. flavus* ATCC 15517, was sent from Dr. G. N. Wogan of the Massachusetts Institute of Technology, to be used as a reference strain in Japan. No aflatoxin-producing strain was found by thin-layer chromatography, ultraviolet spectrophotometry, fluorescent spectrophotometry and yolk-sac inoculation test (*45*).

Matsuura et al. (*46*), of the research group of the Food Research Institute, examined 108 samples of "miso", 28 samples of "rice koji" and 238 strains of "koji mold" for aflatoxin and aflatoxin productivity. Murakami et al (*47*), of the Research Institute of Brewing, examined samples of "koji mold" used in the production of Japanese "sake" wine. These results did not demonstrate that any mold of the *Aspergillus* group now being used for fermentation in brewery industries in Japan produces aflatoxin. In 1965 Kurata et al. (*48*) found, for the first time in Japan, two strains of *A. flavus* capable of producing aflatoxin from wheat flour and bean powder on market. Murakami et al. (*49*) have performed comparative taxonomic studies on aflatoxin-producing *Aspergillus* and the domestic strains of the *A. flavus* group. Manabe et al. (*50*) separated aflatoxins into B_1, B_2, G_1 and G_2 by column chromatography. Uritani et al. (*51*) have been studying the effect of aflatoxin on the regeneration of the plant tissues with interesting results. Yokotsuka et al. (*52*) and Sasaki et al. (*53*) have engaged in studies on fluorescent and nonfluorescent pyrazine compounds produced by koji mold. Terao et al. (*54*) are trying to elucidate the mode of action of aflatoxin on the chicken embryonic liver cells. The research group of the National Institute of Health have investigated various chemical and biological methods for detecting aflatoxin and also the effects of irradiation with γ-ray and ultraviolet upon aflatoxin (*55*). An assay method for aflatoxin using the tissue culture of the synchronized kidney cells has recently been developed (*56*).

Table 1.—Institutions and research areas of mycotoxin studies in Japan

Institution	Mycology	Chemistry and biochemistry	Toxicology, pharmacology, and pathology	Standard assay methods
National institutions:				
National Institute of Health		X	X	X
National Institute of Hygienic Sciences	X	X	X	X
Food Research Institute	X	X	X	X
Research Institute of Brewing	X			
Research Institute of Sciences		X		
Universities:				
University of Tokyo:				
Faculty of Medicine			X	
Institute of Medical Science			X	
University of Chiba:				
Faculty of Pharmacology		X		
Institute of Food Microbiology		X		
Science University: Faculty of Pharmacology		X	X	
University of Nagoya: Faculty of Agricultural Chemistry		X	X	
Tokyo Agricultural College			X	
Nippon Veterinary and Zootechnical College			X	
Private laboratory: Kikkoman Central Research Institute	X	X	X	

The Japanese institutions where mycotoxin studies are performed and the research areas in which they are engaged are summarized in table 1.

Future mycotoxicological studies in Japan should be directed at agricultural commodities of both imported and domestic origin, at agricultural products for both human and auimal consumption, and at food products including fermented foods related to the eating habits of the Japanese people. The projects of immediate importance are:

(1) To study the ecology of the mycotoxin-producing fungi affecting field crops and contaminating the agricultural commodities.

(2) To establish precise and rapid chemical assay methods for detection of mycotoxins in foods and feeds.

(3) To establish practical methods for bioassay of mycotoxins produced by fungi in foods and feeds.

(4) To study the possible hazardous effects on human health of the animal products from the livestock raised on mycotoxic feeds.

(5) To study the epidemiology of such diseases as cancer of the alimentary tract, hypertension, etc., prevailing among the inhabitants of certain areas in Japan, to find out whether or not mycotoxin is involved in the cause of such diseases.

(6) To develop practical methods to detoxify mycotoxins in foods and feeds on a large scale.

The mycotoxin studies in Japan, especially those performed in the national institutions, have come into a new phase. This phase began in 1965 when the panels on toxic micro-organisms were included in the United States-Japan Cooperation on the Development and Utilization of Natural Resources (UJNR). The studies of aflatoxin and many other mycotoxins in Japan were greatly stimulated by this cooperative program.

It became possible for the scientists in both countries to exchange directly the most up-to-date information on mycotoxins which resulted in a great contribution to the development of the studies in Japan. This contribution will be enhanced by this Hawaiian Conference. In order to solve the problems described above, cooperative work among scientists in different fields must be continued in Japan. When we look back someday in the future, I believe we will find that a great contribution was rendered by this Hawaiian Conference to the progress of the studies in Japan and to the cooperative efforts between the United States and Japan.

References

(1) JOFFE, A. Z. 1960. Toxicity and antibiotic properties of some *Fusaria*. Bull. Res. Counc. of Israel *8D*: 81–95.

(2) FORGACS, J., and W. T. CARLL. 1962. Mycotoxicoses. Adv. Vet. Sci. 7: 273–387.

(3) SAKAKI, J. 1891. Toxicological studies on moldy rice. Report 1. J. Tokyo Medical Soc. 5: 1097.

(4) MIYAKE, I., H. NAITO, and H. TSUNODA. 1940. Studies on the production of toxin in the saprophyte-growing rice grains under storage. Beikoku Riyo Kenkyujo Hokoku. 1: 1–29.

(5) MIYAKE, I. 1960. Studien uber die Pilze der Reispflanze in Japan. J. Coll. Agri. Tokyo *11*: 237–276.

(6) MIYAKE, I. 1947. *Penicillium toxicarium* growing on the yellow mouldy rice. Niishin Igaku *34:* 161.

(7) TSUNODA, H., and Y. HARUKI. 1949. On the cultivation of *Penicillium toxicarium* Miyake and its toxin-production. Rept. Food Res. Inst., *2:* 157–164.

(8) HIRATA, Y. 1947. On the products of mould. Substances from mould rice. (pt. 3.), Structure and properties I., J. Chem. Soc. Japan, *68:* 104–105.; Substances from mould rice. (pt. 4), Structure and properties II. J. Chem. Soc. Japan *68:* 105–106.

(9) SAKABE, N., T. GOTO, and Y. HIRATA. 1964. The structure of citreoviridin, a toxic compound produced by *P. citreo-viride* molded on rice. Tetrahedron Letter *27:* 1825–1830.

(10) SAKAI, F. 1955. Experiment studies on rice yellowsis caused by *Penicillium citrinum* Thom and toxicity especially kidney-damaging effect of citrinin pigment produced by the fungus. Folia Pharmacol. Japan. 431–442.

(11) TSUNODA, H. 1951. Studies on the toxicity of the substance produced on the cereals by a *Penicillium* sp. under the storage. Japan. J. Nutrition *9:* 1–6.

(12) KOBAYASHI, Y., K. URAGUCHI, R. SAKAI, T. TATSUNO, M. TSUKIOKA, Y. SAKAI, T. SATO, M. MIYAKE, M. SAITO, M. ENOMOTO, T. SHIKATA, and T. ISHIKO. 1959. Toxicological studies on the yellowed rice by *P. islandicum* Sopp. III. Experimental verification of primary hepatic carcinoma of rats by long-term feeding with the fungus-growing rice. Proc. Japan Acad. *35:* 501–506.

(13) MIYAKE, M., M. SAITO, M. ENOMOTO, T. SHIKATA, T. ISHIKO, K. URAGUCHI, F. SAKAI, T. TATSUNO, M. TSUKIOKA, and Y. NOGUCHI. 1959. Development of primary hepatic carcinoma in rats by long-term feeding with the yellowed rice by *P. islandicum* Sopp.—with study on influence of fungus-growing rice on DAB carcinogenesis in rats. Gann *50:* 117–118.

(14) SAITO, M. 1959. Liver cirrhosis induced by metabolites of *Penicillium islandicum* Sopp. Acta Path. Japan. *9:* 785–790.

(15) ENOMOTO, M. 1959. Histopathological studies on adenomatous nodules of liver induced in mice by *Penicillium islandicum* Sopp. Acta Path. Japan. *9:* 189–215.

(16) ISHIKO, T. 1959. Histopathological studies on the injuries of various organs of mice and rats fed with "yellowed rice" by *Penicillium islandicum* Sopp. Especially on the pathological findings of the other organs associated with the liver injuries. Trans. Soc. Path. Japan. *48:* 867–892.

(17) SHIBATA, S., and I. KITAGAWA. 1956. Metabolic products of fungi. X. The structure of Rubroskyrin and its relation to the structure of Luteoskyrin. Pharm. Bull. Tokyo *4:* 309–313.

(18) SHIBATA, S., and I. KITAGAWA. 1960. Metabolic products of fungi. XVI. The structures of Rubroskyrin and Leuteoskyrin. Pharm. Bull. Tokyo *8:* 884–888.

(19) MARUMO, S. 1959. Islanditoxin, a toxic metabolite produced by *Penicillium islandicum* Sopp. Pt. III., Bull. Agri. Chem. Soc. Japan *23:* 428–431.

(20) URAGUCHI, K., F. SAKAI, M. TSUKIOKA, Y. NOGUCHI, T. TATSUNO, M. SAITO, M. ENOMOTO, T. ISHIKO, T. SHIKATA, and M. MIYAKE. 1961. Acute and chronic toxicity in mice and rats of the fungus mat of *Penicillium islandicum* Sopp added to the diet. Japan. J. Exp. Med. *31:* 435–461.

(21) MOROOKA, N., N. NAKANO, and N. UCHIDA. 1966. Biochemical and histopathological studies on the tumor-developing livers of mice fed on the diets containing luteoskyrin. Japan. J. Med. Sci. Biol. *19:* 293–303.

(22) UENO, Y., I. UENO, T. TATSUNO, and K. URAGUCHI. 1964. Les Effect de la Luteoskyrine, Substance toxicque du *Penicillium islandicum* Sopp, sur le Gonflemnet des Mitochondries. Japan. J. Exp. Med. *34:* 197–209

(23) UMEDA, M. 1964. Cytotoxic effects of the mycotoxins of *Penicillium islandicum* Sopp, Luteoskyrin and chlorine-containing peptide on Chang's liver cells and Hela cells. Acta Path. Japan. *14*(3): 373–394.

(24) HORI, M., and T. YAMAMOTO. 1953. Studies on the chemical constituents of poisonous substances from *Penicillium* (Hori-Yamamoto Strain). I. Morphology and characters of the *Penicillium* separated. J. Pharmacol. Soc. Japan *73:* 1097–1101.

(25) YAMAMOTO, T. 1954. Studies on the poison-producing mold isolated from dry malt. IV. On the toxicity. J. Pharmacol. Soc. Japan *74:* 810–812.

(26) UKAI, T., Y. YAMAMOTO, and T. YAMAMOTO. 1954. Studies on the poisonous substance from a strain of *Penicillium* (Hori-Yamamoto strain). II. Culture method of Hori-Yamamoto strain and chemical structure of its poisonous substance. J. Pharmacol. Soc. Japan *74:* 450–454.

(27) IIZUKA, H, and M. IIDA. 1962. Maltoryzine, a new metabolite produced by a strain of *Aspergillus oryzae* var. *microsporus* isolated from the poisonous malt sprout. Nature *196:* 681–682.

(28) OKUBO, Y., N. URAKAMI, T. HAYAMA, Y. SETO, T. MIURA, Y. KANO, S. MOTOYOSHI, S. YAMAMOTO, K. ISHIDA, H. IIZUKA, and M. IIDA. 1955. Note on some cases of malt rootlet poisoning in dairy cattle. Japan J. Vet. Sci. *17:* 144–151.

(29) HIRAYAMA, S., and M. YAMAMOTO. 1950. Biological studies on the poisonous wheat flour. (2). Eisei Shikenjo Hokoku *67:* 117–121.

(30) TAKEDA, S., K. OGASAWARA, H. OHARA, and T. ONISHI. 1953. Studies on the food poisoning caused by the *Fusarium* scab disease of wheat and barley. (Pt. 4.) Animal test for toxic substances obtained from deteriorated wheat grain. Rep. Hokkaido Inst. Public Health *4:* 22–28.

(31) TSUNODA, H., O. TSURUTA, and S. MATSUNAMI. 1958. Researches on the micro-organisms which deteriorate the stored cereals. XVI. Studies on rice parasitic molds, *Gibberella* and *Fusarium*. Results on animal test. Rep. Food Res. Inst. *13:* 26-28.

(32) URAGUCHI, K., Y. SAKAI, T. TATSUNO, H. WAKAMATSU. 1958. Toxicological approach to metabolites of *Fusarium roseum* and other "Red" molds growing on rice, wheat and other cereal grains (1). Folia Pharmacol. Japon. *54:* 127.

(33) IKEDA, Y., Y. OMORI, T. FURUYA, and M. ICHINOE. 1964. Experimental studies on some causal *Fusarium* for the wheat and barley scab. IV. Feeding test in mice. Eisei Shikenjo Hokoku *82:* 130–132.

(34) KURATA, H., S. UDAGAWA, F. SAKABE. 1964. Experimental studies on some causal *Fusarium* of the wheat and barley scab. I–III. Eisei Shikenjo Hokoku *82:* 123–130.

(35) TSUNODA, H., N. TOYAZAKI, N. MOROOKA, N. NAKANO, H. YOSHIYAMA, K. OKUBO, and M. ISODA. 1968. Researches on the micro-organisms which deteriorate the stored cereals and grains. (Pt. 34.) Detection of injurious strains and properties of their toxic substance of scab *Fusarium* blight grown on the wheat. Rep. Food Res. Inst. *23:* 89–116.

(36) OKUBO, K., and M. ISODA. 1967. Studies on the essential nature of intoxication by the products of *Fusarium nivale*. 1. Histopathological examination of experimental acute intoxication by crude products of *Fusarium nivale*. Bull. Nippon Vet. and Zootech. College *16*: 22–42.

(37) TSUNODA, H., O. TSURUTA, M. TAKAHASHI. 1959. Researches for the micro-organisms which deteriorate the stored cereals. XIX. Parasites of imported rice. (3). Rep. Food Res. Inst. *13*: 38–42.

(38) TSUNODA, H. 1961. Researches for the micro-organisms which deteriorate the stored cereals. XXVI. Classification of genus *Penicillium* which is parasitic on the rice. Rep. Food Res. Inst. *15*: 98–110.

(39) TSURUTA, O. 1962. A study on the parasitism and control of micro-organisms affecting stored rice with specific reference to family Aspergillaceae. J. Medical Soc. Toho Univ. *9*: 1–16.

(40) IIZUKA, H. 1958. Studies on the micro-organisms found in Thai and Buruma rice. Pt. II. On the microflora of Burma rice. J. Gen. Appl. Microbiol. *4*: 108–119.

(41) UDAGAWA, S. 1959. Taxonomic studies of fungi on stored rice grains. III. *Penicillium* group (*Penicillium* and related genera). J. Agr. Sci. Tokyo *5*: 5–21.

(42) INAGAKI, N. 1960. Study on fungi in foodstuff from standpoint of food sanitation. Japan. J. Pub. Health *12*: 1123–1136.

(43) KURATA, H., S. UDAGAWA, M. ICHINOE, Y. KAWASAKI, M. TAKADA, M. TAZAWA, A. KOIZUMI, and H. TANABE. 1968. Studies on the population of toxigenic fungi in foodstuffs. III. Mycoflora of milled rice harvested in 1965. J. Food Hygienic Soc. Japan *9*(1): 23–28.

(44) AIBARA, K. and K. MIYAKI. 1965. Aflatoxin, Shokuhin Esisei Kenkyu *15*: 19–25.

(45) AIBARA. K., and K. MIYAKI. 1966. Paper presented at the Annual meeting of the Agricultural Chemical Society of Japan, Tokyo. (April.)

(46) MATSUURA, S., and M. MANABE. 1967. Paper presented at the Annual meeting of the Agricultural Chemical Society of Japan, Tokyo. (April.)

(47) MURAKAMI, H., TAKASE, S., and K. KUWABARA. 1968. Production of fluorescent substances in rice Koji and their identification by absorption spectra. J. Gen. Appl. Microbiol. *14*: 97–110.

(48) KURATA, H., H. TANABE, K. KANOTA, S. UDAGAWA, and M. ICHINOE. 1968. Studies on the population of toxigenic fungi in foodstuffs. IV. Aflatoxin producing fungi isolated from foodstuffs in Japan. J. Food Hyg. Soc. Japan *9*: 29–34.

(49) MURAKAMI, H., K. OUWAKI, and S. TAKASE. 1966. An aflatoxin strain, ATCC–15517. J. Gen. Appl. Microbiol. *12*: 195–206.

(50) MANABE, M., S. MATSUURA, and M. NAKANO. 1967. Isolation and quantitative analysis for aflatoxins B_1, B_2, G_1, G_2 by thin-layer and liquid chromatographies. J. Agr. Chem. Soc. Japan *41*: 592–598.

(51) URITANI, I., T. ASAHI, R. MAJIMA, and Z. MORI. These proceedings.

(52) YOKOTSUKA, T., M. SASAKI, Y. ASAO, and A. NOBUHARA. 1966. Production of fluorescent compounds other than aflatoxins by Japanese industrial molds. Biochemistry of some foodborne microbial toxins. M.I.T. press. 131–152.

(53) SASAKI, M., Y. ASAO, and T. YOKOTSUKA. 1968. Studies on the compound produced by molds (V). Isolation of nonfluorescent pyradine compounds. Pt. 2. J. Agri. Chem. Soc. Japan *42*: 351–355.

(54) TERAO, K., and K. MIYAKI. 1967. The effect of aflatoxin on chick-embryo liver cells. Expt. Cell Research *48*: 151–155.

(55) MIYAKI, K., K. AIBARA, and T. MIURA. 1967. Resistance of aflatoxin to chemical and biological changes by gamma-irradiation. "Microbiological problems in food preservation by irradiation," International Atomic Energy Agency, pp. 57–64.

(56) AIBARA, K., and Y. YOSHIKURA. 1968. Synchronized culture as an assay system for aflatoxin. Biochim. Biophys. Acta. In press.

(57) UENO, Y., and K. FUKUSHIMA. 1968. Inhibition of protein and DNA syntheses in Ehrlich ascites tumour by nivalenol, a toxic principle of *Fusarium nivale*-growing rice Experientia *24*: 1032–1033.

PERSPECTIVES ON THE MYCOTOXIN PROBLEM IN THE UNITED STATES

by George W. Irving, Jr.
Administrator, Agricultural Research Service,
U.S. Department of Agriculture, Washington, D.C. 20250

It is a pleasure to be with you today to discuss a problem that is truly international in character. Because the molds that produce mycotoxins have been found on crops in many parts of the world, the research being conducted with these organisms cannot be circumscribed by geography.

I need not belabor the point that toxin-producing molds are extremely hardy. Most of them have existed for thousands of years. And certain toxic symptoms noted in both man and animals have long been known to be caused by molds. Until the extensive poultry losses in England in 1960, however, mycotoxicosis was in fact a neglected disease. Only limited research effort was devoted to understanding mycotoxins or to developing control methods.

After the English outbreak was traced to imported peanut meal that had become contaminated with a very common mold, *Aspergillus flavus*, additional resources were directed to this field of work. Discovery of aflatoxin and the subsequent identification of a family of aflatoxins, toxic compounds produced by this mold, stimulated interest, concern, and research effort in the scientific community.

In the United States, we were concerned when we detected aflatoxin in two of our oilseed crops, peanuts and cottonseed. The existence of this problem in our country was first indicated by two research studies reported in 1963. In April of that year, a research group in California reported that a high incidence of liver cancers had occurred in hatchery rainbow trout. A dry ration containing an oilseed meal was the prime suspect. The other study was conducted by Professor Salmon of Auburn University and involved feeding a domestic peanut meal, as a major source of protein, to rats. The rats developed a high incidence of liver cancers.

With these indications that we could have a potentially serious domestic problem caused by toxic molds, the U.S. Department of Agriculture began to expand the scope of its mycotoxin studies. Other agencies investigating the problem are the Food and Drug Administration, the National Institutes of Health, the National Science Foundation, and many of our State agricultural experiment stations. USDA has established and maintained effective liaison with all of these agencies, as well as with industry groups.

By starting early and moving ahead aggressively with this work, USDA's Agricultural Research Service has become the leader in mycotoxin research in the United States. Our major efforts are directed toward aflatoxin production, detection, and decontamination; the incidence of aflatoxin in various crops; how aflatoxin affects animals; and what other mycotoxins are capable of causing similar problems.

Fortunately, mycotoxin problems in the United States are still more potential than actual. We have experienced no large-scale difficulties. And although there is as yet very little factual information concerning possible hazards to human health, we feel that the precautions we are taking assure the absence of any problems in this respect with our human food supply.

Effects of Mycotoxins

We have been able to observe the effects of aflatoxin on animals and plants. Its toxicity has been demonstrated in rainbow trout, rats, brine shrimp, insects, protozoa, chickens, turkeys, ducks, pheasants, goats, swine, guinea pigs, and cattle. It inhibits some bacteria, and it can cause chlorophyll deficiency and inhibit seed germination in green plants.

Mycotoxins, then, could cause livestock losses, but this may not be the biggest problem they pose. There is some evidence that long term consumption of aflatoxin-contaminated feeds can reduce animal growth if the contamination is present at sufficiently high levels. This could have an economic impact on worldwide meat production.

In all of these considerations, there is a very large if. Mycotoxins could become a problem if we do not develop a thorough understanding of them and formulate effective ways for dealing with them. I fully anticipate that a successful cooperative research program, combined with continued efficiency and good practices on the part of our farmers and food processors, will keep mycotoxins out of our food and feed marketing channels. This is more than just wishful thinking on my part. Our domestic peanut industry, for example, has instituted voluntary rules and procedures that assure safe and wholesome peanuts for food uses.

Cooperative Regulation of Peanut Marketing

We know that the incidence of aflatoxin contamination in our domestic peanut crop can vary from season to season as a result of temperature and moisture conditions occurring at harvest. A survey, conducted in Georgia during the 1966 harvesting season, showed that approximately 5 percent of over 2,000 samples of farmers' stock peanuts contained aflatoxin. Within the 5 percent, a relatively few kernels can be the principal source of contamination.

Assuming that we can project this on a national scale, only a small portion of the total crop could be implicated. When contamination is found in any peanuts destined for market, the entire lot is remilled. Then, if the contaminated nuts are not removed, or if the lot continues to show a positive reading, the peanuts are diverted into other channels. This is accomplished through a cooperative program involving USDA, the Food and Drug Administration, and the peanut industry itself.

This program has produced benefits for everyone concerned. Program costs to the Government have been reduced. Although the cost of raw peanuts to manufacturers is up slightly, quality is higher. The industry growth rate is up; lower quality peanuts are being diverted from food trade channels; and the quality and safety of peanut products reaching consumers is no doubt at its highest level.

Crops Affected

Based on the research reported in 1963, we knew that aflatoxin could occur naturally in our domestic peanuts. We did not know whether or not toxic strains of the *Aspergillus flavus* mold occurred in such other domestic agricultural commodities as cottonseed, soybeans, wheat, corn, sorghum, and oats. Later surveys that we made of these crops indicate that such contamination is possible.

Because of the extensive trade in soybeans between Japan and the United States, you will be interested in the information we are developing on soybeans. Laboratory samples of all the commodities I mentioned, including soybeans, were inoculated with *Aspergillus flavus*. The mold grew luxuriantly on each commodity and produced some aflatoxin on each. It did not, however, grow as well on soybean samples as it did on samples of the other commodities.

As far as cotton is concerned, we have encountered the *A. flavus* mold in seed harvested at a few field locations throughout the U.S. Cotton Belt. But the percentages of infected seeds and the levels of aflatoxin have been in the main very low; and just as we have noted with peanuts, aflatoxin contamination in cotton appears to be concentrated in a very few seeds. Nothing in the data we have obtained so far indicated a major problem in more than perhaps a very few restricted areas.

Crops other than peanuts and cotton appear to be affected to lesser degrees. Sampling programs recently established by the Food and Drug Administration should help us to determine the extent of this contamination. Several different foods and food products are being checked.

When available, quantitative and statistical evaluations should also be helpful to us in projecting our research needs.

Cost of Research

In fiscal year 1968, USDA had about $1,800,000 available for research on deleterious molds and their control. The 1968 expenditures for the toxic mold research program of the State agricultural experiment stations were over $600,000. Research on mycotoxins is also supported by grants from the National Science Foundation, National Institutes of Health, and other granting agencies.

Within USDA, these funds support research in six general problem areas. Several of our people will discuss aspects of our work later in these proceedings. At this point, I would like to review each problem area in more general terms.

Problem Area No. 1

The first problem area involves investigating the entire range of conditions under which aflatoxin is produced. This is really basic to our entire effort, because aflatoxin is not produced until the environmental conditions are favorable for growth and development of the fungus.

Moisture and temperature are the chief limiting factors that determine mold growth. If grain is stored in closed containers on a hot, humid day, and later subjected to a drop in temperature, mold can grow from moisture condensing on the grain. As for temperature, we have determined that aflatoxin forms readily at about 28° C. Yields of different aflatoxins, however, vary with differences in temperature and moisture. Aeration is another important influence, since all aflatoxin-producing fungi require air for growth. Condition of the crop itself likewise plays a role. For example, when the seedcoat is broken because of insect damage, mechanical breakage during harvesting, or excessive heating in drying, the seed is much more vulnerable to mold invasion.

Apparently, most contamination problems occur during post-harvest handling and treatment. Once we determine the precise causative factors under field conditions, our scientists can begin developing new or modified technology to eliminate the difficulties. Our marketing specialists are also working on ways to prevent molds from developing in stored products.

Problem Area No. 2

The second set of problems with which we are working is in the development of rapid and accurate methods to detect aflatoxin contamination.

Present detection systems are effective, but in many cases they are complicated and time-consuming. We are still modifying and refining these systems, as well as developing better ones. One of the newest was developed by our market research specialists and is a direct and rapid visual technique for identifying molds in lots of farmers' stock peanuts at the point of first inspection. In early tests, it was found that even untrained or inexperienced persons could, after a brief training period, identify *A. flavus* in peanuts correctly 87 percent of the time. A manual for translating these test results into practical grading instructions is being prepared.

Another detection method, developed by one of our biochemists, permits checking a peanut sample in about 15 minutes at the marketing site. With this millicolumn chromatographic procedure, it is possible to determine both the presence and the amount of aflatoxin in a sample.

Recent modifications in an aqueous acetone procedure have improved both the accuracy and precision of aflatoxin estimates in cottonseed. Developing improved biological assay techniques is also included in our detection work.

Problem Area No. 3

When contamination is detected, the next step is to develop methods for removing it.

If the problem is present in a relatively small number of seeds, we have an excellent opportunity for mechanical removal. In peanuts, for example, a small number of contaminated kernels may make objective representative sampling difficult, but it makes economical culling feasible. This physical separation could include hand-picking, photoelectric sorting, and use of mechanical sorters.

In case the contamination cannot be removed mechanically, it may be possible to extract it with solvents during processing. We have developed such a method for removing aflatoxin from ground peanuts or peanut meal. This extraction system, which involved using acetone, hexane, and water, was originally developed to remove gossypol and oil from cottonseed meals. We later found that it also works very effectively with peanuts.

Our scientists are exploring still other possibilities. These include degrading, destroying, or otherwise inactivating the aflatoxins by heat, chemical, or biological means.

Problem Area No. 4

We hope to determine the scale on which decontamination is necessary through our work in this area, surveying the incidence of aflatoxin in various crops.

Our survey of aflatoxin in corn, wheat, sorghum, oats, and soybeans began in 1963, when samples of all grades of each of these grains were collected from principal commercial markets. Aflatoxin was detected in only 52 out of the 3,548 samples analyzed. This involved 35 out of 1,311 corn samples; two out of 534 wheat samples; six out of 533 sorghum samples; two out of 304 oat samples; and seven out of 866 soybean samples.

Most of the samples in which aflatoxin was detected were taken from lower grades of the commodities involved. No sample contained more than 19 parts per billion of aflatoxin, and 25 of the samples contained less than seven parts per billion.

As part of this work, we also conduct periodic surveys of the incidence of aflatoxin in cottonseed, cottonseed meal, peanuts, rice, and grains that have been placed in storage.

Problem Area No. 5

All of the problems that I have discussed so far deal with the presence of aflatoxins in agricultural commodities. To evaluate the dangers that contaminated feeds pose to livestock, we are conducting animal feeding experiments. These tests will determine the effect of aflatoxins on the various species, as well as determining whether or not they can be transmitted in edible animal products.

Practical feeding trials involving swine and beef cattle have been investigated and the tissues of these animals have been biologically and chemically analyzed for aflatoxin. We found no evidence that the dietary aflatoxin in the ration was transmitted into edible portions of these animals. Our scientists used these same approaches in work with dairy cows and poultry. Tests involving these two kinds of animals are still being evaluated.

Problem Area No. 6

As explained above, most of our work to date has focused on the aflatoxins. We do, however, recognize that these materials are only a part of the total problem. This problem area then, is concerned with isolating and characterizing new mycotoxins that may occur in our food and feed products.

Some of these mycotoxins are produced by fungi that are parasitic on living plants, including grasses, cereal crops, and legumes. Others are produced by fungi that cause moldiness in stored grains, feeds, and other relatively dry products.

Research on other mycotoxins is providing us with more complete information on strains of fungi that can produce them. The toxins, in turn, are being isolated, analyzed, and tested.

This particular problem area underscores a need that we feel for expanding the scope of this work in order to forestall any future problems. It also provides us with an opportunity to apply and confirm many of the things we have learned in our aflatoxin studies.

Immediate Needs

We regard all six of these areas as vital to the eventual solution of our mycotoxin problems. Of immediate concern to us is insuring that wholesome food products and livestock feeds will continue to flow to their respective markets in an orderly and efficient manner. Research can help us to do this in two ways.

One way is to develop very rapid methods for detecting aflatoxin in specific commodities. In the case of corn, for example, there may be a lapse of as little as 48 hours between the time a carload arrives at a processing plant and the time it is shipped out as a finished product. To avoid delays in processing during this time interval, we would need to develop a 30- to 60-minute assay for clearing each carload after arrival.

Another immediate problem is to develop more effective ways to save contaminated crops for use as food or feed. I have already mentioned some of the decontamination methods we are testing. Chemical treatments show particular promise. But before we can formulate and recommend any such methods, we must establish what, if anything, these treatments do to the commodity's nutritive value. We must also establish that the finished product contains no deleterious residues that might result from degradation products of the mycotoxins.

There are, of course, other immediate problems related to our research. I mention these two because they seem to me to be particularly critical at this point.

On an overall basis, our evaluation of the problem could be stated more simply. We feel that it is important, that it may be serious, and that the amount of research attention we are devoting to it is well justified.

SOME BIOASSAY METHODS FOR MYCOTOXINS

by ROBERT F. BROWN
Division of Microbiology, Food and Drug Administration, Washington, D.C. 20204

Introduction

Mycotoxins represent a group of toxic fungal metabolites which have been found to contaminate some foods. Some of these compounds have been shown to have a high order of acute toxicity to certain animal species and have exhibited potent carcinogenic properties (*20*). Many cases of illness or death in cattle, swine, flocks of chickens and turkeys, as well as other animals, are believed to have been caused by mycotoxins contaminating animal feeds (*15*). The demonstration of various biological effects resulting from the ingestion of contaminated foods by experimental animals has emphasized the potential public health hazard which might arise from contamination of the food supply by mycotoxins (*10, 20*). The U.S. Food and Drug Administration, as well as other public health organizations, is well aware of the desirability of keeping foods free of these toxic compounds.

Bioassay is defined as a determination of the potency of a physical, chemical, or biological agent by means of a biological indicator (*7*). The indicators of biological activity are the measurable responses provoked by these agents in a surviving organism or tissue. A variety of biological indicators may supply these responses. These may be whole organisms, isolated organs or tissues, and populations of cells. The object of bioassay is to establish a relative potency of a compound and to supply an estimate of the reliability of the potency (*7*).

Several principles have been given for estimating the relative potencies of compounds by comparison with their biochemical, physiological, and toxicological effects. The following are a few of the principles that one should consider in developing a precise bioassay (*7*):

(1) The biological indicator chosen should be closely related to the significant effect of the compound. For example, if the significant characteristic is carcinogenicity, then the biological indicator should be one in which the induction of neoplasm can be clearly shown.

(2) Dose-response curves should be established which are linear over a wide range of dose concentrations.

(3) A highly purified and carefully preserved standard preparation of the material that is to be bioassayed must be used as a reference for activity.

(4) The assay should be planned so that the log dose-response curves of the preparation whose potency is to be determined are parallel with the reference standard.

(5) The relative potency should be estimated by comparing the log-dose of the unknown with the log-dose of the standard that produces an effect of equal magnitude.

(6) The error of the estimated potency should be calculated from the internal evidence of the bioassay.

(7) To keep precision, reliability, and ease of computations high, the bioassay should be conducted under a rigid experimental design.

Development of precise bioassay methods for most mycotoxins is difficult because most practical chemical analytical procedures produce only crude preparations which may contain related compounds that also have biological activity. Chemical assay for mycotoxins depends on extraction and chromatographic separation with presumptive identification by comparison with reference standards on a thin-layer chromatographic plate (*6*). The possibility exists that nontoxic compounds in nature may have a similar chromatographic behavior.

Bioassay for mycotoxins has been utilized primarily to provide an additional confirmation of the identity established by chemical means. A number of biological tests have been developed for this purpose. Bacteria (*6, 12, 21*), brine shrimp (*2*), chick embryo (*19*), day-old ducklings (*4*), calf kidney cells (*5*), embryonic lung cells (*8*), human Chang liver cells (*8*), zebra fish (*1*), insects (*14*), mollusc eggs (*18*), fungi (*3*), rainbow trout (*9*), and albinism in plants (*17*) are among the biological organisms which have been utilized in these tests.

Methods

The aflatoxins have been identified as a mixture of closely related metabolites produced by some strains of the mold *Aspergillus flavus*. This mixture has been characterized chemically as substituted difuranocoumarins and acts as a very potent toxin in some animal species. Since its initial discovery and isolation aflatoxin has been evaluated in a greater variety of biological systems than any other mycotoxin.

Bacterial inhibition.—In regulatory work, the extensive research equipment and highly trained personnel required for some biological tests are disadvantages. Tests should be as simple and rapid as is practicable. Growth inhibition of bacterial test organisms, a technique which has been applied to the determination of aflatoxins (6), has the advantages of speed and simplicity over other biological assays developed as tests to confirm chemical determinations. This method utilizes aflatoxin B_1 of the highest available purity such as is used in other current biological tests; it can be performed in any microbiological laboratory; and it provides a response within 15 hours. It is based on the growth inhibition of *Bacillus megaterium* in response to aflatoxin B_1. Among 329 micro-organisms tested with crude aflatoxins, *B. megaterium* was found to be the most sensitive (3).

This method utilizes standard antibiotic zone inhibition techniques. Known quantities of aflatoxin B_1 dissolved in chloroform are applied to 1/4-inch paper disks (Schleicher and Schuell No. 740–E). After complete evaporation of the chloroform, the disks are placed on *B. megaterium* tryptone-glucose-yeast (TGY) agar plates. The medium is composed of TGY with 1.0 percent agar, adjusted to pH 6.2, and seeded with 1 percent of a spore suspension of *B. megaterium* containing approximately 1×10^{10} spores per milliliter (1:99, spore suspension: TGY medium). After thorough mixing, 4 ml. of the seeded agar medium is added to each Petri dish (100 mm. wide x 15 mm. deep), distributed evenly by tilting plates from side to side with a circular motion, and allowed to harden on a level surface. The plates are incubated at 35° to 37° C. for 15 to 18 hours. Any aflatoxin present diffuses into the medium surrounding the disk and forms a zone of growth inhibition.

Inhibition is detectable with 1 μg. of aflatoxin B_1 as early as 7 hours after incubation; well-defined zones of inhibition are produced after 15 to 18 hours. Crude aflatoxin, mixtures of B_1 and G_1, highly purified aflatoxin B_1, crude ochratoxin, and 70 percent pure ochratoxin A all give comparable results. Chloroform-impregnated disks and sample extracts free of aflatoxins are carried through the procedure as controls. No zones of inhibition occur. Crude extracts from *Fusarium tricinctum* and *Chaetomium globosum* also inhibit the organism. Patulin gives inhibition at 4 to 8 μg. per disk.

Stained smears made of the organism from the margin of the zone of inhibition have revealed aberrant forms consisting of elongated cells. These cells may be compared with those observed in cultures of *Escherichia coli* which had been exposed to aflatoxin and indicated that the mechanism of cell division has been somewhat damaged (21). *Flavobacterium aurantiacum* grown in the presence of aflatoxin also develops aberrant cells (12). In this case, the enhanced length of the cells is the most striking change; in addition, the ends of these cells are swollen and often branched. Giant cell formation has also been reported after exposure of heteroploid human embryonic lung cells to 0.1 p.p.m. of aflatoxin (11).

Brine shrimp.—An alternate method, which also is relatively simple and rapid, and which can be carried out in most laboratories, utilizes the brine shrimp, *Artemia salina* (2). The use of the brine shrimp in a bioassay technique of this kind has several distinct advantages. This test can be conducted in 24 hours. Highly trained personnel and specialized apparatus are not necessary. It also is unnecessary to maintain living cultures of test organisms. The eggs of *Artemia* are easily obtainable from pet shops at a moderate price. These eggs will remain viable for several years when they are stored in a dry condition. The eggs hatch in less than 24 hours at 27° C. in artificial sea water with a specific gravity of 1.02. The environment of the larvae from hatch until the end of the experiment can be easily controlled. Brine shrimp of uniform vitality can be obtained by selecting larvae that swim from a darkened to an illuminated environment. The brine shrimp has been used for bioassay in testing anesthetics, insecticides, antibiotics, and radioisotopes.

The brine shrimp eggs are placed on one side of the barrier in the brine shrimp rearing dish. The hatched larvae are able to swim through the openings in the barrier. A light source at the side of the dish attracts the swimming larvae through the barrier and also influences them to congregate in one location, so that they may be more easily drawn up in sufficient numbers with a pipette.

The tests are conducted in U.S. Plant Industry Station watch glasses. These are similar to Syracuse watch glasses but are smaller: 8 mm. deep and with an inside diameter of 20 mm. The desired quantity of aflatoxin B_1 dissolved in chloroform is delivered into each dish. The chloroform is then removed by evaporation on a steam bath. Approximately 30 to 50 brine shrimp larvae are drawn up with 0.5 ml. of artificial sea water by means of a graduated 1 ml. pipette and transferred to each watch glass in the test. Aflatoxin B_1 is soluble in artificial sea water up to about 15 μg. per 0.5 ml. The sensitivity of the test is below the upper solubility limits. A population of up to about 50 brine shrimp larvae can be maintained in 0.5 ml. artificial sea water without adverse effects on test results. The watch glasses are maintained at

37.5° C. for 24 hours underneath inverted Wheaton preparation dishes. The percent inactive shrimp are calculated after the 24-hour period.

Mortality was greater than 90 percent after 24 hours at dose levels of 1.0 µg. per ml. and above. The lowest level of aflatoxin tested was 0.5 µg. per ml., which produced 61 percent mortality. Preliminary testing with partially purified ochratoxin has revealed an order of toxicity approximately one-fifth that of aflatoxin B_1. Mortality was 15 percent at 1.0 µg. per ml. and 23 percent at 2.0 µg. per ml. The highest dose level tested was 16.0 µg. per ml., which produced 49 percent mortality. An acetone extract of a culture of *Fusarium tricinctum* produced 100 percent mortality at 16 hours after 1 µl. of this extract had been added to the test dish and the chloroform evaporated. The same results occurred at all dose levels up through 20 µl. These data are shown in figure 1.

Chicken embryo assay.—The chicken embryo assay is one of the most satisfactory assays for confirming the chemical identification of aflatoxin and it is presently being used by the Food and Drug Admin-

istration. Next to the duckling test this is the most frequently used bioassay. Upon the report that as little as 0.3 µg. of crude aflatoxin caused the death in 2 days of 5-day-old chicken embryos (*16*), a bioassay technique utilizing the chicken embryo was developed (*19*). This amount of crude aflatoxin is 1/200th the amount required for a positive result in day-old ducklings.

Preliminary studies using the chicken embryo method have revealed a decreasing order of toxicity for toxic fungal metabolites as follows: B_1, B_2, M_1, aspertoxin, G_1, G_2, and crude ochratoxin. No toxicity to the chicken embryo was exhibited by aflatoxin B_{2a} or hemiacetal of aflatoxin at approximately 80 times the dose level used for aflatoxin B_1. This information is given on table 1.

The technique used for the chicken embryo involves a choice of two routes of injection or administration: either directly into the yolk or into the air cell. Air cell injection has proved to be more sensitive than the yolk injection route, as is indicated on table 1. In addition to avoid contamination, use of the yolk route requires that the injections be carried out in an isolator box with a sterile atmosphere created by using formaldehyde vapors (*13*). Use of the air cell route for injection does not require this isolator box procedure.

When using the air cell route, chromatographically pure aflatoxin B_1 or another mycotoxin is injected into the air cells of fertile White Leghorn eggs before incubation. Before injection the eggs are candled in order to discard those that are defective, the exact location of the air cell is outlined with a pencil (*13*), and a hole about 5 mm. in diameter is drilled into the shell over the air cell. The test solution is then deposited on the egg membrane and the hole is sealed with adhesive cellophane tape, with care not to cover the entire air cell. The volume injected into the air cell is generally restricted to 0.04 ml. or less.

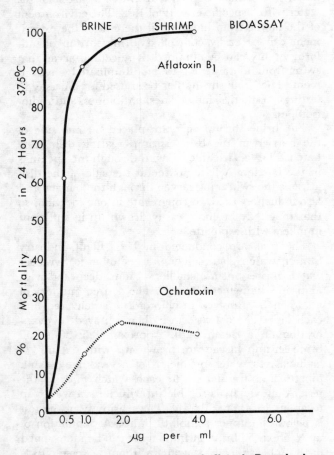

Figure 1.—Brine shrimp bioassay of aflatoxin B_1 and ochratoxin.

Table 1.—Toxicity of mycotoxins in the chicken embryo[1]

Aflatoxin	LD₅₀	
	Air cell injection µg./egg	Yolk injection µg./egg
B_1	0.025	0.048
B_2	.125	
M_1	.2	
Aspertoxin	.7	.7
G_1	1.1	
G_2	2.7	
Ochratoxin	5 to 10	
B_{2a} (Hemiacetal)	None at 0.20 µg./egg	

[1]From Kraybill, H. F. (in press) presented at Session on Toxicological Problems in Agriculture and Industry at International Seminar on Occupational Health Problems in Developing Countries, Lagos, Nigeria, Apr. 1–6, 1968.

Table 2.—Protocol for aflatoxin B₁ assay in the chicken embryo[1]

| Number of eggs | Quantity injected | | Expected mortality percent | Material injected |
	ml.	μg.		
20 or more_____	0.020	0.20	100	Test (unknown sample).
Do_____	.010	.10	100	Test 10 μg./ml.
Do_____	.005	.05	90	Do.
Do_____	.0025	.025	50	Do.
Do_____	.020	.20	100	Aflatoxin B₁ standard.
Do[1]_____	.010	.10	90	Aflatoxin 10 μg./ml.
Do[1]_____	.005	.05	50	Do.
Do_____	.02	---------------	<20	Solvent (ethanol).
Do[1]_____	.01	---------------	<10	Do.
Do[1]_____	.005	---------------	<10	Do.
30 or more_____	---------------	---------------	<20	Noninjected controls.

[1]Levels to be included when a new standard is employed, a new solvent is obtained, or when the eggs come from a new flock.

Table 2 gives the protocol for setting up a routine test for aflatoxin. Propylene glycol was the solvent originally chosen, but because of its high viscosity, it presents problems in the handling and injection of solutions. Any nontoxic solvent which is capable of solubilizing the mycotoxins may be used. Ethanol has proved to be an ideal solvent in this assay since the dose-response curve is the same as that obtained with propylene glycol and it produces very low background toxicity at the levels used. The protocol will depend to some extent on the sensitivity of the particular egg supply to the specific mycotoxin. Under the conditions used (19), the dose-response curve for aflatoxin B₁ covers a rather narrow range: from about 0.10 μg. per egg, which produces 100 percent mortality, to 0.01 μg. per egg, which produces no effect, at the 21st day. A dose-response curve for aflatoxin toxicity is given in figure 2. This figure compares the re-sults of both the yolk and air cell injection routes.

The number of eggs used per level and the number of dose levels for a test sample may be smaller than indicated in table 2 if sufficient material is not available. All levels corresponding to those used for the unknown should be included when a new standard is employed, when a new supply of solvent is obtained, or when the eggs come from a new flock. These levels are marked with an asterisk on table 2. A sufficient number of noninjected controls should always be included to check on the fertility and hatchability of the eggs used, and as a monitor of the incubator conditions.

After injection the eggs are allowed to remain undisturbed in a vertical position with the air cell up for about an hour to allow the material to disperse. The injected eggs are then put into incubator trays with the large end up and the trays are placed into a forced-draft incubator, which automatically rotates hourly and is maintained at an optimum temperature of 38° C. and a relative humidity of 60 percent (13).

The eggs are candled daily from the fourth incubation day on, at which time all nonviable embryos are removed. The evaluation is based on the mortality at 21 days, although mortality with eggs receiving higher levels of aflatoxin (0.05μg./egg or greater) is seen as early as the fourth day after incubation. Over 500 samples have been examined for aflatoxin contamination using this method. Its correlation with chemical assays is excellent.

In addition to toxicity, aflatoxin severely retards growth, an effect readily observed in embryos 10 days old or older. The embryos also undergo considerable hemorrhaging and generalized edema. When crude ochratoxin is administered, preliminary observations show that all embryos have malformed beaks ranging from a cleft palate to complete absence of the beak. The eyes may be absent or greatly reduced in size if the upper beak is absent. Preliminary studies with crude extracts of *Fusarium tricinctum* have demon-

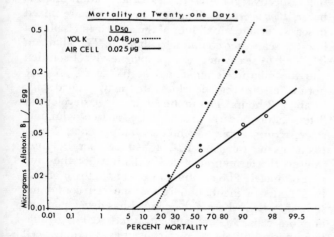

Figure 2.—Toxicity of aflatoxin B₁ in the chicken embryo: mortality at 21 days. LD₅₀: yolk, 0.048 μg.; air cell 0.025 μg. Open circles: yolk injection. Closed circles: air cell injection. From Verrett et al. (1964) J. Assoc. Offic. Anal. Chemists 47:1003–1006.

strated a toxicity to the embryos comparable to that of aflatoxin B_1.

Ducklings.—The use of day-old ducklings, combined with chemical identification of aflatoxin, is probably one of the most widely used and accepted confirmatory procedures for aflatoxin identification (11a). The two factors contributing to the widespread use of the test are sensitivity to aflatoxin injury and the almost immediate induction of bile duct proliferation. The relatively specific response of bile duct proliferation, which can be found a few days after a single dose of aflatoxin, can be said to make the assay unique.

The Peking white duckling has generally been regarded as the variety of choice and the assay uses day-old ducklings weighing approximately 50 g. A semisynthetic diet is used rather than a commercial preparation. The toxin can be administered either as a single dose or over a 5-day period. Propylene glycol is the vehicle most frequently used for aflatoxin formulations. The results should include both the acute LD_{50} and measurement of the bile-duct proliferation.

The lethal effects of aflatoxin to day-old ducklings are usually seen within the first 72 hours after administration, although a 6- to 7-day period may be essential to determine the absolute endpoint. The single-dose LD_{50} for day-old ducklings has been reported by various authors to be 0.36 to 1.0 mg. per kg. body weight. The order of toxicity of the aflatoxins is given in table 3 (10a). The reduction in toxicity averages a factor of about 4.5 between B_1 and B_2, and G_1 and G_2. The average factor for the reduction in toxicity between B_1 and G_1, and B_2 and G_2 is 2.0. Aflatoxin M_1 is of the same order of toxicity as B_1 and a fourfold decrease in toxicity occurs in the case of M_2.

Acute bile duct proliferation reaches a maximum in 3 days, and then regresses with subsequent repair of the liver parenchyma (4). A bile duct hyperplasia score is presented in table 4 comparing aflatoxins B_1, B_2, and G_1 (10a). The evaluation of toxicity is by

Table 3.—Lethality of aflatoxins in ducklings[1]

Aflatoxin	Oral—7-day LD_{50}[2] μg./50 g.
B_1	18.2
M_1	16.6
G_1	39.2
M_2	62.0
B_2	84.4
G_2	172.5

[1]From Kraybill, H. F. (in press) presented at Session on Toxicological Problems in Agriculture and Industry at International Seminar on Occupational Health Problems in Developing Countries, Lagos, Nigeria, Apr. 1–6, 1968.
[2]Administered to day-old (50 g.) ducklings.

Table 4.—Bile duct hyperplasia response to crystalline aflatoxins in ducklings (7- to 8-day assay)

Average bile duct hyperplasia score[2]	B_1 μg./day[3]	B_2 μg./day[3]	G_1 μg./day[3]
0	----------	----------	0.78
6	----------	----------	1.56
10	0.39	----------	3.13
16	0.78	10.0	6.25
20	----------	16.0	12.50
30	1.56	40.0	25.00

[1]From Kraybill, H. F. (in press) presented at Session on Toxicological Problems in Agriculture and Industry at International Seminar on Occupational Health Problems in Developing Countries, Lagos, Nigeria, Apr. 1–6, 1968.
[2]Individual tissues scored on a scale of 0 to 4 + (x 10), 6 animals per group, no mortalities.
[3]Administered orally for 5 consecutive days in 0.1 ml. propylene glycol.

histologic examination of the liver. The relative order of response in terms of the index is $B_1 > G_1 > B_2$, which compares with the single dose oral LD_{50} or the 7 day oral LD_{50} values reported elsewhere. The duckling test with its relatively specific response in a comparatively short period of time has become the assay of choice in many laboratories.

Marine borer.—Another method which has received attention involves the response of fertilized eggs of the mollusc, *Bankia setaceae* (Tryon) to aflatoxin (18). This response is very dramatic and positive in that aflatoxin B_1 inhibits cell cleavage in fertilized mollusc eggs without preventing fertilization or nuclear division. This test does not require extensive research equipment, sterile techniques, or highly trained personnel.

Eggs and sperm are removed by dissection from the respective gonadal tissues of the adult marine borer, *Bankia setaceae*. The eggs and sperm are mixed in sea water and an aliquot of the suspension is placed into the sea water containing aflatoxin. The aflatoxin is added to sea water as a propylene glycol solution and the mixture is incubated at 10° to 20° C. The normal fertilized egg develops into the two-celled stage in about 2 hours. The multicellular stage develops in 3 to 4 hours and the trochophore, or free-swimming stage, requires about 18 hours. The presence of aflatoxin in the range of 0.05 to 40 μg. per milliliter inhibits the formation of cell walls but not the division of nuclei. The resultant effect of aflatoxin after 3 to 5 hours of incubation is a single cell containing several nuclei, whereas the control has developed two or more cells. At low concentrations (0.05 μg. aflatoxin per milliliter), a few fertilized eggs undergo cell division. However, the development of larvae ceases before reaching the trochophore stage.

The presence or absence of the swimming larval state can be used as an indicator. Many eggs can be observed at one time in a very small volume of sea water. For this observation a concentration of only 0.005 µg. aflatoxin per µl. of solution is necessary. If a low-powered microscope (70X) is used for making the observations on cell division, a concentration of 0.05 µg. aflatoxin per µl. of solution is required.

Zebra fish.—The zebra fish, *Brachydanio rerio*, has also been proposed as a bioassay test organism (*1*). The eggs of this species will produce larvae in 3 to 4 days at room temperature. Because the eggs are transparent the progress of normal or abnormal development is easily observed under test conditions. The eggs are obtained during the evening by separating gravid females and twice the number of males. These are placed into special breeding traps with a 10-mesh screen floor hooked on the walls of an aquarium set aside for breeding. Underneath the traps, on the aquarium floor, finger bowls are provided for the collection of eggs. The female fish drop their eggs within about 30 minutes early in the morning. The bowls are then removed and the eggs are separated from fecal matter and debris. The eggs are placed into Petri dishes with distilled water and allowed to develop. After 3 to 4 days the larvae hatch out with considerable embryonic yolk and need no feeding or special care before being used.

Small glass planchets are used as test containers with 29 to 30 test organisms per 2 ml. test solution per container. The test solution is prepared by dissolving 5 µg. of the toxin in 0.04 ml. of acetone and diluting to 5 ml. with distilled water. Lower concentrations are prepared by further dilution with water containing 0.8 percent acetone. The 0.8 percent acetone is harmless to the test organisms.

The larvae show abnormal movements within about 30 minutes after exposure to 1 µg./ml. and become moribund in 5 to 6 hours. The color of the yolk sphere darkens slightly and a kink appears in the larval tail after 20 hours. The larvae die in 24 to 36 hours. The yolk sphere is either ruptured or completely dislodged before death.

Conclusions

The bioassay methods described are some of those most frequently used as confirmatory tests following chemical identification of aflatoxins. In this type of test, the ease and speed of conducting an assay that gives a biological response to the presence of a mycotoxin is important. It is desirable that such a test be as rapid as possible and not require extensive equipment or highly trained personnel.

The bacterial zone inhibition test and the brine shrimp test are rapid and easy to perform. The *B. megaterium* test can give results in as little as 15 to 18 hours at the 1 µg. level, and detection is possible as

early as 7 hours after incubation. The brine shrimp test gives positive results at the same level in 24 hours. The larvae of the zebra fish, *Brachydanio rerio*, are reported to give an observable response to 1 µg. per ml. of aflatoxin B_1 within 30 minutes, but collecting eggs and maintaining a living culture of animals present problems. The multinucleated stage of the fertilized egg of the marine borer, *Bankia setaceae*, can be observed within 3 to 5 hours at 0.05 µg. aflatoxin per milliliter. The marine borer, however, is not commonly available as a test organism (*18*).

The chicken embryo bioassay utilizing the air cell injection route is the most sensitive testing procedure. The complete assay requires 21 days, although a positive response and hence confirmation of toxicity is observed at 4 days with the higher dose levels.

Although it is necessary to use considerably larger quantities of aflatoxin for the test with day-old ducklings, the response of bile duct proliferation within 3 days is said to be a specific indication of aflatoxin toxicity. The multinucleated stage of the fertilized egg of the marine borer is considered by some also to be a specific response to aflatoxin. Similar interference by aflatoxin with the mechanism of cell division in other types of cells, such as *B. megaterium*, probably is related (*6, 11, 12, 21*). The malformation of the beak in the chicken embryo possibly may be a specific indicator of crude ochratoxin toxicity.

The quantities of aflatoxin necessary for a confirmatory test are an important consideration because the supply of aflatoxin may be limited. Therefore, the quantity required for such a test must be maintained within practical limits. Extraction of 10 µg. of aflatoxin from a sample is considered to be within the practical limits. One µg. of this amount is used for chemical assay. The remainder can be used for bioassay.

A confirmatory brine shrimp test covering the 0.5, 1.0, and 2.0 µg./ml. levels in assay medium can be performed with less than 2.0 µg. of aflatoxin because this test can be conducted in only 0.5 ml. of sea water. Such a test utilizing *B. megaterium* and zone inhibition can be carried out with 5.5 µg. of aflatoxin to supply two 1.5 µg. disks and one 2.5 µg. disk. A routine chicken embryo test usually is conducted with 7 to 9 µg. of aflatoxin but an assay can be carried out with as little as 1 µg. (0.1 µg./egg in 10 eggs). Although the marine borer bioassay gives positive results at a level of 0.05 µg. aflatoxin per ml., no total volume is specified for conducting the test. Observation of the swimming larval state can be used as an indicator at 0.005 µg. of aflatoxin per µl. of solution. Five µg. of aflatoxin is necessary for the zebra fish bioassay.

The development of mycotoxin bioassay has been largely devoted to aflatoxin. The discovery of additional mycotoxins has made it important to apply these methods to other mycotoxins. Aflatoxins B_2, G_1, G_2, M_1, and M_2 have all undergone some testing together with aspertoxin, ochratoxin, patulin, and the mycotoxin produced by *Fusarium tricinctum*. All of these compounds have been tested with the chicken embryo and have elicited a toxic response. The duckling has been tested against most of the aflatoxins. *B. megaterium* provides an effective test against highly purified aflatoxin B_1, mixtures of B_1 and G_1, crude aflatoxin, 70 percent pure ochratoxin A, crude ochratoxin, crude extracts from *Fusarium tricinctum* and *Chaetomium globosum*, and patulin. The brine shrimp has been tested effectively against highly purified aflatoxin B_1, ochratoxin, and crude extract from *Fusarium tricinctum*.

The estimation of relative potency by bioassay generally is less precise than a quantitative determination by chemical assay (7). Biological assay is important, however, because these tests can use crude extracts of mycotoxins or compounds of unknown chemical identification.

A number of bioassay methods have not been described. This is not meant to imply that these are not effective methods. Many methods require highly specialized procedures and equipment or greater lengths of time, and as such, are not practical for routine use as confirmatory tests for chemical assays of mycotoxins.

References

(1) ABEDI, Z. H., and W. P. McKINLEY. 1968. Zebra fish eggs and larvae as aflatoxin bioassay test organisms. J. Assoc. Offic. Anal. Chemists 51: 902–904.

(2) BROWN, R. F., J. D. WILDMAN, and R. M. EPPLEY. 1968. Temperature-dose relationships with aflatoxin on the brine shrimp, *Artemia salina*. J. Assoc. Offic. Anal. Chemists 51: 905–906.

(3) BURMEISTER, H. R., and C. W. HESSELTINE. 1966. Survey of the sensitivity of microorganisms to aflatoxin. Appl. Microbiol. 14: 403–404.

(4) BUTLER, W. H. 1964. Acute liver injury to ducklings as a result of aflatoxin poisoning. J. Pathol. Bacteriol. 88: 189–196.

(5) CHILDS, V. A., and M. S. LEGATOR. 1966. Induction of thymidine kinase by aflatoxin. Life Sci. 5: 1053–1056.

(6) CLEMENTS, N. L. 1968. Rapid confirmatory test for aflatoxin B_1, using *Bacillus megaterium*. J. Assoc. Offic. Anal. Chemists 51: 1192–1194.

(7) DiPALMA, J. R. 1965. Drill's Pharmacology in Medicine. McGraw-Hill Book Co., New York.

(8) GABLIKS, J., W. SCHAEFFER, L. FRIEDMAN, and G. WOGAN. 1965. Effect of aflatoxin B_1 on cell cultures. J. Bacteriol. 90: 720–723.

(9) JACKSON, E. W., H. WOLF, and R. O. SINNHUBER. 1968. The relationship of hepatoma in rainbow trout to aflatoxin contamination and cottonseed meal. Cancer Res. 28: 987–991.

(10) KRAYBILL, H. F., and M. B. SHIMKIN. 1964. Carcinogenesis related to foods contaminated by processing and fungal metabolites. Advan. Cancer Res. 8: 191–248.

(10a) KRAYBILL, H. F. 1968. Presented at Session on Toxicological Problems in Agriculture and Industry at International Seminar on Occupational Health Problems in Developing Countries, Lagos, Nigeria, Apr. 1–6, 1968. In press.

(11) LEGATOR, M. S., S. M. ZUFFANTE, and A. R. HARP. 1965. Aflatoxin: Effect on cultured heteroploid human embryonic lung cells. Nature 208: 345–347.

(11a) LEGATOR, M. S. Ch. 5, Biological Assay of Aflatoxin. *In* "Aflatoxin—Scientific Background, Control, and Implications." L. Goldblatt (ed.), Academic Press, New York. In press.

(12) LILLEHOJ, E. B., A. CIEGLER, and H. H. HALL. 1966. Aflatoxin B_1 uptake by *Flavobacterium aurantiacum* and resulting toxic effects. J. Bacteriol. 93: 464–471.

(13) McLAUGHLIN, J., J. P. MARLIAC, M. J. VERRETT, M. K. MUTCHLER, and O. G. FITZHUGH. 1963. The injection of chemicals into the yolk sac of fertile eggs prior to incubation as a toxicity test. Toxicol. Appl. Pharmacol. 5: 760–771.

(14) MATSUMARA, F., and S. G. KNIGHT. 1967. Toxicity and chemo-sterilizing activity of aflatoxin against insects. J. Econ. Entomol. 60: 871–872.

(15) NELSON, G. H., C. M. CHRISTENSEN, and C. J. MIROCHA. 1966. Feeds, fungi, and animal health. Minn. Sci. 23: 12–13.

(16) PLATT, B. S., R. J. C. STEWART, and S. R. GUPTA. 1962. The chick embryo as a test organism for toxic substances in food. Proc. Nutr. Soc. Engl. Scot. 21: 30–31.

(17) SCHOENTAL, R., and A. F. WHITE. 1965. Aflatoxins and albinism in plants. Nature 205: 57–58.

(18) TOWNSLEY, P. M., and E. G. H. LEE. 1967. Response of fertilized eggs of the mollusc, *Bankia setaceae*, to aflatoxin. J. Assoc. Offic. Anal. Chemists 50: 361–363.

(19) VERRETT, M. J., J. P., MARLIAC, and J. McLAUGHLIN. 1964. Use of the chick embryo in the assay of aflatoxin toxicity. J. Assoc. Offic. Anal. Chemists 47: 1003–1006.

(20) WOGAN, G. N. 1966. Chemical nature and biological effects of the aflatoxins. Bacteriol. Rev. 30: 460–470.

(21) WRAGG, J. B., V. C. ROSS, and M. S. LEGATOR. 1967. Effect of aflatoxin B_1 on the deoxyribonucleic acid polymerase of *Escherichia coli*. Proc. Soc. Exptl. Biol. Med. 125: 1052–1055.

SYNCHRONIZED CULTURE AS AN ASSAY SYSTEM OF AFLATOXIN

by HIROSHI YOSHIKURA *and* KAGEAKI AIBARA
Department of Pathology
and Department of Feed Research
National Institute of Health, Tokyo, Japan

Summary

Effect of aflatoxin B_1 on the synchronized cultures of C3H2K cells was investigated. The synchronization was based on the density dependent inhibition of the cell growth and the induction of cell replication by a change of medium. Aflatoxin B_1 inhibited both DNA synthesis and mitosis. At a concentration of 1.0 μg./ml. of aflatoxin B_1, no mitosis occurred. The maximum incorporation of ^{3}H-thymidine was about 50 percent of the control, although DNA synthesis occurred in a synchronized fashion and no delay of DNA synthesis was observed. At lower concentrations, 0.008 or 0.04 μg./ml. only the delay of the mitosis was observed. RNA synthesis was not as severely inhibited by the toxin as it was by actinomycin D.

Introduction

The development of an assay system is essential for the screening as well as for the analysis of any antimetabolite. As an assay system, the tissue culture cell system is one of the convenient ones, since usually it requires a shorter period of time and is less expensive than assay *in vivo*. However, as long as the assay is based on cytopathic effects or other nonspecific changes of the cells, such an assay can hardly be regarded as specific. In this respect, application of synchronized cultures as an assay system should be of great value, since it makes it possible to examine the effects of a given antimetabolite upon individual stages of the cell cycle. Inhibition of mitosis may be the consequence of the inhibition of metabolic events in the preceding G_2, S, or G_1 periods, or due to primary inhibition of induction of mitosis. In unsynchronized cultures, analysis of this kind is not always easy. To give another instance, RNA synthesis is not uniform during the whole cell cycle. Each RNA synthesized at each stage of the cell cycle is different from all others, quantitatively and possibly qualitatively. Synchronized culture facilitate analysis of the effect of an antimetabolite upon each type of RNA synthesis.

One of the authors and his associates developed synchronized culture of a mouse cell line, the C3H2K cell line (*15, 16*). The cells originated from the kidney tissues of a newborn C3H/He mouse and possess properties quite similar to those of 3T3 cells (*14*). The cells were sensitive to density dependent inhibition of cell growth (*13*). The cells stopped growing at a low cell density in the G_1 phase, and after a change of medium, all the cells divided in a synchronized fashion only once.

This report deals with the preliminary experiments on assay of aflatoxin B_1 in the synchronized culture and analysis of the action of the toxin upon the cell cycle.

Materials and Methods

Cell culture.—C3H2K cells originating from the kidney tissues of a newborn C3H/He mouse were used. The culture medium consisted of eight parts Eagle's minimal essential medium, one part calf serum and one part tryptose phosphate broth. The cells were subcultured when they became confluent.

Estimation of DNA and RNA synthesis.—C3H2K cells were suspended in the culture medium in the concentration of 5×10^5 cells/ml. The cell suspension, in an amount of 0.2 ml., was mounted on 18-mm. round coverslips and placed in 60 mm. petri dishes. After incubation overnight, 4 ml. of culture medium was added to each petri dish. The culture medium was replaced with fresh medium 7 to 10 days later. To estimate the DNA synthesis, ^{3}H-thymidine (0.25 μC./ml.) was added to one of the petri dishes containing two coverslips. Thirty minutes later, the incorporation was stopped by fixing the cells with a solution consisting of three parts ethanol and one part of acetic acid, followed by extraction with 2 percent perchloric acid for 20 minutes at 4° C. and washing in running water for 30 minutes. The coverslips placed in planchets were dried in the air and directly set in a window-less, gas-flow counter.

To estimate the RNA synthesis, ^{3}H-uridine (0.25 μC./ml.) was incorporated for 30 minutes in the

19

presence of about thousandfold molecular excess of cold thymidine. The procedures which followed were the same as those described above for estimating the DNA synthesis.

Estimation of mitotic cell population.—When the medium was replaced with fresh medium in the stationary phase, refractile cells in mitosis appeared in a synchronized fashion. Such refractile cells in a fixed area (0.2 x 2.0 cm.) were counted under the inverted microscope at intervals. Dumbbell-shaped cells in the telophase were counted as one. Of course, this method is but a gross estimation of mitotic activity of the cells. For the more accurate analysis, cells from late prophase to late telophase in the stained preparation were counted. However, for the usual assay, the former method was performed because of its simplicity.

Estimation of cell growth.—Fifty thousand C3H2K cells were seeded into each tube with a square bottom of 2 x 4 cm.^{2}. At intervals, the cultures in two tubes were trypsinized and the cell numbers were counted. The doubling time of the cells in the logarithmic phase was about 40 hours. The cells stopped growing at a cell density of about 3.5×10^4 cells per cm^2. On the 13th day of incubation, the culture fluid was replaced with fresh medium. The cell number doubled in about 48 hours. No further cell division occurred unless the medium was changed again. The grade of multiplication was calculated by dividing number of cells at 72 hours, after the change of medium, by number of cells before the change of medium.

Preparation of aflatoxin B_1.—Aflatoxin B_1 was dissolved into distilled water by shaking at room temperature overnight. The concentration of the toxin was checked before the experiments and was adjusted to 10.0 μg./ml.

Results

Sequence of DNA and RNA synthesis and mitosis.—The sequence of DNA and RNA synthesis and that of mitosis are demonstrated in figure 1. The DNA synthesis began to increase at about 10 hours and reached its maximum at 20 hours. Mitosis occurred about 10 hours later than the DNA synthesis. Immediately after the renewal of the culture medium, a sharp peak of ^{3}H-uridine uptake was observed. There was another peak just before the DNA synthesis.

Effect of aflatoxin upon synchronized cell division.—When the culture fluid was replaced with fresh medium containing 1.0 μg./ml. of aflatoxin B_1, no mitosis occurred (fig. 2) and no increase in cell number (fig. 3) resulted.

At this concentration, the cells remained apparently normal for several days. At lower concentrations of aflatoxin B_1, 0.008, 0.04 or 0.2 μg./ml., the delay of mitosis was observed (fig. 2). At concentrations

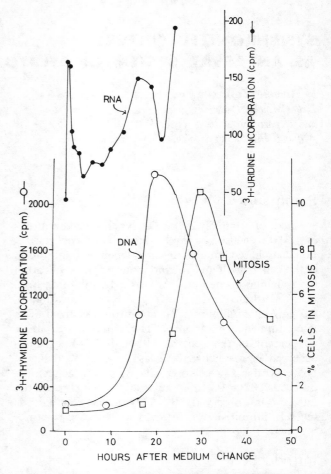

Figure 1.—Sequence of DNA and RNA synthesis and mitosis of synchronized culture of C3H2K cells.

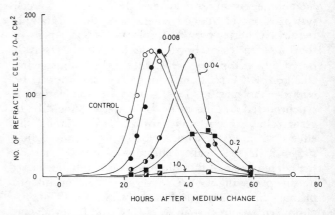

Figure 2.—Effect of aflatoxin B_1 on mitosis ○ Controls; ● 0.008 μg., ◑ 0.04 μg., ■ 0.2 μg., ◪ 1.0 μg. aflatoxin per ml.

of 0.008 and 0.04 μg./ml., however, the grade of multiplication was about 2; i.e., all the cells divided (fig. 3).

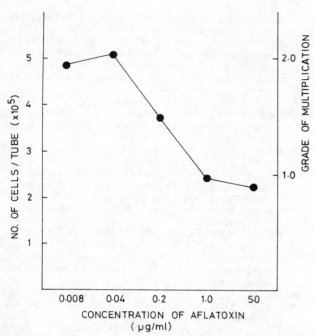

Figure 3.—Effect of aflatoxin B₁ upon the dividing cell population after change of medium.

When similar experiments were performed using actinomycin D, no such apparent mitotic delay was observed (fig. 4).

Effect of aflatoxin upon DNA and RNA synthesis.—When the culture fluid was replaced with fresh medium containing 1.0 μg./ml. of aflatoxin B₁, DNA synthesis was inhibited to nearly 50 percent of the control (fig. 5). The peak of DNA synthesis was at 20 hours after change of medium both in aflatoxin B₁-containing medium and in the control medium.

The effect of aflatoxin B₁ upon RNA synthesis was not so marked as that of actinomycin D (fig. 6).

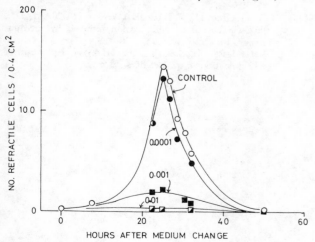

Figure 4.—Effect of actinomycin D on mitosis ○ control; ● 0.0001 μg., ▦ 0.001 μg., ◪ 0.01 μg. actinomycin per ml.

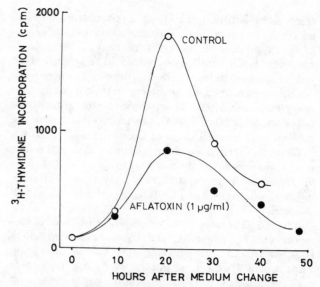

Figure 5.—Effect of aflatoxin B₁ upon DNA synthesis.

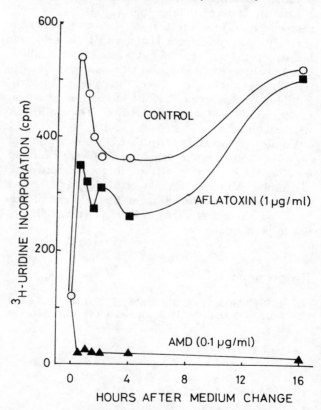

Figure 6.—Effect of aflatoxin B₁ and actinomycin D (AMD) on RNA synthesis.

Discussion

Our preliminary experiments demonstrated that aflatoxin B₁ inhibited DNA synthesis and mitosis. RNA synthesis was not so severely inhibited by the toxin as by actinomycin D. At a concentration of 1.0 μg./ml. of aflatoxin B_1, the maximum incorporation of ^{3}H-thymidine was about 50 percent of the control, although DNA synthesis occurred in a synchronized fashion and no delay of DNA synthesis was observed. At this concentration, however, mitotic activity was completely inhibited. Thus, the delay of mitosis was not due to that of DNA synthesis but due to the inhibition of the cell cycle in G_2 or onset of mitosis.

Close similarities between aflatoxin and actinomycin D were reported by many authors (*1, 2, 3, 4, 6, 7, 9, 11, 12*). In our system, however, the inhibitory effect of aflatoxin B_1 upon RNA synthesis was not so marked.

The LD_{50} value of aflatoxin B_1 and that of actinomycin D, when assayed in embryonated chick eggs, were 0.3 μg. per egg and 2.2 μg. per egg, respectively (Aibara, unpublished data). In our *in vitro* system, however, the minimum concentration of aflatoxin inhibiting cell replication and that of actinomycin D were 0.2 μg./ml. and 0.001 μg./ml., respectively. Thus, on the weight basis, although the effect of actinomycin D upon C3H2K cells was far stronger than that of aflatoxin B_1, the killing effect of actinomycin D upon embryonated chick eggs was almost equal to, or weaker than that of aflatoxin B_1. These data suggest that the mechanism of action of aflatoxin B_1 and that of actinomycin D are different from each other.

Legator (*10*) demonstrated that DNA synthesis and mitosis of human embryonic lung cells were inhibited by aflatoxin B_1. Our results are in good accord with his results. Although Gabliks et al. (*8*), and Daniel (*5*), reported cytotoxic effects of aflatoxin in cell cultures, cytotoxicity of aflatoxin B_1 in C3H2K cells was not so pronounced.

References

(*1*) BERNHARD, W., C. FRYSSINET, C. LAFARGE, and E. LE BRETON. 1965. Lésions nucléolaires précoces provoquées par l'aflatoxine dans les cellules hépatiques du Rat. Comptes Rendus *261:* 1785–1788.

(*2*) CLIFFORD, J. I., and K. R. REES. 1966. Aflatoxin: A site of action in the rat liver cell. Nature *209:* 312–313.

(*3*) CLIFFORD, J. I., and K. R. REES. 1967. The interaction of aflatoxins with purines and purine nucleosides. Biochem. J. *103:* 467–471.

(*4*) CLIFFORD, J. I., K. R. REES, and M. E. M. STEVENS. 1967. The effect of the aflatoxins B_1, G_1, and G_2 on protein and nucleic acid synthesis in rat liver. Biochem. J. *103:* 258–261.

(*5*) DANIEL, M. R. 1965. *In vitro* assay systems for aflatoxin. Brit. J. Exp. Path. *46:* 183–188.

(*6*) DERECONDO, A., C. FRAYSSINET, C. LAFARGE, and E. LE BRETON. 1965. Inhibition de la synthée du DNA par l'aflatoxine B_1 au cours de l'hypertrophie compensatrice du foie chez le Rat. Comptes Rendus *261:* 1409–1412.

(*7*) DERECONDO, A., C. FRAYSSINET, C. LAFARGE, and E. LE BRETON. 1966. Action de l'aflatoxine sur le métabolisme du DNA au cours de l'hypertrophie compensatrice du foie apres hepatectomie partielle. Biochim. Biophys. Acta *119:* 322–330.

(*8*) GABLIKS, J., W. SCHAEFFER, L. FRIEDMAN, and G. N. WOGAN. 1965. Effect of aflatoxin B_1 on cell culture. J. Bacteriol. *90:* 720–733.

(*9*) KING, A. M. Q., and B. H. NICHOLSON. 1967. Effect of aflatoxin B_1 on a deoxyribonucleic acid-dependent ribonucleic acid polymerase *in vitro*. Biochem. J. *104:* 69–70.

(*10*) LEGATOR, M. 1966. Biological effects of aflatoxin in cell culture. Bacteriol. Rev. *30:* 471–477.

(*11*) MOULE, Y., and C. FRAYSSINET. 1968. Effect of aflatoxin on transcription in liver cell. Nature *218:* 93–95.

(*12*) SPORN, M. B., C. W. DINGMAN, H. L. PHELPS, and G. N. WOGAN. 1966. Aflatoxin B_1: Binding to DNA *in vitro* and alteration of RNA metabolism *in vivo*. Science *151:* 1539–1541.

(*13*) STOKER, M. G. P., and H. RUBIN. 1967. Density dependent inhibition of cell growth in culture. Nature *215:* 171–172.

(*14*) TODARO, G. J., G. LAZAR, and H. GREEN. 1965. The initiation of cell division in a contact-inhibited mammalian cell line. J. Cell Comp. Physiol. *66:* 325–333.

(*15*) YOSHIKURA, H., Y. HIROKAWA, and M. YAMADA. 1967. Synchronized cell division induced by medium change. Exp. Cell Res. *48:* 226–228.

(*16*) YOSHIKURA, H., and Y. HIROKAWA. Induction of cell replication. Exp. Cell Res. in press.

ISOLATION AND QUANTITATIVE ANALYSIS OF FOUR AFLATOXINS (B_1, B_2, G_1, AND G_2) BY THIN-LAYER AND LIQUID CHROMATOGRAPHY

by Masaru Manabe, Shinji Matsuura,* *and* Masahiro Nakano
Food Research Institute, Ministry of Agriculture and Forestry, Japan

Summary

Various kinds of absorbent and solvent were examined to separate four aflatoxins by thin-layer chromatography. They were well separated from each other by development with 5 percent acetone in chloroform, in the case of Silica gel G (Merck) as adsorbent, and also with 1 to 3 percent methanol in chloroform, in the case of Silica gel HR (Merck).

Liquid chromatography employing various kinds of columns, for instance, alumina, silica gel, and Sephadex G–10, G–25 and LH–20, were examined. Sephadex G–10 column showed good result for the mutual separation of four aflatoxins. Crude aflatoxins were dissolved in a minimal volume of methanol, and placed on the Sephadex G–10 column, which was developed and eluted with 1 percent aqueous methanol or with distilled water. The first fraction was a mixture of pigments, and then aflatoxins G_2, B_2, G_1, and B_1 were successively eluted. Furthermore, the quantitative analysis of 10 μg. or more of aflatoxin was possible by this chromatographic method, within 10 percent error.

Introduction

Numerous reports on studies on aflatoxin (AF) have appeared since it was made clear, in England, in 1960, that a very strong carcinogenic substance was produced by a strain of fungus which had been identified as *Aspergillus flavus*. In some reports, methods are described for the separation and quantitative analysis of AF by thin-layer chromatography (TLC) and liquid chromatography (LC). In TLC generally, silica gel has been used as the adsorbent and there are many examples of the use of methanol-chloroform developers. It is difficult, however, always to maintain uniform activity of the silica gel thin layer and there have been many cases in which separation and quantitative analysis was difficult due to fluctuation in the Rf of the four kinds of AF (B_1, B_2, G_1, and G_2) when the thin layer varied. In view of this, the au-

thors sought a TLC method which would be suitable for mutual separation of the four kinds of AF.

With regard to LC, there is the report of Shotwell et al. (6) on the separation and refining of AF–B_1 using a silicic acid column. Stubblefield et al. (7) and Robertson et al. (5) recently presented methods of separation and refining of four AF's using silicic acid and silica gel columns. Pigments are present in the crude AF mixture extracted from the samples with solvent. As these pigments act in a manner similar to AF in the separation and purification of the four kinds of AF, it was necessary to carry out decolorization treatment beforehand. Many methods for removing coloring matter present in AF have been reported (1, 2, 4) but these had the defects of either complicated operation or insufficient decolorization. The authors studied methods for separation of the four kinds of AF by LC with separation of the admixed coloring matter, and a method was developed. Also, a study was made on methods for separation, purification, and quantitative analysis of the four kinds of AF using LC.

Materials and Methods

Preparation of crude AF mixture.—The crude AF mixture used as sample was prepared by culturing the AF-producing strain, *Aspergillus flavus* ATCC 15517. A mixture of 100 parts by weight of cracked wheat used for soy sauce fermentation and 60 parts by weight of water was used as the culture medium. Eighty grams of the culture medium was placed in a 500-ml. Erlenmeyer flask, provided with a sterilized cotton plug, sterilized, and the aforementioned strain was inoculated onto the medium and was cultured for 1 week at 30° C. After the culture had grown out, it was sterilized with steam at 100° C. for 1 hour and the AF of the contents extracted with chloroform in a large Soxhlet extractor. The extraction liquid was dried with anhydrous sodium sulfate, filtered to remove sodium sulfate, concentrated under reduced pressure at 40° C. A precipitate was produced, by adding to the extract, 10 times its volume of hexane, and collected by centrifugation. The precipitate was then dissolved in a small quantity of chloroform, added to a 20 x 200 mm. silica gel column and eluted with chloroform-methanol (99:1). The eluted AF portion was collected, concentrated under reduced pressure again, and the substance which was reprecipitated with hexane was used in the chromatographic tests as the crude AF mixture.

TLC of AF.—Adsorbents were Aluminum oxide G (Merck), containing about 15 percent of calcium sulfate; Silica gel G (Merck), containing about 13 percent of calcium sulfate; Silica gel HR (Merck), silica gel only. Developers were chloroform, methanol, ethanol, acetone, benzene, hexane, ethyl acetate, butanol, etc., and the ascending technique was the method of development.

LC of AF.—Carriers employed were aluminum oxide (Merck), silica gel (Mallinckrodt) and Sephadex G–10, G–25, LH–20 (Pharmacia Fine Chemicals). Eluants used were chloroform, methanol, ethanol, acetone, ethyl acetate, pure water, etc. The chromatograph column dimensions were of sizes, 8 x 500 mm., 10 x 300 mm., and 15 x 300 mm.

Results and Discussion

TLC of AF with aluminum oxide G (8).—Methanol-chloroform developers were investigated but keeping the degree of activity of the thin-layer constant was more difficult than in case of silica gel and also separation was not satisfactory.

TLC of AF with silica gel C.—There are numerous reports on the use of silica gel thin layer (*1, 2, 3, 5*) and generally methanol-chloroform developers have been used. The results of our investigation on separation using silica gel G as thin layer, containing about 13 percent of calcium sulfate, and employing methanol-chloroform as the developer with varying methanol concentrations, are shown in figure 1. The mutual separation of the four kinds of AF was good when the methanol concentration was about 3 percent. However, the separation of AF–B_1 and B_2, and AF–G_1 and G_2 were unsatisfactory depending on the activity condition of the thin layer and there were many cases in which B_1 and B_2, and G_1 and G_2 appeared at the same spot. In view of this, an attempt was made to find developers which were more suitable for the separation. Acetone-chloroform was found to be satisfactory. The change in the separation when the acetone concentration was varied is shown in figure 2. The separation of B_1 and B_2 was good with an acetone-chloroform developer and particularly at an acetone concentration of 5 to 10 percent. The separation of B_2 and G_1 was poorer than in case of methanol-chloroform developers but, from the overall point of view, better separations were obtained by use of acetone-chloroform than by use of methanol-chloroform.

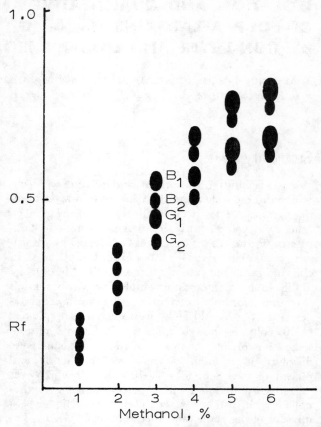

Figure 1—TLC chromatogram of aflatoxin mix; adsorbent: Silica gel G; developer: Methanol-chloroform.

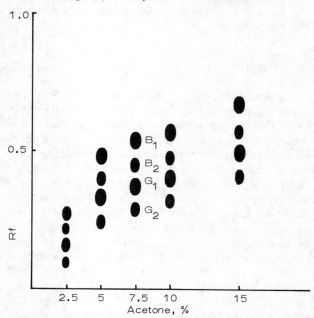

Figure 2.—TLC chromatogram of aflatoxin mix; adsorbent: Silica gel G; developer: Acetone-chloroform.

TLC of AF with silica gel HR.—As Silica gel G contains about 13 percent calcium sulfate, a study was carried out on Silica gel HR which does not contain any calcium sulfate being composed only of silica gel. This comparison was made in order to find out what effect calcium sulfate had on the separations. A test was carried out on this thin layer using methanol-chloroform and acetone-chloroform developers and it was found that good separation of the four kinds of AF was obtained with methanol-chloroform. A comparison of Silica gel HR and Silica gel G is shown in figure 3. It is clear from this that good separation was obtained with acetone-chloroform developer in case of Silica gel G thin layer and with methanol-chloroform in case of Silica gel HR.

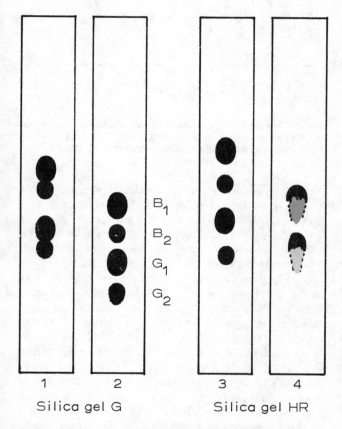

1   2   3   4

Silica gel G   Silica gel HR

Figure 3.—TLC chromatogram of aflatoxin mix: (1) 3 percent methanol in chloroform; (2) 5 percent acetone in chloroform; (3) 3 percent methanol in chloroform; (4) 5 percent acetone in chloroform.

LC of AF, aluminum oxide.—When a crude AF mixture is added to an aluminum oxide column and extracted with a chloroform solvent containing 1 percent methanol, AF–G_1 and G_2 are absorbed by the column and only AF–B_1 and B_2 are eluted selectively. Methanol and ethanol, which are strong elution agents, were tested for elution of AF–G_1 and G_2 but they could not be eluted. This column had the characteristic of eluting only AF–B_1 and B_2; the separation of the four kinds of AF was inefficient; also the pigments mixed in the crude AF mixture could not be removed.

LC of AF on silica gel.—The experiment employed 100-mesh silica gel and methanol-chloroform or acetone-chloroform, which had been used in TLC, as the developers. When methanol-chloroform was used, separation of the four kinds of AF was not possible since they were eluted together when the methanol concentration was over 2 percent. Separation of the four kinds of AF was observed when the methanol content was below 1 percent but pigments could not be removed. In the case of acetone-chloroform, good separation was indicated with the acetone concentration at 5 percent but the pigments could not be separated from the AF. When carrying out elution with this 5 percent acetone concentration, the silica gel was packed in the chromatograph tube with an elution agent saturated with water so that the column contained some moisture. In the separation with this column, first AF–B_1 was eluted followed by B_2, G_1, and G_2. Separation was better, the slower the rate of elution, and the AF layer became disturbed and separation was inefficient, if elution was carried out under pressure using a micro-pump. Elution was carried out with descending solvent at the rate of 15 ml. per hour and the results of measurements by absorption at 363 mμ, of 15 ml. fractions, are shown in figure 4. The defect of the silica gel column is that it was difficult to maintain the activity of the silica gel constant. There were cases in which separation was inefficient depending on the column, thus it had poor reproducibility. Also, in case of AF–B_1, fluorescence became weaker as it advanced through the column and consequently, it appeared that it changed gradually in the column. We consider this silica gel column not to be suitable for separation and purification.

LC of AF on Sephadex.—As the molecular weights of the four kinds of AF range from 312 to 330, a study was carried out with Sephadex G–10 which has the finest network among Sephadexes used for gel filtration. Sephadex G–25, which has a coarser network than this, and Sephadex LH–20, which can be used with organic solvents, were also studied because AF is very soluble in organic solvents.

Sephadex G–10 is normally used with aqueous solutions but since the crude AF mixture is difficultly soluble in water, it was dissolved in methanol for application to the column. Since Sephadex swollen with water shrinks in organic solvent, dry Sephadex G–10 was first swollen with an aqueous 1 percent methanol solution and then packed in the chromatograph tube and equilibrated. The elution liquid was

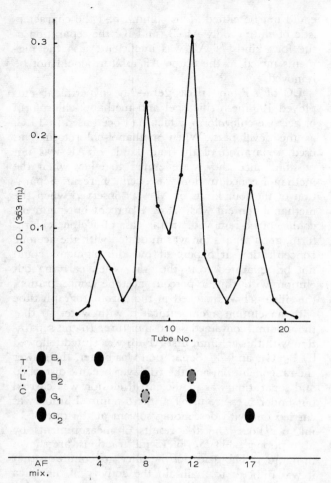

Above : Fractionation of Aflatoxin Mix. on a 8X500 mm
Column of Silica gel.
Eluant : 5% acetone in chloroform
Below : Chromatogram of Fractionated Aflatoxin on TLC.

Figure 4.—Above: Fractionation of aflatoxin mix on a 8 x 500 mm. column of silica gel; eluant: 5 percent acetone in chloroform. Below: Chromatogram of fractionated aflatoxin on TLC.

collected in fractions of 4.5 ml. each. The measurements of absorption of 363 mμ, and the TLC of absorption peak fractions are shown in figure 5. The four kinds of AF were mutually separated by this method, and at the same time, the pigments were removed. The sequence of elution was, the brown pigment became two layers and was eluted, then AF–G_2, B_2, G_1, and B_1 were eluted, in that order. The yellow pigment was adsorbed on the column and was not eluted. The optimum elution rate for the separations was 20 ml. per hour and it was also possible to employ elution under pressure, using a pump.

The elution liquid composition was varied in order to find the optimal conditions for separation through Sephadex G–10 using the same procedure as described

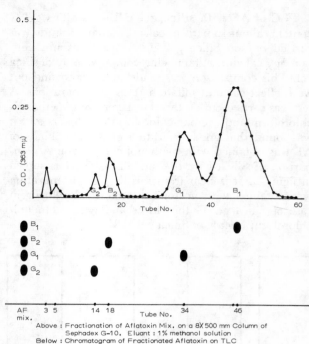

Above : Fractionation of Aflatoxin Mix. on a 8X500 mm Column of
Sephadex G–10. Eluant : 1% methanol solution
Below : Chromatogram of Fractionated Aflatoxin on TLC

Figure 5.—Above: Fractionation of aflatoxin mix on a 8 x 500 mm. column of Sephadex G–10; eluant: 1 percent methanol solution. Below: Chromatogram of fractionated aflatoxin on TLC.

above. Aqueous 50 percent methanol was employed to see the effect of increasing the concentration of methanol; 0.05M NaCl solution to test the effect of adding a solute; 0.1M acetic acid solution to test the effect of acidification; and pure water was also used. The results are shown in figures 6 through 9.

The best separation of the four kinds of AF was obtained when pure water was the eluant, while elutions with the other solutions was inefficient. In view of this, the separation of the four kinds of AF by aqueous 1 percent methanol solution and pure water were studied by measuring the elution peaks of the four kinds of AF, automatically, using Japan Electric Co.'s Universal Spectrum Analyzer, and distribution coefficients (Kd) were calculated. According to the distribution coefficients (table 1), the separation of the four kinds of AF by elution with pure water was best but not too different from 1 percent methanol. The distribution coefficients of AF were larger than 1 in both solvents, from which it can be seen that the adsorption effect is larger than the gel filtration effect. It is believed that good separation obtained with Sephadex G–10 was due to the following two reasons.

Firstly, Sephadex G–10 contains some carboxyl radicals, although the quantity is very small. Therefore, the adsorption of the alkaline radical increases when this is present in the sample if water is used as

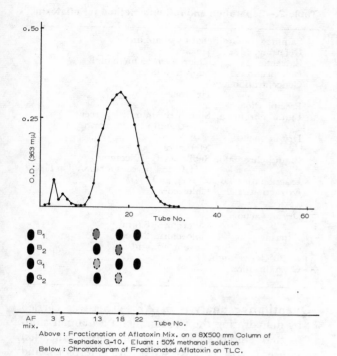

Figure 6.—Above: Fractionation of aflatoxin mix on a 8 x 500 mm. column of Sephadex G–10; eluant: 50 percent methanol solution. Below: Chromatogram of fractionated aflatoxin on TLC.

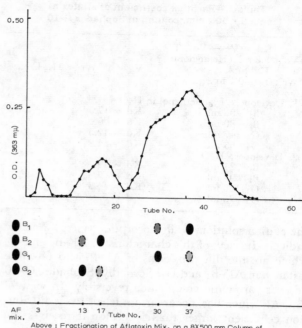

Figure 8.—Above: Fractionation of aflatoxin mix on a 8 x 500 mm. column of Sephadex G–10; eluant: M/10 acetic acid solution. Below: Chromatogram of fractionated aflatoxin on TLC.

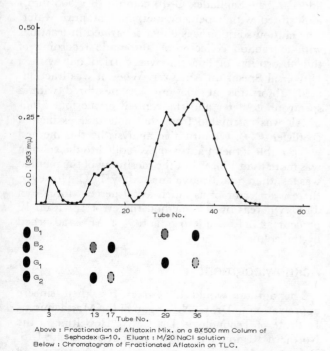

Figure 7.—Above: Fractionation of aflatoxin mix on a 8 x 500 mm. column of Sephadex G–10; eluant: M/20 NaCl solution. Below: Chromatogram of fractionated aflatoxin on TLC.

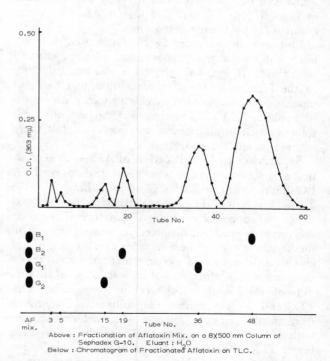

Figure 9.—Above: Fractionation of aflatoxin mix on a 8 x 500 mm. column of Sephadex G–10; eluant: H₂O. Below: Chromatogram of fractionated aflatoxin on TLC.

Table 1.—Partition coefficient of aflatoxin on a 8 x 500 mm. column of Sephadex G–10

$$Kd = Ve - Vo/Vi$$

Vo : 8.8 ml. (Hemoglobin).
a : 11.14 g. $Vi = a$ $Wr = 11.14$ ml.
Wr : 1.0 ± 0.1 ml./g.
Ve :
1. Developer: 1% methanol in H_2O

	Ve	Kd
B_1	203 ml.	$Kd = 17.5$
B_2	80 ml.	$Kd = 6.4$
G_1	147 ml.	$Kd = 12.5$
G_2	63 ml.	$Kd = 4.9$

2. Developer: H_2O

	Ve	Kd
B_1	224 ml.	$Kd = 19.2$
B_2	93 ml.	$Kd = 7.5$
G_1	168 ml.	$Kd = 14.3$
G_2	75 ml.	$Kd = 5.9$

Table 2.—Separation and refining method for aflatoxin

Sample (contaminated by aflatoxin).
Defatting _____ Hexane.
Extraction _____ Chloroform or methanol.
Dehydration _____ Sodium sulfate.
Concentration
                                    Hexane.
Precipitation
Liquid chromato. Silica gel column, 1 percent.
                                    methanol in chloroform.
Dry in vacuo.
                                    Methanol.
Liquid chromato. Sephadex G–10 column
                                    H_2O or 1 percent methanol in H_2O.
Fractionation (B_1, B_2, G_1, and G_2).
Extraction _____ Chloroform.

Shotwell etal.:
Dry in vacuo.
                                    Chloroform 6.6 ml.
Filtering   Chloroform 2.0 ml.
                                    Hexane 16.5 ml.
At 20°C. overnight.
Crystallization.

the elution solution, while adsorption is less for acidic radicals. In view of this characteristic, AF–B_2 and G_2 which are the dihydro forms of AF–B_1 and G_1 elute faster than AF–B_1 and G_1. Secondly, Sephadex G–10 adsorbs aromatic compounds reversibly. In view of this, AF which has a coumarin nucleus has a distribution coefficient larger than 1 because it receives the adsorption effect but, at the same time, it receives the gel filtration effect. Consequently, the G group elutes faster than the B group because the structures of AF–G_1 and AF–G_2 are larger than those of AF–B_1 and AF–B_2, respectively, since they contain one oxygen atom in excess. Other factors other than the above can be considered but it is felt that the order of elution (G_2, B_2, G_1, and B_1) is adequately accounted for by these two reasons.

Elution with Sephadex G–25 was carried out with pure water since good separation had been effected with the G–10 gel, but separation was unsatisfactory as the four kinds of AF were eluted together and separation of the pigment was inefficient. With regard to Sephadex LH–20, elution was carried out with solvents such as chloroform and methanol but there was practically no separation.

Separation and purification of AF.—The separation and refining process which was devised, used the LC method with Sephadex G–10 as is shown in table 2. The first half of the process is the same as described for preparation of the crude AF mixture. The crude AF mixture was then dissolved in a small amount of methanol, added to the Sephadex G–10 column and eluted with aqueous 1 percent methanol solution or pure water. The elution solution was collected in fractions of 10 ml. each and the fractions were assayed by TLC and UV absorption. The collected AF solutions were transferred to a separatory funnel and shaken with chloroform to extract AF into the chloroform layer. This chloroform solution was dried under reduced pressure and the procedure thereafter was of Shotwell et al. (6). The final products were white crystals of each of the four kinds of AF.

Quantitative analysis of AF.—This was carried out by dehydrating the test sample in a manner similar to that employed in the separation purification procedure. It was then extracted with chloroform and the extract solution dried under reduced pressure to remove the solvent. The extracted material was then dissolved in a fixed amount of methanol. A suitable quantity of this concentrate (less than 0.5 ml.) was added to the Sephadex G–10 column (8 x 500 mm.) and eluted with 1 percent methanol or pure water. The elution solution was either separated in fractions with a fraction collector or automatic recording of the absorption of 363 mμ was carried out with a Universal Spectrum Analyzer. When it was fractionated, absorption at 363 mμ was measured with a spectrophotometer and the content of the four kinds of AF was calculated from the molecular extinction coefficients (4). Quantitative analysis by this method was possible if the quantity of AF added to the column was more than 10 μg., but the sensitivity of the method was less than quantitative analysis by TLC. However, there is an error of as much as 20 percent in case of TLC, whereas by this method the error is within 10 percent as only a micro quantity of AF is adsorbed by the column.

Acknowledgment

The authors would like to express their sincere appreciation to Dr. G. N. Wogan of the Massachusetts Institute of Technology, Dr. C. W. Hesseltine of the Northern Regional Research Laboratory of the U.S. Department of Agriculture, and Dr. T. Yokotsuka of the Central Research Institute of Kikkoman Shoyu Co., Ltd., for supplying the strain ATCC 15517 and the standard aflatoxins.

References

(1) CAMPBELL, A. D., and J. T. FUNKHOUSER. 1966. Collaborative study on the analysis of aflatoxins in peanut butter. J. Assoc. Official Agricultural Chemists *49:* 730–739.

(2) CHEN, S., and L. FRIDMAN. 1966. Aflatoxin determination in seed meal. J. Assoc. Official Agricultural Chemists *49:* 28–33.

(3) HARTLEY, R. D., B. F. NESBITT, and J. O'KELLY. 1963. Toxic metabolites of *Aspergillus flavus*. Nature *198:* 1056–1058.

(4) PONS, W. A., A. F. CUCULLU, JR., L. S. LEE, J. A. ROBERTSON, A. O. FRANZ, and L. A. GOLDBLATT. 1966. Determination of aflatoxins in agricultural products: Use of aqueous acetone for extraction. J. Assoc. Official Agricultural Chemists *49:* 554–562.

(5) ROBERTSON, J. A., W. A. PONS, JR., and L. A. GOLDBLATT. 1967. Preparation of aflatoxins and determination of their ultraviolet and fluorescent characteristics. J. Agric. Food Chem. *15:* 798–801.

(6) SHOTWELL, O. L., C. W. HESSELTINE, R. D. STUBBLEFIELD, and W. G. SORENSON. 1966. Production of aflatoxin on rice. Appl. Microbiol. *14:* 425–428.

(7) STUBBLEFIELD, R. D., O. L. SHOTWELL, and G. M. SHANNON. 1967. Aflatoxins B_1, B_2, G_1, and G_2; separation and purification by column chromatography. Paper presented at the 58th annual meeting of Association of Official Agricultural Chemists, New Orleans, May 7–10.

(8) TRAGER, W., L. STOLOFF, and A. D. CAMPBELL. 1964. A comparison of assay procedures for aflatoxin in peanut products. J. Assoc. Official Agricultural Chemists *47:* 993–1001.

(9) WOGAN, G. N. 1966. Chemical nature and biological effects of the aflatoxins. Bacteriol. Rev. *30:* 460–470.

OBJECTIVE DETERMINATION OF AFLATOXINS B_1, B_2, G_1, AND G_2 BY FLUORODENSITOMETRY

by LEO A. GOLDBLATT
Oilseed Crops Laboratory, Southern Utilization Research and Development Division, Agricultural Research Service, U.S. Department of Agriculture, New Orleans, La. 70119

Summary

Aflatoxin contents are usually estimated by visual comparison on thin-layer chromatographic plates (TLC) of the fluorescence intensities of separated aflatoxin spots obtained from aliquots of sample extracts and from aflatoxin standards chromatographed on the same plate. Such analyses are accurate to no more than about ±20 percent. Objective fluorodensitometric measurements permit estimations with a precision of ±2 to 3 percent for aflatoxins B_1 and G_1 and of ±5 percent for B_2 and G_2. In a collaborative study by eight laboratories on the TLC resolution and fluorodensitometric measurement of aflatoxins B_1, B_2, G_1, and G_2 added to a purified cottonseed meal, coefficients of variation for individual aflatoxin measurements ranged from ±4 to 10 percent, and amounted to ±5 percent for total aflatoxins, with average recoveries of 93 to 99 percent of the amounts added. Both the accuracy and the precision of estimates of aflatoxin content are significantly improved by fluorodensitometric measurements. A fluorodensitometric measurement system, its operation, and its application to determination of aflatoxins in cottonseed products are described. The order and relative fluorescence response of aflatoxins B_1, B_2, G_1, and G_2 on the precision of fluorodensitometric measurements are discussed.

Introduction

Most procedures for the determination of the aflatoxin content of agricultural products are based upon the fluorescent characteristics of the compounds for quantitation.

Typically, samples are first extracted with an appropriate solvent, the extracts are concentrated and partially purified, and the individual aflatoxins in aliquots of the partially purified extracts are further purified and resolved by thin-layer chromatography (TLC) on silica gel coated plates. The aflatoxin contents of the aliquots are then estimated by visual comparison of the fluorescence intensities of the separated aflatoxin spots from the sample aliquots with those of appropriate aflatoxin standards chromato-graphed on the same plate while exposed to long-wave (365 mμ) ultraviolet (UV) radiation. The intensity of the fluorescence of aflatoxins makes possible the visual detection of as little as 3 to 4 x 10^{-4} μg. (0.3 to 0.4 nanogram) of aflatoxin B_1 or G_1 on a TLC plate [3] and thus affords the basis of an extremely sensitive procedure. But, analysis by visual comparison of fluorescence intensities must at best be regarded as only semiquantitative. Due to differences in visual acuity, eye fatigue, and the difficulty of estimating small differences in fluorescence intensity with the eye visual analysis is accurate to no more than about ±20 percent. Thus Beckwith and Stoloff [2] in a study of the error associated with the visual comparison of fluorescent aflatoxin spots on a TLC plate found that the precision limit for visual comparison, determined under ideal conditions of juxtaposition of spots of aflatoxin and freedom from extract interference, was 20 percent. They concluded "the precision limit of visual comparison procedures used in aflatoxin methods can be no better than ±20 percent for a single observation and, under operating conditions, it is probably close to ±28 percent."

Both the accuracy and precision of aflatoxin determinations would undoubtedly be improved by a more objective instrumental procedure. The first effort to use an objective method seems to have been based on oscillographic polarography [4]. Aflatoxins B_1 and G_1 were found to give characteristic oscillopolarographic traces. The diffusion current was reported to be proportional to concentration and suitable for quantitative analysis of fairly pure preparations but satisfactory methods do not appear to have been developed for adequate purification of extracts from naturally contaminated materials.

Nabney and Nesbitt [5] utilized ultraviolet absorption spectrophotometry as the basis for an objective procedure for the determination of aflatoxins, particularly aflatoxin B_1. In this procedure concentrated chloroform solutions of partially purified extracts were streaked across plates coated with Kieselgel G and the plates were developed successively with diethyl ether and then with chloroform:methanol to separate the aflatoxins into discrete bands. The bands were scraped off, eluted with methanol, and the aflatoxin contents of the methanol extracts were estimated by absorption spectrophotometry at 363 mμ. Some 3 to 10 μg. of isolated aflatoxins were required for accurate measurements, as absorption is much less sensitive for the aflatoxins than is fluorescence, by a factor of 1,000 or more. Multiple plates were processed to obtain sufficient B_2 for measurement but even so the technique was limited to analysis of materials high in aflatoxin content.

An instrumental procedure for the determination of aflatoxin B_1 directly on TLC plates using a densitometer equipped for measurement of fluorescence was first proposed by Ayres and Sinnhuber (1). They found that a logarithmic function of emitted fluorescence energy and concentration when plotted on semilog paper was linear over a concentration range of about 2.5 to 15 x 10^{-4} μg. of aflatoxin B_1 per spot and used the procedure for estimating the aflatoxin B_1 content of extracts from cottonseed meals. Shortly thereafter, we undertook to explore more fully the parameters involved in the measurement of the solid state fluorescence of aflatoxins on TLC plates (8). This included study of the linearity of emitted fluorescence to concentration, the relative response of individual aflatoxins, the constancy of the response, the precision of solid state fluorescence measurements and the conditions for adequate resolution of the individual aflatoxins. Satisfactory resolution of the aflatoxins is critical for fluorodensitometric methods and a procedure for calculation of numerical resolution factors to evaluate the degree of resolution on TLC plates has recently been proposed (7).

Densitometric Measurement System

A schematic outline of the basic fluorometric densitometry measurement system is shown in figure 1. Briefly, the procedure involves placing a developed TLC plate (gel layer downward) on a motor driven stage, positioning the aflatoxin spots over a primary slit for exposure to a beam of filtered long-wave ultraviolet radiation, scanning the aflatoxin spots, passing the emitted fluorescence radiation through a narrow collimating slit and secondary filter to a photomultiplier tube, and recording the output (8).

We used a Photovolt model 530 densitometer (manufactured by the Photovolt Corp., New York, N.Y. 10010)[1] equipped with a long-wave (320 to 390 mμ) UV lamp, No. 365 primary filter and 6 x 19 mm. primary slit; a stage for TLC plates equipped with an automatic drive (1 inch per minute) and also with a manual rack; a search unit containing a 0.1 x 15-mm. collimating slit, a No. 465 secondary filter

[1]Use of a company and/or product name does not imply endorsement by the Department of Agriculture to the exclusion of others which may also be suitable.

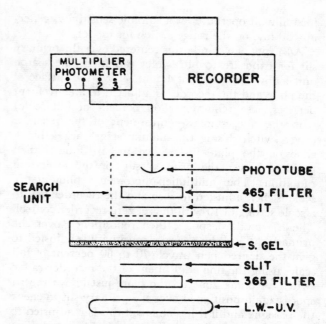

Figure 1.—Schematic diagram of densitometer-recorder.

and a UV sensitive phototube No. 28B; and a No. 520–A multiplier-photometer. With this is used a recorder (Varicord model 43 with a 4-inch per minute chart speed) equipped with an automatic recording integrator (Integraph model 49). We modified the stage by replacing the original rounded tongue with an 8.5-inch long aluminum **T** bar to permit better lateral alinement of the TLC plates. The equipment is operated in a dimly illuminated room and is allowed to warm up for at least 10 minutes before measurements are made.

Operation of Measurement System

The operation of recording the fluorescence emission response of various aflatoxin spots may be illustrated using B_1 as an example. A standard 20 x 20 cm. silica-gel-coated TLC plate is spotted with suitable aliquots of the unknown and of a standard of known aflatoxin content. The plate is developed with any suitable developing solvent and air dried in the dark for about 15 minutes. About 0.5 inch of the gel is removed from the top and bottom edges of the developed plate and small protective guides (made from 26-gage aluminum, 7.5 inches long x 0.5 inches wide with a $\frac{5}{32}$-inch channel) are slipped over the top and bottom edges. The plate is placed on the stage, gel layer down, so that the direction of scan will be downward from above the B_1 spot toward the origin, and securely butted against the **T** bar. The multiplier-photometer is set at suitable sensitivity (position 3 for model 520–A) and the recorder is set for millivolt operation at a suitable sensitivity, generally 50 mv. on the range switch for model 43.

A B_1 spot of a standard is centered over the primary slit for exposure to ultraviolet radiation, the search unit is lowered to about 1 mm. above the surface of the plate and the recorder is adjusted to a convenient pen response (commonly 60 percent of full scale) with the fine, stepless, adjustment of the recorder range switch. Using the manual stage rack a blank zone on the plate just above the B_1 spot is then positioned over the primary slit for the excitation radiation. The multiplier-photometer photometric scale is then adjusted to zero and the recorder pen to a scale setting of 10 with the set zero recorder control. The B_1 standard spot is then repositioned over the primary slit and the recorder sensitivity is adjusted to give the desired pen travel, 70 to 80 percent of full scale, using the fine adjustment of the recorder range switch. A blank zone on the plate just above the B_1 spot is again positioned over the primary slit to check the baseline and if it has changed this is readjusted to a baseline value of 10 with the set zero control. The recorder chart drive is then activated, the automatic integrator set for minimum baseline count (about 1 count per 10 seconds), and the plate is scanned by activating the automatic stage drive. The plate is scanned from above the B_1 spot toward the origin. All operations prior to the scan should be performed as quickly as possible to ensure minimum exposure of aflatoxin to UV radiation. The recorder sensitivity adjustment as set for the first B_1 standard spot should not be changed during subsequent scans on the same plate. However, the baseline should be checked between scans and should be readjusted with the recorder set zero control if necessary.

A recorder trace of a chromatogram on a TLC plate of a standard solution of the four aflatoxins B_1, B_2, G_1, and G_2 is shown in figure 2. It may be seen that the four aflatoxins are well resolved and the peaks return essentially to the baseline between the individual aflatoxins. This is especially noteworthy as the densitometer is even more sensitive than the eye in detecting trace fluorescence. In the figure shown here (fig. 2) the aflatoxin B_1 content of the aliquot of the standard spotted amounted to 0.005 μg.; i.e., 5 nanograms. Detailed descriptions of applicable procedures and operations will be found in publications by Pons et al. (8, 9).

Fluorescence Response of Aflatoxins B_1, B_2, G_1, and G_2

The relationship between recorded peak areas of emitted fluorescence of aflatoxins and concentration was found to be linear over a range of at least 3 to 105×10^{-4} μg. of aflatoxin B_1 and 2 to 70×10^{-4}

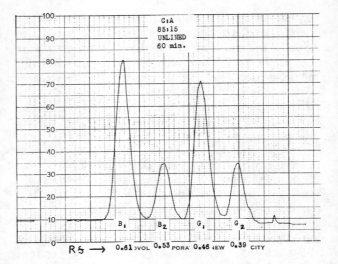

Figure 2.—Recorder trace of aflatoxins B_1, B_2, G_1, and G_2 on TLC plate.

μg. of aflatoxin G_1 per spot (8). The linearity of the area-concentration relationship for aflatoxins B_1, B_2, G_1, and G_2 over a more limited range is shown graphically in figure 3. From this figure it can be seen that although for each aflatoxin the relationship between area and concentration is linear the aflatoxins differ in the magnitude of their fluorescence intensities. The slopes of the curves indicate a relative response $B_2 > G_2 > B_1 > G_1$. The magnitude of the relative response values is influenced by the transmission characteristics of the secondary filter. This is illustrated in table 1 in which is shown results obtained using Silica Gel G–HR coated plates and Nos. 445 and 465 filters. The excitation maxima for the four aflatoxins are all about 368 to 369 mμ but the fluorescence emission maxima for aflatoxins B_1, B_2, G_1, and G_2 in the solid state on silica gel are 432, 427, 455, and 450 mμ, respectively (10). The 445 filter has maximum transmittance at 435 mμ with a UV cutoff at about 390 mμ while the 465 filter has maximum transmittance at 460 mμ with a UV cutoff at 400 mμ (8). Accordingly, the 445 filter discriminates in favor of B_1 and B_2 with a reduction in the G_1 and G_2 response. Inasmuch as the 465 filter gave a much more nearly equivalent response of B_1:G_1 and B_2:G_2 it was selected for general use. With either filter the relative response for these silica gel-coated plates is in the same order viz: $B_2 > G_2 > B_1 > G_1$, but the ratios differ.

The response ratios are not highly reproducible physical constants as they are influenced not only by the filters but also by the type of silica gel used and still other factors including the duration and intensity of previous exposure to UV radiation (8). In experiments with three types of silica gels the response ratios of B_2:B_1 ranged from 1.6 to 2.8 and of G_2:G_1

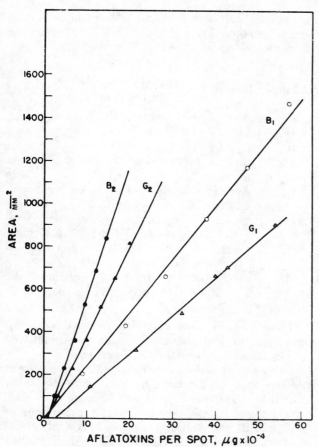

Figure 3.—Linearity of fluorescense response (area) versus concentration relationship for aflatoxins B₁, B₂, G₁, and G₂.

cence response ratios are found in solvents and the order as well as the magnitude of the relative fluorescence intensities may differ in various solvents and in the solid state on silica gel. The order and relative intensities of fluorescence of the aflatoxins in several solvents and in the solid state as reported by Robertson and Pons (10) are given in table 2.

Table 1.—Relative fluorescence intensities of aflatoxins on plates coated with Silica Gel G–HR[1]

Aflatoxin	$\mu g. \times 10^{-4}$ spotted	445 filter[2]		465 filter[2]	
		$\mu g. \times 10^{-4}$[3]	Relative response	$\mu g. \times 10^{-4}$[3]	Relative response
B₂ -----	33.8	3.02	4.9	3.11	3.3
G₂ ----	36.1	1.66	2.7	2.84	3.0
B₁ -----	68.2	1.25	2.0	1.36	1.4
G₁ ----	102.4	.62	1.0	.95	1.0

[1]From reference (8).
[2]Approximate wavelength of maximum transmittance.
[3]From integrator area counts.
NOTES
    Ratio B₂ : B₁,   2.4 : 1,   2.3 : 1.
    Ratio G₂ : G₁,   2.7 : 1,   3.0 : 1.

Precision of Fluorodensitometric Measurements

Estimates of precision from measurement of pure aflatoxins B₁ and G₁ on TLC plates indicated a measurement precision, as expressed by coefficients of variation, of ±2 to 4 percent (8). Stubblefield et al. (11) employed fluorodensitometric measurements to estimate aflatoxins produced by cultures of A. flavus and reported average deviations of ±2 to 3 percent for aflatoxins B₁ and G₁ and ±5 percent for B₂ and G₂. Beckwith and Stoloff (2) have reported attainable precision of about 5 percent for fluorodensitometric measurements of aflatoxins. In a collaborative study by eight laboratories on the TLC resolution and fluorodensitometric measurements of aflatoxins B₁, B₂, G₁, and G₂ added to a purified cottonseed meal extract coefficients of variation for individual aflatoxin

from 2.2 to 3.7. Thus the use of authentic reference standards of each aflatoxin is an absolute requirement in fluorodensitometric analysis. Obviously, however, the heretofore common practice in visual estimation of the aflatoxin B₂ content of unknowns by comparison with the B₁ standard and of the G₂ content by comparison with the G₁ standard may result in overestimation of aflatoxins B₂ and G₂ by a factor of 2 to 3. It may be noted that even greater variations in fluores-

Table 2.—Order and relative intensities of aflatoxin fluorescence in solution and solid state[1]

Measurement conditions	Instrument used	Fluorescence order	Relative intensity			
			B₁	B₂	G₁	G₂
Methanol solvents ----------	Baird -----------	G₂ > B₂ > G₁ > B₁ -------	1.0	8.8	1.7	14.8
Ethanol solvents ------------do-----------		G₂ > B₂ > G₁ > B₁ -------	1.0	2.7	1.4	4.7
Chloroform solvents ------------do-----------		G₂ > G₁ > B₂ > B₁ -------	1.0	1.3	31.0	34.0
Acetonitrile solvents ----------	Aminco -----------	G₂ > G₁ > B₂ > B₁ -------	1.0	6.1	54.1	72.7
Silica gel—Solid ------------do-----------		B₂ > G₂ > B₁ > G₁ -------	1.5	6.6	1.0	4.2
Silica gel—Solid -----------	Densitometer ------	B₂ > G₂ > B₁ > G₁ -------	1.4	3.3	1.0	3.0

[1]From reference (10).

measurements ranged from ±4 to 10 percent, and ±5 percent for total aflatoxins with average recoveries of 93 to 99 percent of the amounts added (6).

Determination of Aflatoxins in Cottonseed Products

An improved fluorodensitometric method for the determination of aflatoxins in cottonseed products has recently been reported (9). This paper should be consulted for full details of the procedures and techniques. The procedure for preparation of the extract may be outlined very briefly, as follows:

A 25-g. ground sample is extracted with 250 ml. of a mixed solvent (acetone:water:acetic acid, 850:150:8) on a mechanical shaker. The extract is filtered and an aliquot (50 percent) is partially purified by treatment with lead acetate and filtered and an aliquot (80 percent) of this filtrate is partitioned into chloroform. The chloroform soluble portion is further cleaned up using a short column of silica gel, first washing with a mixture of diethyl ether:hexane to remove interfering fluorescent materials and then eluting aflatoxins with chloroform:acetone.

The evaporated eluate, which now contains relatively little extraneous interfering impurity, is taken up in exactly 0.5 ml. chloroform for Preliminary TLC. In this step 2, 5 and 10 μl. aliquots of the extract are used to determine the approximate aflatoxin content as judged by visual comparison with aflatoxin standards. Based upon the results of the Preliminary TLC evaluation the volume of purified extract is adjusted to optimum dilution for densitometric analysis (9). Appropriate duplicate sample aliquots along with duplicate 5 μl. aliquots of an aflatoxin standard are spotted on a TLC plate, placing the spots 2 cm. apart along an imaginary line about 4 cm. from the bottom of the plate. A line is scribed across the top about 12 to 13 cm. beyond the origin and the plate is developed, in an upright position in an unlined unequilibrated tank with 150 ml. of development solvent (chloroform:acetone:isopropanol, 850:125:25) until the solvent front reaches the scribed line. A development solvent of chloroform:acetone (85:15) is equally satisfactory. The plate is removed, air dried in the dark for about 15 minutes and measured with the densitometer according to the procedure given in the section entitled "Operation of Measurement System." If a plate is inspected visually prior to measurement, a low-wattage UV lamp should be used and exposure time should be held to a minimum.

We use integrator area counts to calculate aflatoxin contents. Triangulation of the peaks of the recorder trace may, of course, also be used to determine areas. Integrator area counts are determined (9) for each aflatoxin peak averaging the counts for each aflatoxin

in the duplicate standard and sample aliquots. Aflatoxin B_1 content of the sample is calculated according to the following equation:

$$\text{Aflatoxin } B_1 \text{ (ppb)} = \frac{(A_x)(V_s)(C_s)(S_D) \times 1.04}{(A_s)(V_x)(W)}$$

(A_x) = Average area count of the B_1 sample spot.
(V_s) = μl. of standard spotted.
(C_s) = μg. of B_1 per ml. of standard.
(S_D) = Sample dilution; volume of final extract in μl.
(A_s) = Average area count of the B_1 standard spot.
(V_x) = μl. of sample extract spotted.
(W) = grams of original sample represented by the final sample extract; 10 if 25 g. of original sample was taken and the indicated aliquots were used.
1.04 = correction factor for the 3.4 percent of the sample extract used for Preliminary TLC.

The same procedure is used for aflatoxins B_2, G_1, and G_2 (if present) substituting the appropriate area counts, aliquots, and standard concentrations.

Using this procedure a precision of ±2 to 4 percent was reported (9) for the estimation of aflatoxins B_1 and B_2 in cottonseed meal and average recoveries ranged from 89 to 100 percent of the amounts of aflatoxins B_1, B_2, G_1, and G_2 added to typical cottonseed products. The procedure has also been applied to peanuts, peanut butter, mixed feeds, and other agricultural products with satisfactory results.

The procedure described is currently the subject of a collaborative study for the determination of aflatoxins in cottonseed products with some collaborators determining the aflatoxins both by visual estimation and densitometrically. However, the results of several investigations (1, 2, 6, 8, 9, 11) on the precision and accuracy of fluorodensitometric estimation of aflatoxins thus far reported suggest that the technique is a reasonably precise and accurate analytical tool, and superior to visual estimation.

Acknowledgment

The contributions and cooperation of A. F. Cucullu, F. G. Dollear, A. O. Franz, Jr., L. S. Lee, W. A. Pons, Jr., and J. A. Robertson are gratefully acknowledged.

References

(1) AYRES, J. L., and R. O. SINNHUBER. 1966. Fluorodensitometry of aflatoxin on thin-layer plates. J. Am. Oil Chemists' Soc. 43: 423–424.
(2) BECKWITH, A. C., and L. STOLOFF. 1968. Fluoro-

densitometric measurements of aflatoxin thin layer chromatograms. J. Assoc. Offic. Anal. Chemists *51*: 602–608.

(*3*) COOMES, T. J., P. C. CROWTHER, B. J. FRANCIS, and L. STEVENS. 1965. The detection and estimation of aflatoxins in groundnuts and groundnut materials. Analyst *90*: 492–496.

(*4*) GARJAN, R. J., S. NESHEIM, and A. D. CAMPBELL. 1964. Note on identification of aflatoxins by oscillographic polarography. J. Assoc. Offic. Agr. Chemists *47*: 27–28.

(*5*) NABNEY, J., and B. F. NESBITT. 1965. A spectrophotometric method for determining the aflatoxins. Analyst *90*: 155–160.

(*6*) PONS, W. A., Jr. 1968. Fluorodensitometric measurements of aflatoxins on TLC plates. J. Assoc. Offic. Anal. Chemists *51*: 913–914.

(*7*) PONS, W. A., Jr., and L. A. GOLDBLATT. 1968. Instrumental evaluation of aflatoxin resolution on TLC plates. J. Assoc. Offic. Anal. Chemists *51*: 1194–1197.

(*8*) PONS, W. A., Jr., J. A. ROBERTSON, and L. A. GOLDBLATT. 1966. Objective fluorometric measurement of aflatoxins on TLC plates. J. Am. Oil Chemists' Soc. *43*: 665–669.

(*9*) PONS, W. A., Jr., A. F. CUCULLU, A. O. FRANZ, and L. A. GOLDBLATT. 1968. Improved objective fluorodensitometric determination of aflatoxins in cottonseed products. J. Am. Oil Chemists' Soc. *45*: 694–699.

(*10*) ROBERTSON, J. A., and W. A. PONS, Jr. 1968. Solid state fluorescence emission of aflatoxins on silica gel. J. Assoc. Offic. Anal. Chemists *51*: 1190–1192.

(*11*) STUBBLEFIELD, R. D., O. L. SHOTWELL, C. W. HESSELTINE, M. L. SMITH, and H. H. HALL. 1967. Production of aflatoxin on wheat and oats: Measurement with a recording densitometer. Appl. Microbiol. *15*: 186–190.

CHEMICAL METHODS FOR MYCOTOXINS

by A. D. Campbell

Division of Food Chemistry and Technology, Bureau of Science, Food and Drug Administration, Department of Health, Education, and Welfare, Washington, D.C. 20204

Summary

Chemical methods for the detection and estimation of mycotoxins are discussed. The need for different methods for the aflatoxins for various commodities and for particular requirements such as those for regulatory and for manufacturing plant control purposes is emphasized. The methods for the lesser known mycotoxins such as ochratoxin, zearalenone, patulin, sterigmatocystin, and aflatoxin M are presented with emphasis on their limitations and areas where improvements are desired. The need for performance standards for the highly variable reagents such as column silica gels and TLC silica gels used in these methods are discussed. Recent trends in methods for sample preparation are presented.

Methods have been developed for the chemical analysis of several of the mycotoxins. In some instances a method has received limited application, but in others considerable information has been accumulated by the more general application of the method to the control of practical problems. At this time aflatoxin is still the mycotoxin about which most is known and is the one for which a large amount of information has been accumulated by the practical application in the regulation and control of peanuts, Brazil nuts, and cottonseed used for food by man and animals.

The following aspects of the overall mycotoxin problem will be discussed:

(1) Sampling and sample preparation;
(2) Aflatoxin methods currently in use for specific applications;
(3) Methods for other mycotoxins;
(4) Chemical confirmation methods.

Sampling and Sample Preparation

Sampling and sample preparation are particularly difficult problems because of the nature of mycotoxin contaminations. It has been shown that the major part of the total contamination of a lot can be accounted for by a relatively few, highly contaminated units. This has been determined by carrying out aflatoxin analyses on a number of individual kernels. Such data have been reported for peanuts (*1*), cotton-seed (*2*), corn and Brazil nuts (*3*) and are presented in table 1.

This finding points out the nature of the contamination and the need to resort to the collection of relatively large samples to ascertain the extent of contamination of a given lot. In the case of shelled peanuts, it is common practice in the U.S. Department of Agriculture to make a composite sample from 25 percent of the bags. However, there is evidence that even this extensive sampling may not give an entirely representative sample of the lot. In dealing with bulk shipment or cargos involving large numbers of bags, it is not practical to carry out such extensive sampling. Some groups in the United States take a "lot sample" ranging from 15 to 45 pounds of peanuts, then grind and blend 8 to 10 pounds to give a homogeneous mass from which a portion can be taken for the chemical analysis.

Regarding sample preparation, we have effectively used the neutron activation of a few kernels of nuts to evaluate the homogeneity of analytical samples prepared by various means for lot samples. In this technique, several kernels are made radioactive, and these are then added to the lot sample which is ground, mixed, and portions removed for accurate and precise radioactivity measurement. Statistical treatment of the data obtained gives a good measure of the homogeneity of the samples prepared by a particular method (*3*). Nuts in the shell have presented a more

Table 1.—Assay of single kernels for aflatoxins

Selection	Commodity				
	Peanuts	Cotton-seed	Corn		Brazil nuts
	Defects	Random	Defects	Random	Defects
No. examined__	40	150	10	256	100
No. positive____	22	28	5	0	5
	μg. total aflatoxins per gm kernel				
Range:					
Low_____	Trace	0.07	Trace	-------	0.05
High_____	1,100	600	8	-------	25

[1]Defects were visually defective kernels and random refers to the selection of kernels in a random manner.

difficult problem than shelled nuts because of the additional effort and time required for shelling. We have found that it is not necessary to remove the shells of peanuts, walnuts, filberts, almonds, pecans, and Brazil nuts because these shells do not interfere with the chemical analyses. Considerable time is saved by grinding the entire nut. In addition, we find that hard shells such as those of Brazil nuts are excellent grinding aids and are very effective in producing homogeneous analytical samples in some types of grinders.

The Hobart vertical cutter mixer (VCM) is an effective piece of equipment for producing homogeneous samples. Approximately 25 pounds of nuts can be handled at one time in the 40-quart size bowl. Figure 1 illustrates this equipment.

Unshelled Brazil nuts were the first nuts to be ground in the VCM. One radioactive nut in 25 pounds gave a dilution factor of approximately one in 1,600. Grinding and blending for 2 minutes produced a finely ground sample and the radioactivity measurements on portions gave a coefficient of variation of 3 percent, indicating excellent homogeneity. When shelled peanuts with a dilution factor of approximately 10,000 were processed in the same manner, a nonhomogeneous mass with a coefficient of variation of 204 percent was obtained. Reducing the dilution factor to approximately 2,500 produced a coefficient of variation of 96 percent. It became apparent that the great difference between Brazil nuts in the shell and shelled peanuts was due to the grinding action of the hard Brazil nut shells. Oyster shell does not interfere with the subsequent aflatoxin chemical analysis and was selected as a grinding aid for shelled peanuts. An equal portion of shell and nuts produced a mass with a 2 percent coefficient of variation, indicating excellent homogeneity.

The hard shells from other nuts, such as walnuts and pecans, are also effective in producing homogeneous samples. Even the relatively soft shell of almonds gave a material with an 8 percent coefficient of variation. This degree of homogeneity for sample preparation is still considered satisfactory in view of the relatively large coefficients of variation associated with current aflatoxin methods. In practice we find that an overall method coefficient of variation of about 15 percent is to be expected in most laboratories. However, at least one recently conducted collaborative study produced somewhat better results (4).

Figure 1.—Hobart vertical cutter-mixer (VCM–40).

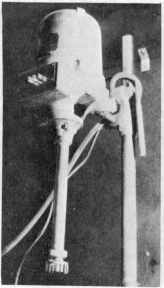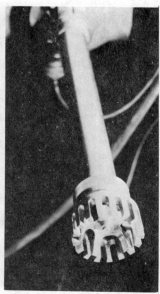

Figure 2.—Right: Willems polytron. Left: Baur mill.

Table 2.—Methods of sample preparation

Commodity	Sample preparation	Dilution	Through 40 mesh (percent)	50 g. sample CV[1] (percent)
Peanuts, shelled...............	VCM, blunt rotor.............	{9,750} {2,570}	30	204 96
Do....................	VCM, sharp rotor...................................		52	....
Do....................	VCM, blunt rotor + oyster shell..	12,600	75	2
Do....................	Bauer + heptane } + polytron}	4,700	99	1
Brazil nuts, in shell.............	VCM, blunt rotor.............	1,590	90	3
Walnuts, in shell................	....do......................	1,600	70	3
Pecans, in shell.................	....do......................	1,800	80	4
Almonds, in shell...............	....do.............	2,900	50	8

[1]Coefficient of variation.

A homogeneous sample of peanuts can also be prepared by the use of a burr-type mill (such as a Baur mill) in conjunction with a Polytron homogenizer. Figure 2 shows a Baur mill, a polytron, and the grinding head of the polytron. A paste is formed from the peanuts by passing them through the burr mill and heptane is added to the peanut paste to make a fluid mixture. The polytron is then employed to further grind and blend to effectively produce a homogeneous sample. The data in table 2 summarize the above experiments on sample preparation.

Analysis

In all of the methods, the aflatoxins are extracted with suitable solvents such as aqueous methanol, chloroform and methanol, and aqueous acetone. The interfering substances extracted along with the aflatoxins are removed by column chromatography or liquid-liquid partition chromatography. The aflatoxins are further separated by thin-layer chromatography, and the amounts of aflatoxin are estimated visually under UV illumination or by fluorescence densitometry by comparison with standards.

Table 3.—Methods and use

Method	Commodity	Use
AOAC Celite (5)..	Peanuts........	USDA (25,000 analyses in 1967).
	Grain.........	USDA surveys.
AOAC CB (6)....	Peanuts........	FDA.
	Grains.........	Industry laboratories.
Liquid-liquid.....	Peanuts........	Manufacturing control.
Waltking (9)......	Peanut butter..	(45–90 min.)
Pons (12)........	Cottonseed....	USDA survey.
Pons (4).........	...do........	USDA research.
Mycotoxin....... Multidetection.... Eppley (13)...... }	Corn........	USDA survey.

Some of the currently used methods for aflatoxin analyses are listed in table 3. The AOAC Celite method (5) has been used by the U.S. Department of Agriculture for the control of peanuts and peanut butter. They carried out approximately 25,000 analyses in 1967 with this method, and it has been estimated that they will use it for approximately 30,000 analyses in 1968. This method has also been used for surveys of grain by the USDA.

The AOAC CB method (6) has been effectively used for peanuts, peanut products, grains and is also useful for a number of other commodities. This is presently the method of choice in the Food and Drug Administration laboratories (FDA), the Canadian Food and Drug Directorate laboratories and is in use in some industrial laboratories. The CB procedure is quite versatile and can be scaled up or down to effectively handle single kernels to kilogram size samples. It is particularly useful for the larger samples which are required to obtain sufficient aflatoxin for confirmatory tests (7). This procedure has also been studied collaboratively by the Trace Substances Committee of IUPAC (International Union of Pure and Applied Chemistry) and was published this year as a provisional IUPAC method (8).

Waltking et al. (9) modified the FDA liquid-liquid clean-up procedure (10) to give a very rapid and practical method particularly useful for manufacturing quality control. The authors estimate an elapsed time of 90 minutes from start to finish. This time can be reduced to 60 minutes by using the small thin-layer chromatography plates described by Eppley (11). Waltking has recently incorporated some additional timesaving steps so that an analysis can be carried out in as little as 45 minutes. This modified method should be very useful for manufacturing control purposes.

Analysis of cottonseed for aflatoxin presents some problems because of inherent interferences. The method of Pons et al. (12) has been used for research and extensive surveys by the Department of Agriculture. Recently an improved method by Pons (4) has been collaboratively studied and was adopted as official, first action at the 1968 AOAC Annual Meeting. The data from the collaborative study indicate that it will be a very effective method for aflatoxin analysis in cottonseed.

The mycotoxin multidetection system of Eppley (13) is being used by the U.S. Department of Agriculture for a survey in which several hundred selected corn samples are being analyzed for aflatoxins, zearalenone, and ochratoxin. Shotwell et al. (14) reported the first natural contamination of a commodity (corn) with ochratoxin, using this method.

Although it would be very desirable to have one method which could be effectively used to analyze all materials for aflatoxins, it has become quite evident that for the present this is not practical. As previously mentioned, some commodities (e.g. cottonseed), are not adaptable to existing methods because of some unique interference or other qualities. Work has been going on in a number of laboratories to develop effective methods for particular commodities.

Aflatoxin M is currently under study. Purchase et al (15, 16) used a method developed in their laboratory to analyze 22 samples of market milk from South Africa. Five of the samples were found to contain aflatoxin; two of these were estimated to contain 0.16 μg. per kg. and lesser amounts were formed in the others. Additional samples were obtained from these two sources and subsequent analysis revealed aflatoxin M in one sample. The aflatoxins were extracted from several gallons of sample from this source and, when fed to ducklings produced the typical liver lesions. This indicates that the method of Purchase et al. is very sensitive and should be useful as an analytical tool. However, a collaborative study with this method and several other unpublished methods was conducted earlier under IUPAC auspices and the results were disappointing. It appears that the instability of the aflatoxin M standard used in the study was largely responsible for the difficulties encountered.

More recently Masri et al. (17) reported that aflatoxin M is stable in dried milk and also stable in the highly purified crystallized form, but that the semi-purified preparations are not stable. The current TLC methods do not separate aflatoxin M_1 from M_2; however, Holzapfel et al. (18) have developed a formamide-impregnated paper chromatographic method which will separate the two. Aspertoxin has the same TLC Rf using a 10 percent acetone—90 percent chloroform solvent system; however, aspertoxin is separated from aflatoxin M with a 10 percent acetic acid—90 percent chloroform solvent system or a 10 percent pyridine—90 percent chloroform solvent system (19).

Both AOAC peanut procedures and the Eppley multidetection procedure have been successfully used for the aflatoxin analysis of whole corn. However, a sizable amount of corn in the United States is processed by wet milling to obtain starch, corn sugar, and corn syrup as the primary products. These primary products can be readily analyzed but the by-products of the process such as steep water, gluten meal, corn germ meal, and gluten feeds require some special cleanup techniques. Dr. R. J. Smith, the AOAC referee for this topic, has developed methods that appear to be adequate, but they have not yet been tested by collaborative study. However, they have been effectively used to carry out research investigating the fate of aflatoxin in the wet milling process (20).

Experience has shown that while most grains are quite easily analyzed, some do present analytical problems. Dr. Shotwell, the AOAC referee for cereal grains, has reported on problems associated with interfering fluorescent material from the hulls of oats (21). She has described a TLC solvent system capable of resolving these interfering substances from the aflatoxins. Some samples of wheat and malted barley also present some interference difficulties. In many instances it has been found that a common procedure can be employed for the extraction and cleanup of the aflatoxins for a number of grains and that the interfering substances from a particular grain can be overcome by employing a TLC solvent system capable of resolving the aflatoxins and interfering substances.

Coffee, cocoa, and tea are difficult to analyze. The alkaloids are a cause of much of the difficulty because caffeine and theobromine have very nearly the same solubility characteristics as the aflatoxins, and the solvent extraction systems remove both simultaneously. The problem then is one of separating a small amount of aflatoxins from a relatively large amount of alkaloids.

Dr. Levi, the AOAC associate referee for coffee, working with Borker (22), and Scott (23) have published methods for coffee employing Florisil in the cleanup step of the procedures. We have not found Florisil to be uniform from lot to lot in its ability to bind the aflatoxins. Losses of up to 75 percent of added B_1 and as much as 100 percent of the G aflatoxins have been observed in our laboratories. In spite of these losses the methods are still very sensitive for aflatoxin B_1. Employing Levi's method, we have been able to detect as little as 2μg. of added aflatoxin B_1 in green coffee.

Dr. Scott, the AOAC associate referee for cocoa and tea, has recently published a method for green cocoa which uses a silver nitrate precipitation step to separate the aflatoxins (24). A collaborative study of the method is under consideration. The method is not effective for roasted cocoa, however. Tea presents one of the most challenging analytical problems encountered to date because of some interferences in addition to the alkaloids, and efficient methods are yet to be developed.

Mixed feeds present one of the most difficult aflatoxin analytical problems due to the number of ingredients which contain interfering substances. Some of these ingredients, such as the corn wet milling byproducts, cottonseed meal, and alfalfa meal are difficult to analyze even by themselves, and the difficulties are much greater when they are mixed. Also, the need for the detection of very low levels of contamination in some feeds, such as trout rations, can present additional problems. For example, the U.S. Fish and Wildlife contracts for these rations specify 1 μg. or less aflatoxins per 1 kg. Mr. Virgil Hill, the AOAC referee for mycotoxins in mixed feeds, is actively pursuing the problem.

Reagent Performance Tests

Experience is revealing the importance of the use of performance tests for some of the troublesome reagents such as the silica gels and filter-aids used in aflatoxin analyses. The AOAC methods specify silica gel GHR because, when they were written several years ago, this was the best silica gel available and the only one capable of consistently resolving the four aflatoxins. Many laboratories have subsequently experienced difficulty in obtaining satisfactory supplies of GHR and currently at least two or three different brands are available which are superior to the one specified in the AOAC methods. A recommendation was made by the associate referee for aflatoxin methods and adopted in 1968 to amend the AOAC procedures to allow for the use of a TLC silica gel which: (a) Resolves the aflatoxins to give four distinct fluorescent spots, and (b) resolves any particular interfering substances of products being analyzed from the aflatoxins. We understand that in practice many laboratories have already discontinued the use of the specified silica gel for more acceptable brands. We recommend that the performance standards procedure of Pons and Goldblatt (25), employing densitometry, be used when possible. It is hoped that the silica gel suppliers will consistently produce products which will meet the stringent requirements of aflatoxin analyses.

Hyflo Super-Cel[1] is specified as a filter aid in the CB procedure (6). No differences were observed between the performance of 13 lots studied for uniformity. However, Filter Cel (another filter-aid sold by the same company) tenaciously held the aflatoxins.

[1]Trade name of a filter-aid produced and sold by Johns-Manville Corp.

We recommend that all new lots of filter-aids be checked for their suitability before they are used.

Column silica gels are currently under study and preliminary results indicate that it may also be necessary to develop performance standards for these. Various batches of Florisil, another adsorbent used in column chromatography, were found to behave differently in the development of the methods for green coffee.

Other Mycotoxins

Some of the more recent developments in the mycotoxin field will require analytical procedures before their significance as health hazards can be properly evaluated. Figure 3 shows some of the naturally occurring compounds closely related to sterigmatocystin, a mycotoxin isolated and characterized by Bullock et al. (26) which is reported by Dickens et al. (27) and by Purchase and van der Watt (28) to be a carcinogen. O-Methylsterigmatocystin was isolated from an aflatoxin-producing strain of Aspergillus flavus by Burkhardt and Forgacs (29). Aspertoxin has been obtained from two different isolates of A. flavus, and its chemical structure was established independently and at very nearly the same time by Waiss et al. (30) and Rodricks et al. (31). Aspertoxin has been shown to be toxic to chicken embryos (19) and zebra fish larvae (32). It is fluorescent but considerably less so than the aflatoxins. This indicates that other techniques will be needed for satisfactory methods. Holzapfel et al. (33) have published a method for sterigmatocystin based on silica gel TLC fluorescence, however, this method is relatively insensitive. A more recent report from Vorster and Purchase (34) describes a more sensitive method based on the conversion of sterigmatocystin to its more highly fluorescent monoacetate derivative.

Patulin is a toxic metabolite produced by a number of molds, some of which are associated with food

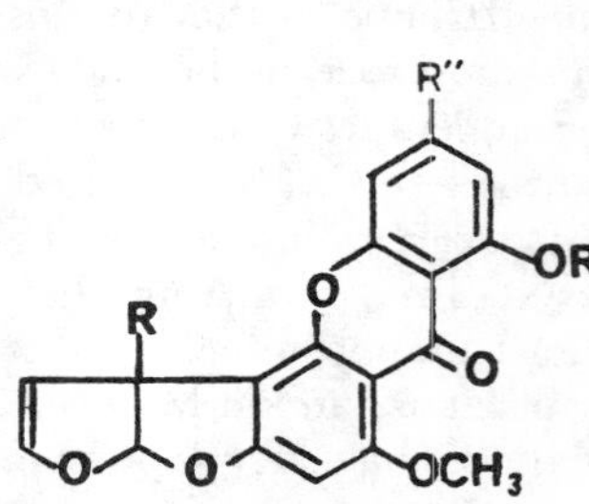

STERIGMATOCYSTIN (R=R'=R''=H)
6-METHOXYSTERIGMATOCYSTIN (R=R'=H, R''=OCH$_3$)
O-METHYLSTERIGMATOCYSTIN (R=R''=H, R'=CH$_3$)
ASPERTOXIN (R=OH, R'=CH$_3$, R''=H)

Figure 3.—The Sterigmatocystin group of DHFF compounds.

spoilage. One of these, *Penicillium expansum*, is responsible for much of the storage rot in apples, and patulin has been found in apple juice obtained from apples afflicted with rots caused by this mold. Patulin is toxic to a number of organisms and has been shown to be a carcinogen for some warm-blooded animals (*35*).

Several methods for patulin are available based on color reactions. A disadvantage of the colorimetric reactions is relatively poor sensitivity. Pohland et al. (*36*) of our laboratories are developing a GLC method which is quite sensitive. The patulin is readily extracted from apple juice by ethyl ether and the acetate is formed using acetic anhydride in pyridine. The reaction requires about 15 hours for completion and, because the reaction product is not stable, the GLC analysis must be carried out within one day after preparation of the derivative. He has also formed the silyl ether and the chloro acetate derivatives. The silyl ether has a number of undesirable characteristics but the chloro acetate is particularly attractive because the chlorine atom allows for the use of the very sensitive electron capture detector.

Steyn and Holzapfel (*37*) have recently reported an additional ochratoxin, the methyl ester of ochratoxin A (fig. 4). They report it to be as toxic as A and, contrary to an earlier report (*38*), now find that ochratoxin C, the ethyl ester, is likewise as toxic as A. Emphasis on analysis to date has been placed on ochratoxin A, but with the new toxicity information on the esters, it now appears that methodology should be capable of detecting the three closely related toxins in order to effectively evaluate the potential hazard from this group of toxins.

Mirocha et al. (*39*) reported another estrogenic compound closely related to zearalenone, the toxic metabolite produced by *Gibberella zeae*. More recently they (*40*) reported a number of closely related compounds. Published methods of Eppley (*13*), and Mirocha et al. (*41*), determine zearalenone alone. In light of these recently discovered, closely related compounds, consideration should be given to methods capable of detecting this group of compounds.

Chemical Confirmation Methods

Confirmation methods have particular significance for regulatory agencies as well as for research and investigational studies, but they are of much less importance for control purposes. In the latter instance the analysts are usually quite familiar with the particular material being analyzed and the extraneous fluorescence and interference associated with the particular material.

The chemical derivative test (*7*) of Andrellos and Reid (*42*) is reliable for the aflatoxins. We find that a

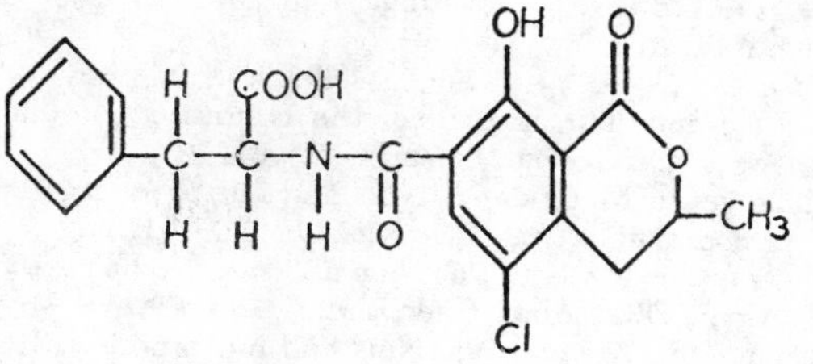

Figure 4.—Structure of ochratoxin A.

good test can be obtained with approximately 1 μg. of "TLC pure B₁." However, the ease with which it can be carried out depends greatly upon the extent of the contamination of the sample. As mentioned earlier, however, when the analyst is quite familiar with the commodity he can rely more heavily on past experience and a different solvent system can be used effectively (*43*). For example, some peanut products contain a fluorescent material easily confused with the G aflatoxins when using the acetone-chloroform solvent system. This same material has approximately the same Rf as the B aflatoxins when using the benzene-ethanol-water system. Consequently, both of the AOAC procedures for peanuts specify the use of a confirmation solvent system for the G aflatoxins.

Ochratoxin A can be confirmed by transferring it into aqueous sodium bicarbonate with subsequent reformation of the ochratoxin A by acidification. In addition, "TLC pure ochratoxin A" can be obtained from silica gel preparatory plates, and the methyl or ethyl esters can be formed and observed by TLC. This technique was recently used by Shotwell (*14*) to confirm a naturally occurring ochratoxin contamination in corn. This is the first report of a natural occurrence of this toxin.

Zearalenone contamination can be verified by Mirocha's (*41*) GLC method using the silyl ester derivatives.

Experience with the aflatoxins and ochratoxins has shown that it is not uncommon to encounter fluorescent materials which can be easily misinterpreted as the toxin. Consequently, it is reasonable to expect that confirmation methods will be required for the recently discovered mycotoxins in order to evaluate their potential as food toxins.

References

(*1*) CUCULLU, A. E., L. S. LEE, R. Y. MAYNE, and L. A. GOLDBLATT. 1966. Determination of aflatoxins in individual peanuts and peanut sections. J. Amer. Oil Chemists' Soc. *43*: 89–92.

(*2*) WHITTEN, M. E., Cotton Gin and Oil Mill Press. Dec. 17, 1966. Pp. 7–8.

(*3*) STOLOFF, L., A. D. CAMPBELL, A. C. BECKWITH, S. NESHEIM, J. S. WINBUSH, Jr., and O. M.

FORDHAM, JR. J. Amer. Oil Chemists' Soc. (to be published).

(4) PONS, W. A., JR. 1969. Collaborative study on the determination of aflatoxins in cottonseed products. J. Assoc. Offic. Anal. Chemists 52: 61–72.

(5) Changes in Methods 25. Nuts and nut products, 1966. J. Assoc. Offic. Anal. Chemists 49: 229–231.

(6) Changes in Methods 25. Nuts and nut products, 1968. J. Amer. Offic. Anal. Chemists 51: 485–488.

(7) Changes in Methods 25. Nuts and nut products, 1967. J. Assoc. Offic. Anal. Chemists 50: 214–216.

(8) ANONYMOUS, International Union of Pure and Applied Chemistry, Information Bulletin No. 31, March 1968. Pp. 35–43.

(9) WALTKING, A. E., G. BLEFFERT, and M. KIERNAN. 1968. An improved rapid physiochemical assay method for aflatoxin in peanuts and peanut products. J. Amer. Oil Chemists' Soc. 45: 880–884.

(10) CAMPBELL, A. D., E. DORSEY, and R. M. EPPLEY. 1964. Rapid procedure for extraction of aflatoxin from peanuts, peanut meal and peanut butter for bioassay. J. Assoc. Offic. Anal. Chemists 47: 1002–1003.

(11) EPPLEY, R. M. 1969. J. Assoc. Offic. Anal. Chemists 52: 311.

(12) PONS, W. A., JR., A. F. CUCULLU, L. S. LEE, J. A. ROBERTSON, A. O. FRANZ, and L. A. GOLDBLATT. 1966. Determination of aflatoxins in agricultural products: Use of aqueous acetone for extraction. J. Assoc. Offic. Anal. Chemists 49: 554–562.

(13) EPPLEY, R. M. 1968. Screening method for zearalenone, aflatoxin, and ochratoxin. J. Assoc. Offic. Anal. Chemists 51: 74–78.

(14) SHOTWELL, O., C. W. HESSELTINE, and M. L. GOULDEN. 1969. Note on the natural occurrence of ochratoxin A. J. Assoc. Offic. Anal. Chemists 52: 81–83.

(15) PURCHASE, I. F. H., and M. SYEYN. 1967. Estimation of aflatoxin M in milk. J. Assoc. Offic. Anal. Chemists 50: 363–366.

(16) PURCHASE, I. F. H., and L. J. VORSTER. 1968. South African Med. J. 42: 219.

(17) MASRI, M. S., J. R. PAGE, and V. C. GARCIA. 1968. Analysis for aflatoxin M in milk. J. Assoc. Offic. Anal. Chemists 51: 594–600.

(18) HOLZAPFEL, C. W., P. S. STEYN, and I. PURCHASE. 1966. Isolation and structure of aflatoxins M_1 and M_2. Tetrahedron Ltrs. 25: 2799–2803.

(19) RODRICKS, J. V., K. R. HENERY-LOGAN, A. D. CAMPBELL, L. STOLOFF, and M. J. VERRETT. 1968. Isolation of a new toxin from cultures of Aspergillus flavus. Nature 217: 668.

(20) RUARK, R. G., and S. A. WATSON. 1968. Survey of mycotoxin potentially in the wet-milling industry. (Summary). Proceedings of the Mycotoxin Research Seminar, June 8–9, 1967, Washington, D.C., p. 11.

(21) SHOTWELL, O. L., G. M. SHANNON, M. L. GOULDEN, M. S. MILBURN, and H. H. HALL. 1968. Factors in oats that could be mistaken for aflatoxin. Cereal Chem. 45: 236–241.

(22) LEVI, C. P., and E. BORKER. 1968. Survey of green coffee for potential aflatoxin contamination. J. Assoc. Offic. Anal. Chemists 51: 600–602.

(23) SCOTT, P. M. 1968. Note on analysis of aflatoxins in green coffee. J. Assoc. Offic. Anal. Chemists 51: 609.

(24) SCOTT, P. M. 1969. Analysis of cocoa beans for aflatoxins. J. Assoc. Offic. Anal. Chemists 52: 72–74.

(25) PONS, W. A., JR., and L. GOLDBLATT. 1968. Instrumental evaluation of aflatoxin resolution on TLC plates. J. Assoc. Offic. Anal. Chemists 51: 1194–1197.

(26) BULLOCK, E., J. C. ROBERTS, and J. G. UNDERWOOD. 1962. Studies in mycological chemistry. XI. The structure of isosterigmatocystin and an amended structure for sterigmatocystin. J. Chem. Soc.: 4179–4183.

(27) DICKENS, F., H. E. H. JONES, and H. B. WAYNFORTH. 1966. Oral, subcutaneous and intratracheal administration of carcinogenic lactones and related substances: The intratracheal administration of cigarette tar in the rat. Brit. J. Cancer 20: 134.

(28) PURCHASE, I. F. H., and J. J. VAN DER WATT. Food and Cosmet. Toxicol., in press.

(29) BURKHARDT, H. J., and J. FORGACS. 1968. O-Methylsterigmatocystin, a new metabolite from Aspergillus flavus, Link ex Fries. Tetrahedron 24: 717–720.

(30) WAISS, A. C., JR., M. WILEY, D. R. BLACK, and R. E. LUNDIN. 1968. 3–Hydroxy–6, 7–dimethoxydifuroxanthone. A new metabolite from Aspergillus flavus. Tetrahedron Ltrs. 28: 3207–3210.

(31) RODRICKS, J. V., E. LUSTIG, A. D. CAMPBELL, L. STOLOFF, and K. R. HENERY-LOGAN. 1968. Aspertoxin. A hydroxy derivative of O-methylsterigmatocystin from aflatoxin-producing cultures of Aspergillus flavus. Tetrahedron Ltrs. 25: 2975–2978.

(32) ABEDI, Z. H. Canadian Food and Drug Directorate, personal communication, 1968.

(33) HOLZAPFEL, C. W., I. F. H. PURCHASE, and P. S. STEYN. 1966. South African Med. J. (Supplement, South African J. Nutr.) 40: 1100.

(34) VORSTER, L. J., and I. F. H. PURCHASE. 1968. A method for the determination of sterigmatocystin in grain and oilseeds. Analyst 93: 694–696.

(35) SINGH, J. 1967. In Antibiotics 1: 621–630, by D. Gottlieb and P. D. Shaw, Springer–Verlag, Berlin.

(36) POHLAND, A. E., K. SANDERS, and C. THORPE, Paper No. 73 presented at the 82nd Annual Meeting of the Assoc. Offic. Anal. Chemists, Oct. 15, 1968.

(37) STEYN, P. S., and C. W. HOLZAPFEL. 1967. J. South African Chem. Inst. 20: 186–189.

(38) VAN DER MERWE, K. J., P. S. STEYN, and L. FOURIE 1965. Mycotoxins. II. The constitution of ochratoxins A, B, and C, metabolites of Aspergillus ochraceus Wilh. J. Chem. Soc.: 7083–7088.

(39) MIROCHA, C. J., C. M. CHRISTENSEN, and G. H. NELSON. 1968. Toxic metabolites produced by fungi implicated in mycotoxicoses. Biotech. Bioeng. 10: 469–482.

(40) MIROCHA, C. J., C. M. CHRISTENSEN, and G. H. NELSON, J. Agr. Food Chem. In press.

(41) MIROCHA, C. J., C. M. CHRISTENSEN, and G. H. NELSON, 1967. Estrogenic metabolite produced by Fusarium graminearum in stored corn. Appl. Microbiol. 15: 497–503.

(42) ANDRELLOS, P. J., and G. R. REID. 1964. Confirmatory tests for aflatoxin B_1. J. Assoc. Offic. Anal. Chemists 47: 801–803.

(43) NESHEIM, S. J. Am. Oil Chemists Soc. In press.

ENVIRONMENTAL FACTORS AFFECTING THE PRODUCTION OF AFLATOXIN

by Norman D. Davis *and* Urban L. Diener
Botany and Plant Pathology Department,
Auburn University Agricultural Experiment Station, Auburn, Ala. 36830

Summary

The influence of temperature, relative humidity, oxygen, and carbon dioxide on aflatoxin production by Aspergillus flavus in peanuts (*Arachis hypogaea*) and soybeans (*Glycine max*) was investigated under controlled environments.

The lower limiting temperature for aflatoxin production was about 12° C., whereas the upper limiting temperature was approximately 41° C. at 99 percent relative humidity. The limiting relative humidity and temperature varied slightly depending on kind and quality of seed. The ratio of aflatoxin B_1 to G_1 varied with temperature; generally, the ratio was approximately one at 30° C., less than one at temperatures below 30° C., and more than one at temperatures above 30° C. The limiting relative humidity was approximately 83 percent or higher at 30° C., varying with the kind and quality of the substrate and length of the incubation period.

Reducing oxygen concentration generally reduced aflatoxin production, notably so when oxygen was reduced from 5 to 1 percent. Aflatoxin production decreased with increasing concentrations of carbon dioxide from 0.03 to 100 percent. The inhibitory effect of carbon dioxide on aflatoxin production was greatly enhanced with a decrease in temperature and relative humidity. Aflatoxin was not produced in peanuts stored 14 days at 86 percent RH in 60 and 40 percent carbon dioxide at 25° C., and at 92 and 86 percent RH in 20 percent carbon dioxide at 17° C.

Introduction

Four environmental factors which affect the production of aflatoxin by Aspergillus flavus growing on peanuts have been extensively investigated at Auburn University. These are relative humidity, temperature, oxygen, and carbon dioxide (*5, 6, 7, 8, 11, 13*). Factors affecting the production of aflatoxin in soybeans (*9*) and in nutrient solution (*1, 2, 3, 4, 5, 10*) have also been studied. This report summarizes much of the data obtained in our laboratory concerning the effect of relative humidity (RH), temperature, oxygen (O_2), and carbon dioxide (CO_2) on aflatoxin production by A. flavus.

Materials and Methods

Relative humidity and temperature studies.—Studies concerned with RH and temperature were conducted using eight Blue M Power-O-Matic 60 (model CFR-7752C) saturable reactor, proportionally controlled, refrigerated, humidity cabinets having 10 ft.^{3} working chambers, 7-day recording psychrometers, and self-contained water purification systems. Both peanuts (*Arachis hypogaea* L. "Early Runner" and "Florigiant") (*5, 6, 7, 8*) and soybeans (*Glycine max* "Bragg") (*9*) have been studied. Peanut substrates consisted of sound mature kernels; broken mature kernels simulating "damaged" and "loose shelled" kernels; immature kernels or "pegs"; and kernels from peanuts incubated with intact shells or unshelled peanuts.

Seed were inoculated by spraying with a suspension of spores (A. flavus, isolate Ala-6) calculated to give approximately 12 to 15 million spores per 900 g. of seed. Seed were incubated at various combinations of temperature (10 to 45° C.) and RH (70 to 99 percent) for intervals of 7, 21, 42, and 84 days. Aflatoxin was quantitatively determined using the method of Pons and Goldblatt (*12*). Materials and methods used in relative humidity and temperature studies have been described fully elsewhere (*5, 6, 7, 8*).

Oxygen and carbon dioxide studies.—Sound, mature kernels of Early Runner peanuts were surface-disinfested with 1 percent sodium hypochlorite for 2 minutes and sprayed with a suspension of spores of A. flavus. Inoculated peanuts were placed in 1.25-liter culture flasks (150 to 200 g. of peanuts per flask) and gas mixtures of specified composition and controlled relative humidity passed through the culture vessel (150 to 250 cc. per min.) for 2 weeks. The culture vessels were partially submerged in a controlled-temperature water bath. Materials, methods, and apparatus used in these experiments have been fully described elsewhere (*11, 13*). Aflatoxin was quantitatively determined as previously described (*12*).

Results and Discussion

Temperature studies.—The effects of temperature on aflatoxin production by *A. flavus* growing on peanuts, soybeans, and synthetic medium (*3*) are illustrated in tables 1, 2, and 3, respectively. Generally, the proportion of aflatoxin B_1 to G_1 increased directly with temperature. In most studies, the ratio was approximately one at 30° C., greater than one at temperatures above 30° C., and less than one at temperatures below 30° C. The ratio *per se* varied with the quality and nature of the substrate as well as with temperature. From these and other studies (*5, 6, 7, 8, 9*), it appears that aflatoxin G_1 is less stable than B_1 at temperatures above 30° C., and that this accounts for the different ratios observed at different temperatures.

The lowest temperature at which aflatoxin production ordinarily occurred was approximately 14° C. in peanuts (table 1) and 13° C. in soybeans (table 2). However, some aflatoxin has been found at 12° C. in extensively damaged peanut kernels (*6*). The lowest temperature for aflatoxin production in synthetic nutrient solution (table 3) was 20° C. Little or no fungus growth occurred in nutrient solution at 15° C. The upper temperature for aflatoxin production was 40° C. in peanuts (table 1) and soybeans (table 2), and 35° C. in nutrient solution (table 3).

Relative humidity studies.—The effect of RH on growth and aflatoxin production in peanuts (*6*) and soybeans (*9*) is presented in tables 4 and 5, respectively. The lowest RH for aflatoxin production in peanuts was approximately 84 percent (table 4): no aflatoxin was produced in peanuts at 82 percent RH. The lowest RH for aflatoxin production in soybeans was approximately 92 percent (table 5).

The limiting RH for aflatoxin production in sound mature kernels was 83.5±0.5 percent RH, whereas the limiting temperatures were 13.5°±0.5° C. and

Table 1.—Aflatoxin production by Aspergillus flavus in sterile sound mature peanuts incubated for 21 days at 99 percent RH

Temperature (degrees centigrade)	Aflatoxins		Ratio, $B_1:G_1$
	B_1 (µg./g.)	G_1 (µg./g.)	
12	0	0	-----------
14	1.7	1.4	1.2
15	6.9	17.6	.4
20	84.2	213.3	.4
25	83.3	159.9	.5
30	94.9	106.6	.9
35	126.6	53.3	2.4
40	2.5	1.0	2.5
43	(^{1})	(^{1})	(^{1})

^{1}Trace or less than 1 µg./kg.

Table 2.—Aflatoxin production by Aspergillus flavus in soybeans incubated for 21 days at 99 percent RH

Temperature (degrees centigrade)	Aflatoxins		Ratio, $B_1:G_1$
	B_1 (µg./g.)	G_1 (µg./g.)	
10	0	0	-----------
13	.1	.1	-----------
17	.4	.1	-----------
20	22.7	60.3	0.4
25	41.3	140.3	.3
30	138.3	156.8	.9
35	49.5	22.4	2.2
38	11.1	1.5	7.4
40	.3	(^{1})	-----------
44	0	0	-----------

^{1}Trace or less than 1 µg./kg.

Table 3.—Aflatoxin production by Aspergillus flavus in synthetic nutrient solution incubated 21 days in stationary culture

Temperature (degrees centigrade)	Aflatoxins		Ratio, $B_1:G_1$
	B_1 (µg./ 100 ml.)	G_1 (µg./ 100 ml.)	
15	0	0	-----------
20	460	4,000	0.1
25	1,150	6,000	.2
30	3,450	3,000	1.1
35	1,150	400	2.9
40	0	0	-----------

Table 4.—Aflatoxin production by Aspergillus flavus in sterile sound mature peanuts incubated for 21 days at 30° C.

Relative humidity (Percent)	Total aflatoxin (µg./g.)
82	0
83	(^{1})
84	.5
85	1.9
87	29.8
90	60.1
95	92.7
99	190.5

^{1}Trace or less than 1 µg./kg.

Table 5.—Aflatoxin production by Aspergillus flavus in soybeans incubated for 21 days at 30° C.

Relative humidity (Percent)	Aflatoxin (µg./g.)
85	(^{1})
87	(^{1})
92	1.6
95	4.3
99	376.3

^{1}Trace or less than 1 µg./kg.

40.5°±0.5° C. (table 6). Long incubation periods (84 days) were used with stored unsterile peanuts as these data would have greater applied significance. The limiting RH and upper limiting temperature for broken mature or damaged kernels were the same as for sound mature kernels; i.e., 83.5±0.5 percent RH and 40.5°±0.5° C. (table 7). Damaged kernels developed aflatoxin at lower temperatures (12° C. for sterile and 13° C. for unsterile peanuts) than sound mature kernels. At the reduced temperature of 20° C., the limiting RH for mature kernels (sound or broken) was 84.5±1.5 percent. The limiting RH and upper limiting temperature for immature kernels were the same as for the other shelled peanuts, but the lower limiting temperature was 14.5°±0.5° C., which was slightly higher than for mature kernels (table 8). At 20° C., aflatoxin developed at 89 percent RH in 84 days (table 8). The limiting relative humidity for aflatoxin formation in kernels from unshelled peanuts was 85.5 ±0.5 percent and the limiting temperatures were 17° ± 1° C. and 40.5°±0.5° C. (table 9). Peanuts in the shell appeared to be slightly more resistant to A. flavus invasion and aflatoxin formation than shelled kernels; however, this resistance was primarily associated with living kernels from freshly dug, surface disinfested pods of stored farmer's stock peanuts. At 20° C. there was little fungus invasion and aflatoxin formed except at the highest RH.

Generally, it appears that the limiting relative humidity for aflatoxin elaboration in agricultural commodities is 83.5±0.5 percent depending on the nature of the substrate and length of the storage period. "Safe Storage" moisture to avoid A. flavus growth and aflatoxin formation then appears to be that moisture content of the agricultural commodity that is in equilibrium with a RH of 83 percent or less. This moisture is in the range of 9 to 10 percent for peanuts and 17 to 18 percent for soybeans. The lower limiting temperature for aflatoxin elaboration in peanuts and soybeans was about 12.5°±0.5° C. except that in the case of heat-treated (sterile), damaged kernels aflatoxin formed at 12° C. The upper limiting temperature for aflatoxin was 40.5°±0.5° C. for all peanut

Table 6.—Limiting environments for aflatoxin production by Aspergillus flavus in sound mature kernels (21 days)

Limiting environment	Peanuts	
	Heat-killed	Unsterile
RH at 30° C	85.5 ± 0.5 percent	84.5 ± 0.5 percent. 83.5 ± 0.5 percent.[1]
Temperature at 98 percent RH	13.0° ± 1.0° C	12.0° ± 2.0° C. 13.5° ± 0.5° C.[1]
	40.0° ± 1.5° C	40.5° ± 0.5° C.
RH at 20° C		84.5 ± 1.5 percent.[1]

[1]Incubated 84 days.

Table 7.—Limiting environments for aflatoxin production by Aspergillus flavus in broken mature kernels (21 days)

Limiting environment	Peanuts	
	Heat-killed	Unsterile
RH at 30° C	85.5 ± 0.5 percent	84.5 ± 0.5 percent. 83.5 ± 0.5 percent.[1]
Temperature at 98 percent RH	11.0° ± 1.0° C	12.0° ± 2.0° C. 12.5° ± 0.5° C.[1]
	40.0° ± 1.5° C	40.5° ± 0.5° C.
RH at 20° C		84.5 ± 1.5 percent.[1]

[1]Incubated 84 days.

Table 8.—Limiting environments for aflatoxin production by Aspergillus flavus in immature kernels (21 days)

Limiting environment	Peanuts	
	Heat-killed	Unsterile
RH at 30° C	85.5 ± 0.5 percent	84.5 ± 0.5 percent. 83.5 ± 0.5 percent.[1]
Temperature at 98 percent RH	14.5° ± 0.5° C	12.5° ± 2.5° C. 14.5° ± 0.5° C.[1]
	40.0° ± 1.5° C	41.5° ± 1.5° C.
RH at 20° C		89.0 ± 3.0 percent.[1]

[1]Incubated 84 days.

Table 9.—Limiting environments for aflatoxin production by Aspergillus flavus in kernels from unshelled peanuts (21 days)

Limiting environment	Peanuts		
	Heat-killed	Freshly dug[1]	Unsterile
RH at 30° C	86.5 ± 0.5 percent	84.0 ± 1.0 percent	86.5 ± 0.5 percent. 85.5 ± 0.5 percent.[2]
Temperature at 98 percent RH	13.0° ± 1.0° C	17.5° ± 2.5° C	22.5° ± 2.5° C. 17.0° ± 1.0° C.[2]
	40.0° ± 1.5° C	37.5° ± 2.5° C	40.5° ± 0.5° C.
RH at 20° C			95.0 ± 3.0 percent.[2]

[1]Freshly dug, surface disinfested pods.
[2]Incubated 84 days.

substrates. Growth and sporulation by the fungus were just as profuse at 43° as at 40° C., but no aflatoxin formed.

Oxygen and carbon dioxide studies.—The effect of O_2 on aflatoxin production in peanuts is shown in table 10. Aflatoxin elaboration was not diminished when the O_2 concentration was lowered from 21 to 15 percent; however, a subsequent decrease of O_2 concentration caused a corresponding decrease in aflatoxin. Greatest decreases in aflatoxin production occurred when O_2 was lowered from 5 to 1 percent and from 1 to 0.1 percent.

Aflatoxin elaboration varied inversely with CO_2 concentration (table 11). Virtually no aflatoxin was produced in peanuts stored 2 weeks at 30° C., 99 percent RH, and 100 percent CO_2. However, storage of peanuts in CO_2 concentrations of 80 percent or greater generally led to the development of rancidity, probably due to anaerobic respiratory processes in the seed. Decreasing the temperature enhanced the CO_2 inhibition of aflatoxin elaboration. Aflatoxin elaboration was greatly reduced, but not completely prevented by 60 percent CO_2 at 25° C. and 99 percent RH (table 12). When the RH was decreased to 92 and 86 percent, little or no aflatoxin was produced. Also, virtually no aflatoxin was elaborated at 25° C. and 40 percent CO_2 when the RH was decreased to 86 percent (table 13). However, 20 percent CO_2 inhibited aflatoxin production only slightly at 25° C. regardless of the relative humidity (data not presented).

Table 14 summarizes the results of experiments with 20 percent CO_2 at 17° C. and 99, 92 and 86 percent RH. Virtually no aflatoxin was produced in sound mature peanut kernels stored 2 weeks at 17° C. in 20 percent CO_2 and 92 or 86 percent RH. Little or no rancidity developed under these conditions although slight discoloration of the seed coat was noted in some cases. Conceivably, lowering the temperature further might make it possible to store peanuts in still

lower levels of CO_2 for longer periods of time without risking aflatoxin development. Further research will be necessary to establish the ideal commercial storage conditions, the limitations involved with various types of structures, and the methods of controlling, maintaining, and recording temperature, RH, and gas concentration.

Table 10.—Effect of oxygen on production of aflatoxin by *Aspergillus flavus* on peanuts at 30° C.

Concentration of gases (percent)			Total aflatoxin ($\mu g./g.$)
CO_2	O_2	N_2	
0.03	21	[1]79	511.9
0	15	85	519.3
0	10	90	316.1
0	5	95	154.1
0	1	99	5.9
0	0.1	99.9	.1
Uninoculated check - - - - - - - - - - - - - - - - -			0

[1]Air.

Table 11.—Effect of carbon dioxide on production of aflatoxin by *Aspergillus flavus* in peanuts at 30°C.

Concentration of gases (percent)			Total aflatoxin ($\mu g./g.$)
CO_2	O_2	N_2	
[1]0.03	[1]21	[1]79	299.4
20	20	60	74.6
40	20	40	35.4
60	20	20	19.8
80	20	0	.1
100	0	0	([2])
Uninoculated check - - - - - - - - - - - - - - - - -			0

[1]Air.
[2]0.001 to 0.049 $\mu g./g.$

Table 12.—Effect of relative humidity and 60 percent carbon dioxide concentration on production of aflatoxin by *Aspergillus flavus* on peanuts at 25° C.

Concentration of gases (percent)			RH (percent)	Total aflatoxin ($\mu g./g.$)
CO_2	O_2	N_2		
[1]0.03	[1]21	[1]79	99	206.3
.03	21	79	92	111.9
.03	21	79	86	72.1
60	20	20	99	.2
60	20	20	92	([2])
60	20	20	86	0
Uninoculated check -				0

[1]Air.
[2]0.001 to 0.049 $\mu g./g.$

Table 13.—Effect of relative humidity and 40 percent carbon dioxide concentration on production of aflatoxin by Aspergillus flavus on peanuts at 25° C.

Concentration of gases (percent)				
CO_2	O_2	N_2	RH (percent)	Total aflatoxin ($\mu g./g.$)
[1]0.03	[1]21	[1]79	99	196.6
.03	21	79	92	37.4
.03	21	79	86	11.8
40	20	40	99	3.8
40	20	40	92	.3
40	20	40	86	0
Uninoculated check				0

[1]Air.

Table 14.—Effect of relative humidity and 20 percent carbon dioxide concentration on production of aflatoxin by Aspergillus flavus on peanuts at 17° C.

Concentration of gases (percent)				
CO_2	O_2	N_2	RH (percent)	Total aflatoxin ($\mu g./g.$)
[1]0.03	[1]21	[1]79	99	57.1
.03	21	79	92	2.5
.03	21	79	86	.2
20	20	60	99	.2
20	20	60	92	0
20	20	60	86	([2])
Uninoculated check				0

[1]Air.
[2]0.001 to 0.049 $\mu g./g.$

Acknowledgments

Investigations supported in part by USDA Research Contract 12–13–100–7754 (72) supervised by the Southern Utilization Research Development Division, ARS, USDA, New Orleans, La., and in part by PHS Research Grant No. UI–00147 from the National Center for Urban and Industrial Health.

References

(1) DAVIS, N. D., U. L. DIENER, and D. W. ELDRIDGE. 1966. Production of aflatoxin B_1 and G_1 by Aspergillus flavus in semisynthetic medium. Appl. Microbiol. 14: 378–380.

(2) DAVIS, N. D., and U. L. DIENER. 1967. Inhibition of aflatoxin synthesis by p-amino benzoic acid, potassium sulfite, and potassium fluoride. Appl. Microbiol. 15: 1517–1518.

(3) DAVIS, N. D., U. L. DIENER, and V. P. AGNIHOTRI. 1967. Production of aflatoxins B_1 and G_1 in chemically defined medium. Mycopathol. Mycol. Appl. 31: 251–256.

(4) DAVIS, N. D., and U. L. DIENER. 1968. Growth and aflatoxin production by Aspergillus parasiticus from various carbon sources. Appl. Microbiol. 16: 158–159.

(5) DIENER, U. L., and N. D. DAVIS. 1966. Aflatoxin production by isolates of Aspergillus flavus. Phytopathology 56: 1390–1393.

(6) DIENER, U. L., and N. D. DAVIS. 1967. Limiting temperature and relative humidity for growth and production of aflatoxin and free fatty acids by Aspergillus flavus in sterile peanuts. J. Am. Oil Chem. Soc. 44: 259–263.

(7) DIENER, U. L., and N. D. DAVIS. 1968. Effect of environment on aflatoxin production in freshly dug peanuts. Trop. Sci. 10: 22–28.

(8) DIENER, U. L., and N. D. DAVIS. 1968. Effect of temperature, relative humidity, and time on aflatoxin production in unsterile peanuts. J. Ala. Acad. Sci. 39. In press.

(9) ELDRIDGE, D. W. 1969. Influence of temperature, relative humidity, and fungus mycoflora on growth and aflatoxin synthesis of Aspergillus flavus on soybeans. Ph.D. Dissertation. Auburn University, Auburn, Ala.

(10) HAYES, A. W., N. D. DAVIS, and U. L. DIENER. 1966. Effect of aeration on growth and aflatoxin production by Aspergillus flavus in submerged culture. Appl. Microbiol. 14: 1019–1021.

(11) LANDERS, K. E., N. D. DAVIS, and U. L. DIENER. 1967. Influence of atmospheric gases on aflatoxin production by Aspergillus flavus in peanuts. Phytopathology 57: 1086–1090.

(12) PONS, W. A., and L. A. GOLDBLATT. 1965. The determination of aflatoxins in cottonseed products. J. Am. Oil Chem. Soc. 42: 471–475.

(13) SANDERS, T. H., N. D. DAVIS, and U. L. DIENER. 1968. Effect of carbon dioxide, temperature, and relative humidity on production of aflatoxin in peanuts. J. Am. Oil Chem. Soc. 45: 683–685.

SURVEILLANCE FOR AFLATOXINS OF RICE AND FERMENTED-RICE PRODUCTS IN JAPAN

by SHINJI MATSUURA, MASARU MANABE, *and* TOMOTARO SATO
Food Research Institute, Ministry of Agriculture and Forestry, Japan

Summary

Extensive studies were made to investigate whether or not rice, rice koji, miso, and industrial koji-mold strains (*Aspergillus oryzae*) in Japan contained or produced aflatoxins. Those were suspected products because rice is considered as one of the farm products which may be contaminated with aflatoxins, and miso is made from rice koji (a solid culture of industrial koji-mold strain) and *A. oryzae* is closely related to *Aspergillus flavus* which produces aflatoxins.

Intact rice, rice which was subjected to microbial culture, rice koji, miso, and liquid or solid cultures of koji-mold strain were subjected to extraction of aflatoxin with chloroform. The extract was developed on the thin-layer chromatogram with silica gel as absorbent. When aflatoxin-like substances were detected, their ultraviolet absorption spectra and fluorescence spectra were studied.

Forty-six samples of the domestic rice from all the prefectures in Japan, 11 samples of imported rice, 108 samples of miso from almost all the prefectures, 28 samples of rice koji from various miso factories in eight districts, and 238 strains of the koji-mold were tested. However, no aflatoxin was detected in any of the samples. Even the aflatoxin-like substances which were detected in some samples were found to be different from aflatoxins in their ultraviolet absorption spectra. Therefore, we conclude that no contamination by aflatoxin is observed in the rice and the fermented rice products of Japan.

Introduction

Japan produces about 13 million tons and imports about 500,000 tons of rice every year. Of this rice, both domestic and imported, the greater part is consumed as a staple food while the rest is processed into sake, miso (fermented soybean paste), and other products.

The poisoning of poultry which occurred in England in 1960 led to the discovery that some strains of *A. flavus* produce aflatoxins (16). A number of reports have since been made public describing the distribution of aflatoxins in farm products (4, 6, 8, 10, 17, 18, 20). As one of the farm products which may be contaminated with aflatoxins, rice is mentioned (5, 10) In fact, when strains producing aflatoxins are cultivated using rice as substrate, the toxins are copiously produced (19).

A. flavus and *A. parasiticus* are mold strains common in every region. And 10 to 30 percent of strains are said to produce aflatoxins (14). It was reported that aflatoxin-producing *A. flavus* was present in wheat and red bean flours in Japan (11, 12). In view of this report the authors investigated rice produced in each prefecture of Japan, as well as rice imported from overseas, for the presence of aflatoxins.

On the other hand, since the aflatoxin-producing *A. flavus* is a species closely related to the koji-mold, *A. oryzae*, used in the fermentation of sake and miso, the possible aflatoxin productivity of koji-mold strains ordinarily used in Japan posed a problem. Masuda, et al. (13) investigated several kinds of koji-starters. Hesseltine, et al. (10) tested *A. oryzae* which was isolated from koji-starters, used for the manufacture of miso in Japan, for aflatoxin productivity. Aibara, et al. (1) and Murakami, et al. (15) performed the same assay on more than 140 and 214 koji-mold strains, respectively. Yokotsuka, et al. (22, 23) tested 73 koji-mold strains isolated from koji-starters. Among the tested strains, they noticed some which produced aflatoxin-like substances but none which produced true aflatoxins.

With the object of collecting all the koji-mold strains now in practical use for fermentation of sake and rice miso, the authors procured the parent strains of various koji-starters from the All-Japan Koji-Starter Association, a major koji-molds supply organization in Japan, and added them to the koji-molds collected from main breweries and preserved in the Food Research Institute. All of these strains were tested as to their aflatoxin productivity.

Furthermore, as means of confirming the test results on the basis of actual products, the authors tested comparatively large quantities of rice koji (rice is used as substrate of koji-mold) as well as of miso products collected from miso plants in almost all the prefectures of Japan. As to miso products, Hesseltine, et al. (10) reported that they had not observed the presence of aflatoxin.

The processing of rice and miso in Japan is shown in figures 1 and 2

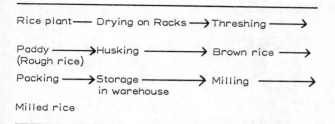

Figure 1.—Processing and storage of rice in Japan.

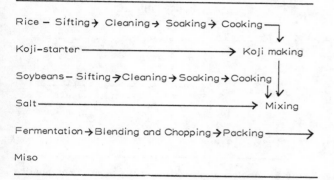

Figure 2.—Flow sheet of miso manufacture.

Materials and Methods

Domestic rice.—One kilogram each of brown rice (stored for 0.5 to 1.5 years), produced either in 1966 or in 1967, was collected from all the 46 prefectures of Japan's eight districts.

Imported rice.—One kilogram each of rice produced in various foreign countries and imported, either in 1966 or in 1967, was collected.

Koji-mold strains.—One hundred and sixty-two strains of major koji-starter parent koji molds, which are in use as starters in production of koji in Japan, and koji molds collected from major breweries and 76 strains of koji molds, preserved in the Food Research Institute, were tested.

Rice koji.—Twenty-eight samples of rice koji which is now being produced at miso plants in Japan were collected from eight districts of Japan. The amount of each sample was 15 kg.

Miso.—One hundred and eight products which are now being produced were collected from miso plants in various prefectures of Japan. The amount of each sample was 1 kg.

Extraction of Aflatoxins

Rice.—As is shown in figure 3, the rice was treated in the following ways: (1) Intact rice, 300 g. was not treated before extraction; (2) cultured rice was produced by adding 8 ml. of sterilized water to 50 g. of the rice and micro-organisms on the surface of its grains were cultivated at 30° C. for 2 to 3 weeks; (3) cultured rice was also produced by steeping 50 g. of rice in 100 ml. of antigormin (containing about 1 percent of effective chlorine) in order to sterilize the surface of the grains. Then, the rice was stirred up in 100 ml. of sterilized water for 30 seconds and washed three times. After draining, micro-organisms inside the rice grains were allowed to grow out at 30° C. for 2 to 3 weeks.

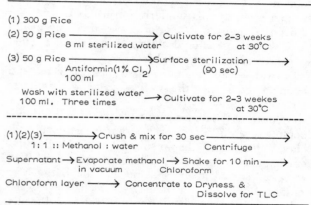

Figure 3.—Analytical procedure of fluorescent compounds in rice.

Each of the intact and treated rice was mixed with a mixture of methanol and water (1:1) and homogenized with a Waring blendor for 30 seconds. After centrifugation, the supernatant was evaporated under reduced pressure to get rid of methanol. Chloroform was added to the residue and the mixture was shaken for 10 minutes. The resultant chloroform layer was concentrated under reduced pressure to make a sample for thin-layer chromatography.

Koji-Mold Strains

Liquid culture.—Both Czapek's medium and Sakaguchi's medium (2) were used. Each koji-mold strain was inoculated on 100 ml. of the medium in a Fernbach flask and cultivated at 30° C. for 7 days under static conditions. On the basis of the methods of Yokotsuka, T., et al. (22), Hartley, R. D., et al. (9), Deiongh, H., et al. (7), the culture liquid was extracted with chloroform. The culture liquid was shaken together with an amount of chloroform corresponding to one-third of its volume. The procedure was repeated three times. The chloroform extracts were condensed, at approximately 50° C., under reduced pressure. The resultant condensate was used as the sample for thin-layer chromatography.

Solid Cultures

Rice.—The domestic rice, milled at an 85 percent retention rate, was washed and steeped in water overnight. After draining and steaming, 40 to 50 g., in terms of the initial weight, was sterilized under pressure in a cotton-stoppered Erlenmeyer flask.

Wheat.—One hundred g. of crushed wheat was stirred up in 60 g. of water and 40 g. of the swollen wheat was similarly sterilized.

Soybean.—Raw soybean and defatted soybean were used. Raw soybean was steeped in warm water (above 15° C.) overnight. After draining, 50 g. of the swollen soybean was similarly sterilized. In the case of defatted soybean, 100 g. of it was stirred up in 120 g. of water and after draining 40 g. of the swollen soybean was similarly sterilized.

Peanut.—Raw peanut was steeped in water and dehulled and 50 g. of the swollen peanut was similarly sterilized.

On each of the above sterile media, three platinum loopfuls of a culture of each strain were inoculated. These cultures were then incubated at 30° C. Twenty-four hours after inoculation, the contents in each flask were well stirred up by shaking and incubation was continued at 30° C. for 6 days.

After completion of culture, each of the solid media was extracted with chloroform by means of Soxhlet's extractor. The extract was concentrated to 30 to 50 ml. under reduced pressure. The concentrate was mixed with either 20 times its volume of petroleum ether or 10 times as much hexane and left to stand overnight in a cold chamber. The resultant precipitate was redissolved in chloroform and was then used as the sample for thin-layer chromatography. In the case of media containing little fat such as rice and wheat, this precipitation procedure was dispensed with.

Rice koji.—As is shown in figure 4, about 15 kg. of rice koji was extracted with a methanol-chloroform mixture (1:9) at 65° to 75° C. for 24 to 36 hours by means of a large extractor. The extract was condensed under reduced pressure. The resultant condensate was diluted up to 100 ml. with a mixture of methanol and water (1:1), mixed with 100 g. of celite No. 545 and was packed in a column. Hexane was allowed to pass through the column in order to remove substances soluble in that solvent. Then, a hexane-chloroform mixture (1:1) was passed through to elute chloroform-soluble substances. The eluate was collected and condensed under reduced pressure to make the sample to be used for thin-layer chromatography.

Miso.—As is shown in figure 5, 200 g. of miso was mixed with 200 ml. of a methanol-water mixture (3:1), shaken for 10 minutes and centrifuged. One hundred ml. of the obtained supernatant was mixed

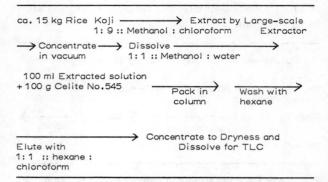

Figure 4.—Analytical procedure of fluorescent compounds in rice koji.

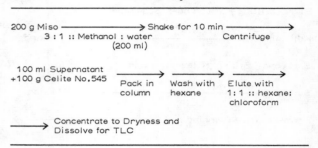

Figure 5.—Analytical procedure of fluorescent compounds in miso (modified FDA method).

with 100 g. of celite No. 545 and packed in a column. From the column a sample for thin-layer chromatography was prepared by the same procedure as described for rice koji.

Detection of aflatoxins.—For adsorbents in the thin-layer chromatography of the above-mentioned samples, Merck's Silica gel G and Silica gel HR were used. The 0.3-mm. thin layer, prepared by the ordinary method, was dried by heating at 105° C. for 2 hours in order to be activated and it was then maintained in a cask filled with desiccated silica gel. As developers, a chloroform-acetone mixture (95:5) was used for the Silica gel G thin layer while a chloroform-methanol mixture (97:3) was used for the Silica gel HR thin layer. Development was performed by the ascending method. After completion of development, the thin layer was observed for emission of fluorescence when illuminated under an ultraviolet ray, wave length of 365 mμ, in the dark. Comparisons of unknown substances were made against standard aflatoxins.

When aflatoxin-like substances were detected, a comparatively large amount of the extract was collected; the whole extract was subjected to thin-layer chromatography; each fluorescent band on the thin layer was collected, extracted with methanol and subjected to thin-layer chromatography again. The extract was measured for its ultraviolet absorption spectrum and fluorescence spectrum.

Results and Discussion

Domestic rice.—By subjecting the extracts of the collected samples to thin-layer chromatography, the authors measured their Rf values close to those of four aflatoxins. The results are shown in figures 6 and 7. The samples with substances showing fluorescent colors similar to those of aflatoxins are marked with ●, while those with none of such substances are marked with ○. Doubtful samples are marked with ◑.

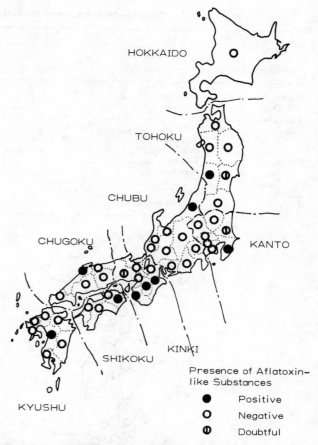

Figure 7.—Distribution of aflatoxin-like substances in domestic rice harvested in 1966 or 1967 from each prefecture of Japan (rice subjected to microbial culture).

Figure 6.—Distribution of aflatoxin-like substances in domestic rice harvested in 1966 or 1967 from each prefecture of Japan (intact rice).

As is shown in figures 6 and 7, of 46 samples of domestic rice, aflatoxin-like substances were detected in five samples of intact rice (plus one doubtful) and in nine samples of rice subjected to microbial culture (plus three doubtful). No aflatoxin-like substances were detected in the remaining 40 samples of intact rice and in the remaining 34 samples of cultured rice.

Imported rice.—On the other hand, as is shown in table 1, of 11 samples of imported rice, aflatoxin-

like substances were detected in three samples of intact rice and in three samples of cultured rice.

Koji-mold strains, liquid culture.—As is shown in table 2, of the collected 238 strains of koji mold, 52 produced aflatoxin-like substances and 25 samples were doubtful.

Koji-mold strains, solid culture.—The results (table 3) obtained by culture on native solid media were almost the same as those obtained by culture on liquid media. The peanut medium, however, showed a different result. The strains which produced aflatoxin-like substances on almost any other medium did not produce them on this medium. But ATCC 15517, an aflatoxin producing strain, produced aflatoxins on all media including the peanut medium.

Rice koji.—As is shown in figure 8, of 28 samples of rice koji, two produced aflatoxin-like substances, while one sample was doubtful.

Miso.—As is shown in figure 9, of the 108 samples tested, aflatoxin-like substances were produced in three samples. Two samples were doubtful.

Table 1.—Distribution of aflatoxin-like substances in imported rice

Producing district	Variety	Grain type	Milling	Aflatoxin-like substances	
				Intact rice	Cultured rice
Burma	Meedone	Long	Milled rice	−	+
Do	Ngasein	do	do	−	−
Thailand		do	do	+	−
U.S.A.	Calrose	Medium	do	+	−
Do	Nato	do	do	−	−
Do	Pearl	Short	do	+	−
China	Jojuku	do	do	−	−
Do	Shochan	do	do	−	+
Do	do	do	Brown rice	−	−
Taiwan	Horai	do	Milled rice	−	−
Spain	Round grain	do	do	−	+

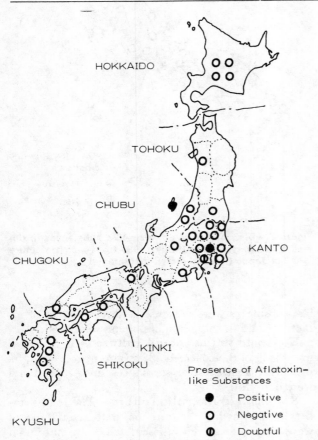

Figure 8.—Distribution of aflatoxin-like substances in rice-koji collected from miso factories located in eight districts of Japan.

Figure 9.—Distribution of aflatoxin-like substances in miso collected from each prefecture of Japan.

Comparison of aflatoxin-like substances with aflatoxins

Of the koji-mold strains which produced aflatoxin-like substances, most produced only two kinds of such substances but some produced as many as five to six kinds. Most of such substances had Rf values close to those of aflatoxin B_1, B_2 and G_1. These strains were mass-cultivated on crushed wheat media; aflatoxin-like substances were separated from those culture media by thin-layer chromatography and the ultraviolet absorption spectra and fluorescence spectra of the

Table 2. Statistics of the koji-molds that produce compounds similar to 4 aflatoxins on Czapek's solution

Usage	Aflatoxin-like fluorescent compounds +	?	−	Aflatoxin +	−	Total
Miso	6	7	34	0	47	47
Shoyu	21	8	36	0	65	65
Sake	4	0	25	0	29	29
Miso or sake	0	0	10	0	10	10
Tamari	3	0	3	0	6	6
Enzyme	0	0	1	0	1	1
Shochu (Spirits)	1	0	3	0	4	4
Ama-zake	1	0	2	0	3	3
The others	16	10	47	0	73	73
Total	52	25	161	0	238	238
Percent	21.8	10.5	67.7	0	100	100

Table 3.—Productivity of aflatoxin-like substances on solid culture by koji-molds

Number of strain	Czapek's solution	Rice	Wheat	Soybean Raw	De-fatted	Peanut
1	+	+	+			
2	+	+	+	+	+	−
3	?	?	?			
4	?	?	?			
5	−	−	−			
6	+	+	+			
7	−	−	−			
8	−	−	−			
9	−	−	−			
10	−	−	−			
11	−	−	−			
12	−	−	−			
13	−	−	−			
14	−	−	−			
15	−	−	−			
16	+	+	+	+	+	−
17	+	+	+			
18	−	−	−			
19	?	?	?			
20	?	+	+	+	+	−
21	?	?	?			
22	?					
23	−	−	−			
24	+	+	+			
25	−	−	−			
26	−	−	−			
27	−	−	−			
28	−	−	−			
29	−	−	−			
30	?	?	?			
31	−	−	−			
32	+	+	+	+	+	−
33	+	+	+			
34	−	−	−			
35	−	−	−			
36	+	+	+			
37	+	+	+			
38	−	−	−			
39	?	?	?			
40	+	+	+	+	+	−
41	+	+	+	+	+	−

aflatoxin-like substances were measured. Some of the results are shown in figures 10 and 11. In the ultra-violet absorption spectra of aflatoxin, absorption peaks are observed at 265 mμ, and 363 mμ. But any of the aflatoxin-like substances produced by the tested koji molds showed no absorption peaks at either 265 mμ, or at 363 mμ, especially in the neighborhood of 363 mμ; i.e. their absorption behavior was quite different from aflatoxins. Yokotsuka, et al. (*22, 23*) separated aflatoxin-like substances whose Rf values were close to those of aflatoxins from culture liquids of koji-molds by chromatography and identified those substances as flavacol and deoxyhydroxy aspergillic acid. But these substances also show no absorption peak in the neighborhood of 363 mμ. From the obtained Rf values and fluorescence colors, it is apparent that the same substances appeared among the aflatoxin-like substances separated by the present authors. The fluorescence spectra did not indicate a difference between aflatoxins and aflatoxin-like substances. Furthermore, although most of the obtained aflatoxin-like substances were hexane-soluble, aflatoxins themselves are insoluble in hexane. Similarly, the aflatoxin-like substances which existed in rice, in microbial cultures, rice koji and miso were found to be different from aflatoxins in their ultraviolet absorption spectra figs. 10 and 11.

In short, in any of the tested samples of rice koji-mold strains, rice koji and miso, the production of aflatoxins was not observed.

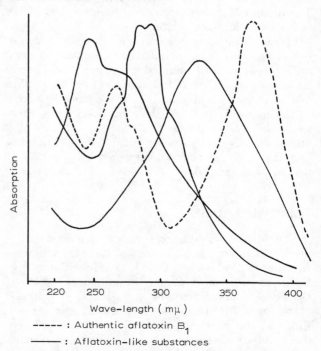

Figure 10.—Ultraviolet absorption spectra blue-purple fluorescent substances (methanol).

----- : Authentic aflatoxin B$_1$

——— : Aflatoxin-like substances

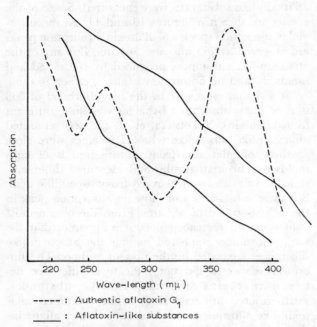

Figure 11.—Ultraviolet absorption spectra green fluorescent substances (methanol).

----- : Authentic aflatoxin G$_1$

——— : Aflatoxin-like substances

Recently G. N. Wogan (21) reported that in an investigation conducted at Bangkok, rice was found to be one of the farm products least contaminated with aflatoxins. He ascribed the reason to methods employed in harvest, storage, and transportation. The present authors confirmed his observations of the absence of aflatoxins in rice.

Likewise, the presented results confirm the fact that in the Japanese miso manufacturing industry, which utilizes molds closely related to aflatoxin-producing ones, no aflatoxins were found in the rice, koji-molds used or in the final product. The results are considered to be highly dependable since in this investigation the authors covered miso manufacturing plants and manufacturers of koji-starter culture throughout Japan, taking into consideration chances for contamination by aflatoxin-producing molds from the outside.

Acknowledgment

The authors would like to express their sincere appreciation to Dr. G. N. Wogan of the Massachusetts Institute of Technology, Dr. C. W. Hesseltine of the Northern Regional Research Laboratory of the U. S. Department of Agriculture and Dr. T. Yokotsuka of the Central Research Institute of Kikkoman Shoyu Co., Ltd., for supplying the strain ATCC 15517 and the standard aflatoxins. They are also very grateful to the Food Agency of Ministry of Agriculture and Forestry, the All Japan Koji-Starter Association and the Japan Miso Cooperative Industrial Association, for supplying the samples of rice, koji-mold, rice koji, and miso, respectively, and to Miss S. Onuma and Mr. T. Mitsuyasu of this Institute for their valuable assistance.

References

(1) AIBARA, K., and K. MIYAKI. 1965. Qualitative and quantitative analysis of aflatoxin. Paper presented at the Annual Meeting of the Agricultural Chemical Society of Japan, in Tokyo, Japan, Apr. 1–4.

(2) ASAI, T. 1956. "Industrial Microbiology." (Asakura Publ. Co., Tokyo) p. 395.

(3) ASAO, T., G. BUCHI, M. M. A. KADER, S. B. CHANG, E. L. WICK, and G. N. WOGAN. 1963. Aflatoxins B and G. J. Amer. Chem. Soc. 85: 1706–1707.

(4) ASHWORTH, L. J. JR., H. W. SCHROEDER, and B. C. LANGLEY. 1965. Aflatoxins: Environmental factors governing occurrence in Spanish peanuts. Science 148: 1228–1229.

(5) BOLLER, R. A. and H. W. SCHROEDER. 1966. Aflatoxin producing potential of Aspergillus flavus-oryzae isolates from rice. Cereal Science Today 11: 342–344.

(6) BORKER, E., N. F. INSALATA, C. P. LEVI, and J. S. WITZEMAN. 1966. Mycotoxins in feeds and foods. Adv. Appl. Microbiol. 8: 315–351.

(7) DEIONGH, H., R. K. BEERTHUIS, R. O. VLES, C. B. BARRETT, and W. O. ORD. 1962. Investigation of the factor in groundnut meal responsible for "turkey X disease," Biochem. Biophys. Acta. 65: 548–551.

(8) GOLDBLATT, L. A. 1968. Aflatoxin and its control. Economic Botany 22: 51–62.

(9) HARTLEY, R. D., B. F. NESBITT, and J. O'KELLY. 1963. Toxic metabolites of Aspergillis flavus. Nature 198: 1056–1058.

(10) HESSELTINE, C. W., O. L. SHOTWELL, J. J. ELLIS, and R. D. STUBBLEFIELD. 1966. Aflatoxin formation by Aspergillus flavus. Bacteriol. Rev. 30: 795–805.

(11) KURATA, H., H. TANABE, K. KANOTA, S. UDAGAWA and M. ICHINOE. 1968. Studies on the population of toxigenic fungi in foodstuffs IV. Aflatoxin producing fungi isolated from foodstuffs in Japan. Journal of the Food Hygienic Society of Japan 9: 29–34.

(12) KURATA, H., S. UDAGAWA, M. ICHINOE, Y. KAWASAKI, M. TAKADA, M. TAZAWA, A. KOIZUMI, and H. TANABE. 1968. Studies on the population of toxigenic fungi in foodstuffs III. Mycoflora of milled rice harvested in 1965. Journal of the Food Hygienic Society of Japan 9: 23–28.

(13) MASUDA, Y., K. MORI, and M. KURATSUNE. 1965. Study on aflatoxin. Paper presented at the 24th Annual Meeting of the Japanese Cancer Association, in Fukuoka, Japan, Oct. 14–16.

(14) MATELES, R. I., and G. N. WOGAN. 1967. Aflatoxins. In Adv. in Microbial Physiol. (A. H. Rose and J. F. Wilkinson, ed.) 1: 25.

(15) MURAKAMI, H., S. TAKASE, and T. ISHII. 1967. Nonproductivity of aflatoxin by Japanese industrial strains of Aspergillus. I. Production of fluorescent substances in agar slant and shaking cultures. J. Gen. and Appl. Microbiol. 13: 323–334.

(16) NESBITT, B. F., J. O'KELLY, K. SARGEANT, and A. SHERIDAN. 1962. Toxic metabolites of Aspergillus flavus. Nature 195: 1062–1063.

(17) SCHROEDER, H. W., and L. J. ASHWORTH, JR. 1965. Aflatoxins in spanish peanuts in relation to pod and kernel condition. Phytopathol. *55:* 464–465.

(18) SCHROEDER, H. W., and H. HEIN, JR. 1967. Aflatoxins; production of the toxins *in vitro* in relation to temperature. Appl. Microbiol. *15:* 441–445.

(19) SHOTWELL, O. L., C. W. HESSELTINE, R. D. STUBBLEFIELD, and W. G. SORENSON. 1966. Production of aflatoxin on rice. Appl. Microbiol. *14:* 425–428.

(20) TABER, R. A., and H. W. SCHROEDER. 1967. Aflatoxin-producing potential of isolates of the *Aspergillus flavus-oryzae* group from peanuts (*Arachis hypogaea*). Appl. Microbiol. *15:* 140–144.

(21) WOGAN, G. N. 1968. Natural toxic substances in foods with special reference to the mycotoxins. Paper presented at the Joint Meeting of Malnutrition Panels, United States-Japan Cooperative Medical Science Program in Tokyo, Aug. 5–7.

(22) YOKOTSUKA, T., M. SASAKI, T. KIKUCHI, Y. ASAO, and A. NOBUHARA. 1967. Studies on the compounds produced by moulds. Pt. 1. Fluorescent compounds produced by Japanese industrial moulds. J. Agric. Chem. Soc. Japan *41:* 32–38.

(23) YOKOTSUKA, T., M. SASAKI, T. KIKUCHI, Y. ASAO, and A. NOBUHARA. 1967. Production of fluorescent compounds other than aflatoxins by Japanese industrial molds. Biochemistry of Some Foodborne Microbial Toxins (The M.I.T. press, Cambridge, Mass.) pp. 131–152.

AFLATOXINS IN RICE IN THE UNITED STATES

by Harry W. Schroeder

USDA, ARS, Market Quality Research Division, College Station, Tex.

Three general conditions are prerequisites of aflatoxin contamination of a food or feed product: (1) The product must be capable of supporting the growth of the toxin-producing fungi and must supply the necessary materials to enable the fungi to produce the toxins; (2) the product must become infested or inoculated with toxin-producing fungi; (3) the inoculated or infested product or crop must be under environmental conditions favorable for growth of the fungi and for production and accumulation of the toxin. Each of these conditions will be examined in relation to its application to rice in the United States.

Reports by numerous investigators have shown that strains of species of the *Aspergillus flavus* group are capable of producing aflatoxins on a wide variety of food and feed products. In 1965, I reported (*4*) that aflatoxin production on autoclaved moist rough rice by an isolate of *A. flavus* approached the quantity produced on autoclaved moist shelled Spanish peanut (fig. 1). Approximately 550 μg. of aflatoxins were produced per gram of rough rice compared with about 650 μg./g. of peanut. Shotwell et al. (*6*) reported yields of 1,000 μg./g. on moist autoclaved milled rice. Thus, there is abundant evidence that rice can be an excellent substrate for the growth of aflatoxin-producing fungi and, subsequently, for the production and accumulation of the toxins. These reports clearly show that rice as a crop meets the first general condition for possible aflatoxin contamination.

The second requirement also has been studied in our laboratory. We have found that the *A. flavus* group of fungi (the principal producers of the aflatoxins) are commonly found associated with rough rice after harvest. We reported in 1961 (*5*) that they were the predominant group of species in rice dried with unheated air. Unpublished studies in our laboratory have shown that the spores of species of the *A. flavus* group are commonly found associated with rough rice immediately after harvest although actual infection of kernels at that time is quite rare. Infection proceeds at a rate determined by the environmental conditions the rice is subjected to after harvest. Apparently the fungal species that produce aflatoxins are prominent in the flora of rice.

Many investigators, however, have shown that iso-

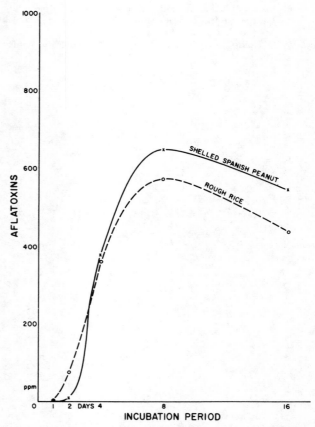

Figure 1.—The production and accumulation of aflatoxins on moist autoclaved rough rice in comparison with the production and accumulation on shelled Spanish peanut.

lates of *A. flavus* may vary greatly in their ability to produce aflatoxins. Our laboratory studied the variability in aflatoxin production by strains of the *A. flavus* group isolated from rice and reported our findings in 1966 (*1*). We studied the mycoflora associated with 282 samples of rough rice from the five major rice-producing States of the United States. The percentages of kernels infected by various fungi were determined by plating surface-disinfected kernels on malt agar containing 7.5 percent NaCl. The distribution of *A. flavus* isolations (table 1) shows that the fungus is associated with rice from all the major rice-producing States and that the frequency of its isolation within the several States can vary widely among samples.

Table 1.—Prevalence of *Aspergillus flavus* species in rough rice samples from 5 states[1]

Percent of infected kernels	Number of samples				
	A	B	C	D	E
0	6				
0.1 to 30	82	10	28	28	24
30.1 to 70	7		21	17	36
>70	1		1	5	15

[1]States identified by alphabetical designation.

The majority of the samples from four of the five States contained 30 percent or less of seeds infested with *A. flavus*.

There were 284 isolates selected at random for determination of their toxin-producing ability. These isolates were maintained on Czapek's solution agar under refrigeration until the test was accomplished. Aflatoxin production was determined by inoculation of each isolate on sterile rough rice and sterile shelled Spanish peanuts. Thirty grams of the respective dry substrate were placed in 250-ml. Erlenmeyer flasks and brought to a suitable moisture content by the addition of 10 ml. of water before being sterilized in an autoclave for 30 minutes at 15 lb./sq. in. The samples were then inoculated with a spore suspension and incubated 10 days at 30° C. Following incubation, the samples were again autoclaved for 30 minutes, frozen, and stored until assayed for aflatoxin content. The toxins were extracted with aqueous acetone after the method of Pons, et al. (*3*) and aflatoxins were detected and quantified by thin-layer chromatography.

To simplify reporting the results of the tests, an aflatoxin-production index was devised (table 2). The isolates were rated from zero through eight. A rating of zero indicates that the isolate failed to produce a detectable quantity of aflatoxin, while eight indicates that it produced more than 250,000 p.p.b. of aflatoxin B_1 or G_1.

Table 2.—Aflatoxin-production index of isolates of the *Aspergillus flavus* group from rice

Aflatoxin production rating	Aflatoxin concentration[1] developed in uniform test (p.p.b.)
0	0
1	1–250
2	251–500
3	501–1000
4	1001–5000
5	5001–10000
6	10001–50000
7	50001–250,000
8	>250,000

[1]Refers to concentration of aflatoxin B_1 or G_1.

The distribution of the isolates from rice, according to this method of rating their ability to produce aflatoxins, is given in figure 2. Toxin-production ability varied over a wide range with the isolates tending to fall into two groups—those producing relatively large amounts of the toxin (comprising roughly 25 percent of the isolates) to those producing little or no toxins (about 75 percent). Sixteen isolates (5.6 percent) did not produce aflatoxin B_1 on rice; 25 (8.8 percent) failed to produce this toxin on peanuts. Aflatoxin G_1 was not produced by 63.7 percent of the isolates on rice or by 66.5 percent on peanuts. This small indication that rice is a better substrate for the production of aflatoxin than peanuts by the isolates from rice is strengthened by another observation. More isolates were in the toxicity class eight when grown on a rice substrate than when grown on a peanut substrate. One isolate produced more than 300,000 p.p.b. of both B_1 and G_1 on both substrates; however, the concentration of B_1 was 317,000 p.p.b. on peanuts compared to 476,000 p.p.b. on rice.

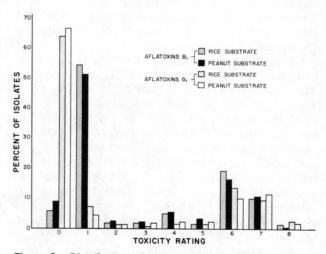

Figure 2.—Distribution of isolates of the *Aspergillus flavus* group from rice according to their ability to produce aflatoxins.

The average of the aflatoxin-production index of all isolates by their respective origins (States) indicated that the toxin-producing ability was well distributed in all States (table 3). Only State B deviated markedly from the overall average index. Since only six isolates were tested from State B, the deviation probably is not significant.

The study just cited clearly shows that the second condition for the contamination of rice with aflatoxins is usually satisfied; namely, rice is often infested or inoculated with toxin-producing fungi during production and marketing. If the third condition were to

Table 3.—The average aflatoxin-production index of *Aspergillus flavus* isolates from rice samples from 5 states

State	Average aflatoxin-production index
A	2.5
B	6.2
C	3.5
D	2.6
E	2.7
Average	2.5

be frequently satisfied also, then an extremely serious problem could exist in the rice industry. That is, a significant portion of the crop might be contaminated with the toxins.

Fortunately, the third condition—the environment in which the crop is kept—is the factor most easily controlled by man. I wish to report some of the results from a study (2) we have made in cooperation with the Transportation and Facilities Division of the Agricultural Research Service that illustrate some of the environmental conditions that could lead to aflatoxin contamination or conversely prevent such contamination.

In the United States, rice is usually harvested at moisture contents ranging from 18 to 22 percent. Moreover, harvest extends from July into November. These factors, coupled with the wide range of climatic conditions found in the rice-growing areas of California and Arkansas to the coastal areas of Texas and Louisiana, indicate that rice is harvested, conditioned, and stored under widely varied conditions, some of which could be favorable for developing aflatoxin contamination as well as other types of microbiological deterioration. To prevent such deterioration, efficient artificial drying systems, using both heated and unheated air, condition the rice crop for storage and further processing.

The experiments which I am reporting were designed to determine the rapidity and extent of aflatoxin production and accumulation in undried rough rice under conditions comparable to those in holding bins in commercial driers. Details of the experimental bin's construction and operation will not be given except to report that each bin had a capacity of about one barrel of rice. It had previously been determined that their design reasonably simulated the conditions in large bins.

These results summarize 2 years of work involving three experiments of nine bins each year. The rice was stored for 21 days in each experiment. We selected three of the most important environmental factors to study; that is: (1) Aeration rate, (2) moisture content, and (3) ambient temperature. Our goal was to

compare the effects of each of these factors by maintaining all other principal factors constant. However, since we cannot control the weather, the availability of varieties, or even the uniformity of rice moisture content within a single truckload, we had to be satisfied with a reasonable approach to that goal.

Table 4 shows the effect of aeration rates. In this particular experiment the ambient temperature averaged about 80° F. during the storage period. The rice went into storage at about 22.0 percent moisture content. Under these conditions, aflatoxins reached a significant concentration within 2 days when aerated at a rate of 0.5 c.f.m. but doubling the airflow rate increased this relatively safe storage period to about 2 weeks. Toxins accumulated to detectable levels very early in the storage period even when the airflow rate was 2.0 c.f.m.

Table 4.—Effect of rate of aeration on aflatoxin development in rice[1]

Airflow rate per barrel c.f.m.	First detected (days in storage)	Maximum concentration (p.p.b.)	Time to reach 30 p.p.b. (days in storage)
0.5	2	857	2
1.0	6	58	15
2.0	2	30	20

[1]Average ambient temperature about 82° F. Initial moisture content about 22.0 percent.

Table 5 shows the development of kernel infection by *A. flavus* in the same experiment. The maximum infection during the storage period did not vary greatly with the aeration rates although the time required to reach the maximum increased as the airflow rate increased. The rate of kernel infection did not reflect the large difference in the rate of aflatoxin accumulation shown in table 4.

Table 5.—Effect of rate of aeration on rice kernel infection by *Aspergillus flavus*[1]

Airflow rate per barrel (c.f.m.)	Range (percent)	Time to reach maximum (days in storage)
0.5	0–43	14
1.0	1–45	15
2.0	0–35	20

[1]Average ambient temperature about 82° F. Initial moisture content about 22.0 percent.

Table 6 shows the effect of initial moisture content. In this experiment, the average ambient temperature was about 80° F. and the airflow rate was 1 c.f.m.

Table 6.—Effect of initial moisture content in aflatoxin development in rice[1]

Initial moisture content (percent wet basis)	First detected (days in storage)	Maximum concentration (p.p.b.)	Time to reach 30 p.p.b. (days in storage)
26.2	3	743	6
22.6	6	94	9
19.8	([2])	--------------------------	

[1] Average ambient temperature about 80° F. Airflow rate—1 c.f.m. per barrel.
[2] Not detected.

per barrel. With initial moisture content at 26.2 percent, aflatoxins were detected after 3 days and reached a level of 30 p.p.b. after 6 days. Reducing the into-storage moisture content to 22.6 percent, doubled the time in storage that the rice remained toxin-free and increased the storage period before the concentration reached 30 p.p.b. to 9 days. A further decrease in initial moisture to 19.8 percent prevented the production of aflatoxins in detectable amounts throughout the 21 days.

This experiment showed a direct relation between *A. flavus* infection of the rice kernel and the initial moisture content (table 7).

Table 7.—Effect of initial moisture content on infection of rice kernels by Aspergillus flavus[1]

Initial moisture content (percent wet basis)	Kernels infected by *A. flavus*	
	Range (percent)	Time to reach maximum (days in storage)
26.2	0–98	18
22.6	0–62	21
19.8	0–32	15

[1] Average ambient temperature about 80° F. Airflow rate—1 c.f.m. per barrel.

Our study of the effect of ambient temperature has more uncontrolled variables affecting the results than the two previous experiments. Table 8, however, illustrates the direct relation between temperature and aflatoxin production and accumulation. With an average ambient temperature of 78° to 82° F., aflatoxins soon developed in high-moisture rice but at about 68° F. the production of aflatoxins in significant amounts was prevented.

Kernel infection by *A. flavus* reached about the same level regardless of ambient temperature; however, the data indicate that the rate of kernel infection was slowed considerably at the lower temperature (table 9).

Table 8.—Effect of ambient temperature on aflatoxin development in rice kernels[1]

Storage period (date)	Average ambient temperature °F.	Aflatoxins		
		First detected (days in storage)	Maximum concentration (p.p.b.)	Time to reach 30 p.p.b. (days in storage)
Aug. 5–25, 1966	82	5	743	8
Sept. 7–28, 1966	78	3	211	9
Oct. 5–26, 1966	67	15	Trace	---------

[1] Initial moisture content about 23 to 25 percent. Airflow rate—1 c.f.m. per barrel.

Table 9.—Effect of ambient temperature on rice kernel infection by A. flavus[1]

Storage period (date)	Average ambient temperature °F.	Kernels infected by *A. flavus*	
		Range (percent)	Time to reach maximum (days in storage)
Aug. 5–25, 1966	82	0–87	8
Sept. 7–28, 1966	78	0–95	6
Oct. 5–26, 1966	68	0–93	15

[1] Initial moisture content about 23 to 25 percent. Airflow rate—1 c.f.m. per barrel.

Obviously, many more similar experiments will be necessary to measure accurately the effects of the many factors and their interactions on the production and accumulation of aflatoxins in undried rice during storage.

The studies I have reported here show how high-moisture rice might become contaminated with aflatoxins. Rice is an excellent substrate for the growth of the toxin-producing organisms and for supporting the production and accumulation of the toxin. Toxin-producing strains of the fungi are widely distributed in rice-growing areas and often are found associated with harvested rice. Moreover, rice often is harvested at moisture contents and under ambient temperatures favorable for the rapid development of aflatoxin contamination. Fortunately, the efficient systems of drying, conditioning, and storing that have been developed to maintain quality in rice after harvest also serve to prevent production and accumulation of aflatoxins. However, efficiency must remain high and the industry must remain alert to prevent the combination of circumstances under which rice could become contaminated with aflatoxins.

References

(1) BOLLER, R. A., and H. W. SCHROEDER. 1966. Aflatoxin-producing potential of *Aspergillus flavus-oryzae* isolates from rice. Cereal Science Today *11:* 433–435.

(2) CALDERWOOD, D. L., and H. W. SCHROEDER. 1968. Aflatoxin development and grade of undried rough rice following prolonged storage in aerated bins. Agricultural Research Service, U.S. Dept. of Agriculture, ARS 52–26. 32 pp.

(3) PONS, W. A. Jr., A. F. CUCULLU, L. S. LEE, J. A. ROBERSON, A. O. FRANZ, and L. A. GOLDBLATT. 1966. Determination of aflatoxins in agricultural products: Use of aqueous acetone for extraction. Jour. Assoc. Official Agric. Chemists *49:* 554–562.

(4) SCHROEDER, H. W. 1965. Factors affecting aflatoxin production *in vitro* by *Aspergillus flavus-oryzae* spp. Peanut Improvement Working Group Meeting. Washington, D.C.

(5) SCHROEDER, H. W., and J. W. SORENSON, Jr. 1961. Mold development in rough rice as affected by aeration during storage. Rice J. *64:* 8–10, 12, 21–23.

(6) SHOTWELL, O. L., C. W. HESSELTINE, R. D. STUBBLEFIELD, and W. G. SORENSON. 1966. Production of aflatoxin on rice. Appl. Microbiol. *14:* 425–428.

MYCOTOXIN RESEARCH IN OILSEEDS

by R. W. Howell*

Crops Research Division, Agricultural Research Service,
U.S. Department of Agriculture, Beltsville, Md. 20705

The aflatoxin problem first came to public attention in an oilseed, namely the peanut or groundnut, *Arachis hypogaea* L. We know now that the problem is not unique to oilseeds, but a special relevance to this group of food crops continues. Peanuts, cottonseed (*Gossypium hirsutum* L.), and soybeans (*Glycine max* (L.) Merr.) excel as sources of high quality protein. The peanut requires a minimum of processing to be a very attractive food. The cottonseed and soybean are major sources of protein for animal feeding and, more recently, of isolated protein for highly nutritious food products. The potential of these crops for meeting food needs of the world is enormous. The presence or threat of mycotoxins continues, therefore, as a cause of grave concern.

Research on mycotoxins in oilseeds has been concentrated on peanuts, cottonseed, and soybeans. I shall therefore limit my discussion to work with these three crops.

Peanuts

In the United States, peanuts are grown in three areas, with different characteristic climates. About a fourth of the acreage is in the southwestern States of Texas and Oklahoma. There is a small acreage in New Mexico. The climate is dry. Irrigation of peanuts in the southwest is increasing and is now used on more than 25 percent of the acreage. Despite the low total rainfall, winds off the Gulf of Mexico bring high humidity and sometimes heavy rains during the harvest season. The harvest season extends from late June to November. The small-seeded Spanish type is grown in the southwest. About half the acreage is in the southeast, Georgia having the largest acreage. The climate is hot and humid. Irrigation is negligible. The harvest season is hot. Both Spanish and Virginia types are grown in nearly equal proportions. About a fourth of the acreage is in the Virginia-Carolina area. The climate during the summer is hot with periods of high humidity but it is cool during harvest. Irrigation is negligible. The large-seeded Virginia-type peanut

is grown here. Aflatoxin has been found in peanuts from all three areas.

Peanuts infected with *Aspergillus flavus* Lk. ex Fr., or contaminated with aflatoxin are being removed from marketing channels before products reach the consumer. Farmers' stock peanuts are segregated at the initial buying point on the basis of mold growth on the seed. Contaminated peanuts go to nonfood uses. Shelled peanuts or recleaned in-shell peanuts destined for roasting in the shell are sampled and assayed for aflatoxin by the Consumer and Marketing Service, U.S. Department of Agriculture. About 4 percent of the lots from the 1967 crop had verified aflatoxin levels of 30 p.p.b. or more. (J. C. Genske. Verbal communication). Levels in most of the contaminated lots do not exceed 30 p.p.b. by very much. It is rare to find a lot with a high level of contamination. Insofar as I know there have been no significant aflatoxin incidents due to peanuts in the United States.

When and how does infection occur? *A. flavus* is a ubiquitous soil fungus with ample opportunity to infect the peanut after the peg enters the ground. There is some evidence that pegs may be infected with *A. flavus* even before penetration of the soil. Such reports are rare, however, and it is probable that infection usually occurs in the soil. At Holland, Virginia, over a 3-year period, *A. flavus* was isolated in low frequency as early as August 3. *A. flavus* was isolated from less than 0.5 percent of the shells and seeds in August, but from 6 and 8 percent of the seeds in September and October. Slightly over 1 percent of the shell isolations produced *A. flavus* in September and October. Aflatoxin was not found in any of the samples analyzed from this study. (K. H. Garren and D. M. Porter. Unpublished annual reports. 1966, 1967). The variety used, Virginia Bunch 46–2, matures at Holland early in October.

A similar study has been conducted at two locations in Texas under both dryland and irrigated conditions (*17*). The percentage of shells infected with *A. flavus* varied from zero to 42 percent on various sampling dates. There was a tendency for higher percentages in the latter part of the season. Of 32 of the infected samples which were assayed, three from each location contained aflatoxin, ranging from 13 to 1,650 p.p.b. Four of these were from irrigated fields and

*Chief, Oilseed and Industrial Crops Research Branch, Crops Research Division, Agricultural Research Service, U.S. Department of Agriculture, Beltsville, Md. 20705.

two from dryland. During this study more than 2,000 pegs were examined. *A. flavus* was isolated from 63 or 3.1 percent. Seed contamination data were not reported.

Examination at marketing points suggested a tendency for a higher frequency of contamination in samples which were harvested during a warm, damp period than in those harvested later when it was cooler and drier. The data were inadequate, however, to establish a statistical probability for this tendency. There was some evidence that crop rotation practices influence the occurrence of aflatoxin (*17*). When the previous crop was peanuts, as many as twice the number of seeds contained internal fungi as when a different crop preceded peanuts. More than half of the samples contained at least a trace of aflatoxin. Fungal contamination or aflatoxin occurred in some samples following each previous cropping pattern.

Peanuts are dug and dried in a windrow for from 2 to several days before pods are removed from the vine. Most of the soil falls away from the pods as they are dug, but ample soil adheres to maintain an inoculum of soil fungi while the pods are in the windrow. Conventional diggers leave the plants and pods in a random arrangement. Diggers which systematically invert the vines leave the pods in a position to dry more readily, thus reducing the time for mold growth and aflatoxin formation.

Pods are of course exposed to the weather while in the windrow. Rain will slow the drying process and may actually increase moisture content of peanuts. Temperature is several degrees higher and drying is more rapid in the inverted windrow than in the conventional windrow. The desired moisture content of less than 25 percent may be reached 2 or more days earlier in the inverted windrow.

More shells and seeds contain *A. flavus* in the conventional windrow. It is interesting to note that *A. flavus* may occur in a higher percentage of seeds than shells. The effect of windrow geometry on aflatoxin formation is not conspicuous during windrowing. Aflatoxin occurred only rarely in samples taken from the windrow. In each such occurrence the samples had been rained on and had been held a full week in the windrow. However, development of aflatoxin during the holding period after combining was related to windrow geometry. The incidence and average level of aflatoxin were consistently very low from inverted rows, compared with about 7 percent incidence and 20 p.p.b. average level from random rows. (J. L. Butler. Unpublished annual report. 1967).

The occurrence and level of aflatoxin in samples at the market reflect the history of the peanuts after digging. The principal aflatoxin hazard occurs following combining, prior to or during drying to the desired storage moisture of 8 to 9 percent. Many more colonies of *A. flavus* can be isolated from slowly dried peanuts than from rapidly dried peanuts. Less than 1 percent of pods dried rapidly to 8 percent moisture contained *A. flavus*, while 4 to 5 percent of those dried slowly were infected. The results were similar whether initial pod moisture was 45 to 55 percent or 18 to 25 percent. (*7*)

Damage caused by mechanical harvesting is a significant factor in fungal invasion. Although combine-harvested pods yielded few colonies at the time of harvest, more than twice as many colonies of *A. flavus* were isolated after drying from peanuts which had been combine-harvested as from those which had been hand picked (*7*). Research to modify harvesting machinery to reduce combine-damage is underway.

Results have varied widely between experiments, reflecting the difficulty of precise control or description of experimental conditions in the field. Fungi, including *A. flavus*, are widely distributed in nature and occur in the shells of virtually all peanut fruits at maturity (*8, 18*). It is probably operationally impossible to establish and maintain a field plot free of *A. flavus* without distorting the ecological balance of the soil environment. However, our studies have not shown a high correlation between the occurrence of aflatoxin in peanuts and climatic, soil, irrigation, fertility, or other environmental variables during crop production. Conditions after harvest, especially during the holding period prior to drying, probably determine whether aflatoxin will be produced.

It is interesting to speculate whether peanut pod development results from symbiotic activities of the peanut and the soil flora. Techniques for producing peanuts under gnotobiotic (germ-free) conditions in the laboratory have been developed by Dr. D. L. Lindsay of Colorado State University. He has been able to exclude fungi from developing pods and seeds, but so far an unidentified bacterium has always appeared by about 90 days after planting.

Factors favoring infection and contamination are the subject of another presentation on this symposium. I shall therefore not further discuss the influence of environmental conditions after harvest. Suffice it to say that there is good evidence that steady drying of peanuts to about 8 percent moisture is highly effective in suppressing mold development (*20*).

The quality of peanuts and peanut products as judged by the consumer is of great importance, more so than in commodities which undergo greater transformation before reaching the consumer. Quality factors are subtle, subjective, and sensitive. The importance of objective measurements, and therefore of the association of aflatoxin with measurable quality factors or constituents, is obvious. Correlations of mold growth score with both fat acidity and aflatoxin content have been reported (*15*). However, in other cases positive correlations have not been found between iodine number, free fatty acids, and aflatoxin concentration or degree of fungal infestation.

What are the mycotoxin hazards attributable to fungi other than *A. flavus*? We have sampled extensively and repeatedly in all peanut producing areas of the United States to identify the fungi which are associated with peanut pods and seeds. Of 2,816 isolations identified at least to genus so far, 2,194 or 78 percent are *Alternaria, Aspergillus, Chaetomium, Fusarium,* or *Penicillium*. The latter is the most frequently isolated, accounting for 30 percent of the total, and its species are dominant in both shells and seeds throughout their development in the soil (*8*).

It is germane to the mycotoxin problem to ask whether these fungi can produce toxin on agricultural commodities. So far, of 231 fungi isolated from peanuts and cultured on moist autoclaved corn or corn and rice, each of which was then fed to two rats or other test animals, 116 have been lethal to one or both animals within 7 days (*3*). Eighty of the isolates were *Penicillium* sp. Forty of these were lethal. Each of the other genera was also lethal in 40 percent or more of the cases. We do not know yet whether these fungi produce toxins when grown on peanuts.

The toxin or toxins have yet been identified chemically. Several workers have examined the aflatoxin production potential of numerous species of *Aspergillus* and *Penicillium* without identifying any aflatoxin producers. Earlier reports that organisms other than *A. flavus* produce aflatoxins are now being questioned (*14*). Whether the toxic material produced by fungi other than *A. flavus* is chemically identical with or different from aflatoxin is a moot point. The presence in peanuts or other food materials of fungi with a toxin-producing potential constitutes a health hazard.

The ultimate objective of our research is to eliminate the mycotoxin problem. What then are possible methods of control? I have already referred to evidence that prompt continuous drying greatly reduces the aflatoxin hazard. This is a recommended procedure. Unfortunately, peanuts must still undergo a period of drying in the field after digging, and during this time are subject to the weather. Equipment that will arrange the plants in a nonrandom fashion has been discussed. Improved versions of diggers, and combines to handle the peanuts more gently, are being developed (*16*).

Chemical controls have received some attention. Pentachloronitrobenzene (PCNB) applied to the soil in barrels (10 liters, 10^{-4}M) at various stages, reduced the number of soil samples from which *A. flavus* was isolated (*9*). Studies with fungicides in the field have been less encouraging. Some of the materials that have been studied are listed below: (*5, 6,* and K. H. Garren and D. M. Porter. Unpublished annual reports. 1966, 1967).

Botran (2,6-dichloro-4-nitroaniline)

D-D(1,3-dichloropropene-1, 2-dichloropropane mixture)

Dexon (p-dimethylaminobenzene diazo sodium sulfonate)

Difolatan (N-(1,1,2,2-tetrachloroethylthio)-4-cyclohexane-1,2-dicarboximide)

Fentin hydroxide (duTer; triphenyl tin hydroxide)

PCNB (pentachloronitrobenzene)

Polyram (polyethylene polymer of zinc carbamates)

SMDC (vapam; sodium N-methyldithiocarbamate dihydrate)

Each of these materials is registered for use on some agricultural commodities and some are registered for nonfood uses on peanuts. None is registered for use on peanuts for food use except PCNB which is registered for *Rhizoctonia* control on peanuts. There is no residue tolerance to PCNB at present, but a petition for a tolerance is pending. None of these materials is registered for *A. flavus* control and based on our results, there is little basis for seeking registration. There are of course no residue tolerances in peanuts.

Promising results have been obtained recently in tests of fungitoxic properties of potassium sorbate and several other food preservatives (*2, 9*). Disinfection of soil with potassium sorbate about 2 months after inoculation reduced the number of *A. flavus* colonies isolated six months later by more than 80 percent (*9*). Acetic acid in 5 percent solution was effective in vitro, against several common fungi of peanuts (*2*). The concentration is of interest because it approximates that of acetic acid in vinegar. These materials have not been used in field tests. Materials such as food preservatives would probably present less of a residue problem than fungicides such as those listed above.

The best control of all would be a peanut variety which is genetically immune to invasion by *A. flavus*. Rao and Tulpule (*19*), of the Indian Council of Medical Research, reported that a toxigenic strain of *A. flavus* failed to produce aflatoxin on the variety U. S. 26 (PI 246388). A check of the reported resistance of this variety to aflatoxin development in two laboratories in the United States and one in England failed to confirm the Indian report. Subsequently, however, a few seeds of U.S. 26 were obtained from the Indian investigators. Again we failed to confirm the Indian report of resistance to aflatoxin development, although aflatoxin was not found in every seed.

Kulkarni (*10*) reported the variety "Asiriya Mwitunde" to be resistant. We have two accessions by this name, PI 268893 and PI 295170, but have not yet checked them for resistance to *A. flavus* or aflatoxin development. Joffe (unpublished report PL 480 grant FG–IS–161, A10–CR–46. 1967) has also reported possible differences in susceptibility between peanut genotypes. This work, too, is unconfirmed.

The usefulness or potential for genetic resistance has thus been explored very little. We have just initiated our first such breeding program with partial support from the United States-Japan medical cooperative program. A plant breeding effort will be a part of this program as soon as suitable genotypes are identified. The possibility that varieties are heterogeneous and do actually contain some resistant genotypes will be explored.

Cotton

Aflatoxins tend to occur infrequently at high levels in U.S. cottonseed at harvest. Naturally infected samples usually contain only aflatoxins B_1 and B_2. Contaminated cotton bolls are principally those produced on the lower third of the plant, where they are exposed longer and to conditions more favorable for *A. flavus* growth than are bolls higher on the plant. The lower part of the plant is subject to longer periods of high humidity each day than the upper part.

As in peanuts, there are probably continuous opportunities for *A. flavus* infection. Examination of cotton soils has shown as many as 5,000 particles of plant debris infested with *A. flavus* per cubic foot of soil. The number of *A. flavus*-infested particles was high, even in fields where there was no significant infestation or aflatoxin contamination of the seed. Artificial increases of humidity by fogging or irrigation have in fact increased the amount of natural infection and contamination under high temperature conditions. Thus the existence of humidity and temperature conditions favorable for fungus growth appears to be the significant variable, rather than *A. flavus* inoculum potential.

Aspergillus flavus has been known for many years as the cause of a boll rot in cotton (*4, 11*). A bright greenish yellow fluorescence (BGY) on the lint is caused by *A. flavus* and is symptomatic of this boll rot. It has occurred most frequently in the Imperial, Colorado, and lower Rio Grande Valleys. High humidities can occur in these areas due to irrigation and to winds off the Gulf of California and the Gulf of Mexico. Aflatoxin in cottonseed has also occurred most often in these same areas.

BGY is a useful indicator of the presence of *Aspergillus flavus* and aflatoxin (*1*). Weathered samples which do not fluoresce may contain aflatoxin, but even so cottonseed lots free of BGY are less likely to contain aflatoxin. Cottonseed produced on soil inoculated with *A. flavus*-contaminated oat seeds have contained a higher percentage of fluorescent seeds and in most cases more aflatoxin than cottonseed from uninoculated soil. BGY is localized in the lint and seed fuzz. The BGY fluorescence has been produced experimentally in many different plants in the laboratory by incubation with *A. flavus* following mechanical damage (*12*). Its occurrence in nature other than in cotton is not known.

The fluorescent compound is a derivative of kojic acid, which was identified by Japanese workers about 1910. It is water soluble and light sensitive. Many derivatives have been characterized, but so far as we know, BGY has not. The fungus forms kojic acid, which is converted, under the influence of peroxidase in the infected higher plant cell, into the typical bright greenish yellow fluorescent material. Many strains of *A. flavus* have been tested for ability to produce the fluorescence in a living cotton fiber and all results have been positive. Some strains of *Alternaria* also produce a fluorescence on the fiber in the field, but this is a whitish fluorescence, easily distinguished from that caused by *A. flavus*. The metabolic relationship of BGY and aflatoxin has not been established, but some relationships have been summarized by Marsh et al. (*12*).

BGY produced no noticeable toxic effects in an egg embryo test when used at a rate of about 13 μg. per egg. A dosage of about 0.02 μg. of aflatoxin B_1 per egg is said to kill half the embryos.

Aspergillus flavus grows and produces aflatoxin primarily on the cottonseed meat (*13*). The hulls of contaminated seeds sometimes contain aflatoxin. The lint is a relatively poor substrate for *A. flavus*, which decomposes cellulose with great difficulty and, unlike many other boll rot fungi, fails to penetrate the fiber wall and enter in the lumen. No difference in the susceptibility of glanded and glandless cotton, with respect to *A. flavus* infection or aflatoxin production has been established. However, present information is limited and has been obtained largely under laboratory conditions.

Aflatoxin is a production problem in cottonseed but, as in peanuts, the greatest buildup of aflatoxin is likely to occur during storage. Storage conditions during the processing season, which may last as long as 10 months, therefore strongly influence the incidence and level of aflatoxin. Cottonseed free of toxin and stored under covered and aerated conditions has generally not developed significant levels of aflatoxin.

Management practices to reduce the humidity in the lower third of the plant have reduced the incidence and level of aflatoxin. A 4 by 4 skip row planting system reduced the aflatoxin level from that in a solid planting. Defoliation of the lower third of the crop with DEF (s,s,s-tributylphosphorotrithioate) accompanying the 4 by 4 skip row pattern, virtually eliminated aflatoxin (L. J. Ashworth, unpublished progress report).

Fungicides have not been considered desirable as controls of aflatoxin in cottonseed because of probable residue problems.

Soybeans

Aflatoxins have been reported in soybeans, but the frequency appears to be much lower than in peanuts and cotton. Soybeans are one of our most widely grown crops, occupying in 1968 more than 41 million acres. The largest acreages were in Illinois, Iowa, and Arkansas, but 12 different States had more than 1 million acres.

We began our studies of aflatoxin in soybeans by assaying laboratory samples from our regional tests in 1964. There were 1,232 samples representing many varieties and production areas, but they had not been collected specifically for aflatoxin studies. Eleven of these samples contained A. flavus. Isolates from six of the 11 samples produced aflatoxin B$_1$. The seeds themselves were not assayed for aflatoxin. The six isolates varied in their aflatoxin-producing potential, one producing 100,000 p.p.b.

During 1965 and 1966 we conducted a comprehensive sampling program throughout the crop production season and for 6 weeks following normal harvest date. This program included 10 varieties at each of 12 to 14 locations, the varieties being grouped in early, midseason, and late categories. Thus, the environmental conditions at any one location were sampled for more than 12 weeks. The 1965 season produced 1,675 samples and the 1966 season 1,439. A. flavus was not isolated from any of these more than 3,100 soybean samples. Many other fungi were isolated, including Alternaria and Fusarium of the species which have proved to be toxin producers when isolated from peanuts. The toxin-producing potential of the isolates from soybeans has not been studied further.

The results of the field sampling program probably remove crop production practices as a significant factor in the aflatoxin problem in soybeans. However, since the opportunity for infection probably exists, the absence of A. flavus from soybean seeds raises interesting questions as to how the soybean escapes. Soybean pods and seeds develop in a "closed canopy" similar to cotton, but the leaves are shed prior to maturation of the crop. Normally, the final stages of ripening proceed rapidly, a drop in seed moisture from 65 percent to less than 20 percent occurring in as short a time as 3 days. The pods and seeds thus usually dry to a safe moisture level before harvest. Soybeans are marketed on a basis of 12 percent moisture, and usually have dried to about this level before they are harvested. They probably constitute a less favorable environment moisture-wise for A. flavus than do peanuts and cotton.

There is the further interesting possibility that soybeans contain some physiological protective mechanism, such as an inhibitor. A. flavus has grown poorly for us on live soybean seed, but it grows luxuriantly on autoclaved soybeans, in contrast to the observation in cotton that the bright greenish yellow fluorescence (BGY) indicative of contamination by A. flavus was produced only on living materials.

We have sought such inhibiting materials in soybeans without much success. Recently, we have seen evidence that magnesium, calcium, and boron, at levels that occur in soybeans, reduce aflatoxin production on a defined medium (J. D. Paxton, unpublished progress report, USDA extramural cooperative agreement 12–14–100–8476(34)). These elements are of particular interest because they occur in soybeans at appreciably higher levels than in the cereals. When magnesium and boron levels in the culture medium were reduced to levels comparable to those in cereals, better fungal growth occurred. The level of these inorganic constituents may have something to do with the poor affinity of A. flavus for soybeans.

Acknowledgments

Appreciation is expressed to numerous persons for assistance in the interpretation of data, permission to use unpublished data, and review of the manuscript. The assistance of W. K. Bailey and K. H. Garren in the section on peanuts, and of P. B. Marsh and J. T. Presley in the section on cottonseed was especially helpful.

References

(1) ASHWORTH, L. J., J. L. MCMEANS, J. L. PYLE, C. M. BROWN, J. W. OSGOOD, and R. E. PONTON. 1968. Aflatoxins in cotton seeds: Influence of weathering on toxin content of seeds and on a method for mechanically sorting seed lots. Phytopathol. 58: 102.

(2) BARNES, G. L. 1968. Proc. Fifth Nat. Peanut Res. Conf. In press.

(3) GARREN, K. H., C. M. CHRISTENSEN, and D. M. PORTER. 1968. Proc. First Int. Congr. Plant Pathol. In press.

(4) HALISKY, P. M., W. C. SCHNATHORST, and M. A. SHAGRUN. 1961. Severity and distribution of cotton boll rots as related to temperature. Phytopathol. 51: 501.

(5) JACKSON, C. R. 1967a. Evaluation of terraclor super X for control of soil-borne pathogens of peanuts in Georgia. Georgia Agr. Exp. Sta. Res. Rept. 4.

(6) JACKSON, C. R. 1967b. Studies on control of peanut pod fungi. Part I. Effects of preplanting soil fumigants on peanut pod surface at harvest. Part II. Value of fungicidal treatment of windrowed peanuts in postharvest reduction of pod-borne fungi and aflatoxins. Georgia Agr. Exp. Sta. Res. Rept. 11.

(7) JACKSON, C. R. 1967c. Development of fungi in peanuts during artificial drying. Georgia Agr. Exp. Sta. Res. Rept. 19.

(8) JACKSON, C. R. 1968. A field study of fungal associations on peanut fruit. Georgia Agr. Exp. Sta. Res. Bull. 26.

(9) JOFFE, A. Z. 1968. Plant Disease Reptr. 52: 718.

(10) KULKARNI, L. G. 1967. "Asiriya mwitunde" groundnut gives good results at Hyderabad. Tropical Abstr. 22, p. 711, q2254.

(11) MARSH, P. B., and T. KERR. 1961. Uncollapsed fibers associated with boll rot in cotton. Plant Disease Rept. 45: 550.

(12) MARSH, P. B., M. E. SIMPSON, T. C. CAMPBELL, A. VASSEF, and J. H. SNIDER. Proc. of USDA Mycotoxin Seminar. In press.

(13) MCMEANS, J. L., L. J. ASHWORTH, and W. A. PONS. 1968. Aflatoxins in hull and meats of cottonseed. J. Am. Oil Chem. Soc. 45: 575.

(14) MISLIVEC, P. B., J. H. HUNTER, and J. TUITE. 1968. Aflatoxin production by the genera Aspergillus and Penicillium. Appl. Microbiol. 16: 1053.

(15) PATTEE, H. E., and S. L. SESSOMS. 1967. Relationship between Aspergillus flavus growth, fat acidity and aflatoxin content in peanuts. J. Am. Oil Chem. Soc. 44: 61.

(16) PEARMAN, G. E., and J. L. BUTLER. 1968. Proc. Assoc. Sou. Agr. Workers. In press.

(17) PETTIT, R. E., and R. A. TABER. 1968. Factors influencing aflatoxin accumulation in peanut kernels and the associated mycoflora. Appl. Microbiol. 16: 1230.

(18) PORTER, D.M., and K. H. GARREN. 1968. An analysis of the endogeocarpic microflora of peanuts in Virginia. Tropical Sci. 10: 100.

(19) RAO, K. S., and P. G. TULPULE. 1967. Varietal differences of groundnut in the production of aflatoxin. Nature 214: 738.

(20) U.S. DEPARTMENT OF AGRICULTURE. 1968. Preventing mycotoxins in farm commodities. U.S. Dept. Agr., Agr. Res. Serv. ARS 20–16.

THE EFFECT OF AFLATOXIN
ON CHICK-EMBRYO LIVER CELLS IN VITRO

by Kiyoshi Terao *and* Komei Miyaki
Institute of Food Microbiology, Chiba University,
Narashino, Chiba, Japan

Summary

In the presence of aflatoxin, cultured parenchymal cells originated from the 12-day-old chick-embryo liver were found to be more susceptible than mesenchymal cells in terms of nucleolus degeneration. Radioautographs with ^{3}H-uridine and ^{3}H-1-leucine revealed that this degeneration of nucleolus caused an inhibition of RNA synthesis followed by protein synthesis. Using the present cell system, the relation between chemical structures and toxicities of aflatoxins (B_1, B_2, and tetrahydrodesoxoaflatoxin B_1) were tested.

Introduction

It is the purpose of this report to summarize findings obtained in our previous publications (*6, 7*). There are three points which we hope to make: (1) As to the effect of aflatoxin on the cultured liver cells, our findings lend further support to the belief that aflatoxin acts specifically on the liver parenchymal cells by means of inhibition of RNA biosynthesis in nucleolus; (2) there are similarities of effects of aflatoxin and actinomycin D, observation of radioautographs reveal that the inhibition of RNA biosynthesis by aflatoxin resembles, at the cytological level, the effects caused by actinomycin D when one observes the behavior of parenchymal cells in our cell system. However, observations on mesenchymal cells in the cell system suggest that the mode of action of aflatoxin is somewhat different from that of actinomycin D; (3) a similarity in chemical structure and wide range in toxicity is revealed when using pure aflatoxin B_1, dihydroaflatoxin B_1 (B_2), and tetrahydrodesoxoaflatoxin B_1 in tests employing primary culture of 12-day-old chick-embryo liver cells.

Materials and Methods

Cell culture.—Freshly dissected livers from 12-day-old chick embryo were prepared for primary culture. After trypsinizing, the cells grown as monolayers in bottle cultures on glass coverslips at 37° C., Eagle's Minimal Essential Medium was supplemented with 5 percent calf serum, 100 units per milliliter penicillin, and 100 μg./ml. streptomycin.

Agents tested.—Crude aflatoxin (a mixture of B and G) was received as a gift from Dr. G. N. Wogan, Massachusetts Institute of Technology. Aflatoxin B_1, aflatoxin B_2, and tetrahydrodesoxoaflatoxin B_1, were prepared by Dr. M. Yamazaki, Institute of Food Microbiology, Chiba University, Japan.

Experiment I.—Crude aflatoxin at a concentration of 100, 50, 10, or 1 μg./ml. was applied for 0.5, 1, 3, 6, 12, or 24 hours. The control culture, incubated in parallel contained no aflatoxin. After fixation with acetic acid-ethanol-formalin, the cells were stained with PAS-Hematoxylin and the areas of nucleoli were calculated as circles or ellipses. One hundred liver parenchymal cells and 100 mesenchymal cells were measured on the same coverslips.

Experiment II.—The cells were treated with crude aflatoxin at concentrations of 10 or 0.3 μg./ml. for 0.5, 3, or 24 hours. For the final 30 minutes each specimen was exposed to ^{3}H-uridine-5-t. (specific activity, 5.0 c./m.mole., Daiichi Chemicals, Tokyo) at a final concentration of 3 μc./ml.

Experiment III.—After the incubation with crude aflatoxin 1 μg./ml. for 5, 15, or 30 minutes the coverslips, with attached growing cells, were rinsed three times with Hank's balanced salt solution and then labeled for 5 hours with ^{3}H-uridine or ^{3}H-1-leucine (specific activity 144 c./m.mole., Daiichi Chemicals, Tokyo) at a final concentration of 3 μg./ml.

Experiment IV.—After the incubation with aflatoxin B_1, B_2, and tetrahydrodesoxoaflatoxin B_1 at the concentration of 10 μg./ml. each, for 5, 15, 30, 60, 180, and 360 minutes, the coverslips were treated as in experiment III and then labeled for 5 hours with ^{3}H-uridine at a final concentration of 3 μc./ml.

In experiments II, III, and IV, the cells were coated with Sakura NRH$_1$ or NRM$_2$ liquid emulsion. After exposure and development of radioautographs, they were then stained with toluidine blue. Incorporation of isotopes was measured by counting silver grains over the various cellular structures, such as the nucleolus, karyoplasm, and cytoplasm for experiments II, and III. For experiment IV, silver grains over cells were measured on the same coverslips.

Results

Experiment I.—The cytological changes after the addition of aflatoxin included a marked quantitative decrease or fading of the liver parenchymal cell nucleoli. At the initial stage, there were few pathological changes in the cytoplasm. Areas of light and dark staining were observed in nucleoli of most of the parenchymal cells in various concentration of the toxin. The nuclear sap become so clear as to make the perinucleolar chromatin prominent. At this stage, a marked shrinkage of the parenchymal cell nuclei was evident. The mesenchymal cells, to the contrary, were less sensitive to the toxic agent. Figures 1 and 2 show control cells and the cells treated with aflatoxin (1 µg./ml.) for 24 hours. It was clearly demonstrated that the sensitiveities of parenchymal and mesenchymal cells against aflatoxin are completely different. After the nucleoli of the parenchymal cells had disappeared, the mesenchymal cells still contained distinct nucleoli. At any concentration of the agent this phenomenon could be observed sooner or later. Even at the stage of complete parenchymal destruction, a few mesenchymal cells remained with prominent nucleoli.

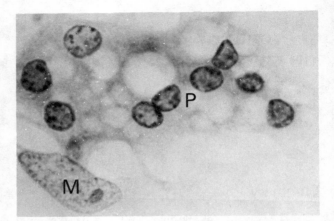

Figure 2.—The cells treated with aflatoxin, 1 µg./ml. for 24 hours. After the nucleoli of the parenchymal cells (P) have disappeared the mesenchymal cell (M) still contain distinct nucleoli.

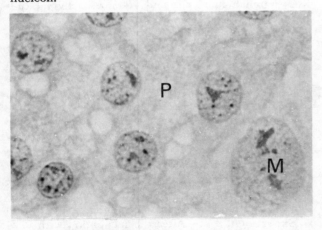

Figure 1.—Control cells. The prominent nucleoli are seen in both parenchymal (P) and mesenchymal (M) cells.

Table 1.—The total areas of nucleoli of parenchymal and mesenchymal cells originated from chick-embryo liver

Exposure time (hour)	Concentration of aflatoxin (µg./ml.)				Control (no aflatoxin)
	100	50	10	1	
Parenchymal cells					
0.5	[1]48.2	88.7	None	None	---------
1	21.6	55.8	82.1	117.2	---------
3	1.6	29.0	75.7	63.4	---------
6	.3	12.8	21.2	56.3	129.3
12		4.6	10.0	32.3	---------
24			3.4	23.9	---------
Mesenchymal cells					
0.5	184.7	255.8	None	None	---------
1	171.3	202.2	355.2	331.9	---------
3	78.6	159.4	361.8	313.2	---------
6	55.7	104.9	305.4	353.7	353.7
12	40.4	77.7	366.9	397.3	---------
24	38.8	45.8	359.7	360.4	---------

[1]Units are $\pi\mu^2$.

NOTE.—100 nucleoli of liver parenchymal cells and 100 nucleoli of mesenchymal cells were measured on the same coverslips.

Table 1 shows the total areas of nucleoli of both parenchymal and mesenchymal liver cells which had originated from 12-day-old chicken embryo. The tendency at the higher concentrations of 100 and 50 µg./ml. was to lower the total areas of nucleoli in both cell types. For example, the total areas of nucleoli of 100 parenchymal cells at 100 µg./ml. was reduced to about 37.2 percent of the control value at 0.5 hour and those of mesenchymal cells, on the other hand, decreased to 52.3 percent. In 3 hours this value dropped to 1.2 percent in the parenchymal cells, whereas in mesenchymal cells it remained at 22 percent of the control. At the low concentrations (10 and 1 µg./ml.), however, distinguishing patterns were seen. For the mesenchymal cells, no significant difference was detectable between the longest and the shortest duration employed, whereas at a concentration of 10 µg./ml., the total areas of nucleoli of 100 parenchymal cells were reduced to 2.6 percent of

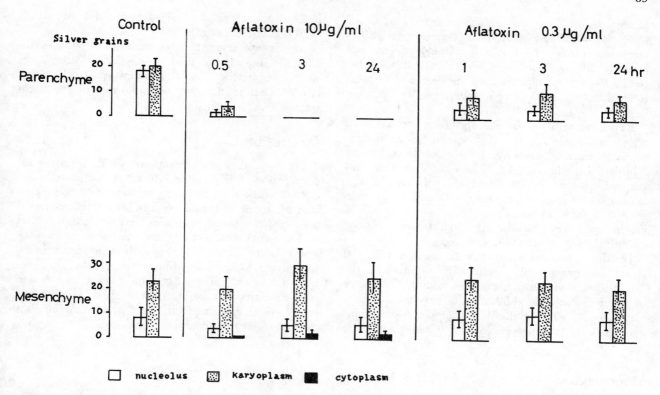

Figure 3.—The distribution of silver grains over the nucleoli, karyoplasm, and cytoplasm of the parenchymal and mesenchymal cells originated from 12-day-old chick-embryo liver cells.

the control value at 24 hours and those in 1 μg./ml. fell to 18.4 percent.

Experiment II.—In the presence of crude aflatoxin at a concentration of 10 μg./ml., the distribution of silver grains over the nucleolus of parenchymal cell was reduced to approximately 12.5 percent of the control value at 30 minutes (fig. 3). Those over the karyoplasm decreased to 35.9 percent. After 3 hours exposure there were no silver grains over either the nucleoli or the karyoplasm. In mesenchymal cells, on the other hand, no significant differences were observed through 24 hours. A few silver grains over the cytoplasm were seen.

In the presence of crude aflatoxin at a concentration of 0.3 μg./ml., the number of silver grains over the nucleoli of the parenchymal cells were reduced to less than 25 percent after 1 hour exposure and those over the karyoplasm were reduced to less than 44.5 percent (fig. 3). But there were no significant differences in the mesenchymal cells during ensuing 24 hours of aflatoxin treatment at this concentration.

Experiment III.—Table 2 shows the distribution of ³H-uridine and ³H-l-leucine incorporation as determined by the average number of silver grains per nucleolus, karyoplasm, and cytoplasm of the parenchymal cells at an early stage. Between 5 and 15

minutes after the administration of aflatoxin, a sudden decrease of labeling by ³H-uridine in the nucleoli was observed. On the other hand, there was no significant reduction of the silver grains over the karyoplasm and cytoplasm in the initial 15 minutes. Data on the labeling pattern by ³H-l-leucine show that silver grains over the nucleolus remained fairly constant in

Table 2.—Distribution of silver grains over the nucleolus, karyoplasm and cytoplasm of the parenchymal cells after the administration of crude aflatoxin, 1 μg./ml.

Duration of treatment (minutes)	Distribution of silver grains over:	Incorporation of ³H-uridine	Incorporation of ³H-leucine
0	Nucleolus	12.9 ± 1.2	5.1 ± 0.7
	Karyoplasm	11.0 ± 1.0	11.8 ± 1.7
	Cytoplasm	20.8 ± 2.2	30.0 ± 2.8
5	Nucleolus	12.0 ± 1.2	5.7 ± 0.5
	Karyoplasm	11.0 ± 0.7	11.7 ± 1.8
	Cytoplasm	19.0 ± 2.6	26.3 ± 3.0
15	Nucleolus	6.0 ± 1.0	4.0 ± 1.3
	Karyoplasm	10.5 ± 1.1	11.1 ± 2.7
	Cytoplasm	20.9 ± 3.1	35.3 ± 4.3
30	Nucleolus	0.2 ± 0.2	0.8 ± 0.6
	Karyoplasm	6.8 ± 1.1	9.0 ± 2.4
	Cytoplasm	9.2 ± 0.8	19.3 ± 3.4

NOTE.—The data represent the grain count average of 36 cells on the same coverslip.

the first 15 minutes. After 30 minutes' exposure of the toxin, however, sudden inhibition appeared. No detectable decrease of labeling in the karyoplasm was observed up to 30 minutes after the treatment. Between 15 and 30 minutes after the exposure to aflatoxin there was a 30 percent lowering of cytoplasmic labeling.

Experiment IV.—In the specimen treated with aflatoxin B_1, 10 $\mu g./ml.$, (fig. 4) the ^3H-uridine incorporation into parenchymal cells has been heavily inhibited by aflatoxin B_1. The reduction of the incorporation was seen within 5 minutes and after 1 hour exposure the silver grains were scarcely seen over the parenchymal cells. Those grains over the mesenchymal cells, on the other hand, were reduced only slightly even after 6 hours' exposure.

In the specimen treated with aflatoxin B_2, 10 $\mu g./ml.$, contrary to the results with aflatoxin B_1, the inhibition was only moderate. The reduction of uptake of ^3H-uridine appeared 30 minutes after the administration of B_2. During the first hour the silver grains decreased to 45.5 percent of the initial stage. The

incorporation of ^3H-uridine was reduced to 40 percent even 6 hours' exposure.

In the specimen treated with tetrahydrodesoxoaflatoxin B_1, 10 $\mu g./ml.$, no significant differences were observed between the intensities of ^3H-uridine labeled cells in the control and those of the toxin treated cells.

Discussion

From cytological observations and data on the incorporation of ^3H-uridine into RNA of cultured liver cells of chicken embryo it was clearly demonstrated that aflatoxin had a strong affinity for parenchymal cells. Different susceptibilities between parenchymal and mesenchymal cells in this cell system to some agents other than aflatoxins, such as actinomycin D, mitomycin C, and acridine orange, have been reported (7). The different cell and nuclear membrane permeabilities to these agents may play a significant role. Growth rate, nucleotide and protein metabolism dissimilarities should also be considered.

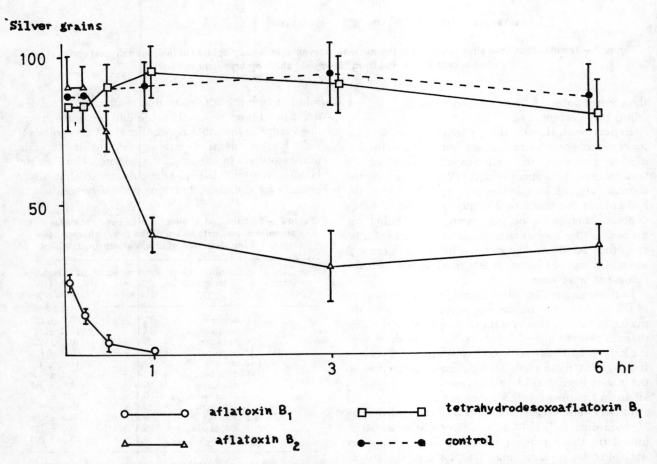

Figure 4.—The incorporation of ^3H-uridine into RNA of liver parenchymal cells after the administration of various aflatoxins.

Zonal transformation of nucleolus in the parenchymal cell at the initial stage may be a secondary change dependent upon disturbance in the configuration of DNA and results in a consequent alteration in RNA and protein synthesis (5).

Altered incorporation of labeled precursor into RNA and labeled amino acid into proteins caused by aflatoxins have been studied in a number of biological system (1, 4, 7, 8). In liver slices from control rats, there was an immediate inhibition of ^{14}C-orotic acid incorporation into RNA, whereas the inhibition of ^{14}C-leucine into protein took some 15 minutes to develop (1). At the optimal concentration of actinomycin D, RNA biosynthesis in the nucleolus is specifically affected, whereas those in the karyoplasm remained fairly constant (3). Present data on radioautograph with ^{3}H-uridine and ^{3}H-1-leucine agree with the data of the above-mentioned experiments. Our results confirmed that a primary effect of aflatoxin was the blocking of RNA biosynthesis especially in the nucleolus. These data are very similar to those on the effects of actinomycin D on the RNA biosynthesis of living cells. In our previous reports, however, it was demonstrated either cytologically or radioautographically, that the action of aflatoxin was somewhat different from that of actinomycin D in cell culture of the chick-embryo liver (6, 7) in that parenchymal cells were more susceptible to aflatoxin than the mesenchymal cells and the former were more resistant to actinomycin D than the latter. The difference between the susceptibilities of the parenchymal and mesenchymal cells to aflatoxin and/or actinomycin D has not yet been satisfactorily explained.

It is obvious from the results mentioned above that the presence of a double bond in difuran structure of aflatoxin B$_1$ markedly affected the biosynthesis of RNA. The fact that tetrahydrodesoxoaflatoxin B$_1$ did not affect RNA biosynthesis has led us to following consideration. The carbonyl group in cyclopentenone portion of B$_1$ and B$_2$ may play an important role in the inhibition of RNA biosynthesis. Various aflatoxins have a wide range in toxicity as determined by their LD$_{50}$ for 1-day-old ducklings. According to Clifford and her collaborators the extent of inhibitory action of various aflatoxins (B$_1$, G$_1$, and G$_2$) on the macromolecular synthetic reactions was proportional to the degree of spectral shift obtained with their interaction with DNA (2). It is thus proposed that their toxicity depends upon this interaction. The double bond in

the difuran structure of B$_1$ and the carbonyl group in cyclopentenone portion of B$_1$ and B$_2$ may relate to the interaction of the toxins with DNA (fig. 5).

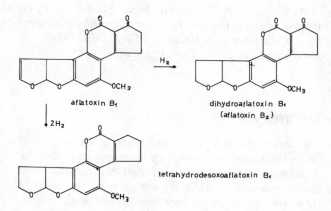

Figure 5.—Chemical structures of aflatoxins; aflatoxin B$_1$, aflatoxin B$_2$ (dihydroaflatoxin B$_1$), and tetrahydrodesoxoaflatoxin B$_1$.

Acknowledgments

The authors wish to thank Dr. M. Yamazaki of the Institute of Food Microbiology, Chiba University, for preparing the purified aflatoxins used in these studies.

References

(1) CLIFFORD, J. I. and K. R. REES. 1966. Aflatoxin: A site of action in the rat liver cells. Nature. 209: 312–313.

(2) CLIFFORD, J. I., K. R. REES, and E. M. STEVENS. 1967. The effect of the aflatoxins B$_1$, G$_1$, and G$_2$ on protein and nucleic acid synthesis in rat liver. Biochem. J. 103: 258–261.

(3) PERRY, R. P. 1963. Selective effects of actinomycin D on the intracellular distribution of RNA synthesis in tissue culture cells. Exp. Cell Res. 29: 400–406.

(4) SMITH, R. H. 1963. The influence of toxins of Aspergillus flavus on the incorporation of ^{14}C-leucine into proteins. Biochem. J. 88: 50–51.

(5) SVOBODA, D., H. J. GRADY, and J. HIGGINSON. 1966. Aflatoxin B$_1$ injury in rat and monkey liver. Amer. J. Pathol. 49: 1023–1051.

(6) TERAO, K. 1967. The effect of aflatoxin on chick-embryo liver cells. Exp. Cell Res. 48: 151–155.

(7) TERAO, K., and K. MIYAKI. 1968. Different susceptibilities of chick embryo liver cells in vitro to aflatoxin, actinomycin D, and mitomycin C. Zeitschr. Krebsforsch. 71: 199–207.

(8) WOGAN, G. N. 1966. Chemical nature and biological effects of the aflatoxins. Bacteriol. Rev. 30: 460–470.

CHRONIC EFFECTS OF AFLATOXIN IN FARM ANIMAL FEEDING STUDIES

by A. C. KEYL, A. N. BOOTH, M. S. MASRI, M. R. GUMBMANN, *and* W. E. GAGNE
Western Regional Research Laboratory, Agricultural Research Service,
U. S. Department of Agriculture, Albany, Calif. 94710,
and Syntex Laboratories, Palo Alto, Calif.

Summary

Practical feeding trials involving swine and beef cattle have been conducted in order to determine the deleterious effects, if any, of graded levels of aflatoxins in the rations. In addition, analyses of the tissues of these treated animals, both chemically and biologically, have been performed in order to determine whether any of the aflatoxins in the rations might be transmitted into the edible meat.

A total of 110 weanling pigs of both sexes were divided into control and treated groups of 10 animals per group and fed dietary levels of aflatoxin in the ration ranging from 0 to 810 p.p.b. for a period of 120 days. No evidence of any toxic effects were observed at levels of 233 p.p.b. dietary aflatoxin or below.

Similarly, 50 cross-bred Hereford steers were fed five dietary levels of aflatoxins ranging from 0 to 1,000 p.p.b. for a period of 4½ months. No evidence of any toxic effects was observed at levels of 300 p.p.b. dietary aflatoxin or below.

No evidence of transmission of dietary aflatoxin in the ration into edible portions of the swine and cattle was observed at any of the levels studied.

The effects of graded dietary levels of aflatoxin B_1 dispersed in cottonseed meal were studied in dairy cattle for determination of the transmission and production of aflatoxin M_1 in milk. Weekly intake of 67 to 200 mg. aflatoxin B_1 produced 70 to 154 p.p.b. aflatoxin M_1 in the lyophilized milk. An important aspect of this study was the finding of complete disappearance of aflatoxin M_1 in the milk after withdrawal of dietary aflatoxin B_1 in a period of 72 hours.

Introduction

In 1964, as a result of joint meetings of the U.S. Department of Agriculture, the Food and Drug Administration and industry research groups, protocols were developed for the purpose of determining: (1) The toxic effects of graded levels of aflatoxin in selected farm animals, and (2) the study of the possible transmission of the aflatoxins in feeds into the tissues, milk, and eggs of appropriate species. The logistic problem of supplying the large quantities of aflatoxin required was assigned to the Fermentation Laboratory of the Northern Regional Research Laboratory, Peoria, Ill., the problem of producing aflatoxin-fortified peanut and cottonseed meals fell to the Oilseed Crops Laboratory of the Southern Regional Research Laboratory, New Orleans, La., the toxicological evaluations were made by the Pharmacology Laboratory of the Western Regional Research Laboratory, Albany, Calif., in conjunction with the Department of Animal Husbandry, University of California, Davis, Calif.

Methods and Results

Swine feeding trials.—The swine feeding trial with aflatoxin-contaminated peanut meals was divided into two parts involving dietary levels of aflatoxin B_1, ranging from 0 (soybean control), 2, 7, 51, 105, and 233 p.p.b. in the first trial, and 0, 6, 465, 600, and 810 p.p.b. in the second trial. The experimental groups at each level consisted of four gilts and six barrows (Duroc-Jersey) starting at approximately 50 lb. weight and finishing at 200 lb. weight at slaughter. The feeding period varied from 110 to 120 days. The diet consisted of a ration comprising 75 percent whole ground barley, 15 percent peanut meal, 5 percent alfalfa meal, 4 percent meat and bone meal, 0.5 percent salt and 0.5 percent vitamin premix.

Up to and including dietary levels of 233 p.p.b. aflatoxin B_1 all results were negative in the sense that no significant differences were noted between control and treated groups with respect to mean weight gains, total feed intake and feed efficiency values (table 1). Blood samples taken four times during this period for hematological and biochemical evaluation revealed no significant differences for hemoglobin, hematocrit, red cell count, white cell count, and differential leukocyte counts. No differences were found with respect to plasma transaminase, NPN, urea N, copper and vitamin A. The only parameter showing a significant increase at the 5 percent probability level was serum alkaline phosphatase. Electrophoretic separation of the albumin and globulin fractions of

Table 1.—Effect of aflatoxin on rate of gain and feed conversion

Kind of meal	Aflatoxin content of ration (p.p.b.)			Average daily gain [1] (kg.)	Gain/feed (kg.)
	B_1	B_2	G_1		
TRIAL 1					
Soybean____	([2])	([2])	([2])	0.58	0.24
Peanut_____	<2	([2])	([2])	.67	.24
Do____	<8	([2])	([2])	.69	.25
Do____	51	([2])	([2])	.65	.25
Do____	105	52	15	.62	.26
Do____	233	([2])	70	.62	.24
TRIAL 2					
Soybean____	([2])	([2])	([2])	0.75a	0.26
Peanut_____	<6	([2])	([2])	.71ab	.26
Do____	450	([2])	30	.68ab	.27
Do____	615	105	45	.60 b	.27
Do____	810	135	60	.47 c	.23

[1]Values with unlike letters are significantly different (P < 0.05).
[2]None detected.

Table 2.—Pig organ weights

Aflatoxin B_1 ration (p.p.b.)	Liver (g.)	Kidney (g.)	Spleen (g.)	Heart (g.)	Adrenals (g.)	Thyroid (g.)
0	714 ± 22	134 ± 4	42	142	1.69	3.1
5.5	749 ± 24	118 ± 5	44	139	1.99	3.06
450	[1]917 ± 41	133 ± 5	51	153	2.0	3.45
615	[1]970 ± 40	136 ± 5	48	153	2.06	3.20
810	[1]1067 ± 39	[1]168 ± 20	58	141	2.26	3.61

[1]P = < 0.01.

these samples revealed no significant difference in the gamma globulin fraction.

At autopsy, no significant differences were found with respect to organ weights (kidneys, liver, spleen, adrenals, and thyroid). Histopathological examination of some 20 tissues showed no pathological abnormalities related to aflatoxin intake.

In the second part of the trial involving relatively high dietary levels of aflatoxin intake (465, 600, and 810 p.p.b.) significant differences were observed at one or more levels between control and treated groups with respect to weight gains, feed efficiency, and organ weights (liver and kidneys) (table 2). Significant elevations of serum alkaline phosphatase, serum, isocitric dehydrogenase, and serum glutamic-oxalacitic transaminase occurred at the 465–800 p.p.b. levels of aflatoxin intake while, correspondingly, a decrease in blood urea nitrogen was observed. Storage of vitamin A in the liver decreased with increasing aflatoxin dosage. Biochemical factors not altered at these dose levels included serum glutamic-pyruvic transaminase and liver alkaline phosphatase. The lowest level of dietary aflatoxin intake which produced histologic lesions was 450 p.p.b. These included karyomegaly, cytoplasmic degeneration and proliferation of fibrous tissue, and bile ductule epithelium. Hepatocellular alinement into tubular-shaped structures and development of centrilobular plexuses occurred at the 810 p.p.b. level. Lipidosis was minimal.

Blood and tissues (lean meat, fat, spleen, liver, and kidneys) were collected at slaughter, lyophilized and then subjected to chemical and biological assays. All tissues including blood showed no chemical or biological evidence of aflatoxin residues detectable by current assay methods. In addition to the conventional assay, 2- and 6-week feeding studies in ducklings were run using weight gain and histopathological examination as criteria of toxic effects possibly due to metabolites of aflatoxin not detectable by current chemical and biological methods.

Cattle feeding trials.—Twenty tons of prime quality California-grown cottonseed meal, containing not less than 41 percent protein and not more than 0.04 percent free gossypol, was purchased locally for the feeding trial. Three tons of this meal was shipped to the Southern Regional Research Laboratory for fortifying with mold (containing aflatoxin) grown on rice at the Northern Regional Research Laboratory. The aflatoxin was produced on a rice substrate at the Northern Regional Research Laboratory, Peoria, Ill., as described by O. L. Shotwell, et al. (3). The procedure used for fortification of the cottonseed meal at the Southern Regional Research Laboratory, New Orleans, La., was described previously (1).

The aflatoxin B_1 content of the fortified meal was 11,000 p.p.b. The composition of the basal ration in percentage was as follows: Alfalfa hay 14, oat hay 6, beet pulp 8, milo 20, barley 24, cottonseed meal 15, fat 2, molasses 10, and salt 1. Vitamin A and a small quantity of oyster shell flour were also added.

Fifty cross-bred beef steers purchased on the open market at age 6 to 8 months and in a body weight range of 400 to 500 pounds were used. The animals were randomly divided and housed in groups of five, two groups of five steers being assigned to each level of aflatoxin fed. Animal weights were recorded initially and at 4-week intervals, each weighing being preceded by withholding of feed and water overnight. Feed consumption records were maintained for each group of five steers.

Blood samples (50 ml.) were taken by jugular vein from 10 steers per week during the feeding trial for hematology and biochemical measurements. Complete autopsies at the rate of five steers per week were initiated when the feeding trial had progressed for 133 days. The last group was slaughtered at 196 days. Organ weights were recorded for liver, kidneys, spleen, heart, and adrenals. Tissues were also preserved in formaldehyde for microscopic examination.

Mean weight gain and feed efficiencies at the end of 133 days are summarized in table 3. Both weight gains and feed efficiencies appear to have been adversely affected, especially when the level of aflatoxin in the ration was increased to 700 and 1,000 p.p.b.

Weekly hematology evaluations were made during the course of the feeding trial. No effects related to aflatoxin intake could be detected from the hematocrit, hemoglobin, red blood cell, and white cell values. The blood cholesterol values were unaffected by the ingestion of aflatoxin.

Table 3.—Beef cattle cottonseed meal (aflatoxin) feeding trial

Ration (p.p.b.)	Mean body weights			
	Initial (lb.)	After 133 days (lb.)	Daily gain (lb.)	Feed efficiency (gain/feed)
Control____	401	734	2.50	0.152
100_____	427	777	2.63	.143
300_____	417	738	2.41	.139
700_____	406	659	1.90	[1] .134
1,000_____	433	[2]679	1.85	[1] .136

[1] 8 steers were confined in metabolism cages for 1 week.
[2] 1 steer died on the 59th day of experiment.

Table 4.—Effect of aflatoxin ingestion on organ weights of beef cattle

Aflatoxin (p.p.b.)	Mean organ weights (grams per 100-pound body weight)				
	Liver	Spleen	Heart	Kidneys (2)	Adrenals (2)
Control____	604	98	193	90	1.5
100_____	[1]662	103	194	98	1.9
300_____	622	83	189	96	1.8
700_____	[1]739	92	208	[1]106	2.1
1,000_____	[1]706	89	193	[1]106	1.6

[1] P = < 0.05.

At autopsy, liver, spleen, heart, kidney, and adrenal weights were recorded (table 4). The organ weights per 100 pounds body weight all appear to be within the range of the control group values with the exception of liver weights which increased when the level of aflatoxin in the ration was 700 p.p.b. or higher. The liver from three of eight steers fed 1,000 p.p.b. and two of 10 steers fed 700 p.p.b. were grossly abnormal being greyish in color, enlarged and having a fibrous (rubbery) texture. Below 700 p.p.b. no gross liver abnormalities were observed.

From these results (excluding the microscopic and blood enzyme studies) it was tentatively concluded that no abnormal effects were produced when the aflatoxin level in the rations was 300 p.p.b. or lower. Evidence of liver damage was observed when the aflatoxin level was 700 p.p.b. or higher.

The serum enzymes, alkaline phosphatase, and malic dehydrogenase increased in activity in response to aflatoxin, while lactic dehydrogenase decreased. Blood urea nitrogen, serum albumin, and total serum protein all decreased. Glutamic-oxalacetic transaminase and isocitric dehydrogenase values were not affected. A possible significant no-effect level of dietary aflatoxin may be estimated from these blood factors to lie between 300 and 700 p.p.b.

Liver glutamic-oxalacetic transaminase, malic and isocitric dehydrogenases all became depressed in response to aflatoxin. No-effect levels were generally estimated to be between 100 to 300 p.p.b. Lipid and vitamin A also decreased, however, with a no-effect level here of 700 to 1,000 p.p.b. Alkaline phosphatase, lactic dehydrogenase, and glycogen values were unaffected.

The microscopic findings in tissues of the cattle were less clearly defined, except at the higher levels (700 to 1,000 p.p.b.), than were found in the examination of the swine tissues. In general, varying degrees of hepatic cell enlargement, enlarged nuclei, and bile duct proliferation was present, the severity of which was not directly related to aflatoxin intake. The lessened intensity of hepatocyte alteration, greater irregularity in location of bile duct proliferation and fibrosis distinguished these lesions from those found in swine.

At slaughter, no chemical or biological evidence of aflatoxin residues were detectable in the tissues. However, blood samples taken from cattle on the highest level (1,000 p.p.b.) showed the presence of traces of aflatoxin B_1 and M_1. Twenty-four hours later when food had been withheld, neither of these compounds was detectable, indicating the rapid clearance of these materials from the blood by the kidneys.

Dairy feeding trials.—The objective of these preliminary experiments was the production of sufficient aflatoxin M_1 for purposes of structure proof. The dietary regimen was not precisely representative of dairy practices because large quantities of contaminated peanut meals were used to provide the aflatoxin B_1 in the diet; however, the effects of dietary aflatoxin B_1 on the aflatoxin M_1 content of the milk are shown in table 5. Aflatoxin M_1 was estimated by the method of Masri et al. (2).

Briefly, whole dried milk was extracted in a Waring Blendor with a measured volume of aqueous methanol (1:1 vol.). After centrifugation, the supernatant was filtered over a thin layer of Celite and the filtrate was

Table 5.—Aflatoxin M in milk from cow 1 while on weekly varying dosage of aflatoxin B$_1$

Weeks on experiment	B$_1$ intake in week (mg.)	Fresh milk for week (lb.)	Average feed intake, lb. per day		M in dry milk (p.p.b.)
			Hay	Concentrate	
1	0.4	428	25.1	24.6	--------
2	67.0	423	22.4	29.4	70
3	89.0	419	25.0	32.0	107
4	120.0	380	23.2	28.1	133
5	169.0	350	24.3	29.7	129
6	206.0	313	23.2	24.0	154
7	175.0	282	22.2	9.0	118
8	0	290	22.7	21.2	18

measured and defatted once with an equal volume of Skellysolve F. Aflatoxin M was extracted from the defatted extract by 3 x ½ vol. of chloroform. The separate chloroform extracts were washed successively in order with two water washes (also kept in order), each was equal to ½ vol. of a single chloroform extract. The washed chloroform extracts were combined and evaporated and the residue was purified on a silica gel cleanup column and the aflatoxin M in the eluate was quantitated after thin-layer chromatography spectrophotometrically or (when concentration in dry milk was less than 5 p.p.b.) by means of visual comparison under ultraviolet light.

An interesting aspect of the study was related to the disappearance of aflatoxin M from the milk following withdrawal of aflatoxin B$_1$. With cow 1 only one analysis was obtained on pooled milk produced in 1 week immediately following the withdrawal. The value obtained was 18 p.p.b. in the dry milk versus 118 p.p.b. for the previous week. More detailed data were obtained with cows 3, 4, and 6, and the results appear in table 6.

A conclusion of practical significance from these data is that milk produced by cows that are known to have consumed aflatoxin contaminated feed would be expected to be essentially free of aflatoxin M after the elapse of relatively only a short period of time following the withdrawal of the contaminated feed.

Conclusions

The design of the reported experiments was practical in nature and conformed to American animal husbandry practices. While the results do not add to the mounting literature attempting to explain the mechanism of action of the aflatoxins, they provide a basis for the establishment of no-effect levels under the reported experimental conditions. The failure to find aflatoxin in the blood of the animals at the highest dietary levels fed, after a 24-hour period of withdrawal of fodder, tends to suggest a method of control of possible transmission of aflatoxins from feed into edible tissues. Extrapolation of these results to other dietary regimens or species is unwarranted.

Acknowledgments

Collaborators in this work included Drs. H. Heitman, Jr., H. F. Hintz, W. N. Garrett, and M. Ronning of the Department of Animal Husbandry, and J. E. Moulton and D. L. Dungworth of the Department of Veterinary Science, University of California, Davis, Calif.

Table 6.—Aflatoxin M in milk from cows 3, 4, and 6 following withdrawal of aflatoxin B$_1$

Cow	Week before withdrawal	Aflatoxin M in dry milk (p.p.b.)				
		Days after withdrawal				
		1	2	3	4	7
3	82	44	17	5	--------	5
4	96	55	27	--------	3	1
6	1,500	718	434	285	160	------

References

(1) HINTZ, H. F., A. N. BOOTH, A. F. CUCULLU, H. K. GARDNER, and H. HEITMAN, Jr. 1967. Aflatoxin toxicity in swine. Proc. Soc. Exptl. Biol. Med. *124:* 266–268.

(2) MASRI, M. S., J. R. PAGE, and V. C. GARCIA. 1968. Analysis for aflatoxin in milk. J. Assoc. Off. Analyt. Chem. *51:* 594–599.

(3) SHOTWELL, O. L., C. W. HESSELTINE, and R. D SORENSON. 1966. Production of aflatoxin on rice. Appl. Microbiol. *14:* 425–428.

INHIBITION OF PROTEIN SYNTHESIS IN ANIMAL CELLS BY NIVALENOL AND RELATED METABOLITES; TOXIC PRINCIPLES OF RICE INFESTED WITH *FUSARIUM NIVALE*

by YOSHIO UENO
Microbial Chemistry, Faculty of Pharmaceutical Science, Science University of Tokyo, Tokyo

Summary

In order to determine the biochemical action of nivalenol and related toxins produced by *Fusarium nivale*, an investigation was made of their effect on protein synthesis in animal cells with the following results: (1) With mice, nivalenol inhibited the *in vivo* uptake of C^{14}-leucine into protein of the spleen and the small intestine; (2) with Ehrlich ascites tumor cells, nivalenol inhibited the uptake of C^{14}-leucine and C^{14}-thymidine without affecting the uptake of C^{14}-uracil and the production of lactic acid; (3) with the whole cell and the cell-free system of rabbit reticulocytes, nivalenol, and fusarenon inhibited protein synthesis at the ribosomal level.

Introduction

Rice infested with *Fusarium nivale* is toxic to mice (5), and two mycotoxins have been isolated from the ethanol extract as the toxic principles. One substance is a white crystal, named nivalenol, m.p. 222° to 223° C., and the other is a white powder, named fusarenon, m.p. 78° to 80° C. (6, 7). Pathological examination has revealed that an ethanol extract of rice infested with *F. nivale*, as well as the isolated toxins, induced in mice degeneration and necrosis of the mucosal epithelium of the small intestine and destructive changes in lymph node, spleen, thymus and bone marrow (3, 5, 6). These pathological findings indicated that the toxins of *F. nivale* affected actively-dividing cells of these tissues. On the other hand, Yates et al. (11, 12) isolated toxic butenolide from metabolites of *F. nivale* (Fries) as causative agent for "tall fescue."

In the present paper, the author investigated the biochemical mode of action of the toxic principles of *F. nivale* and the results obtained indicated that nivalenol and fusarenon inhibited protein synthesis in animal cells, *in vivo* and *in vitro*. Part of this work was reported previously (8, 9).

Materials and Methods

Toxins.—Nivalenol and chemically synthesized butenolide (4-acetamide-4-hydroxy-2-butenoic acid-γ-lactone) were kindly supplied by Dr. T. Tatsuno the Institute of Physical and Chemical Research, Tokyo. Fusarenon was kindly supplied by Dr. Morooka, the National Institute of Health, Tokyo.

In vivo uptake of C^{14}-leucine in mice.—Male mice, of the ddS strain, were administered 40 μg./10 μg. body weight of nivalenol, intraperitoneally, and 1 hour before sacrifice, 1 C./10 μg. of 1-C^{14}-leucine (25 mC./mM.) was injected through the same route. Tissues were rapidly removed and cooled in dry-ice powder. After homogenizing the tissues with ice-cold 10 percent perchloracetic acid (PCA), protein was fractionated according to the method of Magee and Farber (2) in order to count the radioactivity.

Synthesis of macromolecules in tumor cells.—Ehrlich ascites tumor cells, strain 4N, were maintained in ddS-male mice and were harvested from their peritoneal cavities. After washing the cells with ice-cold 0.9 percent NaCl solution, the packed cells were mixed with an equal volume of the saline. For assay of uptake of C^{14}-labeled precursors, 0.2 ml. of the cell suspension was mixed with 0.6 ml. of Locke-Ringer's solution and preincubated at 37° C., with shaking, for 15 minutes in the presence or absence of the toxin. After the preincubation, 0.1 μC of 1-C^{14}-leucine, 2-C^{14}-uracil (21 mC./mM.) or 2-C^{14}-thymidine (50 mC./mM.) was added to the reaction mixture, making a total volume of 1.0 ml. The incubation was continued and after 40 minutes an equal volume of an ice-cold 10 percent PCA was added to the reaction mixture. Acid-insoluble precipitates were fractionated into protein, RNA and DNA according to the method of Reich et al. (4). To study glycolysis of the tumor cells, the cells, suspended in Locke-Ringer's solution, were incubated at 37° C. for 40 minutes in Thunberg tubes, and the lactic acid formed was measured by the method of Barker (1).

Synthesis of protein in rabbit reticulocytes.— Studies on the synthesis of protein in reticulocytes were conducted according to the method of Weinstein et al. (*10*).

Results

Inhibitory effect on nivalenol on in vivo protein synthesis in mice.— When 40 μg./10 g. of nivalenol were administered to mice, the remarkable reduction of the uptake of 1-C^{14}-leucine into protein was found with the spleen tissue and the tissue of the small intestine, and a slight reduction was observed with liver and kidney tissues (table 1).

Table 1.—Inhibitory effect of nivalenol on the in vivo uptake of C^{14}-leucine in mice

Tissue	Incorporation of 1-C^{14}-leucine into protein (cts./min./mg. protein)[1]		
	Control	6 hour	30 hours
Liver	225 (100)	195 (86)	210 (93)
Kidney	271 (100)	210 (77)	308 (113)
Spleen	806 (100)	119 (15)	100 (12)
Small intestine	558 (100)	264 (45)	340 (61)

[1]The parentheses indicate the percent activity of control.

Inhibition of protein and DNA syntheses in tumor cells.— In the case of Ehrlich ascites tumor cells, 1 to 10 μg./ml. of nivalenol inhibited the uptake of 1-C^{14}-leucine and 2-C^{14}-thymidine without affecting the uptake of 2-C^{14}-uracil (figure 1). Furthermore, as shown in tables 2 and 3, the inhibitory action of nivalenol on the syntheses of protein and DNA was remarkable when the cells were preincubated with the toxin and the reduced syntheses did not recover even when the toxin was removed from the incubation mixture.

The effects of toxin on energy metabolism of the cells.— This was studied by observing the action of the toxin on glycolysis. As shown in table 4, nivalenol at

Table 2.—Effects of preincubation of the cell with nivalenol on the synthesis of protein and DNA

Preincubation time (minutes)	Percent activity of control	
	Incorporation of 1-C^{14}-leucine into protein	Incorporation of 2-C^{14}-thymidine into DNA
0	71	81
20	38	57

NOTE.—The tumor cells were preincubated for 0 min. or 20 min. with 10 μg./ml. of the toxin at 37° C., and after adding C^{14}-labeled precursors the cells were continued to incubate for 40 min.

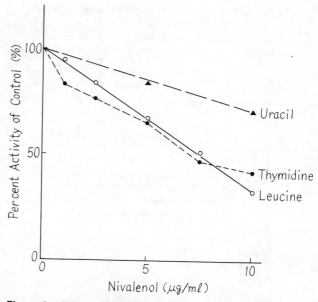

Figure 1.—Effects of nivalenol on the syntheses of protein, DNA and RNA in tumor cells.

Ehrlich ascites tumor, 4N, was preincubated with the toxin at 37° C. for 15 minutes, and after the addition of C^{14}-precursors the reaction mixture was incubated for 40 minutes

Table 3.—Irreversible inactivation of the synthetic activities of protein and DNA in tumor cells by nivalenol

Incubation	Percent activity of control	
	Incorporation of C^{14}-leucine into protein	Incorporation of C^{14}-thymidine into DNA
Without toxin	42	70
With toxin	20	70

NOTE.—The tumor cells were preincubated with 10 μg./ml. of nivalenol for 15 min., and after adding C^{14}-labeled precursors the cells were continued to incubate for 40 min., in the absence or in the presence of the toxin.

concentrations of 5 and 10 μg./ml. did not affect the aerobic or anaerobic formation of lactic acid *in vivo*.

Inhibitory effects of nivalenol and related toxins on the protein synthesis in rabbit reticulocytes.— Comparative effects of nivalenol, fusarenon, and synthetic butenolide on rabbit reticulocytes are shown in table 5. The ED_{50} of nivalenol and fusarenon on protein synthesis in the whole reticulocyte cell was approximately 2.5 μg./ml. whereas butenolide, up to 100 μg./ml., did not inhibit synthesis as measured by uptake of 1-C^{14}-leucine.

In order to further elucidate the inhibitory mechanism of nivalenol and fusarenon on protein synthesis, experiments were conducted with cell-free systems from reticulocytes. As shown in table 6, nivalenol

Table 4.—Effect of nivalenol on the production of lactic acid in tumor cells

Nivalenol (µg./ml.)	Lactic acid produced (µmoles./40 min.)	
	Aerobic	Anaerobic
0	2.6	3.1
5	3.2	3.9
10	2.4	3.1

Table 5.—Comparative toxicities of nivalenol and other toxins on rabbit reticulocytes

Concentration of toxins (µg./ml.)	Percent activity of control in the uptake of 1-C^{14}-leucine		
	Nivalenol	Fusarenon	Butenolide
0	100	100	100
0.1	-------------	91.2	-------------
0.25	-------------	48.4	-------------
0.5	90	20.6	-------------
1.0	86	9.1	100
2.5	49	4.9	100
10	10	-------------	100
20	4	-------------	93
100	-------------	-------------	93

NOTE.—The reticulocytes were preincubated with the toxins for 15 min. at 37° C., and after the addition of C^{14}-leucine to the reaction mixture the cells were incubated for 40 min.

Table 6.—Inhibitory effects of nivalenol and fusarenon on the poly U-dependent incorporation of C^{14}-phenylalanine and C^{14}-phenylalanyl-sRNA into polypeptide in the cell-free system of reticulocytes

Concentration (µg./ml.)	Percent activity of control (percent)			
	Nivalenol		Fusarenon	
	C^{14}-phe	C^{14}-phe -sRNA	C^{14}-phe	C^{14}-phe -sRNA
0.25	-----------	61.7	40.6	82.3
1.0	33.9	37.4	32.9	53.3
2.5	16.8	27.2	--------------------	
5	9.0	--------------------		
10	7.9	--------------------		

NOTE.—Reaction mixture contained the following components (in µmoles. unless otherwise specified); Tris buffer (pH 7.8) 10, magnesium acetate 2, KCl 24, 2-mercaptoethanol 1.2, ATP 0.24, GTP 0.01, phosphoenolpyruvate 1.2, phosphopyruvate kinase 10 µg., poly U 100 µg., 1-C^{14}-phenylalanine 2 m, µmoles. (0.05µC.) or 1-C^{14}-phenylalanyl-sRNA 0.43 mg. (1.510 cts./min.), ribosome 1 mg. and pH 5 enzyme 0.1 mg. Total volume was 0.4 ml. Reaction mixture was incubated at 37° C. for 60 min. In the case of C^{14}-phenylalanyl-sRNA pH 5 enzyme was omitted from the mixture.

and fusarenon inhibited the incorporation of C^{14}-phenylalanine and C^{14}-phenylalanyl-sRNA into polypeptide in a poly U-charged ribosomal system. The inhibitory concentration of the two toxins, for these two reactions, was nearly the same.

Discussion

Tatsuno et al. (5) have shown that the ethanol extract of rice infested with *F. nivale* caused cellular damage in the tissues of mice, especially in bone marrow, thymus, testis, and intestine, and that the isolated toxins caused similar pathological changes in these tissues. These pathological findings suggested that the toxic principles interfere with the syntheses of macromolecules in the cells. Therefore, the present author investigated the effects of toxins on protein synthesis in animal cells such as tissues of mice, tumor cells, and rabbit reticulocytes.

Nivalenol affected the *in vivo* synthesis of protein in tissues of mice, and the synthesis was reduced more markedly in spleen and intestinal tissues than in liver and kidney. This finding suggests that nivalenol affected tissues in which cells are actively dividing, which is in agreement with the pathological findings.

In the case of tumor cells, nivalenol interfered with the synthesis of protein and DNA. This inhibitory action of the toxin proved to be irreversible. However, the inhibition of DNA synthesis by nivalenol was not significant when the toxin was added to the reaction mixture after 15 minutes of the incubation, and the DNA-polymerase of the cell was not directly affected by nivalenol (9). Therefore, the reduced synthesis of DNA is presumably caused by the inhibition of synthesis of an enzyme protein required for DNA synthesis.

Nivalenol and fusarenon inhibited protein synthesis in rabbit reticulocytes, and the inhibitory dose of nivalenol was about 10 times higher than that of fusarenon. However, in the case of the cell-free system of these cells, the two mycotoxins impaired both the incorporation of the free amino acid and amino acid-charged sRNA into polypeptide; the inhibitory concentration of the toxins for two reactions of protein synthesis were nearly the same. These results indicated that the toxins inhibited protein synthesis at the ribosomal level, and that the difference in the inhibitory doses between two toxins observed with the whole cell was presumably caused by the difference in the cellular permeability to the toxins.

On the other hand, toxic butenolide, which was isolated as a causative agent of necrotizing reaction in rabbit skin, proved to be inactive in affecting protein synthesis. In this respect, the mode of action of toxic butenolide is considered to be different from that of nivalenol and fusarenon.

Acknowledgments

This investigation was supported in part by the Cancer Research Grant from the Ministry of Welfare.

References

(*1*) BARKER, S. B. 1957. Preparation and colorimetric determination of lactic acid. Methods of Enzymology. *3*: 24-
1–246.

(*2*) MAGEE, P. N., and F. FARBER. 1962. Toxic liver
injury and carcinogenesis: Methylation of rat liver
nucleic acids by dimethylnitrosamine *in vivo*. Biochem.
J. *83:* 114–124.

(*3*) OKUBO, K., and M. ISODA. 1967. Studies of the
essential nature of intoxication of experimental acute
intoxication by crude products of *Fusarium nivale*. Bull.
of the Nippon Vet. Zootech. College *16:* 22–42 (in
Japanese).

(*4*) REICH, E., R. M. FRANKLIN, A. J. SHOTKIN, and
E. L. TATUM. 1962. Action of actinomycin on animal
cells and viruses. Proc. Natl. Acad. Sci. USA *48:*
1238–1245.

(*5*) TATSUNO, T., N. MOROOKA, M. SAITO, M.
ENOMOTO, M. UMEDA, K. OKUBO, and H.
TSUNODA. 1966. Toxicological studies on the reddish
wheat by *Fusarium graminearum* genera (Report I). Folia
Pharmcol. Japan. *62:* 26–27 (in Japanese).

(*6*) TATSUNO, T., Y. UENO, I. UENO, Y. MORITA,
M. HOSOYA, M. SAITO, M. ENOMOTO, K.
OKUBO, N. MOROOKA, N. NAKANO, and H.
TSUNODA. 1967. Toxicological studies on toxic
metabolites of *Fusarium nivale* II. ibid. In press (in
Japanese).

(*7*) TSUNODA, H., N. TOYAZAKI, N. MOROOKA, N.
NAKANO, H. YOSHIYAMA, K. OKUBO, and M.
ISODA. 1968. Researches on the microorganisms which
deteriorate the stored cereals and grains (pt. 34). Detection of injurious strain and properties of their toxic
substances of scab Fusarium blight grown on the wheat.
Proc. Food Res. Inst. *23:* 89–116 (in Japanese).

(*8*) UENO, Y., M. HOSOYA, Y. MORITA, I. UENO, and
T. TATSUNO. 1968. Inhibition of the protein synthesis in rabbit reticulocytes by nivalenol, a toxic principle isolated from *Fusarium nivale*-growing rice. J.
Biochem. (Tokyo). In press.

(*9*) UENO, Y., and K. FUKUSHIMA, 1968. Inhibition of
protein and DNA syntheses in Ehrlich ascites tumour
by nivalenol, a toxic principle of *Fusarium nivale*-growing
rice. Experientia. In press.

(*10*) WEINSTEIN, I. B., M. OCHOA Jr., and S. M. FRIED-
MAN. 1966. Fidelity in the translation of messenger
ribonucleic acids in mammalian subcellular systems.
Biochemistry *5:* 332–339.

(*11*) YATES, S. G., H. J. TOOKEY, J. J. ELLIS, and H. J.
BURKHARDT. 1967. Toxic butenolide produced by
Fusarium nivale (Fries) Cesati isolated from tall fescue
(*Festuca arundinacea* Schreb.). Tetrahedron Letters 7:
621–623.

(*12*) YATES, S. G., H. L. TOOKEY, J. J. ELLIS, and H. L.
BURKHARDT. 1968. Mycotoxins produced by *Fusar-
ium nivale* isolated from tall fescue (*Festuca arundinacea*
Schreb.). Phytochem. *7:* 139–146.

BIOASSAY OF TOXIC PRINCIPLES OF RICE INFESTED WITH *FUSARIUM NIVALE* EMPLOYING RABBIT RETICULOCYTES

by YOSHIO UENO *and* MASAKATSU HOSOYA
Microbial Chemistry, Faculty of Pharmaceutical Sciences,
Science University of Tokyo, Ichigaya, Tokyo

Nivalenol and fusarenon, toxic principles of rice infested with *Fusarium nivale*, are potent inhibitors of protein synthesis in rabbit reticulocytes (3), Ehrlich ascites tumor (4), cultured cells (2) and *Tetrahymena* (1).

Based on this biochemical character of toxins, the authors examined the possibility of their detection by biochemical mean. The results indicated that with the use of rabbit reticulocytes the toxic principles could be determined biochemically.

Rabbits were injected subcutaneously with 5 mg./kg. of 1.2 percent phenylhydrazine on days 1 through 4, and on day 7 they were bled by cardiac puncture. The blood was centrifuged at 2,000 x g. for 5 minutes, and the pellet, consisting of more than 85 percent reticulocytes, was suspended in two volumes of ice-cold Locke-Ringer's solution. The suspension of the cells, referred as "whole cell," was stored in an ice-cold bath.

For the assay of toxins, 0.1 ml. whole cell suspension, 0.3 ml. Locke-Ringer's solution, 0.05 ml. of test solution were preincubated at 37° C. for 15 minutes. After the preincubation, 0.05 ml. (0.05 µC.) 1-C.^{14}-leucine was added to the reaction mixture and the incubation was continued for 40 minutes. The reaction was stopped by the addition of 0.5 ml. of 10 percent perchloric acid (PCA) and the total reaction mixture was filtered through filter paper which was then washed with 5 percent PCA and ethanol-ether (3:1, v/v). The radioactivity of carbon-14 incorporated was counted by a gas-flow counter.

Using this method, 0.5 µg. of nivalenol and 0.05 µg. of fusarenon could be detected, and the time required for the assay was about two hours. The procedure is schematically illustrated in figure 1.

An example of this test method, applied to the fractionation of toxic principles from rice infested with *F. nivale* is shown in table 1. The inhibitory effect of each fraction on the reticulocytes was paralleled by the lethal dose for mice. This investigation was reported in a previous paper (3).

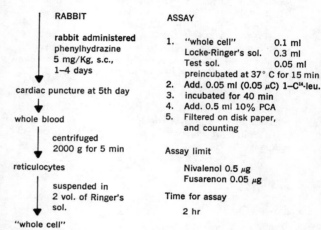

Figure 1.—Method of biochemical detection of nivalenol and fusarenon by rabbit reticulocytes.

Table 1.—Toxicity of the fractions on mice and reticulocytes

Fractions	Lethal dose in mice (mg./10 g.)	Uptake of C^{14}-leucine in reticulocytes Concentration (µg./ml.)	Activity (percent)
Ethanol extract ____ A–I	5–20	—	—
Crude toxin _____ A–II	1	5	90.1
		50	32.6
		100	13.4
Kieselgel—fractions __ A–IV	(1.8)	100	76.7
A–V	.70	100	.5
A–VI	.30	100	.9
A–VII	.60	100	2.2
A–VIII	(1.8)	100	58.3
A–IX	(2.7)	100	89.5
Nivalenol _____ A–X	.10	10	12.0

References

(1) MOROOKA, N., and T. TATSUNO. 1968. Toxic substances (fusarenon and nivalenol) produced by *Fusarium nivale*. These preceedings.

(2) OHTSUBO, K., M. YAMADA, and M. SAITO. 1968. Inhibitory effect of nivalenol, a toxic metabolite of *Fusarium nivale*, on the growth cycle and biopolymer synthesis of HeLa cells. Japan. J. Med. Sci. Biol. *21:* 185–194.

(3) UENO, Y., M. HOSOYA, Y. MORITA, I. UENO, and T. TATSUNO. 1968. Inhibition of the protein synthesis in rabbit reticulocytes by nivalenol, a toxic principle isolated from *Fusarium nivale*-growing rice. J. Biochem. (Tokyo) *64:* 479–485.

(4) UENO, Y., and M. FUKUSHIMA. 1968. Inhibition of protein and DNA syntheses in Ehrlich ascites tumour by nivalenol, a toxic principles of *Fusarium nivale*-growing rice. Experientia. In press.

STUDIES ON THE TARGET INJURIES IN EXPERIMENTAL ANIMALS WITH THE MYCOTOXINS OF *FUSARIUM NIVALE*

by Mamoru Saito *and* Kaoru Okubo
Department of Carcinogenesis and Cancer Susceptibility,
The Institute of Medical Science, The University of Tokyo and Department of Veterinary Pathology
The Nippon Veterinary and Zootechnical College, Kyonan–cho, Musashino City, Tokyo

Summary

The investigation for toxic metabolites of *Fusarium nivale* in Japan was commenced after the heavy damage of wheat with Fusarium in 1963. Marked toxicities of several fungi including one strain of *F. nivale* and two strains of *F. graminearum* were found at that time. The toxicity of moldy rice infested artificially with Fn–2 strain was most prominent. The raw substance extracted from this material was used for the study of chemical isolation.

Specific findings were noticed in experimental animals and also in cultured cells administered with the raw material and the isolated chemical substances, namely nivalenol (Tatsuno), fusarenon (Morooka) and also recently separated fusarenon-X (Ueno). Characteristic findings obtained in the experimental animals consisted of marked damage of the proliferating cells of the hematopoietic tissues in the bone marrow, spleen, thymus and lymph node, and also of the intestinal epithelia and of the testis. These changes were similar to those caused by radiomimetic effect, and the nature of the injuries may reflect the disturbance in DNA and protein synthesis of the cells. Because of the similarities in toxic natures of nivalenol, fusarenon and also fusarenon-X, the principal chemical structure of these substances might closely resemble each other.

It is suggested that more sensitive screening tests for specific toxic properties should be established for the investigation of mycotoxins which may be responsible for various target effects.

Introduction

The so-called red molds, *F. graminearum* (*Giberrella zeae*), *Gibberella fujikuroi*, *F. nivale* and *F. kühnii* have been hitherto noted in the stored food crops in Japan (*40*).

After an accidental toxicosis of 30 human cases (symptoms: vomiting, giddiness and chill) without deaths, occurring in farmers after intake of rice contaminated with fusarium species in Hoya, a rural suburb of Tokyo Metropolis in 1955, toxicological investigation on this contaminated fungus was carried out (*9*). So far only a few organs of the experimental animals have been examined, and only minute injuries have been noticed pathologically.

In 1958, Nishikado (*21*) showed the distribution of wheat, damaged with *Fusarium graminearum*, in Japan (fig. 1). The damage was more marked in the leeward districts of the seasonal winter wind than in other areas.

Following the heavy damage to wheat in the western district of Japan in 1963, the Technical Committee of Agriculture, Forestry and Fishery of the Ministry of Agriculture and Forestry decided to start investigating the red molds of wheat in several research units (*22, 23*). *F. graminearum* was separated in 100 percent and *F. nivale* was separated in 5 or 6 percent of samples from the infected wheat grains obtained from the Agricultural Experimental Station in Kumamoto prefecture. Toxicity screening tests were performed on these fungi by Tsunoda (*41*) of the Food Research Institute, Tokyo, and other fusaria were also separated and tested at the National Agricultural Technical Institute. High toxicities were shown in one strain of *F. nivale* (Fn–2 strain) and two strains of *F. graminearum* (Ishii-strain, Ooita 2 strain) (*11*). Extensive research on the chemical identification of the toxins and the examination of their toxicity have been performed under the close cooperation of Tsunoda (mycologist), Tatsuno, Morooka, and Ueno (chemists), Saito and Ohkubo (pathologists) and other co-workers, and many reports from this project have been published (*14, 25, 26, 27, 32, 33, 35, 36, 37, 38, 39, 42, 43, 45*). Hitherto, there have been many reports and surveys on the toxicity of different species of the genus *Fusarium* throughout the world since Woronin's original report on the damage of wheat in Ussyy district in 1891 (*18, 15, 7, 1, 29, 18, 19, 20, 17, 31, 3, 34, 12, 4, 30, 5, 6, 8, 13, 16, 46, 48, 2, 49, 10, 28*).

This paper describes the specific injuries to the proliferating cells in experimental animals and also to the cultured cells, caused by the mycotoxins of *F. nivale*. These specific injuries were used as the charac-

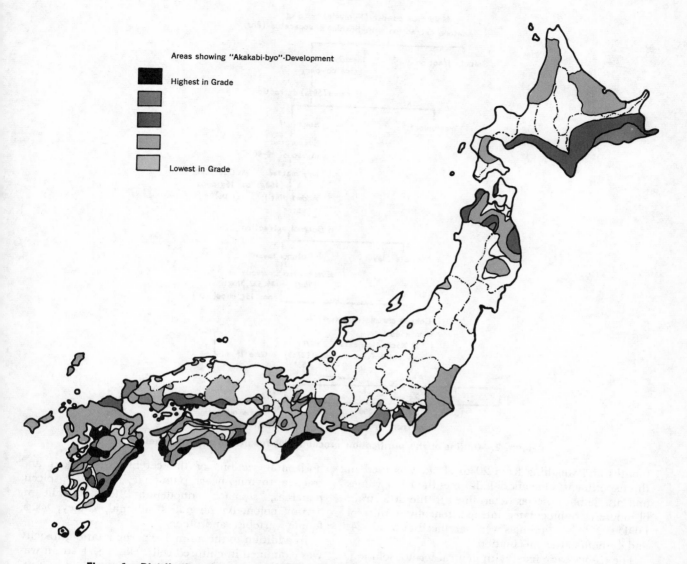

Figure 1.—Distribution of "akakabi-byo" (red mold wheat), occurring in Japan (Nishikado, 1958).

teristics studied to pursue the chemical fractions. Several chemical substances have been isolated to date, and the comparative findings of the injuries with these substances are also presented.

Materials and Methods

Nivalenol (*39*), fusarenon (*42*), fusarenon-X (*45*), raw material, and fractions were tested in this experiment.

The outline of the purification procedure of fusarenon and nivalenol is shown in figure 2, and the chemical and physical properties of fusarenon and nivalenol, are shown in table 1. Recently a new toxic substance, named fusarenon-X, has been isolated from the medium of the stationary culture of *F. nivale* by

Dr. Ueno. The chemical characteristics of fusarenon-X, obtained from the same fractions are somewhat different from fusarenon. For example, the new substance is water soluble, while on the other hand, fusarenon is water insoluble. Fusarenon-X gave nearly the same Rf with fusarenon on thin layer chromatography, but differed in melting point and infrared spectrum (*45*).

In figure 3, the toxicity of the fractions isolated in the vicinity of fusarenon from Kiesel-gel column chromatography is shown. Among them, fraction C–131 and fraction C–301 were also tested for lethal toxicity in each lethal dose in this experiment for the purpose of comparing the toxic properties of the raw material and the isolated substances.

The DDD strain of mouse, age approximately 6

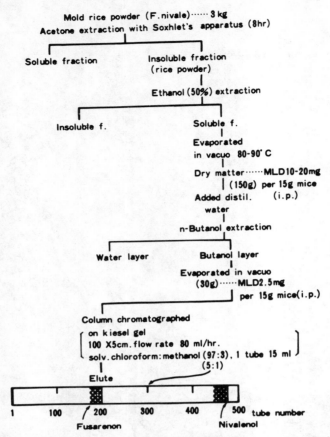

Figure 2.—Outline of the purification procedure of fusarenon and nivalenol.

months and weighing from 20 to 28 g., was used in this experiment. One and a half times the LD_{50} values and also lethal doses as determined in the ddS strain of mouse were inoculated intraperitoneally in mice of DDD strain. The animals were sacrificed at 6, 12, 24, and 48 hours after inoculation.

The tissues were fixed with neutral formol solution. After paraffin and freezing sectionings, they were stained with HE, Giemsa, PAS, Azan, and Sudan III. Tissues examined in this experiment were: Brain (frontal sections of cerebrum and cerebellum, and horizontal sections of the cerebrum), thyroid and trachea, thymus, heart, pulmonary lobe, liver, spleen, pancreas, stomach, duodenum, jejunum, ileum, cecum, colon, lymph nodes, adrenal, kidney, testis, femur, vertebra, and others.

In addition to the animal experimentation, toxicity was examined in cultured cells. HeLa S3T strain was cultured according to the plate panel method in minimum essential medium (Eagle) with 10 percent calf serum. The dilutions of the tested materials is given in table 2.

Results

In the animal experiment, marked toxic injuries were noticed especially in the proliferating cells of the thymus, spleen, lymph nodes, bone marrow, ileum, jejunum, colon, stomach, testis, and hair follicles.

In the thymus, marked karyorrhexis was observed in the cases of fusarenon-X, fusarenon and nivalenol, and slight karyorrhexis in the cases of raw material and C–301. As for the histological distribution of injuries in the thymus, injury was rather marked in the cortex and only slight in the medulla.

Even 6 hours after application, karyorrhexis was

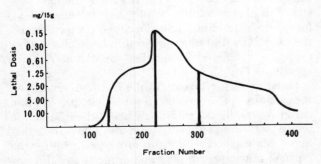

Figure 3.—Toxic substances separated by Kiesel-gel chromatography.

already moderately observed in cases of fusarenon-X, fusarenon and C–301, and slightly in the case of nivalenol. These injuries became more conspicuous after 12 hours with the tested materials except for C–301 and C–131, in which their injuries became remarkable after 24 hours. Nivalenol showed the heaviest injuries. At 48 hours, the findings of all cases improved (fig. 4) (pl. I, figs. 1 and 2).

In the lymph nodes, the main injuries consisted of

Table 1.—Properties of isolated toxic substances of *Fusarium nivale*

Tests	Substances	
	Fusarenon	Nivalenol
Author	Morooka (1968)	Tatsuno (1968)
Crystal m.p.	78–80° C.	222-223° C.
Rf value Toluene-Et-Ac (1:3)	0.35	0.06
20% H_2SO_4 Colour	purple yellowish-green	pink-violet brown
G.C. Retention time	10.3 min.	8.3 min.
Anal. Found		C H O 56.29 37.70 6.01
Calc.		57.68 35.86 6.46
M.W. M.F.		312 $C_{15}H_{20}O_7$
U.V. Spectra.	end absorpt.	λ max 260 mμ
I.R. Spectra. (cm-1)	3570(s)1250(s) 2960(m)1167(m) 1720(s)1080(s) 1685(s)1040(s) 1365(m)	3400(s)2870(m) 3270(s)2740(m) 2980(w)1680(m) (2900(w)1610(m)
(α) t D	$(\alpha)^{24} = +29.6°$ D (EtOH)	$(\alpha)^{24°} = +21.5°$ D (EtOH)

Table 2.—Concentrations of various materials tested for toxicity in HeLa cell tissue culture

Material tested	Microgram per milliliter				
Nivalenol	10,	3.2,	1.0,	0.32,	0.1,
Fusarenon	10,	3.2,	1.0,	0.32,	0.1,
Fusarenon-X	10,	3.2,	1.0,	0.32,	0.1,
Fraction C–131	100,	32,	10,	3.2,	1.0,
Fraction C–301 (dissolved in ethanol)	100,	32,	10,	3.2,	1.0,
Fraction C–301 (suspended in water)	100,	32,	10,	3.2,	1.0,
Raw material (suspended in water)	1000,	320,	100,	32,	10,
Raw material (millipore filtrate)	1000,	320,	100,	32,	10,

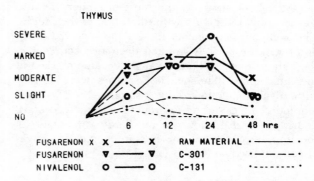

Figure 4.—Toxic injuries with metabolites of *Fusarium nivale* in mouse.

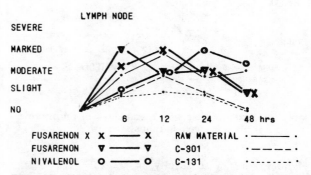

Figure 5.—Toxic injuries with metabolites of *Fusarium nivale* in mouse.

karyorrhexis in a part of the lymph follicles and also slightly in the pulps. Marked damage was noticed in the cases of fusarenon-X, fusarenon, nivalenol and raw material, and only slight in the cases of C–301 and C–131. The greatest injuries in the case of fusarenon were noted at 6 hours, in fusarenon-X and raw material at 12 hours and in nivalenol at 24 hours after inoculation. These findings may indicate that fusarenon acts rather promptly and nivalenol acts rather slowly (fig. 5) (pl. I, fig. 3).

In the spleen, the main injury was marked karyorrhexis in the lymph follicles. Conspicuous damage was noted in the cases of fusarenon-X at all time periods and in case of nivalenol at 24 hours. In the spleen also, fusarenon acted promptly and nivalenol acted rather slowly. Extramedullary hematopoiesis in the spleen was noticed in the later periods of the experiment. This finding may be seen after marked injury of the bone marrows and lymph nodes (fig. 6) (pl. II, fig. 4).

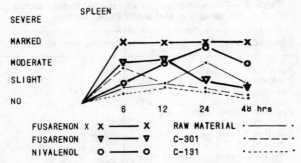

Figure 6.—Toxic injuries with metabolites of *Fusarium nivale* in mouse.

In the bone marrow, the most prominent feature was atrophy of the pulp with dilatation of the sinuses. The cellular components in the pulp decreased in number, an especially marked decrease occurring in the immature cells. These changes became marked at the later times. The heaviest injuries were noticed with nivalenol, followed by fusarenon-X. The most marked changes due to fusarenon were noticed at 12 hours, while at 48 hours, a regenerative tendency of the immature cells of the hematopoietic tissue was already noticeable (fig. 7) (pl. II, figs. 5 and 6).

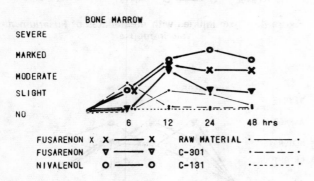

Figure 7.—Toxic injuries with metabolites of *Fusarium nivale* in mouse.

The grades of sensitivity of several parts of the gastrointestinal tract may be lined up as follows: the ileum and jejunum were the highest followed by the colon, duodenum, pyloric gland, and corpus gland. The most prominent injuries were observed in the proliferating foci of the mucosal epithelia. Pathologic mitosis, karyorrhexis, and collapsed necrotic cells were seen. At 48 hours after fusarenon-X inoculation, slough-off of the mucosal epithelia of the ileum was noticed. Besides the epithelial damages, edema and cell infiltration with debris of karyorrhexis were found in the stromal spaces of the mucosa. These stromal findings might be considered as part of the pathogenesis of the so-called catarrhalic change of the

gastrointestinal tract. The heaviest damage with fusarenon-X was seen in the intestinal mucosa. In this area fusarenon acted rather promptly and nivalenol acted rather slowly (fig. 8) (pl. III, figs. 7, 7′, 8, 9, and pl. IV, fig. 10).

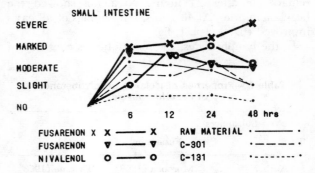

Figure 8.—Toxic injuries with metabolites of *Fusarium nivale* in mouse.

Injuries of the mucosal epithelia were not prominent in the large intestine. In this organ, fusarenon-X showed the peak of the damage 12 hours after inoculation (fig. 9) (pl. IV, fig. 11).

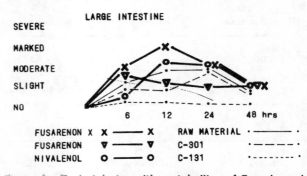

Figure 9.—Toxic injuries with metabolites of *Fusarium nivale* in mouse.

In the testis, cellular injury was also noticed in spermatogenesis. The cellular components were reduced in number, cellular arrangement was irregular, and pycnosis and karyolysis of the blastic cells were also seen (pl. IV, fig. 12).

In the skin, atrophy of the hair follicles and sebaceous glands were noticed.

As for the findings in the other organs, the brain tissue, especially the putamen and cortex of the cerebrum, showed marked perivascular and pericellular edema in the heavily intoxicated cases. Flecky haemorrhages were noticed in the lung, and sometimes the bronchial epithelium does not reach the terminal parts of the bronchiolus with or without bronchitis in the severely intoxicated cases. The liver showed slight damage of Kupffer cells at the periportal regions with slight vacuolar change of the neighbouring liver cells, and loss of glycogen in the liver cells were generally observed. Hematopoietic cells and/or other damaged cell debri were infiltrated into both sinusoidal spaces and portal tracts. The findings of other organs were not so prominent as those described above.

The results of the toxicity test of the various metabolites from *F. nivale* on HeLa S3T strain is illustrated in figure 10.

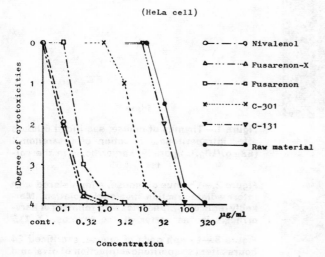

(HeLa cell)

Figure 10.—Comparison of toxicities of metabolites from *Fusarium nivale*.

As for the fractions, C–301 and C–131, collected from the column adjacent to fusarenon, the characteristic injuries in the proliferating cells were lower in grade, especially in the cases of C–301, and almost no injuries in the cases of C–131. Specificities of the lethal injuries caused with C–131 and C–301 were not clear.

Discussion

The primary injuries in the mice inoculated with nivalenol, fusarenon, and fusarenon-X and also raw material were found in the proliferating cells of various organs. Fusarenon-X was the most injurious followed by nivalenol and fusarenon. In this experiment, the doses of each metabolite administered to the DDD strain of mouse were close to the LD_{50} values of nivalenol and fusarenon-X, and to the lethal doses of raw material, column-301 and column-131 found in the ddS strain. Fusarenon was administered with the same dose as nivalenol. Grades of toxicities caused by these applied materials may be ordered as follows: fusarenon-X, nivalenol, fusarenon, raw material, C–301 and C–131.

On the other hand, the cultured cells (HeLa S3T) were exposed to the same test materials in half log dilutions yielding the following order of toxicity: Fusarenon-X, nivalenol, fusarenon, fraction 301, fraction 131 and raw material.

Comparing toxicities found in the animal experiment with those found in the cultured cells shows that there is a good correlation between them, with the exception of the raw material (table 3).

Table 3.—Comparison of lethal doses in HeLa cells and in mice

	HeLa (a) μg./ml.	Mouse (b) μg./10g.	(a):(b)
Nivalenol	*ca.* 0.32	[1]42	1:130
Fusarenon	0.56	[2]42	1:75
Fusarenon-X	0.32	[1]36	1:110
C–131	56	[2]1,660	1:30
C–301	10	[2]822	1:82
Raw material	100	[2]7,000	1:70

[1]LD_{50}.
[2]Lethal doses, estimated.

As stated in the introduction, the toxicity test employing the cultured cells had already been used in pursuing the toxic metabolites in the chemical fractionations (*38*). In that study, the raw material of *Fusarium nivale* caused marked lysis of Chang's liver cells and HeLa cells at the concentration of 10^{-4}; and at that more dilute dose, atrophy of nuclei and multinucleate giant cell formation were observed. In the chemical fractionation, among column filtrates from G–25 sephadex, a cytolytic effect was observed at a concentration of 10^{-5} with column fraction numbers 20 and 21, and the toxicity test with fractions of column fraction numbers 16 to 22 (0.02 ml./10g.) on the mouse lethal effect was shown. The toxicity test with culture cell may be of value in the detection of mycotoxins, especially of the radiomimetic substances. In the animal experiments, thymus, ileum, and spleen are adequate organs for evaluating the radiomimetic activities.

In the gastrointestinal tract, the grades of sensitivities may be considered as follows: Ileum = jejunum > colon ≫ duodenum > pyloric gland > corpus gland. Toxic injuries of the gastrointestinal tract were prominent in the proliferating cells. Karyorrhexis and collapsed necrotic cells accumulated in the glandular spaces. The number of injured cells might be related to the time lag of the effective concentration of the toxins acting in the spaces or in the circulating blood. Probably, when the period of effective concentration of the toxin exceeds the generation time of the blastic cells and/or the lifespan of the glandular epithelia, erosive changes may occur. Sometimes, mitotic cells

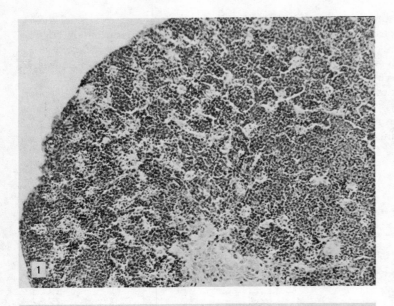

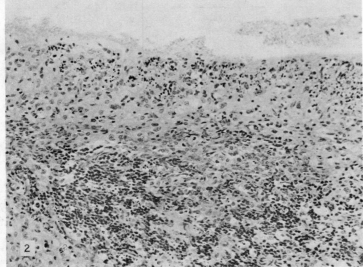

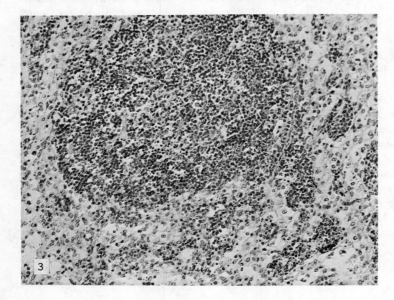

Plate I

Figure 1.—Thymus of mouse, sacrificed 6 hours after intraperitoneal injection of fusarenon-X (63μ.g./10g.). Sporadic karyorrhexis in the cortex.   X 95

Figure 2.—Thymus of mouse, administered with intermediate fraction nivalenol isolation. Markedly reduced lymphocytes with remnant of karyorrhexis in the cortex of the thymus.   X 115

Figure 3.—Lymph node of mouse, sacrificed 24 hours after intraperitoneal injection of nivalenol (63μ.g./10g.). Karyorrhexis is marked in the lymph follicle and slight in the pulp of the lymph node.   X 225

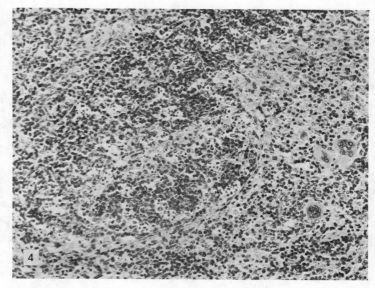

Plate II

Figure 4.—Spleen of mouse, sacrificed 24 hours after injection of fusarenon-X (54µg./10g.). Karyorrhexis in the lymph follicle of the spleen.   X 95

Figure 5.—Vertebra of mouse, sacrificed 48 hours after injection of fusarenon-X (54µg./10g.). In the bone marrow, both atrophy of the pulp and dilation of sinuses are observed. The cellular components are markedly decreased in the pulp.   X 195

Figure 6.—Femur of mouse, sacrificed 24 hours after injection of nivalenol (63µg./10g.). Diminution of the cellular components in the bone marrow.   X   475

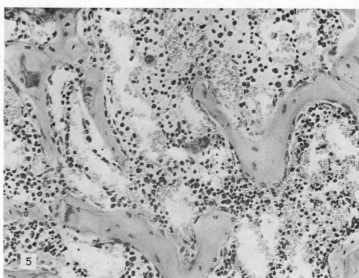

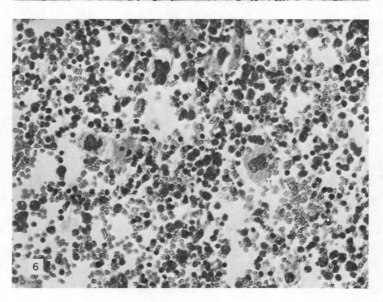

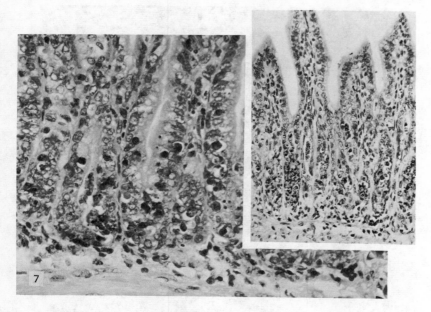

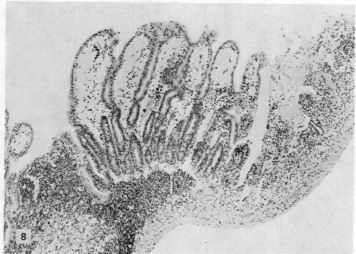

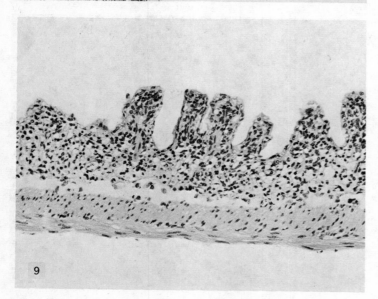

Plate III

Figure 7.—Ileum of mouse, sacrificed 12 hours after injection of nivalenol (63μg./10g.). Pathologic mitoses and karyorrhexis in the proliferating region of intestinal glands of illeum. X 460

Figure 7 (insert).—Ileum of mouse, sacrificed 6 hours after injection of fusarenon-X (63μg./10g.) Accumulation of necrotic cells in grandular spaces with scarcely any damage of the upper part of grandular epithelium.   X 230

Figure 8.—Ileum of mouse, sacrificed 90 hours after injection of intermediate substance of nivalenol isolation. Generalized erosive changes with remnant of grandular epithelium.   X 65

Figure 9.—Ileum of mouse, sacrificed 48 hours after injection of fusarenon-X (54μg./10g.). Generalized erosive changes.   X 230

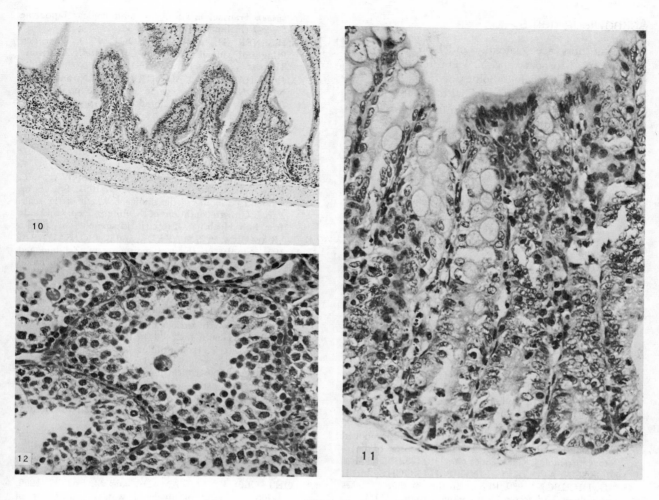

Plate IV

Figure 10.—Ileum of mouse, sacrificed 12 hours after injection of fusarenon-X (54µg./10g.). Cell infiltration found in stromal spaces. X 80

Figure 11.—Colon of mouse, sacrificed 6 hours after injection of fusarenon-X (54µg./10g.). Mitotic injuries observed at the proliferating foci of glandular epithelia of the colon. X 525

Figure 12.—Testis of mouse, sacrificed 48 hours after injection of fusarenon-X (54µg./10g.). Decreased spermatogensis with a typical giant cell formation. X 390

were observed at the upper regions of the glandular epithelium and increased in number. These findings may suggest the existence of mitotic injuries.

According to an experiment of autoradiographical analysis with ^{3}H–thymidine administered to mice along with a small dosage of the toxic metabolite (crude nivalenol) elongation of G–2 phase of the cells of the glandular epithelium of the ileum was observed (33).

Recently work on the toxicities of nivalenol for HeLa cells indicates that both DNA and protein synthesis are inhibited with nivalenol. These findings

also suggest the similarity of the damage with the toxin to those of radiomimetic substances (24, 44). It is quite interesting that the morphological findings of injuries are correlated with evidence found at a molecular level.

In order to detect the toxic metabolites among the numerous products of fungi, especially those found in contaminated food stuffs, more effective screening tests for various toxic effects should be developed. It is needless to emphasize the importance of detection of new fungi especially those growing in the epidemiological circumstances of geographical pathology.

Acknowledgments

The authors are gratefully indebted to Drs. T. Tatsuno, N. Morooka, and Y. Ueno for the supplies of the purified toxic metabolites of *F. nivale;* to Dr. M. Umeda for his cooperation with the toxicity test employing cultured cells, and also to Miss K. Miyata and Mr. S. Matsuo for their technical assistance.

References

(1) ASHLEY, J. N., B. C. HOBB, and H. RAISTRICK. 1937. Studies in the biochemistry of microorganisms. The crystalline colouring matters of *Fusarium culmorum* m (W. G. Smith) Sacc. and related forms, Biochem. J. *31:* 385–397.

(2) BAMBURG, J. R., N. V. RIGGS, and F. M. STRONG. 1968. The structures of toxin from two strains of *Fusarium tricinctum.* Tetrahedron Letters *24:* 3329–3336.

(3) BRIAN, P. W., A. W. DAWKINS, L. F. GROVE, H. G. HEMMING, D. LOWE, and G. L. F. NORRIS. 1961. Phytotoxic compounds produced by *Fusarium equiseti.* J. Exp. Botany *12:* 1–12.

(4) CHRISTENSEN, C. M., G. H. NELSON, and C. J. MIROCHA. 1965. Effect on the white rat uterus of a toxic substance isolated from *Fusarium,* Applied Microbiol. *13:* 653–659.

(5) CURTIN, T. M., and J. TUITE. 1966. Emesis and refusal of feed in swine associated with *Gibberella zeae*-infected corn. Life Science *5:* 1937–1944.

(6) DAWKINS, A. W. 1966. Phytotoxic compounds produced by *Fusarium equisetti.* Part II. The chemistry of diacetoxyscirpenol. J. Chem. Soc. *100:* 116–123.

(7) DICKSON, A. D., K. L. LINK, B. H. ROCHE, and J. G. DICKSON. 1930. Report on the emetic substances in Gibberella-infected barley. Phytopathol. *20:* 132.

(8) GILGAN, M. W., E. B. SMALLEY, and F. M. STRONG. 1966. Isolation and partial characterization of a toxin from *Fusarium tricinctum* on moldy corn. Arch. Biochem. Biophys. *114:* 1–3.

(9) HIRAYAMA, K., and M. YAMAMOTO. 1948. Biological studies on the poisonous wheat flour. Eisei Shikenjo Hokoku *66:* 85–98 (in Japanese).

(10) HOYMAN, W. G. 1941. Concentration and characterization of the emetic principle present in barley infected with *Gibberella saubinetii.* Phytopathol. *31:* 871–885.

(11) IDE, Y., K. SHIMBAYASHI, J. OBARA, and T. YONEMURA. 1967. Toxicities of wheat and rice infected with *Fusarium graminearum* and *Fusarium nivale* for mice and chicks. Bull. Nat. Inst. Animal Health *54:* 34–37 (in Japanese).

(12) JOFFE, A. Z. 1964. Toxin production by cereal fungi causing toxic alimentary Aleukia in Man. "Mycotoxins in Foodstuffs," G. N. Wogan, ed., M.I.T. Press, p. 77–85.

(13) KEYL, A. C., J. C. LEWIS, J. J. ELLIS, S. G. YATES, and H. L. TOOKEY. 1967. Toxic fungi isolated from tall fescue. Mycopathol. et Mycologia Applicata *31:* 329–331.

(14) KONNO, S., and H. FUJIWARA. 1966. On the pathological changes of mice by the extract of red mould rice cultured in laboratory (raw toxic material of *Fusarium*

nivale). Transactiones Societatis Pathologicae Japonicae *55:* 247 (in Japanese).

(15) MIESSNER, H., and G. SCHOOP. 1929. Uber den Pilzgefall amerikanischer "Giftgerste". Deutsche Tierarzt. Wochenschr. *37:* 167–170.

(16) MIROCHA, C. J., C. M. CHRISTENSEN, and G. H. NELSON. 1967. Estrogenic metabolite produced by *Fusarium graminearum* in stored corn., Appl. Microbiol. *15:* 497–503.

(17) MIYAKE, I., M. MATSUNAMI, and H. WAKAMATSU. 1956. Studies on the red disease of barley and wheat grains, J. Tokyo Agricult. Univ. *3:* 83–92 (in Japanese).

(18) NAKAMURA, Y., S. TAKEDA, K. OGASAWARA, T. KARASHIMADA, and K. ANDO. 1951. Studies on the food poisoning of the damaged wheat of the scab. Part I. Growth conditions of the fungus, Rep. Hokkaido Inst. Pub. Health *2:* 35–46. (in Japanese).

(19) NAKAMURA, Y., S. TAKEDA, and K. OGASAWARA. 1951. Studies on the food poisoning of the damaged wheat of the scab. II. On toxicity tests, Rep. Hokkaido Inst. Pub. Health *2:* 47–50 (in Japanese).

(20) NAKAMURA, Y., S., TAKADA, K. OGASAWARA, and T. KONISHI. 1953. Studies on the food poisoning of the damaged wheat of the scab. Part IV. Animal experiment on the toxicity of the fungus, Rep. Hokkaido Inst. Pub. Health *4:* 22–28 (in Japanese).

(21) NISHIKADO, Y. 1958. Studies on the control of Fusarium scab disease of wheat, Data on Agricultural New Technics *97:* 59–220 (in Japanese).

(22) Office of Technical Committee of the Agriculture, Forestry and Fishery. 1964. Progress of the research on the intoxications of domestic animals by the red mould of wheat (in Japanese).

(23) Office of Technical Committee of the Agriculture, Forestry and Fishery. 1965. Data of the research on the intoxication of domestic animals by the red mould of wheat in 1964 and 1965 (in Japanese).

(24) OHTSUBO, K., M. YAMADA, and M. SAITO. 1968. Inhibitory effect of nivalenol, a toxic metabolite of *Fusarium nivale,* on the growth cycle and biopolymer synthesis of HeLa cells, Japan. J. Med. Sci. Biol. *21:* 185–194.

(25) OKUBO, K., M. ISODA, T. SENBOKU, K. SATTA, and S. YUKISADA. 1966. Pathological studies on the poisoning by *Fusarium nivale.* I. Pathological findings of acute poisoning of guinea pig by peroral administration of crude sample. Japan. J. Vet. Sci. *28:* 381 (in Japanese).

(26) OKUBO, K., M. ISODA, T. SENBOKU, H. KAWAMURA, H. KUNIYA, and T. KOBAYASHI. 1966. Studies on the pathology of poisoning of *Fusarium nivale.* II. Experimental acute poisoning of the mice. Japan. J. Vet. Sci. *28:* 489 (in Japanese).

(27) OKUBO, K. and M. ISODA. 1967. Studies on the essential nature of intoxication by the products of *Fusarium nivale.* I. Histopathological examination of experimental acute intoxication by crude products of *Fusarium nivale.* Bull. Nippon Vet. Zootech. College *16:* 22–42 (in Japanese).

(28) OPPERMANN and DOENECKE. 1929. Futterungsversuche mit amerikanischer "Giftgerste". Deutsche Tierarzt. Wochensch. *37:* 165–167.

(29) PLATTNER, RL. A. and N. CLAUSON-KASS, 1945. Uber Lyco-marasmin, den welkstoff aus *Fusarium lycopsersiei* Sacc. Experimentia *1:* 196.

(30) POUTEAU, M. THOUVENOT and M. BARBIER,

1965. La lycomarasmine, phytotoxine de Fusarium oxysporumif. vasinfectum. Comptes rendus Soc. Biol. *260:* 5924–5927.

(*31*) PRENTICE, N., A. D. DICKSON, and J. G. DICKSON. 1959. Production of emetic material by species of Fusarium. Nature *184:* 1319.

(*32*) SAITO, M. and M. ENOMOTO. 1965. On the pathological changes of mice by the toxic metabolite of red mould of wheat, *Fusarium nivale.* Data of the research on the intoxication of domestic animals by the red mould of wheat in 1964 and 1965, Supplement (in Japanese).

(*33*) SAITO, M., M. ENOMOTO, T. YOKOYAMA, K. OHTSUBO, K. YAMAGUCHI and T. TATSUNO. 1967. On the injuries of the alimentary tracts and hematopoietic tissues by the toxic metabolite of red mould of wheat, *Fusarium nivale.* Transactiones Societatis Pathogicae Japonica *56:* 78 (In Japanese).

(*34*) STOB, M., R. S. BALDWIN, F. N. ANDREWS and K. G. GILLETTE. 1962. Isolation of an anabolic, uterotrophic compound from corn infected with *Gibberella zeae.* Nature *196:* 1318.

(*35*) SUGIURA, K., T. KOBANAWA, M. MUNAKATA and K. IKEDA. 1965. Pathologic-histological findings of pigs after feeding of wheat infected with red mould. Data of Research on the Intoxication of Domestic Animals by Wheat Infected with Red Mould (in Japanese).

(*36*) TAKAHASHI, I. and S. KONNO. 1965. On the mortality and their pathological changes of mice by the application of red mould of wheat. Data of research on the intoxication of domestic animals by wheat infected with red mould (in Japanese).

(*37*) TAKAHASHI, I., T. ISHII, T. SHIMADA and S. KONNO. 1966. The experimental study on the toxicity of crude toxin extracted from scab rice. Japan. J. Vet. Sci. *28:* 381 (in Japanese).

(*38*) TATSUNO T., N. MOROOKA, M. SAITO, M. ENOMOTO, M. UMEDA, K. OKUBO, and H. TSUNODA. 1966. Toxicological research on toxic component of metabolites of the red mould (Fusarium group) of the wheat. Folia Pharmacol. Japonica *62:* 26 (in Japanese).

(*39*) TATSUNO, T., Y. UENO, I. UENO, I. MORITA, M. HOSOYA, M. SAITO, M. ENOMOTO, N. MO-ROOKA, N. NAKANO, and H. TSUNODA. 1968. Toxicological research on toxic component of metabolites of the red mould (*Fusarium nivale*) II. Folia Pharmacol. Japonica *64:* 1213 (in Japanese).

(*40*) TSUNODA, H., O. TSURUTA, M. MATSUSUMI, and S. ISHII. 1958. Researches on the micro-organisms on the stored cereals and grains (*14*). Studies on rice parasitic molds, Gibberella and Fusarium. Rep. Food Res. Inst., *12:* 26–33 (in Japanese).

(*41*) TSUNODA, H., O. TSURUTA, M. MATSUSUMI, and S. ISHII. 1958. Researches on the micro-organisms on the stored cereals and grains (*16*) Studies on the fungi of red molds, especially their animal tests. Rep. Food Res. Inst. *13:* 26–28 (in Japanese).

(*42*) TSUNODA, H., N. TOYAZAKI, N. MOROOKA, N. NAKANO, H. YOSHIYAMA, K. OKUBO, and M. ISODA. 1968. Researches on the micro-organisms on the stored cereals and grains. Studies on the isolation of toxic red mould strains from wheat and nature of the Toxin. Rep. Food Res. Inst. *23:* 89–114 (in Japanese).

(*43*) TSUNODA, H. T. TATSUNO, Y. UENO, N. MOROOKA, N. NAKANO, H. YOSHIYAMA, K. OKUBO, and M. ISODA. 1968. Researches on the isolation of toxic red mould strains from the wheat and nature of their Toxins. II. Especially on the isolation of toxic substance from metabolite of *Fusarium nivale* and its pathological findings. Ann. Phytopathol. Soc. Japan *34:* 181 (in Japanese).

(*44*) UENO, Y., M. HOSOYA, and T. TATSUNO. Effect of toxin of *Fusarium nivale* on the polymer synthesis of reticulocytes. Biochem., *39:* 708 (in Japanese).

(*45*) UENO, Y. Personal Communication. 1968.

(*46*) WHITE, E. P. 1967. Isolation of ($\pm$)-2-Acetamido-2,5-dihydro-5-oxyfuran from *Fusarium equiseti,* J. Chem. Soc. *100:* 346–347.

(*47*) WORONIN, M. 1891. Uber das "Taumelgetreide" in Sud-Ussurien. Botanische Zeitung *6:* 81–94.

(*48*) YATES, S. G., H. J. TOOKEY, J. J. ELLIS and H. J. BURKHARDT. 1967. Toxic butenolide produced by *Fusarium nivale* (Fries) Cesati isolated from tall fescue (Festuca arundinacea Schreb.). Tetrahedron Letters *7:* 621–623.

(*49*) YATES, S. G., H. L. TOOKEY, J. J. ELLIS, and H. J. BURKHARDT. 1968. Mycotoxins produced by *Fusarium nivale* isolated from tall fescue (*Festuca arundinacea* Schreb.). Phytochem. *7:* 139–146.

PATHOLOGY OF THE TOXICOSIS PRODUCED IN MICE BY CORN CULTURES OF *PENICILLIUM VIRIDICATUM*

by William W. Carlton, John Tuite, *and* Phil Mislivec
Department of Veterinary Physiology and Pharmacology,
School of Veterinary Science and Medicine,
and Department of Botany and Plant Pathology,
School of Agriculture, Purdue University, Lafayette, Ind. 47907

Summary

Two isolates of *Penicillium viridicatum* were grown on autoclaved corn at 24° C. for 2 weeks. The cultures after treatment with chloroform were dried, ground and incorporated into a purified diet at levels of 50, 33, and 25 percent of the diet. Weanling male albino mice were fed the various diets *ad libitum*. In trial 1, isolate 5 x 3#3 was fed and the mice killed at weekly intervals for study. Isolate 2HA–2 was fed in trial 2 and mice were killed in certain dietary groups after 3, 5, 7, 10, and 14 days of feeding. Body weights were taken at necropsy and at weekly intervals. Liver, heart, spleen, and kidneys were examined microscopically. Both isolates were toxic to mice at the three concentrations, reducing weight gains and causing a high death loss. Gross lesions with both isolates included jaundice, greenish discoloration of the kidneys, and foci of necrosis in the liver. Microscopically, the earliest changes occurred in the bile ducts and included necrosis of epithelium, periductal edema and infiltration with inflammatory cells and later periductal fibrosis. The necrotizing cholangitis affected extra-hepatic ducts as well with similar changes. An obliterative cholangitis developed in some bile ducts whereas others showed hypertrophy and hyperplasia of epithelium. After some time of feeding which varied with the various diets, disseminated focal caseative necrosis of liver cells was the dominant pathologic change, always preceded by lesions in the biliary system. Renal lesions consisted of coagulative necrosis of the epithelium of convoluted tubules followed by calcification in some kidneys and in others by reactive changes in tubular epithelium consisting of cellular and nuclear hypertrophy and increased cytoplasmic basophilia. A variable incidence was noted in the number of mice with lesions. In each group some mice had normal appearing liver and kidneys. The spleen and heart were without lesions.

Introduction

The literature on mycotoxins and the induced mycotoxicoses has reached voluminous proportions and much of the recent literature has appeared since 1960, when the first reports of Turkey "X" disease were published. Studies in Great Britain, Belgium, and United States of America established the toxic origin of the disease, its association with Brazilian peanut meal and certain strains of *Aspergillus flavus*. Aflatoxins elaborated by the fungus were isolated and identified as the toxic metabolites and later were established as potent hepato-carcinogens. Prior to this outburst of research activity, diseases of man and animals of mycotoxin origin were recognized. These diseases included stachybotryotoxicosis (*13, 14*), moldy corn toxicosis of swine (*27*) and horses, facial eczema of ruminants, and alimentary toxic aleukia in man. The latter disease and stachybotryotoxicosis were studied intensively in Russia and no such volume of mycotoxin literature existed in the Western world prior to the studies on aflatoxicosis. The older literature and some of the more recent studies have been reviewed in detail by Forgacs and Carll (*12*) and in the book edited by Wogan (*33*). Other recent reviews include the papers by Abrams (*1*), Brook (*3*), Wogan (*34, 35*), and Schoental (*25*), as well as chapters by Miller (*19*) and Wilson (*31*).

Natural outbreaks of disease and experimental production of toxicosis by certain of the *Penicillia* have been reported (*4, 12*), but the number of published reports is not great. Species incriminated as agents of disease or as toxic to animals include *P. rubrum* (*4, 32*), *P. purpurogenum* (*15*), *P. islandicum* (*20, 26*), *P. oxalicum* (*26*), and *P. urticae* (*36*). In contrast to the report of Scott (*25*), recent studies in our laboratories have established that isolates of *P. viridicatum* were toxic to mice and corn cultures consistently produced gross and microscopic lesions in the liver (*8*). The present studies were concerned with the development of the pathologic changes in mice fed corn cultures of *P. viridicatum*.

Materials and Methods

Preparation of fungal cultures.—Flasks containing 560 g. of popcorn and 225 ml. of water were autoclaved for 75 minutes. The flasks were inoculated with spores of *P. viridicatum* from 6-day-old cultures grown on Czapek's medium. Two isolates, 5x3–#3 and 2HA–2, were studied. The inoculated flasks were incubated at 24° C. for 2 weeks, then were covered with chloroform and stored in a hood overnight. The cultures were transferred to a drying oven at 100° F. for 1 week. After drying, the cultures were ground.

Preparation of experimental diets.—The dried fungal cultures were combined with a purified diet of casein and sucrose supplemented with vitamins and minerals according to the report of Mills and Murry (*18*), with the addition of 10 p.p.m. copper supplied in the form of cupric sulfate. Three dilutions of the fungal cultures were fed with the cultures representing 50, 33, and 25 percent of the diet and are presented in the Tables as ratios of 1:1, 2:1, and 3:1. Control groups received the purified diet only.

Experimental animals.—Male Swiss albino mice were started on the experimental diets at weaning and fed feed and water *ad libitum*. Housing was in an air-conditioned animal room in plastic cages with sanitized Ab-Sorb-Dri as bedding. Mice were weighed at weekly intervals or at the time of necropsy. Mice were killed by decapitation and the livers dissected free and weighed prior to fixation. Tissues collected for histopathologic examination included the liver, kidney, heart, and spleen, and were fixed in 10 percent buffered formalin. Portions of fixed tissues, including samples from each lobe of the liver, were prepared for paraffin sections and stained with hematoxylin and eosin.

Trial 1.—Corn culture of *P. viridicatum*, isolate 5x3#3, was fed in the three dilutions. Five control mice and 10 mice from each of the test groups were killed at weekly intervals. Tissues available for examination for the various groups included 7 and 14 days from the 1:1 group; 7, 14, and 21 days from the 2:1 group; and for 5 weekly intervals from the 3:1 group.

Trial 2.—Isolate 2HA–2 was fed in the three dilutions as in trial 1. The killing schedule was as follows: Control group, 3, 5, 7, 10, 14, and 21 days; 1:1 diet group, 3, 5, and 7 days; 2:1 diet group, 5, 7, 10, and 14 days; and 3:1 diet group, 7, 10, 14, and 21 days.

Results

Weight gains and mortality (trial 1—isolate 5x3#3).—The fungal culture was toxic at all dilutions studied and the severity of the toxic effects followed roughly the concentration fed. Thus, the dilution of 1:1 was extremely toxic and average body weights were reduced by 2 g. after 1 week of feeding with a death loss of 40 percent (table 1). None of the mice of this group survived to the end of the 3rd week. A reduction in weight gains of the 2:1 diet group was

evident after a week and the differences were greater after 2 and 3 weeks. Only eight animals were available for necropsy at the end of 3 weeks feeding. Mortality incidence was 48 percent after 1 week and death loss amounted to 65 percent of the mice after 3 weeks on the diet.

The 3:1 diet was less toxic but average weight gains were reduced after 2 weeks, a difference of 10 g. from average weight of controls. Death losses varied from about 20 percent after 2 weeks to 50 percent at the fifth week.

Necropsy findings.—Gross lesions were generally restricted to the triad of generalized jaundice, liver necrosis, and greenish discoloration of the kidneys. The number of jaundiced mice was greatest in the groups fed the highest concentration of fungal culture and during the first week of the experimental period. Thereafter, the incidence of jaundiced carcasses decreased (table 2). Obvious lesions in the livers of test mice were observed at the end of 2 weeks of feeding and the incidence was similar among the various groups. Great variation existed in the extent of involvement of the livers; some appeared normal whereas others had numerous pinpoint yellowish to greenish foci on the capsular surface. These foci of necrosis were green after fixation. In none of the groups was the incidence of gross liver lesions greater than 50 percent and the incidence did not increase greatly with length of feeding. As many as half of the mice had green kidneys at necropsy. The incidence of pigmented kidneys was greatest in the 1:1 diet group and the number appeared to decrease with length of feeding in the 3:1 diet group, as none of the 10 mice killed after 5 weeks of feeding had green kidneys, although four had gross lesions in the liver (table 2). Other gross changes were not observed in the kidneys. The spleen, heart, lungs, and intestines appeared normal at necropsy.

Liver weights, as a percent of the body weight, were not greatly different among the various groups at the different weeks with the possible exception of the second- and third-week weights of 3:1 diet group (table 3). At these times the percentages were 7.5 and 7.8, the largest observed, indicating slight enlargement of the livers.

Histopathology.—After 1 week, seven livers from the 3:1 diet mice were without lesions with the possible exception of vacuolization of cytoplasm of hepatocytes. This latter change may not represent a specific toxic manifestation of the fungal culture as similar changes, although often not so severe, were observed in livers from control mice. The earliest change noted representing a reaction to the fungal toxin(s) was hypertrophy of the epithelium of intrahepatic bile ducts. Some of these ducts were surrounded by a few inflammatory cells. In another

Table 1.—Growth and mortality data of mice fed *P. viridicatum* culture (Isolate, 5x3-3)

Experimental group	Average weight (g.), week						Mortality, week				
	0	1	2	3	4	5	1	2	3	4	5
Control	11	20	26	31	35	36	0/25	0/20	0/15	0/10	0/5
P. viridicatum, 1:1	12	10	11	---	---	---	20/50	7/20	---	---	---
P. viridicatum, 2:1	11	14	15	19	---	---	1/50	19/39	19/29	---	---
P. viridicatum, 3:1	12	17	16	19	22	23	1/80	14/69	19/59	7/30	10/20

Table 2.—Gross lesions in mice fed *P. viridicatum* culture (Isolate, 5 x 3#3)

Experimental group	Gross lesions														
	Jaundice, week					Liver necrosis, week					Pigmented kidneys, week				
	1	2	3	4	5	1	2	3	4	5	1	2	3	4	5
Control	0/5	0/5	0/5	0/5	0/5	0/5	0/5	0/5	0/5	0/5	0/5	0/5	0/5	0/5	0/5
P. viridicatum, 1:1	10/10	5/9	---	---	---	0/10	4/9	---	---	---	4/10	5/9	---	---	---
P. viridicatum, 2:1	8/10	4/10	1/8	---	---	0/10	5/10	4/8	---	---	2/10	2/10	2/8	---	---
P. viridicatum, 3:1	6/10	4/10	4/10	2/10	0/10	0/10	4/10	5/10	4/10	4/10	0/10	3/10	5/10	2/10	0/10

Table 3.—Body and liver weights of mice fed *P. viridicatum* culture (Isolate, 5 x 3#3)

Experimental group	Average body weight (g.), week					Average liver weight (g.), week					Liver weight, percent body weight, week				
	1	2	3	4	5	1	2	3	4	5	1	2	3	4	5
Control	20.2	25.2	29.8	34.7	36.1	1.22	1.76	1.95	1.93	1.93	6.0	7.0	6.5	5.6	5.3
P. viridicatum, 1:1	10.6	11.4	---	---	---	.64	.77	---	---	---	6.1	6.8	---	---	---
P. viridicatum, 2:1	14.4	14.8	20.6	---	---	.90	.94	1.50	---	---	6.3	6.8	7.3	---	---
P. viridicatum, 3:1	18.0	16.2	18.8	22.3	23.1	1.06	1.23	1.47	1.53	1.37	5.9	7.5	7.8	6.8	5.9

liver the reactive changes in the ductal epithelium had advanced slightly, as hypertrophied cells had hyperchromatic nuclei along with increased amounts of basophilic cytoplasm. In this same liver a few bile ducts showed loss of epithelium accompanied by separation of periductular tissue by edema with infiltration of inflammatory cells, both mononuclear and neutrophilic leukocytes. In the third affected liver, the lesions described above were found along with two areas of necrosis of hepatocytes.

All but one of the livers from 2:1 diet mice had lesions, although the severity varied from lobe to lobe of the same liver as well as among the livers. Half of the livers had a few foci of necrosis and in some of the necrotic areas, "ghosts" of portal structures remained (fig. 1). Hemorrhage was noted in a few of the necrotic foci. Predominant pathologic changes in the livers from the mice of this group were associated with the bile ducts and the surrounding periductal tissues. Alterations varied in severity from reactive changes in epithelium to necrosis. Hypertrophy of

ductal epithelial cells was evidenced by increased nuclear size along with increased amounts of basophilic cytoplasm so the cells were elongated and protruded into the lumen (fig. 2). Hyperplasia of the epithelium resulted in piling up of nuclei (fig. 3). More advanced changes consisted of the formation of fibrous connective tissue consisting mainly of widely separated fibroblasts and little collagen deposition was observed (fig. 4). In some of the collars of connective tissue, inflammatory cells accumulated in variable degrees. In more severely affected bile ducts the epithelium was incomplete due to necrosis and the lumens reduced in size, constricted by proliferated fibroblasts (fig. 5). In a few of the livers some of the intrahepatic ducts contained a protein precipitate which stained eosinophilic but appeared structureless.

Some of the extrahepatic ducts were also affected; they were surrounded by increased amounts of fibrous connective tissue infiltrated with inflammatory cells, mainly neutrophils. The epithelium was either hyperplastic or necrotic and the lumens sometimes con-

All photographs of formalin-fixed material stained with hematoxylin and eosin. Figures 1 to 25 of mice fed 5 x 3 #3 culture, remaining figures of mice fed 2HA–2 isolate.

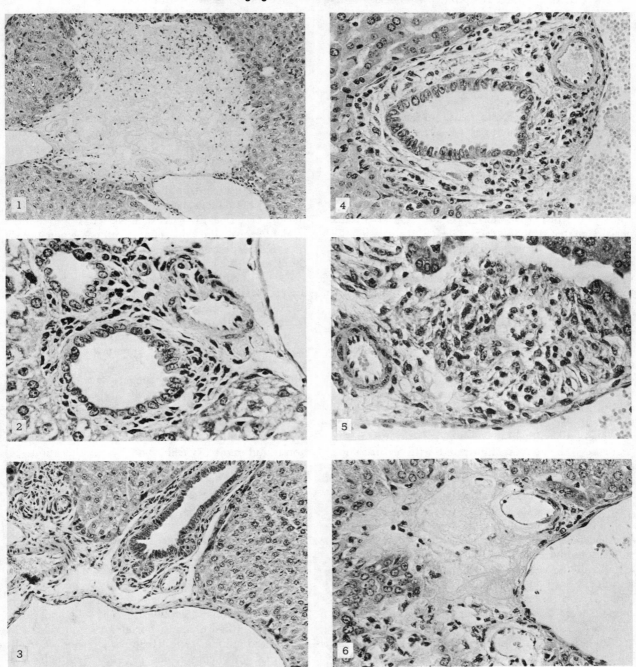

Figure 1.—1:1 diet for 1 week. Focal necrotic area in liver between two veins contain "ghosts" of bile duct and hepatic artery. X 120

Figure 2.—2:1 diet for 1 week. Hypertrophy of bile duct epithelium with apical cytoplasm protruding into duct lumen. X 375

Figure 3.—2:1 diet for 1 week. Hyperplasia and hypertrophy of bile duct epithelium is illustrated. X 150

Figure 4.—2:1 diet for 1 week. Cellular and nuclear hypertrophy is present in the bile duct epithelium accompanied by periductular fibroplasia and inflammatory cell infiltration. X 235

Figure 5.—2:1 diet for 1 week. Necrotizing cholangitis affects a portal bile duct with periductular fibroplasia and cellular accumulations within the lumen. X 300

Figure 6.—1:1 diet for 1 week. Focal necrosis of hepatocytes and portal structures includes portions of a radical of the hepatic artery. X 235

tained eosinophilic debris. Similar protein coagula occurred in the dilated lymphatics which accompanied the extrahepatic bile ducts.

Lesions were more severe and extensive in the livers of the 1:1 diet mice and nine of 10 animals were affected. Disseminated focal caseation necrosis was a feature of the reaction in these livers and the foci generally adjoined the portal region with inclusion of the hepatic artery (fig. 6). There was hemorrhage within some of the necrotic areas and many contained "ghosts" of portal structures (fig. 7).

Pathoanatomic alterations in the intrahepatic bile ducts were as described above and included epithelial cell hypertrophy and hyperplasia, periductular fibroplasia with inflammatory cell infiltration, and necrosis of ductal epithelium accompanied by deposition of eosinophilic protein material (fig. 8). Often the deposited material was structureless but occasionally numerous fine fibrils (suggestive of fibrin) could be discerned. In some livers the periductular fibrosis and infiltration with inflammatory cells were the most remarkable features of the liver pathology. Cholangitis involving the extrahepatic ducts was evident by necrosis of epithelium, periductular fibrous, and edema, and filling of dilated lymphatics with protein coagula (fig. 9). These alterations were also accompanied by accumulations of neutrophils beneath the destroyed epithelium (fig. 10). In a few livers, the gall bladder wall was thickened, there was loss of epithelium and the lumens contained protein debris with inflammatory cells. In one liver, the gall bladder wall was thickened, the epithelium was hyperplastic and lamina propria of the mucosa infiltrated with neutrophilic leukocytes (fig. 11).

After 2 weeks, lesions in the livers of mice fed the 3:1 diet had advanced and resembled the lesions in mice fed 1:1 diet for 1 week. Necrotic foci were observed in seven and in three of these the disseminated focal necrosis was the dominant pathologic feature. Alterations in the biliary system, both intra- and extrahepatic ducts, were the most prominent findings in six mice. Severe vacuolization of liver cell cytoplasm (fig. 12) was observed in only one liver, but milder changes were present in other livers. Pathoanatomic changes of the biliary passages were as described above and included hypertrophy and hyperplasia of epithelium, periductal fibrosis with inflammatory cell infiltration of the connective tissue and portal spaces, and necrosis of epithelium followed in some ducts by obliteration of lumen by encircling connective tissue. In a few livers, the focal necrotic areas had a core of cellular debris, composed mainly of neutrophils and in one liver numerous abscesses occurred in the hepatic parenchyma (fig. 13). In this same liver a large irregular area of necrosis reached the capsular surface, suggesting infarction as the cause. At the base of the

necrotic region, abscesses were observed.

Hepatic lesions were quite variable in mice fed the 2:1 diet for 2 weeks ranging from mild reactive changes in duct epithelium to disseminated focal necrosis. All of the livers had lesions in the biliary system and in some periductal granulation tissue was a dominant lesion, whereas in other livers the obliterative cholangitis was the most striking change (fig. 14). Changes in extrahepatic ducts were severe in some with the necrotizing cholangitis accompanied by granulation tissue and thrombosed lymphatics (fig. 15). Venous thrombosis was observed adjacent to foci of hepatic necrosis (fig. 16). A suppurative choleocystitis was accompanied by ulceration of the mucosa and an intense neutrophilic response.

Disseminated focal caseative necrosis was most often the major lesion in livers of mice fed 1:1 diet for 2 weeks. Necrotizing and reparative changes in biliary passages as described above were found in most of the livers.

Five of the eight surviving mice fed the 2:1 diet for 3 weeks had severe lesions in the livers with disseminated foci of caseative necrosis prominent in most. Extensive infiltration with inflammatory cells, mainly neutrophils, occurred in the portal areas, around the bile ducts and surrounding many of the foci of necrosis. Additional lesions, not observed previously, included reactive changes in hepatocytes, consisting of cellular and nuclear hypertrophy and collapsed parenchyma with cells filled with bile pigment. The increased portal cellularity in other livers included proliferated bile ductule cells and fibroblasts in addition to inflammatory cells. The several alterations described above were found in the biliary system of these mice. In the other three livers, vacuolization of hepatocytes was observed in one and in the other two, mild reactive changes were present in the ductal epithelium.

Five of ten mice of the 3:1 diet group had severe hepatic lesions consisting of disseminated foci of caseative necrosis (fig. 17) with marked cellular infiltration around ducts in portal areas and at periphery of necrotic foci. Portions of increased cellularity in livers was due to proliferated bile ductule cells and fibroblasts (fig. 18). In many portal areas ductule cells were the dominant type. Reactive changes were observed in both hepatic cells and in the epithelium of ducts. Fibrosis occurred around some bile ducts with obliteration of lumens. In the other livers, vacuoles in hepatic cytoplasm were the only changes observed.

No increase in the incidence of severely affected livers occurred during the next 2 weeks of feeding in the 3:1 group. Severe pathologic changes as described above were present in four of 10 livers of mice fed the 3:1 diet for 4 weeks. In the other livers, vacuolization of hepatocytes was the only lesion and it was consid-

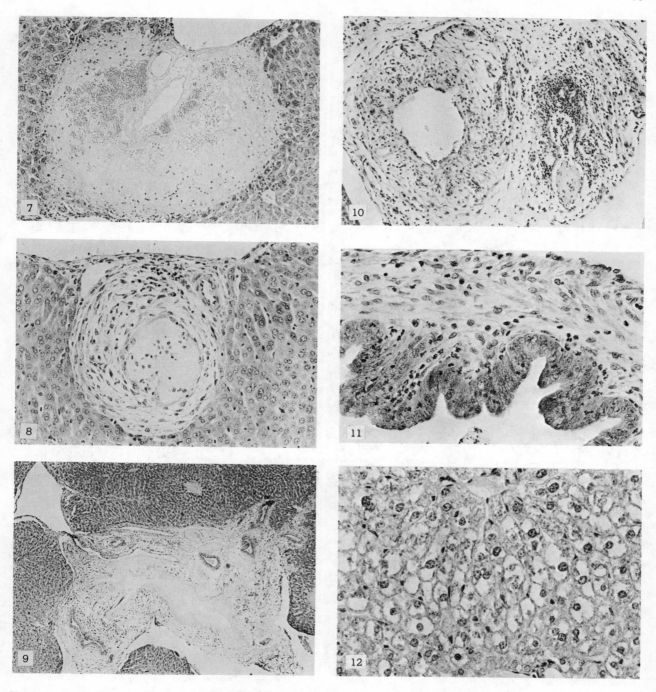

Figure 7.—1:1 diet for 1 week. Area of hepatic necrosis contains erythrocytes and remains of bile duct and hepatic artery. No reaction in parenchyma around necrotic area. X 95

Figure 8.—1:1 diet for 1 week. Periductular fibroplasia containing a few inflammatory cells. The duct epithelium is both attenuated and necrosed and the lumen is plugged with eosinophilic hyaline material containing nuclear debris. X 60

Figure 9.—1:1 diet for 1 week. Necrotizing cholangitis of extrahepatic duct accompanied by fibroplasia and plugging

of lymphatics. Epithelium is destroyed and lumen partially filled with eosinophilic material. X 40

Figure 10.—1:1 diet for 1 week. Necrotizing cholangitis of extrahepatic ducts accompanied by fibroplasia and suppuration. X 95

Figure 11.—1:1 diet for 1 week. Infiltration of the lamina propria of the gall bladder mucosa is illustrated. The epithelium is hyperplastic accompanied by nuclear and cellular hypertrophy. X 235

Figure 12.—3:1 diet for 2 weeks. Severe cytoplasmic vacuolization of hepatocytes. X 235

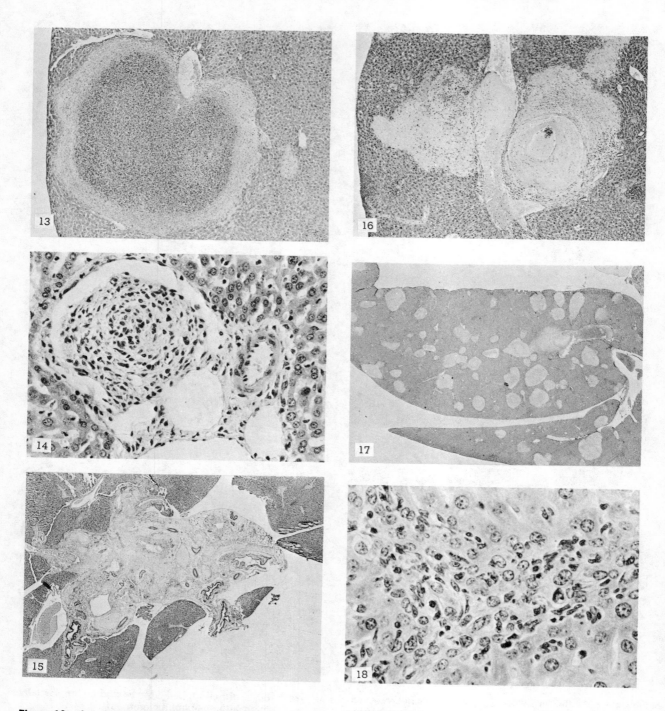

Figure 13.—3:1 diet for 2 weeks. An abscess occupies most of field. It contained a core of cellular debris and neutrophils and was circled by granulation tissue. X 40

Figure 14.—2:1 diet for 2 weeks. Obliterative cholangitis was accompanied by dilatation of periportal lymphatics. X 235

Figure 15.—2:1 diet for 2 weeks. Necrotizing cholangitis of extrahepatic bile duct was accompanied by fibroplasia and thrombosis of lymphatics. X 14

Figure 16.—2:1 diet for 2 weeks. Hepatic necrosis adjacent to radial of hepatic vein containing a fibrin plug adhered to necrosed wall. X 40

Figure 17.—3:1 diet for 3 weeks. Disseminated focal caseative necrosis of hepatocytes is illustrated. X 10

Figure 18.—3:1 diet for 3 weeks. Increased cellularity in periportal zones was due to proliferation of fibroblasts, bile ductule cells and infiltration by leukocytes. X 375

ered to be severe in two livers. After 5 weeks, three of 10 mice had the severe hepatic lesions described above with focal bile duct proliferation a feature in some (figs. 19 and 20). The other livers were considered normal.

Of the 10 mice fed the 3:1 diet for 1 week and killed, two were found to have lesions in the kidney. In one kidney reactive changes were found in the epithelial cells of the convoluted tubules; in the other, vacuole formation occurred within the cytoplasm of tubular epithelium.

All 10 mice of the 2:1 diet group had, after 1 week, lesions in the kidneys. The alterations varied both as to kinds and degree of severity. In half of the kidneys, major changes were restricted to the epithelial cells of the convoluted tubules. Epithelial cells were hypertrophied with enlarged hyperchromatic nuclei containing prominent chromatin clumps and increased basophilia of cytoplasm was observed (fig. 21). Some of the nuclei were quite large and mitotic figures were observed (fig. 22). Hyperplasia of the tubular epithelial cells was common and the proliferated nuclei nearly obliterated the lumens. In some of the tubules the lumens contained bright red amorphous deposits. Such reactive changes were not prominent in two mice in which the main alterations were vacuolization of renal epithelial cells due to accumulation of water or lipids. Three mice had more severe renal lesions consisting of reactive changes in epithelium of certain tubules, necrosis of epithelial cells in others of the convoluted tubules, and cast formation within collecting tubules.

All of the mice fed the 1:1 diet had renal lesions, generally confined to the cortex and of the two general types described above, but more severe. Necrosis of the epithelium of the convoluted tubules (fig. 23) was not accompanied by any inflammatory cells but reactive changes of the epithelial cells of certain tubules did occur. Hyperplasia of epithelium occurred as the only reaction as well.

The severity of the renal lesions did not progress in the mice fed the 3:1 diet for 2 weeks. The kidneys from five mice were considered normal and the only change noted in the other five animals were brownish bile casts within the lumen cortical tubules. The renal changes in the 2:1 fed group also were minimal; six kidneys were considered normal, two had reactive changes of the tubular epithelial cells accompanied by scattered foci of calcification of necrotic renal tubules. Alterations in two other kidneys consisted of dilated tubules, some with casts, and mild reactive changes in tubular epithelium.

Microscopic findings were generally more severe in the kidney of the 1:1 diet group although two were considered normal. The lesions were variable and included those described above: reactive changes of epithelial cells, necrosis of epithelium of convoluted tubules, and apparent dilation of tubules with low, usually squamous, epithelium (fig. 24). A few foci of calcified tubules were observed in three mice. Calcification was extensive in two mice and accompanied the necrosis of tubules (fig. 25).

Renal lesions had not progressed in mice fed the 2:1 diet for 3 weeks. Four of the 10 were considered normal and two had only a few foci of calcification. Two others contained a few foci of reactive tubular epithelium accompanied by scattered necrotic tubules, some calcified, and a few bile casts.

During the third to the fifth week, the alterations observed in the kidneys of mice fed the 3:1 diet decreased in severity and the number affected also decreased. Thus, after 3 weeks, six mice had renal lesions but only one was severely involved. The others had mild to moderate reactive changes in cortical tubular epithelium accompanied by a few bile casts. Eight of ten mice fed the 3:1 diet for 4 weeks were found to have normal appearing kidneys and in the two with lesions only the tubular epithelium was affected. After 5 weeks of feeding, nine of 10 kidneys were considered normal.

Weight gains and mortality (trial 2—isolate 2HA–2).—Average body weights were reduced in all test groups, especially in the 1:1 diet group which was about half the weight of controls (table 4). None of this group survived beyond 7 days of feeding and 50 of 80 mice died. Mortality was less in the 2:1 diet group; one mouse died during the first week and 21 between the first and second week of feeding. Although no deaths occurred during the first week in the group fed 3:1 diet, 21 died between 7 and 14 days of feeding.

Table 4.—Body and liver weights of mice fed *P. viridicatum* culture (2HA–2)

Experimental group	Average body weight, days						Average liver weight, days					Liver weight, percent body weight, days				
	0	3	5	7	10	14	3	5	7	10	14	3	5	7	10	14
Control	11.1	13.7	16.1	18.6	23.4	26.8	0.73	0.99	1.14	1.72	1.87	5.3	6.1	6.1	7.3	6.9
1:1 diet	10.9	11.7	9.4	9.7				.54	.45	.49			4.6	4.8	5.0	
2:1 diet	12.1	NT	13.4	12.7	12.6	12.5	NT	.67	.64	.89	.91	NT	5.0	5.1	7.1	7.2
3:1 diet	11.2	NT	NT	14.1	13.2	13.4	NT	NT	.85	.87	.87	NT	NT	6.0	6.6	6.4

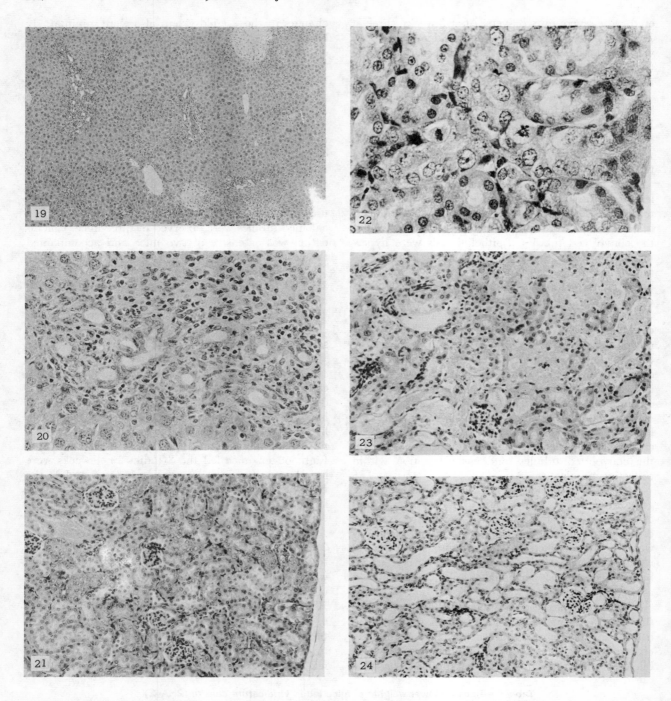

Figure 19.—3:1 diet for 5 weeks. Increased cellularity in portal areas, focal necrosis and focal bile duct hyperplasia are illustrated.   X 45

Figure 20.—3:1 diet for 5 weeks. Numerous bile ducts are located within granulation tissue infiltrated with leukocytes. X 235

Figure 21.—2:1 diet for 1 week. Reactive changes in tubular epithelium included cytoplasmic and nuclear hypertrophy, hyperplasia, and increased cytoplasmic basophillia. X 120

Figure 22.—2:1 diet for 1 week. Mitotic figures and nuclear hypertrophy in reactive tubular epithelium are illustrated. X 375

Figure 23.—1:1 diet for 1 week. Necrosis of convoluted tubules was not accompanied by inflammatory response. X 150

Figure 24.—1:1 diet for 2 weeks. Dilated tubules are lined by attenuated cells resembling squamous epithelium. X 120

Necropsy findings.—Jaundiced carcasses were observed in 12 of 20 test mice killed after 10 days of feeding and 15 of 18 killed after 14 days. The incidence of grossly affected livers was never more than half in the mice killed, until 14 days when 10 of 18 had obvious hepatic lesions (table 5). The gross changes were as described above including greenish discoloration and the presence of few to many pinpoint green to yellow foci on the capsular surface. Prominent lobular markings were observed in livers of some mice and small red foci of apparent hemorrhage in others. The incidence of pigmented kidneys was greatest after 2 weeks of feeding as half of the test mice were affected.

Liver weight, as a percentage of body weight, appeared to be decreased during the early phases of the intoxication, but later the differences among groups were not great.

Histopathology.—Livers from mice fed the 1:1 diet for 3 days were considered normal. However, after 5 days, four of 10 mice had lesions, generally mild, affecting the bile ducts. Pathoanatomic changes included periductular edema with serous exudation into the portal spaces accompanied by necrosis of the biliary epithelium. Cholangitis in other sections was observed with the duct lumen obscured by inflammatory cells, mainly neutrophils. Inflammatory cells also were present in the periportal tissues. Some necrotic bile ducts contained an eosinophilic material, somewhat fibrillar, resembling fibrin. Only two livers from mice fed the 2:1 diet for 5 days were considered abnormal. Necrosis of ductal epithelium was evident as some of the cells were missing and others had pycnotic nuclei. Lumens of some ducts contained plugs with a matrix of fine fibrils. Such material occurred in some dilated lymphatic capillaries. Reactive changes in ductal epithelium consisted of cellular and nuclear hypertrophy with increased basophilia of cytoplasm.

Lesions in the extrahepatic ducts were observed in the 1:1 diet group after 7 days. Necrosis of epithelium was accompanied by cellular infiltration of wall and supporting tissues. Cholangitis with inflammatory cells in wall and lumen was present along with periductular hemorrhage. Six of ten mice were affected

with dominant changes of the biliary system, but marked disseminated foci of necrosis was not seen. Centrolobular necrosis was observed in a single mouse.

Lesions were generally more severe in the livers of 2:1 diet mice after 7 days and were generally restricted to the biliary system and necrotic foci within the hepatic parenchyma was found in one mouse.

Additional features of the liver histopathology in mice fed the 3:1 diet for 7 days included reactive changes in ductal epithelium of hypertrophy and hyperplasia accompanied in some ducts by periductular fibroplasia, often infiltrated with inflammatory cells.

After 2 weeks, more advanced lesions were observed in six of eight mice fed the 2:1 diet. In the livers, the dominant pathologic picture was the disseminated foci of caseative necrosis. All the several changes previously described were observed in the biliary passages. Two mice did not have liver lesions in the sections examined.

Nine mice fed the 3:1 diet for 2 weeks had liver lesions. Although disseminated focal necrosis was a prominent feature in five of these, more acute lesions were present in the biliary system than observed in the 2:1 diet group and was the main feature of the pathologic picture in four mice (fig. 26). Necrotizing choleocystitis occurred and extensive hyperplasia was found in other larger extrahepatic ducts along with fibrosis and cellular infiltration (fig. 27). Obliterative cholangitis (fig. 28) was often observed as was observed in mice fed isolate 5x3–#3.

No lesions were observed in the kidneys of mice fed the 1:1 diet for 3 days. After 5 days half of the mice had renal changes consisting of vacuolization and necrosis of the epithelium of convoluted tubules. Necrosis was evidenced by increased eosinophilia of the cytoplasm and nuclear pycnosis. Of the 10 mice on the 2:1 diet for 5 days, three had similar degenerative and necrotic changes in tubular epithelium.

The number of affected mice increased after 7 days of feedings. Eight of ten mice on the 1:1 diet had renal lesions consisting of tubular degeneration and necrosis with some casts and mild reactive changes were observed in the epithelium of three. Necrosis of tubular epithelium was present in five of 10 mice fed the 2:1 diet for 7 days but reactive changes of the

Table 5.—Gross lesions in mice fed *P. viridicatum* culture (Isolate, 2HA-2)

Experimental group	Jaundice, days					Liver necrosis, days					Pigmented kidneys, days				
	3	5	7	10	14	3	5	7	10	14	3	5	7	10	14
Control	0/5	0/5	0/5	0/5	0/5	0/5	0/5	0/5	0/5	0/5	0/5	0/5	0/5	0/5	0/5
P. viridicatum, 1:1	0/10	0/10	0/10			0/10	0/10	0/10			0/10	0/10	0/10		
P. viridicatum, 2:1	NT	0/10	0/10	8/10	8/8	NT	0/10	3/10	5/10	5/8	NT	0/10	0/10	0/10	5/8
P. viridicatum, 3:1	NT	NT	2/10	4/10	7/10	NT	NT	0/10	4/10	5/10	NT	NT	1/10	2/10	4/10

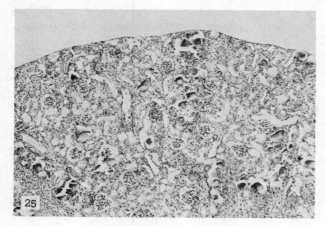

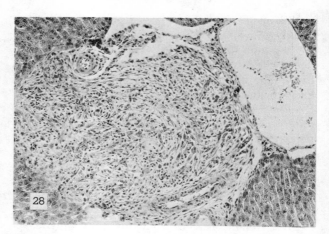

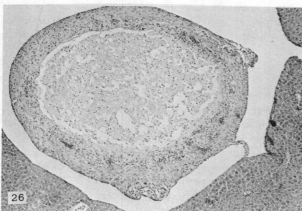

Figure 28.—3:1 diet for 2 weeks. Obliterative cholangitis was a feature of intoxication by both isolates. X 195

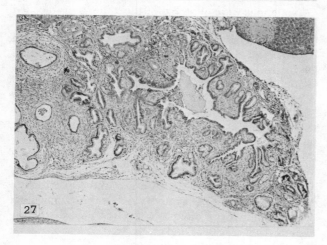

Figure 25.—1:1 diet for 2 weeks. Necrosis of tubular epithelium is accompanied by calcification. X 60

Figure 26.—3:1 diet for 2 weeks. Necrotizing choleocystitis is illustrated. X 45

Figure 27.—3:1 diet for 2 weeks. Extensive hyperplasia of extrahepatic duct epithelium with fibroplasia and cellular infiltration. X 40

epithelial cells occurred in only one. Most of the mice fed the 3:1 diet for 7 days had normal appearing kidneys microscopically and only two were found with reactive tubular epithelium.

No mice fed the 1:1 diet were available for examination after 10 days of feeding. However, eight of 10 fed the 2:1 diet had renal lesions described above with five of eight showing tubular necrosis. The major pathologic finding in the 3:1 diet group was reactive changes in the tubular epithelium as six of 10 were affected and only three showed necrosis of tubules. A few casts, both hyaline and bile, were observed in the affected kidneys.

No further progression of the renal lesions occurred in the two groups examined after 2 weeks of feeding. Of the eight fed the 2:1 diet, kidney changes were minor consisting of a few dilated tubules and bile casts in three and mild reactive changes in two others. Necrosis of tubular epithelium occurred in two of 10 mice fed the 3:1 diet for 2 weeks; three kidneys were considered normal and reactive changes were observed in four.

Discussion

The development of the morphologic lesions in the livers of mice fed corn cultures of *P. viridicatum* followed a fairly definite pattern, although great variations in the severity of the disease among mice of a particular diet group and period of feeding were observed. Thus, some mice would have rather severe hepatic alterations and the livers of cage mates would appear microscopically normal. No explanation for these observations outside of biologic variation can be given at this time. Such great variation in host response to fungal toxins is not unknown. Done, et al. (*10*) has emphasized the wide range in severity of disease within a flock of sheep affected with facial eczema and has described changes in serum chemistry after oral administration of sporidesmin (*11*).

The dominant features of the early lesions in mice were those involving the bile ducts and were the same for the two isolates. Basically, a cholangitis developed with necrosis of epithelium and periportal inflammatory cell infiltration, followed in some other portal areas by fibroplasia and reactive changes of hypertrophy and hyperplasia of duct epithelium. Recovery did not occur in other affected ducts and the expanding necrosis involved other portal structures including the hepatic artery. Often "ghosts" of these structures occurred within foci of necrosis. Not only were intrahepatic ducts affected, but similar necrotic, inflammatory and fibrous alterations were observed in extrahepatic ducts and in the gall bladder. Within both types of bile passages the reparative response resulted in obliteration of the ducts due to the proliferation of fibrous connective tissue. Later, after 1 to 3 weeks, the pathologic picture was dominated by numerous foci of caseative necrosis. When such lesions were observed, it was difficult to find portal structures suggesting they had been destroyed and were obscured by the necrosis. At this time, also, proliferation of bile ducts and bile ductule cells occurred, but this response was late in contrast to the destructive changes in the bile ducts. Other mycotoxins, especially aflatoxin, induce an early marked proliferation of bile ductule cells in several species of animals (*2, 5, 6, 7*). In the duckling, bile ductule cell hyperplasia was used as a bioassay procedure for the identification and estimation of toxic fractions (*23, 24*).

The mycotoxicosis induced in mice by cultures of *P. viridicatum* most resembles the pathologic changes reported in sporidesmin intoxication in sheep (*21, 22*). In the experimental disease in sheep, a marked pericholangitic inflammatory exudation was accompanied by a necrotizing cholecystitis and cholangitis. The formation of granulation tissue with partial stenosis or obliteration of bile ducts followed the acute lesions. These were essentially the major hepatic lesions in the test mice of this study. Whereas, Mortimer (*21*) found vascular occlusive lesions in sheep poisoned with sporidesmin, marked involvement of vessels was not a feature of *P. viridicatum* toxicosis in mice. Slater et al. (*28*) found that the rate responds differently than sheep and certain laboratory rodents to sporidesmin intoxication. He found that the pathologic changes were in the nature of a general inflammatory response, marked by ascites and/or pleural effusions, increased capillary permeability and diarrhea, but the severe hepatic alterations characteristic of the disease in sheep did not occur.

Renal lesions occurred in all groups early in the experimental period and consisted of necrosis of con-voluted tubules followed in some kidneys by calcification and reactive changes in tubular epithelial cells. In affected tubules, cellular and nuclear hypertrophy was accompanied by increased cytoplasmic basophilia, hyperplasia and mitoses. In many kidneys these hyperplastic tubules were the only lesions found, and appeared to develop in the absence of prior tubular necrosis. Thus, these alterations need not be interpreted as regeneration reactions but rather a direct response to the toxin(s) produced by the growth of the fungus in the corn cultures. The necrosis of convoluted tubules may not represent a specific lesion of the mycotoxicosis. The fungal cultures were treated with chloroform and, although the drying period should have removed all traces, some small amount may have persisted. Male mice are extremely sensitive to chloroform and poisoning by this chemical results in extensive necrosis of convoluted tubules (*17*). However, renal lesions have been described in aflatoxicosis in turkeys (*29*) and in ducklings (*22*).

The specific component in the corn cultures responsible for the intoxication has not been established. Aflatoxins as causative agents have been eliminated by at least two observations. The cultures were uniformly negative for aflatoxins by thin-layer chromatography assay and the mouse is relatively insensitive to aflatoxins, whereas, it is extremely susceptible to the toxins of *P. viridicatum*. This species has been little investigated, but certain strains are known to produce a chemical named viridicatin (*9*), which had little antibiotic usefulness. No toxicologic studies of this antibiotic has been published. Certain *Penicillia* are producers of gliotoxin, one of several epidithiadioxopiperazines metabolites of fungi which include chetomin and sporidesmin. Gliotoxin at a dosage of 50 mg./kg. killed injected mice within 24 hours. Half this dose killed 50 percent of the mice and hematuria was a common finding (*16*). Taylor (*29*) has reviewed the epidithiadioxopiperazines but did not indicate that the pathologic features of gliotoxin poisoning have been reported. Extraction studies are presently underway to attempt the isolation and chemical characterization of the mycotoxin(s) produced by *P. viridicatum*.

Acknowledgment

Supported in part by Cooperative Agreement No. 12–14–100–8393, Market Quality Research Division, Agricultural Research Service, USDA.

References

(*1*) ABRAMS, L. 1965. Mycotoxicoses. J. S. Afr. Vet. Med. Assoc. *36:* 5–13.
(*2*) ASPLIN, F. D., and R. B. A. CARNAGHAN. 1961. The toxicity of certain groundnut meals for poultry with

special reference to their effect on ducklings and chickens. Vet. Rec. *73:* 1215–1219.

(3) BROOK, P. J. 1966. Fungus toxins affecting mammals. Ann. Rev. Phytopath. *4:* 171–194.

(4) BURNSIDE, J. E., W. L. SIPPEL, J. FORGACS, W. T. CARLL, M. B. ATWOOD, and E. R. DOLL. 1957. A disease of swine and cattle caused by eating moldy corn. II. Experimental production with pure cultures of molds. Am. J. Vet. Res. *18:* 817–824.

(5) BUTLER, W. H. 1964. Acute liver injury in ducklings as a result of aflatoxin poisoning. J. Path. Bact. *88:* 189–196.

(6) BUTLER, W. H., and J. M. BARNES. 1964. Toxic effects of groundnut meal containing aflatoxin to rats and guinea pigs. Brit. J. Cancer *17:* 699–710.

(7) BUTLER, W. H. 1966. Acute toxicity of aflatoxins B_1 in guinea pigs. J. Path. Bact. *91:* 277–280.

(8) CARLTON, W. W., J. TUITE, and P. MISLIVEC. 1968. Investigations of the toxic effects in mice of certain species of *Penicillium*. Toxicol. App. Pharmacol. In press.

(9) CUNNINGHAM, K., and G. ERREMAN. 1953. The isolation and some chemical properties of viridicatin, a metabolic product of *Penicillium viridicatum*. West I. Biochem. J. *53:* 328–332.

(10) DONE, J., P. H. MORTIMER, and A. TAYLOR. 1960. Some observations on field cases of facial eczema: liver pathology and determinations of serum bilirubin, cholesterol, transaminase, and alkaline phosphatase. Res. Vet. Sci. *1:* 76–83.

(11) DONE, J., P. H. MORTIMER, and A. TAYLOR. 1962. The experimental intoxication of sheep with sporidesmin, a metabolic product of *Pithomyces chartarum*. II. Changes in some serum constituents after oral administration of sporidesmin. Res. Vet. Sci. *3:* 161–171.

(12) FORGACS, J., and W. T. CARLL. 1962. Mycotoxicoses. Adv. Vet. Sci. *7:* 273–382.

(13) FORGACS, J. 1965. Stachybatryotoxicosis and moldy corn toxicosis. In "Mycotoxins in Foodstuffs". B. N. Wogan, ed., M.I.T. press, Cambridge, Mass., pp. 87–104.

(14) FORGACS, J., W. T. CARLL, A. S. HERRING, and W. R. HINSHAW. 1958. Toxicity of *Stachybotrys atra* for animals. Trans. N.Y. Acad. Sci. *20:* 187–208.

(15) FORGACS, J,, H. KOCK, W. T. CARLL, and R. H. WHITE-STEVENS. 1958. Additional studies on the relationship of mycotoxicosis to the poultry hemorrhagic syndrome. Am. J. Vet. Res. *19:* 744–753.

(16) JOHNSON, J. R., W. F. BRUCE, and J. D. DUTHCER. 1943. Gliotoxin, The antibiotic principle of *Gliocladium fimbricatum* I. Production, physical and biological properties. J. Amer. Chem. Soc. *65:* 2005–2009.

(17) HEWITT, H. B. 1956. Renal necrosis in mice after accidental exposure to chloroform. Brit. J. Exp. Path. *37:* 32–39.

(18) MILLS, C. F., and GRACE MURRAY. 1960. The preparation of a semisynthetic diet low in copper for copper-deficiency studies with the rat. J. Sci. Food Agric. *11:* 547–552.

(19) MILLER, J. A. 1966. Tumorigenic and carcinogenic natural products. *In* "Toxicants Occurring Naturally in Foods". Pub. 1354. Nat. Acad. Sci., Nat. Res. Council, Washington, D.C.

(20) MIYAKI, M., M. SAITO, M. ENOMOTO, T. SHIKATA, T. ISHIKO, K. URAGUCHI, T. TATSUNO, M. TSUKIOKA, and Y. SAKAI. 1960. Toxic liver injuries and liver cirrhosis induced in mice and rats through long-term feeding with *Penicillium islandicum* Sopp-growing rice. Acta. Path. Japan *10:* 75–123.

(21) MORTIMER, P. H. 1963. The experimental intoxication of sheep with sporidesmin, a metabolic product of *Pithomyces chartarum*. IV. Histological and histochemical examination of orally-dosed sheep. Res. Vet. Sci. *4:* 166–185.

(22) MORTIMER, P. H., and A. TAYLOR. 1962. The experimental intoxication of sheep with sporidesmin, a metabolic product of *Pithomyces chartarum*. I. Clinical observations and findings at post mortem examination. Res. Vet. Sci. *3:* 147–160.

(23) NEWBERNE, P. M., W. W. CARLTON, and G. N. WOGAN. 1964. Hepatomas in rats and hepatorenal injury in ducklings fed peanut meal or *Aspergillus flavus* extract. Path. Vet. *1:* 105–132.

(24) NEWBERNE, P. M., G. N. WOGAN, W. W. CARLTON, and M. M. ABDEL KADER. 1964. Histopathologic lesions in ducklings caused by *Aspergillus flavus* cultures, culture extracts, and crystalline aflatoxins. Toxicol. Appl. Pharmacol. *6:* 542–556.

(25) SCHOENTAL, REGINA. 1967. Aflatoxins. Ann. Rev. Pharmacol. *7:* 343–346.

(26) SCOTT, D. B. 1965. Toxigenic fungi isolated from cereal and legume products. Mycopath. et Myco App. *25:* 213–222.

(27) SIPPEL, W. L., J. E. BURNSIDE, and M. B. ATWOOD. 1953. A disease of swine and cattle caused by eating moldy corn. Proc. 90th Ann. Meeting Am. Vet. Med. Assoc., Toronto, Canada, pp. 174–181.

(28) SLATER, T. F., U. D. STRAULI, and BARBARA SAWYER. 1964. Sporidesmin poisoning in the rat. I. Chemical changes. Res. Vet. Sci. *5:* 450–472.

(29) TAYLOR, A. 1967. The chemistry and biochemistry of sporidesmins and other 2,5-epidithia-3,6-dioxopiperazines. *In* "Biochemistry of some Foodborne Microbial Toxins," R. I. Mateles and G. N. Wogan eds., M.I.T Press, Cambridge, Mass.

(30) WANNOP, C. C. 1961. The histopathology of turkey "X" disease in Great Britain. Avian Diseases *5:* 371–381.

(31) WILSON, B. J. 1966. Fungal Toxins. *In* "Toxicants Occurring Naturally in Foods". Pub. 1354. Nat. Acad. Sci., Nat. Res. Council, Washington, D.C.

(32) WILSON, B. J., and C. H. WILSON. 1962. Extraction and preliminary characterization of a hepatotoxic substance from cultures of *Penicillium rubrum*. J. Bact. *84:* 283–290.

(33) WOGAN, G. N., editor. 1965. Mycotoxins in Foodstuffs. M.I.T. press, Cambridge, Mass.

(34) WOGAN, G. N. 1966. Chemical nature and biological effects of the aflatoxins. Bact. Reviews *30:* 460–470.

(35) WOGAN, G. N. 1966. Physiologically significant food contaminants. Fed. Proc. *25:* 124–129.

(36) YAMAMOTO, T. 1954. Studies on the poison-producing mold isolated from dry malt. J. Pharm. Soc. Japan *74:* 797–801.

THE BIOCHEMICAL EFFECTS OF AFLATOXINS AND OTHER TOXIC COMPOUNDS RELATED TO PARASITIC FUNGI ON THE METABOLISM OF PLANT TISSUES

by Ikuzo Uritani, Tadashi Asahi,
Reiko Majima, *and* Zyunko Mori*
*Institute for Biochemical Regulation and Laboratory of Biochemistry,
Faculty of Agriculture, Nagoya University, Nagoya, Japan*

Summary

Mycotoxin may be divided into two categories, in a broad sense. One category includes the toxic compounds produced by fungi when they grow on or infect agricultural commodities. The other category consists of toxic compounds produced by agricultural commodities when they are attacked by fungi.

Aflatoxins are the typical group belonging to the first category. In the present study, aflatoxin B_1 caused an increase in the enzymatic activities of supernatant and mitochondrial fractions and also in the number of mitochondria of sweet potato root slices during aging. Aflatoxin B_1 inhibited DNA replication but not the protein synthesis of higher plant tissues.

As one example of the other kind of mycotoxin, which are produced by living agricultural commodities when contaminated by fungi. When the sweet potato is attacked by the fungus pathogen, *Ceratocystis fimbriata*, or any other injurious agent, the root tissue produces more than 10 kinds of bitter substances; the main component of which is ipomeamarone, a sesquiterpene containing a furan ring. The compound inhibits the respiration of sweet potato root tissue as well as *C. fimbriata* and rat liver.

Effects of Aflatoxin on Plant Tissues

Introduction

Aflatoxins are well known to be the toxic metabolites of certain strains of *Aspergillus flavus* which grow on groundnuts or other agricultural commodities.

Many laboratories have reported interesting findings concerning the mode of action of aflatoxins on animal tissues and micro-organisms, showing that toxins depress cell division. As listed in table 1, the depression was shown to be probably due to the inhibition of DNA replication (8, 21) and protein synthesis

(9, 10). It has been shown that the toxins combine with DNA or with histone (7, 29) and inhibit the activities of DNA polymerase and DNA-dependent RNA polymerase (9, 11).

Table 1.—Effects of aflatoxins on animal tissues and micro-organisms

O Depression of cell division.
O Inhibition of DNA replication.
O Inhibition of protein synthesis.
O Formation of complex with DNA or histone.
O Inhibition of DNA polymerase and DNA dependent RNA polymerase activities.

However, few reports are available concerning the effects of aflatoxins on plant tissues (27). There is the evidence for the inhibition of mitosis and protein synthesis in plant tissues by the toxins (6, 22). Interestingly, the toxins seem to have also a gibberelin-like action on plant tissues (17). We have investigated the effects of the toxins on plant tissues in order to elucidate what kinds of events occur in plant tissues infected by *A. flavus*.

Before describing the effects of aflatoxins on plant tissues, some typical events in the biological system we have used will be reviewed. Our laboratory has reported (see table 2) that many kinds of reactions were activated in sweet potato root tissue, when the thinly sliced tissue was incubated at 28° to 30° C. in moist air (30, 34). The respiratory activity of the slices increased during aging (4). Polyphenols such as chlorogenic acid and isochlorogenic acid were syn-

Table 2.—Metabolic changes in sweet potato root tissue in response to injury

O Increase in respiratory activity.
O Synthesis of polyphenols.
O Increase in enzymatic activity:
   Peroxidase, Polyphenol oxidase, Glc-6-P dehyrogenase, 6-P·gluconate dehydrogenase, 5-Dehydroquinate dehyrogenase, Shikimate dehydrogenase, Phenylalanine ammonia-lyase.

---

*Read by K. Aibara.

thesized during incubation (30). Moreover, activities of various enzymes increased during aging. They involved peroxidase (19), polyphenol oxidase (15), glucose 6-phosphate dehydrogenase, 6-phosphogluconate dehydrogenase (25), and some enzymes participating in the polyphenol biosynthesis such as 5-dehydroquinate hydro-lyase, shikimate dehydrogenase and phenylalanine ammonia-lyase (23, 34). The increase in the enzymatic activities has been shown to be inhibited by puromycin and other protein synthesis inhibitors (18, 34). Actinomycin D also inhibited the increase. Thus, the increase in the enzymatic activities in response to injury was due to de novo synthesis of enzyme proteins from amino acids, which process required the synthesis of messenger RNA.

Futhermore, the activity and number of mitochondrial particles in the root tissue also increased during aging of the slice (4). Table 3 indicates the time-course analysis after slicing. The number of Janus green B-stained particles in the fraction increased during incubation, as well as acid-insoluble nitrogen content and cytochrome oxidase activity. The increase in acid-insoluble nitrogen and cytochrome oxidase activity may have been specially related to the increase in the number of mitochondrial particles, and the increased activity may have been an important factor for the increased respiration after slicing, so called wound respiration.

Table 3.— Increase in number of mitochondria particles during aging of slices

Time after slicing (days)	Acid— insoluble nitrogen (percent)	Cytochrome oxidase activity (percent)	Number of particle (percent)
0	100	100	100
1	151	142	112
2	191	359	173
3	189	355	238

The increase in the mitochondrial activity and number was inhibited by some protein synthesis inhibitors, as shown in figure 1. The open circles indicate the changes in the slices incubated without any inhibitor. The square symbols show the changes in the slices treated for 1 hour with blasticidin S (1.3 x 10^{-6} M), a potent protein synthesis inhibitor. The triangles indicate the changes in the slices treated for 1 hour with chloramphenicol (6 x 10^{-3} M), which is known to inhibit the bacterial type of protein synthesis. Blasticidin S inhibited the increase in cytochrome oxidase activity and the number of the particles, as well as peroxidase activity in the supernatant. However, chloramphenicol inhibited the increase in cytochrome oxidase activity and the

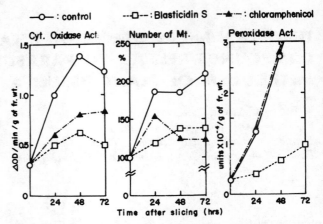

Figure 1.—Effects of inhibitors, blasticidin S and chloramphanicol, on cytochrome oxidase activity, number of mitochondria and peroxidase activity of sweet potato root tissue.

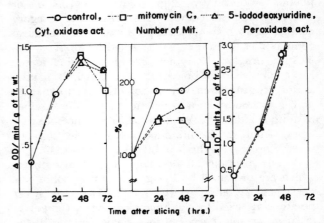

Figure 2.—Effects of inhibitors, mitomycin C and 5-iododeoxyuridine on cytochrome oxidase activity, number of mitochondria and peroxidase activity of sweet potato root tissue.

number of the particles, but did not inhibit the increase in peroxidase activity. Thus, chloramphenicol inhibited only the protein synthesis in the mitochondrial particles and had no effect on the protein synthesis in the cytoplasmic ribosomal fraction. Furthermore, chloramphenicol inhibited only the incorporation of C^{14}-leucine into the mitochondrial protein and did not inhibit the incorporation into the supernatant protein. These results also strengthen the concept that the increase in the mitochondrial number requires an active operation of the protein synthesis system in the particles.

Figure 2 shows the effects of mitomycin C and 5-iododeoxyuridine on the increase in the activities of cytochrome oxidase and peroxidase and the number of mitochondrial particles. The open circles show the changes in the slices incubated without any inhibitor. The squares are the changes in the slices treated with mitomycin C (3 x 10^{-6} M) and the triangles are the changes in the slices treated with 5-iododeoxyuridine (3×10^{-5} M). Interestingly, both inhibitors had no effect on the increase in the enzymatic activities of both cytochrome oxidase and peroxidase. However, the inhibitors depressed the increase in the number of mitochondrial particles. These data suggest to us that the inhibitors for DNA replication inhibited the increase in the number of mitochondrial particles without any effect on the synthesis of enzyme proteins. The activity of a DNA-polymerase in the plant mitochondria may have been inhibited by those inhibitors, as has been shown in isolated yeast mitochondria (35). At the present time, we cannot explain how the inhibitors depress the increase in the number of mitochondrial particles without any effect on the synthesis of cytochrome oxidase. It may be very instructive for elucidating the mode of action of such inhibitors to look at the fine-structure of mitochondria in the inhibitor-treated slices by electron microscopy.

The mode of action of aflatoxins could be elucidated, if aflatoxins affected the increase in the activities of cytochrome oxidase and/or the number of mitochondrial particles; and the effect of aflatoxins would be compared with that of the inhibitors as shown above.

Methods

Preparation of slices.—As indicated in table 4, sweet potato root tissue was sliced and disks, 2 mm. in thickness and 10 mm. in diameter, made by using a cork borer. The 40 disks were washed with water and immersed for 1 hour at room temperature in 100 ml. of 0.05 M phosphate buffer, pH 5.5, containing 1.5×10^{-5} M aflatoxin B_1 in 0.5 percent methanol, with continuous stirring. Then, the disks were wiped and incubated at 28° to 30° C. on filter paper in a moist chamber. In the case of 1.5×10^{-4} M., 0.2 percent N, N-dimethylformamide was used in place of 0.5 percent methanol for the complete dissolution of aflatoxin B_1.

Table 4.—Metabolic changes in sweet potato root tissue in response to injury

Discs of sweet potato tissue:
   (NORIN-1) (10 x 2mm.)
   Incubated for 1 hr. at room temperature in 0.05 M
   Phosphate buffer PH 5.5 containing 0.5 percent
   MetOH with or without AFLATOXIN-B_1
   1.5×10^{-5} M (4.68 μg./ml.)
↓ Incubated at 30° to 28° C. in dry petri dish.
↓ Extraction of enzymes.
⊙ Increase in Peroxidase, Phenylalanine
   ammonialyase, Polyphenol oxidase, Cytochrome
   oxidase, Succinate dehydrogenase and α-Keto
   glutarate dehydrogenase activities.
⊙ Increase in Mitochondria number.
⊙ Inhibition by Protein synthesis inhibitors.

Preparation of toxin.—Aflatoxin B_1 was isolated in a pure form by the extraction from steamed rice grains on which NRRL 2999 strain of *A. flavus* had been grown, according to the method of Hesseltine, Shotwell and others (12, 28).

Preparation of soluble enzyme-containing extract and mitochondrial fraction.—The incubated disks were homogenized with Tris buffer, pH 7.0, containing 0.5 M sucrose and the homogenate was centrifuged for 10 minutes at 300 g. The supernatant fraction was used for the assays of the activities of peroxidase, phenylalanine ammonia-lyase and polyphenol oxidase. The mitochondrial fraction was prepared by centrifuging the supernatant fraction for 20 minutes at 14,000 x g. and by washing the precipitate once and recentrifuging the suspension. The mitochondrial fraction was used for the assays of the activities of cytochrome oxidase, succinate dehydrogenase and α-ketoglutarate dehydrogenase, and for the counting of the number of Janus green B-stained particles (see table 5).

Table 5.—Extraction of enzymes

Tissue 10 g. (incubated):
   Homogenized with 20 ml. of 0.05 M Tris-
     HCl PH 7.0—0.5 M Sucrose—0.01 M EDTA-
     0.1 percent Na isoascorbate for 1.0 min.
   Squeezed through cheese cloth.
   Centrifuged for 10 min. at 300 x g.

Ppt Sup Made up to 25 ml. with homogenizing
         medium and taken off 1.0 ml. for Peroxidase
         and 4.0 ml. for Phenylalaninammonialyase.
         Centrifuged for 20 min. at 14,000 x g.

Sup Ppt Suspended in 0.05 M Tris-HCl
         PH 7.0–0.5 M Sucrose.
         Centrifuged for 20 min. at 14,000 x g.

Sup Ppt Suspended with glass homogenizer and
         made up to 5.0 ml. with washing medium.
     Mitochondrial fraction:
        Mitochondria number.
        Cytochrome oxidase.
        Succinate dehydrogenase.
        α-Ketoglutarate dehydrogenase.

Results

The effects of aflatoxin B_1 on the increase in peroxidase and succinate dehydrogenase activities in response to injury are shown in figure 3. The solid lines show the increasing profiles of the enzymatic activities in the disks not treated with the toxin. The dotted lines show the enzymatic activities in the disks treated with the toxin. The toxin had no effect on the increase in the enzymatic activities in response to injury. The same profiles are observed also in the case of phenylalanine ammonia-lyase.

The effects of aflatoxin B_1 on the increase in cytochrome oxidase activity and the number of mitochondrial particles are shown in figure 4. The toxin had no effect on the increase in the enzymatic activity, but did inhibit the increase in the number of the particles.

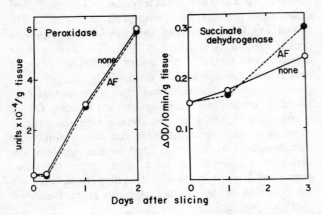

Figure 3.—Effects of aflatoxin B_1 on increase in enzymatic activity in response to injury. (1)

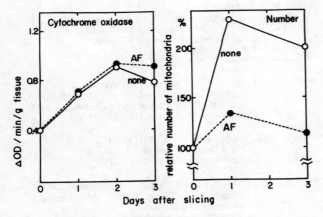

Figure 4.—Effects of aflatoxin B_1 on increase in enzymatic activity in response to injury. (2)

Therefore, the effects of aflatoxin B_1 on the metabolic changes in response to injury resembled the action of mitomycin C and 5-iododeoxyuridine, which are the inhibitors for DNA replication. Thus, it may be supposed that aflatoxin B_1 is a kind of DNA-replication inhibitor, and inhibits the replication of mitochondrial DNA, but the toxin does not inhibit protein synthesis, either in cytoplasmic ribosomal fraction or in the mitochondrial particles in the range of 1.5×10^{-4} to 1.5×10^{-5} M (5). Neither polyphenol oxidase nor α-ketoglutarate dehydrogenase have shown a decrease in the enhanced activity, in the presence of 1.5×10^{-5} M aflatoxin B_1.

It may be concluded that aflatoxins inhibit DNA replication but not protein synthesis in higher plant tissues, in the above concentration range. To make this assumption sure, it may require a study, in more detail, of the mechanism of increase in the mitochondrial number in sweet potato root tissue in response to injury.

Mycotoxins Produced by Living Plant Tissues Contaminated by Fungi

In this section attention will be paid to the other kind of mycotoxins; *i.e.* those which are produced by living agricultural commodities when contaminated by fungi (*31*). As one example, the case of the sweet potato—*Ceratocystis fimbriata* interaction will be mentioned. When sweet potato roots are attacked, either in the field or during storage, by *C. fimbriata, Thielabiopsis basicola, Fusarium oxysporum,* or *Helicobasidium mompa,* bitter substances are produced in infected tissue. Hiura (*13*) isolated the main component and called it ipomeamarone. Later, Kubota and Matsuura (*20*) determined the chemical structure as shown in figure 5 and further isolated ipomeanine, batatic acid, and furan-β-carboxylic acid from the crude oil.

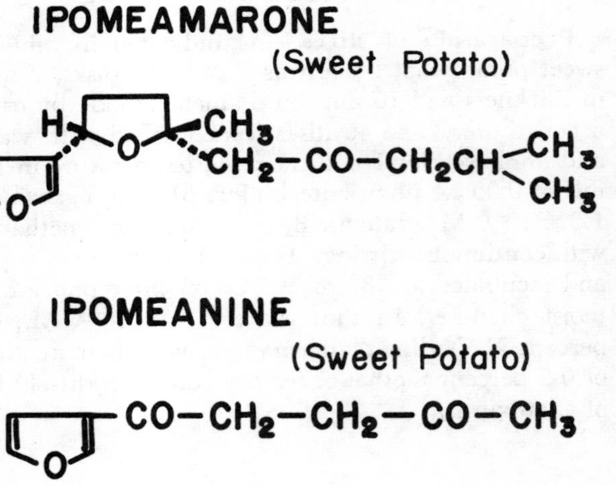

IPOMEAMARONE
(Sweet Potato)

IPOMEANINE
(Sweet Potato)

Figure 5

Akazawa (*1*) found more than 10 kinds of terpene compounds, including ipomeamarone and ipomeanine, by using silica-plate chromatography. The terpene compounds are produced both after fungal penetration and in response to attack by insects (*3*) and treatment with toxic chemicals (*33*). These substances are thus synthesized by the sweet potato tissue itself. They accumulate only in the infected region and in the noninfected tissue very close to the infected area. Moreover, they are rarely found after simple mechanical injury.

Asian people eat the roots of the sweet potato as either a staple food or a main vegetable and feed them to cattle. In the past several decades, death of cattle was sometimes attributed to bad lots of sweet potatoes. The main cause was thought to be the terpene compounds. Ipomeamarone, for example, is a sesquiterpene containing a furan ring and is probably synthesized through the acetyl CoA-mevalonate pathway as shown by radioisotope experiments (2, 16, 26). Such compounds inhibit the growth of C. fimbriata and participate in the defense action of the roots. Investigation of the inhibitory action of some of the fractions eluted from the silica gel plate after chromatography of the crude terpenes shows that the ipomeanine-containing fraction had the highest activity, whereas the impomeamarone-containing fraction had the lowest activity, although all fractions showed antibiotic properties. Ipomeamarone inhibited the respiration of both C. fimbriata and sweet potato and, according to the results obtained with rat liver mitochondria, it acted at some site between the TCA cycle substrates and cytochrome c in the electron transport system (32).

When sweet potato roots are attacked by pathogens, some coumarin derivatives, umbelliferone, scopoletin, esculetin, scopolin (scopoletin-7-β-glucoside), and skimmin (unbelliferone-7-β-glucoside), also accumulate in almost the same region as the terpene compounds (24). Those structures are shown in figure 6. They may also take part in the defense action against fungus penetration and may be harmful to humans, animals, and plants.

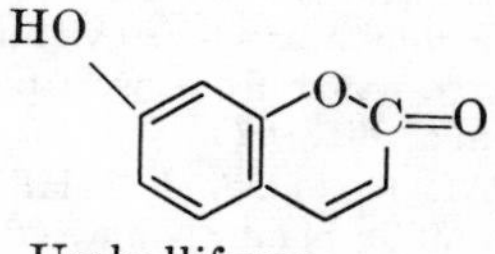

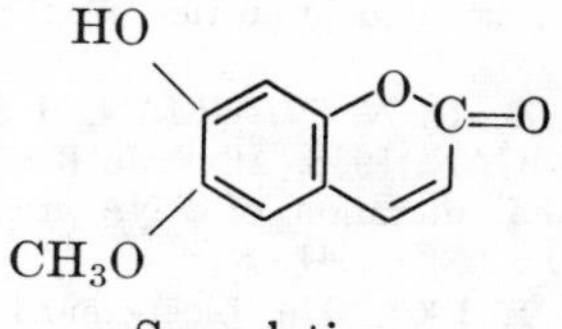

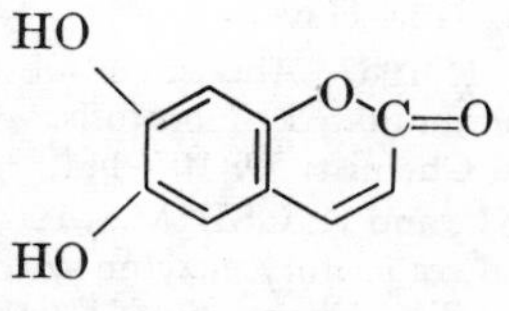

Caffeic acid and its derivatives, such as chlorogenic acid, isochlorogenic acid and methyl caffeate are produced in the noninfected tissue of sweet potato adjacent to the infected region or mechanically injured tissue, as mentioned above (30, 31). Those structures are indicated in figure 7. They probably play a role in the defense action by forming a physical barrier, after being oxidized by polyphenol oxidase which increases in concentration during the period of infec-

Figure 7

Figure 6

tion or injury. According to some experimental results, these compounds seem to be harmless to humans and animals. However, their physiological effect should be reinvestigated because chlorogenic acid shows antigenicity, even though it is a compound of low molecular weight (31). According to the data of Horigome and Kandatsu (14), the oxidation products resulting from the oxidation of p-coumaric acid, caffeic acid, and chlorogenic acid by polyphenol oxidase decrease the pepsin digestibility of the leaf protein from red clover. It should be mentioned that other abnormal substances have been found to be produced by several crops in response to fungal infection.

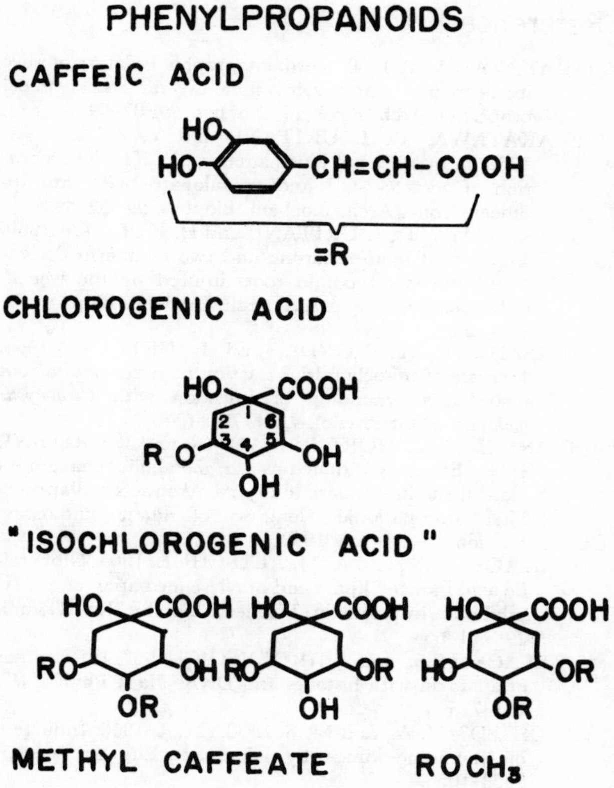

Acknowledgments

The authors wish to thank Dr. Godfrey L. Mann at Southern Regional Research Laboratory in New Orleans; and Dr. C. W. Hesseltine and Dr. O. L. Shotwell at Northern Regional Research Laboratory in Peoria for sending them the standard samples and the cultures and giving them valuable advice.

This research has been financed in part by a grant made by the U.S. Department of Agriculture under Public Law 480.

References

(1) AKAZAWA, T. 1960. Chromatographic isolation of pure ipomeamarone and reinvestigation on its chemical properties. Arch. Biochem. Biophys. *90:* 82–89.

(2) AKAZAWA, T., I. URITANI, and Y. AKAZAWA. 1962. Biosynthesis of ipomeamarone. 1. The incorporation of acetate-2-C^{14} and mevalonate-2-C^{14} into ipomeamarone. Arch. Biochem. Biophys. *99:* 52–59.

(3) AKAZAWA, T., I. URITANI, and H. KUBOTA. 1960. Isolation of ipomeamarone and two coumarin derivatives from sweet potato roots injured by the weevil, *Cylas formicarius elegantulus.* Arch. Biochem. Biophys. *88:* 150–156.

(4) ASAHI, T., Y. HONDA, and I. URITANI. 1966. Increase of mitochondrial fraction in sweet potato root tissue after wounding or infection with *Ceratocystis fimbriata.* Plant Physiol. *41:* 1179–1184.

(5) ASAHI, T., Z. MORI, R. MAJIMA, and I. URITANI. 1968. Effects of aflatoxins on metabolic changes in plant tissue in response to injury. Abstracts of Papers of First International Congress of Plant Pathology, London, 14–26, July 1968.

(6) BLACK, H. S., and A. M. ALTSCHUL. 1965. Gibberellic acid induced lipase and amylase formation and their inhibition by aflatoxin. Biochem. Biophys. Res. Comm. *19:* 661–664.

(7) BLACK, H. S., and B. JIRGENSONS. 1967. Interactions of aflatoxin with histones and DNA. Plant Physiol. *42:* 731–735.

(8) CHILDS, V. A., and M. S. LEGATOR. 1966. Induction of thymidine kinase by aflatoxins. Life Sciences *5:* 1053–1056.

(9) CLIFFORD, J. I., and K. R. REES. 1966. Aflatoxin: a site of action in the rat liver cell. Nature *209:* 312–313.

(10) CLIFFORD, J. I., and K. R. REES. 1967. The action of aflatoxin B$_1$ on the rat liver. Biochem. J. *102:* 65–75.

(11) De RECONDO, A. M., D. FRAYSSINET, C. LAFARGE, and E. Le BRETON. 1966. Action de l'aflatoxine sur le metabolisme du DNA au cours de l'hypertrophie compensatrice du foie apres hepatectomie partielle. Biochim. et Biophys. Acta. *119:* 322–330.

(12) HESSELTINE, C. W., O. L. SHOTWELL, J. J. ELLIS, and R. D. STUBBLEFIELD. 1966. Aflatoxin Formation by *Aspergillus flavus.* Bacteriol. Rev. *30:* 795–805.

(13) HIURA, M. 1941. Studies on storage and rot of sweet potato. 2. Gifu Norin Semmon Gakko Gakujutsu Hokoku *50:* 1–5.

(14) HORIGOME, T., and M. KANDATSU. 1966. Studies on the nutritive value of grass proteins. Pt. XIII. Phenolic substances of red clover leaves and effects of *p*-coumaric, caffeic and chlorogenic acids. J. Agri. Chem. Soc. Japan (Nippon Nogeikagaku Kaishi) *40:* 246–251.

(15) HYODO, H., and I. URITANI. 1967. Properties of polyphenol oxidases produced in sweet potato tissue after wounding. Arch. Biochem. Biophys. *122:* 299–309.

(16) IMASEKI, H., and I. URITANI. 1964. Ipomeamarone accumulation and lipid metabolism in sweet potato infected by the black rot fungus. II. Accumulation mechanism of ipomeamarone in the infected region with special regard to contribution of the noninfected tissue. Plant and Cell Physiol. *5:* 133–143.

(17) JONES, H. C., H. S. BLACK, and A. M. ALTSCHUL. 1967. A comparison of effect of gibberellic acid and aflatoxin in germinating seeds. Nature *214:* 171.

(18) KANAZAWA, Y., H. SHICHI, and I. URITANI. 1965. Biosynthesis of peroxidases in sliced or black rot-infected sweet potato roots. Agricultural and Biological Chemistry *29:* 840–847.

(19) KAWASHIMA, N., and I. URITANI. 1965. Some properties of peroxidase produced in sweet potato infected by the black rot fungus. Plant and Cell Physiol. *6:* 247–265.

(20) KUBOTA, T., and T. MATSUURA. 1953. Chemical studies on the black rot disease of sweet potato. J. Chem. Soc. Japan. *74:* 101–109, 197–199, 248–251, 668–670.

(21) LILIEHOJ, E. B., and A. CIEGLER. 1967. Inhibition of deoxyribonucleic acid synthesis in *Flavobacterium aurantiacum* by aflatoxin B$_1$. J. Bacteriol. *94:* 787–788.

(22) LILLY, L. J. 1965. Induction of chromosome aberrations by aflatoxin. Nature *207:* 433–434.

(23) MINAMIKAWA, T., and I. URITANI. 1965. Phenylalanine ammonialyase in sliced sweet potato roots. J. Biochem. *57:* 678–688.

(24) MINAMIKAWA, T., T. AKAZAWA and I. URITANI. 1963. Analytical study of unbelliferone and scopoletin synthesis in sweet potato roots infected by *Ceratocystis fimbriata.* Plant Physiol. *38:* 493–497.

(25) MUTO, S., T. ASAHI and I. URITANI. 1968. Increase in the dehydrogenase activities of the pentose phosphate pathway in sweet potato root tissue after slicing. Agric. Biol. Chem. *32.* In press.

(26) OSHIMA, K., and I. URITANI. 1968. Enzymatic synthesis of a β-hydroxy-β-methylglutaric acid-derivative by a cell-free system from sweet potato with black rot. J. Biochem. *63:* 617–625.

(27) SCHOENTAL, R., and A. F. WHITE. 1965. Aflatoxins and 'albinism' in plants. Nature *205:* 57–58.

(28) SHOTWELL, O. L., C. W. HESSELTINE, R. D. STUBBLEFIELD, and W. G. SORENSON. 1966. Production of aflatoxin on rice. Applied Microbiol. *14:* 425–428.

(29) SPORN, M. B., D. W. DINGMAN, H. L. PHELPS, and G. N. WOGAN. 1966. Aflatoxin B$_1$: Binding to DNA *in vitro* and alteration of RNA metabolism *in vivo.* Science *151:* 1539–1541.

(30) URITANI, I. 1963. The biochemical basis of disease resistance induced by infection, *In* S. Rich, Perspectives of Biochemical Plant Pathology, pp. 4–19, Conn. Agr. Expt. Sta., New Haven.

(31) URITANI, I. 1967. Abnormal substances produced in fungus-contaminated foodstuffs. J. Assoc. Official Analytical Chemists *50:* 105–114.

(32) URITANI, I., and K. OSHIMA. 1965. Effects of ipomeamarone on respiratory enzyme system in mitochondria. Agric. and Biol. Chem. *29:* 641–648.

(33) URITANI, I., M. URITANI, and H. YAMADA. 1960. Similar metabolic alterations induced in sweet potato

by poisonous chemicals and *Ceratocystis fimbriata*. Phytopathol. *50:* 30–34.

(*34*) URITANI, I., T. ASAHI, H. MINAMIKAWA, H.
HYODO, K. OSHIMA, and M. KOJIMA. 1967. The
relation of metabolic changes in infected plants to
changes in enzymatic activity. *In* C. J. Mirocha and I.

Uritani. The Dynamic Role of Molecular Constituents
in Plant-Parasite Interaction. Association Services Inc.,
pp. 342–356. St. Paul, Minn.

(*35*) WINTERSBERGER, E. 1966. Occurrence of a DNA-
polymerase in isolated yeast mitochondria. Biochem.
Biophys. Res. Comm. *25:* 1–7.

TOXIC SUBSTANCES (FUSARENON AND NIVALENOL) PRODUCED BY *FUSARIUM NIVALE*

by Nobuichi Morooka *and* Takashi Tatsuno
Department of Food Research, National Institute of Health, Shinagawa-ku, Tokyo;
Institute of Physical and Chemical Research, Yamato-Machi, Saitama-ken, Japan

Summary

Metabolic products of *Fusarium nivale* in rice grains, artificially inoculated, were separated by column chromatography on kieselgel. Fusarenon and nivalenol, both toxic metabolites of *F. nivale*, were eluted with chloroform-methanol (97:3) and the same system at a different mixing ratio (5:1), respectively. The chemical formulas proposed for fusarenon and nivalenol are $C_{18}H_{25}O_8N_3$ (as fusarenon-semicarbazone) and $C_{15}H_{20}O_7$, respectively. These substances appeared to be a kind of terpenoid. Fusarenon and nivalenol showed no antimicrobial activity against any species of bacteria, fungi or yeasts that were examined. Fusarenon, at a low concentration, blocks completely the cell division of synchronized and logarithmic phase *Tetrahymena pyriformis* (ciliated protozoon). The toxic effect was suggested to be inhibition of the protein synthesis.

Introduction

Studies on toxic metabolites of fungi of the genus *Fusarium* are reviewed by Dr. Tsunoda (these proceedings), who reports on their taxonomy. We isolated two substances from rice artificially inoculated with *F. nivale*. Toxic metabolites of *Fusarium* had been studied not only in Japan, but also in other countries. Recently, the interesting researches of toxic substances of *Fusarium* species was published by Dawkins (3), Gilgan et al. (4) and Bamburg et al. (1). We were especially interested in the reports by Yates et al. (9), who isolated from *F. nivale* 8-(3-methyl-butyryloxy) diacetoxy-scirpenol, which had also been isolated from *F. tricinctum* by Gilgan and Bamburg. We will report the procedures for purification of the toxic substances, some physicochemical properties in comparison with those of Yates' substances, and the inhibitory effect of fusarenon upon the cell division of *T. pyriformis*.

Methods and Results

Purification of the two toxic metabolites of *F. nivale*.—Inoculation of rice with *F. nivale*. Ninety-eight percent polished rice was washed, soaked in water for 30 minutes and drained. The washed rice was dispensed in flat-bottomed flask of 450 ml. capacities to two-thirds full. The rice in the flasks was autoclaved at 15 pounds for 20 minutes and cooled in the air. Spores of *F. nivale* harvested on Czapeck's agar slants were introduced into the flasks. They were shaken well and incubated at 25° to 27° C. for 20 days. After incubation, the rice was dried in hot air at 45° C. and ground in a mechanical grinder to prepare a powdered material.

Isolation and purification of the toxic substances.—Three kg. of the material was extracted with acetone in a Soxhlet's continuous extractor for 8 hours as shown in figure 1. The extract and the residue were separated. The residue was then extracted with 50 percent alcohol, kept standing for 24 hours and filtered to separate the extract from the residue.

The alcohol extract was concentrated under negative pressure and a solid material of 150 g. was obtained. To this material distilled water was added to make an emulsion, which was extracted with n-butanol. From the n-butanol phase, 30 g. of crude toxic substances were obtained.

The material was adsorbed onto a column of kieselgel (Merck, finer than 0.08 mm., 5 x 100 cm.), which was eluted with chloroform-methanol (97:3) at a flow rate of 80 ml./hr. at room temperature; 15 ml. fractions were collected.

The most toxic substances were eluted in tube numbers 198 to 206. After 400 fractions had been taken, the column was eluted with chloroform-methanol (5:1). Another toxic substance was eluted in fraction numbers 528 to 560. The early eluted toxic substance was named "fusarenon," the late-eluted one "nivalenol." The increase in the toxicity of the substances as purification proceeded is shown in the right column of figure 1. The intraperitoneal MLD of the 50 percent alcohol extract was 10 to 20 mg./mouse (of 15 g. weight); that of the n-butanol extract was 2.5 mg./mouse; the intraperitoneal LD_{50} of the purified fusarenon was 3.5 mg./kg. (mouse); that of the purified nivalenol was 4.0 mg./kg. (mouse).

Figure 2 shows a thin-layer chromatogram of each fraction separated by kieselgel column chromatography of kieselgel F. Plates of 0.25 mm. thickness were developed with chloroform-methanol (97:3) and stained by spraying with 20 percent H_2SO_4 and by heating the plate. Fusarenon was detected in fraction numbers 11 to 12 and had an Rf value of 0.19. These fractions were developed with cyclohexane-chloroform-diethylamine (5:4:1). A spot with an Rf value of 0.25 was detected in the fraction number 251 as in figure 3.

Nivalenol was shown to give a spot with Rf value of 0.45 (fig. 4, fraction No. 4) when developed with chloroform-methanol (5:1) in thin-layer chromatography. Nivalenol, a metabolite of *F. nivale*, can be isolated by adsorbing onto a column of active charcoal and eluting with methanol.

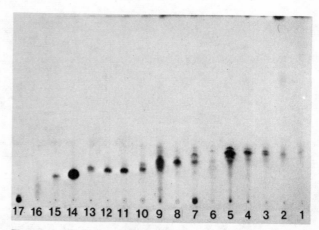

Figure 2.—Thin-layer chromatogram on kieselgel-F of the fractions separated by kieselgel column chromatography. Development was with chloroform-methanol (97:3).

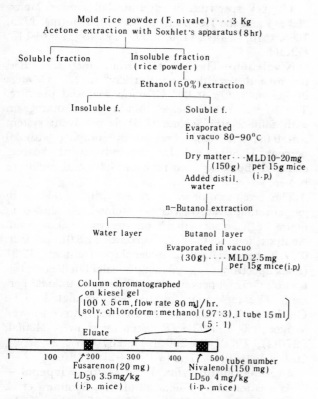

Figure 1.—Outline of the purification procedure of fusarenon and nivalenol.

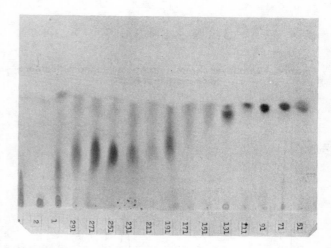

Figure 3.—Thin-layer chromatogram on kieselgel-F of the fraction separated by kieselgel column chromatography. Development was with cyclohexane-chloroform-diethylamine (5:4:1).

Fusarenon, also a metabolite of *F. nivale*, can be isolated by counter current distribution with ethylacetate-water. The toxic action of these substances is reported in a separate report by Dr. M. Saito (these proceedings).

Physicochemical properties of the two substances, fusarenon and nivalenol.—The physicochemical properties of the two toxic compounds and of Yates' compound are tabulated in table 1.

Fusarenon.—The colorless oily material purified as above was crystallized repeatedly in ethylacetate-toluene. The melting point of this crystalline powder was 78° to 80° C. When it was subjected to kieselgel thin-layer chromatography with toluene-ethylacetate as the developing solvent, sprayed with 20 percent H_2SO_4 and followed by heating the plate, a single spot of purple color changing into yellowish green with an Rf value of 0.35 was obtained. The retention time of trimethylsilyl-fusarenon in gas chromatography was 10.3 minutes as shown in figure 5 (2). The MW was 354 (mass spectra). The UV (ultraviolet) spectrum in ethylalcohol showed end absorption only.

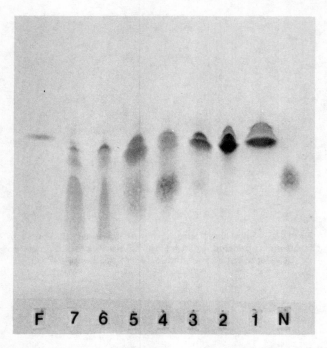

Figure 4.—Thin layer chromatogram developed with chloroform-methanol (5:1).

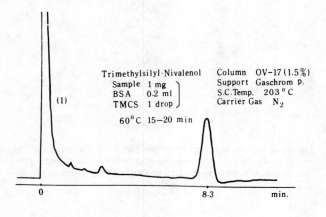

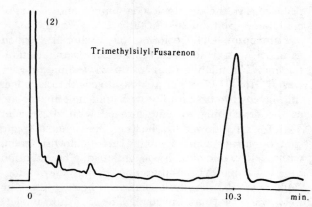

Figure 5.—Gas chromatograms of nivalenol and fusarenon.

The IR (infrared) spectrum, 3570(s), 2960(m), 1720(s), 1685(s), 1365(m), 1250(s), 1167(m), 1080(s), 1040(s). The $[\alpha]_D^{24°} = +29.6°$ (in EtOH).

Fusarenon-semicarbazone.—As described before, it was difficult to obtain fusarenon in the crystalline state. To prove the homogeneity, the material was developed with different solvent systems and subjected to gas chromatography. In these tests, the material behaved as a pure substance.

Fusarenon is combined with semicarbazide to form a semicarbazone. The semicarbazone crystals are colorless and in a plate form, with a melting point of 235° to 236° C. (decomposing point). Analysis found, C:51.71 percent, H:6.12 percent, 0:31.53 percent, N:10.46 percent; the MW was 411 (mass spectra) calculated to c:52.56 percent, H:6.08 percent, 0:31.14 percent, N:10.22 percent. The molecular formula was estimated to be $C_{18}H_{25}O_8N_3$.

The UV spectrum in ethyl alcohol showed λmax. 268 mμ and the IR spectrum 3390(s), 2940(m), 1725, 1665, 1570, 1240(s), 1150, 1080, 1030. $[\alpha]_D^{23°} = +147°$ (EtOH).

Nivalenol.—The crystals from methanol had prisms and a melting point of 222° to 223° C. after drying on P_2O_5 at 80° C. under reduced pressure. The Rf value on kieselgel thin-layer chromatogram with toluene-ethylacetate (1:3) as a solvent system was 0.06. The spot obtained by spraying with 20 percent H_2SO_4 and by the subsequent heating changed the color from pink to violet and finally to brown.

The retention time of trimethylsilyl-nivalenol in gas chromatography was determined. As shown in figure 5 (1), a peak with 8.3 minutes was demonstrated. Analysis found, C:56.29 percent, H:6.01 percent, 0:37.70 percent, and a molecular weight of 312.31 (mass spectrometry), yielding a calculated composition of, C:57.68 percent, H:6.46 percent, 0:35.86 percent. The molecular formula was estimated to be $C_{15}H_{20}O_7$. The UV spectrum in acetonitrile showed λ max. 260 mμ. The IR spectrum showed 3400(s), 3270(s), 2980(w), 2900(m), 2870(m), 2740(w), 1680(m), 1610(w). The $[\alpha]_D^{24°} = +21.5°$ (EtOH).

8-(3-methylbutyryloxy) diacetoxyscirpenol.—This was found by Gilgan et al. (4), Bamburg et al. (1) in *F. tricinctum*. Yates et al. (9) found a similar substance in *F. nivale* which was proved to be identical to 8-(3-methylbutyryloxy) diacetoxyscirpenol. An Rf value of 0.25 was obtained in thin-layer chromatography with a solvent system of toluene-ethylacetate (1:3). When sprayed with concentrated H_2SO_4 and heated, a purple spot appeared. The melting point was 151° to 152° C. Analysis found, C:61.41 percent, H:7.29 percent, 0:31.29 percent. The molecular weight was 466, yielding a calculated composition of C:61.79 percent, H:7.35 percent, 0:30.87 percent.

Table 1.—Comparative physico-chemical properties of the 3 toxic substances

Tests	Substances			
	Fusarenon	Fusarenon-semicarbazone	Nivalenol	8-(3-Methylbutyryloxy) Diacetoxyscirpenol
Author	Tsunoda and Morooka (1968)		Tatsuno (1968)	Gilgan et al. (1966) Bamburg et al. (1968) Yates et al. (1968)
Crystal m.p.	78°–80° C.	235°–236° C. (decomp.)	222°–223° C.	151°–152° C.
Rf value Toluene-Et-Ac (1:3)	0.35		0.06	0.25
20 percent H_2SO_4 Color	purple → yellowish-green		pink → violet → brown	purple
G.C. Retention time	10.3 min.		8.3 min.	
Anal. found Calcd.		C H O N 51.71 6.12 31.53 10.46 52.56 6.08 31.14 10.22	C H O 56.29 6.01 37.70 57.68 6.46 35.86	C H O 61.41 7.29 31.29 61.79 7.35 30.87
M.W. mass spectra M.F.	354 $C_{17}H_{22}O_8$	411 $C_{18}H_{25}O_8N_3$	312 $C_{15}H_{20}O_7$	466 $C_{24}H_{34}O_9$
U.V. spectra	end absorpt.	λmax. 268 mμ	λmax. 260 mμ	end absorpt.
I.R. spectra (cm^{-1})	3570(s) 1250(s) 2960(m) 1167(m) 1720(s) 1080(s) 1685(s) 1040(s) 1365(m)	3390(s) 1240(s) 2940(m) 1150 1725 1080 1665 1030 1570	3400(s) 2870(m) 3270(s) 2740(m) 2980(w) 1680(m) 2900(w) 1610(m)	3400(s) 1635(w) 2940(s) 1365(s) 1720(Vs) 1240(Vs)
$[\alpha]_D^t$	$[\alpha]_D^{24°} = +29.6°$ (EtOH)	$[\alpha]_D^{23°} = +147.0°$ (EtOH)	$[\alpha]_D^{24°} = +21.5°$ (EtOH)	$[\alpha]_D^{24°} = -50°$ (cyclohexane) $[\alpha]_D^{26°} = +15°$ (EtOH)

The molecular formula suggested was $C_{24}H_{34}O_9$. The UV spectrum showed λ max. 187.5 mμ (ϵ19,300). The IR spectrum showed 3400(s), 2940(s), 1635(w), 1365(s), 1240(Vs). The $[\alpha]_D^{24°} = -50°$ (cyclohexane) and the $[\alpha]_D^{26°} = +15°$ (EtOH).

The foregoing results showed that fusarenon and nivalenol isolated by us are different from 8-(3-methyl-butyryloxy) diacetoxy-scirpenol isolated by Gilgan et al. (4), Bamburg et al. (1) and Yates et al. (9). The physicochemical properties of the two substances indicated that they are certain kinds of sesquiterpenoid. The chemical structures of both substances will be reported in the subsequent paper.

Inhibitory action of fusarenon on cell division of T. pyriformis.—Fusarenon at a fixed-concentration (1 mg./ml.) was tested for the possible antimicrobial activity against different bacteria, fungi and yeasts as shown in table 2. None of the organisms tested were inhibited.

The effect of fusarenon upon exponentially growing *T. pyriformis*, a ciliated protozoon, was studied. Different concentration, 1μg./ml., 10μg./ml., 50μg./ml., 100 μg./ml. and 200μg./ml., were tested periodically for their influence upon growth of the organism. As shown in figure 6, fusarenon at 50 to 100 μg./ml. completely inhibited the growth of *T. pyriformis*.

The influence of fusarenon, at the same concentrations as above, upon synchronous division of *T. pyriformis* was examined. As shown in table 3, at 1 μg./ml. it delayed slightly the recommencing of the multiplication and at 10 μg./ml. the effect was great. At 50 to 200 μg./ml. it completely blocked cell multiplication. At 200 μg./ml., spherical dead cells appeared at 9 hours after the addition of fusarenon.

Delays in synchronous division of *T. pyriformis* were

induced by treating the cells with fusarenon at various stages of the division cycle. As seen in figure 7, the delay in the division increased gradually during the first 45 minutes after EHT, followed by a sharp de-

crease in the sensitivity. After the transition-point (45 minutes) up to the synchronous division, the addition of fusarenon did not exert a harmful influence upon the oncoming division. The maximum delay

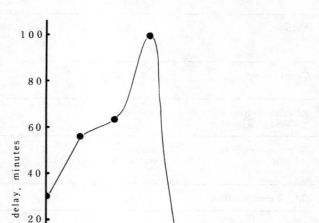

Figure 7.—Delays in synchronous division induced by treating cells of Tetrahymena 200 μg./mg. of fusarenon for 20 min. at various stages.

Table 2.—Antibiotic activity of fusarenon (1 mg./ml.)

MICROORGANISMS TESTED
Micrococcus pyogenes var. *aureus* 209 pp.
Bacillus subtilis 6 and 8.
Pseudomonas aeruginosa.
Escherichia coli ML 1630, KM 1630.
Mycobacterium sp. 607.
Candida albicans.
Trichophyton mentagrophytes.
Piricularia oryzae.
Xanthomonas oryzae.

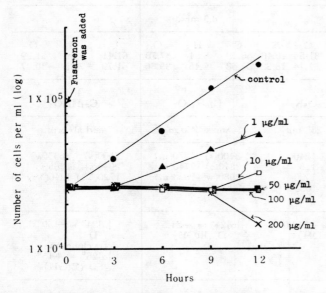

Figure 6.—Effect of fusarenon on exponentially growing Tetrahymena cells.

Table 3.—Effects of various concentrations of fusarenon on synchronous division[1]

Concentration of fusarenon (μg./mg.)	Occurrence of synchronous division[2]	Midpoint of the first synchronous division (minutes after ETH)	Maximum division index (percent)
0	+	75	80
1	+	110	60
10	+	240	40
50	–	–	–
100	–	–	–
200	–	–	–

[1]Fusarenon was added to synchronous cultures at 5 min. after the end of the heat treatment.
[2]Observation was continued up to 300 min. after the end of the heat treatment.

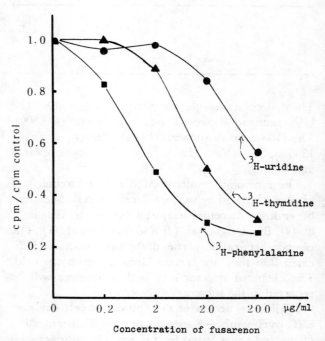

Figure 8.—Effects of fusarenon on incorporation of precursors into nucleic acids and proteins.

was observed about 45 minutes after EHT, in other words, about 30 minutes before a midpoint in fission.

The influence of fusarenon on DNA, RNA and protein syntheses was studied by uptake of ^{3}H-uridine, ^{3}H-thymidine and ^{3}H-phenylalanine by *T. pyriformis* at the exponential phase. Protein synthesis was most seriously affected by the fusarenon treatment. The phenylalanine uptake was inhibited with fusarenon to 50 percent at a concentration of 2 μg./ml. The uptake into DNA and RNA was little influenced with fusarenon at 2 μg./ml. At a higher concentration of fusarenon at 20 μg./ml., the uptake of thymidine was inhibited to 50 percent and at 200 μg./ml., the uptake of uridine was inhibited to 45 percent (figure 8).

References

(*1*) BAMBURG, J. R., N. V. RIGGS, and F. M. STRONG. 1968. The structures of toxins from two strains of *Fusarium tritinctum*. Tetrahedron *24:* 3329–3336.

(*2*) BRIAN, P. W., A. W. DAWKINS, J. F. GROVE, H. G. HEMMING, D. LOWE, and G. L. F. NORRIS. 1961. Phytotoxic compounds produced by *Fusarium equiseti*. J. Exp. Bot. *12:* 1–12.

(*3*) DAWKINS, A. W. 1966. Phytotoxic compounds produced by *Fusarium equiseti*. II. The chemistry of diacetoxyscirpenol. J. Chem. Soc. Series C, No. 1. 116–123.

(*4*) GILGAN, M. W., E. B. SMALLEY, and F. M. STRONG. 1966. Isolation and partial characterization of a toxin from *Fusarium tricinctum* on moldy corn. Arch. Biochem. Biophys. *114:* 1–3.

(*5*) NAKANO, N. 1968. Inhibitory effects of fusarenon on multiplication of *Tetrahymena pyriformis*. Japan J. Med. Sci. Biol. *submitted for publication.*

(*6*) TATSUNO, T. 1968. Recherche toxicologique de la substance metabolique de *Fusarium nivale*. Proc. Symp. Carcinogenic Natural Substances. UICC. In press.

(*7*) TSUNODA, H., N. TOYAZAKI, N. MOROOKA, N. NAKANO, H. YOSHIYAMA, K. OKUBO, and M. ISODA. 1968. Research on the microorganisms which deteriorate the stored cereals and grain. Detection of injurious strains and properties of their toxic substance of scab fusarium blight grown on the wheat. Rep. Food Res. Inst., Ministry of Agriculture and Forestry, Tokyo *23:* 89–116.

(*8*) YATES, S. G., H. L. TOOKEY, and J. J. ELLIS. 1967. Toxic butenolide produced by *Fusarium nivale* (Fries) Cesati isolated from tall fescue (*Festuca arundinacea* Schreb). Tetrahedron Ltrs. *7:* 621–625.

(*9*) YATES, S. G., H. L. TOOKEY, J. J. ELLIS, and H. J. BURKHARDT. 1968. Mycotoxins produced by *Fusarium nivale* isolated from tall fescue (*Festuca arundinacea* Schreb). Phytochemistry *7:* 139–146.

ISOLATION OF TOXIC PRINCIPLES FROM THE CULTURE FILTRATE OF *FUSARIUM NIVALE*

by Yoshio Ueno, Kazue Saito, *and* Hiroshi Tsunoda
Microbial Chemistry, Faculty of Pharmaceutical Sciences, Science University of Tokyo, and The Food Research Institute, the Ministry of Agriculture and Forestry, Tokyo

Rice infested with *Fusarium nivale* is highly toxic to animals. Nivalenol and fusarenon can be isolated from an ethanol extract of the moldy rice, as the toxic principles (*1, 2*).

In the present paper, the authors aim was to isolate these mycotoxins from a culture filtrate of the fungus. The results indicated that nivalenol and a new mycotoxin, fusarenon-X, were obtained from the peptone-supplemented Czapek medium.

F. nivale Fn 2, which was isolated from naturally infested wheat, was cultured at 27° C. on Czapek medium supplemented with 10 g./l. of peptone. After 2 weeks of stationary cultivation, the culture filtrate was mixed with 10 g./l. of active carbon. Toxic principles adsorbed on the carbon were eluted by methanol, and the addition of five volumes of chloroform to the methanol eluate gave a crude toxin. Column chromatography on Kieselgel with chloroform-methanol (97:3 to 5:1) yielded two toxic fractions, numbers 3 and 5, and nivalenol was isolated from number 5, yielding 2 to 3 mg./l.

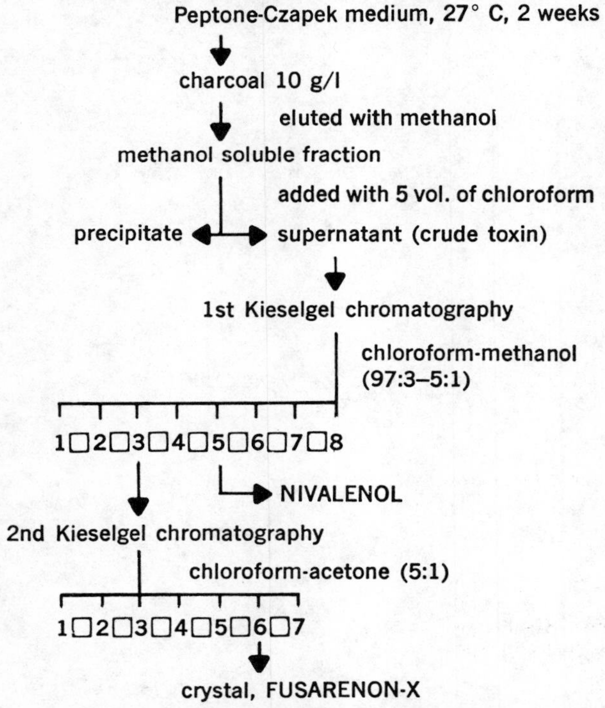

Rechromatography of fraction number 3 on Kieselgel with chloroform-acetone (5:1) yielded three toxic fractions, numbers 2, 3, and 6. A toxic principles was crystallized from fraction number 6 with dichloromethane-n-pentane. The yield was approximately 20 mg./l. This toxin gave nearly the same Rf as fusarenon on TLC, but it differed from fusarenon in melting point and the elemental analysis. Therefore, the authors named it fusarenon-X. Chemical fractionation is schematically represented in figure 1. Chemical and biological characteristics of fusarenon-X are summarized in table 1.

Table 1.—Chemical and biological characteristics of fusarenon-X

m.p. 91°–92° C.
C 5.50, H 54, 83, O 39.67 (%)

TLC (Kieselgel G):		Rf
chloroform:methanol	(5:1)	0.89
chloroform:methanol	(97:3)	0.19
ethylacetate:toluene	(3:1)	0.36

Acute toxicity to mice:
  LD_{50} 3.56 mg./kg. (dd S ♂, i.p.)
Inhibition of protein synthesis in rabbit reticulocytes:
  ID_{50} 0.25 μg./ml.
Inhibition of protein and DNA syntheses in Ehrlich ascites tumor:
  ID_{50} 0.5 μg./ml.

References

(*1*) TATSUNO, T., Y. UENO, I. UENO, Y. MORITA, M. HOSOYA, M. SAITO, M. ENOMOTO, K. OHKUBO, N. MOROOKA, N. NAKANO, and H. TSUNODA. 1967. Toxicological studies on toxic metabolites of *Fusarium nivale* II. Folia Pharmacol. Japon. 64:121 (in Japanese).

(*2*) TSUNODA, H., N. TOYAZAKI, N. MOROOKA, N. NAKANO, H. YOSHIYAMA, K. OHKUBO, and M. ISODA. 1968. Researches on the micro-organisms which deteriorate the stored cereals and grains. 34. Detection of injurious strain and properties of their toxic substances of scab Fusarium blight grown on wheat. Proc. Food Res. Inst. *23:* 89–116 (in Japanese).

Peptone-Czapek medium, 27° C, 2 weeks
↓
charcoal 10 g/l
↓ eluted with methanol
methanol soluble fraction
  added with 5 vol. of chloroform
precipitate ← → supernatant (crude toxin)
↓
1st Kieselgel chromatography
  chloroform-methanol (97:3–5:1)
1☐2☐3☐4☐5☐6☐7☐8
  → NIVALENOL
2nd Kieselgel chromatography
  chloroform-acetone (5:1)
1☐2☐3☐4☐5☐6☐7
↓
crystal, FUSARENON-X

Figure 1.—Fractionation of toxic principles.

BIOSYNTHESIS OF AFLATOXINS

by GEORGE MILNE, MICHEL BIOLLAZ, *and* G. BÜCHI

Department of Chemistry, Massachusetts Institute of Technology, Cambridge, Mass. 02139

Summary

Degradative studies on radioactive aflatoxin-B_1 (*1*) prepared in precursor studies with labeled acetate [1-2^{14}C and 2-^{14}C] and with methyl-^{14}C-methionine are described. The origin of 13 of the 17 carbon atoms present in aflatoxin-B_1 (*1*) was determined and a hypothetical scheme for the biogenesis of the aflatoxins and related mold metabolites consonant with the determined distribution of labels is proposed.

The biosynthetic origin of the aflatoxins, a biologically and structurally remarkable group of metabolites produced by some *Aspergillus* species (*17, 25*), has been the subject of much conflicting speculation (*14, 15, 19, 22*) and several precursor incorporation studies (*1, 11*). An early incorporation study (*1*) implicated phenylalanine as a precursor in aflatoxin biosynthesis by cultures of *A. flavus*. A more recent study (*11*) has excluded this view, and put forward acetate as the probable major biosynthetic contributor. Since the origin in nature of the aflatoxins is not obvious from inspection of their structures, we undertook the determination of the distribution of labels in aflatoxin-B_1 derived from methyl-^{14}C-methionine, [1-^{14}C]- and (2-^{14}C)-acetate.

Materials and Methods

Preparation of labeled aflatoxins.—The aflatoxins were prepared by the addition of methyl-^{14}C-methionine, [1-^{14}C]- or [2-^{14}C]-acetate (New England Nuclear Corp.) to resting cell cultures of *A. flavus* ATTC 15517 metabolizing glucose according to the procedure of Mateles et al. (*11*). The highly active aflatoxin-B_1 was purified by preparative thin layer chromatography and combined with inactive material obtained by column chromatography (*18*) to afford large quantities of labeled aflatoxin-B with activities of about 5 x 10^5 disintegrations per minute per millimole.

Analytical methods.—All degradation products were completely characterized by comparison with known samples or by standard analytical techniques. Acids from Kuhn-Roth oxidations were purified and measured for radioactivity as their corresponding p-bromophenacyl esters or N(α-Naphthyl)-amides.

Carbon dioxide was collected as $BaCO_3$. All samples for radioactivity determinations were weighed on a microgram balance. Pure reagent grade chemicals were used for all reactions as required.

Radioactivity measurements.—All radioactivity measurements were made on a Packard model 3375 Liquid Scintillation Spectrometer. Samples of CO_2 liberated from $BaCO_3$ and trapped in Hyamine 10–X solution (Packard) were measured in 20 cc. of scintillator solution (3 g. of PPO in 1 liter of toluene). All other samples were measured in Bruno Solution (*6*) (15 cc. per vial).

Results

Administration of methyl-^{14}C-methionine yielded radioactive aflatoxin-B_1 which on Zeisel degradation gave methyl iodide containing 97.8 percent of the total radioactivity(*2*). The methyl iodide was characterized and counted as its triethylamine salt. In agreement with this, degradation of [1-^{14}C]- and [2-^{14}C]-acetate labeled aflatoxin yielded triethylmethyl ammonium iodide containing only 0.32 and 0.31 percent of the molar activity, respectively.

Aflatoxin-B_1 prepared from [1-^{14}C]- and [2-^{14}C]-acetate was degraded using the three sequences outlined in schemes I, II, and III, and the distribution of radioactivity found is summarized in tables I, II, III, IV, and V.

The degradation of the bisfuranoid moiety of aflatoxin-B_1 was carried out using both schemes I and II and the distribution of radioactivity for 1-^{14}C-acetate labeled aflatoxin is presented in tables I and II, respectively.

Table 1.—Distribution of labels from 1-^{14}C-acetate incorporation as determined from scheme I

Carbon atoms	Estimated as—	Percent of total radioactivity
C–14 to C–16	p-bromophenacylpropionate	12.01
C–14	CO_2	1.35
C–15, C–16	p-bromophenacylacetate	11.21
C–15	CO_2	8.61
C–16	CO_2	1.21

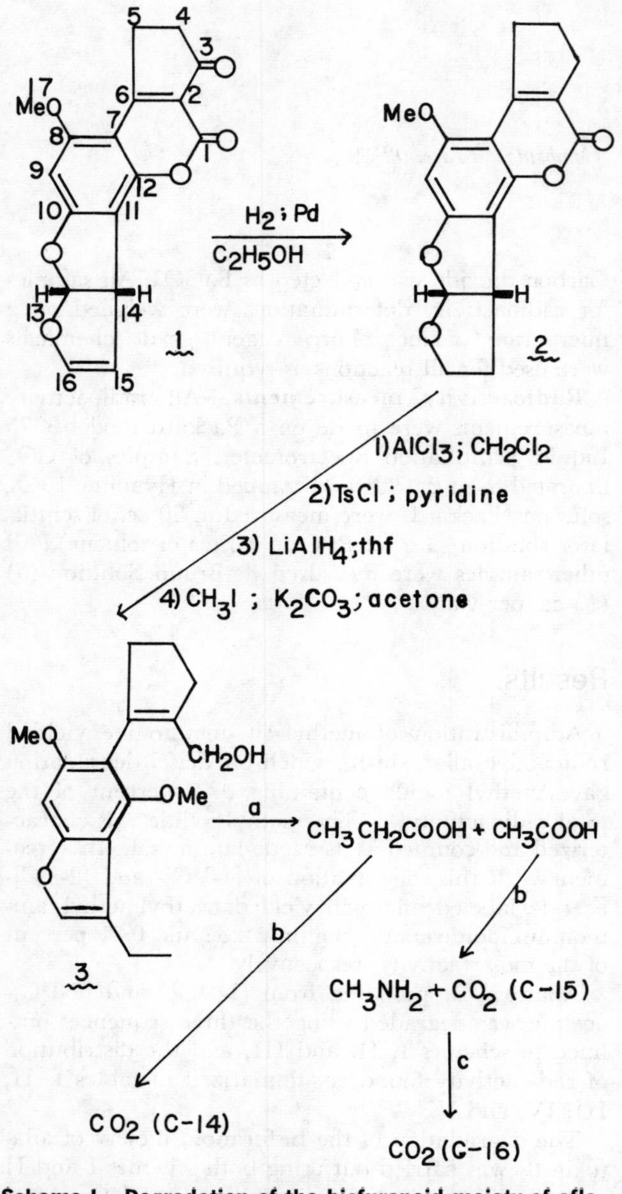

Scheme I.—Degradation of the bisfuranoid moiety of aflatoxin-B₁ to propionic and acetic acid. (a) Kuhn-Roth oxidation.[24] (b)Schmidt degradation.[5] (c) Oxidation with KMnO₄.[5]

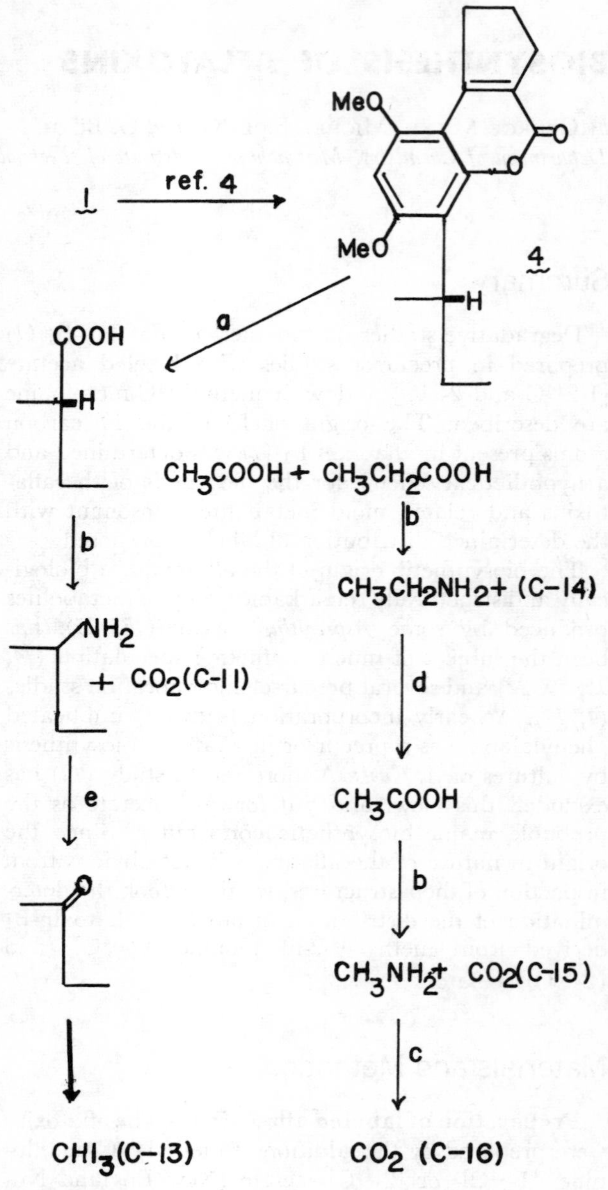

Scheme II.—Degradation of the bisfuranoid moiety of aflatoxin-B₁ to 2-methylbutanoic, propionic, and acetic acid. (a)–(c) same as in scheme I. (d) Oxidation with KMnO₄.[3] (e) Oxidation with NaOCl.[21]

The distribution of labels indicated in table I is not delineated as sharply as in the later degradative studies. Since this particular sample of labeled aflatoxin was not employed again, we are uncertain as to whether this should be ascribed to partial randomization of the labels during the incorporation or to some fault of the degradation. However, the labeling pattern in the bisfuranoid moiety determined for the [1-14C]-acetate incorporation was decisively confirmed by degradation of aflatoxin-B₁ prepared from [2-14C]-acetate, via scheme II. The results of this degradation are given in table III.

Table 2.—Distribution of labels from 1-14C-acetate labeling as determined by scheme II

Carbon atoms	Estimated as—	Percent of total radio-activity
C–11, C–13 to C–16	N(α-naphthyl)-2-methylbutanamide	22.31
C–11	CO₂	.13

Table 3.—Distribution of labels from 2-^{14}C-acetate labeling as determined from scheme II

Carbon atoms	Estimated as—	Percent of total radio-activity
C–11, C–13 to C–16	p-bromophenacyl-2-methylbutanoate	43.26
C–11	CO_2	12.83
C–13	CHI_3	.49
C–14 to C–16	p-bromophenacyl-propionate	28.61
C–14	CO_2	12.78
C–15	CO_2	.49
C–16	CO_2	12.72

Table 4.—Labeling pattern in aflatoxin-B_1 derived from 1-^{14}C-acetate as determined by scheme III

Carbon atoms	Estimated as—	Percent of total radio-activity
C–1 to C–7	p-bromophenacyl-*cis*-2-methylcyclopentanoate	43.84
C–7	CO_2	.14
C–1, C–2	p-bromophenacylacetate	10.37; 11.05
C–2	CO_2	.21
C–1	CO_2	8.52
C–1 to C–6	p-bromophenacylcaproate	44.48
C–6	CO_2	8.89
C–1 to C–5	p-bromophenacylvalerate	32.57
C–5	CO_2	6.77
C–1 to C–4	p-bromophenacylbutyrate	18.57
C–1 to C–3	p-bromophenacylpropionate	21.80

Table 5.—Distribution of labels from 2-^{14}C-acetate incorporation as determined from scheme III

Carbon atoms	Estimated as—	Percent of total radio-activity
C–1 to C–7	p-bromophenacyl-*cis*-2-methylcyclopentanoate	43.06
C–7	CO_2	12.86
C–1, C–2	p-bromophenacylacetate	14.10
C–2	CO_2	12.62
C–1	CO_2	.35
C–1 to C–6	p-bromophenacylcaproate	28.56
C–6	CO_2	.26
C–1 to C–5	p-bromophenacylvalerate	28.67
C–5	CO_2	.35
C–1 to C–4	p-bromophenacylbutyrate	28.47
C–1 to C–3	p-bromophenacylpropionate	14.28

The degradation of the cyclopentenone moiety of aflatoxin-B_1 is described in scheme III. The distribution of labels obtained from the degradation of [1-^{14}C]- and [2-^{14}C]-acetate derived aflatoxin-B_1 by this scheme is shown in tables IV and V, respectively.

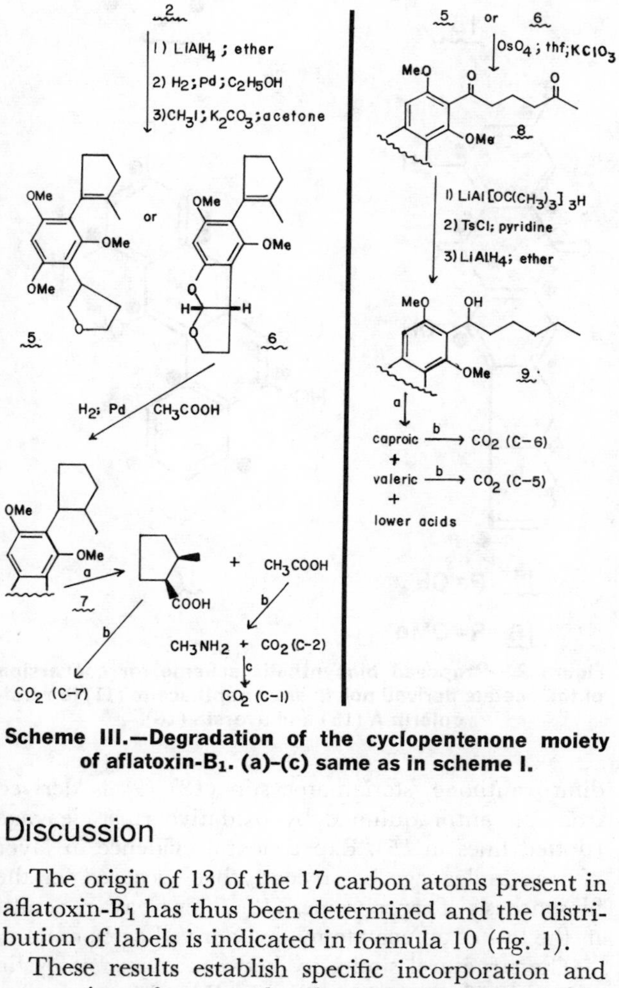

Scheme III.—Degradation of the cyclopentenone moiety of aflatoxin-B_1. (a)–(c) same as in scheme I.

Discussion

The origin of 13 of the 17 carbon atoms present in aflatoxin-B_1 has thus been determined and the distribution of labels is indicated in formula 10 (fig. 1).

These results establish specific incorporation and comparison of measured and calculated radioactivities demand the presence of nine labels (theoretical activ-

ity 11.1 percent per labeled carbon atom) in 1-^{14}C acetate derived aflatoxin-B_1. If it is assumed that the metabolite originated from a nonaacetyl chain, two methyl-derived carbon atoms must have been eliminated. Experimental support for the presence of seven labels (theoretical activity 14.3 percent labeled carbon atom) in radioactive aflatoxin-B_1 prepared from [2-^{14}C]-acetate was secured again by comparison of the measured and calculated radioactivities of the degradation products.

The resulting distribution of labels portrayed in formula 10 is not in accord with that of others (*14, 19, 22*) or implied in Holker and Underwood (*15*), a number of previously proposed biosynthetic schemes. We wish to propose a new hypothesis for the biogenesis of the aflatoxins and related mold metabolites which is consonant with the experimental evidence now in hand.

It is assumed that the postulated nonaacetyl chain is cyclized to give a polyhydroxynapthacene **11** which is oxidized to the endoperoxyanthraquinone **12** which in turn rearranges via the diradical **13** to the aldehyde **14** (see fig. 2). A further isomerization, similar to the

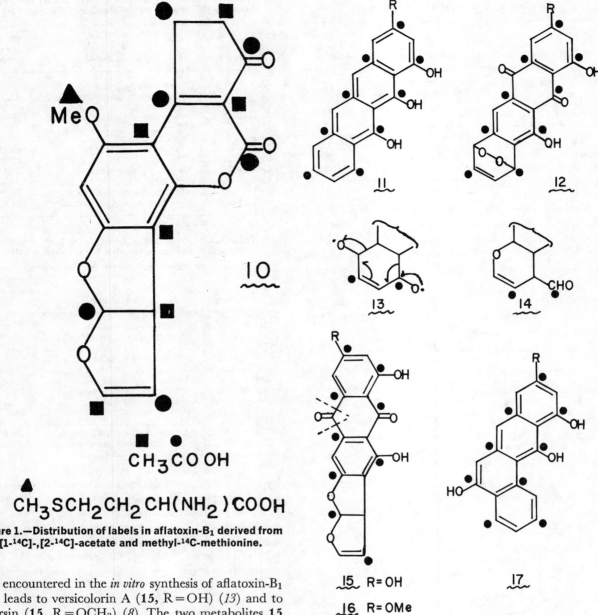

Figure 1.—Distribution of labels in aflatoxin-B₁ derived from [1-¹⁴C]-,[2-¹⁴C]-acetate and methyl-¹⁴C-methionine.

Figure 2.—Proposed biosynthetic scheme for conversion of the acetate derived polyhydroxynapthacene (11) to versicolorin A (15) and aversin (16).

one encountered in the *in vitro* synthesis of aflatoxin-B₁ (*7*), leads to versicolorin A (**15**, R=OH) (*13*) and to aversin (**15**, R=OCH₃) (*8*). The two metabolites **15** and **16** may also arise from the isomeric polyhydroxy-benzanthracene by an entirely analogous sequence leading to the same distribution of labels. The rearrangement of the endoperoxide **12** to the pyran **14** seems to be without chemical precedent, yet it does provide an exceedingly economical and mechanistically not unreasonable pathway to the bisfuran moieties of metabolites elaborated by the genus *Aspergillus*. The employment of the diradical intermediaty **13** is not intended to rule out the possible intermediace of related ionic mechanistic pathways leading to the aldehyde **14**.

It has previously been postulated (*22*) that the

difuroxanthone, sterigmatocystin (**18**) (*9*) is derived from an anthraquinone by oxidative ring cleavage (dotted lines in **15**). Experimental evidence in favor of such a cleavage has recently been secured for the biosynthesis of ergochromes (*12*). This cleavage results in the loss of an acetate methyl derived carbon atom.

The structural similarity between sterigmatocystin (**18**) and aflatoxin-B₁ (**20**) as well as the coexistence of O-methylsterigmatocystin (**19**) (*10*) and aflatoxins

in *A. flavus*, has led to the postulate that a difuroxanthone is an intermediate in the biosynthesis of the
aflatoxins. Two detailed schemes were presented (*15,
22*) but only one (*22*) involving oxidative ring cleavage
(dotted line in *18*), recyclization followed by expulsion
of an acetate *methyl* derived carbon atom, leads to the
distribution of labels in the cyclopentenone moiety as
demanded by our experimental findings (fig. 3).

Since the only experimental evidence available
(*15*) is against sterigmatocystin (**18**) being a precursor
of aflatoxin-B₁ (**20**) in *A. flavus*, one should not over-
look the possibility that the aflatoxins could originate
from a trihydroxybenzanthracene **21** isomeric with **17**
by the route **21** → **22** → **23** → **24** → **20** (fig. 4). We
consider this route to be less attractive, however, in
view of the great preponderance of napthacene as
versus benzanthracene derivatives elaborated in
Nature, tetracycline biosynthesis, and finally the fact
that the cometabolites aflatoxin-B₁ and O-methylsterigmatocystin can be derived from a common
hydroxynapthacene, but not from the same hydroxy-
benzanthracene.

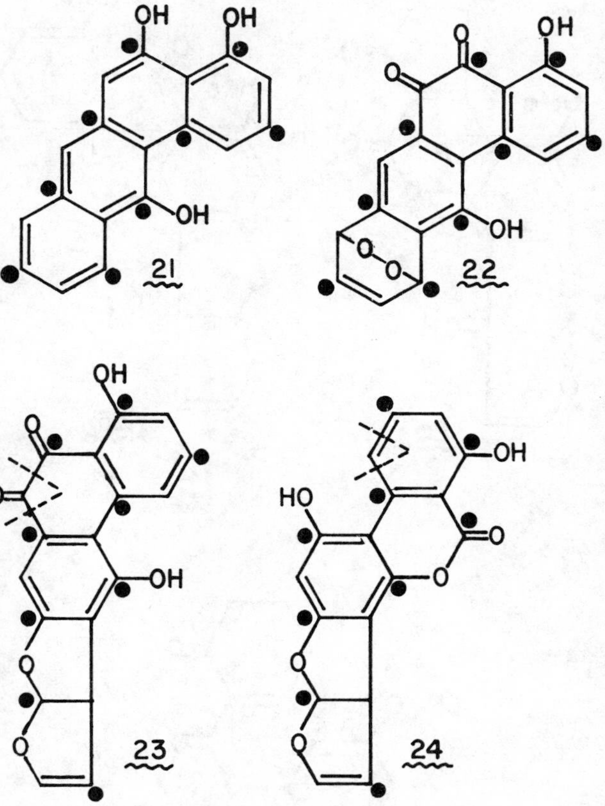

**Figure 4.—An alternative biosynthetic scheme for afla-
toxin-B₁ originating from the acetate derived polyhydroxy
benzanthracene (21) isomeric with 11.**

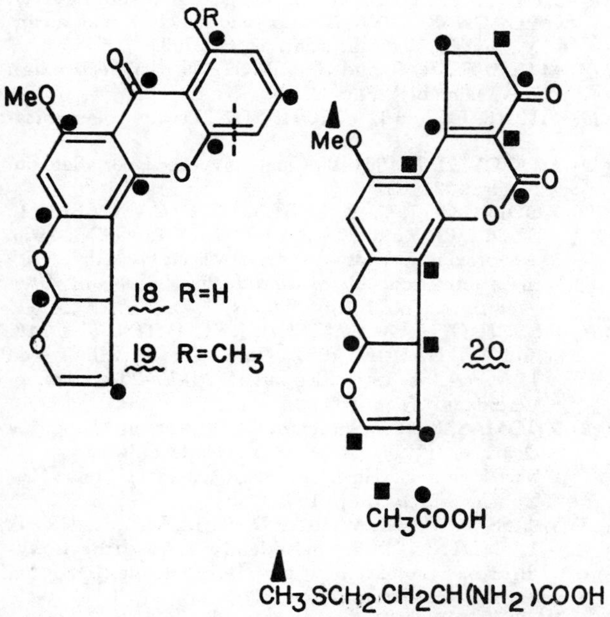

**Figure 3.—Postulated biosynthetic conversion of sterig-
matocystin (18) to aflatoxin-B₁ (20).**

Aflatoxin-M₁(*16*) (**25**) and aspertoxin (*20, 23*) (**26**)
(hydroxy-O-methylsterigmatocystin) (fig. 5) are almost certainly derived from aflatoxin-B₁ (**20**) and
O-methylsterigmatocystin (**19**), respectively, rather
than vice versa because the additional hydroxyl
group present in the bisfuran portion of these metabolites is attached to an acetate methyl group. Finally,
aflatoxin-G₁ (**27**), as compared to aflatoxin-B₁, exhib-

its further branching of the carbon skeleton of the
cyclopentenone moiety and so is almost certainly
derived from aflatoxin-B₁, perhaps by a base catalyzed
Baeyer-Villiger type oxidation.

Acknowledgment

This study was supported by contract No. PH
43–62–468 with the National Cancer Institute, National Institutes of Health.

References

(*1*) ADYE, J., and R. I. MATELES. 1964. Incorporation of
labeled compounds into aflatoxins. Biochim. Biophys.
Acta *86:* 418.

(*2*) BRECHBUHLER, S. We are indebted to Dr. S. Brechbuhler for this determination.

(*3*) BRECHBUHLER, S. 1964. Dissertation, Eidgenossischen
Technischen Hochschule, Zurich.

(*4*) BRECHBUHLER, S., G. BUCHI, and G. MILNE. 1967.
The absolute configuration of the aflatoxins. J. Org.
Chem. *32:* 2641.

(*5*) BRITT, J. J. 1959. Dissertation, Eidgenossischen Technischen Hochschule, Zurich.

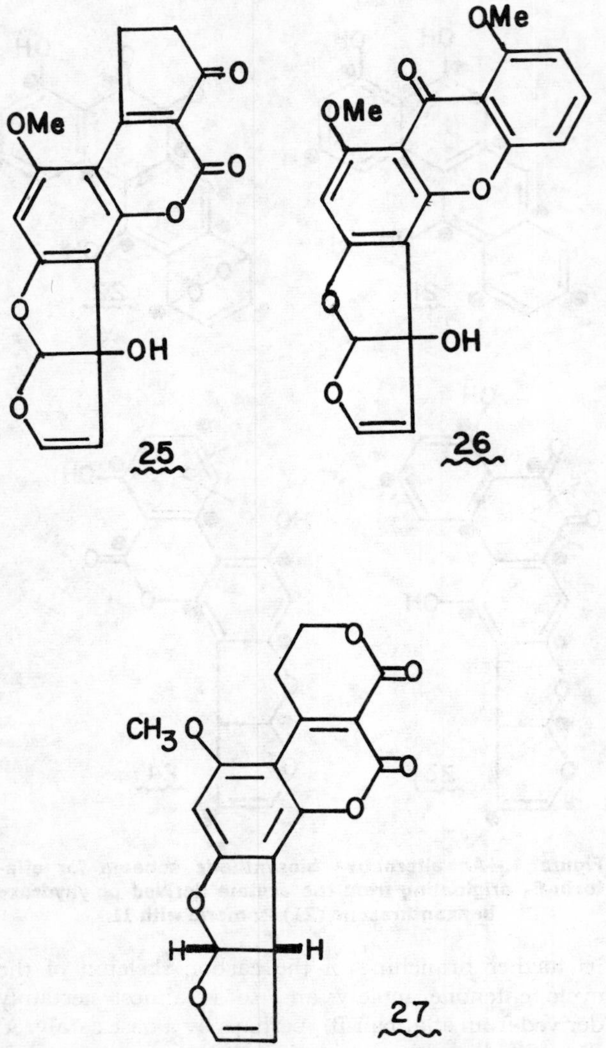

Figure 5.—aflatoxin-M₁ (25), aspertoxin (26) and aflatoxin-G₁ (27).

(6) BRUNO, G. A., and J. E. CHRISTIAN. 1961. Determination of carbon −14 in aqueous bicarbonate solutions by liquid scintillation counting techniques. Application to biological fluids. Anal. Chem. *33:* 1216.

(7) BUCHI, G., D. M. FOULKES, M. KURONO, G. F. MITCHELL, and R. S. SCHNEIDER. 1966 and 1967. The total synthesis of racemic aflatoxin B. J. Am. Chem. Soc. *89:* 6745; *88:* 4534.

(8) BULLOCK, E., J. C. ROBERTS, and J. G. UNDERWOOD. 1962. Studies in mycological chemistry Part XI. The structure of isosterigmatocystin and an amended structure for sterigmatocystin. J. Chem. Soc., 4179.

(9) BULLOCK, E., D. KIRKALDY, J. C. ROBERTS, and J. G. UNDERWOOD. 1963. Studies in mycological chemistry part XII. Two new metabolites from a variant strain of *Aspergillus versicolor* (Vuillemin) *tiraboschi*. J. Chem. Soc., 829.

(10) BURKHARDT, H., and J. FORGACS. 1968. O-methyl sterigmatocystin, a new metabolite from *Aspergillus flavus*, link ex fries. Tetrahedron, *24:* 717.

(11) DONKERSLOOT, J. A., D. P. H. HSIEH, and R. I. MATELES. 1968. Incorporation of precursors into aflatoxin B₁. J. Am. Chem. Soc. In press.

(12) FRANCK, B., F. HUPER, D. GROGER, and D. ERGE. 1968. Biosynthese der ergochrome. Chem. Ber. *101:* 1954.

(13) HAMASAKI, T., Y. HATSUDA, N. TERASHIMA, and M. RENBUTSU. 1967. Studies on the metabolites of *Aspergillus versicolor* (Vuillemin) *tiraboschi*. Part V. Isolation and Structures of three new metabolites, versicolorins A, B, and C. Agr. Biol. Chem. *31:* 11.

(14) HEATHCOTE, J. G., J. J. CHILD, and M. F. DUTTON. 1965. The possible role of kojic acid in the production of aflatoxin by *Aspergillus flavus*. Biochem. J. *95:* 23 p.

(15) HOLKER, J. S. E., and J. G. UNDERWOOD. 1964. A synthesis of a cyclopentenocoumarin structurally related to aflatoxin B. Chem. Ind. (London), 1865.

(16) HOLTZAPFEL, C. W., P. S. STEYN, and I. F. H. PURCHASE. 1966. Isolation and structure of aflatoxins M₂ and M₁. Tetrahedron Letters, 2799.

(17) MATELES, R. I., and G. N. WOGAN. 1967. Aflatoxins. Adv. Microbiol. Phys. *1:* 25.

(18) MILNE, G., and D. S. JOHNSON. Private communication.

(19) MOODY, D. P. 1964. Biogenetic hypothesis for aflatoxin. Nature *202:* 188.

(20) RODRICKS, J. V., E. LUSTIG, A. D. CAMPBELL, L. STOLOFF, and K. R. HENERY-LOGAN. 1968. Aspertoxin, a hydroxy derivative of O-methylsterigmatocystin from aflatoxin-producing cultures of *Aspergillus flavus*. Tetrahedron Letters, 2975.

(21) RUSCHIG, H., W. FRITSCH, J. SCHMIDT-THOME, and W. HAEDE. 1955. Uber die Herstellung von 17α-Oxy-20-ketosteroiden aus 17(20)-En-20-acetaminosteroiden. Ber. *88:* 883.

(22) THOMAS, R. 1965. Biosynthetic pathways involving ring cleavage. In "Biogenesis of Antibiotic Substances", Z. Vanek and Z. Hostalek, eds., Academic Press, New York, N.Y., ch. 13, p. 155.

(23) WAISS, A. C., M. WILEY, D. R. BLACK, and R. E. LUNDIN. 1968. 3-hydroxy-6, 7-dimethoxy-difuroxenthone a new metabolite from *Aspergillus flavus*. Tetrahedron Letters, 3207.

(24) WIESENBERGER, E. 1948. Die mikroanalytische bestimmung von C-methyl-und Acetylgruppen. Microchim. Acta *33:* 51.

(25) WOGAN, G. N. 1966. Chemical nature and biological effects of the aflatoxins. Bacteriol. Rev. *30:* 460.

A NEW MYCOTOXIN PRODUCED BY *ASPERGILLUS CLAVATUS*

by HIROYA TANABE *and* TAKASHI SUZUKI*
National Institute of Hygienic Sciences, Setagaya, Tokyo

Summary

Many kinds of fungal strains were isolated from rice grains, beans, wheat flour, and other foodstuffs during investigations on toxic fungi and mycotoxins contained in Japanese foods.

During these investigations, culture broth of a strain of toxic *Aspergillus clavatus*, isolated from wheat flour, was studied for the isolation and identification of patulin. The broth was treated with activated charcoal, absorbed patulin extracted with moistened acetone, the extract concentrated under suction, and applied to column-chromatography purification. During this process a new toxic compound was isolated in a slightly more polar fraction than that containing patulin. The infrared ultra-violet and nuclear magnetic resanance spectrographic studies carried out on this compound, $C_7H_8O_4$, m.p. 64° C., finally demonstrated it to be identical with $NaBH_4$-reduction product of patulin showing that the structure of the compound was as follows:

The compound was named *ascladiol* and it was found to be one-fourth as toxic as patulin.

Introduction

Extensive investigation of mycotoxin-producing fungi on and in Japanese foods has been carried on in the Laboratory of Mycology, in cooperation with the Laboratory of Food Chemistry of the National Institute of Hygienic Sciences, Japan (*1*).

To date more than 500 samples of various kinds of foods such as flour, rice, beans, and others have been investigated and about 1,500 strains have been isolated. Two strains of *A. flavus* proved to produce aflatoxins. This was the first finding of this kind of

---

*Read by K. Kanota.

fungus in Japan. Among the isolates, liquid cultures or methanol extracts from solid cultures of 170 strains were investigated by bioassay for toxicity, and 31 strains were found to be of considerable toxicity for mice.

One strain of *A. clavatus* (WF–38–11) isolated from wheat flour was among these toxic strains. *A. clavatus* has been known to produce patulin, a strongly toxic metabolite. In order to identify patulin in the culture, its isolation was carried out by the general procedure; i.e. absorption of the toxin by activated charcoal, its elution by moistened acetone and its purification by column chromatography.

During this purification, a new toxic crystalline compound was obtained in slightly more polar fraction than that of patulin. Acute toxicity of this compound was about one-fourth times as strong as patulin. The new toxin was named ascladiol.

Isolation of ascladiol.—Liquid culture (5:1) of *A. clavatus* isolated from wheat flour was filtered and the filtrate obtained was shaken with activated charcoal (50 g.) overnight. The charcoal was centrifuged, washed with water and then extracted with several portions (each 200 ml.) of a mixture of acetone and water (4:1) to elute the adsorbed patulin.

The extracts were combined and concentrated under vacuum down to about 200 ml. The residual water solution was subjected to continuous extraction with ether in an automatic extractor. The ether extract was, evaporated and the residue obtained was mixed with silica gel (5 g.) and applied to a silica gel (30 g.) column for chromatography. Elution was carried out with three portions of a mixture of chloroform and acetone (50:1), yielding fraction 1, 300 ml.; fraction 2, 300 ml.; and fraction 3, 400 ml.; and then eluted with three portions of another mixture of chloroform and acetone (50:2), yielding fraction 4, 300 ml.; fraction 5, 400 ml., and fraction 6, 1,500 ml.

Fractions 1 and 2 contained 250 mg. of oily material which has been under investigation. Fractions 3 and 4 contained 363 mg. of a crystalline substance which proved to be patulin by IR spectrography, thin-layer chromatography and m.p. depression test on admixture with an authentic sample.

From the last fraction, when concentrated and treated with methanol and chloroform, a very hygroscopic crystalline compound was obtained. This was purified by dissolving it in a small amount of methanol, followed by the addition of chloroform, until the solution became turbid, and then being allowed to stand over night in a refrigerator.

Chemical structure of ascladiol.—The crystalline substance, m.p. 65° to 66° C., $C_7H_8O_4$, was subjected to physical and chemical tests to elucidate its chemical structure.

The absorption bands at both of 1,735 cm.$^{-1}$ and 1,750 cm.$^{-1}$, and 3,300 cm.$^{-1}$ in the IR spectrum (KBr tab.) of the compound indicated the presence of a 5-membered lacton ring and associated hydroxyl groups in the molecule. The UV spectrum, measured in ethanol, showed maximum absorption at 271 mμ while that of patulin is at 277 mμ. This shift of 6 mμ toward a short wave length seemed to hint the lack of one exo-double bond in the new compound in comparison with patulin.

The NMR spectrum showed absorption at 6.29 p.p.m. (quartet) and 5.87 p.p.m. (multiplet), each indicating the presence of different one vinyl protons. Broad singlet absorption was also observed at 4.74 p.p.m., indicating the presence of four protons. Since two of these protons disappeared by addition of D_2O into sample solution, it seemed that two hydroxy protons and two methylene protons overlapped each other.

Two other methylene protons were observed at 4.30 p.p.m. This compound seemed not to have aldehyde or ketone groups in the molecule, since it did not react with 2,4-dinitrophenythydrazine.

According to the above data, the chemical structure of the new compound was presumed to be as follows:

Finally, the structure was confirmed by the comparison of physical data with an authentic sample synthesized from patulin by reducing it in ethanol with $NaBH_4$ under very mild conditions 0° to 2° C. for 10 minutes.

References

(1) KURATA, H., and M. ICHINOE. 1967. Studies on the population of toxigenic fungi in foodstuffs. I. Fungal flora of flour-type foodstuffs. J. Food Hyg. Soc. Japan *8*: 237–246.

(2) KURATA, H., and M. ICHINOE. 1967. Studies on the population of toxigenic fungi in foodstuffs. II. Toxigenic determination for the fungal isolates obtained from the flour-type foodstuffs. J. Food Hyg. Soc. Japan *8*: 247–252.

(3) KURATA, H., S. UDAGAWA, M. ICHINOE, Y. KAWASAKE, M. TAKADA, M. TAZAWA, A. KOIZUMI, and H. TANABE. 1968. Studies on the population of toxigenic fungi in foodstuffs. III. Mycoflora of milled rice harvested in 1965. J. Food Hyg. Soc. Japan *9*: 23–28.

(4) KURATA, H., H. TANABE, K. KANOTA, S. UDAGAWA, and M. ICHINOE. 1968. Studies on the population of toxigenic fungi in foodstuffs. IV. Aflatoxin producing fungi isolated from foodstuff in Japan. J. Food Hyg. Soc. Japan *9*: 29–34.

STUDIES ON TOXIC METABOLITES OF PENICILLIUM ROQUEFORTI

by KENZO KANOTA

Department of Medical Supplies, National Institute of Hygienic Sciences, Tokyo

Summary

Isolation and purification of the toxins produced by a toxic strain of *Penicillium roqueforti* was studied. The production of toxic substances by this strain was observed when it was cultured using Czapek's medium, grown at 25° C. in stationary culture. The optimum culture age was about 3 weeks. Koji extract media were found useless for the production of toxins. The culture filtrate was extracted with charcoal, which was collected by centrifugation. The charcoal was extracted using methanol and the solvent layer was concentrated and acidified. The concentrate could be further extracted with acetonitrile. Although the dried material of this fraction was observed to kill mice, it was found to be impure. Silicic acid column chromatography was performed to obtain three kinds of toxic fractions. Toxin 1 was easily crystallized. Its toxicity was rather weak. Partial characterization of this crystal was made. Toxin 2 was a brownish oil. All the mice tested were killed by this fraction. Gross liver damage and hemmorrhage in the alimentary tract were observed. Toxin 3 was the weakest in toxicity among the three fractions. The mycelia proved to have no toxicity.

Introduction

Among the molds which can be isolated from ensilage, *P. roqueforti* is one of the most commonly found (*2, 3*). A toxicosis caused by this mold was reported in 1956. Sudden death of cattle in Kobe was attributed to the ensilage from which strains of *P. roqueforti* had been isolated. The mycelium of one of the strains of this species, obtained from the liquid culture, proved to kill all the mice tested (*4*).

The MR 212–2 strain of *P. roqueforti*, which had been isolated from a milled-rice sample by Dr. Kurata and his coworkers, was found toxic. However the toxicity was not as severe as that of *P. islandicum*, *P. expansum*, and *Aspergillus clavatus* which were obtained from the same origin (*1*).

Although it did not always follow that all of *P. roqueforti* strains were toxic it was of great interest to elucidate the situation since this is an essential fungus used in the manufacture of "roquefort cheese" and is one of the strains that can be isolated frequently from foods.

The author has attempted to isolate and elucidate the nature of the toxins produced by this strain.

Materials and Methods

Detection of toxins.—The toxicity of the fractions, obtained during the course of purification of the toxic substances, was tested by intraperitoneal injection of a solution of each fraction in propylene glycol. Male, strain dd mice, weighing 15 to 18 g. were used as test animals. Toxicity was determined by mortality, loss of body weight for 4 days after injection and the gross pathological findings of the tested animals.

Mold culture.—Czapek's medium, containing 50 g. of sucrose per liter, was used for the mold culture. It was grown at 25° C. in stationary culture. Optimum cultural age for toxin production was approximately 3 weeks.

The yield of toxins was thought to be proportional to the mycelial growth, and a good mycelial growth depended upon the pH of the medium. About 10 g. of mycelial growth resulted when the final pH was about 4.0, but when the pH became higher than 4.5, the yield decreased rapidly. Production of toxic substances was restricted to the culture using Czapek's medium. Koji extract media were found useless for the production of toxin under any cultural conditions. It would be interesting to find the conditions necessary for optimal toxin production.

The mycelia of this strain showed no toxicity. This differed from previous reports. And it was suggested that there might be some kinds of toxins which *P. roqueforti* can produce, one kind being water soluble and the other insoluble.

Extraction of toxins.—The culture filtrate was treated with 1 percent of active charcoal. After centrifugation the charcoal was collected and treated with methanol to elute the toxins. The methanol layer was concentrated *in vacuo* to yield a brownish oil. Two of five mice were killed by this fraction within several hours after injection of 0.2 ml. (fig. 1). The yield of this fraction was about 12 g./l. of broth when the growth of mold was heavy.

Trials to increase the toxicity of this fraction made

it clear that an acetonitrile extraction of the oil, dissolved in a few milliliters of N/1 HCl was very effective. The concentrate of the resultant fraction killed all the mice tested. Thin-layer chromatography (TLC) of this extract revealed that this fraction was not yet pure. Subsequently silicic acid column chromatography was performed, which yielded three fractions, all of which were toxic to mice.

Toxin-1 was obtained from the eluate, which resulted from percolation of two parts of methanol and

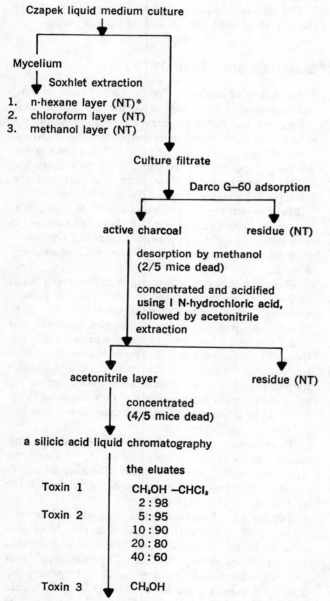

*(NT) means not toxic to mice.

Figure 1.—Scheme of extraction of the toxic metabolites of *Penicillium roqueforti* MR 212–2.

98 parts of chloroform; and toxin-2 from five parts of methanol and 95 parts of chloroform; and toxin-3 was from methanol.

Toxin-1 was easily crystallized. Its toxicity was rather weak. Intraperitoneal injection of 20 mg. of this crude substance per mouse caused decrement of body weight but was not lethal. The yield was about 150 mg./20 l. of broth when the culture was well formed. Toxin-2 was a brownish oil. All the mice tested were killed by injection of 0.2 ml. of this fraction. At autopsy gross damage in liver and hemorrhage in alimentary tracts were observed. Toxin-3 was the weakest in toxicity.

Elucidation of physical properties of toxin 1.— From the crude preparation of toxin-1, a tetragonal crystal was obtained, once from methanol-ether and then twice from methanol-chloroform. The vacuum dried (1 mm. Hg. at room temperature) material melted at 86° to 87° C. Toxin-1 was soluble in water, methanol, acetone and pyridine; slightly soluble in chloroform and insoluble in ether and n-hexane.

This chromatographed as a single spot on Kieselgel G (E. Merck AG Darmstadt) TLC plate. RF values were 0.50 and 0.60, respectively, when methanol-chloroform (1:3) and acetone-chloroform (1:5) were used as developer. The spot did not fluoresce in ultraviolet light. The color developed, when the TLC plate was sprayed with cesium sulfate solution and heated in an oven at 180° C., was white at first and then became gray.

Elemental analysis showed that it contained 40.57 percent of C, 5.86 percent of H. Nitrogen was not detected. Possible formulae from such analytical data were either $C_7H_{11}O_7$ (for C:40.60 percent, H:5.36 percent) or $C_7H_{12}O_7$ (C:40.31 percent, H:5.81 percent).

The mass spectrum of the crystal (using JEOL–OIS model, double focusing mass spectrometer, ionizing energy: 75 eV, accelerating voltage 7 kV, and sample temperature 90° C.) indicated a millimass number 189.0361 as the parent peak of toxin-1. The possible molecular formula which corresponded to the millimass was only $C_7H_9O_6$ (Anal. Calcd. for 189.0396) since nitrogen was not included in the compound.

A solution of 2.6 mg. of the crystalline toxin in 10 ml. of ethanol was transparent to ultraviolet light of wavelength longer than 220 mμ.

Figure 2–a shows the infrared spectrum of toxin-1. It did not yield the characteristic peaks of an aromatic compound. Absorptions at 3,400, 1,365 and 1,150 cm⁻¹ suggest the existence of hydroxyl function, presumably secondary or tertiary alcohol. Methylation procedure by diazomethane caused a shortening of the absorptions at 3,400 and 1,150 and the peak at 1,365 almost disappeared (fig. 2–b).

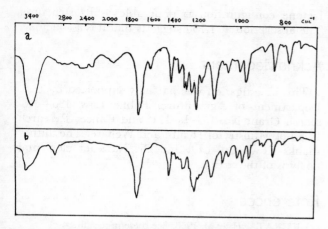

Figure 2.—Infrared spectra of toxin 1 and its methyl derivative (a) toxin 1, (b) methylated Toxin 1. KBr disc.

Increment of γCH at 2,870 by methylation was also apparent. An abnormal spectral pattern from 1,900 to 3,000 cm^{-1} depends upon stretching vibration of intramolecular association of hydroxyl and carbonyl groups. Methylation of hydroxyl function stops such association and causes the disappearance of these peaks.

Gas chromatography of toxin-1 has not been successful even when a highly polar column was utilized, but the methyl derivative was easily chromatographed, using nonpolar stationary phases such as SE–30 and OV–17. According to the gas chromatogram (fig. 3) a minor peak leads the major; presumably the minor peak corresponds to the fully methylated derivative and the major peak to a partially methylated derivative.

The millimass number of methylated toxin-1 was 235.0804 which denoted $C_9H_{15}O_7$ (Anal. Calcd. for 235.0817).

The absorptions of toxin-1 at 1,730, 1,215, and 1,150 cm^{-1} indicates that this substance contains an ester or lactone structure.

Figure 4 shows the NMR spectrum of a deuterochloroform solution of toxin-1. The signal at 4, 7τ depends upon hydroxyl function, and its τ value is easily varied by raising the temperature.

Discussion

It is very strange that the mass number of the parent peak of toxin-1 is odd, as it neither contains nitrogen nor does it have a spectrum characteristic of a compound which gives an odd mass number.

The difference between the data of elemental analysis and mass spectrometry is H_2O or H_3O. There are some examples of such differences, for instance in the case of polyalcohol, where, as the result of being

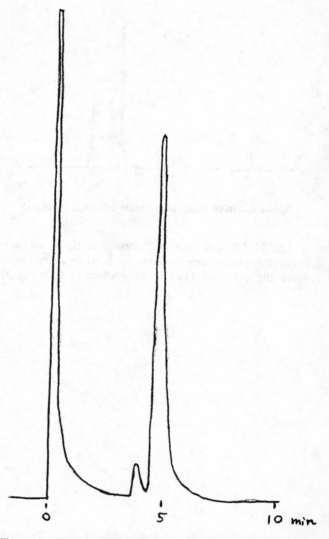

Figure 3.—Gas chromatogram of methylated toxin 1. Gas chromatographic condition:
Column: SE-30, 5 percent on Chromosorb G (HMDS treated) 4 mm. x 1.8 m. glass column, 170° C.
Injection port: 180° C.
Detector: 200° C.
Carrier: Nitrogen 50 ml./min.

deprived of H_2O in the ionizing chamber, a parent peak 18 less than the native mass number was observed. Toxin-1 may be such a case. Another explanation for the lack of one proton could be that it was due to the discharging of one hydrogen radical, although such a case is very rare. Further studies on this subject must be made. Methylated toxin-1 also has an odd number, 235, and if the phenomenon of discharging of one hydrogen radical is applied, the difference between the elemental composition of toxin-1 and its methylated derivative is C_2H_4 which means two hydroxyls are methylated.

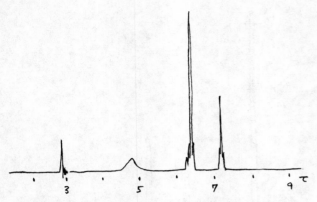

Figure 4.—NMR spectrum of toxin 1 (CDCl₃ solution).

The NMR spectrum indicated that there was no methyl function neighboring to carbon atom, and from the point of view of its molecular formula a lactone configuration is preferable as its structure. The absorption at 1,730 suggests that it is a δ-lactone.

Acknowledgment

This investigation was partially supported by U.S. Department of Agriculture, Public Law 480—Research Grant No. FG–Ja–121, and Cancer Research Fund of Ministry of Health and Welfare. The author thanks Kowa Co. Ltd. and Dr. Nara for elemental analysis of the toxins.

References

(1) KURATA, H. et al. 1968. See these proceedings.
(2) NAKANE, M. 1946. On the molds of ensilage. J. Appl. Mycol. *1:* 17–29.
(3) ibid. *1:* 30–41.
(4) TSUBAKI, K. 1956. *Penicillium* isolated from toxic ensilage. Trans. Mycol. Soc. Japan *1:* 6–7.

PYRAZINE COMPOUNDS PRODUCED BY MOLDS

by Tamotsu Yokotsuka, Yasuo Asao, Masaoki Sasaki, *and* Katsunori Oshita
Central Research Institute of Kikkoman Shoyu Co., Ltd.
399 Noda, Noda-shi, Chiba-ken, Japan

Summary

This report describes the chemical characterization of two kinds of new fluorescent pyrazine compounds which were isolated from cultures of seed mold widely used in the Japanese fermentation industry. Six new nonfluorescent pyrazine compounds were also isolated from the same culture and the structures of five were determined, including aspergillic acid and hydroxy-aspergillic acid. Nontoxicity of fluorescent pyrazine compounds and some toxicity of the nonfluorescent compounds was established by intraperitoneal injection into mice.

Introduction

Some investigators (1, 2, 3) have reported the existence of fluorescent compounds, produced by molds, whose Rf values in chromatography resemble those of aflatoxins. We did not find aflatoxin producing strains among the seed molds that are widely used in the Japanese fermentation food industries. Instead, we frequently found fluorescent metabolites of molds, the Rf values and fluorescence of which were similar to those of aflatoxin B or G. Eight kinds of pyrazine compound were isolated and five of them were characterized to be of the structures shown in figures 1 and 2 (4, 5). These results were reported in a Symposium on Mycotoxins, at the American Chemical Society annual meeting, New York, September 12, 1966 (6). The important findings of that report were as follows:

None of the 73 seed culture of starter strains of aspergilli produced aflatoxin when tested under our conditions. These findings confirmed the 1965 reports of Hesseltine et al. (1), Aibara and Miyaki (2), and

Sample	B0	B1	B2			B3
Assigned chemical structure						
Name of compound	2-hydroxy-3·6-di-sec-butyl pyrazine	deoxy-aspergillic acid	flavacol			——
Molecular formula	$C_{12}H_{20}ON_2$	$C_{12}H_{20}ON_2$	$C_{12}H_{20}ON_2$			——
Yield, mg/L Czapek Dox medium	67 / 260	225 / 140	145 / 140			trace amount
mod. Meyer medium	108 / 100					
mp °C sample	129	83	144			117
authentic sample	——	103–104	148.5–149			——
Analysis	C H N	C H N	C H N			
analytical	69.1 9.3 13.3	70.1 9.6 13.4	69.4 9.4 13.8			——
calculated	69.2 9.6 13.5	69.2 9.6 13.5	69.2 9.6 13.5			

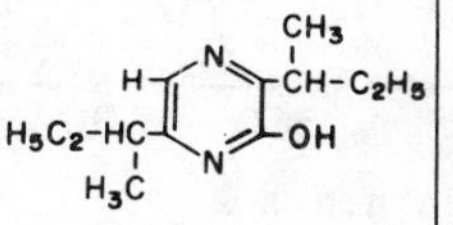

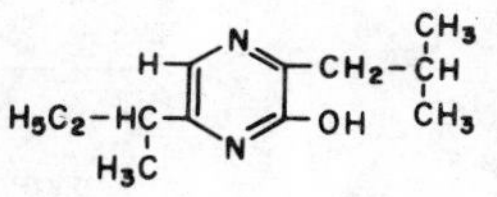

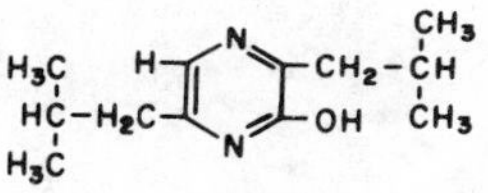

Figure 1.—Characterization of compounds B0–B3 of aspergillic X–1.

133

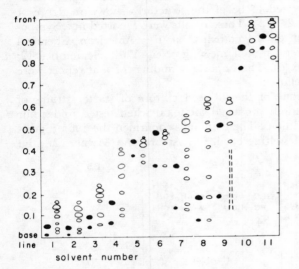

Sample	B4	B5	B6	B7
Assigned chemical structure				
Name of compound	Deoxyhydroxyaspergillic acid	____	2-Hydroxy-6-(1-hydroxy isopropyl)-3-isobutyl-pyrazine	____
Molecular formula	$C_{12}H_{20}O_2N_2$		$C_{11}H_{18}O_2N_2$	$C_{11}H_{18}O_2N_2$
Yield, mg/L Czapek Dox medium	trace amount			
mod. Meyer medium	339/100	311/100 (mix. of B5 and B6)		240
mp °C sample	107	153–154	133–134.5	158–159
authentic sample	105–106			
Analysis analytical	C 64.4 H 8.9 N 12.4	____	C 62.9 H 8.3 N 13.1	C 62.9 H 8.6 N 13.0
calculated	C 64.3 H 8.9 N 12.5		C 62.9 H 8.6 N 13.3	C 62.9 H 8.6 N 13.3

Figure 2.—Characterization of compounds B4–B7 of aspergillic X–1.

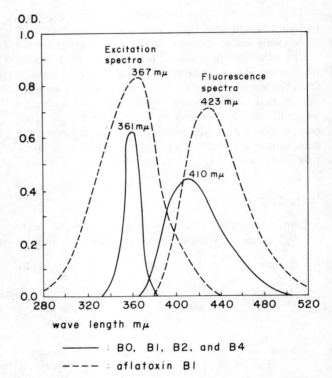

Masuda et al. (3). Approximately one-third of the strains tested produced compounds, displaying Rf values (fig. 3), and fluorescence data (fig. 4) similar to aflatoxins under some experimental conditions. However, isolation and characterization demonstrated that these compounds differed markedly in chemical structure from aflatoxins. Aflatoxins B-like compounds were related to each other, with the pyrazine ring common to their structures. This was indicated by similar ultraviolet spectra with absorption at 310 to 330 mμ (fig. 5) and similar infrared spectra with

—— : B0, B1, B2, and B4

- - - - : aflatoxin B1

Figure 4.—Excitation and fluorescence spectra of B0–B4 compounds.

adsorbent : Kieselgel G,   0.5 mm thickness

samples : aflatoxin B1 and G1, black spot on
left side of each column
aflatoxin B-like compounds, B0 to
B8 from the top on right side

solvent No. 1 : benzene, ethylacetate	3/1
2 : benzene, acetone	3/1
3 : chloroform, ethylacetate	3/1
4 : benzene, ethylacetate, ethanol	30/19/1
5 : chloroform, methanol	97/3
6 : benzene, ethanol	9/1
7 : chloroform, ethylacetate, ethanol	30/19/1
8 : ethylacetate, hexane	3/1
9 : chloroform, acetone	3/1
10 : ethylacetate, methanol	3/1
11 : acetone, hexane	3/1

Figure 3.—Variation of Rf values of aflatoxin B-like compounds of aspergillic X–1 with different solvent system.

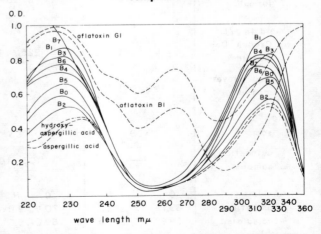

Figure 5.—UV absorption spectra of compounds B0–B7 in ethanol.

absorption at 1,600 cm.$^{-1}$. Nonfluorescent compounds, aspergillic acid (7) and hydroxy-aspergillic acid (8) were also isolated. It was confirmed that when these compounds have 2-hydroxy pyrazine rings they give fluorescence but when the No. 1 nitrogen is of an oxide structure they give no fluorescence, as far as the isolated compounds are concerned. The maximum absorption in infrared spectra at approximately 950 cm.$^{-1}$ seemed to be associated with these differences These conclusions offered some suggestions for possible chemical structures of the unknown compounds isolated.

In the present report we describe the chemical characterization of two kinds of fluorescent pyrazine compounds that were isolated subsequent to our previous report (6). Six kinds of new nonfluorescent pyrazine compound were also isolated from the same culture and the structures of five were determined, including aspergillic acid and hydroxyaspergillic acid. Toxicity of these compounds was tested by intraperitoneal injection into mice.

Materials and Methods

I. SEPARATION OF PYRAZINE COMPOUNDS.

Mold strain tested.—*Aspergillus sojae* X–1.

Medium.—Modified Mayer's medium believed to be the best for producing pyrazine compounds was prepared in accordance with the method of S. Nakamura (9) to the following composition: sucrose 50.0 g., polypeptone 20.0 g., KH_2PO_4 5.0 g., $MgSo_4.7H_2O$ 2.5 g., $CaHPO_4$ 2.5 g., water 1,000.0 ml., final pH 6.0 to 7.0.

Cultural conditions.—One liter of the medium, autoclaved in a 5-liter Fernbach flask, was inoculated with organisms from seed culture and incubated for 15 days at 30° C.

Separation of fluorescent pyrazine compounds.— This fractionation method is shown in figure 6. The separation of these similar compounds by direct use of thin-layer chromatography was very difficult. Moreover, the amount which could be spotted was limited. Taking advantage of the difference in the

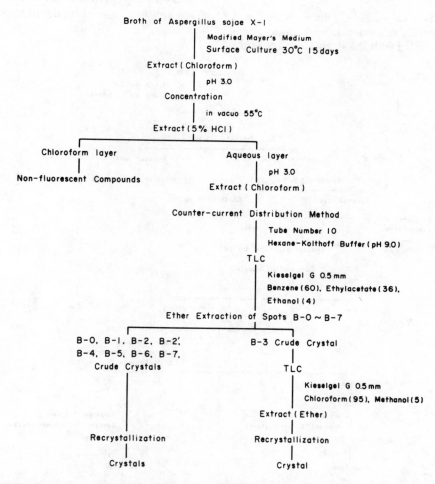

Figure 6.—Separation of fluorescent pyrazine compounds from culture of *Aspergillus sojae* X–1.

side chains at position 6, those of B4 and B6 being hydroxylated while those of B0, B1, B2 and B2' not being hydroxylated, a rough separation of two groups of the compounds was achieved by using counter-current distribution (*10*), followed by thin layer chromatography.

Separation of nonfluorescent pyrazine compounds.—This fractionation method is shown in figure 7. Thin layer chromatography, column chromatography, fractional extraction (*11, 12*), repeated recrystallization (*8*), and counter-current distribution (*8, 13*) have been applied by others for the separation of nonfluorescent pyrazine compounds, such as aspergillic acid, hydroxyaspergillic acid, muta-aspergillic acid (*13*), neoaspergillic acid (*14*), neohydroxyaspergillic acid (*11*), and pulcherriminic acid (*15*). But these methods were ineffective for the perfect separation of the closely similar structures of the compounds studied by us. In our hands good separation was achieved by converting the compounds to cupric salts which are readily soluble in nonpolar solvents (*16, 17*).

Biological tests.—Crystalline, fluorescent, and nonfluorescent pyrazine compounds were injected intraperitoneally into mice (ddOM strain, average body weight 20 g.) by personnel of the Institute of Physical and Chemical Research. Changes of weight and mortality of the animals were observed for 1 week.

II. ASSAY OF ASPERGILLIC ACID IN SHOYU KOJI.

Mold strain tested.—*Aspergillus sojae* X–1 was the strain employed. It is the most prolific aspergillic acid producer that was screened out of wild strains of *A. sojae* I. *A. sojae* KS is the common industrial molds used in this process.

Koji manufacture (mold culturing).—Cultivation of molds was carried out in 1 liter Fernbach flasks containing 15 g. of defatted soy beans. Soybeans in the Fernbach flasks were moistened with 15 ml. tapwater and then were steamed for 20 minutes and cooled. Crushed wheat (15 g.) was added to the cooked soybeans. The mixture was autoclaved at 15 pounds for 30 minutes. It was then inoculated with organisms from agar slants and incubated at 30° C. If the mixture (koji) packed in clumps, the material was loosened by shaking each flask vigorously.

Assay of aspergillic acid.—Aspergillic acid in the shoyu koji was assayed by the method shown in figure 8.

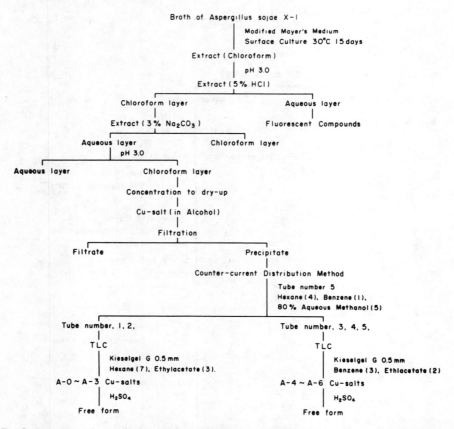

Figure 7.—Separation of non-fluorescent pyrazine compounds from culture of *Aspergillus sojae* X–1.

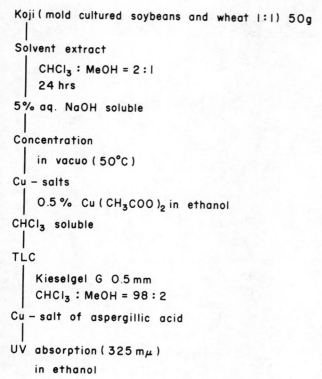

Koji (mold cultured soybeans and wheat 1:1) 50g

Solvent extract
  CHCl$_3$: MeOH = 2 : 1
  24 hrs

5% aq. NaOH soluble

Concentration
  in vacuo (50°C)

Cu – salts
  0.5 % Cu (CH$_3$COO)$_2$ in ethanol

CHCl$_3$ soluble

TLC
  Kieselgel G 0.5 mm
  CHCl$_3$: MeOH = 98 : 2

Cu – salt of aspergillic acid

UV absorption (325 mμ)
  in ethanol

Figure 8.—Determination of aspergillic acid in koji.

Results

Comparison of fluorescent and nonfluorescent pyrazine compounds in UV and IR spectra.—The similarity of ultraviolet and infrared absorption maxima and fluorescent and nonfluorescent pyrazine compounds, A0 to A5, are shown in figures 9 and 10, respectively.

Compounds	λmax mμ	λmax mμ
B – 0 ~ B – 6	227 ~ 231.5	312 ~ 327
A – 0 ~ A – 5	232 ~ 233.5	325 ~ 327

Solvent : Ethanol

Figuree 9.—Ultraviolet-absorption maxima of pyrazine compounds.

			Wavenumber (cm^{-1})			
Fluorescent	—	—	1650	—	950	—
Non – fluorescent	2400	2060	1640	1580	—	700

(KBr)

Figure 10.—Difference between fluorescent and nonfluorescent pyrazine compounds in infrared spectra.

CHARACTERIZATION OF ISOLATED COMPOUNDS:

B2′ compound.—This compound when isolated proved to be the corresponding synthetic deoxymuta-aspergillic acid (*18*) by infrared spectrum. (Kindly supplied by Dr. S. Nakamura.) This compound was newly isolated from nature.

B3 compound.—The isolated B3 was found to be identical with the hydrazine reduction (*8*) product of A4, and the reduction product of A4 by red phosphorus and hydriodic acid (*8*) proved to be the B0 compound, of which the chemical structure was already determined. R. G. Mecitich (*12*) in discussing the NMR spectra of the pyrazine compounds, pointed out the effect of the structure of the side chains; i.e. that the signals of the ten proton triplet centered at about 9.1τ were due to two ethyl group, that the three proton doublet centered at about 8.8τ and multiplet with τ values 6.6 to 6.9, respectively, indicated the presence of the grouping -C-CH$_3$. These findings indicated that the side chain at the position 3 of B3 was a *sec*-butyl structure. On the other hand, the three-proton singlet about 8.4τ, absence of multiplet with τ values about 7.4 to 7.6 in B0, together with the infrared spectra, indicated that the side chain at position 6 was also *sec*-butyl structure and was hydroxylated. Multiplet with τ value 7.9 to 8.2 was assigned to the CH$_2$ protons in the 3 and 6 *sec*-butyl side chain. Therefore, B3 compound was identified to be 2-hydroxy-6(1-hydroxy-1-methylprophyl) -3-*sec*-butylpyrazine. This is a new compound.

A0 compound.—Free form of cupric-salt of A0 was a yellow oil. The hydrazine reduction (*11*) product of A0 was shown to be the corresponding 2-hydroxy-3, 6-di-*sec*-butylpyrazine. Then the structure of A0 was identified as 2-hydroxy-3, 6-di-*sec*-butylpyrazine 1-oxide.

A1 compound.—Free form of A1 was also a yellow oil. The reduction of A1 with hydrazine (*8*) gave colorless crystals but its structure has not been identified as yet.

A2 compound.—This was characterized to be aspergillic acid by its infrared spectrum.

A3 compound.—The product on reduction of A3 with hydrazine (*8*) corresponded to 2-hydroxy-3-isobutyl-6-isopropylpyrazine by its infrared spectrum. Then the A3 structure was identified to be 2-hydroxy-3-isobutyl-6-isopropylpyrazine 1-oxide. This compared in figures 11, 12, and 13.

A4 compound.—The reductive product of A4 with hydriodic acid in phosphoric acid and the product on reduction of A4 with hydrazine (*8*) were shown to be B0 and B3, respectively. Therefor the A4 compound was identified to be 2-hydroxy-6-(1-hydroxy-1methylpropyl)-3-*sec*-butylpyrazine 1-oxide. This is a new compound.

A5 compound.—Its structure was characterized to be hydroxyaspergillic acid (8) by its infrared spectrum.

The properties of these purified compounds are compared in figures 11, 12, and 13.

Sample	B-2′	B-3
Assigned Chemical Structure	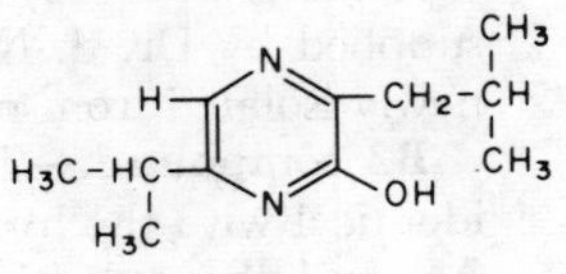	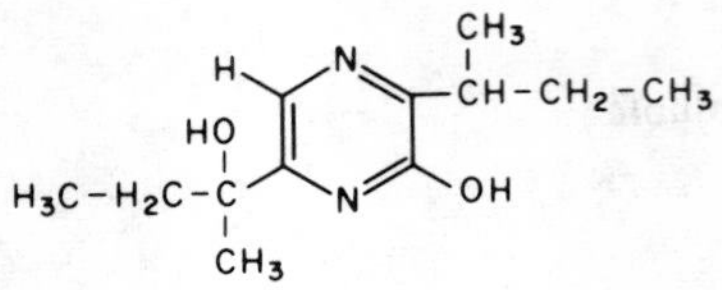
Name of Compounds	Deoxymuta–aspergillic acid	2-Hydroxy-6-(1-hydroxy-1-methylpropyl)-3-sec buthylpyrazine
Molecular Formula	$C_{11}H_{18}ON_2$	$C_{12}H_{20}O_2N_2$
Yield mg/L Mod. Mayer Medium	60/70	22/70
mp °C Sample	111	120~120.5
Authentic Sample	109	120~120.5

Analysis	C	H	N	C	H	N
Analytical	68.4	9.3	14.3	64.1	8.8	12.4
Calculated	68.0	9.3	14.4	64.3	9.0	12.5

Figure 11.—Characterization of compounds B2′ and B3 of *Aspergillus sojae* X–1.

Sample	A-0	A-1	A-2
Assigned Chemical Structure	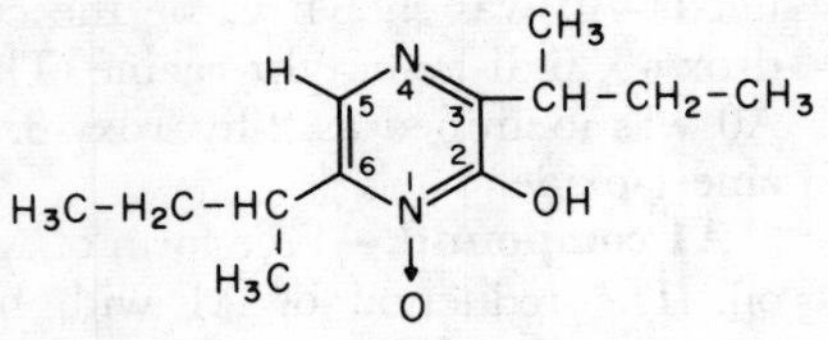	—	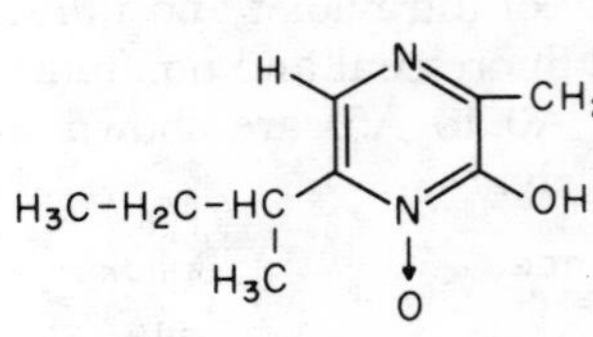
Name of Compounds	2-Hydroxy-3,6-di-sec-butylpyrazine 1-oxide		Aspergillic acid
Molecular Formula	$C_{12}H_{20}O_2N_2$		$C_{12}H_{20}O_2N_2$
Yield. mg/60L Mod. Mayer Medium	136.8	192.4	2449
mp °C Sample	Oil	Oil	95~96
Authentic Sample	—	—	97~99

Figure 12.—Characterization of compounds AO ~ A2 of *Aspergillus sojae* X–1.

Biological testing.—The crystals of fluorescent pyrazine compounds B0 to B6, excluding B5 and B7, were injected intraperitoneally into mice. Because of shortage of samples only three mice were tested for each dosage, 250 mg. and 500 mg./kg. Nontoxicity was confirmed, as shown in figure 14. The same test for toxicity was applied to the nonfluorescent pyrazine compounds, for the total mixture and for each of the separated compounds (fig. 15). The toxicity of aspergillic acid and hydroxyaspergillic acid have been previously reported in literature (9, 13). Judging from these results the toxicity of these compounds seems to be similar to that of aspergillic acid, LD$_{50}$ approximately 100 mg./kg.

Assay of aspergillic acid in koji.—*A. sojae* X–1 began production of aspergillic acid after the end of third day of cultivation. In the case of the ordinary industrial mold, strains I and KS began production 4 to 10 days, respectively, after inoculation (fig. 16).

Discussion

Pyrazine compounds of No. 1-N-oxide structure, such as aspergillic acid, are generally hardly soluble in water, but their toxicity cannot be overlooked. Among Japanese fermented foods, shoyu consists of water soluble ingredients, mirin contains 15 percent alcohol and in case of miso the total mold-culture material is fermented and served as is. Mirin is an alcoholic seasoning, which is prepared by saccharifying mold-cultured rice in 35 percent alcohol, and miso is prepared by enzymatically degrading the mixture of cooked soybeans and molded rice, or barley, or wheat, or corn in the presence of about 10 percent of salt, along with some yeast fermentation.

Thus, it is important to check the content of these mold-cultured materials for toxic pyrazine compounds. The production of aspergillic acid by the strains of *Aspergillus* that are widely used in Japanese industries were checked and 26 strains among 68 gave positive results (19), when they were cultured in modified Mayer's medium by surface culture at 30° C. for more than 10 days. But in the Japanese food fermentation industries, molds are always cultured on solid materials for only 2 or 3 days. In our solid cultures, just as in the industrial method, even *A. sojae* X–1 began production of aspergillic acid only after the end of third day of cultivation, and in case of the ordinary industrial molds (*Aspergillus sojae*, strains I and KS) only 4 and 10 days after inoculation (fig. 7). Thus one can conclude that it is easy to avoid the contamination with aspergillic acid in koji culture by selecting suitable strains of mold. In production of shoyu, molds are usually cultured on equal amounts of a mixture of soybeans and wheat of about 50 percent moisture; 500 g. of mold-cultured material corresponds to 1 liter of shoyu. The average consump-

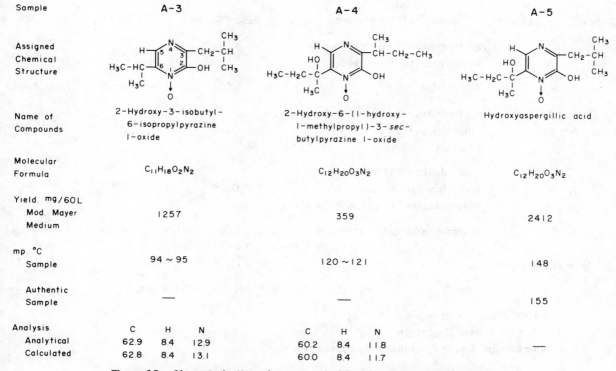

Sample	A–3			A–4			A–5
Assigned Chemical Structure							
Name of Compounds	2-Hydroxy-3-isobutyl-6-isopropylpyrazine 1-oxide			2-Hydroxy-6-(1-hydroxy-1-methylpropyl)-3-*sec*-butylpyrazine 1-oxide			Hydroxyaspergillic acid
Molecular Formula	C$_{11}$H$_{18}$O$_2$N$_2$			C$_{12}$H$_{20}$O$_3$N$_2$			C$_{12}$H$_{20}$O$_3$N$_2$
Yield. mg/60L Mod. Mayer Medium	1257			359			2412
mp °C Sample	94 ~ 95			120 ~ 121			148
Authentic Sample	—			—			155
Analysis	C	H	N	C	H	N	—
Analytical	62.9	8.4	12.9	60.2	8.4	11.8	
Calculated	62.8	8.4	13.1	60.0	8.4	11.7	

Figure 13.—Characterization of compounds A3 ~ A5 of *Aspergillus sojae* X–1.

Abbreviated Mark	Name of Compound	250 mg/kg	500 mg/kg
B-0	2-Hydroxy-3, 6-di-*sec*-butylpyrazine	—	0/3*
B-1	Deoxyaspergillic acid	0/3	—
B-2	Flavacol	0/3	0/3
B-2'	Deoxymuta-aspergillic acid	0/3	0/3
B-3	2-Hydroxy-6-(1-hydroxy-1-methylpropyl)-3-*sec*-butylpyrazine	—	0/3
B-4	Deoxyhydroxy-aspergillic acid	0/3	—
B-6	2-Hydroxy-6-(1-hydroxy-isopropyl)-3-isobutyl pyrazine	0/3	0/3

ddOM Mice weighted about 20g (♂)
Intraperitoneal Injection
* Number of Death/Number of Tested Animals

Figure 14.—Biological test of fluorescent pyrazine compounds on mice.

Abbreviated Mark	Name of Compound	62.5 mg/kg	125 mg/kg	250 mg/kg
A-0	2-Hydroxy-3, 6-di-*sec*-butylpyrazine 1-oxide	—	0/3	3/3*
A-2	Aspergillic acid	LD_{50} 100 mg/kg (value of Reference)		
A-3	2-Hydroxy-3-isobutyl-6-isopropylpyrazine-1-oxide	0/3	3/3	—
A-4	2-Hydroxy-6(1-hydroxy-1-methylpropyl)3-*sec*-butylpyrazine 1-oxide	0/3	3/3	—
A-5	Hydroxyaspergillic acid	LD_{50} 100 mg/kg (value of Reference)		
A-mixture		0/3	3/3	3/3
		LD_{50} 119 mg/kg		

ddOM Mice weighted about 20g (♂)
Intraperitoneal Injection
* Number of Death/Number of Tested Animals

Figure 15.—Biological test of nonfluorescent pyrazine compounds on mice.

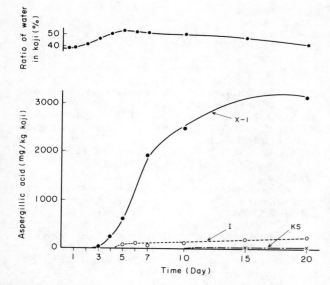

Figure 16.—Formation of aspergillic acid in culture of Aspergillus sojae on soybeans and wheat.

observed, on thin layer chromatographs, many other faint spots of possible fluorescent and nonfluorescent pyrazine compounds. So, the existence in nature of many other pyrazine compounds produced by molds from two molecules of amino acid, for instance, from valine and valine or valine and isoleucine, should be considered.

Acknowledgments

The authors would like to express their sincere appreciation to Dr. K. Sakaguchi and Dr. Y. Sumiki of Tokyo University and to Mr. K. Mogi, president, and all his staff of Kikkoman Shoyu Co., for their very kind interest in our research. They are also very grateful to Dr. S. Suzuki, Mr. Y. Kawashima and Mr. H. Homma of the Institute of Physical and Chemical Research, 4775 Yamato-Machi, Saitarma-Ken, Japan, and to Mr. Y. Kaneko of their laboratory for their valuable assistance.

tion of shoyu in Japan per capita per month is 1 liter; 600 mg./kg. of ether extract of koji, and 300 mg./kg. extract of shoyu correspond to 6 month's consumption of shoyu for a man of 50 kg. body weight. These amounts were injected into mice. The results indicated (fig. 17) that intraperitoneal injection of these amounts of ether extract of koji of shoyu, at the dosage that corresponds to a year of human consumption, did not kill three mice in each case. In addition to the 15 kinds of pyrazine compound that have been isolated to date from culture of molds, muta-aspergillic acid, neoaspergillic acid and neohydroxy-aspergillic acid are also known. These compounds are considered to be condensation products of two molecules of amino acid, as was suggested by J. C. MacDonald (20, 21, 22, 23, 24), such as leucine and leucine, isoleucine and isoleucine, isoleucine and leucine, and valine and leucine, in our case. We have

	300mg/kg**	600mg/kg**	1200mg/kg
Extract of Shoyu (Ether)	0/3*	0/3	—
Extract of Shoyu−koji (Ether)***	—	0/3	0/3

Note :

* ddOM Mice Weighted about 20g
Intraperitoneal Injection
Number of Death / Number of Tested Animals.

** 300mg/kg of extract of shoyu, and 600mg/kg of extract shoyu−koji, for a mouse respectively corresponds 1L monthly intake of shoyu by a man of 50kg weight for 6 months.

*** 10 kinds of industial strain of Aspergillus sojae and Aspergillus sojae X−I, wild strain were tested.

Figure 17.—Biological test of extracts of shoyu and shoyu-koji on mice.

References

(1) HESSELTINE, C. W., O. L. SHOTWELL, J. J. ELLIS, and R. D. STUBBLEFIELD. 1965. Investigation of aflatoxin formation. Personal communication.

(2) AIBARA, K., and K. MIYAKI. 1965. Paper presented at the Annual Meeting of the Agricultural Chemical Society of Japan, Tokyo, p. 86.

(3) MASUDA, Y., K. MORI, and M. KURATSUNE. 1965. Paper presented at the annual meeting of the Japanese Cancer Association. Fukuoka p. 50.

(4) YOKOTSUKA, T., M. SASAKI, T. KIKUCHI, Y. ASAO, and A. NOBUHARA. 1967. Studies on the compounds produced by molds. 1. Fluorescent compounds produced by Japanese industrial molds. J. Agric. Chem. Soc. Japan 41: 32–38.

(5) SASAKI, M., T. KIKUCHI, Y. ASAO, and T. YOKOTSUKA. 1967. Studies on the compounds produced by molds. II. Fluorescent compounds produced by Japanese industrial molds. J. Agric. Chem. Soc. Japan 41: 154–158.

(6) YOKOTSUKA, T., M. SASAKI, T. KIKUCHI, Y. ASAO, and A. NOBUHARA. 1966. Production of fluorescent compounds other than aflatoxins by Japanese industrial molds. In (Mateles, R., and G. N. Wogan, ed.), Biochemistry of some foodborne microbial toxins. The MIT Press.

(7) WHITE, E. C., and J. H. HILL. 1943. Studies on antibacterial products formed by molds. I. Aspergillic acid, a product of a strain of Aspergillus flavus. J. Bacteriol. 45: 433–442.

(8) DUTCHER, J. D. 1957. Aspergillic acid; an antibiotic substance produced by Aspergillus flavus. III. The structure of hydroxyaspergillic acid. J. Biol. Chem. 232: 785–795.

(9) NAKAMURA, S., and T. SHIRO. 1960. Studies on growth inhibition of Hiochi-bacteria, specific saprophytes of sake. IV. Hydroxyaspergillic acid as a growth inhibitant against Hiochi-bacteria. Bull. Agric. Chem. Soc. Japan 23: 418–427.

(10) SASAKI, M., Y. ASAO, and T. YOKOTSUKA. 1968. Studies on the compounds produced by molds. III. Fluorescent compounds produced by Japanese industrial molds. J. Agric. Chem. Soc. Japan *42:* 288–293.

(11) WEISS, U., F. STRELITZ, H. FLON, and I. N. ASHESHOV. 1958. Antibiotic compounds with action against bacterial viruses; Neohydroxyaspergillic acid. Arch. Biochem. Biophys. *74:* 150–157.

(12) MICETICH, R. G., and J. C. MacDONALD. 1964. Metabolites of *Aspergillus sclerotiorum.* J. Chem. Soc. 1507–1510.

(13) NAKAMURA, S., and T. SHIRO. 1961. Studies on growth inhibition of Hiochi-bacteria, specific saprophytes of sake. VI. Muta-aspergillic acid as a new growth inhibitant against Hiochi-bacteria. Agric. Biol. Chem. *25:* 573–579.

(14) MacDONALD, J. C., R. G. MICETICH, and R. H. HASKINS. 1964. Antibiotic activity of neoaspergillic acid. Canadian J. Microbiol. *10:* 90–92.

(15) COOK, H. A., and C. A. SLATER. 1954. Metabolism of wild yeasts. I. Chemical nature of pulcherrimin. J. Institute of Brewing (London) *60:* 213–217.

(16) YOKOTSUKA, T., Y. ASAO, and M. SASAKI. 1968. Studies on the compounds produced by molds. IV. Isolation of nonfluorescent pyrazine compounds. J. Agric. Chem. Soc. Japan *42:* 346–350.

(17) SASAKI, M., Y. ASAO, and T. YOKOTSUKA. 1968. Studies on the compounds produced by molds. V. Isolation of nonfluorescent pyrazine compounds. J. Agric. Chem. Soc. Japan *42:* 351–355.

(18) NAKAMURA, S. 1961. The structure of muta-aspergillic acid. Agric. Biol. Chem. *25:* 74–75.

(19) YOKOTUSKA, T., and K. OSHITA. Unpublished data.

(20) MacDONALD, J. C. 1961. Biosynthesis of aspergillic acid. J. Biol. Chem. *236:* 512–514.

(21) MacDONALD, J. C. 1962. Biosynthesis of hydroxyaspergillic acid. J. Biol. Chem. *240:* 1977–1981.

(22) MICETICK, R. G., and J. C. MacDONALD. 1965. Biosynthesis of neoaspergillic acid and neohydroxyaspergillic acid. J. Biol. Chem. *240:* 1692–1695.

(23) MacDONALD, J. C. 1965. Biosynthesis of pulcherriminic acid. Biochem. J. *96:* 533–538.

(24) MacDONALD, J. C. 1967. Aspergillic acid and related compounds. *In* (Gottlieb, D., and Shaw, P. D., ed.). *Antibiotics 2, Biosynthesis.* Springer-Verlag Berlin, Heidelberg, New York, pp. 43–51.

MICRO-ORGANISMS WHICH DETERIORATE STORED CEREALS AND GRAINS

by HIROSHI TSUNODA
Food Research Institute, Ministry of Agriculture and Forestry, Tokyo

The History of the Research

During some periods of history, Japanese nationals have suffered from beri-beri ("kakke"), a disease known to be peculiar to the rice-consuming nations. Clarification of the etiology was not achieved even through the animal experiments using injured rice conducted in 1891 by Dr. Junjiro Sakaki (*115, 116, 117*).

During the periods of Japan-China War (1894–95) and the Japan-Russian War (1904–5) considerable numbers of soldiers and sailors suffered from kakke. It was assumed that the kakke was caused by the rice diet and the ration was successfully improved by adding barley. Subsequently the number of cases of kakke decreased among the military.

The above experiments were resumed by Dr. Yutaka Teruuchi (*135*) in 1929, but his results also failed to find a clear relationship between the kakke and injured rice, probably due to complex infection with various mold strains and the substances thereby produced in naturally developed diseased rice.

Dr. Umetaro Suzuki enlightened the vitamin aspect of the problem in 1911–12, and collaborating with Dr. Shimazono of the faculty of internal medicine of Tokyo University, reached the conclusion that the cause of kakke was a deficiency of vitamin B$_1$.

Meanwhile, it was suspected that the cause of kakke had been chronic poisoning by some product of some kind of mold developing on stored rice. This idea was hypothesized by Prof. Ichiro Miyake of Tokyo Agricultural University.

No factor relating to kakke was found throughout a series of experiments conducted from 1916 through 1922. These experiments involved the feeding of mice with diseased rice which had been artificially inoculated with strains of *Oospora* sp. (*1*) (redding of grains), *Abisidia* sp. (*68*) (moldy rice grains), and *Penicillium commune* Thom. (*68*) (mosu-mai—Japan's local expression for chalklike rice). The three mold species had been isolated from natural infestations of rice.

A diseased rice of yellow coloration was found in rice imported into Japan proper from Formosa in 1937. A study by Prof. Ichiro Miyake, Dr. Hiroshi Naito, and Dr. Hiroshi Tsunoda showed that the cause of this so-called yellow rice was due to infection by *P. citreo-viride* Biouge (*P. toxicarium* Miyake) of unpolished rice during storage (*50, 51, 52, 53, 70, 74*).

Unpolished rice inoculated with *P. citreo-viride*, isolated from the naturally developed diseased rice, was tested by oral administration to rats. Using the diseased rice as 100 percent of the diet was fatal to rats, with paralysis in the hind legs after 8 days of feeding; with diseased rice as 50 percent of the diet, after 20 days and even in the case of diseased rice as low as 10 percent of the diet, fatalities occurred in one-half of the animals within 1 month. No characteristic anatomical changes were observed with the exception of an enlargement of the heart. Characteristic nervous signs were observed following parenteral injection of ether extracts of the diseased rice. Paralysis of the hind legs and subsequent respiratory paralysis of the experimental animals were observed by Miyake et al. (*70*).

Collaborative works on mycotoxin were started in 1940 at the request of Japanese Government to the faculty of medicine of Tokyo University (Dr. Kenji Uraguchi) (*198, 199, 200, 201, 202, 203, 204, 205, 206, 207, 208, 209, 210, 211, 212*).

Through the collaborative studies on this problem, the chemical structure of the toxic substance was proposed by Y. Hirata (*8*) as in fig. 1. Named Citreoviridin (*8, 9, 10, 142*), its characteristics were: m.p. 107° to 111° C., stable to heat, labile to ultraviolet radiation, exhibiting a deep yellow fluorescence. It is noteworthy that the signs of poisoning in the experimental animals consuming raw materials contaminated with the citreoviridin were similar to those observed in the human cases of "kakke-shoshin"; namely, cardiac attack of kakke disease with cardiac weakness and ascending type of paralysis. *P. ochrosalmoeum* Udagawa also produces a substance structurally identical to citreoviridin (*120*). Recently

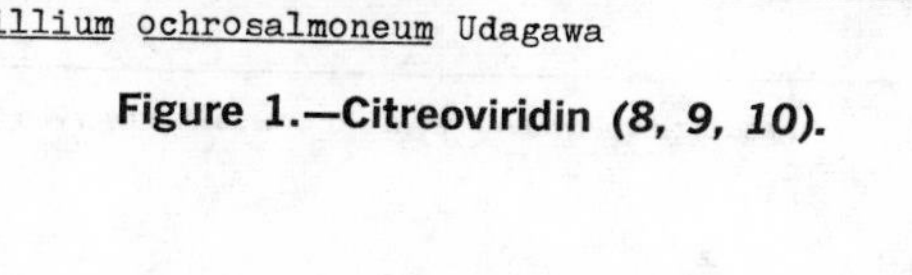

Penicillium citreo-viride Biourge (P. toxicarium Miyake)
Penicillium ochrosalmoneum Udagawa

Figure 1.—Citreoviridin (8, 9, 10).

similar results were obtained with the isolated citreoviridin by Dr. Uraguchi.

These were essentially the historical outlines of mycotoxin studies during the prewar (World War II) periods.

Micro-Organisms Parasitic on Grains and Cereals in the Field

In countries of high humidity such as Japan, it is important to know the plant hosts of parasites, the condition of their cultivation, the strains involved and so on, before one can decide on the storage conditions of cereals or grains. From 1938 to 1967, harvested products of rice, wheat, barley, soybean, and other crops were subjected to examination of causes of their field injuries. The results of the examination are shown in table 1.

Schizomycetes: *Bacillus subtilis* (157), *Xanthomonas itoana* (43), *Xanthomonas atroviridigena* (71, 72), *Pseudomonas sp.* (152); Ascomycetes: *Gibberella zeae* (165, 166, 167), *Gibberella fujikuroi* (165, 166, 167); Fungi imperfecti: *Helminthosporium*, *Nigrospora*, *Cladosporium* (176), *Fusarium* (162) (*F. nivale*, *F. kuknii*), *Curvularia* and *Epicoccum* (176) were often found associated with Japanese domestic rice.

Table 1.—Micro-organisms parasitic to the Graminea plants in field (177)

Class	Genus	Species	Animal test[1]	Host
Schizomycetes	Bacillus	B. subtilis sp.	Nontoxic	Rice.
	Pseudomonas	Pseudomonas sp.	do	Do.
	Xanthomonas	X. itoana (43, 45)	do	Do.
		X. atroviridigena (71)	do	Do.
		X. cinnamona (65)	do	Do.
Ascomycetes	Claviceps	C. purpurea	Toxic	Cereals.
	Ophiobolus	O. miyabeanus	Not tested	Rice.
		O. graminis	do	Do.
	Cochliobolus	C. miyabeanus	do	Do.
	Gibberella	G. zeae	Toxic	Cereals.
		G. fujikuroi	Not tested	Rice.
	Nectria		do	Do.
	Pleospora	P. trichostoma	do	Do.
	Ustilaginoidea	U. virens	Toxic	Do.
	Sclerotinia	S. sclerotiorum	Not tested	Soybeans.
		S. trifoliorum	do	Feed crops.
Basidiomycetes	Ustilago	U. hordei	do	Barley.
		U. zeae	do	Corn.
	Tilletia	T. foetida	Toxic	Wheat.
		T. caries	do	Do.
	Corticium	C. rolfsii	Not tested	Soybeans.
	Pellicularia	P. sasakii	do	Rice.
Fungi imperfecti	Alternaria	A. oryzae	do	Rice, wheat.
		A. tritici	do	Wheat.
	Ascochyta	A. sojaecola	do	Soybeans.
	Botrytis		do	Rice.
	Colletotrichum	C. graminicolum	do	Leguminase.
	Diplodia	D. natalensis	do	Peanut.
	Epicoccum	E. neglectum	Nontoxic	Rice.
		E. oryzae	do	Do.
	Helminthosprium	H. gramincum	do	Rice, wheat.
		H. turcicum	do	Do.
	Isaria		do	Rice.
	Nigrospora	N. sphaeria	do	Rice, wheat.
		N. oryzae (43, 44)	do	Do.
	Phoma	P. glumarum	do	Rice.
	Pestalotia		do	Do.
	Piricularia	P. oryzae	do	Do.
	Septoria	S. nodorum	do	Do.
		S. tritici	do	Do.
	Torula		do	Do.
	Cladosporium	C. herbarum	do	Rice, wheat.
	Fusarium	F. nivale	Toxic	Rice, wheat.
		F. oxysporum	do	Wheat.
		F. kuknii	Not tested	Rice.
		F. poae	Toxic	Wheat.
	Curvularia	C. lunata	Not tested	Rice.

[1]Animal test: Feeding experiments with rats, usually observed for at least 60 days.

Micro-Organisms Parasitic to Stored Rice

Those microorganisms infecting the grain during the harvest, during hulling by contamination from soil or sand, or deriving from straw packaging will grow on rice when the conditions of temperature and humidity, optimal for their development are fulfilled. Examination results on those kinds of infestation are given in table 2.

When the moisture content of rice is below 14 percent, no development of mold is observed for at least 1 year in most cases. *Aspergillus glaucus* develops when the moisture content is 14 to 15 percent and at approximately 15 percent moisture *P. citreo-viride* develops (*90, 92*). Many kinds of mold develop at 15 to 17 percent moisture, and moisture content higher than 18 percent permit the growth of Mucor, Oospora, Rhizopus and even bacteria.

Infestation is limited in the case of wheat storage in dry conditions probably due to the poor development of Aspergillus species at low content.

Aspergillaceae Grown on Stored Rice (180, 187).

Isolation and identification of micro-organisms were carried out during the 1940–60 period. Imported products were subjected to the same examination as Japanese domestic products by the stratified location sampling carried out by the inspection section of the food agency.

Aspergillus group.—As shown in table 3, more than 30 strains of micro-organisms were recorded. In table 3, the species listed from *A. repens* to *A. amstelodami*, (the *Aspergillus glaucus* group) induced injuries mostly to Japanese domestic rice (*155*). That group is known as the cause of dark coloration of Japanese rice harvested from the northeastern prefectures and is seen in the summer time.

A. glaucus, A. clavatus, A. fumigatus, A. nidulans, A. versicolor, A. terreus, A. candidus, A. wentii, A. oryzae, and *A. ochraceus* were frequently found on imported rice, the frequency varying according to the country of their origin (*165, 166, 167*).

Penicillium group.—As shown in table 4, approximately 50 strains were found to contaminate rice, among them, those possessing toxicity being listed in tables 4 and 5. The degree of their toxicity varied according to the kinds of the host, the isolated strain and conditions of incubation, but the most highly toxic belong to Asymmetrica, Fasiculata, and Biverticillata-symmetrica.

Table 2.—Micro-organisms parasitic to the stored grains (177)

Class	Genus	Species	Animal test[1]	Host
Phycomycetes	Abisidia	Abisidia sp.	Nontoxic	Rice.
	Mucor		do	Rice, wheat.
	Rhizopus	R. chinensis	do	Do.
		R. tritici	do	Do.
	Syncephalastrum		Not tested	Rice.
	Thamnidium		do	Do.
Ascomycetes	Aspergillus	31 races	5 races, toxic	Do.
	Penicillium	47 races	14 races, toxic	Do.
	Chaetomium		Not tested	Wheat, barley.
	Emericella		do	Rice.
	Eurotium		do	Do.
	Monascus		Nontoxic	Do.
	Sordaria		Not tested	Do.
	Torulopsis		do	Do.
	Saccharomyces		Nontoxic	Do.
Fungi imperfecti	Brachysoporium		Not tested	Do.
	Candida	C. albicans	do	Do.
	Cephalosporium		do	Do.
	Monilia		do	Do.
	Oospora	Oospora sp.	Nontoxic	Do.
	Paccilomyces	P. varioti	do	Do.
	Scopulariopsis	S. brevicaulis		
		S. brevi var. glabra	do	Do.
		S. melanospora		
	Sporotium		do	Do.
	Stemphylium		Not tested	Do.
	Tricothecium	T. roseum	Nontoxic	Do.
	Trichoderma	T. lignorum	do	Do.
	Spicaria	S. violacea	do	Do.
Actinomycetales-streptomyces		S. flavovirens	Soil smell	Do.

[1]Animal test: Feeding experiments with rats, usually observed for at least 60 days.

Table 3.—Aspergilli parasitic to the stored rice (15, 177)

Species	Animal test[1]	Host	Damage[2]
A. clavatus, Desm	Toxic:patulin	Rice, Barley	+++
A. gigantens, Behmer	do	Rice	++
A. repens (cda), Debary	Nontoxic	do	+++
A. chevalieri, (Mang), Thom et Church	do	do	+++
A. mangini, n. Camb	do	do	+
A. restricus, G. Smith	do	do	+
A. amstelodami, (Mang), Thom et Church	do	do	+++
A. fumigatus, Fresenius	do	do	+++
A. fischeri, Wehmer	Not tested	do	+
A. nidulans (Eidam), Wint	Nontoxic	do	+++
A. variecolor, (Berk et Br), Thom	do	do	+
A. unguis, (Emite-Weitet et Gaydin), Thom et Church	Not tested	do	+
A. ustus, (Bainier), Thom et Church	do	do	+
A. sydowi, (Bain et Sart), Thom et Church	Nontoxic	do	+++
A. versicolor (Vuill), Tiraboschi	do	do	+++
A. terreus, Thom	Toxic:citrinin	do	+++
A. candidus, Link	do	Rice, Wheat	+++
A. niger, van Tieghem	Not tested	Rice	+++
A. japanicus, Saito	do	do	
A. awamori, Nakagawa	Nontoxic	do	+++
A. carbonarius, (Bain), Thom	Not tested	do	+
A. phaenicis, (cda), Thom	do	do	+
A. wentii, Wehmer	Nontoxic	do	+++
A. terricola, Marchal	do	do	+++
A. tamarii, Kita	do	do	+++
A. oryzae (Aheburg), Cohn	do	do	+++
A. flavus, Link	Toxic:aflatoxin	do	
A. ochraceus, Wilhelm	Toxic:ochratoxin	do	+++
A. elegans, Gasperini	Not tested	do	+
A. ostianus, Wehmer	do	do	+
A. quercinus (Bain), Thom et Church	do	do	+

[1]Animal test: Feeding experiments with rats, usually observed for at least 60 days.
[2]Damage: Marked +++, moderate ++, slight +.

Instances of Poisoning Caused by Naturally Developed Diseased Rice

During the periods when rice inspection had been entrusted to the Federal Association of Rice Brokers, there were no records concerning cases of rice poisoning.

The Japanese Government enacted the "Rice Act" in 1921 and rice inspection has been performed since then under the provision of the act. The frequency of kakke cases has tended to decrease since that time. Rice inspection and guidance in rice storage technology has been under direct governmental supervision since 1946 when these activities involved the total rice crop of Japan. No case of kakke has been reported in recent years. *P. citreo-viride* could readily be isolated from any sample before the war, but at the present time, it is very difficult to find this species in any rice. Thus, there may be a correlation between the low frequency of beri-beri (kakke) and the rarity of this mold in rice. No case of rice poisoning was reported in 1954 and 1955, probably because rice imported into Japan was inspected for the toxicity. The rice which proved to be positive for toxicity (135,000 tons) was diverted to produce alcohol for industrial use in 1955, based on the report of a govern-

mental committee constituted of toxicologists and statisticians.

Other than those mentioned in table 6, there have been three cases suspected as *Fusarium* poisoning from rice cakes, and two other cases from brewed rice beverage (koji juice) reported from Kyushu.

The experimental studies on the toxicities of the important fungi growing on the grains in Japan are described below.

***Penicillium islandicum* Sopp, (143, 144) (islandia yellowed rice (146), hepatotoxic yellowed rice.—** This organism was isolated from Egyptian yellow-brown rice imported into Japan in 1948. The mold is derived from soil, so that this type of infection arises from contamination from soil or sand at the time of rice hulling. When the moisture content of rice rises higher than 16 percent and in the presence of a high temperature, the mold grows and yields toxicity. Three types of strains were found which differed in the chemical structure of substances produced (104). As shown in the table 7 Islanditoxin (62, 63, 64, 65), a kind of peptide, is assumed to be produced more or less by any one of the three strains.

Material of the greatest toxicity may be obtained under the following conditions: moisture content of the host rice kept 16 to 20 percent in well aerated

Table 4.—Penicillia parasitic to the stored rice (14, 177, 170)

Species	Animal test[1]	Host	Damage[2]
P. thomii, Maire	Not tested	Rice	
P. cinnamopurpureum, Abe	do	do	+
P. frequentans, Westling	Nontoxic	do	+
P. multicolor, Gig-Manoi et Parad	do	do	+ +
P. Hirayamae, Udagawa	do	do	+
P. purpurrescens, (Sopp) n Camb	do	do	+
P. implicatum, Biourge	Toxic:citrinin	do	+
P. decumbens, Thom	Nontoxic	do	+ + +
P. citreo-vivide, Biourge	Toxic:citreoviridin, citrinin	do	+
P. roseo-purpureum, Dierckx	Nontoxic	do	+ + +
P. fuscum, (Sopp) Thom	do	do	+
P. adametzi, Zaleski	do	do	+
P. vinaceum, Gilman et Abbott	do	do	+
P. phoeniceum, van Beyma	do	do	+
P. capsulatum, Raper et Fennell	do	do	+
P. Waksmani, Zaleski	do	do	+ +
P. Ochrosalmoneum, Udagawa	Toxic:citreoviridin	do	+ +
P. lilacinum, Thom	Nontoxic	do	+
P. citrinum, Thom	Toxic:citrinin	do	+
P. chrysogenum, Thom	Nontoxic	do	+ + +
P. notatum, Westling	do	do	+ + +
P. oxalicum, Currie et Thom	Toxic	do	+ + +
P. roqueforti, Thom	Nontoxic	do	+ +
P. phialosparum, Udagawa	do	do	
P. commune, Thom	Toxic?	do	+ + +
P. namyslowskii, Zaleski	Nontoxic	do	+
P. viridicatum, Westling	Cron:toxic	do	+ +
P. cyclopium Westling (moldy smell grain)	Nontoxic	do	+ + +
P. expansum, Link	Toxic:patulin	do	+
P. urticae, Bainier	do	Barley:rice	+ + +
P. granulatum, Bainier	Nontoxic	Rice	+
P. claviforme, Bainier	Toxic:patulin	do	+
P. stipitatum, Thom	Nontoxic	do	+
P. vermiculatum, Dangerud	Not tested	do	+
P. wortmanni, Klocker	Toxic:Rugulosin	do	+
P. spiculisporum, Lehman	Not tested	do	+
P. funiculosum, Thom	do	do	+
P. islandicum, Sopp	Toxic:Ruteoskyrin, Islanditoxin (Peptide)	do	+ + +
P. piceum, Raper et Fennell	Nontoxic	do	+ +
P. brunneum, Udagawa	Toxic:Rugulosin	do	+
P. purpurogenum, Stoll	Nontoxic	Grains	+ +
P. rubrum, Stoll	do	Rice	
P. rugulosum, Thom (16)	Toxic:Rugulosin	do	+ + +
P. concavo-rugulosum, Abe (17)	do	do	+
P. tardum, Thom	do	do	+ + +
P. diversum, Raper et Fennell	Nontoxic	do	+
P. heuquei, Bainier et Sartory	do	Rice, corn	+

[1]Animal test: Feeding experiments with rats, usually observed for at least 60 days.
[2]Damage: Marked + + +, moderate + +, slight +.

Table 5.—Group of toxic Penicillium, parasitic to stored rice

Monoverticillata	P. implicatum	Citrinin.
Asymmetrica—Divaricata	P. citreo-virid	Citreoviridin, citrinin.
Asy.—Velutina	P. ochrosalmoneum	Citreoviridin.
	P. oxalicum	Toxic: Patulin?
Asy.—Fasiculata	P. viridicatum	Rice: Notnoxic, Corntoxic.
	P. urticae	Patulin.
	P. expansum	Do.
	P. claviform	Do.
	P. wortmanni	Rugulosin.
	P. islandicum	Luteoskyrin, Islanditoxin.
Biverticillata—Symmetrica	P. brunneum	Rugulosin.
	P. rugulosum	Do.
	P. concavo-rugulosum	Do.
	P. tardum	Do.

Table 6.—Cases of poisoning by molds

Year	Location	Substance	Strain	Subjects	Diagnosis	Notes
1944	Gilolo Island	Overseas rice	*Penicillum islandicum*	Human	Anasarica (leg)	In regiment soldiers.
1946	Nakano area, Tokyo	Wheat flour	*Gibberella zeae*	do	Vomiting	Numbers (*11, 13*).
1952	Kobe—City including suburb.	Malt root (embryo)	*Penicillium urticae*	Milch cow	Hemorrhage, fatal	118 head (*3, 229, 230, 231, 232*).
1954	Tokyo, Chiba Prefecture.	Commercial food	*Aspergillus oryzae* var. *microsporus.*	do	Fatal poisoning	40 head (*18, 19, 24*)
1954 to 1955	Japan	Overseas rice	Putrefied and toxic	135,000 tons of rice		Made imposible to distribute as the dietary ration.
1954	Osaka	Oats from Hokkaido	*Gibberella zeae*	Horse		Supply forbidden.
1955	Hoya, Tokyo	Rice land crop	*G. zeae* and *F. nivale*	Human	Vomiting	30 persons (*162, 164*).
1955	Ibaragi, Tochigi, Kanagawa, Kochi— Prefectures.	do	*Gibberella zeae*	do	do	4 families (*162, 164*).
1960	Metropolitan Police Bureau.	Cooked rice	*Penicillium citrinum*	do	Fever, benumbed	1 family
1963	Nagano Prefecture.	Commercial food	*Penicillium islandicum*	Chick	Fatal	2,891 head (*178*).
1963	Tokachi area, Hokkaido.	Corn	*Gibberella zeae*	Sheep	do	30 to 40 head.

petri dishes incubating at temperatures of 25° to 28° C. for 20 days. In the case of Czapek solution medium, stirred cultivation or tank culture are not recommended if one wishes to successfully obtain toxicity equal to those obtained from the direct rice inoculation method.

In 1950, an experiment was performed by the author with rats fed a diet containing 46.5 percent artificially infected rice. Autopsy of the rats dead after 36 to 40 days of the feeding revealed cirrhotic livers, suggesting firstly, the development of the liver cirrhosis by toxic metabolites of *Penicillium islandicum* (*2, 46, 78, 79, 80, 81, 82, 83, 143, 144, 146*). Some of the pathologists doubted the observation of liver cirrhosis at that time. However, the experiment was repeated by the author with rats fed a diet containing 10 percent moldy rice and again the development of liver cirrhosis occurred within 100 days. Extensive studies, with cooperation of chemists, toxicologists,

and pathologists in Tokyo, have been performed on acute and chronic toxicities of this fungus since 1952. Two toxic metabolites were isolated, luteoskyrin and a chlorine-containing peptide. Luteoskyrin (*88, 89*) caused centrolobular necrosis of the liver in both rats and mice. The peptide was also the hepatotoxin causing the damage in the perilobular areas of the liver. Long-term feeding of both metabolites as well as moldy rice infested with *Penicillium islandicum* induced liver tumors in rats and mice (*2, 37, 38, 79, 80, 81, 82, 83, 85, 86, 87, 88, 89, 105, 106, 107, 108*). Diagnostic and histological changes toward malignancy in the liver were found to be fatty infiltration of the liver and cirrhosis when poisoned by any one of the strains of the flavoskyrin type or islandicin type, while those changes induced by the erythroskyrin type led to fatty liver and centrolobular necrosis, thus yielding variations in toxicity characteristics among the strains (fig. 2).

Table 7.—Types of Penicillium islandicum classified by the produced substances

P. islandicum	Flavoskyrin type (NRRL1175). Colony: yellowish orange. Reverse: yellowish orange.	Chrysopkanic. Skyrin. Flavoskylin toxic.	Islanditoxin, Chlorine containing peptide, toxic.
	Islandicin type (generally develops in high frequency). Colony: orange. Reverse: reddish brown.	Islandicin. Rubroskyrin toxic. iridoskyrin. Catenarin.	
	Erythroskyrin type (turkish and japanese rice). Colony: dark orange-greenish gray. Reverse: dark brownish gray-yellowish orange.	Luteoskyrin toxic. Skyrin. Erythroskyrin. Erythroskyrin. (Rubroskyrin).	

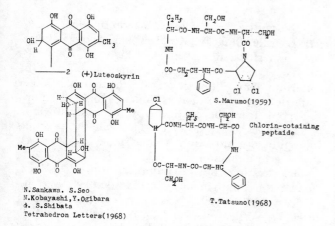

N.Sankawa. S.Seo
N.Kobayashi,Y.Ogibara
a. S.Shibata
Tetrahedron Letters(1968)

T.Tatsuno(1968)

Figure 2.—Luteoskyrin (120).

Penicillium citrinum Thom; Thailand yellowed rice (49, 148, 151, 192).

Rice imported into Japan from Thailand around 1951 had been found to be contaminated with the mold, hence this current designation. The rice injured by the mold reveals yellowish coloration over the whole surface of the grain or yellowish spots, and the colored part gives yellow fluorescence under exposure to ultraviolet radiation.

The organism is characterized by a deep bluish-green velveteen colony, brown in the central areas, with a yellow pigment which crystallized out at the reverse of the colony. It yields the citrinin reaction with hydrochloric acid and Lugol's solution giving a deep reddish brown color.

In order to prepare an artificially diseased rice with this mold, it is necessary to use well polished rice and to supply sufficient water for production of citrinin. When those optimal conditions are fulfilled, yellow-disease rice can be obtained at 25° C. after 48 hours' incubation. Oral administration of a diet containing 10 to 30 percent of diseased rice killed all the experimental rats within 3 months. The cause of death was due to renal necrosis, accompanied by swelling of the kidney (109, 110, 111). Urinary excretion was 2.5 fold the normal rate. Dilatation of the renal tubules occurred because of incapability of removal of accumulated water. A. terreus, A. candidus, P. implicatum and P. citreoviride produce citrinin (fig. 3).

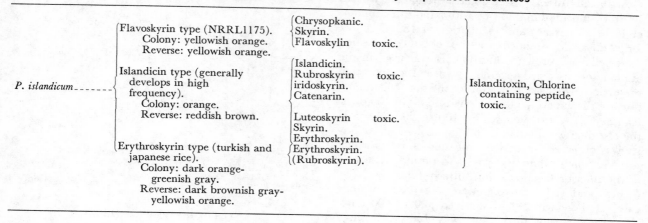

Raistrick (1935)

A.terreus Thom
A.candidus Link
P.implicatum Biourge
P.citreo-viride Biourge

Figure 3.—Citrinin (120).

Penicillium brunneum Udagawa (172, 173, 174).

Among Penicillium species, a considerable number produce rugulosin. Many of these are species classified in the Biverticillata-Symmetrica group; namely, P. brunneum, P. wortmanni, P. rugulosum, P. concavo-regulosum, and P. tardum. P. brunneum was found by Dr. Shinichi Udagawa in imported rice. It is also considered to be present in Japan judging from the fact that it was isolated by the author from a sample of rice cake made of Japanese rice (176).

The colony of P. brunneum is velveteen, yellow-orange or grayish brown, unsmooth surface, dull yellow-orange reverse. This species is the most copious producer of rugulosin among the rugulosin producing strains.

Artificially diseased rice could be obtained by this strain by inoculation into rice with a moisture content of 16 to 20 percent and incubation at 15° to 28° C. for 20 days. The diseased rice, thus obtained, revealed dark yellowish brown coloration. It was used in the animal test as dried ground powder. Incorporating the toxic powder as 10 percent of the diet, killed one-third of the experimental mice within 50 to 100 days. Another one-third died within 100 to 200 days and the rest died within 300 to 400 days. A fine granularity was observed in the livers of those animals which survived longer than 100 days. An unsmooth surface of the interior liver partition, utterly reformed liver, ascites, and renal necrosis were observed in some cases of those which had survived 300 to 400 days. Fatty degeneration in the liver was observed in those dying acutely; this was accompanied by cell infiltration at the periportal area.

Those chronically poisoned, having survived more than 150 days, revealed the following diagnostic signs and histological characters: connection of the cell infiltration change between the periportal areas or cell infiltration between periportal and central areas in the advanced cases, no fibrosis variety in size of nuclei of the liver cells or considerable proliferation of the bile duct. These variations are nearly identical to those obtained in the poisoning cases by luteoskyrin. More severe changes were observed in the renal tissue than in the liver when the experimental rats were administered a diet containing dried mold, cultivated in Czapek solution, incorporated as 50 per 1,000 to 25 per 1,000 parts of the diet. The manner of the changes and damages observed in the kidney were found to be identical to those observed in citrinin poisoning cases (fig. 4).

Studies on the Toxicity of Scab, Fusarium Blight (26, 27, 34, 50, 51, 59)

Damage caused by Fusarium.—The damage caused by this organism in wheat, barley, oats, rye, and other crops is worldwide. Extraordinary damage was reported in 1901 from Hokkaido, in 1914 from around the Kanto district and in 1963 from all the western Japan proper when the production of wheat and other crops was reduced to half of the usual crops. In Japan, when the long rainy spring season fell during the harvest time of wheat, barley and other crops, greater damage by this mold was recorded. No method to prevent it had been devised.

Even when the gross statistical crop of wheat and other crops show a normal level, damage by this mold to rice, wheat, maize corn, oats and to some kinds of feed grass have been reported from every district of this country.

Fusarium damage is depicted in the map of Japan

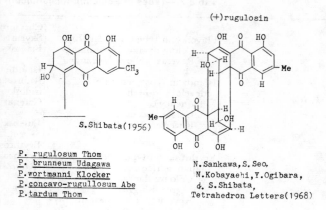

(+)rugulosin

S. Shibata (1956)

P. rugulosum Thom
P. brunneum Udagawa
P. wortmanni Klocker
P. concavo-rugullosum Abe
P. tardum Thom

N. Sankawa, S. Seo,
N. Kobayaehi, Y. Ogibara,
d. S. Shibata,
Tetrahedron Letters (1968)

Figure 4.—Rugulosin (120).

as reported by Dr. Giichi Nishikado in 1958 (96, 97, 98). Kyushu, Shikoku, Kinki, Tokai, Aomori Prefectures and Hokkaido are areas of high frequency (fig. 5). To explain the fact that Japan is plagued by Fusarium damage to a greater degree than most other countries, some investigators assume a flight of Fusarium spores from the continent by the seasonal winds.

Difficulties exist due to the fact that the products injured by this mold do not show stable toxicity when supplied to human or livestock.

Classification of Fusarium group.—Classification of this group involves great complexity. It includes more than 100 species and sub species according to H. W. Wollenweber and O. A. Rinkin's classification system (225) which is based on parasitism of plant hosts (table 8). W. C. Synder and N. H. Hansen have proposed another classification system on a morphological basis which includes approximately 100 different species.

Fusarium found in rice, wheat and other crops produced in Japan.—Inspection of Japanese domestic rice reveals F. graminearum to be found with the highest frequency, followed by F. fujikuroi, F. nivale and F. kuhunii. In wheat and other crops F. graminearum also in the highest frequency, followed by F. nivale, F. poae, F. oxysporum, in that order.

As already stated, extraordinary damage occurred in the western districts of Japan in 1963. At that time the damage was compounded because the injured products had been fed to livestock resulting in severe poisoning and even deaths. The Agricultural, Forestry, and Fisheries Research Council ordered investigations on the tolerance of various kinds of livestock to the toxin derived from the Fusarium-damaged crops, and investigations on the permissable degree of mixing such crops into feeds and on nature of the toxic substance involved.

After isolation of strains from a wheat sample ob-

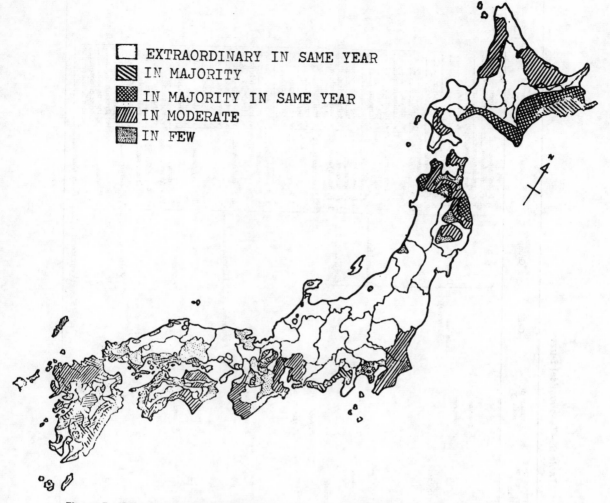

Figure 5.—Distribution of fusarium damages in wheat and barley. Fusarium positive area of Japan.

tained in Kumamoto Prefectural Laboratory of Agriculture (Kyushu), *F. graminearum* and *F. nivale* were found by the author and others. Dr. Tominaga of the Agricultural Engineering Research Station also isolated 61 strains of *F. graminearum* from the wheat samples. Subsequent toxicity screening tests were performed on all of these strains.

Screening of toxic strains.—Polypeptone (10 g.) and yeast extract (5 g.) (Difco) were added per one liter of Czapek's solution. Toxicity was determined by parenteral injection of mice with 0.5 ml. of the culture per 10 g. body weight. The following results were obtained: Three strains killed the test mouse within 24 hours. No. 36 and Oita No. 7 (Noken, Agricultural Research Laboratory) belonging to *F. graminearum* and *F. nivale* (F. n–2) strains No. 55 of *F. graminearum*, Tokuho No. 2, Hiroshima No. 6, Atsugi "W" No. 20, T. No. 21 and Ishii No. 26 yielded

culture fluids which did not kill the mice but caused extraordinary congestion of the ear auricle of the animals.

Selection of the strains which were to be subjected to the toxicity test was based on the fact that strain F. n–2 had copious conidia, which was preferable to *F. graminearum* which had few conidia on liquid media. *F. graminearum* toxicity will be studied using the same technic derived by experience with F. n–2 from which the toxic substance will have been purified.

Survey of studies on Fusarium toxicity.—Cooked rice is the Japanese staple food. It is considered probable that every Japanese national consumes some Fusarium contaminated rice. The result of inspection for Fusarium contamination of 205 domestic rice samples, obtained from many places and covering all of Japan's districts, showed the following. The maximum contamination rate was as high as 39.5 per-

Table 8.—Taxonomical Survey

Genus	Group	Species	Varieties	System by Snyder and Hansen
Fusarium (Nectria)	Eupionnotes	1. F. aquaeductum	v. medium.	
		2. F. melanochlorum.		
		3. F. merismoides	v. chlamydosporale.	
			v. crassum.	
		4. F. covisperum.	v. nectrioides.	
		5. F. dimerum	v. violaceum.	F. episphaeria.
			v. pusillum.	
		6. F. flavum.		
	Macroconia	1. F. expansum.		
		2. F. buxicola.		
		3. F. sphaeriae.		
		4. F. coccophilum.		
		5. F. gigas.		
	Spicarioides	1. F. decemcellulare.		F. rigidiuscula.
	Submicrocera	1. F. cerasi.		
		2. F. ciliatum.		F. ciliatum.
Fusarium (calonectria)	Pseudomicrocera	1. F. juranum.		
		2. F. orthoconium.	v. majus.	
	Arachnites	1. F. nivale.	v. majus.	F. nivale.
		2. F. kuhnii.		
		3. F. lavarum.		
	Sporatrichiella	1. F. poae.		
		2. F. chlamydosporum.		
		3. F. tricinctum.		F. tricinctum.
		4. F. sporotrichioides.	v. minus.	
		2. F. graminum.		
Fusarium	Roseum	2. F. avenaceum.	v. pallens.	
			v. volutum.	
		3. F. detonianum.		
		4. F. arthrosporioides.		
		1. F. semitectum.	v. majus.	
	Arthrosporiella	2. F. camptoceras.		
		3. F. diversisporum.		
		4. F. concolor.		
		5. F. anguioides.	v. bullatum.	F. roseum.
	Gibbosum	1. F. equiseti.	v. compactum.	
			v. caudatum.	
			v. acuminatum.	
		2. F. scirpi.	v. filiferum.	
			v. longipes.	

Strains of toxicity	Genus	Group	Species	Varieties	System by Snyder and Hansen
	Fusarium (Gibberella)	Discolor	1. F. heterosporum.	v. congoense.	
				v. negundinis.	
			2. F. reticulatum.		
F. graminearum.			3. F. graminearum.	v. minus.	
			4. F. sambucinum.	v. cereale.	
F. culmorum.			5. F. culmorum.		
			6. F. flacciferum.	v. humi.	
			7. F. tumidum.	v. sublunatum.	
			8. F. sublunatum.	v. elongatum.	
			9. F. macroceras.		
			10. F. trichothecioides.		
			11. F. bactridioides.	v. minus.	
				v. uncinatum.	F. lateritium.
		Lateritium	1. F. lateritium.	v. mori.	
				v. majus.	
				v. longum.	
		Liseola	2. F. stibboides.		
			3. F. sarcochroum.	v. minus.	
			1. F. lactis.	v. subglutinans.	
			2. F. neoceras.	v. anthophilum.	F. moniliforme.
			3. F. moniliforme.	v. pisi.	
	Fusarium	Elegans	1. F. orthoceras.	v. apii.	
				v. longius.	
				v. betae.	
			2. F. conglutinans.	v. callistephi.	
				v. citrinum.	
			3. F. lini.		
			4. F. bostrycoides.		
			5. F. angustum.	v. tracheiphilum.	
				v. blasticola.	F. oxysporum.
			6. F. bulbigenum.	v. lycopersici.	
				v. batatas.	
				v. niveum.	
				v. awantiacum.	
				v. nicotinae.	
			7. F. oxysporum.	v. cubense.	
				v. gladioli.	
				v. medicaginis.	
			8. F. dianthi.		
F. redolens.			9. F. vasinfectum.	v. zonatum.	
				v. lutulatum.	
			10. F. redolens.	v. radicicola.	
	Fusarium (Hypomyces)	Martiella	1. F. javanicum.	v. ensiforme.	
			2. F. coeruleum.	v. minus.	
F. scirpi.				v. striatum.	
F. solani.			3. F. solani.	v. martii.	F. solani.
				v. adnncisporum.	
				v. eumartii.	
		Ventricosum	1. F. argillaceum.		

¹System by Wollen, Weber and Reinking.

cent in third-class rice; only nine samples were negative among the 205 samples conducted. Third-class wheat in 1958 had the highest contamination rate among the wheat inspected, 77 percent of samples showed contamination; among 176 samples only 39 were negative. About 1959, the inspection section of the food agency concerned itself with the permissible level of contamination which could be allowed. A mixing rate of 5 percent by visible inspection was decided on as being permissable. As suggested by poisoning cases, the toxicity in normal consumption is not excessive, but judging from the described results of the examinations for contamination, it is considered that Japanese nationals consume some infected grains in every meal.

F. graminearum (*99, 101*) also could be involved in accidental poisoning. However, the chronic nature of the toxicity makes research more difficult, as observed in the already mentioned case in sheep in Hokkaido (Tokachi district) where the toxic damage was disclosed only after parasitized maize corn had been supplied as feed for half a year.

Studies on the Toxicity of *Fusarium nivale* (*162, 164, 179*)-Morphology of isolated strains. The colony of the strain obtained in Kumamoto Prefectural Laboratory of Agriculture in 1963 from an injured wheat grain was floccose, pink colored, with the reverse eluting a purple pigment. The conidia were crescent-shaped or spindle-shaped, 3.5 to 4.5 x 10 to 31 microns in size, with zero or three septa and attached at the top of one or three sterigmata, extending from twiglike branches of conidiophores (fig. 6). These characters were found to be completely identical to the referral strain, *F. nivale* NRRL 3249, obtained by courtesy of Dr. C. W. Hesseltine.[1]

Relationships between the kind of the medium and its toxicity.—Toxicity of this strain was found to be unstable when cultivated in Czapek's medium when peptone and yeast extract were added. A stationary culture was preferable to an agitated culture. Because of circumstances and convenience for collaborative work, it was decided to use material extracted from cultures cultivated on rice for this study. Strength of the produced toxin was compared with toxins produced on a variety of other kinds of hosts including strain F. n–2 artificially inoculated onto wheat, oat, corn, naked barley, and soybean. The length of the survival period of experimental rats, fed F. n–2 infested rice as 80 or 50 percent of their diet, was measured. As depicted in figure 7, the strongest toxicity and the least deviation of the length of the survival period were obtained in the case of rice

---

[1]*F. nivale* NRRL 3249 was identified by Dr. Ellis. According to a personal communication from Dr. C. W. Hesseltine, NRRL 3249 is classified as an abnormal strain of *Fusarium tricinctum* by Dr. W. C. Snyder.

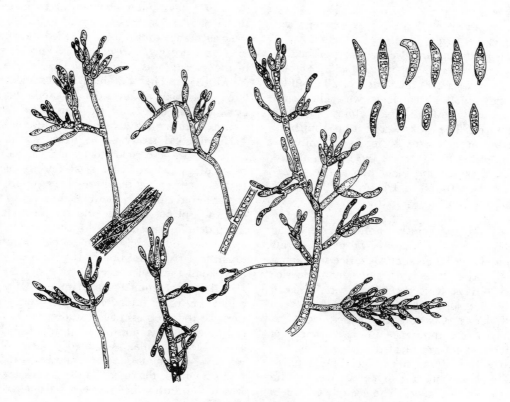

Figure 6.—*Fusarium nivale.*

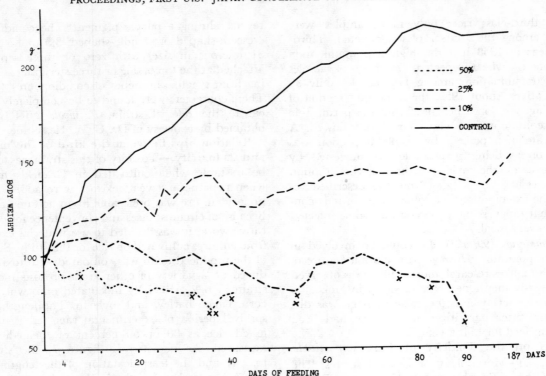

Figure 7.—Deviation in survival periods of rats fed the artificially inoculated rice.

grown cultures. From this evidence, the original host of the toxin-producer used in this experiment was thought to have been rice.

Host rice specification.—Rice grain, polished to 98 percent yield (2 percent of unpolished rice grain removed), was immersed in tap water for 30 minutes. Cultivation flasks (450 ml. capacity) were filled with 300 ml. of the wet rice from which almost all water had been removed. The flasks were cotton stoppered, sterilized in the autoclave at 15 lb. for 20 minutes. After cooling, strain F. n–2 was inoculated, mixed well (by hard shaking) and incubated at 25° to 27° C. for 20 days and ground to a toxic rice flour. The flour was subjected to further extraction of the toxic substance.

Toxicity of the artificially molded rice.—The results are shown in fig. 8. The survival period of rats fed a diet containing 50 percent toxic rice was found to be 8 to 40 days; those fed 25 percent toxic rice died at 56 to 90 days. Rats, receiving toxic rice as 10 percent of the diet, survived to the end of the experiment at 187 days. Considerable toxicity can be assumed because of a difference in body weight of 60 g. from those of control rats fed a normal diet.

Toxin extraction.—The toxic rice thus prepared was washed with acetone for 8 hours. Acetone did not elute out toxic substances. The acetone extracted residue was immersed in 50 percent alcohol at 45° C.

for 1 to 2 days. After filtration and concentration of the alcohol extract *in vacuo* at 80° to 90° C., the crude toxic substance thus obtained, killed the experimental mice at a dosage of 10 to 20 mg. Further refinement of the process was devised by Drs. T. Tatsuno and N. Morooka. They obtained a substance which differed in its toxic nature from that reported by Gilgan (1966), Yates (1967), or Dawkins (1966), so the substances were termed nivalenol and fusarenon.

Histological study.—The items which are to be described are also reported by Dr. M. Saito in these proceedings. Main histological findings consisted of marked injuries in the proliferating cells of the intestinal epithelium, hematopoietic tissues in the bone marrow, spleen, thymus, and lymph node. Cases of sheep deaths, especially well bred ones, often reported from Hokkaido might have been attributed to this toxin, if a risky assumption is permitted. No matter how small the daily dose, if this substance was consumed by a human for presumably 60 years, there might be some unfavorable influence. Moreover, through the progress of the studies on F. n–2 and *F. graminearum*, it is possible that the causes of unaccountable leukemia, associated diseases of the bone marrow, inflammation or cancer of the digestive tracts might be disclosed. Thus, the research group to which the author belongs has started its work with great hope.

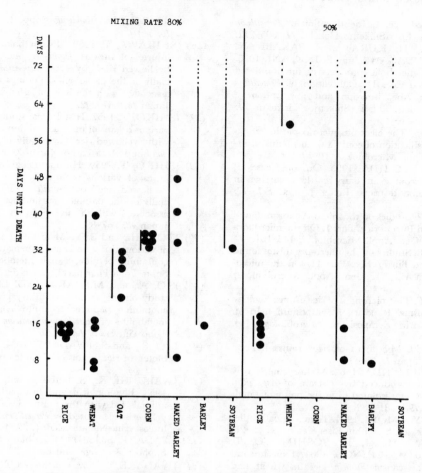

Figure 8.—Rat experiment of fusarium (F. n–2) inoculated rice.

References

(1) AOI, M. 1921. Studies on the pathogen of reddish rice grains. Bull. Agr. Exp. Sta. *45:* 29–69.

(2) ENOMOTO, M. 1959. Histopathological studies on adenomatous nodules of liver induced in mice by *Penicillium islandicum* Sopp. Acta. Path. Japan. *9:* 189–215.

(3) HORI, M., T. SUZUKI, and T. YAMAMOTO. 1954. Some pathogenic fungus isolated from the dry malt which was causal agent for the death of dairy cow. Shokuhin Eisei Kenkyu *4:* 45–48.

(4) HORI, M. 1956. Studies on the toxigenicity of "yellowsis rice". Ann. Rept. Kobe Hyg. Inst. 190–199.

(5) HORI, M., and T. YAMAMOTO. 1953. Studies on the chemical constitutents of poisonous substances from *Penicillium* (Hori-Yamamoto Strain). I. Morphology and Characters of the Penicillium Separated. J. Pharmacol. Soc. Japan *73:* 1097–1101.

(6) HATADA, M. 1954. O-hen-mai (yellowsis rice). Shokuhin Eisei Kenkyu *4:* 39–47.

(7) HIRAYAMA, S. 1954. The detection method for the pathogenic fungi on rice grain. Shokuhin Eisei Kenkyu *4:* 11–16.

(8) HIRATA, Y. 1947. On the products of mould. Poisonous substance from mouldy rice. I. Extraction. Chem. Soc. Japan *68:* 63.

(9) HIRATA, Y. 1947. On the products of mould. Poisonous substance from mouldy rice. II. Molecular formula. J. Chem. Soc. Japan *68:* 74–75.

(10) HIRATA, Y. 1947. On the products of mould. Substances from mouldy rice. III. Structure and properties. Chem. Soc. Japan *68:*104–105; Substances from mouldy rice. IV. Structure and properties 2. J. Chem. Soc. Japan *68:* 105–106.

(11) HIRAYAMA, S., and M. YAMAMOTO. 1948. Biological studies on the poisonous wheat flour (1). Eisei Shikenjo Hokoku *66:* 85–98.

(12) HIRAYAMA, S., and M. YAMAMOTO. 1948. Studies on the antibacterial substance obtained from *Aspergillus fumigatus.* Eisei Shikenjo Hokoku *66:* 123–138.

(13) HIRAYAMA, S., and M. YAMAMOTO. 1950. Biological studies on the poisonous flour. Eisei Shikenjo Hokoku *67:* 117–121.

(14) HIRAYAMA, S., and S. UDAGAWA. 1957. Taxonomic studies of fungi on stored rice grains. I. *Penicillium* group (Penicillia and related genera) Bull. Faculty Agri., Mie University *14:* 21.

(15) HIRAYAMA, S., and S. UDAGAWA. 1958. Taxonomic studies of fungi on stored rice grains. II. *Aspergillus* group. Bull. Faculty Agri., Mie University *16:* 7.

(16) HIRAYAMA, S., H. KURATA, F. SAKABE, N. INAGAKI, S. UDAGAWA, and S. IKETANI. 1965. Studies on the metabolic products of fungi isolated

from deteriorated rice. I. Identification of *Penicillium rugulosum* Thom. Eisei Shikenjo Hokoku *74*: 305–312.

(*17*) HIRAYAMA, S., H. KURATA, F. SAKABE, N. INAGAKI, S. UDAGAWA, and S. IKETANI. 1956. Studies on the metabolic products of fungi isolated from deteriorated rice. II. Cultivation of *Penicillium concavo-rugulosum* Abe, isolation and purification of metabolic products. Eisei Shikenjo Hokoku *74*: 313–316.

(*18*) IIZUKA, H. 1955. The electron microscopic investigation on the classification of conidia of the genus *Aspergillus*. J. Gen. Appl. Microbiol. *1*: 10–17.

(*19*) IIZUKA, H., and M. IIDA. 1955. On some cases of malt rootlet poisoning in dairy cattle occurring in Tokyo and Chiba districts. Japan J. Vet. Sci. *17*: 145–151.

(*20*) IIZUKA, H. 1957. Studies on the micro-organisms found in Thai rice and Burma rice. Part I. On the microflora of Thai rice. J. Gen. Appl. Microbiol. *3*: 146–161.

(*21*) IIZUKA, H. 1958. Studies on the micro-organisms found in Thai rice and Burma rice. Part II. On the microflora of Burma rice. J. Gen. Appl. Microbiol. *4*: 108–119.

(*22*) IIZUKA, H. 1960. The microflora of rice grains. Ecology of micro-organisms. Reports of Symposium held on Nov. 17–18, I.A.M. Symposia on Microbiology, No. II.

(*23*) IIZUKA, H. 1960. Microflora of rice grains. J. Food Hygienic Soc. Japan *1*: 17–29.

(*24*) IIZUKA, H., and M. IIDA. 1962. Maltoryzine, a new toxic metabolite produced by a strain of *Aspergillus oryzae* var. *microsporus* isolated from the poisonous malt sprout. Nature *196*: 681–682.

(*25*) IKEDA, Y., and Y. OMORI. 1954. Toxicological studies on the yellowsis rice. Shokuhin Eisei Kenkyu *4*: 23–28.

(*26*) IKEDA, Y., Y. OMORI, H. YOSHIMOTO, T. FURUYA, and M. ICHINOE. 1964. Experimental studies on some causal *Fusaria* for the wheat and barley scab. IV. Feeding test in mice. Eisei Shikenjo Hokoku *82*: 130–132.

(*27*) IKEDA, Y., Y. OMORI, H. YOSHIMOTO, T. FURUYA, and M. ICHINOE. 1964. Experimental studies on some causal Fusaria for the wheat and barley scab. V. Acute toxicity test of cultural extracts and medium in mice. Eisei Shikenjo Hokoku *82*: 132–133.

(*28*) INAGAKI, N., and M. IKEDA. 1959. Studies on the fungi isolated from foods. I. Method for the isolation of the fungi in powdered foods. Eisei Shikenjo Hokoku *77*: 341–366.

(*29*) INAGAKI, N., and M. IKEDA. 1959. Studies on the fungi isolated from foods. II. Identification of Penicillia and Aspergilli isolated from flours. Eisei Shikenjo Hokoku *77*: 347–366.

(*30*) INAGAKI, N. 1960. Study on fungi in foodstuff from standpoint of food sanitation. Japan J. Pub. Health *12*: 1123–1136.

(*31*) INAGAKI, N., and Y. TAKAHASHI. 1961. Fungi growing upon cold stored meat. I. Eisei Shikenjo Hokoku *79*: 293–296.

(*32*) INAGAKI, N., and Y. TAKAHASHI. 1961. Fungi growing upon cold stored meat. II. Eisei Shikenjo Hokoku *79*: 297–302.

(*33*) INAGAKI, N. 1961. On the mold contamination of skim dry milk. J. Food Hyg. Soc. Japan *2*: 44–46.

(*34*) INAGAKI, N. 1962. *Fusarium* scab disease of cereals and its food poisoning. Shokuhin Eisei Kenkyu *12*: 29–31.

(*35*) ITANO, T. 1959. Pathological studies on the toxicity of the *Penicillium islandicum* Sopp. J. Nara Med. Assoc. *10*: 1–16.

(*36*) ISHIKAWA, T. 1959. Histopathological studies on the injuries of various organs of mice and rats fed with "yellowed rice" by *Penicillium islandicum* Sopp., especially on the pathological findings of the other organs associated with the liver injuries. Trans. Soc. Pathol. Japan *48*: 867–892.

(*37*) ISHIKO, T. 1957. Histological studies on the injuries of various organs of mice and albino rats except liver, fed with "yellowed rice" artificially polluted by *P. islandicum* Sopp. Acta Pathol Japan *7*: 368.

(*38*) ISHIKO, T. 1959. Histopathological studies on the injuries of various organs of mice and rats fed with "yellowed rice" by *Penicillium islandicum* Sopp. Especially on the pathological findings of the other organs associated with the liver injuries. Trans. Soc. Pathol. Japan *48*: 867–892.

(*39*) ITOH, H., and S. YAMASAWA. 1962. The influence of various drugs on acute intoxication due to chlorine-containing peptide, a toxic metabolite of *P. islandicum* Sopp. Folia Pharmacol. Japan *58*: 90.

(*40*) ITO, A., and M. HARA, 1965. Electron microscopic study on the acute liver injury produced by chlorine containing peptide (Islanditoxin), isolated from the metabolites of *Penicillium islandicum* Sopp. J. Med. Soc. Toho University *12*: 62–66.

(*41*) ITO, S., and S. IWADARE. 1934. Studies on the red blotch of rice grains. Hokkaido Agr. Exp. Sta. Rept. *31*: 1–84.

(*42*) IWABUCHI, K., S. USUDA, and T. KUROKAWA. 1958. Physiological and histopathological studies on animals fed with the musty rice. III. Studies on the yellowsis rice caused by *Penicillium islandicum* Sopp and luteoskyrin. Niigata Med. J. *72*: 445–450.

(*43*) IWADARE, S. 1931. On the black rot of rice grains. J. Sapporo Soc. Agr. and Forest *22*: 458–459.

(*44*) IWADARE, S. 1932. On the red blotch of rice grain. J. Sapporo Soc. Agr. and Forest *23*: 357–358.

(*45*) IWADARE, S. 1936. On the geographical distribution of the black rot of rice grains and the relation of atmospheric temperature to the outbreak of the disease. Hokkaido Agric. Exp. Sta. Rept. *36*: 1–52.

(*46*) Division of Food Hygiene, The Ministry of Health and Welfare. 1965. On Aflatoxin. Shokuhin Eisei Kenkyo *15*: 83–88.

(*47*) KIMURA, T. 1958. Studies on the damaged rice (3). On the effects of remilling of the damaged rice. Niigata EKS. Gh. *89*: 1–21.

(*48*) KIMURA, T. 1959. Studies on the damaged rice (4). *Penicillium lilacium* isolated from the domestic rice grain. Niigata EKS. Gh. *91*: 1–12.

(*49*) KOBAYASHI, M., K. IWABUCHI, and H. TSUNODA. 1958. Physiological and histopathological studies on animals fed with the musty rice. II. Studies on the yellowsis rice caused by *Penicillium islandicum* Sopp. and *Penicillium citrinum* Thom. Niigata Med. J. *72*: 337–345.

(*50*) KOBAYASHI, M., and K. IWABUCHI. 1957. Pathological and physiological studies on the influence of feeding animals with musty rice. I. Studies with yellowsis rice caused by *Penicillium toxicarium* Miyake. Niigata Med. J. *71*: 512–516.

(*51*) KOBAYASHI, Y. 1961. Toxicological studies on yellowed rice. Nisshin Igaku *48*: 279–287.

(*52*) KOBAYASHI, Y., and K. URAGUCHI. 1944. Toxicological study on the yellow mouldy rice. Nanpo

Igaku Kenkyu-siryo 2: 1–10, Nanpo Kagaku Kenkyu Kai in Tokyo Imperial University.

(53) KOBAYASHI, M., and K. IWABUCHI. 1957. Pathological physiological studies on the influence of feeding animals with musty rice. I. Studies with yellowsis rice caused by *Penicillium toxicarium* Miyake. Niigata Med. J. 71: 512–516.

(54) KOBAYASHI, M., K. IWABUCHI, and H. TSUNODA. 1958. Physiological and histopathological studies on animals fed with the musty rice. II. Studies on the yellowsis rice caused by *Penicillium islandicum* Sopp and *Penicillium citrinum* Thom. Niigata Med. J. 72: 339–345.

(55) KOBAYASHI, Y., K. URAGUCHI, F. SAKAI, T. TATSUNO, M. TSUKIOKA, Y. SAKAI, T. SATO, M. MIYAKE, M. SAITO, M. ENOMOTO, T. SHIKATA, and T. ISHIKO. 1958. Toxicological studies on the yellowed rice by *P. islandicum* Sopp. I. Experimental approach to liver injuries by long-term feedings with the noxious fungus on mice and rats. Proc. Japan Acad. 34: 139–144.

(56) KOBAYASHI, Y., K. URAGUCHI, F. SAKAI, T. TATSUNO, M. TSUKIOKA, Y. SAKAI, T. SATO, M. MIYAKE, M. SAITO, M. ENOMOTO, T. SHIKATA, and T. ISHIKO. 1958. Toxicological studies on the yellowed rice by *P. islandicum* Sopp. II. Isolation of the two toxic substances from the noxious fungus, and their chemical and biological properties. Proc. Japan Acad. 34: 736–741.

(57) KOBAYASHI, Y., K. URAGUCHI, F. SAKAI, T. TATSUNO, M. TSUKIOKA, Y. SAKAI, T. SATO, M. MIYAKE, M. SAITO, M. ENOMOTO, T. SHIKATA, and T. ISHIKO. 1959. Toxicological studies on the yellowed rice by *P. islandicum* Sopp. III. Experimental verification of primary hepatic carcinoma of rats by long-term feeding with the fungus-growing rice. Proc. Japan Acad. 35: 501–506.

(58) KOBAYASHI, Y., and K. URAGUCHI. 1959. The further development of the researches on the poison of the yellowed rice "o-hen-mai". Nihon Iji Shinpo 1822: 3–7.

(59) KURATA, H., F. SAKABE, and S. UDAGAWA. 1964. Experimental studies on some causal *Fusaria* for the wheat and barley scab. I. Determinative method for isolation of pathogenic fungi and relation between seed discoloration and degree of *Fusaria* isolation. Eisei Shikenjo Hokoku 82: 123–125.

(60) KURATA, H., F. SAKABE, and S. UDAGAWA. 1964. Experimental studies on some causal *Fusaria* for the wheat and barley scab. II. Identification of the wheat and barley scab fungus and its allied species. Eisei Shikenjo Hokoku 82: 125–129.

(61) KURATA, H., S. UDAGAWA, and F. SAKABE. 1964. Experimental studies on some causal *Fusaria* for the wheat and barley scab. III. The influence of various media on the formation of conidia of *Fusarium* isolates. Eisei Shikenjo Hokoku 82: 129–130.

(62) MARUMO, S. 1955. Islanditoxin, a toxic metabolite produced by *Penicillium islandicum* Sopp. Part I. Bull. Agri. Chem. Soc. Japan 19: 258–262.

(63) MARUMO, S. 1955. Islanditoxin, a toxic metabolite produced by *Penicillium islandicum* Sopp. Part II. Bull. Agr. Chem. Soc. Japan 19: 262–265.

(64) MARUMO, S., and Y. SUMIKI. 1955. Islanditoxin, a toxic metabolite produced by *Penicillium* Sopp. J. Agri. Chem. Soc. Japan 29: 305–306.

(65) MARUMO, S. 1959. Islanditoxin, a toxic metabolite produced by *Penicillium islandicum* Sopp. Part III. Bull. Agri. Chem. Soc. Japan 23: 428–431.

(66) MATSUNO, T., S. MATSUMOTO, and M. OMORI. 1955, 1956. Pathological study on the toxic substance of Islandia Yellowsis Rice. Ann. Rept. Kobe Municipal Hygienic Laboratory 140: 270–272, 1955; 141: 1956.

(67) MIYAKE, I. 1910. Studien uber die Pilze der Reisplanze in Japan. J. Coll. Agri. Tokyo, 11: 237–276.

(68) MIYAKE, I., and K. TAKADA. 1922. Studies on the pathogen of "Fuke" and "Moss" rice. Bull. Agr. Exp. Sta. Nishigahara 45.

(69) MIYAKE, I., and H. TSUNODA. 1968. Studies on cinnamon-discolored rice grain (Ebi-mai). Byo-chugai-zattsushi 25: 9.

(70) MIYAKE, I., H. NAITO, and H. TSUNODA. 1940. Studies on the production of toxin in the soprophyte-growing rice grains under storage. Beikoku Riyo Kenkyujo Hokoku 1: 1–29.

(71) MIYAKE, I., and H. TSUNODA. 1941. Studies on the black-spot of rice grain (Meguro-mai) (previously report). Byo-chugai Zatsushi 28: 480–484.

(72) MIYAKE, I., and H. TSUNODA. 1941. Studies on the black-spot of rice grain (Meguro-mai) 2. Byo-chugai Zatsushi 28: 551–559.

(73) MIYAKE, I. 1941. Studies on the production of the toxic substances on the stored rice grain spoilage by fungi. Ann. Phytopath. Soc. Japan 11: 28–39.

(74) MIYAKE, I. 1947. *Penicillium to_icarium* growing on the yellow mouldy rice. Niishin Igaku 34: 161.

(75) MIYAKE, I. 1955. On the problem of remilled yellow rice (II). Koshu-Eisei 17: 57–59.

(76) MIYAKE, I., Y. MATSUNAMI, and H. WAKAMATSU. 1956. Studies on the infested part of the rice-grain, called "wou-hen-mai" (yellow diseased rice). J. Agr. Sci., Tokyo Nogyo Daigaku 3: 43–51.

(77) MIYAKE, I., Y. MATSUNAMI, and H. WAKAMATSU. 1956. Studies on the distribution of fungi in a diseased rice grain. J. Agr. Sci., Tokyo Nogyo Daigaku 3: 53–81.

(78) MIYAKE, I., Y. MATSUNAMI, and H. WAKAMATSU. 1956. Studies on the red disease of barley and wheat grains. J. Agr. Sci., Tokyo Nogyo Daigaku 3: 83–38.

(79) MIYAKE, M., M. SAITO, M. ENOMOTO, K. URAGUCHI, M. TSUKIOKA, Y. IKEDA, and Y. OMORI. 1955. Histological studies on the liver injury due to the toxic substances of *Penicillium islandicum* Sopp. Acta Pathol. Japan 5: 208.

(80) MIYAKE, M. 1959. Experimental liver cirrhosis produced by "yellowed rice." Sogo Rinsho 8: 134–143.

(81) MIYAKE, M., M. SAITO, M. ENOMOTO, SHIKATA, T. ISHIKO, K. URAGUCHI, F. SAKAI, T. TATSUNO, M. TSUKIOKA, and Y. NOGUCHI. 1959. Development of primary hepatic carcinoma in rats by long-term feeding with the yellowed rice by *Penicillium islandicum* Sopp—with study on influence of fungus-growing rice on DAB carcinogesis in rats. Gann 50: 117–118.

(82) MIYAKE, M. 1960. Pathology of the liver injury due to the toxic substances of yellowed rice. Rinsho Biyori 8: 9–14.

(83) MIYAKE, M., M. SAITO, M. ENOMOTO, T. ISHIKO, K. URAGUCHI, F. SAKAI, T. TATSUNO, M. TSUKIOKA, and Y. SAKAI. 1960. Toxic liver injuries and liver cirrhosis induced in mice and rats through long-term feeding with *Penicillium islandicum* Sopp growing rice. Acta Path. Japan 10: 95–123.

(84) MIYAKE, K., and K. AIBARA. 1965. "Aflatoxin" J. Food Hygienic Soc. Japan 6: 1–9.

(85) MOROOKA, N. 1956. Studies on the toxic products of *P. islandicum* No. 1 on a toxic pigment produced by surface culture. Japan J. Med. Sci. and Biol. *9:* 121–127.

(86) MOROOKA, N., N. NAKANO, T. MIURA, N. UCHIDA, and M. OKUGI. 1964. Observation on development of tumors in the livers of mice by diet containing luteoskyrin (Toxic pigment of *P. islandicum* Sopp) Japan J. Nutrition *22:* 94–101.

(87) MOROOKA, N., N. NAKANO, T. MIURA, N. UCHIDA, and M. OKUGI. 1964. Comparative studies on the enzyme activities in the mice liver cells of normal regenerating and tumour developed. Japan J. Nutrition *22:* 163–172.

(88) MOROOKA, N., N. NAKANO. 1967. Metabolism of ^{32}S-Cystine in the liver of mice fed on low protein diet containing luteoskyrin. Japan J. Med. Sci. Biol. *20:* 501–504.

(89) MOROOKA, N., N. NAKANO, and N. UCHIDA. 1966. Biochemical and histopathological studies on the tumor-developing livers of mice fed on the diets containing luteoskyrin. J. Med. Sci. Biol. *19:* 293–303.

(90) NAITO, H. 1955. Supplemental studies on the yellowsis rice. Rept. Food Res. Inst. *10:* 21–39.

(91) NAITO, H., M. MATSUNO, and M. KIKUCHI. 1956. Fumigation test of imported rice. (Fumigation effects on *Penicillium islandicum*, and *Penicillium citrium*) Rept. Food Res. Inst. *11:* 129.

(92) NAITO, H. 1964. Revision of *Penicillium toxicarium* Miyake (Rice yellowsis mold) Rept. Food Res. Instit. *18:* 75.

(93) NOGUCHI, S., and K. FUKUI. 1957. Serum cholesterol of the rabbits fed with *Penicillium islandicum* Sopp infested rice. Sogo Igaku *14:* 193–196.

(94) NOGUCHI, Y. 1959. Sexual differences in the poisoning on the liver damages induced in mice by *P. islandicum* Sopp growing rice, fungus mat and toxic substances. Folia Pharmacol. Japan *56:* 126–139.

(95) NOGUCHI, Y., K. URAGUCHI, M. ENOMOTO, and M. SAITO. 1962. Examination on the action of luteoskyrin in the liver damage with continuous and intermittent long administrations. Folia Pharmacol. Japan *58:* 90.

(96) NISHIKADO, Y. 1957–58. Studies on the control of Fusarium scab disease of wheat (I) Agricultural Insti. Okayama Univ. *45:* 59–85.

(97) NISHIKADO, Y. 1957–58. Studies on the control of *Fusarium* scab disease of wheat (II) Agri. Insti. Okayama Univ. *45:* 14–158.

(98) NISHIKADO, Y. 1957–58. Studies on the control of *Fusarium* scab disease of wheat (III) Agri. Insti. Okayama Univ. *45:* 159–220.

(99) OGASAWARA, K. 1965. On the food poisoning caused by *Fusarium* scab disease. J. Food Hyg. Soc. Japan *6:* 81–82.

(100) OGASAWARA, K., T. KARASHIMADA, S. MEJIKA, M. YANASE, K. ANDO, T. SUGII, and K. SHINPO. 1957. Experimental study on the toxicity of Italian remilled rice and its rice-bran. Rep. of Hokkaido Inst. Pub. Health 145–159.

(101) OGASAWARA, K. 1957. On the food poisoning caused by cereals—special reference to the food poisoning by the *Fusarium* scab disease of wheat and barley. Shokuhin Eisei Kenkyu *7:* 31–36.

(102) OHMORI, Y., C. ISONO, and H. UCHIDA. 1954. On toxicity of Thailand and yellowsis rice and Islandia yellowsis rice. Folia Pharmacol. Japan *50:* 246.

(103) OSHIMA, Y. et al. 1959. Studies on the vascular effect of a chlorine containing peptide produced by *Penicillium islandicum* Sopp (a toxic component of the contaminated rice) Sogo Igaku *16:* 341–344.

(104) SAIGO, M., K. OGURA, and H. TSUNODA. 1963. Studies on the toxic substances produced by *Penicillium islandicum* and their taxonomic relations to its type differences. J. Food Hyg. Soc. Japan *4:* 85–92.

(105) SAITO, M. 1955. Poison of "yellowed rice" and liver—especially on the liver injury due to toxic fungi, *Penicillium islandicum* Sopp. Saishin Igaku *10:* 760–769.

(106) SAITO, M., M. ENOMOTO, T. SHIKATA, et al. 1956. Experimental research of liver cirrhosis induced by feeding of "yellowed rice", artificially polluted by *Penicillium islandicum* Sopp. Acta Path. Japan *6:* 397–398.

(107) SAITO, M., M. ENOMOTO, T. ISHIKO, T. SHIKATA, and M. TSUKIOKA. 1958. Experimental studies on the histogenesis of liver injuries due to toxic substances of *Penicillium islandicum* Sopp. Acta Path. Japan *8:* 512.

(108) SAITO, M. 1959. Liver cirrhosis induced by metabolites of *Penicillium islandicum* Sopp. Acta Pathol. Japan *9:* 785–790.

(109) SAKAI, F. 1955. Experimental studies on rice yellowsis caused by *P. citrinum* Thom and toxicity especially kidney-damaging effect of citrinin pigment produced by the fungus. Folia Pharmacol. Japan. *51:* 431–442.

(110) SAKAI, F., and K. URAGUCHI. 1955. Researches for the possibility of chronic intoxication through long-term oral toxicity testing in rats of the yellowed rice toxic principle. Pharmacological studies on the toxicity of the yellowed rice "O-hen-mai." VII. Niishin Igaku *42:* 609–617.

(111) SAKAI, F. 1955. An experimental study on the toxic effect especially on the kidney of "yellowed rice" polluted by *Penicillium citrinum* Thom., as well as of Citrinin, a pigment isolated from the mould. Folia Pharmacol. Japan *51:* 431–442.

(112) SAKAI, F., M. TSUKIOKA, T. TATSUNO, et al. 1956. Toxicity of the so-called "O-hen-mai" detected from the recently imported foreign rice. VII. Folia Pharmacol. Japan *52:* 246.

(113) SAKAGUCHI, K., and K. YAMADA. 1944. On the morphology and classification of Aspergilli. J. Agr. Chem. Soc. Japan *20:* 65–73 and 141–154.

(114) SAKAGUCHI, K., H. IIZUKA, and J. OKAMOTO. 1951. On *Aspergillus flavus* Link as Koji mold. J. Agr. Chem. Soc. Japan *25:* 79–81.

(115) SAKAKI, J. 1891. Toxicological studies on the deteriorated rice infested by fungi. Tokyo Med. Assoc. *5:* 1097–1115.; Tokyo Iji Shinpo 703–704.

(116) SAKAKI, J. 1893. Relationship between the cause of beriberi and eating of rice. Tokyo Iji Shinpo 364–369; 417–420.

(117) SAKAKI, J. 1902. Studies on the poisonous rice grain. Kokkaiiji *180:* 15.

(118) SHIBATA, S., M. TAKIDO, and T. NAKAJIMA. 1955. Metabolic products of fungi. VII. Paper chromatography of the coloring matters of *Penicillium islandicum* Sopp. Chem. Pharm. Bull. (Tokyo) *3:* 286–290.

(119) SHIBATA, S. 1956. Anthraquinones produced by fungi. Kagaku *26:* 391–396.

(120) SHIBATA, S., S. NATORI, and S. UDAGAWA. 1964. List of fungal products. University of Tokyo Press, Tokyo, Japan, pp. 1–170

(121) SHIMOMURA, I., and K. NISHIMOTO. 1955. Microscopical anatomy of deteriorated rice. Eisei Shikenjo Hokoku *73:* 197–199.

(122) SUGIMURA, K. 1961, 1960. Researches on amino acids in animal organs, Part 2. Influence of the administration of the rice infested by *P. islandicum* Sopp or the toxic substance extracted on the amino acid distribution of animal organs. Rept. Food Res. Inst. *15:* 153. Folia Pharm. Japan *56:* 317–338.

(123) TAKAHASHI, K. 1955. Clinical studies on the yellowsis rice. Shizen *10:* 4–10.

(124) TAKEDA, S., K. OGASAWARA, T. KARASHI-MADA, K. ANDO. 1951. Studies on the food poisoning caused by *Fusarium* scab disease of wheat. Part I. On growth condition of *Fusaria*. Rept. of Hokkaido Insti. Pub. Health *2:* 35–46.

(125) TAKEDA, S., K. OGASAWARA. 1951. Studies on the food poisoning of deteriorated wheat caused by *Fusarium* scab disease. Part 2. Test on the toxicity. Rept. of Hokkaido Inst. Pub. Health *2:* 47–50.

(126) TAKEDA, S., and K. OGASAWARA. 1952. Studies on the food poisoning caused by the *Fusarium* scab disease of wheat and barley. Part 3. Chemical change of main substances of deteriorated wheat grain. Rept. of Hokkaido Inst. Pub. Health *3:* 15–19.

(127) TAKEDA, S., K. OGASAWARA, H. OHARA, and T. ONISHI. 1953. Studies on the food poisoning caused by the *Fusarium* scab disease of wheat and barley. Part 4. Animal test for toxic substances obtained from deteriorated wheat grain. Rept. of Hokkaido Inst. Pub. Health *4:* 22–28.

(128) TANAKA, I., Y. UENO, and K. URAGUCHI. 1960. Effect of luteoskyrin and chlorine-containing peptide, toxic components of *P. islandicum* Sopp. on the intermediary metabolism of liver. 1. On the respiratory enzyme systems. Folia Pharmacol. Soc. Japan *56:* 166.

(129) TANAKA, I., Y. UENO, and K. URAGUCHI. 1961. Effects of leuteoskyrin and chlorine containing peptide, toxic components of *P. islandicum* Sopp. on the intermediary metabolism of liver. III. Effects on oxidative phosphorylation. Folia Pharmacol. Japan *57:* 156.

(130) TANAKA, Y., S. HIRAYAMA, H. KURATA, F. SAKABE, and N. INAGAKI. 1957. Studies on the Technique of the Isolation for the presence of rice grain Fungi. I. Eisei Shikenjo Hokoku *75:* 443–459.

(131) TATSUNO, T., M. TSUKIOKA, Y. SAKAI, et al. 1955. Recherche sur la substance toxique du riz jauni. Chem. Pharm. Bull. (Tokyo) *3:* 476–477.

(132) TATSUNO, T., Y. SAKAI, M. TSUKIOKA, et al. 1957. Toxicity of the socalled "O-hen-mai" detected from the recently imported foreign rice IX. Folia Pharmacol. Japan *52:* 231.

(133) TATSUNO, T., H. WAKAMATSU, T. SATO, et al. 1957. On a method for detection of yellowish rice infected by *Penicillium islandicum*. I. J. Pharm. Soc. Japan *77:* 680–691.

(134) TATSUNO, T., H. WAKAMATSU, T. SATO, et al. 1957. On a method for detection of yellowish rice infected by *Penicillium islandicum*. II. J. Pharm. Soc. Japan *77:* 692–693.

(135) TERUUCHI, Y., C. WADA, and T. OHYAMA. 1928. On oryzatoxin contained in polished rice. J. Japan Soc. Internal Med. *16:* 825.

(136) TOCHINAI, Y. 1932. The black rot of rice grains caused by *Pseudomonas itoana*, n. sp. Ann. Phytopath. Soc. Japan *2:* 453–457.

(137) TOYAMA, Y. 1956. How can we solve the trouble of "yellowsis rice" Koshu Eisei *19:* 21–24.

(138) TORIKAI, T. 1942. Feeding examination of the socalled "yellow mouldy rice." Japan J. Gastroenterol. *41:* 478–490.

(139) TSUKIOKA, M., K. URAGUCHI, and M. ENOMOTO. 1957. Toxicity of the socalled "O-hen-mai" detected from the recently imported foreign rice. VIII. Folia Pharmacol. Japan *53:* 231.

(140) TSUKIOKA, M. 1959. Experimental approach through BSP retention test to the toxic liver-injuries due to *P. islandicum* Sopp-growing rice, fungus mat and toxic substances. Folia Pharmacol. Japan *55:* 1367–1389.

(141) TSUKIOKA, M., Y. HOZUMI, and K. URAGUCHI. 1959. Toxicity of the socalled "O-hen-mai" detected from the recently imported foreign rice. X. Folia Pharmacol. Japan *56:* 41.

(142) TSUNODA, H., and Y. HARUKI. 1949. On the cultivation of *Penicillium toxicarium* Miyake and its toxin-production. Rept. Food Reser. Inst. *2:* 157–164.

(143) TSUNODA, H. 1950. Studies on a poisonous substance produced on the cereals by a *Penicillium* sp. under the storage. Japan J. Nutrition *8:* 185–199.

(144) TSUNODA, H. 1951. Studies on a poisonous substance produced on cereals by a *Penicillium* sp. under the storage. Japan J. Nutrition *9:* 1–6.

(145) TSUNODA, H. 1951. Studies on the toxicity of the substance produced by a species of *Penicillium* which grows in storage grains. Medicine and Biology *18:* 187–190.

(146) TSUNODA, H. 1953. Researches on the micro-organisms which deteriorate the stored cereals and grains. I. Studies on the micro-organisms which cause the "Islandia yellowsis rice." Rept. Food Res. Inst. *8:* 41.

(147) TSUNODA, H., and O. TSURUTA. 1953. Researches on the micro-organisms which deteriorate the stored cereals and grains. II. Studies on the effect of fumigation of methyl bromide to *Penicillium islandicum* Sopp which causes "Islandia yellowsis rice." Rept. Food Res. Inst. *8:* 69–76.

(148) TSUNODA, H. 1953. Study on damage of stored rice, caused by micro-organisms. III. On yellowsis rice from Thailand. Rept. Food Res. Inst. *8:* 77–81.

(149) TSUNODA, H., and O. TSURUTA. 1954. Researches on the micro-organisms which deteriorate the stored cereals and grains. IV. Misclassified yellowsis rice. Rept. Food Res. Inst. *9:* 163–167.

(150) TSUNODA, H., and O. TSURUTA. 1954. Review of yellowsis rice. Imported Food Assoc. Office.

(151) TSUNODA, H. 1954. Researches for micro-organisms which deteriorate the stored cereals and grains. V. On the species name of Thailand yellowsis rice. Rept. Food Res. Inst. *9:* 169.

(152) TSUNODA, H. 1954. Researches on the micro-organisms which deteriorate the stored cereals and grains. VI. Researches on rotted rice "Monas." Rept. Food Res. Inst. *9:* 171–179.

(153) TSUNODA, H. 1954. Fungi isolated from the yellowsis rice. Shokuhin Eisei Kenkyu *4:* 7–10.

(154) TSUNODA, H. 1955. Yellowsis Rice and Fungi. Shizen *10:* 20–24.

(155) TSUNODA, H., and O. TSURUTA. 1955. Researches on the micro-organisms which deteriorate the stored cereals and grains. VII. The classification of the rotted rice "Kokuhen (Black discoloured)." Rept. Food Res. Inst. *10:* 55–59.

(156) TSUNODA, H., and O. TSURUTA, 1955. Researches on the micro-organisms which deteriorate the stored cereals and grains. VIII. A new strain found in the yellowed rice growing during the rice storage. Rept. Food. Res. Inst. *10:* 61–67.

(157) TSUNODA. H., N. MOROOKA, and N. NAKANO.

1955. Researches on the micro-organisms which deteriorate the stored cereals and grains. IX. Studies on the "Sublitis yellowsis rice." Rept. Food Res. Inst. *10:* 69–76.

(*158*) TSUNODA, H., and Y. TOBE. 1956. Researches on the micro-organisms which deteriorate the stored cereals and grains. X. Mathematical-statistical research for method of testing effectiveness of sterilization by fumigant. Rept. Food Res. Inst. *11:* 137–143.

(*159*) TSUNODA, H., and O. TSURUTA. 1956. Researches on the micro-organisms which deteriorate the stored cereals and grains. XI. Technique of fumigation with methylbromide, a sterilizing agent of cereal storage. Rept. Food Res. Inst. *11:* 144–145.

(*160*) TSUNODA, H., and O. TSURUTA. 1956. Researches on the micro-organisms which deteriorate the stored cereals and grains. XII. Sampling for examination of rice parasite. Rept. Food Res. Inst. *11:* 146–150.

(*161*) TSUNODA, H., and O. TSURUTA. 1957. Researches on the micro-organisms which deteriorate the stored cereals and grains. XIII. Studies on *Penicillium islandicum* Sopp recently obtained from Egyptian rice. Rept. Food Res. Inst. *12:* 24–25.

(*162*) TSUNODA, H., O. TSURUTA, S. MATSUNAMI, and S. ISHII. 1957. Researches on the micro-organisms which deteriorate the stored cereals and grains. XIV. Studies on rice parasitic molds. *Gibberella* and *Fusarium.* Rept. Food Res. Inst.

(*163*) TSUNODA, H., and Y. TOBE. 1957. Researches on the micro-organisms which deteriorate the stored cereals. XV. The effect of surface moisture of fumigated materials on fumigation by methylbromide. Rept. Food Res. Inst. *12:* 34–36.

(*164*) TSUNODA, H., O. TSURUTA, S. MATSUNAMI. 1958. Researches on the micro-organisms which deteriorate the stored cereals. XVI. Studies on rice parasitic molds. Gibberella and Fusarium; results on animal test. Rept. Food Res. Inst. *13:* 26–28.

(*165*) TSUNODA, H., O. TSURUTA, M. TAKAHASHI. 1958. Researches on the micro-organisms which deteriorate the stored cereals. XVII. Parasites of imported rice (1). Rept. Food Res. Inst. *13:* 29–42.

(*166*) TSUNODA, H., O. TSURUTA, M. TAKAHASHI. 1959. Researches for the micro-organisms which deteriorate the stored cereals. XVIII. Parasites of imported rice (2). Rept. Food Res. Inst. *13:* 34–37.

(*167*) TSUNODA, H., O. TSURUTA, M. TAKAHASHI. 1959. Researches for the micro-organisms which deteriorate the stored cereals. XIX. Parasites of imported rice (3). Rept. Food Res. Inst. *13:* 38–42.

(*168*) TSUNODA, H., O. TSURUTA, M. TAKAHASHI, M. IKEBE, T. SUGIMOTO, and Y. MATSUDA. 1959. Researches for the micro-organisms which deteriorate the stored cereals. XXIII. An examination on quality of domestic nonglutinous brown rice of aquatic culture. Rept. Food Res. Inst. *14:* 42–53.

(*169*) TSUNODA, H., T. SUGIMOTO, and O. TSURUTA. 1959. Researches for the micro-organisms which deteriorate the stored cereals. XXV. Studies on soil smelling yellowsis rice. Rept. Food Res. Inst. *14:* 58–61.

(*170*) TSUNODA, H. 1961. Researches for the micro-organisms which deteriorate the stored cereals. XXVI. Classification of genus *Penicillium* which is parasitic on the rice. Rept. Food Res. Inst. *15:* 98–110.

(*171*) TSUNODA, H., M. SAIGO, K. OGURA. 1966. A toxicological study on cultivable conditions of *Penicillium islandicum.* J. Agr. Sci. Commemoration Issue of 70th Anniversary Tokyo Nogyo Daigaku. 288–300.

(*172*) TSUNODA, H. 1961. Studies on *Penicillium brunneum* Udagawa nov. sp., parasitic to rice storage. I. J. Food Hygienic Soc. Japan *2:* 33–35.

(*173*) TSUNODA, H. 1962. Studies on *Penicillium brunneum* Udagawa nov. sp., parasitic to rice storage. II. Animal test. Food Hyg. Soc. Japan *3:* 347–351.

(*174*) TSUNODA, H. 1963. Micro-organisms which effect deterioration of stored cereals. XXIX. *Penicillium brunneum* Udagawa isolated from stored rice. Rept. Food Res. Inst. *17:* 238–248.

(*175*) TSUNODA, H. 1963. Micro-organisms of spoiled rice in storage. Food—Its Science and Technology. Suppl. pp. 161.

(*176*) TSUNODA, H. 1965. Research on the micro-organisms which deteriorate the stored cereals and grains. Part 31. On the Molds Parasitic to Mochi (Rice Cake). Rept. Food Res. Inst. *19:* 8–14.

(*177*) TSUNODA, H. 1964. Studies on toxicity of fungi parasitic on stored rice and grains. The diagnosis and treatment. *52:* 313–318.

(*178*) TSUNODA, H., and S. ITO. 1965. Research on the micro-organisms which deteriorate the stored cereals and grains. Part 32. On toxication of chick observed at Nagano prefecture. Rept. Food Res. Inst. *19:* 15–20.

(*179*) TSUNODA, H., N. TOYAZAKI, N. MOROOKA, N. MAKANO, H. YOSHIYAMA, K. OKUBO, M. ISODA. 1968. Researches on the micro-organisms which deteriorate the stored cereals and grains (part 34). Detection of injurious strains and properties of their toxic substance of scab, fusarium blight grown on the wheat. Rept. Food Res. Inst. *23:* 89–116.

(*180*) TSURUTA, O., and H. TSUNODA. 1959. Researches on the micro-organisms which deteriorate the stored cereals. XX. An examination on appearance frequency among countries, of *Aspergillaceae,* the main organism introductive to mildew putrefaction of imported rice. Rept. Food Res. Inst. *20:* 32–34.

(*181*) TSURUTA, O., and H. TSUNODA. 1959. Researches on the micro-organisms which deteriorate the stored cereals. XXI. Transition of moisture amount of stored rice in warehouse. Rept. Food Res. Inst. *14:* 35–37.

(*182*) TSURUTA, O., and H. TSUNODA. 1959. Researches on the micro-organisms which deteriorate the stored cereals. XXII. Parasitical state of *Fusarium* to domestic wheat and aquatic nonglutinous whole rice. Rept. Food Res. Inst. *14:* 38–41.

(*183*) TSURUTA, O., T. SUGIMOTO, T. MATSUDA, and H. TSUNODA. 1959. Researches on the micro-organisms which deteriorate the stored cereals. XXIV. The fundamental studies on the methods of package of rice storage. Rept. Food Res. Inst. *14:* 54–57.

(*184*) TSURUTA, O. 1960. The statistic studies on the parasitic micro-organisms infest in the imported and stored rice grains. Shokuryo Hokan Sousho *17:* 1–144.

(*185*) TSURUTA, O. 1962. Micro-organisms which effect deterioration of stored cereals. XXVII. Antagonism of the strains. Rept. Food Res. Inst. *16:* 54–58.

(*186*) TSURUTA, O. 1962. Micro-organisms which effect deterioration of stored cereals. XXVIII. The effects of the product in culture medium of *Pen. purpurogenum* on the growth of other Eumycetes. Rept. Food Res. Inst. *16:* 59–64.

(*187*) TSURUTA, O. 1962. A study on the parasitism and control of micro-organisms affecting stored rice with specific reference to family Aspergillaceae. J. Medical Soc. Toho Univ. *9:* 1–16.

(*188*) TSURUTA, O. 1963. Researches on the micro-organisms which deteriorate the stored cereals and grains.

XXX. Low temperature storage system of cereals observation on growth of injurious micro-organisms under the conditions concerning the storage system. Rept. Food Res. Inst. *17:* 249–251.

(*189*) TSURUTA, O. 1963. Review of the studies on the *Fusarium* scab disease of cereals. Division of Examination, Bureau of Food and Agricultural Products 1–24, 1963. (Mimeograph).

(*190*) UCHIDA, N. 1957. Histopathologic changes of organs in mice fed with molded rice (*Penicillium islandicum* Sopp) and those in mice given extracts of the mold. Acta Path. Japan *7:* 463.

(*191*) UCHIDA, N., and Y. EGASHIRA. 1957. Histopathologic findings in monkeys fed with molded rice (*Penicillium islandicum* Sopp) for a long time. Acta Path. Japan *7:* 463.

(*192*) UDAGAWA, S., Y. HASHIMOTO, and S. HIRAYAMA. 1956. Comparative studies on the citrinin producing activity among the different isolates of *Penicillium citrinum* Thom, Eisei-shikenjo Hokoku *74:* 299–303.

(*193*) UDAGAWA, S. 1962. Relation of Fungi to the deterioration of stored grains. Hakko Kyokaishi *20:* 1–7.

(*194*) UKAI, T., Y. YAMAMOTO, and T. YAMAMOTO. 1954. Studies on the poisonous substance from a strain of *Penicillium* (Hori-Yamamoto Strain). II. Culture method of Hori-Yamamoto strain and chemical structure of its poisonous substance. J. Pharmacol. Soc. Japan *74:* 450–454.

(*195*) UENO, Y., and I. UENO. 1964. Effects of luteoskyrin and chlorine-containing peptide, toxic components of *P. islandicum* Sopp., on the intermediary metabolism of the liver. VI. On the inhibitory action of luteoskyrin on Na$^+$ + K$^+$-activated ATPase. Folia Pharmacol. Japan *60:* 111.

(*196*) UENO, I. 1965. Effects of luteoskyrin and chlorine-containing peptide, toxic components of *P. islandicum* Sopp., on the intermediary metabolism of the liver. VII. Inhibitory action of luteoskyrin upon the mitochondrial oxidative phosphorylation. Folia Pharmacol. Japan *61:* 146.

(*197*) UMEDA, M. 1964. Cytotoxic effects of the mycotoxins of *Penicillium islandicum* Sopp, luteoskyrin and chlorine-containing peptide on changs liver cells and Hela cells. Acta. Path. Japan *14:* 373–394.

(*198*) URAGUCHI, K. 1942. Pharmacological studies on the extract of the yellow mouldy rice, "O-hen-mai." I. Folia Pharmacol. Japan *34:* 39–40.

(*199*) URAGUCHI, K. 1947. Existence of toxic substance in the mouldy rice. Pharmacological studies on the toxicity of the yellowed rice, "O-hen-mai." I. Nisshin Igaku, *34:* 155–161.

(*200*) URAGUCHI, K. 1947. Some chemical properties of the toxic substances isolated from the yellowsis rice. Pharmacological studies on the toxicity of yellowed rice, "O-hen-mai." II. Nisshin Igaku *34:* 224–229.

(*201*) URAGUCHI, K. 1948. Activity of vitamine to the occurrence of acute poisoning caused by yellowsis rice. Pharmacological studies on the toxicity of yellowed rice, "O-hen-mai." III. Nisshin Igaku *35:* 166–170.

(*202*) URAGUCHI, K. 1949. Pharmacological studies on the toxicity of the yellowed rice "O-hen-mai." IV. Characteristic toxicity of the poisonous substances in yellowsis rice on acute poisoning. Nisshin Igaku *36:* 13–18.

(*203*) URAGUCHI, K. 1950. Pharmacological studies on the toxicity of yellowed rice. V. Acute symptoms in vertebrates poisoned by the yellowed rice. Nisshin Igaku *37:* 337–343.

(*204*) URAGUCHI, K. 1954. Various kinds of yellowsis rice and their characters of toxicity. Koshu Eisei *16:* 53–55.

(*205*) URAGUCHI, K., F. SAKAI, and M. TSUKIOKA. 1954. Toxicity of the socalled "O-hen-mai" detected from the recently imported foreign rice. I. Folia Pharmacol. Japan *50:* 63.

(*206*) URAGUCHI, K., F. SAKAI, and M. TSUKIOKA. 1954. Toxicity of the socalled "O-hen-mai" detected from the recently imported foreign rice. II. Folia Pharmacol. Japan *50:* 146.

(*207*) URAGUCHI, K. 1954. The present situation in studies on toxicity of yellowsis rice. J. Japan Med. Assoc. *32:* 507–514.

(*208*) URAGUCHI, K., M. SAITO, M. TSUNODA, et al. 1955. Toxicity of the socalled "O-hen-mai" detected from the recently imported foreign rice. IV. Folia Pharmacol. Japan *51:* 105–106.

(*209*) URAGUCHI, K., T. TATSUNO, F. SAKA, et al. 1955. Toxicity of the socalled "O-hen-mai" detected from the recently imported foreign rice. V. Folia Pharmacol. Japan *51:* 154–155.

(*210*) URAGUCHI, K., F. SAKAI, and S. MORI. 1955. Site of action and cause of death in the acute poisoning of the yellowed rice toxic principle. (Pharmacological studies on the toxicity of the yellowsis rice "O-hen-mai" VIII.) Nisshin Igaku *42:* 690–695.

(*211*) URAGUCHI, K., and F. SAKAI. 1955. Influence of previous administrations into mice to the yellowed rice toxic principle (Extracted from the *Penicillium toxicarium*-polluted rice grains) upon the acute poisoning due to lethal doses of the same principle. (Pharmacological studies on the toxicity of the yellowed rice "O-hen-mai" VI). Nisshin Igaku *42:* 512–518.

(*212*) URAGUCHI, K., T. TATSUNO, M. TSUKIOKA, et al. 1956. Toxicity of the socalled "O-hen-mai" detected from the recently imported foreign rice. VI. Folia Pharmacol. Japan *52:* 225–226.

(*213*) URAGUCHI, K. 1959. Toxicity of *P. islandicum*-growing moldy rice. Medicine of Japan in 1959, (Proc. 15th General Assembly of Japan Med. Congress, Tokyo) *1:* 313–319.

(*214*) URAGUCHI, K. 1960. Liver injury caused by yellowsis rice. Clinical Pathology *8:* 1–8.

(*215*) URAGUCHI, K., Y. KOBAYASHI, M. MIYAKE, et al. 1961. Toxicological approach to the metabolites of *Penicillium islandicum* Sopp growing on the yellowed rice. Japan J. Exp. Med. *31:* 1–18.

(*216*) URAGUCHI, K., T. TATSUNO, M. MIYAKE, et al. 1961. Isolation of two toxic agents, luteoskyrin and chlorine-containing peptide, from the metabolites of *Penicillium islandicum* Sopp, with some properties thereof. Japan J. Exp. Med. *31:* 19–46.

(*217*) URAGUCHI, K., F. SAKAI, M. TSUKIOKA, Y. NOGUCHI, T. TATSUNO, M. SAITO, M. ENOMOTO, T. ISHIKO, T. SHIKATA, and M. MIYAKE. 1961. Acute and chronic toxicity in mice and rats of the fungus mat of *Penicillium islandicum* Sopp added to the diet. Japan J. Exp. Med. *31:* 435–461.

(*218*) URAGUCHI, K. 1962. Malignant hepatoma and socalled carcinogens, with special reference to the toxicity of luteoskyrin in a small dose. Folia Pharmacol. Japan *58:* 45.

(*219*) URAGUCHI, K., Y. NOGUCHI, and M. OKUGI. 1962. Comparative susceptibility of various strained mice to the *P. islandicum* growing rice poisoning. Folia Pharmacol. Japan *58:* 147.

(220) URAGUCHI, K. 1963. Analytical approach to the yellowed rice poisoning, through acute and chronic liver injurious actions of *Penicillium islandicum* metabolic poisons, luteoskyrin and chlorine-containing peptide. Folia Pharmacol. Japan *59:* 61.

(221) URAGUCHI, K. 1963. Some experiments on the yellowsis rice—On the standpoint of chronic poisoning. Sogo Igaku *20:* 13–22.

(222) URAGUCHI, K., Y. NAGUCHI, T. TATSUNO, M. SAITO, and M. ENOMOTO. 1964. Comparative study on toxicological spectrum of the liver damage due to luteoskyrin and chlorine-containing peptide, mycotoxins of *P. islandicum* Sopp. Folia Pharmacol. Japan *60:* 71.

(223) WATANABE, A. 1950. Study on culture of fungi causes the yellowsis rice. Pharmacological Laboratory 12–13.

(224) WATANABE, Y., K. ITO, and Y. YANADA. Present status of food hygienic examination for the imported rice. Shokuhin Eisei Kenkyu *4:* 45–61.

(225) WOLLEN WEBER, H. W., and O. A. REINKING. 1935. "Die Fusarien."

(226) YAMADA, Y. 1946. On the accident of food poisoning by cereal powder at Nagano Pref. Sogo Igaku *3:* 587–588.

(227) YAMADA, T. 1959. Angiological studies on chlorine containing peptide produced by *Penicillium islandicum* Sopp. Sogo Igaku *16:* 902.

(228) YAMAGUCHI, S., and M. KIKUCHI. 1964. Notes on the production of Organic Acids and mycelial pigments during growth of *Penicillium islandicum*. Bot. Mag. (Tokyo) *77:* 49–53.

(229) YAMAMOTO, T. 1954. Studies on the poison-producing mold isolated from dry malts. I. Distribution, isolation, cultivation and formation of the toxic substance. J. Pharm. Soc. Japan *74:* 797–801.

(230) YAMAMOTO, T. 1954. Studies on the poison-producing mold isolated from dry malt. II. Physiological properties. J. Pharm. Soc. Japan *74:* 801–806.

(231) YAMAMOTO, T. 1954. Studies on the poison-producing mold isolated from dry malt. III. Physiological properties. J. Pharm. Soc. Japan *74:* 806–810.

(232) YAMAMOTO, T. 1954. Studies on the poison-producing mold isolated from dry malt. IV. On the toxicity. J Pharm. Soc. Japan *74:* 810–812.

(233) YAMAMOTO, T. 1955. Studies on the metabolic products of *Penicillium islandicum* Sopp. I. J. Pharm. Soc. Japan *75:* 512–514.

(234) YAMAMOTO, T. 1955. Studies on the metabolic products of *Penicillium islandicum* Sopp. II. Composition of culture filtrate (Addendum) J. Pharm. Soc. Japan *75:* 761–763.

(235) YAMAMOTO, I. 1955, 1956. Study on *Aspergillus candidus* isolated from damaged rice. Ann. Rept. Kobe Municipal Hygienic Laboratory 75–89, 1955; 34–42, 1956.

(236) YAMAMOTO, T., I. YAMAMOTO, A. HAMAGUCHI, Y. MATSUMOTO, K. SAWADA, Y. YAMAMOTO. 1955, 1956. Biochemical studies on the molds isolated from foodstuffs. I. On *Penicillium tardum* (on the yellowsis rice caused by *Pen. tardum*) II. On the metabolite of *Pen. implicatum* Biourge isolated from damaged rice. III. On the metabolite of *Asp. repens* isolated from damaged rice. IV. On the Penicillia isolated from domestic rice. Ann. Rept. Kobe Municipal Hygienic Laboratory 90–101, 1955; 43–48, 1956.

(237) YAMAMOTO, T. 1955. Studies on the poison-producing mold isolated from dry malts. V. Patulin production fermented by *Penicillium urticae* Bainier. VI. Toxicity and biological activities of Patulin and its derivatives. VII. Detection and micro-activity assay of Patulin. Ann. Rept. Kobe Municipal Hygienic Laboratory pp. 57–67, 68–71, 72–74.

MYCOTOXICOSES ASSOCIATED WITH MOLDY CORN

by E. B. Smalley, W. F. O. Marasas, F. M. Strong, J. R. Bamburg, R. E. Nichols, *and* N. R. Kosuri
Department of Plant Pathology, Biochemistry and Veterinary Science, University of Wisconsin, Madison

Summary

Toxicosis in farm animals after ingestion of moldy corn is an irregularly occurring problem of long standing in the Midwestern United States. Toxin producing strains of *Aspergillus flavus*, *Alternaria tenuis*, *Cephalosporium* sp., *Epicoccum nigrum*, *Fusarium moniliforme*, *F. roseum*, *F. tricinctum*, *Paecilomyces varioti*, *Trichoderma lignorum*, and *Trichothecium roseum* are frequently isolated from such corn. Certain of the isolates of *F. roseum* from moldy corn produce the estrogenic compound zearalenone (RAL). Stob et al. (45), Christensen et al. (10) and Mirocha et al. (32) have shown this compound to be the cause of the vulvo-vaginitis phase of the problem. Several of the other fungi produce toxic spiroepoxy metabolties called trichothecanes. Isolates of *F. tricinctum* produce diacetoxyscirpenol (3-hydroxy-4, 15-diacetoxy-12 13-epoxy-Δ^9-trichothecene) and T–2 toxin (3-hydroxy-4,15-diacetoxy-8-(3-methylbutyryloxy) 12, 13-epoxy-Δ^9-trichothecene) as their major toxic metabolites. Certain isolates of *F. roseum* also produce diacetoxyscirpenol. *Trichothecium roseum* and *Trichoderma lignorum*, respectively, are known to produce the similar compounds trichothecin (4-isocrotonyloxy (-12, 13-epoxy-Δ^9-trichothecene-8-one) and trichodermin (4-acetoxy(-12,13-epoxy-Δ^9-trichothecene)). One Wisconsin isolate of *T. lignorum* also produced small quantities of T–2 toxin. Certain species of *Cephalosporium* are known to produce the toxic spiroepoxy metabolite crotocin (4-isocrotonyloxy-7,8;12,13-diepoxy-Δ^9-trichothecene). The acute oral LD_{50} of crystalline T–2 toxin was 4 mg./kg. in rats and 6.5 mg./kg. in trout. Sublethal and lethal doses in rats caused increases in blood clotting and prothrombin times. Heart rate and blood pressure in rats following lethal or sublethal doses first dropped below normal, then increased above normal and gradually declined. Respiration rates followed similar patterns. Resting metabolic rates decreased in both sublethal and lethal doses. Low dose, long term feeding trials with T–2 toxin did not induce cancer in rats or trout.

Introduction

The development of toxicosis in farm animals after ingestion of moldy corn (*Zea mays* L.) is an irregularly occurring problem of long-standing importance in the United States and elsewhere (2, 3, 6, 8, 12, 16, 20, 21, 35, 41). The problem has become particularly important in Wisconsin and other Midwestern States in recent years, and severe outbreaks have occurred in association with the 1962, 1964, and 1965 corn crops (1, 10, 11, 13, 22, 43). Lesser outbreaks have occurred sporadically in other years. These problems have been primarily associated with corn, late-to-mature, and high in moisture at the time of the first killing frosts (28). This corn, when stored in conventional cribs without artificial drying is often quite moldy by early spring. The general moldy corn problem has been the subject of several recent comprehensive reviews (8, 18, 19, 20, 21), and this review will not include many of these subjects except as they relate to our moldy corn problems in Wisconsin and the Midwestern United States.

Animal Symptoms

A variety of animal problems with a multitude of symptoms has been observed in association with ingestion of such moldy corn. For example, in an outbreak year, one can expect many cases of vulvo-vaginitis in swine and particularly in the young gilts. Symptoms of this problem include enlarged and elevated vulvae, enlarged mammary glands and in severe cases, prolapse of the vagina and death. Similar associated estrogenic effects in swine and cattle may often include abortion and infertility. Another equally widespread part of the problem complex includes general digestive disorders in various farm animals accompanied by diarrhea, often bloody, milk reduction, unthriftiness, lack of weight gain and general feed refusal. Cases of nervous twitching, encephalitis, or leuco-encephalomalacia and death are less common, but occur occasionally. In still other cases, the death of the farm animals is not accompanied by obvious symptoms. Another major problem associated with ingestion of moldy corn is death of the farm animal as the result of massive hemorrhagic lesions in the stomach, heart, intestines, lungs, bladder, and kidneys. These symptoms probably constitute the hemorrhagic syndrome as described by Forgacs (18, 19, 20), Albright, et al. (1), and others (40, 41) (fig. 1).

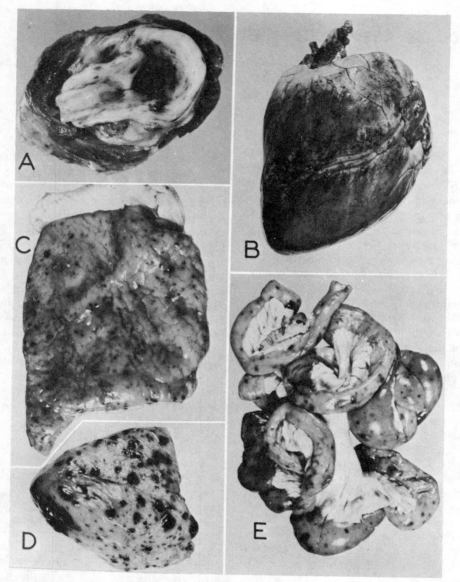

Figure 1.—Lethal hemorrhagic lesions developing in a pig following ingestion of moldy corn.

Estrogenic Syndrome

Several authors have reported a condition in female swine ingesting moldy feeds resulting in a swelling of the vulva and subsequent prolapse of the vagina. McNutt, et al. (*35*) first reported the condition which they called vulvovaginitis from Wisconsin in 1928. McErlean (*34*) in Ireland reported a similar condition and postulated that the syndrome was caused by an estrogen produced by molds in the feeds.

Christensen et al. (*10*) described the "estrogenic syndrome" in swine in detail. They indicated that affected swine develop swollen, edematous vulva in the young females, while testes of the young male

pigs become shrunken. Enlarged mammary glands are present in the young of both sexes and abortion often occurs in pregnant sows. The condition and causal agent has been studied in detail by Stob et al. (*45*), Christensen et al. (*10*), Urry et al. (*47*) and Mirocha et al. (*32*).

Stob et al. (*45*) reported the purification of a metabolite from *Gibberella zeae* (*F. roseum* 'graminearum') exhibiting anabolic and marked uterotrophic activity. During 1957–58 they observed seven widely separated swine herds showing vulval hypertrophy and occasional vaginal eversion along with prominent mammary glands in both sexes. This condition was reproduced in 4 days in pigs fed corn infected with *Gibberella zeae.*

The active fungal metabolite proved to be 6-(10-hydroxy-6-oxo-1-unidecenyl) beta resorcylic acid mu lactone (fig. 2), named zearalenone (*47*).

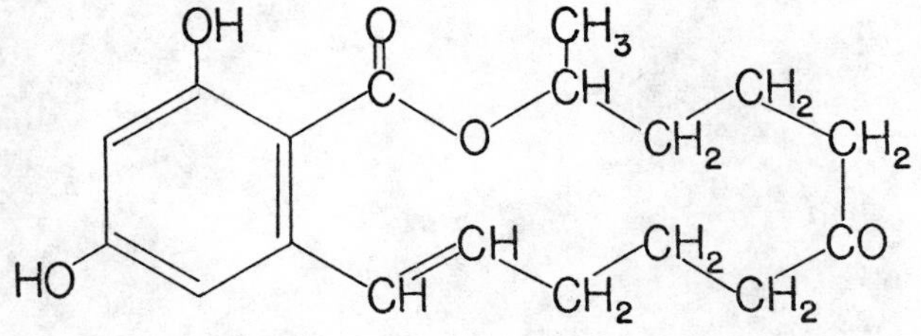

Figure 2.—Zearalenone [6-(10-hydroxy-6-oxo-1-unidecenyl) beta resorcylic acid mu lactone], the toxin from *Gibberella zeae* causing vulvo-vaginitis.

This work has been confirmed by Christensen et al. (*10*) and Mirocha et al. (*32*) who indicate that evidence is now conclusive that the "estrogenic syndrome" is caused by eating grains, especially invaded by certain strains of *F. roseum* 'graminearum' (*G. zeae*). They found that a period of low temperature, or alternating moderate and low temperatures is necessary for the production of the toxin. Mirocha (*32*) confirmed that their compound (F–2) was identical to the previously described zearalenone.

Mirocha et al. (*33*) found that purified zearalenone when injected into white, weanling, virgin female rats resulted in an increase in fresh weight of uterus with increasing doses giving increased response. Uterus fresh weights three times greater than the controls developed when 650 µg. of the compound was administered over a 7-day period. Little or no effect was noted below the 20 µg. dose. Animals given 40 µg. over the same period doubled their body weights. Higher doses gave no further growth increases. In other studies (*33*) these same workers showed that the compound was produced most abundantly in pure culture if the culture was given a 12° C. cold treatment prior to incubation at higher temperatures. No zearalenone was produced in pure culture at 25° C. No real difference in production was obtained when either corn or rice was used as a substrate.

More recently, zearalenone has been shown to play a striking role in the production of perithecia by *F. roseum* and other fungi (*9, 15, 38*). High concentrations of the compound in the culture media limit perithecial production in many fungi, while low concentrations cause stimulation of perithecial production. Single ascospore isolates of *F. roseum* which readily produce perithecia produce less zearalenone in culture than those not producing perithecia (*15*).

The role which zearalenone and other recently discovered compounds (*33*) may play in the infertility and abortion problems in cattle and other farm animals has not yet been established.

Toxin Producing Fungi

Penicillium rubrum from moldy corn has been associated with a hemmorrhagic disease in swine and other animals in the southern United States (*6, 20, 41*). *A. flavus* has also been implicated, but these results seem doubtful since the animal symptoms which developed were atypical of those presently understood as typical symptoms of aflatoxicosis (*8, 49*). Recently, however, Cysewski et al. (*13*) in studies with pigs using purified and crude aflatoxin preparations found that doses of 2 to 3 mg./kg. aflatoxin are capable of causing an acute disease in young swine. They indicated that clinical and pathologic changes were comparable to those in naturally affected animals reported by Sippel et al. (*41*). Sisk et al. (*42*) were not able to produce such drastic changes at 0.08 to 0.30 mg./kg. Toxins of *P. rubrum* were partially purified by Wilson (*48*). Recently rubratoxins A and B have been purified and partially characterized (*27, 36, 37, 46*). Toxin-producing strains of *A. flavus*, *P. cyclopium*, and *P. palitans* from moldy corn have been associated with the hemorrhagic syndrome in cattle in the northern areas of the United States (*1*). Another hemorrhagic disease in poultry has been associated with ingestion of corn containing moldy mixed feeds contaminated with toxin producing isolates of *A. chevalieri*, *A. clavatus*, *A. flavus*, *A. fumigatus*, *A. glancus*, *Paecilomyces variati*, *P. citrinum*, and *P. rubrum* (*18, 19*). Thus, although many toxin producing fungi have been associated with hemorrhagic diseases in farm animals, their exact role as causal agents remains unclear.

Since initiation of our research in Wisconsin on this problem, we have isolated a great diversity of fungi from moldy corn samples associated with severe animal toxicity. Although there was considerable variation in the species of fungi isolated from different samples, the most commonly isolated fungi included: *F. moniliforme*, *F. roseum*, (*Gibberella zeae*), *Epicoccum nigrum*, *F. tricinctum*, *Trichoderma lignorum*, *Cladosporium herbarum*, *Alternaria tenuis*, *Trichothecium roseum*, *Nigrospora* sp., *Paecilomyces varioti*, *Acromoniella atra*, *Papulospora* sp., (*Melanospora* sp.) *A. versicolor*, *A. flavus*, *A. candidus*, *A. fumigatus*, *P. cyclopium*, *P. oxalicum*, *P. rubrum*, and several members of the Mucorales including: *Mucor fragilis*, *Mucor alternans*, *Mucor pusillus*, *Rhizopus rhizopodiformis*, *Absidia corymbifera* and others. Some of these fungi have previously been recognized as toxin producers (*8*).

Pure cultures of these fungi from moldy corn were tested in a variety of ways to determine their toxin producing potential when grown on various culture substrates over a range of temperatures. Test animals included guinea pigs, rats, mice, cattle, chickens and ducks. Assay procedures included free choice oral feedings, force feedings, skin tests and intraperitoneal injections. One of the most useful testing procedures made use of topically applied pure culture concentrates to the skin of unwounded, shaved laboratory animals. Pure cultures of contaminated moldy feeds were first extracted with diethyl ether or ethylacetate and after solvent evaporation the remaining residues resuspended in olive oil, acetone, ethylacetate or dimethylsulfoxide were applied at approximately 5 mg. per application. The results of the skin assay ranged from a just noticeable skin reaction with the formation of a slight scab after 3 to 5 days to inflammation, hemorrhage, and heavy scab formation in the same period. Application of highly toxic concentrates often led to death in 48 to 72 hours with little or no noticeable skin response (fig. 3).

It was interesting to find that of the many fungi isolated and tested for toxin production only a limited number proved to be potent toxin producers as determined by the skin test. Although toxin-producing strains of *Fusarium roseum*, *Trichothecium roseum*, *Fusarium moniliforme*, *Nigrospora* sp., *Epicoccum nigrum*, *Aspergillus flavus*, *Papulospora* sp., *Aspergillus versicolor*, *Trichoderma lignorum* and others were present, clearly the most active toxin producers were isolates of *Fusarium tricinctum* (table 1).

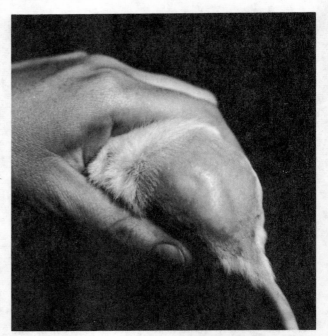

Table 1.—Dermal toxicity on albino rats of residues from ethyl acetate extracts of fungus cultures from moldy corn

| Fungus species | Isolates tested | Number inducing[1] | | |
		Severe reaction or death	Mild reaction	No reaction
Fusarium tricinctum	29	22	4	3
Fusarium roseum	11	0	11	0
Tricothecium roseum	1	1	0	0
Fusarium moniliforme	10	0	10	0
Nigrospora sp.	4	2	2	0
Epicoccum nigrum	2	0	2	0
Papulospora sp.	3	0	2	1
Aspergillus versicolor	1	1	0	0
Trichoderma lignorum	3	0	2	1

[1]Values for dermal toxicity were the averaged results from 2 treated rats. No reactions were obtained on rats treated with residues from extracted sterile culture media.

The mouse injection test revealed in addition toxin producing isolates of *Cephalosporium* sp., *Cladosporium herbarum*, *Alternaria tenuis*, *Paecilomyces variota*, *Helminthosporium turcicum*, and *Ustilago maydis*. Studies by Mirocha, et al. (*33*) revealed that the most commonly

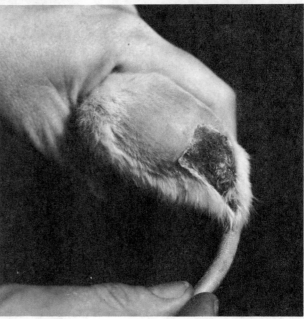

Figure 3.—Typical skin response (lower picture) on shaved albino rat following topical application of residues of ethyl acetate extracted toxic fungus culture. The other animal was treated with extracted sterile culture media.

isolated toxin producing fungi from "corn, feeds and foods" were species of *Alternaria*, *Aspergillus*, *Chaetomium*, *Cladosporium*, *Fusarium*, and *Penicillium*. More detailed studies were carried out by this group with toxins produced by *Chaetomium globosum* from corn and from commercially manufactured animal feeds. Several isolates grown on moist corn killed rats in 4 to 5 days after the rats had consumed less than 5 g. of infested corn per animal. Symptoms included disturbance of the central nervous system, coma and death. Gross necropsy lesions consisted of subdural hemorrhage and hemorrhagic enteritis. The *Chaetomium* toxin was harmless in pigs. The toxin has not been characterized chemically.

Factors Influencing Toxin Production by *Fusarium tricinctum*

Research in our laboratory at the University of Wisconsin has been concentrated on the toxins produced by *Fusarium tricinctum*. The fungus was among those most commonly isolated from corn associated with toxicity and appeared to produce large quantities of a potent toxin. Factors influencing toxin production by *F. tricinctum* were studied in detail in order to produce sufficient crude toxin for studies on the chemical structure of the toxins. It is also of interest to note that in their taxonomic revision of the genus *Fusarium*, Snyder and Hanson (*44*) considered that all species in the group Sporotrichiella of the older classification system of Wollenweber and Reinking (*50*) could be placed in the single variable species *F. tricinctum*. Thus our *F. tricinctum* includes such species as *F. poae*, *F. chlamydosporum*, and *F. sporotrichioides*. This is of particular interest since in the years following World War II a severe toxicosis developed in the Soviet Union when humans consumed millet which had been allowed to winter under the snow. Many people died from this disease which has been called alimentary toxic aleukia (*19, 29*). *F. sporotrichioides* was considered one of the principal toxin producing fungi in this millet. The principal symptoms in humans after ingestion of the toxic millet were anemia, increased clotting time, hemorrhages in the skin, nose, mouth, and gastrointestinal tract, kidneys, and subsequent death. A purified compound, sporofusariogenin, has been reported to be the toxic product (*39*).

Taxonomically, the *F. tricinctum* isolates from moldy corn appeared to be closely related to the organisms suspected of causing alimentary toxic aleukia in the Soviet Union. As with other *Fusarium* species, *F. tricinctum* exhibits considerable variation between isolates, and indeed between single conidial isolates from the same source. All isolates, however, produced the characteristic lemon to pear-shaped microconidia diagnostic for *F. tricinctum* (fig. 4). Regardless of the source of the *F. tricinctum* isolate, most of the isolates produced toxic metabolites which could be detected using the rat skin assay (table 2). As with many other mycotoxin-producing fungi, temperature and substrate markedly influenced the degree of toxin production (table 3) (*21*). Low incubation temperatures favored toxin production in liquid culture. At higher temperatures in liquid culture less toxin was produced and after long incubation, the toxin was apparently degraded.

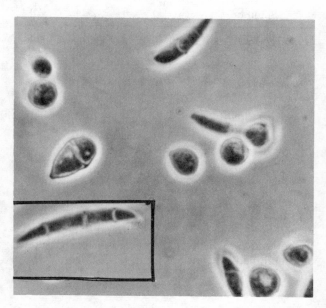

Figure 4.—Typical microconidia and macroconidia of *Fusarium tricinctum*.

Table 2.—Dermal toxicity of residues from ethyl acetate extracts of *Fusarium tricinctum* cultures on albino rats

Source	Number tested	Severe reaction or death	Mild reaction	No reaction
		Number inducing[1]		
Field corn	17	16	1	0
Sweet corn	12	6	3	3
Carnation	2	2	0	0
Oats	2	1	1	0
Sorghum	2	2	0	0
Wheat	2	1	1	0
Fescue	1	1	0	0
Grass hay	1	1	0	0
Turf grass	1	0	1	0
Cranberry	1	1	0	0

[1]Values for dermal toxicity were the averaged results from 2 treated rats. No reactions were obtained on rats treated with residues from extracted sterile culture media.

Toxin Purification and Characterization

Using the rat skin test as an assay tool with one isolate of *F. tricinctum* (B24 from moldy sweet corn), a purification procedure was developed which yielded a highly toxic crystalline product (*21, 22*). This compound proved to be identical with a sesquiterpenoid

Table 3.—Effect of temperature on toxin production by *Fusarium tricinctum* (T–5)[1]

Substrate	Time (weeks)	Temperature (C.)		
		8	14	20
Cracked corn_____	1	1.5	2.5	[2]2.5
	2	1.5	5.0	2.0
	4	5.0	1.0	1.0
Gregories liquid medium (mat)_____	1	0	1.5	1.0
	2	2.0	2.0	1.5
	4	5.0	3.0	3.0
Gregories liquid medium (broth)_____	1	2.5	3.0	4.0
	2	5.0	3.0	3.0
	4	5.0	2.0	2.0

[1]Toxicity determined by topical applications of residues from diethyl ether extracted cultures on shaved albino rats.

[2]Skin reactions: 0 = no reaction; 5 = death.

4,15-diacetoxyscirp-9-en-3-ol or in more recent nomenclature 3-hydroxy-4,15-diacetoxy-12,13-epoxy-Δ^9-trichothecene, which had previously been isolated and identified by Dawkins et al. (*7, 14*), from *F. scirpi* and *F. equiseti* (*3*) (fig. 5).

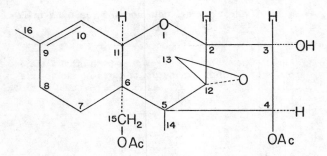

Figure 5.—The structure of diacetoxyscirpenol (B–24 toxin) [3-hydroxy-4,15-diacetoxy-12,13-epoxy-Δ^9-trichothecene] from *Fusarium scirpi*, *Fusarium equiseti* (both *F. roseum*), and *Fusarium tricinctum*.

After a time, isolate B24 lost its ability to produce extensive amounts of toxin and was discarded in favor of a more potent toxin-producing strain (T–2). From this strain of *F. tricinctum* a second pure crystalline toxin was isolated which has been called T–2 toxin. This compound was shown to be 3-hydroxy-4,15-diacetoxy-8-(3-methylbutyryloxy)-12,13-epoxy-Δ^9-trichothecene (*3, 4*) (fig. 6). When this latter strain of *F. tricinctum* was grown at temperatures above 20° C. another toxic metabolite, 4-Desacetoxy T—2 toxin was produced in relatively large quantities above 20° C. (*2*).

Isolates of *F. tricinctum* also produce a still different toxin, a butenolide characterized as 4-acetamido, 4-hydroxy, 2-butenoic acid-γ-lactone (*51*). Apparently

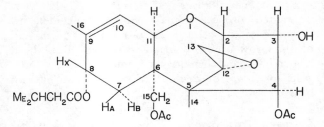

Figure 6.—The structure of T–2 toxin [3-hydroxy-4,15-diacetoxy-8-(3-methylbutyryloxy)-12,13-epoxy-Δ^9-trichothecene] from *Fusarium tricinctum*.

the ratios of the toxins produced by the T–2 isolate of *F. tricinctum* are dependent upon substrate, with high production of T–2 toxin taking place on soybean meal, corn steep liquor media and with production of the butenolide on some autoclaved small cereals or rich agar cultures (*43*).

Certain species of *Cephalosporium* are also known to produce the trichothecene crotocin (4-isocrotonyloxy)-7,8-12,13-diepoxy-Δ^9-trichothene (*23, 24, 26*) (fig. 7). The structures of these scirpene or trichothecene (*25*) compounds are quite interesting in view of the fact that other fungus species associated with moldy corn have previously been reported to produce similar compounds. Certain isolates of *F. roseum*, as indicated, produce diacetoxyscirpenol. *Trichothecium roseum* and *Trichoderma lignorum*, respectively, produced the similar compounds trichothecin (4-isocrotonyloxy-12,13-epoxy-Δ^9-trichothecen-8-one) (*3, 17*) and trichodermin (4-acetoxy-12,13-epoxy-Δ^9-trichothecene) (*3, 25*) (fig. 8). When the double bond of T–2 toxin is removed by hydrogenation, the com-

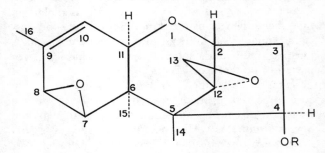

R = $-\overset{O}{\overset{\|}{C}}CH = CHCH_3$ CROTOCIN

R = H   CROTOCOL

Figure 7.—The structure of crotocin [4-(2-butenoxy)-7,8-12,13-diepoxy-Δ^9-trichothecene] from *Cephalosporium*

R = $\overset{O}{\overset{\|}{C}}CH = CHCH^3$.

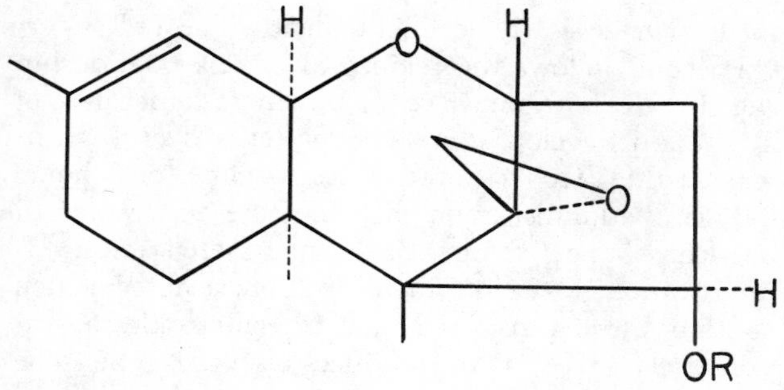

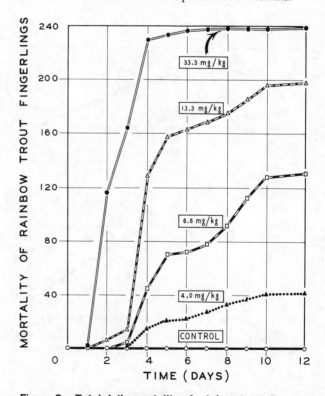

R = Ac TRICHODERMIN
R = H TRICHODERMOL = RORIDIN C

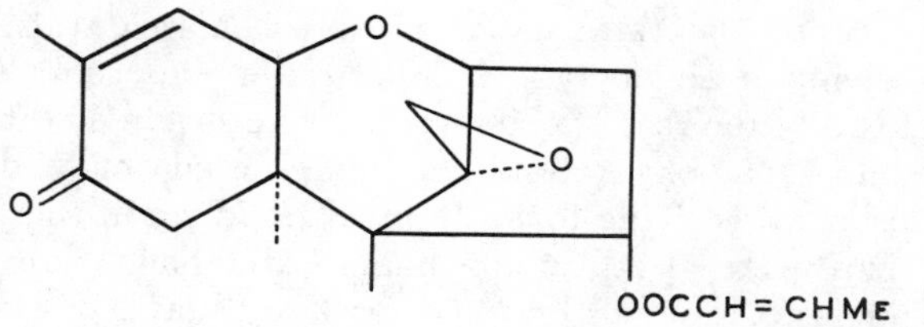

OOCCH = CHMe

TRICHOTHECIN

Figure 8.—Trichothecenes from fungi associated with moldy corn toxicosis.

pound retains its animal toxicity. However, when the epoxide ring is opened to obtain the compound 3, 4, 8, 12, 15-pentahydroxy-Δ^9-trichothecene, it becomes nontoxic (2). Thus the toxicity of this compound is closely associated with the epoxy ring.

Trichothecin, trichodermin and crotocin have not presently been demonstrated to be produced by isolates of their respective fungi from moldy corn. Very recently one isolate of *T. lignorum* has been shown to produce small quantities of T-2 toxin (5).

Animal Studies

The crude toxin from the T-2 isolate and the crystalline toxin when it became available were used in animal tests to determine dose effect and responses to the toxin. Rainbow trout proved to be extremely responsive animals and the acute oral LD_{50} for the crystalline T-2 toxin was about 6.1 mg./kg. (30, 31) (fig. 9). This figure was possibly too high because of losses in the water during feeding (30).

In rats the LD_{50} of the crude toxin (frozen dried cultures) was 160 mg./kg. orally and for the crystalline toxin 3.8 mg./kg. The toxin in concentrations as low as 4 mg./kg. produced striking pathological signs in

rainbow trout fingerlings, notably a shedding of the intestinal mucosa and severe edema with fluid in the body cavities and behind the eyes.

Very low concentrations of another group of mycotoxins, the aflatoxins, at 2 to 80 parts per billion in the daily diet, have been found to induce hepatoma in rainbow trout and rats. In view of these findings long-term feeding studies were performed with rainbow trout and rats to determine pathological responses of these animals to low doses of T-2 toxin, and to determine whether this toxin plays a role in hepatomagenesis. One thousand fish in each treatment received daily doses of 200 or 400 p.p.b. of T-2 toxin, respectively, in their diet for 1 year. No evidence of neoplasia or the development of hepatoma was found (31). Similar results were obtained in feeding trials with rats. Thus, long-term feeding trials with rainbow trout and albino rats indicated that T—2 toxin is not carcinogenic, at least in the concentration used in these experiments. Low doses of the toxin fed to rainbow trout over a period of 12 months actually had a small growth-promoting effect. Albino rats consumed up to 20 times the single dose of LD_{50} when the T-2 toxin was administered in low concentrations in their feed over a period of 8 months.

Figure 9.—Total daily mortality of rainbow trout fingerlings fed pellets treated with *Fusarium tricinctum* toxin in ethyl acetate and control pellets treated only with ethyl acetate. Concentration of toxin is expressed as milligram toxin per kilogram fish.

The pronounced skin and epithelium tissue irritating properties of T–2 toxin at concentrations of 2 to 15 parts per million in the diet was evident, in that feeding such diets to albino rats resulted in severe inflammation of the nose and mouth. This observation suggested that the T–2 toxin might cause skin cancer if applied to the skin in low doses over a long time period. Application of various amounts of T–2 toxin to the backs of white mice, with and without subsequent applications of Croton oil, over a period of 10 weeks failed to induce any papillomas. The fact that no papillomas developed in any of the treatments suggests that this toxin is not a skin carcinogen. Thus, the evidence obtained from long-term low-dose feeding trials with rainbow trout and albino rats as well as from the mouse-papilloma studies indicates that T–2 toxin is noncarcinogenic. This is in striking contrast to the aflatoxins which are potent liver carcinogens at extremely low concentrations.

Sublethal doses of crude T–2 toxin in rats resulted in increased clotting and prothrombin times up to 8 hours or more after treatment (fig. 10). Heart rates and amplitude increase slightly following oral toxin administrations then drop sharply below normal followed by another and greater increase. After 6 hours the heart rate slowly declines to death. The T–P/interval second follows the reciprocal of this relationship (fig. 11). Respiration in rats following a lethal dose of T–2 toxin develops the same patterns over time as seen in the ECG response. Rates decline for 3 hours following administration then increase above normal between 4 and 6 hours. Seven hours after toxin administration, a decline in respiration is noted which continues to death (fig. 12). Intravenous administration of crude T–2 toxin produces essentially the same effect upon the rat's heart rate as seen in oral administration. The initial drop and sudden increase, however, develop within 1 hour instead of the 4 hours required for oral administration. In the same trial, blood pressure in the treated animal follows the same pattern (fig. 13).

Metabolic rates in fasted and nonfasted rats receiving a single oral administration of crude T–2 toxin at the rate of 100 mg./kg. were strikingly different. Metabolic rates in animals fasted for 2 days prior to receiving toxin declined rapidly and the animals were dead in 48 hours. Metabolic rates in nonfasted animals declined for 1 to 2 days, but later increased to normal. None of the nonfasted animals died (fig. 14).

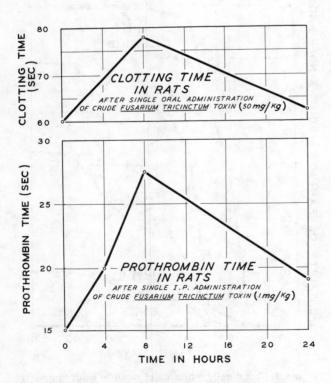

Figure 10.—Clotting time and prothrombin time in young rats following administration of crude (frozen dried cultures) T–2 toxin. Each point represents the averaged results from five treated animals.

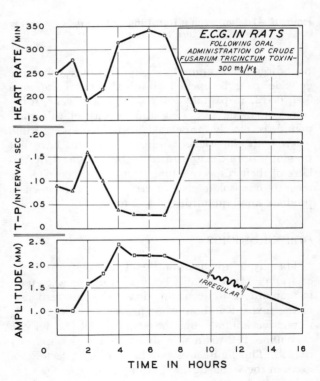

Figure 11.—ECG in young rats following oral administration of crude (frozen dried cultures) T–2 toxin. Each point represents the averaged results from five treated animals.

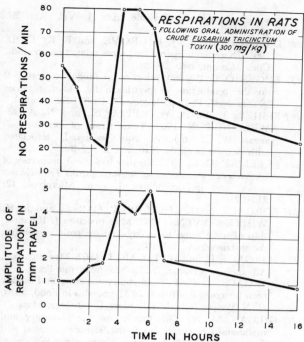

Figure 12.—Respirations in rats (average results from five treated animals) following oral administration of crude T–2 toxin.

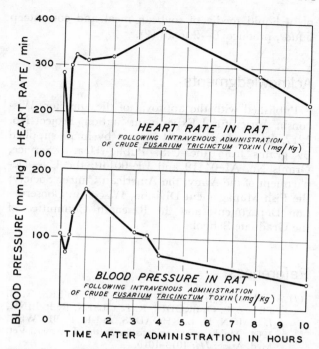

Figure 13.—Heart rate and blood pressure in rats receiving lethal intravenous administrations of crude (frozen dried cultures) of T–2 toxin. Each point represents the averaged results from five treated animals.

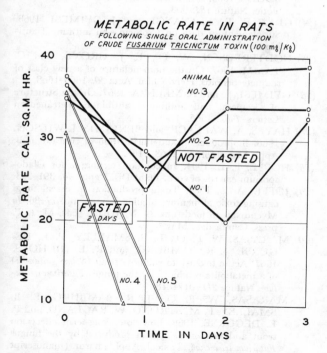

Figure 14.—Metabolic rates in fasted and nonfasted rats following a single oral administration of crude T–2 toxin (100 mg./kg.).

Discussion

Evidence for involvement of any or all the trichothecane-type compounds in moldy corn toxicosis is still circumstantial. Toxin-producing isolates of these trichocane-producing fungi have been isolated from moldy corn, but only a few of them have been studied for their ability to produce trichothecanes in corn. Even though all these fungi may eventually be shown to produce these compounds in pure culture, it still remains necessary to show that they are actually present in moldy corn in sufficient concentrations to cause disease. Until recently, procedures for analysis of trichothecane compounds from crude moldy corn were not available. Recent studies have shown that, using a gas chromatographic method for separation of these compounds, it may be possible to determine their concentration in the natural corn products (2). In preliminary trials the parent alcohols of the naturally occurring trichothecane compounds could be separated as their trimethylsilyl ethers by gas-liquid chromatography (5). T–2 toxin has been identified in extracts of *F. tricinctum* infected corn by chromatographing an aliquot of the extract after converting the toxin to its trimethylsilyl ether (2).

Using this technique with extracts from pure cultures, it has been shown that all toxin producing isolates of *F. tricinctum* in our collection, when grown, on a liquid media of soybean meal and corn steep liquor, produce T—2 toxin (2).

Acknowledgments

Published with the approval of the Director, Wisconsin Agricultural Experiment Station, Project No. 1217. Research supported in part by funds supplied by grants from the U.S. Public Health Service, Grants No. AI–04419 and EF–00140; the U.S. Department of the Army; the American Cancer Society; the Fish Management Division, Wisconsin Conservation Department; and the Research Committee of the Graduate School.

References

(1) ALBRIGHT, J. L., S. D. AUST, J. H. BYERS, T. E. FRITZ, B. O. BRODIE, R. E. OLSEN, R. P. LINK, J. SIMON, H. E. RHOADES, and R. L. BREWER. 1964. Moldy corn toxicosis in cattle. J. Amer. Vet. Med. Assoc. 144: 1013–1019.

(2) BAMBURG, J. R. 1969. Mycotoxins of the trichothecane family produced by cereal molds. Ph. D. Thesis, University of Wisconsin. 161 pp.

(3) BAMBURG, J. R., W. F. O. MARASAS, N. V. RIGGS, E. B. SMALLEY, and F. M. STRONG. 1968. Toxic spiro-epoxy compounds from Fusaria and other hyphomycetes. Biotechnol. and Bioeng. 10: 445–455.

(4) BAMBURG, J. R., N. V. RIGGS, and F. M. STRONG. 1968. The structure of toxins from two strains of Fusarium tricinctum. Tetrahedron 24: 3329–3336.

(5) BAMBURG, J. R. and F. M. STRONG. 1968. Unpublished research.

(6) BURNSIDE, J. E., W. L. SIPPEL, J. FORGACS, W. T. CARLL, M. B. ATWOOD, and E. R. DOLL. 1957. A disease of swine caused by eating moldy corn. II. Experimental production with pure cultures of molds. Am. J. Vet. Res. 18: 817–824.

(7) BRIAN, P. W., A. W. DAWKINS, J. F. GROVE, H. G. HEMMING, D. LOWE, and G. L. F. NORRIS. 1961. J. Expt. 12(34): 1–2.

(8) BROOK, P. J., and E. P. WHITE. 1966. Fungus toxins affecting mammals. Ann. Rev. Phytopathology 4: 171–194.

(9) CALDWELL, R. W., and J. TUITE. 1968. Zearalenone production among Fusarium species. Phytopathology 58: 1046 (Abstr.).

(10) CHRISTENSEN, C. M., G. H. NELSON, and C. J. MIROCHA. 1965. Effect on the white rat uterus of a toxic substance isolated from Fusarium. Appl. Microbiol. 13: 653–659.

(11) CHRISTENSEN, C. M., G. H. NELSON, C. J. MIROCHA, FERN BATES, and C. E. DORWORTH. 1966. Toxicity to rats of corn invaded by Chaetomium globosum. Appl. Microbiol. 14: 774–777.

(12) CURTIN, T. M., and J. TUITE. 1966. Emesis and refusal of feed in swine associated with Gibberella zeae-infected corn. Life Sciences 5: 1937–1944.

(13) CYESWSKI, S. J., A. C. PIER, G. W. ENGSTRONE, J. L. RICHARD, R. W. DOUGHERTY, and J. R. THURSTON. 1968. Clinical pathologic features of

acute aflatoxicosis of swine. Am. J. Vet. Res. 29: 1577–1590.

(14) DAWKINS, A. W., J. F. GROVE, and B. K. TIDD. 1965. Diacetoxyscirpenol and some related compounds. Chem. Comm. 1965: 27–28.

(15) EUGENIO, C. P. 1968. Effect of the fungal estrogen F–2 on the production of perithecia by Fusarium roseum 'graminearum'. Phytopathology 58: 1050–1051 (Abstr.).

(16) FISHER, E. E., A. W. KELLOCK, and N. A. M. WELLINGTON. 1967. Toxic strain of Fusarium culmorum (W. G. Sm.) Sorc. from Zea mays L., associated with sickness in cattle. Nature 215: 322–323.

(17) FREEMAN, G. G. 1955. Further biological properties of trichothecin, an antifungal substance from Trichothecium roseum, and its derivatives. J. Gen. Microbiol. 12: 213–221.

(18) FORGACS, J., H. KOCH, W. T. CARLL, and R. H. WHITE-STEVENS. 1962. Mycotoxicoses I. Relationship of toxic fungi to moldy-feed toxicosis in poultry. Avian Diseases 6: 363–380.

(19) FORGACS, J., and W. T. CARLL. 1962. Mycotoxicosis. Advances in Vet. Sci. 7: 273–383. Academic Press, N.Y.

(20) FORGACS, J. 1964. Stachybotryotoxicosis and moldy corn toxicosis. P. 87–104. In Mycotoxins in Food Stuffs. G. N. Wogan (ed). M.I.T. press, Cambridge, Mass.

(21) GILGAN, M. W. 1965. Studies on the chemistry and metabolism of the toxins from Fusarium tricinctum and Lathyrus adoratus. Ph. D. Thesis. University of Wisconsin, 98 pp.

(22) GILGAN, M. W., E. B. SMALLEY, and F. M. STRONG. 1966. Isolation and partial characterization of a toxin from Fusarium tricinctum on moldy corn. Arch. Biochem. Biophys. 114: 1–3.

(23) GLAZ, E. T., E. SCHEIBER, J. GYIMESI, I. HORVATH, K. STECZEK, A. SZENTIRMAI, and G. BOHUS. 1959. A new trichothecin-like antifungal antibiotic. Nature 184: 908.

(24) GLAZ, E. T., E. CSANGI, and J. GYIMESI. 1966. Supplementary data on Crotocin—an antifungal antibiotic. Nature 212: 617–618.

(25) GODTFREDSEN, W. O., F. J. GROVE, and C. TAMM. 1967. On the nomenclature of a new class of sesqueterpenoids. Helv. Chim. Acta 50: 1666–1668.

(26) GYIMESI, J., and A. MELERA. 1967. On the Structure of Crotocin, and antifungal antibiotic. Tetrahedron Letters. 1967: 1665.

(27) HAYES, A. WALLACE, and BENJAMIN J. WILSON. 1968. Bioproduction and purification of rubratoxin B. Appl. Microbiol. 16: 1163–1167.

(28) HOPPE, P. E. 1964. Inoculation technique for Cladosporium ear rot of corn. Plant Dis. Reptr. 48: 391–393.

(29) JOFFE, A. Z. 1964. Toxin production in cereal fungi causing toxic alimentary aleukia in man. pp. 77–86. In Mycotoxins in foodstuffs. G. N. Wogan (ed). M. I. T. press, Cambridge, Mass.

(30) MARASAS, W. F. O., E. B. SMALLEY, P. E. DEGURSE, J. R. BAMBURG, and R. E. NICHOLS. 1967. Acute toxicity to rainbow trout (Salmo gairdnerii) of a metabolite produced by the fungus Fusarium tricinctum. Nature 214: 817–818.

(31) MARASAS, W. F. O., J. R. BAMBURG, E. B. SMALLEY, F. M. STRONG, W. RAGLAND, and P. E. DEGURSE. 1968. Low-dose, long-term effects on trout and rats of T–2 toxin produced by the fungus Fusarium tricinctum. Toxicol. Appl. Pharm. (manuscript prepared for submission).

(32) MIROCHA, C. J., C. M. CHRISTENSEN, and G. H. NELSON. 1967. Estrogenic metabolite produced by

Fusarium graminearum in stored corn. Appl. Microbiol. *15:* 497–503.

(*33*) MIROCHA, C. J., C. M. CHRISTENSEN, and G. H. NELSON. 1968. Toxic metabolites produced by fungi implicated in mycotoxicosis. Biotech. and Bioeng. *10:* 469–482.

(*34*) McERLEAN, B. A. 1952. Vulvovaginitis in swine. Vet. Rec. *64:* 539–540.

(*35*) McNUTT, S. H., P. PURWIN, and C. MURRAY. 1928. Vulvovaginitis in swine. J. Am. Vet. Med. Assoc. *73:* 484.

(*36*) MOSS, M. O., F. V. ROBINSON, and A. B. WOOD. 1967. Observations on the structure of toxins from *Penicillium rubrum.* Chem. and Ind. *1967:* 755–757.

(*37*) MOSS, M. O., F. V. ROBINSON, and A. B. WOOD. 1968. Rubratoxin B, a toxic metabolite of *Penicillium rubrum.* Chem. and Ind. *1968:* 587–588.

(*38*) NELSON, R. R., C. J. MIROCHA, D. HUISINGH, and A. TIJERINA-MENCHACA. 1968 Effects of F–2, on estrogenic metabolite from Fusarium, on sexual reproduction of certain ascomycetes. Phytopathology *58:* 1061–1062 (Abstr.).

(*39*) OLIFSON, L. E. 1957. Toxins isolated from overwintering cereals and their chemical nature. Monitor, Orenburg Sect. of the U. S. S. R., D. J. Mendeleyev Chem. Soc. *7:* 21–35. *In Russian.*

(*40*) SCHUMAIER, G., B. PANDA, H. M. DeVOLT, N. C. LAFFER, and R. D. CREEK. 1961. Hemorrhagic lesions in chickens resembling naturally occurring "Hemorrhagic Syndrome" produced experimentally by mycotoxins. Poult. Sci. *40:* 1132–1134.

(*41*) SIPPEL, W. L., J. E. BURNSIDE, and M. B. ATWOOD. 1953. A disease of swine and cattle caused by eating moldy corn. Proc. Book AVMA (*1953*)*:* 174–181.

(*42*) SISK, D. B., W. W. CARLTON, and T. M. CURTIN. 1968. Experimental aflatoxicosis in young swine. Am. J. Vet. Res. *29:* 1591–1602.

(*43*) SMALLEY, E. B. 1968. Unpublished research.

(*44*) SNYDER, W. C., and H. N. HANSEN. 1945. The species concept in Fusarium with reference to discolor and other sections. Am. J. Bot. *32:* 657–666.

(*45*) STOB, M., R. S. BALDWIN, J. TUITE, F. N. ANDREWS, and K. G. GILLETTE. 1962. Isolation of an anabolic, uterotrophic compound from corn infected with *Gibberella zeae.* Nature *196:* 1318.

(*46*) TOWNSEND, R. J., M. O. MOSS, and H. M. PECK. 1966. Isolation and characterization of hepatotoxins from *Pencillium rubrum.* J. Pharm. Pharmac. *18:* 471–473.

(*47*) URRY, W. H., H. L. WEHRMEISTER, E. B. HODGE, and P. H. HIDY. 1966. The structure of zearalenone. Tetrahedron Letters (*1966*)*:* 3109–3114.

(*48*) WILSON, B. J. and C. H. WILSON. 1962. Extraction and preliminary characterization of a hepatotoxic substance from cultures of *Pencillium rubrum.* J. Bact. *84:* 283–290.

(*49*) WOGAN, G. N. 1966. Chemical nature and biological effects of the Aflatoxins. Bact. Rev. *30:* 460–470.

(*50*) WOLLENWEBBER, H. W., and O. A. REINKING. 1935. Die Fusarien. Paul Parey, Berlin.

(*51*) YATES, S. G., H. L. TOOKEY, J. J. ELLIS, and H. J. BURKHARDT. 1968. Mycotoxins produced by *Fusarium nivale* isolated from tall fescue (*Festuca arundinacea* Schreb.). Phytochemistry *7:* 139–146.

OCCURRENCE AND DISTRIBUTION OF MYCOTOXIN PRODUCERS IN JAPANESE FOODS

by Shun-Ichi Udagawa, Masakatsu Ichinoe, *and* Hiroshi Kurata
Laboratory of Mycology, National Institute of Hygienic Sciences, Tokyo

Summary

The fungus flora of more than 26 kinds of foods in Japan, including polished rice, other cereal grains and their products, legumes, fermented foods, dried fishes, and edible seaweeds, has been determined and summarized. Except for a few cases, members of the Aspergillaceae were predominant in the flora throughout the surveys. The polished rice harvested in 1965–66 was considered to have been maintained and handled under good conditions of sanitation. The following species isolated have known or suspected toxigenic abilities in experimental animals: *Aspergillus clavatus, A. chevalieri, A. flavus, A. fumigatus, A. ochraceus, A. oryzae, A. versicolor, Penicillium citreo-viride, P. citrinum, P. cyclopium, P. expansum, P. islandicum, P. ochrosalmoneum, P. oxalicum, P. puberulum, P. purpurogenum, P. roqueforti, P. rugulosum, Fusarium nivale* and *Pithomyces chartarum.*

Introduction

Since the hepatotoxic metabolites known as aflatoxins were found in the outbreak of "Turkey X" disease in England in 1960, the prevalence of mycotoxicoses has become an increasing problem in the world. In Japan, the study of mycotoxins and their effects is well described by the work on toxic yellowed rices, which have been defined as the deterioration of rice grains by some species of Penicillia such as *P. citreo-viride* (syn. *P. toxicarium*), *P. citrinum* and *P. islandicum.*

Although the exact significance of the presence of mycotoxin-producing fungi has not yet been defined thoroughly, enumeration and identification of fungi encountered in cereal grains and other various types of foods are important in understanding the evaluation of their safety as foods for human consumption. Our routine work on the mycological examination of imported and domestic polished rice over the past 15 years has led to a remarkable development of an etiological survey for the detection of naturally occurring carcinogens in Japanese foods and for the elucidation of the natural history of cancer. Although the elimination of active carcinogenic agents in human environment is very difficult, the research needs in this field are practically unlimited for cancer prevention.

In the present report, results of mycological examinations of stored rice grains (mostly imported), fungi in market flours, mycoflora of domestic polished rice, and mycological surveys of the Japanese foods with regard to the detection of carcinogens are summarized. To the isolates belonging to *A. ochraceus* group, an attempt of assay for ochratoxin producing activity was also made. A further investigation of the toxigenicity of the isolates obtained from these surveys will be presented in the subsequent report.

Materials and Methods

The following food samples were collected for the mycological surveys in this paper: Rice grains (unhulled, rough, and polished rice), rice flour, wheat and barley grains, wheat flour, soybeans, soybean flour, red beans, red bean flour, kidneybeans, broad beans, potato starch, buckwheat flour, miso (soybean paste), shoyu (soy sauce), moromi (mash), tsukemono (Japanese pickles), nukamiso (pickled vegetables in a mixture of rice bran, salt, and water), mugikoji (molded masses of barley grains), niboshi (dried small sardines), dried fishes, edible seaweeds, noodle, etc.

Numbers and kinds of fungi in cereal grain samples were estimated by the official method (5) recommended by the Ministry of Health and Welfare for the microbiological examination of imported foods, with minor modifications to suit present needs. To enumerate invading fungi, 50 to 100 kernels from each sample were plated, following surface washing with sterile water, on culture media. The two culture media used were Czapek-Dox agar for isolation of storage molds such as *Aspergillus* and *Penicillium* and glucose-peptone agar for a more extensive range of fungi including field invaders. Prior to culturing, about 10 g. of the grains were washed aseptically with 10 successive volumes of sterile distilled water to remove surface contaminants. Then, the washed grains were placed onto the surface of slants oc Czapek agar or plates of glucose-peptone agar.

On the other hand, surveys of the microflora associated with the fermented foods such as miso, shoyu and tsukemono, flours, noodle, dried fishes, and niboshi, etc., were usually conducted by the quantitative dilution plate method. Enumeration was accomplished by placing 1 to 10 g. of sample into a Waring blender which homogenized the sample for 3 minutes at high speed with 40 ml. of sterile 0.05 percent plain agar water. Appropriate dilutions (mostly at 10^{-3} level) of blended materials were cultured on Czapek agar, potato-dextrose agar or glucose-peptone agar. In addition, MY 20 agar (peptone, 5 g.; yeast extract, 3 g.; malt extract, 3 g.; glucose, 200 g.; agar, 20 g.; and water, 1 liter; after Raper and Fennell (7)) was used to estimate numbers of halophilic fungi in the salty foods and dried foods. An addition of 100 mg. per l. of chloramphenicol to the media was effective for inhibition of bacterial growth.

After incubation for 10 to 14 days at 25° C., the number and types of fungal colonies appearing on the slants or plates were recorded and representative colonies were selected. Members of Aspergillaceae and potentially toxigenic fungi such as *Fusarium* were identified. Other fungi were identified only as far as the genus, with some exceptions. The manuals of Thom and Raper (8), Raper and Thom (6), and Raper and Fennell (7) have been followed in determining species of the two common genera *Aspergillus* and *Pencillium*.

Results and Discussion

Mycological examinations for the presence of mycotoxin producers in the 1954–67 stored rice grains. Our routine work during 1954–67 was designed to demonstrate the frequency of occurrence of mycotoxin-producing fungi and the constituent members of microflora of the stored rice grains in Japan (4). A total of 3,014 samples of rough and polished rice, the majority representing imported rice from more than 10 different countries, were assayed. The composition of the microflora of the stored rice grains is summarized in table 1. During this sampling period, *Aspergillus* and *Penicillium* accounted for about 20 percent of the total micro-organisms isolated.

Aspergillus species were very frequently encountered on 1954, 1963, and 1967 samples, as shown in table 1. Through the surveys of 1955–57, a total of 14,000 isolations of *Aspergillus*, representing 10 different groups, were made from 1,600 samples of rice grains, most of which had been imported from Thailand, Burma, Formosa, United States, China, Spain, and Italy. *A. flavus-oryzae* and *A. candidus* were the groups most frequently found; the *A. glaucus* group accounted for 21.5 percent of the isolations. Other common groups recovered were *A. niger*, *A. versicolor*, and *A. terreus*. The *Aspergillus* contents of the 1964–67 samples,

Table 1.—Summary of average micro-organisms contents of the imported and domestic rice grains during 1954–67

Micro-organisms	Year and number of samples surveyed (percent)				
	1954 (392)	1955 (698)	1956 (496)	1957 (350)	1958 (457)
Aspergillus spp.	23.0	6.0	8.0	10.0	8.5
Penicillium spp.	8.0	4.0	7.0	2.5	4.5
Other fungi	11.0	5.0	9.0	11.5	8.5
Streptomyces	5.0	3.0	4.0	4.0	2.5
Bacteria and yeasts	53.0	82.0	72.0	72.0	76.0
	1959 (239)	1960 (97)	1961 (3)	1962 (52)	1963 (124)
Aspergillus spp.	14.0	15.0	5.0	9.0	25.0
Penicillium spp.	8.5	4.5	0.	23.5	5.0
Other fungi	16.0	11.5	4.0	4.5	17.0
Streptomyces	5.0	2.5	1.0	13.0	7.0
Bacteria and yeasts	56.5	66.5	90.0	50.0	46.0
	1964 (24)	1965 (70)	1966 (4)	1967 (8)	Total (3,014)
Aspergillus spp.	3.0	9.0	3.5	21.5	12.0
Penicillium spp.	3.0	4.0	3.5	21.5	7.0
Other fungi	11.0	6.0	4.5	7.5	9.0
Streptomyces	11.0	1.0	3.5	1.0	3.5
Bacteria and yeasts	72.0	80.0	85.0	48.5	68.5

which had been imported from Thailand, Burma, Formosa, and China, were essentially the same; but 66 percent of the *Aspergillus* were made up of two widely distributed groups of *A. glaucus* and *A. versicolor*.

Particular attention has been given to the occurrence of *Penicillium* species in the samples because of their importance as causes of various types of mycotoxicoses. The presence of three species, *P. citreo-viride*, *P. citrinum*, and *P. islandicum*, was checked especially as an index for determining the sanitary condition of the imported polished rice. Of the total 8,000 isolates from the 1955–57 rice grains, members of *P. citrinum* and *P. cyclopium* series were the most prevalent and formed respectively, 10 percent of the total Penicillia, followed by *P. funiculosum* series (most of *P. islandicum*), *P. chrysogenum* series, and *P. rugulosum* series. Similar data were found in the 1964–67 samples. *P. viridicatum* series was most frequently encountered in the samples, accounting for 26 percent of the *Penicillium* isolates. Other common fungi found associated with the rice grains were some members of the order Mucorales, *Alternaria* species, *Cladosporium* species, *Helminthosporium* species, *Paecilomyces varioti*, *Scopulariopsis brevicaulis*, and *Trichoderma viride*. Two genera of Fungi Imperfecti, *Fusarium* and *Monilia* were also frequently found from the domestic rice samples.

In 1957 an outbreak of food poisoning (acute diarrhea) among four families of the Japanese farmers occurred at two localities, Kanagawa and Kagoshima Prefectures, respectively, in central and southern Japan. Table 2 shows that it was due to the consumption of moldy rice heavily infected with *F. graminearum* and *F. nivale* under the rainy condition.

Although great variations existed in the mycological quality of the samples tested during 1959–61, 21 percent of the 593 samples of imported rice from Thailand, Burma, Formosa, and China were in poor sanitary condition and were rejected as a result.

Fungi in cereal and legume products as market foods.—In 1960, in order to determine the frequency of occurrence of mycotoxin-producing fungi in market foods (*2*), a total of 100 samples of the following flours were collected from central Japan: 50 of wheat, 15 of rice, 15 of soybean, six of red bean, five of buckwheat, four of kidneybean, and five of potato starch. Twenty-five genera of molds and some yeasts were isolated from these samples, as seen in table 3. In most flours the frequently encountered and widely distributed fungi were those belonging to the genera *Penicillium*, *Aspergillus*, and *Cladosporium*. Yeast species also occurred in about 32 percent of the samples. *Penicillium* was recovered from slightly more than 80 percent of the samples of wheat and rice, whereas this group was found in only about 30 percent of the samples in soybean flour. In wheat and rice flours, the second most prevalent group of organisms was *Aspergillus*, with frequency of 68 and 60 percent each. On the other hand, soybean flour yielded this organism in 40 percent of the samples.

As indicated in table 3, *P. citrinum*, *A. flavus*, *A. verisolor*, and *Cladosporium sphaerospermum* were the most commonly isolated species in 26, 21, 19, and 18 percent of the samples, respectively. Except for the above four species, the predominant organisms in wheat flour also included *P. notatum* and *P. islandicum*. In addition, *P. lanosum*, *A. oryzae*, *A. ochraceus*, *Paecilomyces varioti*, and *Cladosporium cladosporioides* were commonly found in the other types of flours. Fungal counts of

20 samples of wheat flour ranged from 50 to 2,050/g. and averaged 540/g.

Mycoflora of domestic polished rice harvested in 1965–1966.—The fungus flora of 219 samples of polished rice, which were harvested in 1965 and collected from 132 Prefectural Public Health Stations in nine geographical regions of Japan (fig. 1), was determined (*3*). Various kinds of fungi were recovered from 65 percent of the total samples, whereas the remainder (35 percent) did not yield any fungi. Of the 143 positive samples, 83 percent contained only one to five isolates per 50 g. During this survey, 835 isolations of fungi, representing more than 25 different genera, were made from domestic polished rice. These are listed in order of frequency in table 4. Microscopic observations revealed that the contaminating fungi were predominately *Aspergillus* (51 percent of the total isolates), *Penicillium* (9 percent), *Fusarium* (5 percent) and *Cladosporium* species (5 percent). *Aspergillus* species were observed in 23 percent of the samples analyzed and accounted for the greatest amount of fungal mass. *A. repens* was by far the commonest species of this genus, representing 67 percent of the isolates collected from the 426 colonies. No other species formed more than 8 percent of the total colonies of this genus. Some plant pathogenic genera such as *Helminthosporium*, *Trichoconis*, *Phoma* and *Piricularia* were sometimes frequently isolated.

To compare mycological sanitation of domestic polished rice consumed in different urban communities, a similar survey was made on collections from five cities in 1966 (fig. 1). The cities were: Tokyo (population 8,900,000), Osaka (3,130,000), Nagoya (1,950,000), Sapporo (820,000), and Fukuoka (785,000). A total of 573 fungi were isolated from 140 samples. In 64 percent of samples collected from Nagoya city, no isolations of fungal contaminants were obtained. Of the samples of the remaining four cities, about 40 to 45 percent were associated with one to two colonies per 50 g. A list of the 22 genera

Table 2.—Mycological detection of the deterioration of domestic rice grains associated with Fusarium-mycotoxicosis in 1957

Organisms	Number of isolated from 500 gr. of samples		Organisms	Number of isolated from 500 gr. of samples	
	Rough rice	Polished rice		Rough rice	Polished rice
Penicillium			*Cladosporium*	4	8
P. cyclopium	3		*Fusarium*	291	79
P. chrysogenum		1	*Helminthosporium*	20	9
P. brevi-compactum	4		*Chaetomium*		1
Penicillium spp		6	*Epicoccum*	5	2
Aspergillus			Unknown fungi	54	75
A. flavus-oryzae		29	Total fungi	385	225
A. candidus		1	Streptomyces	1	
A. fumigatus		6	Bacteria, yeasts	298	348
Aspergillus spp		1	Total micro-		
Phycomycetes	4	7	organisms	684	573

Table 3.—Frequency of occurrence of fungal species in the market flour-type foodstuffs

Fungi	Percentage of occurrence of fungi per samples				
	Wheat flour (50)[1]	Rice flour (15)	Soybean flour (15)	Various flours (20)	Total (100)
Penicillium	84	80	33.3	70	66.8
P. citrinum	42	13.3	----	15	26
P. lanosum	24	20	----	15	26
P. notatum	22	6.7	6.7	5	16
P. viridicatum	24	6.7	----	15	16
P. islandicum	20	6.7	----	10	15
P. ochraceum	10	13.3	----	5	12
P. spinulosum	18	----	6.7	20	11
P. rugulosum	8	----	6.7	----	10
P. cyaneo-fulvum	8	6.7	6.7	5	7
P. frequentans	6	6.7	----	5	6
P. chrysogenum	8	6.7	6.7	5	6
P. corymbiferum	2	----	----	5	5
P. cyclopium	6	6.7	6.7	10	5
P. waksmani	6	6.7	----	----	4
Penicillium spp	40	20	6.7	10	4
Aspergillus	68	60	40	20	25
A. flavus	28	20	20	5	47
A. versicolor	26	----	20	10	21
A. candidus	18	6.7	----	----	19
A. terreus	6	13.3	6.7	10	11
A. chevalieri	8	6.7	6.7	10	8
A. amstelodami	10	----	----	----	6
A. clavatus	8	6.7	----	----	5
A. ochraceus	2	6.7	13.3	----	5
A. oryzae	2	20	----	----	4
Cladosporium	36	33.3	13.3	40	30.6
C. sphaerospermum	26	6.7	13.3	10	18
C. cladosporioides	8	20	----	25	12
Cladosporium spp	4	6.7	----	5	4
Mucor spp	2	33.3	13.3	10	10
Paecilomyces varioti	6	33.3	----	5	10
Alternaria tenuis	10	----	----	5	9
Trichothecium roseum	12	----	----	10	7
Trichoderma viride	----	6.7	13.3	----	7
Phoma spp	----	6.7	----	5	4
Fusarium spp	----	6.7	13.3	15	4
? Calcarisporium	4	20	6.7	----	4
Yeasts	30	40	20	30	32

[1]Number of samples examined.

NOTE:—Miscellaneous species (total percentage less than 3): *Absidia* spp., *Acremoniella atra*, *Arthrinium phaeospermum*, *Aspergillus* 7 spp., *Cephalosporium* sp., *Chaetomium* sp., *Cladosporium herbarum*, *C. macrocarpum*, *Epicoccum nigrum*, *Monochaetia* sp., *Nigrospora* sp., *Penicillium* 26 spp., *Ramularia* sp., *Rhizopus* spp., *Scopulariopsis brevicaulis*, *Stemphylium* sp., *Syncephalastrum* sp., and *Trichocladium asperum*.

Table 4.—List of the genera and the frequency of occurrence of fungi isolated from polished rice harvested in 1965

Fungi	Number of isolates	Percentage of occurrence	Miscellaneous genera[1]
Aspergillus	426	51.0	*Alternaria.*
Hemispora	92	11.0	*Cephalotrichum.*
Penicillium	77	9.0	*Chaetomium.*
Fusarium	41	5.0	*Chrysosporium.*
Cladosporium	40	5.0	*Coniothyrium.*
Helminthosporium	33	4.0	*Curvularia.*
Trichoconis	20	2.5	*Epicoccum.*
Phoma	20	2.5	*Gliomastix.*
Piricularia	9	1.0	*Mucor.*
Miscellaneous genera.	37	4.5	*Nigrospora.*
Mycelia sterilia	19	2.0	*Rhizopus.*
Unknown fungi	21	2.5	*Scopulariopsis.*
Total	835	100.0	*Septoria.*

[1]Percentage of occurrence less than 1.

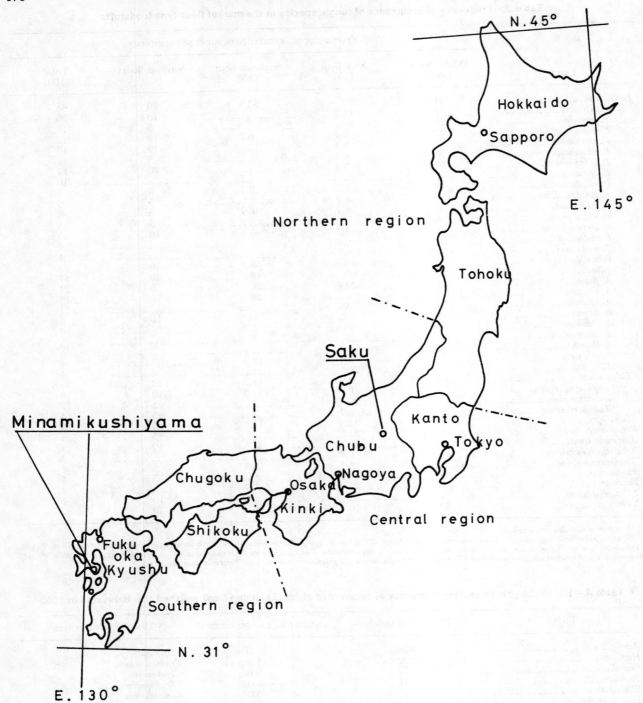

Figure 1.—Map of sampling locations.

and their frequency of occurrence is given in table 5. In this survey, *A. repens* was still the most prevalent (22 percent of the samples isolated), followed by *A. amstelodami* (18 percent, and *A. versicolor* (18 percent).

The results obtained in the two surveys indicated that the majority of domestic polished rice harvested in 1965–66 had been maintained and handled under good sanitary conditions.

Mycological surveys of the Japanese foods for the detection of carcinogens in natural products.— In the summer of 1967, the Cancer Research Division of the Institute of Medical Sciences, the University of

Table 5.—List of the genera and the frequency of occurrence of fungi isolated from polished rice harvested in 1966

Fungi	Number of isolates	Percentage of occurrence	Miscellaneous genera[1]
Penicillium	148	26.0	Alternaria.
Hemispora	117	21.0	Arthrinium.
Aspergillus	98	17.0	Botrytis.
Monilia	63	11.0	Cephalosporium.
Cladosporium	25	4.5	Curvularia.
Fusarium	18	3.0	Helicoceras.
Trichoconis	18	3.0	Monascus.
Helminthosporium	13	2.5	Nigrospora.
Epicoccum	11	2.0	Paecilomyces.
Miscellaneous genera.	23	4.0	Phoma.
Mycelia sterilia	26	5.0	Tritirachium.
Unknown genera	6	1.0	Wardomyces.
Total	573	100.0	

[1]Percentage of occurrence less than 1 percent.

Tokyo (Prof. M. Saito), provided an opportunity for our group to collect various kinds of the Japanese foods in conjunction with municipal corporations at two rural communities in central and southern Japan. To give a solution of the many complex factors involved in the cause of diseases—particularly those that are often fatal, such as cancer and cardiovascular diseases, extensive surveys have been conducted by the research organization in the fields of epidemiology, nutriology, clinics, and histopathology. Different geographical areas often present marked differences in mortality from a given disease and mortality statistics have served as the basis for the geographical study of disease. Thus, the first survey was designated for farm families, the highland inhabitants of Saku city in Nagano Prefecture (fig. 1), where the highest incidence of hypertension and gastric cancer was estimated. It is interesting to note that large amounts of salt have been fed there in the customary diet containing miso, soy sauce, and pickles. Because mortality from hepatoma in Nagasaki Prefecture, southern Japan, remained at a high level throughout the past decade, the coastal families of fishermen and those engaged in agriculture combined with fishery at Minamikushiyama village (fig. 1) were chosen for the second survey. Production and consumption of dried small sardines are characteristic for the food survey of this coastal region. It appeared of interest to investigate further the relationship between the high incidence of these diseases and the food peculiarities of the inhabitants.

For the survey, a total of 668 samples of the following foods were collected from the 88 families of Saku City and 57 families of Minamikushiyama Village: miso, shoyu, moromi, tsukemono, nukamiso, polished rice, wheat grain, flours, legumes, dried small sardines, and miscellaneous foods. The majority of collected samples was homemade devoid of the influence of food additives.

About 350 isolates of fungi in 23 genera, representing three mucors, four ascomycetes, and 16 deuteromycetes, were recorded from the collection of six kinds of foods from Saku. From the mycoflora of these foods, table 6 gives the distribution of halophilic and nonhalophilic species belonging to *Aspergillus*. The number of halophilic *Aspergillus* in the fermented foods was much less than those of polished rice, although the analysis on MY 20 agar medium was used for determining the fungi in these samples. This is surprising, since the fermented foods such as miso, shoyu and tsukemono are usually known as highly salty. A possible explanation is that the incidence of the other halophilic micro-organisms, for example the growth of *Pediococcus halophilus* and *Streptococcus faecalis* (bacteria) and *Saccharomyces rouxii* (yeast), could have influenced significantly the results with the mycoflora of fermented foods. Of the halophilic populations described here, *A. repens* was the most prevalent. *A. versicolor* comprised the second most widely distributed group in the milled rice survey, showing a frequency of 21 to 50 percent of the total samples. *A. flavus* and *A. oryzae*, two of the molds isolated from the fermented foods, are worthy of notice, probably coming primarily from koji materials (the starters).

Penicillium species isolated from the foods of Saku city and their evaluation are presented in table 7. The two Penicillia isolated with greatest frequency and in the largest numbers from polished rice were *P. phoeniceum* and *P. roseopurpureum*. Both of these have not only been the subject of limited distribution in nature, but little is actually known regarding their possible importance in the deterioration processes of cereal grains. In spite of its rather low population, *P. waksmani* was probably the most ubiquitous species to be found on the miso and shoyu samples. It is also noticeable that the fungal contamination of all samples

Table 6.—Occurrence of *Aspergillus* species in the foods of Saku City†

Fungi	Miso (52)[1]	Shoyu (17)	Moromi (3)	Tsukemono (13)	Nukamiso (3)	Polished rice (16)
Halophilic group:						
A. amstelodami					*	+
A. chevalieri					*	+
A. conicus		*	++		**	+++
A. repens			+		*	+
A restrictus		*	+		*	+++
A. ruber		*			*	+
A. umbrosus						
Nonhalophilic group:						
A. candidus	*		***		*	+
A. flavus	*					
A. japonicus	*	*	+			
A. niger	*			*	*	
A. oryzae	****	++			*	
A. sydowi	*	*	++		*	
A. terreus	*	*			***	+
A. versicolor	*	*			*	
Aspergillus spp		*				

[1]Numbers of the estimated samples.
†See the following for symbol key, tables 6 through 11.

Abundance (numbers of isolates per sample)	Frequency (percent of respective samples recorded)
* — 1–10 (scanty).	+ — 1–20 (rare).
** — 11–20 (fairly abundant).	++ — 21–40 (fairly wide).
*** — 21–50 (abundant).	+++ — 41–60 (wide).
**** — 51–100 (very abundant).	++++ — 61–80 (very wide).
***** — More than 100 (extremely abundant).	+++++ — 81–100 (extremely wide).

Table 7.—Occurrence of *Penicillium* species in the foods of Saku City

Fungi	Miso (52)[1]	Shoyu (17)	Moromi (3)	Tsukemono (13)	Nukamiso (3)	Polished rice (16)
Monoverticillata:						
P. citreo-viride	*				*	
P. decumbens	*	*			*	
P. frequentans	*	+			*	
P. implicatum					****	+
P. phoeniceum					***	+++
P. roseo-purpureum						
P. waksmani	*	++	*	++++	*	
Eupenicillium sp						
Asymmetrica:						
P. chrysogenum			**		*	
P. citrinum	*		**	**	*	
P. cyclopium	****	+			*	
P. italicum				*		
P. janthinellum	****	+			*	
P. notatum					*	
P. oxalicum	**	+	+		**	++
P. martensii				*	*	
P. puberulum	*****	+		++	*	
P. roqueforti	*				*	
P. steckii	*	*				
P. stoloniferum	*	*	*			
P. viridicatum				*		
Penicillium sp						
Biverticillata:						
P. purpurogenum	*				*	
P. rugulosum	*				*	
P. variabile	*	*	+			
P. vermiculatum	*					

NOTE.—For symbol indications see table 6.
[1]Numbers of the estimated samples.

of miso, when stored under poor sanitary conditions, was attributed to asymmetric Penicillia such as *P. cyclopium*, *P. puberulum* and *P. janthinellum*.

A total of over 470 cultures of fungi belonged to 23 genera has been isolated from the 23 kinds of foods analyzed in the Minamikushiyama survey. As shown in table 8, the analyses of *Aspergillus* species revealed certain differences as well as certain similarities between these two surveys. Through the survey at the Minamikushiyama Village, no halophilic Aspergilli were found in the fermented foods, while large amounts of *A. glaucus* group or *A. restrictus* group were recovered from the samples of wheat grains, dried small sardines, and edible seaweeds. The most common species in these groups were *A. amstelodami*, *A. gracilis*, *A. penicilloides*, *A. restrictus*, and *A. ruber*. Other representatives recovered were *A. tamarii* from Japanese pickles and *A. oryzae* from kidneybeans. Finally, the most striking finding was a high frequency of the incidence of *A. ochraceus* group in five kinds of the foods. An assay of these isolates for ochratoxin A producing potential will be reported later.

Table 9 illustrates the abundance and distribution of Penicillia isolated from the Minamikushiyama's foods. In the samples of miso, *P. waksmani* was the persistent contaminant most frequently found. *P. phoeniceum* was also widely distributed in polished rice, while *P. herquei* was repeatedly isolated from kidneybeans. Of the other Fungi Imperfecti, *Fusarium nivale* and *Phoma* sp. formed two of the more noticeable components of the fungus flora of wheat grains. From the kidneybean samples, a large number of isolates of *Cladosporium cladosporioides* was collected.

The summarized patterns of the two surveys are indicated in tables 10 and 11. Of the large number of fungi known to be associated with many kinds of foods it is of interest to note that so few of them occur on fermented foods such as moromi (mash), tsukemono (Japanese pickles), and nukamiso (pickled vegetables in a mixture of rice bran, salt, and water). Mycoflora of moromi was made up of *Absidia* sp., *Syncephalastrum racemosum*, *Syncephalastrum* sp., and *Aspergillus flavus*. Two imperfect genera, *Candida* and *Geotrichum*, constituted important components of the fungus population of tsukemono. Only a limited species, *A. oryzae*, was present in the majority of nukamiso samples surveyed, usually with a high population of 21 to 50 isolates per sample. A halophilic fungus, *Hemispora stellata* (formerly known as *Catenularia fuliginea*), regularly occurs in sweets and jelly, and in the surveys,

Table 8.—Occurrence of *Aspergillus* species in the foods of Minamikushiyama Village

Fungi	Foods						
	Miso (9)[1]	Tsukemono (5)	Polished rice (12)	Wheat (5)	Legumes (4)	Flours (10)	Dried sardines (10)
Halophilic group:							
A. amstelodami				***	*	+	* ++
A. chevalieri		*	+	**	*	+	* ++
A. conicus				*	*	+	
A. gracilis					*	+	
A. mangini					*	+	***** +
A. penicilloides							* +
A. repens	*	+++		**	*	+	***** ++
A. restrictus	*	+		*	*	+	***** +++
A. ruber					*	++	***** ++++
A. umbrosus	*	+			*	+	
Nonhalophilic group:							
A. aculeatus				*			
A. candidus			*				
A. clavatus				*			
A. foetidus		*	+				
A. fumigatus		*	+	*			
A. nidulans				*			
A. niger		*	+	*	*		
A. ochraceus	*		++++	*	***	* ++	* +++
A. oryzae				*	***	*	+
A. petrakii			***	+			
A. sclerotiorum							
A. sydowi	*	++	*		*	+	
A. tamarii		*****	*	+			
A. terreus				*			
A. terreus var. africanus						*	++
A. versicolor	**	+	+++	*	*	* ++	*

NOTE.—For symbol indications see table 6. Isolations from miscellaneous foods: *A. deflectus*, *A. fischeri*, and *A. phoenicis*.
[1] Numbers of the estimated samples.

Table 9.—Occurrence of *Penicillium* species in the foods of Minamikushiyama Village

Fungi	Food				
	Miso (9)[1]	Polished rice (12)	Wheat (5)	Legumes (4)	Flours (10)
Monoverticillata:					
P. citreo-viride	*	+	-------	-------	-------
P. decumbens	*	++	-------	-------	-------
P. frequentans	*	+	-------	-------	-------
P. phoeniceum	*	+++	*	-------	* ++
P. waksmani	***** +	-------	-------	-------	-------
Asymmetrica:					
P. casei				**	+
P. chrysogenum			*	-------	-------
P. citrinum	*	++	*	* *	* ++
P. cyclopium	*			***	
P. herquei				***	
P. lanosum	*	+			
P. lilacinum				*	
P. notatum	*			*	
P. ochrosalmoneum				*	* +
P. oxalicum	*	+	*	*	* +
P. paxilli	*	+	-------	-------	
P. phialosporum	*	+			
P. puberulum	*	+		*	* +
P. putterillii	*	+			
P. steckii	*	+			* ++
P. viridicatum		+			
Biverticillata:					
P. islandicum	*	+	-------	-------	* +
P. piceum				*	+
P. purpurogenum	*	+	-------	-------	* +
P. purpurogenum var. rubrisclerotium	*	+	-------	-------	
P. rugulosum				*	+
P. variabile				*	+

[1]Numbers of the estimated samples.
NOTE.—For symbol indications see table 6.

Table 10.—Summarized occurrence of fungi in the Japanese foods from Saku City and Minamikushiyama Village

Fungi	Fermented foods					
	Miso		Shoyu	Moromi	Tsukemono	Nukamiso
Absidia spp	**			***		
Mucor spp				***		
Syncephalastrum racemosum				****		
Syncephalastrum sp				****		
Aspergillus repens		*	++	***		
Aspergillus flavus	*			***		
Aspergillus oryzae	****	+			* *****	***
Aspergillus tamarii					*****	
Aspergillus sydowi	*	++	*	++		
Aspergillus versicolor	**	+	*			
Penicillium waksmani	*****	++	*	++++		
Penicillium janthinellum	****	+				*
Penicillium cyclopium	****	+			**	+
Penicillium puberulum	*****	+			* ++	*
Candida spp					*****	
Geotrichum candidum	*				****	++

NOTE.—For symbol indications see table 6.

had been found frequently upon a wide variety of foods including polished rice, flours, and dried small sardines. The following species isolated have known or suspected toxigenic abilities in experimental animals: *A. clavatus, A. chevalieri, A. flavus, A. fumigatus, A. ochraceus, A. oryzae, A. versicolor, Penicillium citreoviride, P. citrinum, P. cyclopium, P. expansum, P. islandicum, P. ochrosalmoneum, P. oxalicum, P. puberulum P. purpurogenum, P. roqueforti, P. rugulosum, Fusarium nivale,* and *Pithomyces chartarum.*

Table 11.—Summarized occurrence of fungi in the Japanese foods from Saku City and Minamikushiyama Village

Fungi	Cereal and dried foods							
	Polished rice		Wheat	Legumes	Flours		Dried sardines	
Rhizopus spp				**				
Aspergillus amstelodami			***		*	+	*	++
Aspergillus gracilis					*	+	*****	+
Aspergillus penicilloides					*	+	****	++
Aspergillus repens	**	+++	**		*	+	*****	+++
Aspergillus restrictus	*	+	*			++	*****	++++
Aspergillus ruber	*	+++			*	+	***	+
Aspergillus oryzae			*	***	*	+		
Aspergillus ochraceus	*	+++++	***		*	++	*	+++
Aspergillus versicolor	***	+++	*	*	*	++	*	+
Penicillium phoeniceum	****	+++	*		*	++		
Penicillium roseo-purpureum	***	++++						
Penicillium citrinum		++	*		*	++		
Penicillium herquei				***				
Hemispora stellata	***	+++++			*	+++	*	+
Candida spp	*	+++						
Getroichum candidum	***	+						
Cladosporium cladosporioides	*	++	*	***	*	+		
Fusarium nivale	*	+		***				
Phoma spp	*	+		****				

NOTE.—For symbol indications see table 6.

Ochratoxin-producing activity of isolates of the *Aspergillus ochraceus* group from the Japanese foods.—Following the aflatoxin problem, much attention has been focused recently on ochratoxin A, a hepatotoxic metabolite produced by the *A. ochraceus* group of fungi. Because members of *A. ochraceus* group are ubiquitous, their existence in the Japanese foods is neither surprising nor unusual. In Japan, however, there have been no previous reports published to date on the occurrence of this toxin as well as on its distribution in nature. Thus, during the course of the above described surveys on the Japanese foods, an attempt was made to detect the presence of ochratoxin producing strains in the 33 isolates belonging to *A. ochraceus* group. Following the procedure described by Ferreira (*1*), the organisms were grown in shake-flask culture for 6 days at 25° C. on medium containing (per liter) sucrose, 30 g.; glutamic acid, 10 g.; KH_2PO_4, 1 g.; KCl, 0.5 g.; $MgSO_4 \cdot 7H_2O$, 0.5g.; and the necessary amounts of trace elements. The cultural filtrates of each isolate were acidified to pH 2–3 with HCl, extracted with chloroform in a separatory funnel, and the chloroform was evaporated on a steam bath. The presence of ochratoxins and other products in the extracts was determined by thin-layer chromatography in comparison with spots of the following 13 previously known metabolites: ochratoxins A, B, C; penicillic acid; ochracin; aspergillic acid; muta-aspergillic acid; hydroxyaspergillic acid; orsellinic acid; everninic acid; isoeverninic acid; orcinol; and orcinol methyl ether. Two solvent systems were used on two types of migration media. The first system: Develop on acidified Silica Gel G (Mallinckrodt) treated with 3 percent oxalic acid in benzene-methyl alcohol-ethyl acetate (15:2:1, v/v/v). The second system: Develop on Silica Gel G in ethyl acetate-isopropanol-water (5:2:1, v/v/v). All metabolites were detected by UV light and by spraying with a potassium permanganate solution.

Of the total of 33 isolates, only two strains, isolated from red bean and spice, were positive for the ochratoxin-producing ability at levels detectable by TLC. The most noticeable observation was that the majority of the isolates produced large amounts of penicillic acid. The highest yield of this substance amounted to 700 mg. per l. of medium. Further work is in progress on the chemical identification of ochratoxin-like substances and other interesting metabolites in the cultures of *A. ochraceus* isolates and will be reported at a future date.

Acknowledgments

These investigations are supported in part by Public Law 480 research grant, No. FG–Ja–121, of the U.S. Department of Agriculture, and cancer research funds of the Ministry of Health and Welfare and the Ministry of Education, Japan.

The authors wish to thank Dr. M. Ishidate, director, Drs. S. Iwahara and S. Natori, the National Insititute of Hygienic Sciences, Tokyo, and Prof. M. Saito, the Institute of Medical Sciences, University of Tokyo, for many helpful discussions and suggestions.

Thanks are also due to Dr. H. W. Schroeder, the Field Crops and Animal Products Research Branch, U.S. Department of Agriculture, College Station, Tex., for his helpful suggestions and critical evaluation of the manuscript. Space does not permit listing the names of the Institute's co-operators whose full professional assistance was essential for the conduct of these surveys.

References

(1) FERREIRA, N. P. 1967. Recent advances in research on ochratoxin. Part 2. Microbiological aspects, pp. 157–168. In R. I. Mateles, and G. N. Wogan (ed.), Biochemistry of some foodborne microbial toxins. MIT press, Cambridge, Mass.

(2) KURATA, H., and M. ICHINOE. 1967. Studies on the population of toxigenic fungi in foodstuffs. I. Fungal flora of flour-type foodstuffs. J. Food Hyg. Soc. Japan 8: 237–246.

(3) KURATA, H., S. UDAGAWA, M. ICHINOE, Y. KAWASAKI, M. TAKADA, M. TAZAWA, A. KOIZUMI, and H. TANABE. 1967. Studies on the population of toxigenic fungi in foodstuffs. III. Mycoflora of milled rice harvested in 1965. J. Food Hyg. Soc. Japan 9: 23–28.

(4) KURATA, H., F. SAKABE, S. UDAGAWA, M. ICHINOE, M. SUZUKI, and N. TAKAHASHI. 1968. A mycological examination of the 1954–67's stored rice grains for the presence of mycotoxin producers. Bull. Natl. Inst. Hyg. Sci. Japan 85: In press.

(5) Ministry of Health and Welfare, Japan. 1959. Standard methods for the examination of foods. Revised edition. Tokyo. (Shokuhin Eisei Kensa Shishin (i).) See also Kurata, H., K. Ogasawara, and V. L. Frampton. 1956. Microflora of milled rice. Cereal Chem. 34: 47–55, and Tanaka, Y., S. Hirayama, H. Kurata, F. Sakabe, N. Inagaki, T. Matsushima, and S. Udagawa. 1957. Studies on technique for the isolation for the presence of rice grain fungi. I. Bull. Natl. Hyg. Lab. 75: 443–459.

(6) RAPER, K. B., and C. THOM. 1949. A manual of the Penicillia, p. 875. Williams & Wilkins Co., Baltimore.

(7) RAPER, K. B., and D. I. FENNELL. 1965. The genus Aspergillus, p. 686. Williams & Wilkins Co., Baltimore.

(8) THOM, C., and K. B. RAPER. 1945. A manual of the Aspergilli, p. 373. Williams & Wilkins Co., Baltimore.

OCCURRENCE OF MYCOTOXINS IN *ASPERGILLUS**

by G. Semeniuk, G. S. Harshfield, C. W. Carlson, C. W. Hesseltine, *and* W. F. Kwolek
South Dakota State University, Brookings, S. Dak. 57006, and
Northern Regional Research Laboratory, Peoria, Ill. 61604

Summary

Two hundred and forty-seven cultures of 63 *Aspergillus* species from 10 to 18 taxonomic groups were each tested for mycotoxic properties on chicks and mice by feeding them molded wheat and soybeans in 50 percent diet mixes. Thirty-two cultures on one or both substrates were toxic to chicks, while 42 were toxic to mice—toxicity being defined as the death of three or more chicks or mice from the five or six on test. Nineteen cultures on one or both substrates were toxic to both chicks and mice: one each of *A. flavus* and *A. ochraceus*, two of *A. janus*, two of *A. sclerotiorum*, three of *A. quercinus*, four of *A. melleus*, and six of *A. sulphureus*. The one culture of *A. ochraceus*, two of *A. melleus*, and one of *A. sulphureus* produced much ochratoxin; the others produced trace or nondetectable amounts of this toxin. Cultures on both substrates toxic to both chicks and mice were one culture each of *A. quercinus* and *A. ochraceus*, two of *A. sclerotiorum*, three of *A. melleus*, and four of *A. sulphureus*. Thirty-two cultures were toxic only on one substrate to only one of the two animal types. Fifty-two nontoxic cultures stunted the growth of one or both animal types on one or both substrates. Gross and histological lesions were uniformly characteristic from aflatoxin-producing cultures, not from other toxigenic cultures.

Introduction

Aspergilli are ubiquitous colonizers of plant materials. They are commonly associated with deteriorating food and feed, wherein and whereon they develop, contribute to the deterioration process, and leave their own bodies and excreted products as residues. Such bodies and products are a potential hazard to the health of humans and animals that ingest them. So far, about one-fifth of 132 species of the genus (*3*) have been tested for mycotoxic properties (*4*) and 12 of these were found to be toxigenic. Because aflatoxin produced by *A. flavus* and *A. parasiticus* was shown to have high hepatotoxicity and hepatocarcinogenicity, the need was great to appraise other *Aspergilli* for toxigenicity. To meet this need, a testing program was undertaken with a portion of the large collection of *Aspergillus* species at the USDA Northern Regional Research Laboratory, Peoria, Ill. The following is a progress report of that testing.

Methods and Materials

Tests consisted of feeding *ad libitum* wheat and soybeans molded with each culture to six Swiss white weanling mice (male and female, Gopher State Caviary, St. Paul, Minn.) and six cockerel chicks (Dekalb 131 or Shayer Starcross 288 hybrids) per substrate.

Each test comprised a unit of 23 or 24 cultures on each substrate, and one to four controls of each substrate. A unit comprised species of a taxonomic group including all strains to be tested of a species. Each molded and nonmolded substrate was mixed 50 percent with an appropriate basal feed, formulated to provide diets of isocaloric and isonitrogenous value between wheat and soybeans (table 1).

Table 1.—Composition of basal feeds used in preparing 50 percent diet mixes of molded wheat and molded soybeans for chicks and mice

Components	Basal feed formulations for—	
	Molded wheat	Molded soybeans
	Weight proportions, percent	
Yellow corn	12.5	
Soybean meal	25.0	
Alfalfa meal	2.0	2.0
Glucose monohydrate[1]		40.0
Dicalcium phosphate	2.0	2.0
Limestone	1.0	1.0
Salt	.5	.5
Vitamin mix[2]	.5	.5
DL-Methionine	.1	.1
Yellow grease	7.0	
Cellulose[3]		4.5

[1]Cerelose, produced by Corn Products, Inc., Argo, Ill.
[2]Containing, per kilogram, 1,100,000 IU vitamin A, 440,000 ICU vitamin D3, 4,400 IU vitamin E, 220 mg. menadione, 880 mg. riboflavin, 1,760 mg. pantothenic acid, 8.8 g. niacin, 88 g. choline, 1.76 mg. cobalamine, and 22 g. ethoxyquin. For the soybean mixes, other additives were made to provide, per kilogram, 4.4 mg. thiamine, 4.4 mg. pyridoxine, 0.22 mg. biotin, and 0.2 percent DL-Methionine.
[3]Solka-floc 100, a product of Brown Co., Berline, N.H.

*South Dakota Agricultural Experiment Station Journal Series No. 841.

Molded wheat and soybeans were produced in groups of 11 or 12 cultures of one or more species including all strains to be tested of a species. Good quality Scout winter wheat and Chippewa soybeans with about 8 percent moisture were used. The substrates were cracked in a roller mill in approximately 100-kg. amounts, screened free of fine particles, and eleven or twelve 3.6-kg. lots placed in individual plastic sacks. Each lot was wetted with 1 l. of tap water, shaken several times thereafter to prevent caking, and equilibrated 1 or 2 days at 4° C. Thereupon, each lot (wheat one day and soybeans the next, or vice-versa) was divided between two flat paper bags (4 ply, 48 cm. wide, 80 cm. long) which were then laid flat on an autoclave wire-mesh rack. The grain within each bag was spread uniformly over the inside surface. The mouth of the bag was then folded once and stapled shut. After autoclaving, 30 minutes at 121° C. and cooling, the content of each pair of bags was dumped into a clear polyethylene flat sack (3 mil thick, 48 cm. wide, 112 cm. long). The sack previously had been rinsed with 70 percent ethanol and drained. The transferred grain was inoculated immediately. The inoculum was a 7- to 10-day-old sporulating culture developed on 20 to 30 g. of corresponding sterilized grain in a 300-ml. Erlenmeyer flask. All flask cultures were established directly from spores present on agarslant cultures received from the Peoria Laboratory.

Molding of grain in each plastic sack was promoted by laying the sack flat on a tiered shelf in a darkroom at 23° to 30° C., by uniformly spreading the content to the full width of the sack, and by tenting the sack with a centrally placed 15 cm. long sterilized wooden stick. The content of each sack was shaken daily, or less often, depending on the apparent progress of mold growth. After 5 or 6 days for slow-growing cultures, the molded grain from each sack was spread thinly to dry for 3 or 4 days on paper in a shaded, dry greenhouse. The dried material was then ground in a coffee bean grinder and mixed with an appropriate basal feed. For 50 percent mixes, 2.25 kg. of ground moldy grain was needed for chicks; 0.45 kg. was needed for mice.

Mice were housed in suspended wire cages and fed from one-hole cups, one per cage; chicks were housed in thermostated standard chick batteries and fed from a trough. Dead and terminally killed chicks and mice were examined grossly for pathological lesions of internal organs and histologically for liver and kidney cellular changes. In the absence of death within a cage or pen, one animal, at least, was examined histologically.

A least significant difference factor, at a one chance in 20 probability level, of average weight gain between any two cages or pens of four to six animals in each test was determined from the analysis of variance, on the basis of logarithms of the data. A single factor was determined for all three weighings of mice, for the last two of chicks, for the average of these weighings, and for the ratio of the last weighing weight to the first. Significant differences at first were assessed from nonmoldy control feeds, but later they were assessed from the average of all feeds.

Results

At this writing, 247 cultures of 63 *Aspergillus* species from 10 of 18 taxonomic groups (table 2) were tested for mycotoxic properties to chicks and mice on wheat and soybean substrates. This covered 14 chick and 13 mouse trials, each trial with 300 to 336 animals.

Table 2.—Species group and number of NRRL cultures of *Aspergillus* species tested for mycotoxic properties

Species group	Species and number of cultures
Clavatus	Clavatus (4), giganteus (2).
Flavus	Flavus (9 + 2 var.), oryzae (11 + 1 var.), parasiticus (3).
Versicolor	Granulosus (1), janus (3), pulvinus (1), sydowi (10), versicolor (10).
Candidus	Candidus (10).
Ochraceus	Auricomus (2), elegans (1), melleus (7), ochraceus (10), ostianus (1), petrakii (1), quercinus (6), sclerotiorum (2), sulphureus (10).
Restrictus	Caesiellus (1), conicus (3), gracilis (2), penicilloides (1), restrictus (9).
Fumigatus	Auratus (1), brevipes (1), duricaulis (1), fischeri (2 + 3 var.), fumigatus (7 + 1 var.), quadricinctus (2), stramenius (1), viridi-nutans (1).
Niger	Aculeatus (2), awamori (3), carbonarius (3), ellipticus (1), ficuum (2), foetidus (2 + 2 var.), heteromorphus (1), japonicus (2), niger (10), phoenicus (4), pulverulentis (1), tubingensis (1).
Glaucus	Amstelodami (10), athecius (1), carnoyi (1), chevalieri (9 + 2 var.), cristatus (2), echinulatus (3), mangini (3), medius (1), montevidensis (1), niveo-glaucus (3), proliferans (1), pseudoglaucus (2), repens (10), ruber (10), tonophilus (1), umbrosus (2).
Flavipes	Flavipes (10).

Toxic cultures.—On one or both substrates, 55 cultures, or 22 percent of those tested, were toxic to one or both animal types (three or more deaths in five or six animals): 32 were toxic to chicks, 42 were toxic to mice, and 19 were toxic to both chicks and mice (table 3). The 19 were: one culture each of *A. flavus* and *A. ochraceus*, two of *A. janus*, two of *A. sclerotiorum*, three of *A. quercinus*, four of *A. melleus*,

Table 3.—NRRL cultures of *Aspergillus* species on wheat and soybeans toxic or growth stunting to chicks or mice, with indications for low-feed consumption

Species	NRRL Number	Chicks		Mice	
		Soybean	Wheat	Soybean	Wheat
Giganteus	10			S[1]	S
Clavatus	A-14, 106		S[1]		S
Do	4			Sr	
Do	A-14, 542				S[1]
Flavus	450			S	
Do	2999	Ts[1]	Ts[1]	Ts[1]	S[1]
Do	A-14, 205			S	S
Do	A-14, 210			S	S[1]
Oryzae	A-51	S[1]			
Do	468		S	S[1]	
Do	506		S	S	
Do	699		S[1]	Sr	
Oryzae v. effusus	1958		S[1]		
Parasiticus	465	Ts	Ts[1]		S[1]
Sydowi	242	S			
Do	A-12, 469		S		
Do	A-12, 981		S		
Janus	1787		Ts	S	T
Do	1936		Ts		T[1]
Candidus	309	T			
Do	310	Ts			
Do	A-12, 395	T			
Do	A-12, 329	Ts[1]			
Do	1720	S[1]			
Granulosus	1932				T[1]
Quercinus	392		Ts	Sr	T[1]
Do	394	T	Ts	T[1]	T[1]
Do	396	T	S	T[1]	
Do	A-13, 493	S	S	S[1]	
Do	A-13, 494	S[1]		T[1]	
Ochraceus	3174	T	T	T[1]	T[1]
Do	398		S		
Do	399		S		
Do	400	S	S		S[1]
Do	410		S		
Do	2864	S	S		
Sclerotiorum	415	T[1]	T[1]		
Do	4901	T[1]	Ts[1]	T	Ts[1]
Sulphureus	386	T[1]	Ts[1]	T[1]	Ts[1]
Do	387			Ts	
Do	389			T	
Do	4077	T[1]	T[1]	T[1]	T[1]
Do	A-829	T[1]	Ts[1]	T	
Do	A-830	T[1]	Ts[1]	Ts[1]	
Do	A-832	T[1]	Ts[1]	T	T
Do	A-6924	T[1]	T[1]	T	T[1]
Melleus	416	S[1]			
Do	5103	T[1]		T	
Do	A-975			Sr	
Do	A-993	T[1]	T[1]	T[1]	T[1]
Do	A-2305			Ts	
Do	2306	T[1]	T[1]	T[1]	
Do	A-13, 653	T[1]	T[1]	T[1]	T[1]
Elegans	4850			S	
Restrictus	145			S	
Do	148			S	
Do	151			T	
Do	154			S	
Conicus	641	(1)		Sr	
Gracilis	4962				S
Penicilloides	4548				T[1]
Fumigatus	171	S	r		T
Do	A-12, 248	S[1]	S	S[1]	(1)
Do	A-12, 386	S[1]	S	T[1]	T
Do	A-13, 658	S			
Do	A-15, 151				T[1]
Fumigatus v. Ellipticus	5109	Ts	S[1]		
Viridi-nutans	4365	T			

Table 3.—NRRL cultures of *Aspergillus* species on wheat and soybeans toxic or growth stunting to chicks or mice, with indications for low-feed consumption—Continued

Species	NRRL Number	Chicks		Mice	
		Soybeans	Wheat	Soybeans	Wheat
Brevipes	4078			r	T¹
Fischeri	181		S¹	T¹	
Fischeri v. Spinosus.	5034		S		
Quadricinctus	2154	S	S	Ts¹	
Carbonarius	370	Ts		S	
Aculeatus	358	T			
Ficuum	364	S		S	
Foetidus	341		S¹		
Foetidus v. Pallidus.	4797	T¹	(¹)	(¹)	
Japonicus	1782	Sr			
Phoenicis	2253	T¹	Sr	S¹	S¹
Do	4757	T¹			
Tubingensis	4866				Ts¹
Niger	3			S¹	
Do	326	T¹	Sr		
Do	330	Sr		S¹	Sr¹
Do	367				Ts¹
Do	A–208		Sr		
Do	A–314		Sr		(¹)
Do	A–412	S¹	Sr	S¹	
Repens	11	r		S¹	
Do	14				S
Do	47			S¹	
Do	A–12, 277			S¹	
Do	A–12, 409	S			
Do	A–12, 480			T¹	T
Pseudoglaucus	38	S			
Ruber	52		S¹	S¹	
Do	53		S¹	S	
Do	A–12, 460	S			
Tonophilus	5124				Ts
Chevalieri	79			Sr	
Do	80				T
Do	81				S
Do	A–12, 406			S	
Do	A–12, 673			S	
Chevalieri v. Multisporus.	88		S		
Amstelodami	110				T
Do	A–12, 675	S			
Flavipes	531				T
Do	1618				S
Do	1723		S		T
Do	1959			Sr	T
Cristatus	4222		(¹)	S	
Medius	246		S		
Echinulatus	137	S¹			

¹Low-feed consumption.

NOTES.—T = toxic; 3 or more chicks or mice killed of 5 or 6 on test; S = growth stunting; s = growth stunting of survivors; r = low-growth ratio of final to initial weights.

and six of *A. sulphureus*. On both substrates, 15 were toxic to chicks, 13 were toxic to mice, and 11 were toxic to both chicks and mice. The 11 included one culture each of *A. quercinus* and *A. ochraceus*, two of *A. sclerotiorum*, three of *A. melleus*, and four of *A. sulphureus*. A culture of *A. flavus*, of *A. parasiticus*, and of *A. fumigatus* could be added to this list if growth stunting from the other substrate or to the other animal type is taken for toxicity.

Growth stunting by nontoxic cultures.—Fifty-nine nontoxic cultures (24 percent) stunted the growth of one or both animal types on one or both substrates (table 3). Thirty-five stunted the growth of chicks, 37 of mice, and 13 of both chicks and mice. The 13 represented one culture each of *A. clavatus*, *A. quercinus*, *A. ochraceus*, *A. fumigatus*, *A. ficuum*, and *A. amstelodami;* two of *A. ruber;* two of *A. niger;* and three of *A. oryzae*. Mice were stunted on both substrates by single cultures of *A. giganteus*, *A. niger* and *A. flavus;* chicks were stunted on both substrates by one culture each of *A. niger*, *A. quercinus*, and *A. fumigatus*, and by two of *A. ochraceus*.

Growth stunting by toxic cultures.—Growth stunting generally was associated with toxicity expression.

However, a culture toxic to only one animal on one substrate often did not stunt growth of the other animal type on the same or other substrate. Of 44 cultures toxic to one or both animal types on one or the other substrate, only 17 stunted growth where there was no toxicity. The others stunted only where there was toxicity. The results support a low-order expectancy of stunting from a toxic culture where there is no toxicity.

Low-feed consumption.—Of 102 toxic combinations of 55 toxic cultures, two substrates, and two animal types, 66 showed low-feed consumption, while of 20 nontoxic growth stunting combinations of these same items, nine showed low-feed consumption (table 3). By contrast, of 80 growth stunting combinations of 59 nontoxic cultures, two substrates, and two animal types, 28 resulted in low-feed consumption. Low-feed consumption appeared to be associated more with toxic cultures than with growth-stunting nontoxic ones.

Pathology.—Lesions from aflatoxin toxicity to liver and kidneys of chicks fed toxigenic cultures of *A. flavus* and *A. parasiticus* were those abundantly described by other investigators (*1*). These included yellow, tan, or reddish mottled livers grossly. Microscopic changes included strong eosinophilic staining, abundance of foamy cells, vacuolation of cytoplasm, karyorrhexis, necrosis of hepatic cells, and regeneration to form acinus-like structures. A variable degree of bile duct proliferation was present. Other changes also included tan-colored kidneys, swollen and protruding from their bony fossae, with abnormally abundant proteinaceous debris in swollen, convoluted tubules, and with degeneration of tubular epithelial cells. Kidney lesions in mice consisted of mild swelling of convoluted tubules around the midzone of the cortex outside the medulla, and a swelling of parenchyma cells. Such lesions, especially in chicks, were so distinctive that their presence in chick livers from other cultured feeds raised questions as to whether the feeds were contaminated with *A. flavus* or *A. parasiticus*. In each of four instances the suspicion was borne out with detection of the toxin and of one or other of these species in the feed.

Lesions in dead or terminally killed chicks and mice fed other toxigenic cultures generally were nondistinctive, nonconsistent among cell mates, and often not different from nontoxigenic cultures or control feeds. This lack of distinctiveness was surprising and disconcerting as lesions described for ochratoxin A in rats as tubular necrosis of the kidney, mild degeneration of the liver, and enteritis (*2*) were presumed distinctive and readily obtainable. Lesions from 16 highly toxigenic cultures of *A. quercinus*, *A. sclerotiorum*, *A. sulphureus*, *A. ochraceus*, and *A. melleus*, of which

some of the last three produced much ochratoxin, were as follows: (*a*) No gross lesions in 93 and 76 dead chicks on molded soybean and wheat, respectively, and in three and 14 surviving chicks on these feeds killed at test termination; and (*b*) no gross lesions in about one-half of 101 and 58 dead mice on these same substrates, hemorrhagic or mucoid enteritis in about one-fifth of these, abscessed lungs, abscessed abdominal cavity, pleural fluid, and tanned mottled, abscessed, or enlarged livers in the rest of them. Surviving mice killed at the end of the test were free of such abnormalities, and their livers were free of internal changes.

Lesions from other Aspergilli were similarly inconsistent among cellmates, but a pattern seemed to emerge for some species when lesions types were pooled from a number of cultures and from related species. Thus, for the *A. fumigatus* group, air-sac infection and discolored livers in chicks appeared associated principally with *A. fumigatus*, and less with *A. duricaulis* and *A. fischeri;* whereas pneumonia and lung abscesses, enteritis, and enlarged liver and spleen in mice appeared associated with all species of the group, except with *A. viridi-nutans*, and *A. stramenius*.

For the *A. niger* group, no gross lesion or histological abnormality in liver and kidneys was noted in dead or terminally killed chicks. In mice, kidneys were pale, with interstitial nephritis and fibrosis; convoluted tubules were swollen and cystic, with occasional casts. Livers were free of significant lesions. Pneumonia with occasional lung abscesses, cervical abscesses, and enteritis were general in dead or terminally killed mice from all species tested within this group.

For the *A. glaucus* group, gross and histological lesions in liver and kidneys of chicks were absent, or they were like those from control feeds. Pneumonia, with or without lung abscesses, discolored kidneys or liver, or both, with or without abscesses, enlarged spleen, cervical abscesses, and enteritis were common with mice on *A. ruber*, *A. chevalieri*, *A. cristatus*, and *A. tonophilus* cultures, and absent or nearly absent on *A. amstelodami*, *A. montevidensis*, *A. athecius*, *A. proliferans*, *A. umbrosus*, *A. mangini*, *A. echinulatus*, *A. niveo-glaucus*, and *A. cristatus* cultures. The pathological difference between these groupings of *Aspergillus* species may reflect differences between batches of mice more than a real difference between the groupings.

For *A. clavatus*, *A. flavus*, *A. versicolor*, *A. candidus*, and *A. restrictus* groups, and excluding single cultures of *A. flavus* and of *A. parasiticus* discussed above, no gross liver and kidney tissue lesions were detected in either chicks or mice. The exceptions to this were cultures of *A. janus* on wheat from which four or six mice died with abscessed lungs and liver, and with enteritis.

Discussion

The range of response of chicks and mice to molded wheat and soybeans in our test in some measure parallels the response of ducklings, mice and rats to corn molded with other *Aspergillus* cultures tested by Scott (*4*). This investigator fed 104 cultures of 26 *Aspergillus* spp. to groups of three Pekin ducklings and found that 27 cultures of 12 species killed all birds within 2 weeks. Thereupon he fed the 27 cultures to mice and rats and found that only five cultures in different species killed all 10 mice and all 10 rats on test within 4 weeks; one culture in another species killed three mice and eight rats, and one culture in still a third species only stunted the average growth of both mice and rats. The differential response of chicks and mice to molded wheat and soybeans in our tests and the differential response of ducklings, mice, and rats to molded corn in Scott's test would tend to support the thesis that mycotoxicity is an interaction effect between culture, substrate, and animal. On this basis, one might possibly conclude that any *Aspergillus* culture may be toxigenic in some particular combination of interacting factors, and that no toxigenic culture will be toxigenic under all circumstances.

Of some concern on the animal side of our tests was the presence at necropsy of varying degrees of gross and histological lesions that occurred independently of the kind of feed the animals were on. Such lesions were believed due to latent infections that came with the batches of animals received. Lesions in chicks were omphalitis, and liver erythroleukosis and its associated hemorrhages, fat infiltrations, and enlarged spleen. Lesions in mice were liver murine viral hepatitis with its scattered foci of mononuclear and polymorphonuclear cells, and small to large granulomatous lesions. A *Corynebacterium* was isolated from a gross caseous abscess in a liver. No assessment was made of the effect such infections had on animal response to moldy feed.

Acknowledgments

This investigation was supported by Agricultural Research Service Contract No. 12–14–100–8323(71), U.S. Department of Agriculture.

We gratefully acknowledge the technical assistance of Dr. Mingtan Lai, postdoctorate research assistant in plant pathology, for aflatoxin and ochratoxin assays, and of John G. Gregoriades, graduate research assistant in animal science, for chick feeding tests.

References

(*1*) NEWBERNE, P. M., W. W. CARLTON, and G. N. WOGAN. 1964. Hepatomas in rats and hepatorenal injury in ducklings fed peanut meal or *Aspergillus flavus* extract. Path. Vet. *1*: 105–132.

(*2*) PURCHASE, I. F. H., and W. NEL. 1967. Recent advances in research on ochratoxin, pp. 153–156. R. I. Mateles, and G. N. Wogan (ed.) *In* Biochemistry of some foodborne microbial toxins. The M.I.T. press, Cambridge, Mass.

(*3*) RAPER, K. B., and DOROTHY I. FENNELL. 1965. The genus Aspergillus. The Williams & Wilkins Co., Baltimore, Md.

(*4*) SCOTT, DE B. 1965. Toxigenic fungi isolated from cereal and legume products. Mycopathol. Mycol. Appl. *25*: 213–222.

SOME CONSIDERATIONS ON A BIOLOGICAL METHOD FOR THE DETECTION OF MYCOTOXINS IN JAPANESE FOODS

by Masakatsu Ichinoe, Shun-Ichi Udagawa, Masako Tazawa, *and* Hiroshi Kurata
Laboratory of Mycology, Department of Microbiology,
National Institute of Hygienic Sciences, Tokyo

Summary

Preliminary studies of three different methods to test for acute toxicity have been carried out in order to devise a rapid, simplified, and precise screening method for a large-scale study of mycotoxins and to provide information concerning the mycotoxic status of Japanese foods.

The first method employed subcutaneous injection of mice with filtrates of fungal cultures from two different kinds of liquid media and the second employed methanol extracts from cultures on solid medium. Cultures of fungal isolates from flour-type foods and domestic rice were employed in these tests. A third method, the chicken embryo method, was also investigated for its applicability as a myotoxin assay. The latter method employed representative toxic and nontoxic strains of fungi and six kinds of pure mycotoxins.

The fungus metabolites of *Penicillium islandicum*, *Aspergillus clavatus*, and *A. ochraceus* from the flour foods and *P. expansum* and *P. islandicum* from the domestic rice proved to be highly toxic to mice by subcutaneous injection. Precise and simplified bioassay for large scale mycotoxin screening is discussed in this paper.

Introduction

Since 1965, a mycotoxicological study on Japanese foodstuffs has been designed and carried out to provide information concerning the mycotoxic status of Japanese foods.

Prior to the present study, an extensive mycological survey on wheat flour and other kinds of flour (6) and rice (8) had been carried out using the cultural procedure and then testing representative fungal isolates for toxigenicity. During course of these studies, the authors were often faced with the difficult problem of choosing a biological assay which was the most reliable method for the detection of toxic fungi, especially for the first screening step. Feeding trails, or force-feeding of experimental animals by stomach tube, had been frequently applied by earlier workers (3, 15, 16, 18). Intraperitoneal or subcutaneous injection of fungal metabolite had been used principally for the determination of acute toxicity of some fungal metabolites and etiological research.

On the other hand, some mycotoxin research groups (2, 3, 5) have successfully employed testing by dermal toxicity in the rabbit skin with ether or methanol extracts of fungal substrates. In a large scale of examination, such as the present study, feeding trials were not feasible for preliminary testing because of the troublesome necessity for preparation of moldy feed. Therefore, subcutaneous injection of cultural filtrates of methanol extracts of solid cultures were used. Subsequently, the possibile usefulness of the chicken embryo technique for mycotoxin assay was investigated using both known and suspected strains of toxic fungi.

Methods and Results

Toxicity test I, preliminary investigations (7).— These were carried out in order to compare the applicability of toxicity tests using two different procedures of administration; feeding animals with fungus infected substrates and subcutaneous injection of filtrates of fungus cultures. Four species and 12 strains of known or suspected toxic fungi which had been isolated from foodstuffs were employed.

For the feeding trials, moldly feed was made of fungus infected corn meal mixed with equal amounts of the commercial mouse diet. Culture filtrates of the fungi were prepared from two liquid media of either glucose-peptone (GP medium) or Czapek-Dox (Cz medium) medium cultured for 3 weeks at 25° C. In the case of the subcutaneous administration, a single dose of 0.5 ml. of filtrate was injected subcutaneously into the back of a mouse.

Male mice, 15 to 18 g., were caged in groups of five and were allowed feed and water *ad libitum*. All surviving animals were killed and autopsy performed on the 4th to 7th day after the start of the investigation. Control mice were given the commercial mouse diet or the same dose of uninoculated culture medium.

Table 1 shows the results of the comparative in-

Table 1.—Preliminary toxicity tests for the determination of mycotoxigenicity

Fungus species and strain no.	Origin	Feeding trials[1]	Subcutaneous injection	
			GP medium	Cz medium
Aspergillus flavus:				
WF–3–8	Wheat flour	+	−	−
WF–8–1	do	−	−	−
RF–5–1	Rice flour	−	−	+
ATCC–15517	Aflatoxin producing strain	+	−	+
Aspergillus clavatus:				
WF–44–10	Wheat flour	+	+	++
WF–38–11	do	−	+	++
RF–7–1	Rice flour	n.d.	+	++
Aspergillus ochraceus:				
WF–18–6	Wheat flour	+	+	+
SF–13–1	Soybean flour	++	+	+
RF–9–5	Rice flour	−	−	+
Aspergillus fumigatus:				
WF–14–2	Wheat flour	n.d.	+	−
WF–41–7	do	+	−	−

[1]Solid medium of fungus-infected corn meal mixed with mouse diet.

NOTES.— ++, highly toxic, all test animals died; +, mildly toxic, one or two animals died; ±, slightly toxic, loss of body weight; −, nontoxic; n.d., no data.

vestigation. In general, it appears that toxic effect demonstrated by feeding was greater than by subcutaneous injection. The toxic effect with subcutaneous injection was judged to be less sensitive than feeding, still, it should be emphasized that its use as a biological assay has points in its favor. The subcutaneous method is a more rapid and simplified technique for the detection of toxicity because it does not require the complicated handling and troublesome preparation of moldly feed. Therefore, subcutaneous administration of mice was applied in our subsequent toxicity tests. As the toxic effects were different when the fungus was cultured in the different media, it was essential that both media be used for our screening tests.

It was interesting to note that the aflatoxin producing strains of *A. flavus* (ATCC–15517 and WF–3–8) had not revealed their toxigenicity in our investigation. This might be attributed to the low susceptibility of the mouse to aflatoxin as reported by Allcroft and Carnaghan (*1*).

Toxicity test II, subcutaneous injection of culture filtrates.—Based on the decision described above, subcutaneous administration of culture filtrates of fungi to mice were applied on a large scale. The 88 representative strains of fungi were utilized. These were selected from the group of flour-borne fungi, which had been investigated and collected by the authors (*6*). Test method and an assessment of toxicity were made in the same manner as described in the preliminary investigation (toxicity test I).

Approximately 10 percent of examined fungi were found to be highly toxic by this bioassay method (table 2). In the test on culture filtrates from the GP-medium, all mice were killed by the injection of culture filtrates of four strains of *P. islandicum*. Seventeen strains of fungi, including *P. citrinum*, *P. islandicum*, *P. viridicatum*, *P. ochraceum*, *P. spinulosum*, *A. candidus*, *A. clavatus*, *A. versicolor*, *A. ochraceus*, and *A. fumigatus*, were mildly toxic to mice. On the other hand, when employing culture filtrates from Cz-medium, only one strain of *P. islandicum* and five strains of *A. clavatus* were highly toxic. Eight mildly toxic strains including *P. citrinum*, *P. viridicatum*, *P. ochraceum*, *A. flavus*, and *A. ochraceus* were detected.

These results indicated that there was considerable difference in mycotoxin production depending on the kind of substrate on which test fungi were grown. As far as artificial media being employed for the screening test, the disadvantage of choosing a medium was unavoidable. Therefore, it was felt that the natural substrate from which the fungi had been isolated, such as corn, wheat meal, and rice etc., should be employed for the bioassay. Furthermore, no toxic effects had been detected from the 10 strains of *A. flavus* tested. This result seemed reasonable because the mouse has been recognized as an aflatoxin resistant animal, since routine chemical assay for the aflatoxin revealed that the two strains of *A. flavus* were characterized as aflatoxin producers (*9*). From these results, it should be noted that the cultural filtrate method used in this test was not suitable for the detection of aflatoxin.

As far as the bioassay for mycotoxin is concerned, subcutaneous injection of culture filtrates which possibly contained extracellular fungal metabolites, was applicable only for the detection of certain strains of toxic fungi and could not be assumed as an ade-

Table 2.—Summarized data of toxicity test, II in mice with the 88 representative strains of fungi isolated from various kinds of flour

Fungi	Number of strains examined	Toxicity on GP medium			Toxicity on Cz medium		
		High[1]	Mild[1]	None[1]	High	Mild	None
Penicillium:							
P. citrinum	10		1	9		2	8
P. islandicum	10	4	2	4	1		9
P. notatum	5			5			5
P. viridicatum	5		2	3		1	4
P. lanosum	3			3			3
P. ochraceum	3		1	2		1	2
P. spinulosum	3		1	2			3
Aspergillus:							
A. flavus	10			10		1	9
A. candidus	5		3	2			5
A. clavatus	5		3	2	5		
A. versicolor	5		1	4			5
A. ochraceus	3		2	1		3	
A. terreus	3			3			3
A. fumigatus	2		1	1			2
Other fungi:							
Cladosporium sphaerospermum	5			5			5
Trichothecium roseum	5			5			5
Alternaria tenuis	3			3			3
Paecilomyces varioti	3			3			3
Total:	88	4	17	67	6	8	74
Total, percent		4.5	19.3	76.2	6.8	9.1	84.1

[1]For degree of toxicity see footnote, table 1.

quate bioassay for screening a large number of unknown toxin producers.

Toxicity test III, subcutaneous injection of culture filtrate and methanol extracts from solid substrate (10).—In the toxicity test II, only culture filtrates were investigated. By this method it was shown that toxic properties produced in the mycelium might not be contained in the culture filtrate. Thus an improved method for toxicity determination was investigated using the methanol extracts of solid cultures of the fungi. The 82 representative strains of fungi isolated from milled rice, which were harvested in 1965, were examined.

For the preparation of methanol extract, rough rice was soaked in tap water and drained. The moistened rice was then placed in Roux flasks and 10 ml. of water was added to each flask before sterilization. After inoculation of fungus, the flasks were cultured for 4 weeks at 25° C. The moldly mass was first dried at 70° C. and then crushed and powdered in a Waring Blendor. The powder was extracted with methanol for 24 hours in a Soxhlet apparatus. The methanol extract was concentrated in a rotary evaporator *in vacuo.* For use in the toxicity tests, the concentrated methanol extract was dissolved in propylene glycol. Doses of 250 and 1,250 mg./kg. body weight, respectively, were administered to male mice, 15 to 18 g. The 1,250 mg./kg. seemed to be the maximum dose for the screening step. Culture filtrates

used in this test were identical to the previous test (toxicity test II).

Table 3 shows the toxicities of a representative group of fungi, comparing their liquid culture filtrates and their methanol extracts. Different degrees of toxicity were shown, depending on different substrates, but in the case of *P. islandicum* (MR–206–6) culture, the toxicity was evident in both liquid and solid cultures. It is suggested that this strain has the ability to produce at least two different kinds of toxic substance (15, 16); producing islanditoxin in the culture filtrate and luteoskyrin in the mycelium. The islanditoxin, a chlorine-containing cyclic peptide, was confirmed by our chemical assay.

The Cz-medium culture of *P. expansum* (MR–212–3) was recognized as highly toxic, but no toxic effect was noticed from the GP-medium. Patulin and other newly disclosed toxic compounds were detected by chemical analysis. The other eight strains of fungi exhibited toxicity which were submitted to more detailed toxicity tests.

The summarized data of toxicity test III, on all strains tested, are presented in table 4. Two strains of highly toxic fungi (2.4 percent) were detected by the toxicity test III. In the *Penicillium* group, the fungal metabolites of *P. expansum* and *P. islandicum* were recognized as highly toxic and metabolites of one strain each of *P. cyclopium*, *P. cyclopium* var. *echinulatum*, *P. decumbens*, and *P. expansum* and two strains

Table 3.—Detailed results of toxicity test III showing a group of toxic strains of fungi isolated from milled rice

Fungal species	Strain number (MR–)	Liquid culture Toxicity (dose 0.5 ml./mouse) GP-medium[1]	Cz-medium[2]	Solid culture Toxicity (dose mg./kg.)[3] 250	1,250
Penicillium:					
P. cyclopium West. var. *echinulatum* T. & R.	188–1	−	±	−	+
P. decumbens Thom	163–2	−	±	−	+
P. expansum Link	72–3	±	−	−	+
	212–3	−	++	+	
P. islandicum Sopp	202–6	++	±	+	++
P. roqueforti Thom	212–2	±	−	±	+
	219–2	−	−	±	±
Aspergillus:					
A. mangini Thom and Raper	208–4	±	±	−	
A. versicolor (Vuil.) Tirab.	163–1	−	−	+	+

For symbols, see table 1.
[1]Glucose-peptone medium filtrate.
[2]Czapeck solution medium filtrate.
[3]Methanol extracts.

Table 4.—Summary of toxicity test III with 82 representative strains of fungi isolated from milled rice by means of the subcutaneous injection of culture filtrates and methanol extracts into mice

Fungi	Number of strains examined	Toxicity High[1]	Mild[1]	None[1]
Penicillium (series):				
P. cyclopium	8		2	6
P. citrinum	7			7
P. chrysogenum	6			6
P. decumbens	3		1	2
P. roqueforti	3		2	1
P. viridicatum	3			3
P. canescens	2			2
P. commune	2			2
P. expansum	2	1	1	
P. frequentans	2			2
P. rugulosum	2			2
P. digitatum	1			1
P. funiculosum	1	1		
P. implicatum	1			1
P. terrestre	1			1
Aspergillus (groups):				
A. glaucus	11		1	10
A. versicolor	6		1	5
A. flavus	3			3
A. candidus	2			2
A. nidulans	1			1
A. ochraceus	1			1
Other fungi:				
Fusarium spp.	3			3
Cladosporium cladosporioides	2			2
Helminthosporium oryzae	2			2
Phoma spp.	2			2
Trichoconis padowickii	2			2
Alternaria tenuis	1			1
Piricularia oryzae	1			1
Chaetomium globosum	1			1
Total	82	2	8	72
Total, percent	82	2.4	9.7	87.9

[1]For degree of toxicity, see footnote table 1.

of *P. roqueforti* were determined as mildly toxic to mice. In the *Aspergillus* group, no highly toxic strain was disclosed by this study, but one strain each of *A. mangini* (a member of *A. glaucus* group) and *A. versicolor* proved to be mildly toxic. The other fungi belonging to Ascomycetes and Fungi Imperfecti did not exhibit toxicity. Comparing the results of toxicity test III with the previous test II using culture filtrates alone, unexpectedly revealed that this method seemed to be not only insensitive for the detection of toxic fungi but also was not simple or rapid.

Toxicity test IV, chicken embryo test.—The sensitivity of the chicken embryo to mycotoxins was examined by injection with two kinds of materials: Culture filtrates of mycotoxin producing mold and propylene glycol solutions of pure mycotoxins. The species and strains of fungi examined and their corresponding mycotoxins are listed below:

```
A. flavus (WF-3-8)_____Aflatoxin B₁
                                   and B₂, Kojic
                                   acid.
A. clavatus (WF-38-11)_____Patulin,
                                   Ascladiol.
A. ochraceus (SF-13-1)_____Penicillic
                                   acid.
P. islandicum (WF-18-1)_____Luteoskyrin,
                                   Islanditoxin.
P. expansum (MR-212-3)_____Patulin.
P. citrinum (MR-205-3)_____Citrinin.
```

Ochratoxin has not yet been found in the metabolites of *A. ochraceus* by our chemical assay. The other two strains of *A. flavus*, MR-169-1 and RF-5-1, as shown in table 5, were not aflatoxin producing strains.

Yolk sacs of embryonating (96 hours of incubation), White Leghorn eggs were injected with 0.05 ml. of culture filtrates of both of the Cz- and GP-media or with a solution of the pure mycotoxin dissolved in propylene glycol. The egg was observed for embryo viability for 48 hours after injection. Control eggs were injected with uninoculated media and solvent. Noninjected eggs were also incubated in the same manner to provide the necessary information on the background mortality. Parallel toxicity tests were carried out on mice by subcutaneous administration with culture filtrates of fungi, as had been employed in the previous experiment.

The effects on the culture filtrates are presented in table 5. The toxicity of culture filtrates of *A. flavus* (WF-3-8) was readily confirmed. This toxicity was more conspicuous in the GP-medium than in the Cz-medium. On the other hand, *P. islandicum* which had been confirmed as a toxic strain in mice was not toxic in the chicken embryo. The Cz-medium culture of *A. clavatus* induced 40 percent mortality in the embryos; which was similar to the result in mice. A highly toxic effect was disclosed in both culture fil-

trates of *Fusarium* sp., isolated from samples of milled rice, although toxicity of the fungus had not been demonstrated in toxicity test III. Further toxicity tests on this fungus are now being carried out.

The results of the chicken embryo test on pure mycotoxins are shown in table 6. Aflatoxin B₁ obtained from *A. flavus* (WF-3-8) showed the highest toxicity; however, the other mycotoxins tested exhibited no appreciable toxic effect. Only 30 percent of mortality was revealed by patulin, from which a higher mortality had been expected. Mycotoxin injection prior to incubation (*12*) was an unreliable procedure for the determination of toxigenicity because of high mortality even in the control eggs.

Since studies on chicken embryo test have been initiated just recently, the applicability of this test for mycotoxin screening has not yet been thoroughly evaluated, however, it is the authors' impression that the embryo method seems to be inadequate for large scale screening, even though the method is simple and rapid.

Table 5.—Results of toxicity by chicken embryo test on toxic or nontoxic fungal culture filtrates

Fungal species	GP medium chicken embryo	Mice	Cz medium chicken embryo	Mice
Aspergillus flavus (WF-3-8)	[1]10/10	—	4/10	—
Aspergillus flavus (MR-169-1)	2/10	—	0/10	—
Aspergillus flavus (RF-5-1)	0/10	—	0/10	—
Aspergillus clavatus (WF-38-11)	2/10	—	4/10	++
Aspergillus ochraceus (SF-13-1)	1/10	—	0/10	—
Penicillium islandicum (WF-18-1)	0/10	++	1/10	—
Penicillium expansum (MR-212-3)	1/10	—	10/10	++
Penicillium citrinum (MR-205-3)	0/10	—	3/10	—
Fusarium sp. (MR-39-1)	10/10	—	5/10	—
Cladosporium cladosporioides (MR-20-1)	0/10	—	0/10	—
Alternaria tenuis (MR-28-1)	0/10	—	0/10	—
Control media	1/10	—	1/10	—
Nontreatment	0/10, 0/10			

[1]Dead embryos per total inoculated.
For symbols see table 1.

Discussion

Several techniques for the mycotoxin bioassay have been developed and are under study. A bioassay of mycotoxins as a screening step was reported in 1960

Table 6.—Results of toxicity by chicken embryo test on various kinds of crystalline mycotoxins

Mycotoxins	Dose (mg. per egg)	Age of embryo	
		Prior to incubation	96 hours of incubation
Aflatoxin B₁	0.4	[1]10/10	10/10
Kojic acid	.5	2/10	2/10
Patulin	.6	5/10	3/10
Penicillic acid	.5	5/10	1/10
Luteoskyrin	.5	3/10	2/10
Citrinin	.5	3/10	1/10
Control:			
Propylene glycol	.05	1/10	1/10
Nontreatment		4/10	0/10

[1]Dead embryos per total inoculated.

by Joffe (5), who employed the skin test in rabbits, utilizing ether extracts from moldly substrates. Forgacs (3) also reported successful results utilizing the dermal toxicity test on some experimental animals and some livestock. Burnside et al. (2) studied toxic metabolites of *P. rubrum* and reported that it caused death of swine and cattle and discussed four fundamental toxicity methods for mycotoxin assay, including skin test and chicken embryo tests with mold culture filtrates. More recently, in South Africa, Scott (13) reported the results of extensive toxicity tests, utilizing feeding of ducklings and fruitful results were obtained. A bioassay using the chicken embryo has been developed by Verrett et al. (17), since Spensley (14) discovered its high sensitivity to aflatoxin. A cell culture method has been described by Legator et al. (11). Gablik et al. (4) found the cell culture assay to give more precise and rapid results than the duckling test.

A simplified, ideal, and authorized method, has not as yet, been provided for mycotoxin screening. Each one of these methods mentioned above has its own merits and demerits making it difficult to decide on a method of choice. Furthermore, there are so many related and contributing factors which might influence the production of toxic metabolites of fungi, such as, kinds of culture media employed, temperature and period for culture, routes of administration, levels of dosage, and kinds of experimental animals. For these reasons, it should be anticipated that the use of only a single, limited method in large scale screening tests would not provide satisfactory results. The authors have carried out several assay methods for large scale mycotoxin screening: Force feeding of moldy feed, subcutaneous injection of culture filtrates or methanol extracts of solid culture of fungi to mice, and injection of culture filtrates into the yolk sac of embryonating chicken eggs. From the results obtained it is concluded that unfortunately no ideal method

has yet been discovered, however, it is the authors' impression that subcutaneous administration of fungal culture filtrates to mice could be a useful procedure for large scale assays. The cell culture method might be useful, despite the present authors' lack of experience with the method. It is our conception that some combined methods might be employed for the large-scale mycotoxin survey, because each method has its advantages and disadvantages.

Acknowledgments

The authors would like to express their sincere appreciation to Dr. M. Ishidate, Dr. I. Kawashiro, Dr. S. Iwahara of the National Institute of Hygienic Sciences, Tokyo; Dr. K. Uraguchi, Dr. M. Saito, Dr. M. Okudaira of Tokyo University; Dr. H. W. Schroeder of Field Crops Animal Products Research Station, Texas; Dr. Leo A. Goldblatt of Southern Utilization Research and Development Division, New Orleans, USDA; and Dr. T. Miyaki of Chiba University for their very kind interest and advice in our research, and to Dr. F. Sakabe, Mr. Y. Kawasaki, and Mr. M. Takada, of their laboratory, for their valuable assistance.

This research is supported in part by a Public Law 480 research grant, No. FG–Ja–121, of the U.S. Department of Agriculture, and Cancer Research Foundation of the Ministry of Health and Welfare, to whom the authors are indebted.

References

(1) ALLCROFT, R., and R. B. A. CARNAGHAN. 1962. Groundnut toxicity; an examination for toxin in human food products from animal fed toxic groundnut meal. Vet. Rec. *75:* 259–263.

(2) BURNSIDE, J. E., W. L. SIPPEL, J. FORGACS, W. T. CARLL, M. B. ATWOOD, and E. R. DOLL. 1957. A disease of swine and cattle caused by eating moldy corn. II. Experimental production with pure cultures of molds. Amer. J. Vet. Res. *18:* 817–824.

(3) FORGACS, J., W. T. CARLL, A. S. HERRING, and B. G. MAHLANDT. 1954. A toxic *Aspergillus clavatus* isolated from feed pellets. Amer. J. Hyg. *60:* 15–26.

(4) GABLIKS, J., W. SCHAEFFER, L. FRIEDMAN, and G. WOGAN. 1965. Effect of aflatoxin B₁ on cell culture. J. Bacteriol. *90:* 720–723.

(5) JOFFE, A. Z. 1960. The mycoflora of overwintered cereals and its toxicity. Bull. Res. Counc. Israel *9D:* 101–126.

(6) KURATA, H., and M. ICHINOE. 1967. Studies on the population of toxigenic fungi in foodstuffs. I. Fungal flora of flour-type foodstuffs. J. Food Hyg. Soc. Japan *8:* 237–246.

(7) KURATA, H., and M. ICHINOE. 1967. Studies on the population of toxigenic fungi on foodstuffs. II. Toxigenic determination for the fungal isolates obtained from the flour-type foodstuffs. J. Food Hyg. Soc. Japan *8:* 247–252.

(*8*) KURATA, H., S. UDAGAWA, M. ICHINOE, Y. KAWASAKI, M. TAKADA, M. TAZAWA, A. KOIZUMI, and H. TANABE. 1968. Studies on the population of toxigenic fungi in foodstuffs. III. Myco-flora of milled rice harvested in 1965. J. Food Hyg. Soc. Japan *9:* 23–28.

(*9*) KURATA, H., H. TANABE, K. KANOTA, S. UDAGAWA, and M. ICHINOE. 1968. Studies on the population of toxigenic fungi in foodstuffs. IV. Aflatoxin producing fungi isolated from foodstuffs in Japan. J. Food Hyg. Soc. Japan *9:* 29–34.

(*10*) KURATA, H., S. UDAGAWA, M. ICHINOE, Y. KAWASAKI, M. TAZAWA, J. TANAKA, and H. TANABE. 1968. Studies on the population of toxigenic fungi in foodstuffs. V. Acute toxicity test for representa-tive species of fungal isolates from milled rice harvested in 1965. J. Food Hyg. Soc. Japan *9.* In press.

(*11*) LEGATOR, M. S. and A. WITHROW. 1964. Aflatoxin: Effect on mitotic division in cultured embryonic lung cells. J. Assoc. Official. Agr. Chemists *47:* 1007–1009.

(*12*) McLAUGHLIN, J. JR., J. MARLIAC, M. J. VERRETT, M. K. MUTCHLER, and O. G. FITZHUGH. 1963. The injection of chemicals into the yolk sac of fertile eggs prior to incubation as a toxicity test. Toxicol. Appl. Pharmacol. *5:* 760–771.

(*13*) SCOTT, D. B. 1965. Toxigenic fungi isolated from cereal and legume products. Mycopath. Mycol. Appl. *25:* 213–222.

(*14*) SPENSLEY, P. C. 1963. Aflatoxins, reactive principle in turkey "X" disease. Endeavour *22:* 75.

(*15*) TSUNODA, H. 1951. Studies on a poisonous substance produced on the cereals by a Penicillium sp. under the storage. Japan. J. Nutrition *9:* 1–6.

(*16*) URAGUCHI, K., T. TATSUNO, M. TSUKIOKA, F. SAKAI, Y. SAKAI, O. YONEMITSU, H. ITO, M. MIYAKE, M. SAITO, M. ENOMOTO, T. SHI-KATA, and T. ISHIKO. 1961. Isolation of two toxic agents, luteoskyrin and chlorine containing peptide, from the metabolites of *Penicillium islandicum* Sopp, with some properties thereof. Japan. J. Exp. Med. *31:* 19–46.

(*17*) VERRETT, M. J., J. P. MARLIAC, and J. McLAUGHLIN JR. 1964. Use of the chicken embryo in the assay of aflatoxin toxicity. J. Assoc. Official Agr. Chemists *47:* 1003–1006.

(*18*) YAMAMOTO, T. 1954. Studies on the poison-producing mold isolated from dry malt. J. Pharm. Soc. Japan *74:* 797–812.

MYCOLOGICAL DIFFERENCES BETWEEN THE PRODUCER AND NONPRODUCER OF AFLATOXIN OF *ASPERGILLUS*

by Hideya Murakami *and* Meiji Suzuki
Research Institute of Brewing, Tax Administration Agency,
2–6 Takinogawa, Kita-Ku, Tokyo

Summary

The following mycological characteristics were found to be the most common in the aflatoxin producing strains: Color of conidial heads green even in old culture; the reverse side of colony wrinkled and colored; presences of sclerotia, globose to subglobose vesicles, biseriate sterigmata and conidiophore with roughened walls; high productivities of pigment, total acid and kojic acid; low abilities of browning rice koji and of production of deferriferrichromes.

Three strains were selected from 160 industrial strains as mycologically somewhat similar to the aflatoxin producing strains, all of which, however, were proved not to produce aflatoxin. Four out of 29 aflatoxin strains were also found not to produce aflatoxin. Therefore, it was concluded that the mycological characters described above, are the necessary ones to a fungus for the production of aflatoxin but that the fungus having these characters may not always produce aflatoxin. Finally, the aflatoxin strains were placed in the *Aspergillus flavus* series, taxonomically.

Introduction

For the purpose of excluding even a trace amount of aflatoxin, impossible to be detected chemically from foods and drink, one of the most feasible methods is to make clear the mycological differences between the producer and nonproducer of aflatoxin. One can then exclude any strains similar to the producer from the microbiological industries. Such procedures will also serve to provide cultures for the study of the physiological mechanism of aflatoxin formation.

In this paper we report on the mycological characters of 29 aflatoxin strains and compare them with those of Japanese industrial strains which were proved previously not to produce an aflatoxin. We also consider the mycological differences between *A. oryzae* and *A. flavus*.

Materials and Methods

Microorganisms.—Most of the aflatoxin strains were sent from the Northern Utilization Research and Development Division (Peoria, Ill.) and some of them from the Tropical Products Institute (London), the National Institute of Health (Japan) and the National Institute of Hygienic Science (Tokyo). The industrial strains were isolated by the authors from starter koji (tane koji) in Japan, and some were received from the Institute of General and Applied Microbiology, University of Tokyo. The type cultures of *A. oryzae* and *A. flavus* were received from the Department of Bacteriology, University of Wisconsin, and from several institutes of the type-culture collections in Japan.

Culture and analysis.—The Czapek agar and Adye and Mateles' medium (*1*) were used for morphological study and for determination of aflatoxin productivity, respectively. Rice-koji extract (Ballg. 8, pH 4–5) was used for the determination of total acid and kojic acid (*2, 3*). Kojic acid in this paper means any substance showing a red color after addition of $FeCl_3$ solution to the cultured broth.

The arrangement of sterigmata and formation of sclerotia were observed on the fungus culture cultivated on rice koji extract-agar at 24° C. for 10 days and on the giant colony incubated at 34° C. for 10 days in Czapek agar, respectively, which proved to be the most favorable conditions for the appearance of these mycological characteristics (*4*).

Rice kojis were made using 10 g. of polished rice in 100 ml. flasks by the same culture method as that reported previously (*5*). After cultivation, the cultures were steeped in 50 ml. of distilled water for 1 hour with occasional stirring and then filtered. To 5 ml. of the filtrate, 0.5 ml. of aqueous solution of $FeCl_3$, containing 100 p.p.m. of Fe, and 0.5 ml. of the citric acid buffer solution (pH 4.0) were added. After keeping the mixture at 60° C. for 30 minutes, it was analyzed with a Hitachi model EPO–B spectrophotometer, at 430 mμ, using a cell of 10-mm. light path, in which 5 ml. and 0.5 ml. of distilled water were used as controls of the filtrate and the $FeCl_3$ solution, respectively. The productivity of deferriferrichromes by fungus (*6, 7*) was expressed as the DF value. The DF values of fungi were determined by the mean values obtained by three replications of the culture and determination for each strain, because the DF values of the fungi varied sensitively with the conditions of culture.

The residual matter on the filter paper was kept at room temperature for 1 to 2 days and the degree of their browning was compared, each with the other.

Selection of the industrial strains.—From the results obtained it seemed that there were some common mycological characteristics in the aflatoxin strains. The characteristics of 160 industrial strains were compared with those of aflatoxin strains. This led to the selection of three industrial strains as the strains mycologically most similar, although not identical, to the aflatoxin strains.

Results and Discussion

Common characteristics of aflatoxin strains.—Color of old cultures kept the green tint and did not become brown, as is usually seen in *A. oryzae*. The reverse side of the colonies was wrinkled when cultured at both 34° and 24° C., and was deeply colored brown, reddish brown, brownish orange, van Dyke brown or sometimes brownish black. Sclerotia were found in every strain, with two exceptions of NRRL 465 and NRRL A4018b; their numbers varying from few to innumerable. The strain ATCC 155 17 was found to produce some sclerotia in this experiment, contrary to a previous observation (*8*). Vesicles were usually globose to subglobose and sometimes oval shaped, and larger than about 25μ to 30μ in diameter. Sterigmata were arranged more or less in two series in every strain with an exception of NRRL A4018b, which was in one series. Walls of conidiophores were very roughened. Conidia were usually smaller than about 4.6μ to 4.8μ, but those of prominently roughened walls were somewhat larger.

Pigments were produced abundantly, showing yellowish brown, reddish brown, or brown, except for one strain NRRL A4018b which lacked pigment. High productivity of total acid and kojic acid was also one of the most evident characteristics. It is well known that a producer of sclerotia usually has high productivity of acid (*9*). Rice kojis were not browned in almost every strain, and the DF values were usually small. Seven strains having conidia with prominently roughened walls, NRRL 2999, NRRL 3145, NRRL 465, NRRL A11613 and NRRL A12353, ATCC 15517 and CMI 89717 showed the smallest DF values and produced the largest amount of aflatoxin, with the highest stability of production among all the strains tested. Four strains, NRRL A4018b, A12267, A12268 and RIB 4026 (Research Institute of Brewing), proved not to produce aflatoxin by thin-layer chromatography, of which three strains other than NRRL A4018b (uniseriate) had the common charac-

teristics of aflatoxin strain (biseriate).

The principal characters of 25 aflatoxin strain are summarized in table 1. From this table, the aflatoxin

Table 1.—Some principal characters of 25 aflatoxin producing strains of the *Aspergillus*

Mycological character	Number of strains
Type of conidial head:	
Loosely radiate	[1]7
Radiate, broom-like, columnar	18
Presence of sclerotia	[2]24
Having conidia of prominently roughened walls	7
Conidial size:	
Larger than 4.8μ to 5.0μ	[2]6
Smaller than 4.6μ to 4.8μ	19
Total acid shown by titer of 0.1N NaOH/10 ml. of medium:	
Higher than 3.0 ml.	[3]18
Lower than 2.8 ml.	[4]7
Browning of rice koji:	
Not browned	21
Slightly browned	[4]4
DF value of rice koji:	
Larger than 0.06	[4]5
Smaller than 0.05	20
Relative fluorescence energy:	
Larger than 10,000	[5]8

[1]All of them have conidia with prominently roughened walls (represented by NRRL 465).
[2]NRRL 465 is not included. It is a prominent strain.
[3]All the prominent strains other than NRRL 465 are included.
[4]The great majority of industrial strains showed titers ranging from 0.5 to 2.6 ml.
[5]None of the prominent strains are included.
[6]Including only 1 strain RIB 4027 of which conidial walls are not so roughened.

strains can be classified into two groups. One is a group of the strains like *A. parasiticus* Speare having conidia of prominently roughened walls and another is that of the strains like *A. flavus* Link having conidia with not so roughened walls. Thus, they seemed to be included in the *A. flavus* series by Thom and Church (*10*).

Aflatoxin productivity of the industrial strains.—None of the 160 industrial strains were found to have exactly the same mycological characteristics as those of the aflatoxin strain. However, three strains, RIB 410, RIB 433, and RIB 537, were selected as those somewhat similar to the aflatoxin strains in terms of color of old culture, wrinkles, and colors on reverse side of colony, biseriate sterigmata and production of pigment and kojic acid. Some of their mycological characters are compared with those of aflatoxin strains (see table 2). After culturing them in 1 liter of Adye and Mateles' medium and/or 1 kg. of polished rice, their productivities of aflatoxin were examined by the usual method and they were proved not to produce any aflatoxin. It seems that many mycological characteristics of a fungus need to be studied in order to identify it as a possible producer of aflatoxins.

Mycological differences between *A. oryzae* and *A. flavus*.—It is of major importance that the producer of aflatoxin belongs to the *A. flavus* series and not to the *A. oryzae* series. The mycological characters of *A. oryzae* and *A. flavus* varied so continuously with the strain that their differences have been difficult to find. The authors, however, found that they have different abilities to produce kojic acid and to brown rice kojis as shown in table 3. All the type cultures of *A. flavus* did not brown rice koji while those of *A. oryzae* did so. The aflatoxin strains did not brown rice kojis.

The great majority of industrial strains browned their rice kojis with diverse grades of browning. A few strains of *A. oryzae* did not brown their rice kojis; all of such strains were nonproducers of kojic acid.

Table 2.—Mycological characters of the aflatoxin strains and industrial strains selected

| | Group of strains | | | | |
| | Aflatoxin strain | | Industrial strain[1] | | |
Mycological character	Conidia of prominently roughened walls	Conidia with not so roughened walls	Conidia of prominently roughened walls [2]410	[2]433	Conidia with not so roughened walls 537
Length of stalk	Short	Short	Long	Long	Short.
Conidial size	Middle	Small	Small	Small	Large.
Presence of sclerotia	Yes	Yes	No	No	Yes.
Production of kojic acid	Much	Much	Little	Much	Much.
Production of pigment	do	do	do	do	Little.
Coloration of hydroquinone	No	No	No	No	Yes.
Reduction of methylene blue	Yes	Yes	do	Yes	No.
Browning of rice koji	No	No	do	do	Yes.
DF value	Small	Small	Small	Small	Large.

[1]The morphological characters such as color of old culture, wrinkles and colors on the reverse side of colony, and arrangement of sterigmata, were similar to those of aflatoxin strains.
[2]These strains were isolated from some kinds of koji as wild strains about 50 and 20 years ago, respectively.

Table 3.—Mycological characters of the type cultures of *A. oryzae* and *A. flavus*

Group of strains	Strain Number	Biseriate sterigmata	Total acid (0.1N NaOH ml./10 ml. of rice-koji extract)	Kojic acid[1]	Amylase activity	Coloration of hydroquinone	Reduction of methyleneblue	DF value	Browning by air
			Production					Rice koji	
A. oryzae	NI 5177	++	0.2–0.3	−	+	+++	+++	+	++
	OUT 5039	−	0.6–1.1	−	−	+++++	+++	++	+
	IFO 5239	−	1.2–1.5	+++	+++	++++	++	++	+++
	WB 447	+++	0.8–1.1	−	−	+++	+	+	+++
A. flavus	NI 5051	−	0.4–0.7	+++	+	+	++	±	−
	OUT 5004	−	0.6–0.8	−	++	++++	+++	±	−
	IFO 4053	++++	0.4–1.3	+	−	+++++	+++	±	±[2]
	WB 482	++	1.6–2.7	++++	++++	−	+++	+++	−

[1]The results are those when the strains were cultured in rice-koji extract at 24° C. for 15 to 30 days; if the other medium was used, they were changed.
[2]When cultured on some kinds of imported rice, scarcely browned.
NOTES.—Signs − and +, in this table show respectively, absence of the characters concerned and, in proportion to the number of +, presence of the more evident, abundant to strong characters concerned.

Acknowledgments

This work would not have been possible without the series of aflatoxin producing strains and type cultures of *A. oryzae* and *A. flavus* sent from Dr. C. W. Hesseltine, Northern Utilization Research and Development Division, and Prof. Dr. K. B. Raper, University of Wisconsin, respectively. The authors wish to express their thanks to them, and to Mrs. A. J. Wallbridge, the Tropical Products Institute, and to the institutes in Japan for their supply of aflatoxin strains and the type cultures of *A. oryzae* and *A. flavus*.

The authors are grateful for the encouragement of Prof. Emeritus Dr. K. Sakaguchi, University of Tokyo, and also acknowledge the cooperation of Messrs. the late S. Takase, H. Sagawa, Y. Ogino, M. Makino and N. Sato, the Research Institute of Brewing.

References

(*1*) ADYE, J., and R. I. MATELES. 1964. Incorporation of labeled compounds into aflatoxin. Biochim. Biophys. Acta. *86:* 418–420.

(*2*) MURAKAMI, H., A. SUZUKI, K. OWAKI, and K. KUWABARA. 1965. On the physiological characters of the yellow green Aspergilli. Report of the Research Institute of Brewing *137:* 12–18 (in Japanese).

(*3*) MURAKAMI, H., Y. KIEDA, S. HYOTO, T. ISHII, and K. KUWABARA. 1965. On the yellow green Aspergilli with conidia of prominently roughened walls. Ibid., *137:* 19–27 (in Japanese).

(*4*) MURAKAMI, H., Y. OGINO, M. MAKINO, and K. OWAKI. 1967. On the stability of mycological characters in comparison of the parent strains with their mutants. Ibid., *139:* 6–15 (in Japanese).

(*5*) MURAKAMI, H., S. TAKASE, and K. KUWABARA. 1968. Production of fluorescent substances in rice koji and their identification by absorption spectrum. J. Gen. Applied Microbiol. 97–110.

(*6*) TADENUMA, M., and S. SATO. 1967. Presence of ferrichrysin as iron containing colorant in sake. Agri. Biol. Chem. *31:* 1482–1489.

(*7*) MURAKAMI, H., M. MAKINO, N. SATO, M. FUJIJI, and S. TAKASE. 1967. Productivity of ferrichromes by the yellow greenspored Aspergilli and its relation to other mycological characters. Report of the Res. Inst. of Brewing, *139:* 1–5 (in Japanese).

(*8*) MURAKAMI, H., K. OWAKI, and S. TAKASE. 1966. An aflatoxin strain ATCC 15517. J. Gen. Appl. Microbiol. *12:* 195–206.

(*9*) SAKAGUCHI, K. 1928. Production of acid and alcohol by genus *Aspergillus*. J. Agri. Chem. Soc. Japan *4:* 203–213 (in Japanese).

(*10*) THOM, C., and M. B. CHURCH. 1926. *The Aspergilli*. The Williams & Wilkins Co., Baltimore.

PRODUCTION OF VARIOUS AFLATOXINS BY STRAINS OF THE *ASPERGILLUS FLAVUS* SERIES

by C. W. Hesseltine, Odette L. Shotwell, Mabel Smith, J. J. Ellis, Elsie Vandegraft, *and* Gail Shannon

Northern Regional Research Laboratory, Northern Utilization Research and Development Division, Agricultural Research Service, U.S. Department of Agriculture, Peoria, Ill. 61604

Summary

Sixty-seven strains of the *Aspergillus flavus* group, most of which reportedly produce aflatoxin, were grown on three different substrates under two different fermentation conditions. Yields of aflatoxins B_1, G_1, and M were determined for each fermentation. All strains that produced G_1 also produced B_1. All strains that produced aflatoxin M produced it at a ratio to B_1 of from 0.007 to 0.020. Several distinct taxa were present. Consistently 11 of 14 *A. parasiticus* strains produced all aflatoxins. In the remaining three strains, the levels of B_1 were very low and no M was detected. A second group of five strains formed numerous large sclerotia on Czapek's agar and, likewise, formed all the aflatoxins. The third and largest group represented by *A. flavus* produced only aflatoxins B_1 and M but no G_1; in six strains no aflatoxin was detectable. One very unusual strain, which does not appear to belong to any of the groups studied, had extremely high levels of B_1 (1,257 μg./g.) but no G_1. This strain sporulates poorly and produces many small sclerotia that are much smaller than those seen in *A. flavus*.

Reports in the literature indicate great variability of isolates of *A. flavus* Link ex Fries in their ability to produce aflatoxins. Several papers state that some isolates produce only aflatoxin B_1 and no G_1. Diener and Davis (*3*) reported 23 isolates out of 26 produced aflatoxin B_1; the remaining formed both B_1 and G_1. In another laboratory, Taber and Schroeder (*12*), investigating isolates of *A. flavus* from U.S. peanuts, found no isolate that produced aflatoxins G_1 or G_2.

The objectives of our investigation were: (1). To discover the best strains that would produce aflatoxins M_1 and M_2, recently discovered by Holzapfel, Steyn, and Purchase (*5*) in peanuts; (2) to determine the variation in aflatoxin yields in as many aflatoxin-producing cultures in the ARS Culture Collection as possible; and (3) to determine whether there was any relationship between the kinds and yields of aflatoxin and the taxonomy of the different species in the *A. flavus* series.

Aflatoxins M_1 and M_2 are of interest because they were originally found in milk by Allcroft and Carnaghan (*1*). On the basis of chromatographic data of extracts of peanuts molded with *A. flavus*, de Iongh et al. (*2*) suggested that aflatoxins M_1 and M_2 were identical with the toxic material from milk. Holzapfel et al. (*5*) were able to isolate aflatoxins M_1 and M_2 from urine of sheep fed a mixture of aflatoxins and they determined the structures of the new aflatoxins to be as follows:

Masri et al. (*7*) demonstrated that fermented rice, prepared in our Laboratory with *A. parasiticus* strain NRRL 2999, contains aflatoxin M_1.

Materials and Methods

Fermentation.—All *A. flavus* series cultures selected for this study either were reported to produce or were suspected of producing aflatoxin. The source and equivalent identification numbers of the 67 cultures used are given under results. Each culture was grown on potato dextrose agar (PDA) at 28° C. for 2 weeks to obtain conidia for inoculum. At this time, 10 ml. of sterile tap water was added to each slant. Seven milliliters of a spore suspension was used to inoculate 200 g. of pearled wheat or rice in Fernbach flasks. Each flask containing long grain white rice had 50 ml. of tap water added. The flasks were allowed to stand at room temperature for 2 hours, and then they were sterilized and cooled. After flasks containing pearled Conley hard red wheat had 70 ml. of tap water added, they were allowed to stand overnight, autoclaved, and cooled. A liquid fermentation medium, earlier found to be excellent for the formation of aflatoxin, was prepared by adding 10 g. of rice flour (made from long grain white rice) to 200 ml. of tap water in 500-ml. Erlenmeyer flasks. After sterilizing and cooling, these flasks were inoculated with 3 ml. of a spore suspension described above.

All flasks were then placed on a Gump[1] shaker at 28° C. At the end of 48 and 72 hours, 5 ml. of sterile tap water was added to each flask containing the solid rice and wheat substrates. At the end of 5 days, all flasks were harvested and steamed; then the pH of the liquid medium was determined.

Assay procedure.—Moldy wheat or rice (25 g.) was extracted by mixing for 5 minutes with 250 ml. water in a Waring Blendor, followed by mixing the aqueous slurry in the blendor for 5 minutes with 250 ml. of chloroform as described by Lee (6). Blended mixtures were centrifuged and filtered, and filtrates concentrated to dryness under nitrogen, according to Stubblefield et al. (11). Residues were made up to 10 ml. with chloroform for thin-layer chromatography (TLC).

Fifty-milliliter portions of culture liquors were mixed thoroughly with acid-washed Celite 545 (50 g.) and packed tightly with the aid of a tamping rod into a column (5.2 cm. i.d.) plugged at the bottom with Pyrex wool. The packed column was washed first with hexane (400 ml.) and then eluted with chloroform (600 ml.). After the eluate was collected and concentrated to dryness under nitrogen, the residue was taken up in chloroform (1 ml.) for TLC.

Aflatoxins B_1, G_1, and M were determined quantitatively by TLC with a recording densitometer (11). The developing solvent for B_1 and G_1 was acetone:chloroform (1:9, v/v) and for M, methanol:chloroform (7:93, v/v). Aflatoxins B_2 and G_2, although produced along with B_1 and G_1, were not determined. Aflatoxins M_1 and M_2 did not separate with the solvent system used. Aflatoxin M was determined quantitatively by comparing with a B_1 standard, assuming that the fluorescence of M_1 and M_2 is three times the intensity of B_1 as reported by Holzapfel et al. (5).

Preparative thin-layer chromatography.—Thin-layer plates (20 x 20 cm.) were coated with silica gel (Adsorbosil-1; Applied Science Laboratories, State College, Pa.), to a thickness of 0.5 mm. and activated for 2 hours at 105° C. The chloroform solution (500 μl.) of material extracted from moldy rice or wheat was transferred to the origin line of a plate applying 10 μl. at a time. Plates were first developed approximately 19 cm. with anhydrous ether in an unlined, unequilibrated tank and airdried 30 minutes. The dried plates were then developed approximately 16 cm. with methanol:chloroform (7:93, v/v). The area containing aflatoxin M, as located with ultraviolet light, was outlined with a needle and the silica gel was collected from the area with a thin-layer plate scraper as described by Stoloff (10). Aflatoxin M was eluted from silica gel with portions of ACS methanol (total volume, 30 ml.), and eluate was concentrated on a steam bath under nitrogen to volume of about 5 ml. (was not taken to dryness). The ultraviolet absorption spectra of solutions were obtained on a Beckman DB–G spectrophotometer.

Results

Table 1 shows the equivalent culture numbers of other investigators and the source of each isolate. The amounts of aflatoxin from the solid substrates, rice, and wheat, are given in μg./g. of substrate while the yields in the liquid medium are given in milligrams per liter. Each aflatoxin value is the average of duplicate assays on two fermentations. The final pH of the liquid medium at the completion of the fermentation is also the average of two fermentations. In some instances, if the assay values of the two fermentations were quite different, additional fermentations were run.

Aflatoxin M was identified by TLC and confirmed by ultraviolet absorption. The spectra of M preparations eluted from thin-layer plates had absorption peaks at 227, 266, and 358 mμ. corresponding to those reported by Holzapfel et al. (5).

The initial group of isolates belong to *A. parasiticus* Speare, a species first isolated in Hawaii from mealy bugs in sugarcane. Additional papers will describe the taxonomy and biochemical characteristics of the 14 strains of *A. parasiticus* studied. Of the 14 strains, four are Speare's original isolate, but each was carried in a different collection over many years and varies considerably from the others in its ability to form aflatoxin. Another strain, NRRL 465, considered to be typical of the species, has been in pure culture for at least 45 years and is a rather high producer of aflatoxin. Besides the isolate from Hawaii, others came from South Africa, Argentina, and Southern United States. Since we did not find *A. parasiticus* in our flour microbiology studies (4), we suspect that this species may be geographically restricted to the tropical regions of the world.

Note should be taken that all strains, except NRRL 504 which is a low toxin producer, tend to produce final pH's below 5 and often below 4 in the liquid media. Growth on the liquid rice medium is very luxuriant. The highest toxin production occurs upon the solid substrate, wheat. All strains, except some

---

[1]The mention of firm names or trade products does not imply that they are endorsed or recommended by the Department of Agriculture over other firms or similar products not mentioned.

which have been in culture collections for many years, produce aflatoxins B_1, G_1, and M.

Upon potato dextrose and Czapek's solution agars, the colonies of all isolates are relatively low and dark green as contrasted to the yellow green of *A. flavus*. The reverse of the colonies is typically yellowish to drab and often irregularly wrinkled. No pigment typically is produced although occasionally a faint diffusible yellow pigment may be encountered. The conidial heads are globose with the conidial chains arranged in a diffuse fashion. Conidia do not shatter readily. Also, some strains do produce sclerotia under certain circumstances. For example, NRRL 3145 was observed to form sclerotia on potato dextrose agar and on Czapek's solution agar. This condition is contrary to the situation in *A. parasiticus* as described by Raper and Fennell (*8*).

The NRRL 3161 group of five strains are closely related to *A. parasiticus* because each produces good yields of aflatoxins B_1 and G_1 and low levels of M.

Table 1.—Survey of strains of the *Aspergillus flavus* series for the production of aflatoxin B_1, G_1 and M

| Source and collection numbers | Substrate | Medium | Final pH | Aflatoxin µg./g. on R and W, mg./l. in L | | | |
				B_1	G_1	M	M/B_1
A. parasiticus							
NRRL 465. ?		R		160	85	1.3	0.008
Received 1922 from Takamine's		W		226	105	2.4	.010
Laboratory, ATCC 16,869.		L	4.2	22	15	0.2	.010
NRRL 502.	Mealy bug of	R		0.09	Trace	ND	--
Type from Speare, Hawaii 1913.	sugarcane.	W		0.5	0.2	ND	--
CMI 15,957, ATCC 1018.		L	4.4	ND	ND	ND	--
Thom 3509.							
NRRL 504. ?		R		0.06	ND	ND	--
From Fawcett, Calif. 1929.		W		0.09	ND	ND	--
CMI 92,876.		L	5.4	ND	ND	ND	--
NRRL 2999.	Uganda peanuts	R		467	109	2.2	.005
CMI 91,019b, Austwick V		W		930	415	3.4	.004
3734/10, WB 5013.		L	3.3	21	3	0.07	.003
NRRL 3000.	do	R		268	69	1.2	.005
CMI 89,717, TPI T–12,		W		413	268	2.3	.006
R. C. Codner UG 3.		L	3.9	12	6	0.08	.008
NRRL 3145.	South African	R		452	228	3.4	.007
CMI 93,080, Austwick V 4065/4.	peanuts.	W		641	594	5.4	.008
		L	3.9	14	13	0.10	.007
NRRL 3240.	Uganda peanuts	R		461	116	2	.004
MIT, Austwick V 3734/10,		W		625	277	2.3	.004
TPI M 001, ATCC 15,517,		L	3.1	10	2	0.03	.003
CMI 120,920.							
A–3313.	Soil, Argentina	R		121	46	0.7	.005
J. Winitzky, M-1-361, Buenos		W		196	134	0.8	.004
Aires, Argentina, 1950.		L	4.8	0.12	0.06	ND	--
CMI 91,019.							
A–3842.	Sugarcane stalks	R		1	0.7	0.007	.006
B. A. Bourne, U. S. Sugar Corp.,		W		0.2	0.1	ND	--
No. 52 F-10.		L	4.8	ND	ND	ND	--
A–13360.	Mealy bug of	R		50	54	0.6	.012
CMI 15,957 (11), same as	sugarcane.	W		201	193	2	.009
NRRL 502 but carried		L	4.8	0.2	0.1	0.001	.007
separately for many years.							
A–13441.	Rough rice	R		411	111	1.5	.004
H. W. Schroeder 64–R8, Texas.		W		604	253	1.9	.003
		L	3.1	6	0.5	0.02	.002
A–14330.	Peanuts	R		113	20	0.34	.003
U. Diener, Alabama 6.		W		450	139	1.3	.003
		L	3.2	18	2	0.04	.002
A–14694.	Same as NRRL 502.	R		54	19	0.33	.006
CMI 15,957 (VI) IFO 4082,		W		73	59	0.5	.006
Thom 3509. Same as NRRL 502		L	4.8	4	4	0.04	.010
but carried separately for many							
years.							
A–14695.	Same as NRRL 502.	R		0.04	0.023	ND	--
CMI 15,957 (VII), NRRL 502.		W		0.38	0.1	ND	--
Thom 3509, IFO 4351.		L	3.4	ND	ND	ND	--

Table 1.—Survey of strains of the *Aspergillus flavus* series for the production of aflatoxin B₁, G₁ and M—continued

Source and collection numbers	Substrate	Medium	Final pH	Aflatoxin μg./g. on R and W, mg./l. in L			
				B_1	G_1	M	M/B_1
Strains intermediate between *A. parasiticus* and *A. flavus*							
A–3161. A. C. Keyl, Western Regional Research Laboratory (isolated by Forgacs).	*Cycas circinalis* Sclerotia.	R	----------	248	210	2.4	0.009
		W	----------	82	107	1.2	.014
		L	5.3	18	8.4	0.10	.005
A–13671. A. F. Schindler, M 93, FDA. ATCC 15,546.	Moldy wheat	R	----------	64	54	0.5	.008
		W	----------	95	125	1.0	.011
		L	5.7	18	16	0.1	.005
A–13794. F. A. Hodges, M 93, FDA. ATCC 15,546.	do	R	----------	14	8.2	0.09	.006
		W	----------	4	3.3	0.04	.01
		L	5.1	0.4	0.33	0.0006	.002
A–14329. U. Diener, 33–ATCC 15,548, Hodges M–90. From J. Forgacs.	Cycad	R	----------	337	313	2.6	.008
		W	----------	147	205	1.8	.012
		L	4.9	28	12	0.12	.004
A–15619. C. R. Benjamin, C–641.	Pine sawfly (*Diprion similis*).	R	----------	218	302	1.8	.008
		W	----------	281	380	1.5	.005
		L	6.0	28	44	0.2	.006
A. flavus							
NRRL 482. *A. flavus*. From Westerdijk, CBS 1909, CMI 16,145, ATCC 1003.	?	R	----------	ND	ND	ND	--
		W	----------	ND	ND	ND	--
		L	6.7	ND	ND	ND	--
NRRL 3357. F. A. Hodges, M–52, FDA.	Moldy peanuts	R	----------	105	ND	0.5	0.004
		W	----------	87	ND	0.4	.004
		L	5.8	10	ND	0.03	.003
A–4018b. J. Forgacs, P-1, CMI 92,875.	Toxic bran	R	----------	ND	ND	ND	--
		W	----------	ND	ND	ND	--
		L	4.9	ND	ND	ND	--
A–11606. CMI 91,546, Austwick V 3734/14.	Uganda peanuts	R	----------	12	ND	0.08	.006
		W	----------	ND	ND	ND	--
		L	5.6	ND	ND	ND	
A–11607. CMI 91,547, Austwick V 3734/15.	do	R	----------	100	ND	0.22	.002
		W	----------	37	ND	0.04	.001
		L	5.2	0.06	ND	ND	--
A–11608. CMI 91,548, Austwick V 3827/30.	Brazilian peanuts	R	----------	15	ND	0.06	.004
		W	----------	16	ND	ND	--
		L	5.5	2	ND	0.009	.005
A–11609. CMI 91,549, Austwick V 3827/31.	do	R	----------	0.7	ND	ND	--
		W	----------	ND	ND	ND	--
		L	4.7	0.5	ND	ND	--
A–11610. CMI 91,550, Austwick V 3827/32.	do	R	----------	22	ND	0.08	.004
		W	----------	4	ND	ND	--
		L	5.6	0.3	ND	ND	--
A–12140. U. L. Diener, CD 571-1 f24.	Peanuts	R	----------	16	ND	0.08	.005
		W	----------	1	ND	ND	--
		L	4.5	0.04	ND	ND	--
A–12268. F. A. Hodges, M 26, FDA.	Turkey feed mix	R	----------	ND	ND	ND	--
		W	----------	ND	ND	ND	--
		L	5.6	ND	ND	ND	--
A–12353. J. C. Lewis, No. 6b, Western Regional Research Laboratory.	Cottonseed hulls	R	----------	5.4	ND	0.02	.004
		W	----------	11	ND	0.02	.002
		L	5.2	8	ND	0.008	.001
A–12589. F. A. Hodges, M–51, FDA.	Moldy peanuts	R	----------	4.2	ND	0.02	.004
		W	----------	37	ND	0.06	.002
		L	5.0	3	ND	0.01	.004
A–12591. F. A. Hodges, M–53, FDA.	do	R	----------	97	ND	0.4	.004
		W	----------	29	ND	0.1	.003
		L	5.4	4	ND	Trace	--
A–12592. F. A. Hodges, M–54, FDA.	do	R	----------	4	ND	0.02	.005
		W	----------	1	ND	ND	--
		L	5.0	ND	ND	ND	--
A–12593. F. A. Hodges, M–66, FDA.	do	R	----------	20	ND	0.09	.005
		W	----------	38	ND	Trace	--
		L	5.1	3	ND	0.01	.003

Table 1.—Survey of strains of the *Aspergillus flavus* series for the production of aflatoxin B₁, G₁ and M—continued

Source and collection numbers	Substrate	Medium	Final pH	Aflatoxin µg./g. on R and W, mg./l. in L			M/B₁
				B₁	G₁	M	
A. flavus — continued							
A–13072. Van der Walt, No. 500, South Africa.	Maize meal	R	----------	2	ND	ND	--
		W	----------	ND	ND	ND	--
		L	5.2	ND	ND	ND	--
A–13438. L. Ajello, Atlanta, Ga.	Air sac of African parrot.	R	----------	0.3	0.08	ND	--
		W	----------	ND	ND	ND	--
		L	4.7	0.002	ND	ND	--
A–13454. NRRL	Moldy crambe seed	R	----------	Trace	ND	ND	--
		W	----------	ND	ND	ND	--
		L	5.3	ND	ND	ND	--
A–13505. NRRL	Sorghum	R	----------	7	ND	0.02	.003
		W	----------	67	ND	0.1	.001
		L	4.2	0.1	ND	ND	--
A–13668. A. F. Schindler, M–177, FDA.	Poultry feed	R	----------	ND	ND	ND	--
		W	----------	ND	ND	ND	--
		L	5.5	ND	ND	ND	--
A–13772. NRRL	Peanut meal	R	----------	57	ND	0.3	.005
		W	----------	257	ND	0.5	.002
		L	5.3	3	ND	0.009	.003
A–14152. NRRL	Corn, Minnesota	R	----------	ND	ND	ND	--
		W	----------	ND	ND	ND	--
		L	5.1	ND	ND	ND	--
A–15618. C. R. Benjamin, C–649.	Forest weevils Hylobis pales	R	----------	0.02	0.04	ND	--
		W	----------	ND	ND	ND	--
		L	4.6	ND	ND	ND	--
A–15647. NRRL	Moldy corn, Pakistan.	R	----------	0.1	0.01	ND	--
		W	----------	ND	ND	ND	--
		L	5.3	ND	ND	ND	--
A–15648. NRRL	do	R	----------	ND	ND	ND	--
		W	----------	ND	ND	ND	--
		L	4.4	Trace	ND	ND	--
A–15649. NRRL	do	R	----------	ND	ND	ND	--
		W	----------	ND	ND	ND	--
		L	5.2	ND	ND	ND	--
A–15650. NRRL	do	R	----------	ND	ND	ND	--
		W	----------	ND	ND	ND	--
		L	5.5	0.06	0.1	ND	--
Morphological atypical *A. flavus* strains							
A–12141. U. L. Diener, CD 571–1 f25.	Peanuts	R	----------	4	ND	0.02	0.005
		W	----------	0.5	ND	ND	--
		L	6.1	0.01	0.001	ND	--
A–12267 F. A. Hodges, M 25, FDA.	Moldy peanuts	R	----------	ND	ND	ND	--
		W	----------	ND	ND	ND	--
		L	4.8	ND	ND	ND	--
A–13071. Van der Walt, No. 501, South Africa.	Maize meal	R	----------	2	2	Trace	--
		W	----------	10	15	0.06	.006
		L	5.1	0.02	0.03	ND	--
A–13594. J. Forgacs.	From *Cycas circinalis*, Guam (Sclerotial fern).	R	----------	19	17	0.2	.009
		W	----------	7	11	0.08	.010
		L	6.8	1	3	0.01	.008
A–13596. J. Forgacs	From *Cycas circinalis*, Guam.	R	----------	7	6	0.07	.009
		W	----------	9	16	0.08	.009
		L	6.4	2	4	0.01	.005
A–13663. A. F Schindler, M–172, FDA.	Cocoa beans	R	----------	ND	ND	ND	--
		W	----------	ND	ND	ND	--
		L	4.7	0.002	ND	ND	--
A–13672. A. F. Schindler, M–122, FDA.	Peanuts	R	----------	ND	ND	ND	--
		W	----------	ND	ND	ND	--
		L	6.7	ND	ND	ND	--
A–13795. F. A. Hodges, M–93, FDA. F—See above ATCC 15,546.	Moldy wheat	R	----------	13	8	0.08	.008
		W	----------	4	2	0.05	.013
		L	4.8	0.3	0.2	--	--

Table 1.—Survey of strains of the *Aspergillus flavus* series for the production of aflatoxin B₁, G₁ and M—continued

Source and collection numbers	Substrate	Medium	Final pH	Aflatoxin μg./g. on R and W, mg./l. in L			
				B_1	G_1	M	M/B_1
Morphological atypical A. flavus strains—continued							
A–14327.	Peanuts	R	----------	0.2	Trace	ND	--
U. Diener, Alabama 1.		W	----------	0.05	ND	ND	--
		L	6.8	0.002	Trace	ND	--
A–14328.	do	R	----------	0.2	ND	ND	--
U. Diener, Alabama 8.		W	----------	0.04	Trace	ND	--
		L	6.8	0.002	Trace	ND	--
A–15418.	Peanut meal	R	----------	5	Trace	0.02	.004
J. P. Voets, Gent, Belgium, 1967.		W	----------	38	ND	ND	--
		L	4.7	0.2	ND	ND	--
A–15651. NRRL	Moldy corn	R	----------	0.1	ND	ND	--
Lahore, Pakistan.		W	----------	ND	ND	ND	--
		L	5.6	ND	ND	ND	--
New taxon							
A–11611.	Nigerian peanuts	R	----------	64	43	0.4	.007
CMI 91,552, Austwick V		W	----------	90	90	0.6	.006
4030/6.		L	5.6	23	20	0.03	.001
A–11612.	do	R	----------	2	0.7	ND	--
CMI 93,070, Austwick V		W	----------	18	20	0.1	.007
4104/6.		L	5.6	0.5	0.3	0.004	.007
NRRL 3251.	Walnuts	R	----------	1,257	ND	6	.005
A. F. Schindler, M–141, FDA.		W	----------	1,188	ND	4	.003
		L	5.1	22	ND	0.06	.003
A. flavus from alkali bees							
NRRL 3353.	Diseased alkali bees	R	----------	19	5	0.2	0.011
D. Shemanuki, No. 126, Bee		W	----------	56	62	0.8	.014
Disease Investigations		L	5.5	106	35	0.7	.006
Laramie, Wyo.							
A–13837.	do	R	----------	ND	ND	ND	----------
D. Shemanuki, No. 129, Bee		W	----------	ND	ND	ND	----------
Disease Investigations		L	5.2	0.04	0.01	0.0003	.008
Laramie, Wyo.							
A–13838.	do	R	----------	31	28	0.6	.016
D. Shemanuki, No. 130, Bee		W	----------	48	48	0.6	.013
Disease Investigations		L	5.8	18	22	0.4	.020
Laramie, Wyo.							
A. leporis							
NRRL 3216.	Dung of white tail	R	----------	ND	ND	ND	--
M. Christensen, RMF 99,	jack rabbit,	W	----------	ND	ND	ND	--
ATCC 16,490.	Wyoming.	L	6.3	ND	ND	ND	--
A–15811.	Soil, Wyoming	R	----------	ND	ND	ND	--
M. Christensen, RMF 2050.		W	----------	ND	ND	ND	--
		L	6.2	ND	ND	ND	--
A–15812.	do	R	----------	ND	ND	ND	--
M. Christensen, RMF 2110.		W	----------	ND	ND	ND	--
		L	6.2	ND	ND	ND	--

NOTE: R =rice; W =wheat; L =liquid medium; ND =none detected.

These isolates came from the United States, except for NRRL 3161which was isolated from cycads from Polynesia. Two isolates from moldy wheat are presumably the same but differ considerably in activity. Like *A. parasiticus*, one strain was isolated from an insect attacked by the mold. Like *A. parasiticus*, growth of the five strains was luxuriant in the liquid media, but all isolates had a final pH above 5 except one strain (*4*, *9*). Unlike *A. parasiticus*, but like *A. flavus*, colonies are yellow green, and brown sclerotia are produced by every isolate on both PDA and Czapek's solution agar. These are about 0.75 to 1 mm. in diameter. The conidial heads are diffuse, globose, and the conidiophores are approximately of the same length as *A. parasiticus*. The conidiophores and conidia are roughened and the sterigmata are both uniseriate and biseriate. The conidial chains tend not to shatter when the culture tube is tapped.

The largest group of isolates studied belongs in *A. flavus*, in the strict sense represented by many strains, These isolates came from all over the world—Africa. Brazil, and the United States. In liquid culture, the pH range is from 4.2 to 5.8 except for NRRL 482, a nonaflatoxin producer which has a high pH. Out of the 27 strains examined, six formed no aflatoxin and five produced only traces. The remaining 16 strains produce aflatoxin B_1 but no G_1 except for traces in four strains. Also, the levels of aflatoxin B_1 formed are relatively lower than those encountered in *A. parasiticus* and in the NRRL 3161 group. Like *A. parasiticus*, if appreciable yields of B_1 are formed, then M is also produced at low levels.

The 27 strains all agree fairly well in colony color and growth appearance with NRRL 482, which is considered to be a typical strain of the species according to Raper and Fennell (*8*). Some produced an abundance of dark brown sclerotia ranging in size from 400μ to $1,000\mu$.

The conidiophores and conidia were uniformly roughened. The sterigmata were biseriate, at least in part, in every one of the 27 isolates. In almost all instances, conidial chains shattered quite readily. None appeared to be members of the *A. flavus* variety *columnaris*. No isolate produced a diffusible pigment in the two agar media used and the reverse of the colonies was pigmented similarly to that seen in *A. parasiticus*, except the wrinkled characteristic was absent on Czapek's solution agar.

A fourth group is made up of 12 isolates which are morphologically atypical of *A. flavus*. They form aflatoxins B_1 and G_1 in low levels as well as M. Two strains form none. If B_1 was formed, then usually G_1 and M were also detectable. In one-half of the isolates, the pH of the medium was above six. The strains in this group came from cycads, peanuts, wheat, cocoa beans, and corn.

Colonies of these isolates are yellow green, with reverse colony color from white to yellowish. No pigment is formed in agar. Some strains produce sclerotia typical of *A. flavus* in appearance and size. The roughened conidiophores form diffuse to somewhat columnar conidial heads. All conidia are roughened and are produced on biseriate sterigmata. (One strain was uniseriate.) The chains of spores are readily shattered when a test tube culture is gently tapped.

The fifth group is represented by three strains and one of these is unique only in that it forms very high levels of B_1 (1257 $\mu g./g.$) but produces no G_1. This isolate came from walnuts, while the other two were isolated from Nigerian peanuts. Each of the isolates produces M in small amounts. The pH of the fermentation broth is about the same, 5.1 to 5.6.

In culture, all isolates seemed identical. Although the colonies appear brown, this color is due to the enormous numbers of microsclerotia formed to the almost complete exclusion of conidiophores. The color of the conidia, however, is yellow green, similar to *A. flavus*. The colony reverse on Czapek's solution agar is wrinkled and appears brown because of the sclerotial color. No pigment is present in the agar. The conidiophores are about the height of those of *A. parasiticus* and roughened as are the conidia. The sterigmata are biseriate, the conidial heads are diffuse, and the conidia chains do not shatter. The sclerotia are produced in enormous numbers and are only about 300μ in diameter; hence, they seem much smaller than those seen in *A. parasiticus* and *A. flavus*.

A sixth group is represented by three strains, each isolated from alkali bees in Wyoming. These strains vary in their ability to produce aflatoxins, although all form B_1, G_1, and small amounts of M. The fermentation pH range is 5.2 to 5.8, and one strain (NRRL 3353) forms more aflatoxin B_1 in liquid media than on solid wheat or rice.

Colonies of the alkali bee isolates are yellow green, lack sclerotia, have a yellow to orange reverse, and typically show a diffuse yellow pigment. The roughened conidiophores are tall with diffuse conidial heads. The chains of rough conidia sometimes shatter in one strain but not in the other two. All three strains have biseriate sterigmata.

In addition to these groups, three isolates of *A. leporis* Christensen were studied, but in none of them was any aflatoxin detected. This species belongs in the *A. flavus* group and was described after Raper and Fennell's book was published.

Discussion

Although this study was restricted to only 67 strains of the *A. flavus* series, known to produce or suspected of producing aflatoxin, several definite conclusions can be drawn about the formation of these toxins by this group of fungi. In the examination of all strains, aflatoxin G_1 was never made without B_1, and the ratio of G_1 to B_1 varied with different strains. Aflatoxins B_2 and G_2 never appeared without B_1 and G_1, respectively.

One purpose of our study was to find a strain that would produce aflatoxin M in high yields, but the ratio of M to B_1 never exceeded 0.016 on solid substrates. In one liquid culture out of 67 such fermentations examined, the ratio of M to B did equal 0.020, but yields of M were so low as to make isolation unprofitable The average ratio of M to B was 0.006. Yields of M were not improved meaningfully by changing species or fermentation conditions. These conditions included submerged fermentation in 20-liter fermentors, in liquid rice medium in Fernbach flasks, and in solid wheat and rice shaken in Fernbach flasks. In studies carried out by Dr. George Semeniuk (South Dakota State University, Plant Pathology Department, Brookings, S. D. 57006) under a research contract, it was shown that yields of M also did not increase when soybeans and wheat were molded with little aeration in plastic bags.

The exact ratio of M to G and that of M to B depend on the taxonomic group and substrate. The ratio of M to B or to G is more nearly constant when one substrate or strain from one taxonomic group is considered. Ratios can be predicted fairly accurately for the production of aflatoxins by strains of one group on a single substrate.

A statistical analysis of all the data reveals significant sources of variation in the production of aflatoxins, that is, taxonomic groups of Aspergilli, strains within groups, and media. There is evidence, however, of interactions between media and groups and between media and strains. In general, more aflatoxin B_1 than G_1 is produced on rice and in liquid culture. Wheat is the best substrate we found for aflatoxin G_1 production, a result which supports our observations in earlier studies (6, 11). Strains of *A. parasiticus* produce higher yields of aflatoxin on wheat than either on rice or in liquid media.

Variations in yields among specific species and strains cannot be separated from variations at different pH's in liquid medium. It is highly unlikely that yields are associated with pH alone.

Several specific groups of strains of the *A. flavus* series can be recognized on the basis of their aflatoxin yields and on the basis of their morphological classification. These groups are as follows:

(1) *A. parasiticus* is a valid species that regularly produces large amounts of aflatoxins B_1 and G_1. This species can be distinguished from *A. flavus* because of its low colonies having a deep green color, and because on Czapek's solution agar the colonies are irregularly wrinkled in reverse. Its conidial heads are regularly globose with conidial chains radiating from the vesicle and these chains remain firmly intact. Contrary to what is published on the species, sclerotia similar to *A. flavus* are formed in some strains. The strains used in this study when grown in liquid medium greatly lowered the pH. Based on a rather limited number of sources for cultures, this species appears to be geographically restricted to the tropics.

(2) Intermediate between *A. parasiticus* and *A. flavus sensu stricto* are five strains resembling *A. flavus* in their yellow-green colonies, which possess dark brown sclerotia. All possess both uniseriate and biseriate sterigmata, a characteristic of *A. flavus*. Its members fail to produce the low pH's in liquid media seen in *A. parasiticus*. However, like *A. parasiticus*, all strains produce aflatoxins B_1 and G_1 in high amounts, the conidial heads are all globose, and the conidial chains radiate and do not shatter. We consider this group to be a member of the *A. flavus* species.

(3) *A. flavus sensu stricto* may or may not produce aflatoxin. When it is produced, the amount is lower than that produced by the first two groups. Many isolates do not produce any G_1 or if they do, then the quantity is very low. The highest level of B_1 encountered on rice was 105 μg./g. Isolates came from all over the world. Colonies are yellow green in color and with or without brown sclerotia. Every isolate had some biseriate sterigmata. In most instances, the spore chains shatter readily and the conidial heads were variable in shape.

(4) In addition to the *A. flavus* strains, 12 additional strains are more variable morphologically but nevertheless are retained in *A. flavus*.

(5) This group is represented by three strains, one of which forms very high levels of aflatoxin B_1 and no G. The other two form relatively low amounts of B_1 and G_1. In all other respects, the three isolates are alike. They differ from *A. flavus* and *A. parasiticus* by having enormous numbers of microsclerotia measuring only

about 300μ in diameter. Hence, the surface and underside of the colonies appear brown in color and on Czapek's solution agar the colonies are irregularly wrinkled. However, the few conidial heads are yellow-green. The conidia and conidiophores are roughened like the other members of the series. The sterigmata are biseriate. Conidial heads, however, are diffuse and globose like *A. parasiticus* and conidial chains do not appear to shatter. This group represents a new taxon, which will be described in a subsequent paper.

(6) The sixth group may not actually represent a real one since all the isolates came from alkali bees. Each isolate makes aflatoxins B_1 and G_1 and one strain makes more aflatoxin B_1 on liquid medium than on the solid substrates, a condition not encountered before. All cultures are yellow-green, lack sclerotia, and are unlike all other isolates by having a yellow, diffusible pigment and a bright yellow to orange colony reverse. All strains have biseriate sterigmata like *A. flavus*.

Another publication will describe the morphological and biochemical relationships of the above aflatoxins strains. The new taxon will likewise be described and named.

References

(1) ALLCROFT, R., and R. B. A. CARNAGHAN. 1963. Groundnut toxicity: An examination for toxin in human food products from animals fed toxic groundnut meal. Vet. Rec. 75: 259–263.

(2) DE IONGH, H., R. O. VLES, and J. G. VAN PELT. 1964. Milk of mammals fed an aflatoxin-containing diet. Nature 202: 466–467.

(3) DIENER, L., and N. D. DAVIS. 1966. Aflatoxin production by isolates of *Aspergillus flavus*. Phytopathology 56: 1390–1393.

(4) GRAVES, R. R., and C. W. HESSELTINE. 1966. Fungi in flour and refrigerated dough products. Mycopathol. Mycol. Appl. 29: 277–290.

(5) HOLZAPFEL, C. W., P. S. STEYN, and I. F. H. PURCHASE. 1966. Isolation and structure of aflatoxins M_1 and M_2. Tetrahedron Ltrs. 25: 2799–2803.

(6) LEE, W. V. 1965. Quantitative determination of aflatoxin in groundnut products. Analyst 90: 305–307.

(7) MASRI, M. S., R. E. LUNDIN, J. R. PAGE, and V. C. GARCIA. 1967. Crystalline aflatoxin M_1 from urine and milk. Nature 215: 753–755.

(8) RAPER, K. B., and D. I. FENNELL. 1965. The genus Aspergillus. The Williams & Wilkens Co., Baltimore, Md.

(9) SHOTWELL, O. L., C. W. HESSELTINE, R. D. STUBBLEFIELD, and W. G. SORENSON. 1966. Production of aflatoxin in rice. Appl. Microbiol. 14: 425–428.

(10) STOLOFF, L. 1967. Collaborative study of a method for the identification of aflatoxin B_1 by derivative formation. J. Assoc. Offic. Anal. Chem. 50: 354–360.

(11) STUBBLEFIELD, R. D., O. L. SHOTWELL, C. W. HESSELTINE, M. L. SMITH, and H. H. HALL. 1967. Production of aflatoxin on wheat and oats: Measurement with a recording densitometer. Appl. Microbiol. 15: 186–190.

(12) TABER, R. A., and H. W. SCHROEDER. 1967. Aflatoxin-producing potential of isolates of the *Aspergillus flavus-oryzae* group from peanuts (*Arachis hypogaea*). Appl. Microbiol. 15: 140–144.

EFFECTS OF ULTRAVIOLET IRRADIATION ON THE DESTRUCTION OF AFLATOXIN B₁

by KAGEAKI AIBARA *and* SABURO YAMAGISHI
Department of Food Research, National Institute of Health, Tokyo, and
Faculty of Pharmacology, University of Chiba, Chiba, Japan

Summary

We investigated such physicochemical procedures as ultraviolet spectrophotometry, fluorescence spectrophotometry and thin-layer chromatography applicable to quantitative analysis for aflatoxins. In ultraviolet spectrophometry, from the concentration response curve for pure aflatoxin B₁, at 363 mμ an optical density value of 1.0 corresponds to about 14 μg./ml. of aflatoxin B₁ in EtOH.* However, if the substances showing maximum absorption at 363 mμ were present in a material to be tested, accurate determination was not possible.

Fluorescence spectrophotometry is a highly sensitive method for determination of aflatoxin, but the position of the peak of fluorescence energy distribution and the fluorescence intensity vary, depending upon the solvent used. Aflatoxin B₁ in MeOH* solution gave the largest fluorescence intensity. On the other hand, some degradation products showed an emission more intense than aflatoxin B₁. Aflatoxin B₁ at concentrations higher than 50 μg./ml. showed a marked concentration quenching. Therefore, further studies are needed for the determination of fluorescence spectrophotometry.

Thin-layer chromatographic densitometry was the most hopeful method for quantitative determination of aflatoxin. Aflatoxin B₁ was dissolved in MeOH, EtOH, benzene or chloroform at a concentration of 10 μg./ml. Destruction experiments were performed with these solutions by irradiation with an ultraviolet lamp at various distances and for varying times. It appeared that destruction by UV irradiation with doses smaller than a certain limit proceeded as a first-order reaction.

One of the irradiation products was separated by column chromatography and compared with the original aflatoxin B₁ by ultraviolet spectrophotometry, infrared spectrophotometry and mass spectrometry. In fragmentation of this substance by electron impact, a marked intense peak at mass over energy (m/e) 149 appeared, which was considered to be stable. As indicated by the mass spectrometry, photodimerization of the coumarin moiety might have occurred prior to the degradation of the aflatoxin B₁ molecule.

Introduction

There has been much study on the destruction of aflatoxins by chemicals, but there is only meager information on the effects of ultraviolet and gamma irradiation on aflatoxins.

The research group of the Food and Drug Administration reported that new fluorescent photoproducts were induced by UV light acting on aflatoxin B₁ situated on silica gel thin-layer plates (*1*). From a practical standpoint, this work suggested that interception of UV light is essential for the quantitative determination of aflatoxin B₁ by thin-layer chromatography.

One of the authors demonstrated the resistance of aflatoxin to gamma irradiation, chemically and biologically. Aflatoxins, particularly when in solid state, are quite stable against irradiation. They were only partially destroyed with 30 M-rads or larger doses (*4*). Dr. Wogan and his collaborators have been working with the kinetics of destruction of aflatoxin B₁ in chloroform by gamma irradiation (personal communication).

The present report consists of two parts. In the first part, we will discuss the chemical assay methods of aflatoxin B₁ and its related compounds; ultraviolet spectrophotometry, fluorescence spectrophotometry and thin-layer chromatographic densitometry. Then, the effect of UV irradiation on the destruction of aflatoxin B₁ in organic solvents will be described. In the second part, we will describe one of the degradation products separated by column chromatography from the 6-hour irradiated aflatoxin B₁. The physicochemical properties of the product were investigated by thin-layer chromatography, ultraviolet spectrophotometry, infrared spectrophotometry and mass spectrometry.

---

*EtOH and MeOH will be used to designate ethanol and methanol, respectively.

EXPERIMENT I—KINETIC STUDIES

Materials and Methods

Aflatoxin.—The molecular extinction coefficient of aflatoxin B_1 crystal in EtOH was 22,200 and its mass spectrum is shown in figure 1.

Reagents.—All organic solvents used were of reagent grade. Chloroform was redistilled to remove a stabilizer just before use for each experiment.

Fertile egg.—Ninety-six-hour incubated, fertile chicken eggs were used for the toxicity test.

Duckling.—One-day-old ducklings, Campbell strain, were used for the confirmation test of toxicity.

Ultraviolet irradiation.—The concentration of aflatoxin B_1 in each solvent (EtOH, MeOH, Benzene or $CHCL_3$) was adjusted to 10 µg./ml. A handmade reaction chamber for the irradiation treatment was used. All the inner surfaces of the chamber were covered with frosted black cloth to avoid reflection of UV rays. The top of a UV lamp (UV-ray oscillator, NIKKO SEIKI model NY–2, 100 W) was embedded at the center in the chamber floor and test samples in quartz cuvettes were placed at required distances (5, 10, or 20 cm.) from the lamp. After irradiation for a certain period (0.5, 1, 2, 4, or 8 minutes), the remaining aflatoxin B_1 was determined quantitatively by physicochemical and biological methods. The volume of the solvent in each reaction cuvette was adjusted to the original volume after the irradiation, when necessary.

Ultraviolet spectrophotometry.—The UV-absorption spectrum of each irradiated sample was compared with that of the nonirradiated aflatoxin B_1 control solution by an automatic recording spectrophotometer (SHIMAZU MPS–50).

Fluorescence spectrophotometry.—The changes in fluorescence energy distribution caused by the irradiation were determined by an automatic recording fluorospectrophotometer (SHIMAZU GF–16).

Thin-layer chromatography and its densitometry.—Identification of aflatoxin B_1 and its degradation products was accomplished by a thin-layer chromatogram on BIO–SIL A (0.50 mm. thick, activated at 110° C. for 60 minutes) with a mixture of chloroform-acetone (90:10 to 87:13, v/v, depending on atmospheric humidity) as developing solvent. The chromatogram was recorded by a fluorescence densitometer (OZUMOR type SD–91).

Toxicity test.—The residual toxicity of the irradiated samples was determined by the yolk sac inoculation test using 96-hour incubated fertile eggs. The solvent of the irradiated sample was removed carefully in the dark and under vacuum. The residue was dissolved in 0.1 ml. of EtOH and the necessary dilutions were made with sterilized water. Each dilution was injected in 0.2 ml. amounts into the yolk sac of the eggs with a tuberculin syringe. Fifteen to fifty eggs were used for each dilution of each sample to determine the LD_{50} value after 48 hours' observation. The surviving eggs were continuously incubated after checking the LD_{50} until hatching. The chicks were

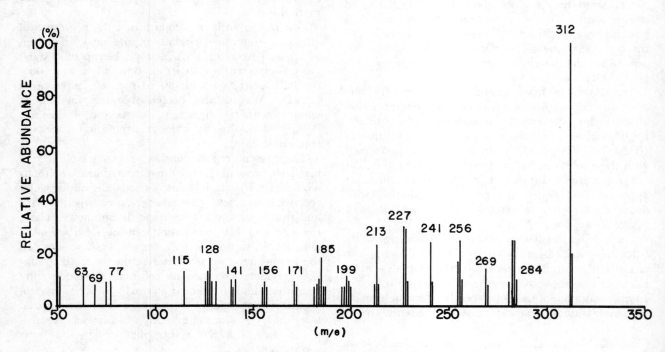

Figure 1.—Mass spectrum of aflatoxin B_1.

subsequently observed for any teratogenic effect of aflatoxin B_1 and/or its destruction products.

Duckling test.—A half-milliliter of the diluted sample was administered to 1-day-old duckling orally with a nylon cannula directly into the stomach.

Results and Discussion

As demonstrated in figure 1, aflatoxin B_1 used in this experiment was in the form of a highly pure crystal from the results of mass spectrometry. The molecular extinction coefficient of this material was 22,200 in EtOH.

The optical densities at 363 mμ of serially diluted aflatoxin B_1 solutions in EtOH were plotted against the concentration and the UV absorption standard curve is shown in figure 2.

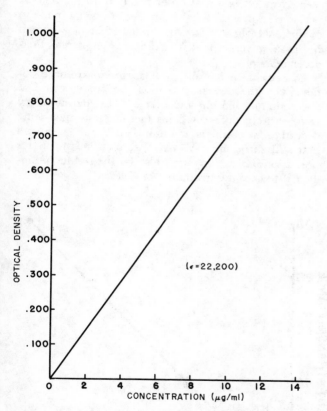

Figure 2.—Standard curve of aflatoxin B_1 in ethanol determined by ultraviolet spectrophotometry.

For the quantitative measurement of aflatoxin B_1 by UV spectrophotometry, there were several important factors to be carefully controlled, such as the correction factor of the spectrophotometer, purity of the sample to be tested, the kind of solvent used, etc. For the unknown samples extracted from natural materials, however, it could be estimated roughly that the optical density at 363 mμ of a 10 μg./ml. concentration was approximately 0.7, in other words, a concentration of 14 μg./ml. shows an OD value of approximately 1.0.

The fluorescence energy distribution peak of aflatoxin B_1 in reagent grade chloroform (undistilled) was 425 mμ with an excitation wavelength of 363 mμ and in distilled chloroform it was 410 mμ. The peak position and intensity of fluorescent emission varied, depending upon the solvent used, as shown in table 1. Aflatoxin B_1 in MeOH showed the strongest intensity among the solutions generally used in aflatoxin studies. It is very difficult to correlate the intensities or the peak positions of each aflatoxin solution to the chemical or physicochemical properties of the solvent itself. The fluorescence intensity of each solution can be controlled by the adjustment of the instrument such as the energy level of the excitation lamp, the slit width, and the sensitivity of the automatic detector. Under the controlled conditions of the instrument, however, the peak widths at half height of the fluorescence energy distribution, in different solvents, were constant; although the fluorescence intensities and the peak positions greatly changed. The intensity was quite stable during the processes of measurement, even in MeOH, for over 20 minutes if the sample contained no impurities. Another interesting and important characteristic of aflatoxin B_1 as a fluorescent substance is the concentration quenching phenomenon.

As shown in figures 3 and 4, the fluorescence intensity of aflatoxin B_1 in methanol, and also in EtOH or $CHCl_3$, markedly decreased at concentrations higher than 50 μg./ml. This phenomenon indicates that selecting the appropriate range of concentration is one of the most important factors in determining aflatoxin or other materials of unknown concentration.

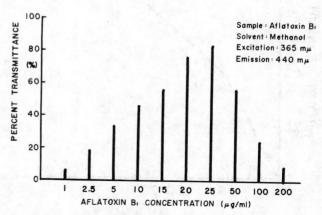

Figure 3.—Effect of aflatoxin B_1 concentration in methanol on the quenching of fluorescence.

Table 1.—Solvent effect on fluorescence energy distribution of aflatoxin B₁ excited at 363 mμ

Solvent	Peak position (mμ)	Slit level	Half width	Relative emission
Methanol	433	0.20	6.85	100
Ethanol	431	.20	6.85	43
Butanol	427	.20	6.85	43
Propylene glycol	435	.20	6.85	70
Methanol	433	.38	7.20	100
Distilled water	445	.38	7.20	23
Methanol	433	.41	6.85	100
Chloroform	412	.41	6.85	2
Chloroform	412	2.00	7.60	[1]100 (2)
Acetone	415	2.00	7.60	43 (0.9)
Benzene		2.00		0 (0)

[1]Relative emission against methanol.

A fluorescence densitometer was used for the instrumental determination of thin-layer chromatogram of aflatoxin B₁ and its destruction products (fig. 5). The results were considerably affected if the thickness or smoothness of the adsorbent layer on plates varied and the transparency was different from one plate to another in the instrumental determination. The concentration-response curve given in figure 6 was calibrated from quantitative graphical representations of the intensities of fluorescent spots of serial dilutions of the aflatoxin B₁ standard on the same plate. The

fiducial limit was confirmed with respect to each concentration at the 95 percent probability level. For quantitative determinations of unknown samples, a standard aflatoxin B₁ of one or more concentrations should be spotted on the same plate.

As demonstrated in figure 7, aflatoxin B₁ dissolved in different organic solvents was degraded by UV irradiation. The degradation patterns varied from one to another depending upon the kind of solvent used, the distance between the UV light source and the sample, and the exposure time. Aflatoxin B₁ remaining after irradiation was determined by ultraviolet spectrophotometry and TLC densitometry. The percentages of the remaining amounts against the control were plotted versus the exposure time on semilogarithmic coordinate paper.

The degradation curves of aflatoxin B₁ in MeQH and CHCl₃ (fig. 7) and EtOH and benzene (fig. 8) seemed to follow a first order reaction during a short period of exposure. Further studies are being made to confirm whether or not the destruction of aflatoxin B₁, in a solvent, by UV irradiation is a real first-order reaction.

As is clear in figure 8, the degradation curve obtained by the determination of the changes of UV absorption at 363 mμ and that by TLC densitometry were entirely different. This fact suggests that some degradation products maintain chemical structures that still show the UV absorption at 363 mμ. This presumption was supported also by the results of biological tests of the irradiated samples.

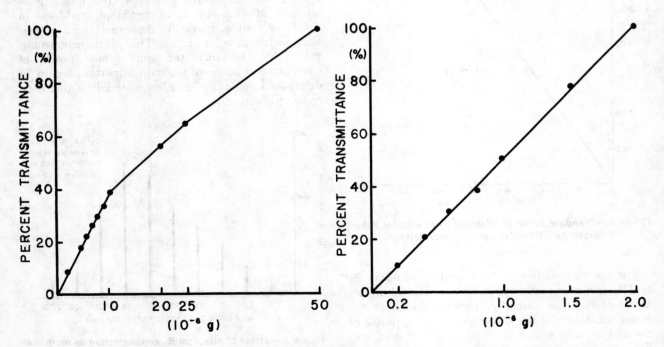

Figure 4.—Effect of the concentration of aflatoxin B₁ in ethanol on the quenching of fluorescence.

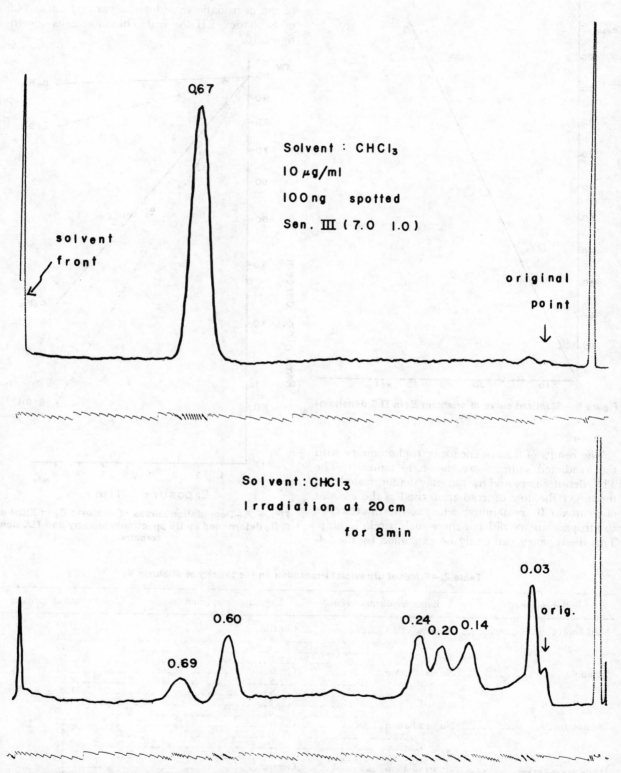

Solvent : CHCl₃
10 μg/ml
100ng   spotted
Sen . III (7.0   1.0)

Figure 5.—Instrumental determination of thin-layer chromatogram of aflatoxin B₁ and its destruction products by an OZUMOR fluorescence densitometer type SD–91.

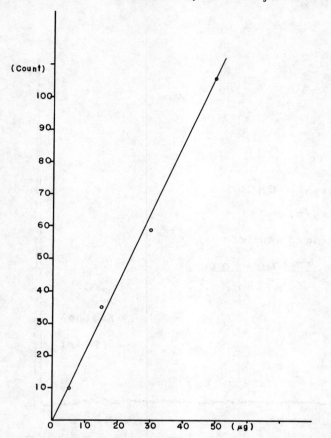

Figure 6.—Standard curve of aflatoxin B₁ in TLC densitometry.

lowing experiment. A fluorescence intensity of more than twice that of aflatoxin B_1 was found in a fraction of the degradation products, separated on a column of Sephadex LH 20 with chloroform, as shown in figure 10.

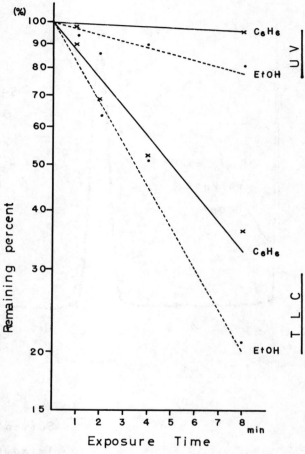

Figure 7.—Degradation curves of aflatoxin B₁ in EtOH and C₆H₆ determined by UV spectrophotometry and TLC densitometry.

The results of fluorescence spectrophotometry with the irradiated samples are shown in figure 9. The TLC densitometry and the bioassay demonstrated that the larger the dose of irradiation the less the amount of aflatoxin B_1 remaining; whereas the fluorescence spectrophotometry did not show such a relationship. This discrepancy can easily be explained by the fol-

Table 2.—Effect of ultraviolet irradiation on the toxicity of aflatoxin B₁

Solvent used	Exposure distance (cm.)	Exposure time (minutes)	LD₅₀ value (µg. per egg)
Methanol	No irradiation	Control	0.23
	5	2	.61
	5	4	.72
	5	8	.96
Ethanol	No irradiation	Control	.31
	5	2	.59
	5	4	1.50
	10	4	.92
	20	4	.56
Chloroform	No irradiation	Control	.23
	5	0.5	.41
	5	2	.48
	5	8	.75
Water	No irradiation	Control	.27
	5	1	.33

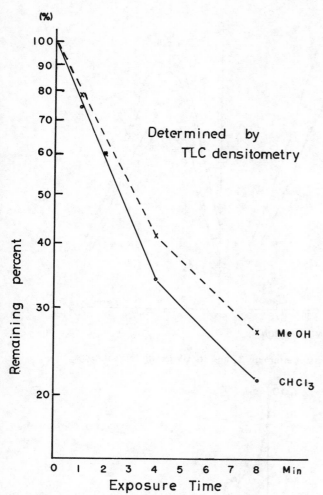

Figure 8.—Degradation curves of aflatoxin B₁ in MeOH and CHCl₃ determined by TLC densitometry.

From this evidence, the high fluorescence intensity of the 8-minute irradiated sample consisted of, not only the intensity of aflatoxin B₁ remaining, but also that of the degradation products.

The remaining toxicities of irradiated aflatoxin B₁ in methanol, ethanol, chloroform, or water, determined by the yolk sac inoculation test, are shown in table 2.

EXPERIMENT II—DEGRADATION PRODUCTS

In addition to the kinetic studies of the degradation of aflatoxin B₁ by UV irradiation, described previously, we have been trying to isolate the degradation products from the irradiated samples. The UV source used for this preparative treatment was a high-

pressure immersion mercury lamp (100 w.). Wavelengths shorter than 280 mμ were excluded with a filter, Pyrex 7740, so that the emission line was mainly 360 mμ.

The aflatoxin B₁ used in this experiment had been purified by column chromatography and still contained aflatoxin B₂, at about 20 percent, according to the mass spectrum. Ten mg. of aflatoxin B₁ was dissolved in 300 ml. of methanol and the solution was irradiated in the reaction tube into which the lamp was inserted.

The destruction pattern of aflatoxin B₁ in terms of UV spectral change is presented in figure 11. The most characteristic of the absorption maxima of aflatoxin, 363 mμ, rapidly decreased throughout the period of irradiation. The destruction curve seemed to follow a first-order reaction. The toxicity decreased according to the decrease in UV absorption. Since the appearance of a new absorption maximum at around 290 mμ was observed in response to decrease of the absorption at 363 mμ, some alteration of the conjugation system may have taken place in aflatoxin B₁. The spectral change in IR absorption also suggests an alteration in the structure. The $\nu_{max}^{CHCl_3}$ of the 19-hour irradiated aflatoxin B₁ were as follows: 1745, 1730 (shoulder), 1621, 1360, 1200 (broad) cm⁻¹. At least four fluorescent products other than aflatoxin B₁ were separated into seven fractions from this sample by chromatography on the column of Kieselgel G. The λ_{max}^{EtOH} of the fractions are indicated in table 3.

Table 3.—Absorption maxima in EtOH of the degradation products fractionated by column chromatography

Fraction number	$\lambda \dfrac{EtOH}{max}$	(mμ)
1	[1]220, 256	290
2	224, 280	
3	220, 289	
4	220, 289	
5	220, 266	295, 362
6	221, 266	290, 362
7[1]	[1]220, 261	[1]290

[1]Shoulder.
[2]$\underline{CHCl_3}$ of No. 7 fraction were 1730, 1640, 1600, 1435, 1420, and 1200 max
cm⁻¹.

To obtain the alteration products, a methanol solution of aflatoxin B₁ was irradiated for 6 hours in the reaction tube. After the removal of the MeOH- and the CHCl₃-soluble portions, the product was chromatographed on a column of Kieselgel G are separated into nine factions according to the fluorescent zones as shown in figure 12.

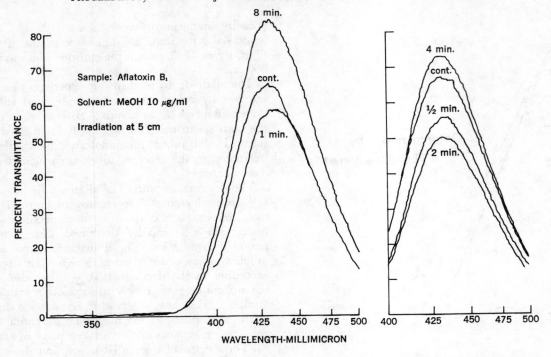

Figure 9.—Fluorescence energy distribution patterns of aflatoxin B₁ and its UV irradiated samples.

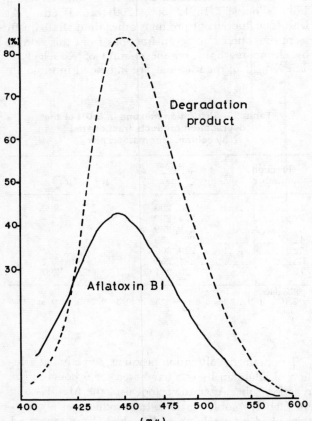

Figure 10.—Fluorescence energy distribution patterns of aflatoxin B₁ and its degradation product isolated from preparative thin-layer chromatoplates.

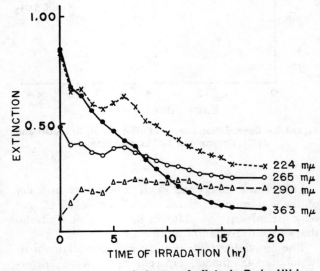

Figure 11.—UV spectral change of aflatoxin B₁ by UV irradiation.

Fraction No. 1, giving a yellow-green fluorescence, had a R_f value of 0.84 on a TLC plate, and its $\lambda_{max}^{CHCl_3}$ were 264, 276 and 282 mμ. The IR-absorption spectrum of the fraction is shown in figure 13. In fragmentation of this fraction by electron impact, a marked intensive peak at m/e 149, considered to be stable, appeared as shown in figure 14. However, further experiment will be needed to determine whether or not this fraction is composed of a single substance.

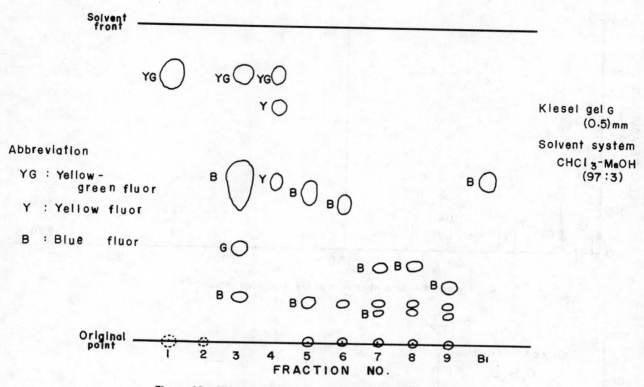

Figure 12.—Thin-layer chromatogram of aflatoxin B₁ irradiated.

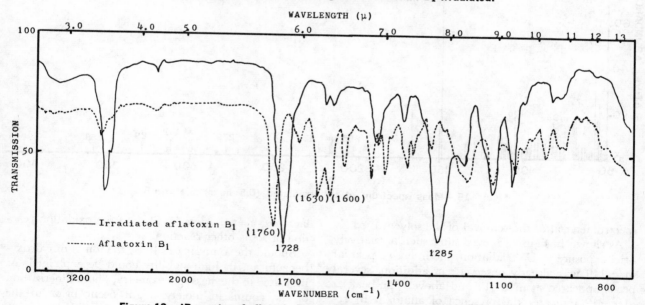

Figure 13.—IR spectra of aflatoxin B₁ and its UV irradiation (6 hours) sample.

From the observation of metastable ions, it might be possible that the ion at m/e 223, 205, or 167 was fragmented into an extremely intensive peak at m/e 149. On the other hand, the fragmentation pattern of aflatoxin B₁ obtained by electron impact (fig. 1) was quite different from that of the product mentioned above. The ion at m/e 149 was not observed with aflatoxin.

To get information on the alteration of aflatoxin B₁ in a short period of UV irradiation, it was irradiated for 30 minutes. The whole of the reaction products, without separation, were analyzed by the mass

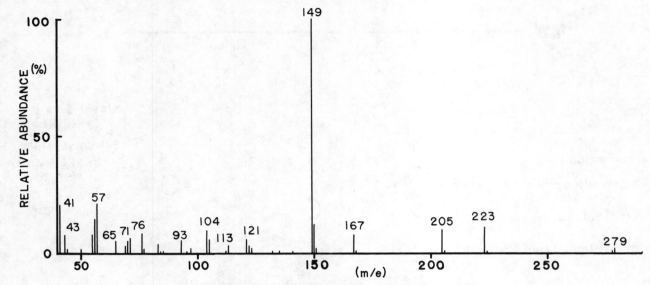

Figure 14.—Mass spectrum of UV irradiated aflatoxin B₁.

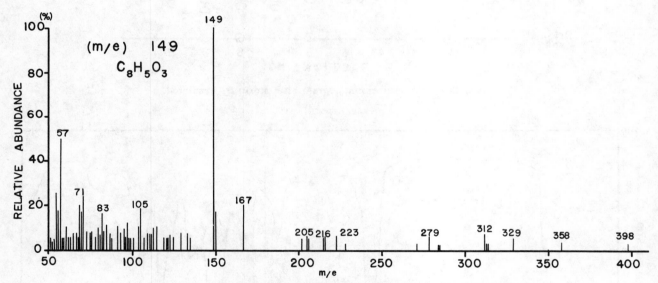

Figure 15.—Mass spectrum of UV irradiated (0.5 hour) aflatoxin B₁.

spectrometer after the removal of the solvent used.

As shown in figure 15, even after such a relatively brief exposure to UV radiation, the intensive peak at m/e 149 was already observed; in addition, several peaks appeared at m/e 312 and above. The peak at m/e 312 indicates the presence of aflatoxin B₁ remaining.

The formula, $C_8H_5O_3$, was given to the ion at m/e 149 by the use of the high-resolution mass spectrometry. From the results, it seems to be possible that such a rapid and complex reaction may have occurred in aflatoxin B₁ when irradiated, similar to the photo-dimerization reactions with coumarins (2) or pyrones (3, 5), the fragmentation reaction as reported with

lactones or enol esters (6, 7), and the oxidation reaction or some other reaction.

Should the ion at m/e 149 be the ion of dihydroxy-benzofuran, its high stability could be explained. As indicated in the mass spectrometry, photodimerization of the coumarin moiety might occur prior to the fragmentation which results in the possible formation of the precursor of dihydroxybenzofuran.

Acknowledgments

The authors wish to thank Dr. G. N. Wogan, Massachusetts Institute of Technology, for providing standard aflatoxin B₁ and for his helpful suggestions.

Thanks are also due to Misses K. Kariya and I. Honma for technical assistance. The investigation was performed in cooperation with International Atomic Energy Agency.

References

(1) ANDRELLOS, P. J., A. C. BECKWITH, and R. M. EPPLEY. 1967. Photochemical changes of aflatoxin B₁, Journal of AOAC *50:* 346–350.

(2) ANET, R. 1962. The photodimers of coumarin and related compounds. Canad. J. Chem. *40:* 1249.

(3) COREY, E. J., and J. STREITH. 1964. Internal photo-addition reactions of 2-pyrone and N-methyl-2-pyridone: A new synthetic approach to cyclobutadiene. J. Am. Chem. Soc. *86:* 950.

(4) MIYAKI, K., K. AIBARA, and T. MIURA. 1967. *In* "Microbiological problems in food preservation by irradiation". International Atomic Energy Agency, pp. 57–64.

(5) PADWA, A. and R. HARTMAN. 1964. The photochemistry of 4, 5-dimethyl-2-pyrone. J. Am. Chem. Soc. *86:* 4212.

(6) YOGEV, V., M. GORODETSKY, and Y. MAZUR. 1964. Photochemistry of enolic systems. I. Irradiation of enol acetates. J. Am. Chem. Soc. *86:* 5208.

(7) YOGEV, A. ,and Y. MAZUR. 1965. Irradiation of enol lactones. J. Am. Chem. Soc. *87:* 3520.

BOTULISM

• • •

PERSPECTIVES OF THE BOTULISM PROBLEMS IN JAPAN

by Ryosuke Murata*
Second Department of Bacteriology, National Institute of Health,
Shinagawa-ku, Tokyo 141, Japan

In May 1951, at Iwanai, Hokkaido, a total of 14 persons who partook the same herring "izushi" became ill and four of them died. The disaster was at first suspected to be murder by some poison. The postmortem examinations failed to identify the possible cause of the deaths. Drs. Y. Nakamura, H. Iida, and other staff members of the Hokkaido Institute of Public Health, Sapporo, started bacteriological examinations of the incriminated izushi. All known pathogenic organisms were ruled out. An extract of the izushi killed mice in a few hours with the characteristic symptoms, the guitar-shaped abdomen and the abdominal breathing. Botulinum antitoxins types A and B failed to neutralize the toxin; but antitoxin type E completely neutralized the toxin. This was the first outbreak of botulism in Japan and the eighth known type E outbreak in the world (19).

Since this Iwanai outbreak, at least 57 outbreaks of botulism have occurred in Japan, mostly in Hokkaido and some in four different prefectures in the northernmost part of Honshu. There have been at least 321 cases and 85 deaths with an average fatality rate of 26.5 percent. The epidemiology of botulism in Japan will be presented by Dr. H. Iida.

Many other cases and deaths with similar symptoms after eating izushi had been recorded before 1951 in Hokkaido and Tohoku areas (15, 20). No doubt a large number of these cases must have been botulism.

Of all the outbreaks in Japan, only one was reported to have been due to type B toxin (18); all the rest were due to type E toxin. In addition to human botulism, type C botulism occurred among captive minks in 1960 and 1964 in Hokkaido. The mink outbreaks will be detailed by Dr. T. Karashimada.

In 1962, as many as 55 persons became intoxicated at Toyotomi, Hokkaido, after eating commercial products of herring "kirikomi." This was the largest scale outbreak in this country and perhaps in the world. Fortunately, only one death occurred; all the other 54 cases recovered, although 15 were seriously ill and another 26 were moderately ill. A Japanese preparation of type E antitoxin was administered to all the seriously and moderately ill cases; none of them died (9). In the period of 9 years since 1959, only four deaths have been reported in Hokkaido,

possibly because it has become the general rule to administer type E antitoxin to the cases of izushi poisoning by the physicians even before the bacteriological examinations are performed.

It is noteworthy that all the 57 outbreaks, except two, have been caused by izushi or kirikomi, which are similar kinds of food containing fermented raw fish. Of the other two outbreaks, one was due to the trout eggs (8) and the other to a commercially canned mackerel (35).

Izushi and kirikomi are traditional Japanese fermented food made of raw fresh water or salt water fish. Izushi contains other ingredients, in addition to fish, such as cooked rice and occasionally raw vegetables. The fish are dressed and soaked in water for a few days to remove the blood. The soaked fish are sliced and then packed in a container with "koji" (malted rice) to allow fermentation for a few weeks. Kanzawa and Iida (11) demonstrated that most of the toxin is produced in the fish meat before the initiation of fermentation. The acid produced by the fermentation protects the preformed toxin, which is mostly in the stable macromolecular form (28). The nature of the toxin in izushi will be detailed by Dr. G. Sakaguchi. Izushi and kirikomi are always eaten without cooking, since cooking destroys the delicate flavor and the acceptability.

The distribution of spores of *C. botulinum* has extensively been investigated in Japan. The details will be presented by Dr. H. Iida and by Dr. E. Kodama. Nakamura et al. (21) examined a total of 2,300 soil samples collected in Hokkaido and demonstrated type E organisms in 82 samples (3.6 percent). Kanzawa (10) demonstrated type E organisms in 30 (9.5 percent) out of 315 soil samples taken along the Ishikari River, Hokkaido, from the mouth to 50 km. upstream. He also demonstrated type E organisms in seven (23 percent) of 30 samples of coastal sand.

From the dead, floating fish taken from Hachiro Lagoon, Akita, type E organisms were demonstrated in very high frequency; 83 percent in one survey and 92 percent in the other. The corresponding figure with fresh fish at the fish market in Akita was 0.4 percent (15). The same authors demonstrated type E organisms at a rate of 12 percent in homemade and commercial izushi in Akita. Kobayashi (14) isolated

---
*Read by G. Sakaguchi.

two type E cultures from mud samples collected at the Central Fish Market, Tokyo. Yamagata (*34*) isolated three type E strains from soil samples taken in Yamaguchi prefecture, where no outbreak has been reported. More recently, Kanzawa and his associates conducted an extensive survey for *C. botulinum* in Hokkaido. The results will be presented by Dr. K. Kanzawa. They detected type E spores in higher rates than before.

Type A organisms had been isolated in Kyushu area before the Iwanai outbreak (*33*) and later were isolated in Akita prefecture (*16*). The type B outbreak due to izushi (*18*) was mentioned previously. The mink outbreaks, mentioned before, were caused by the meat of a sperm whale caught off the coast of Hokkaido and by the meat of a horse which died with colic-like symptoms. It is certain, therefore, that in addition to type E, types A, B, and C spores may be distributed in this country, although no type B or C organisms have been isolated during the soil surveys.

The efficiency of detecting the spores of *C. botulinum* or any other organisms may vary depending on the method employed. In fact, the percentage of positive soil and other samples has gradually increased in the past years. Establishing a worldwide standardized method for isolating *C. botulinum*, including enrichments, selective or differential culture medium, etc. is desired.

Culture media for *C. botulinum* type E consisting of fish extract was devised by Saeki (*24*). Kanzawa and his associates have used the centrifugal precipitate of washings of relatively large amounts of soil samples in phosphate buffer (pH 7) as inocula in their recent surveys. The influence of other microorganisms in the enrichment cultures seems to be important. Sakaguchi and Tohyama (*30, 31*) found an activation of type E toxin by an enzyme produced by contaminating organisms. Inhibition or enhancement of growth and toxin production of type E organisms by various aerobic microorganisms was studied by Karashimada and Inoue (*12*). Organisms very similar to *C. botulinum*, type E, producing no toxin, were often found on agar plates inoculated with soil or fish samples (*21*). Nontoxic variants of *C. botulinum*, type E, originally found by Dolman (*2*) and designated as "OS" and "TP" variants were often encountered in this country (*6*).

Subtyping type E organisms by the agglutination reaction was attempted by Ono and Rei (*23*) and Ono (*22*). Dr. K. Yamamoto will present their results on agglutination tests. Agglutination tests, if practicable in every laboratory, will be of use not only in epidemiological work, but also identifying nontoxic variants of *C. botulinum* type E.

For the moment, identification of *C. botulinum* must be entirely dependent upon the mouse injection and the neutralization tests with the specific antitoxins. The deaths of mice from type E botulism seem to be quicker than from other types, but it takes at least 24 hours to quantitate the toxin. A quicker determination of the toxin by measuring the time from intravenous injection into mice to death was originally studied by Boroff and Fleck (*1*) with type A toxin. Their method applied to type E toxins will be reported by Dr. G. Sakaguchi. He proposes an assay method based on the principles of quick determination by intravenous injection and of the relative toxicity against a reference toxin by the parallel-line-assay method. I believe the method will be of value in comparing the toxicities of preparations between different laboratories. I hope other quick and reproducible methods for determining the toxins, preferably without using animals, will also be established.

Besides the ecological, clinical, and epidemiological work on botulism much basic experimental work has been conducted. Due to the prevalence of type E botulism in Japan, most work has been concerned with type E. Sakaguchi and Tohyama (*30, 31*) reported that type E toxin is produced in the form of a virtually nontoxic "precursor" which is activated by a proteinase, produced by contaminating organisms, to become the fully active toxin. This finding was substantiated by Duff et al. (*3*) who found a more marked activation of type E toxin by trypsin. The activation occurs not only in the test tube but also in foods, as well as in the digestive tract of the consumer, playing a very important role in pathogenesis of type E botulism. Therefore, this phenomenon has been paid much interest from medical, biological and chemical viewpoints. Activation seems to occur commonly in other types of toxins, which will be presented by Dr. H. Iida.

Purification of the precursor of type E toxin has been attempted. It was obtained from the bacterial cells in the form of an RNA-protein complex (*25*), but later the RNA was removed by RNAase without affecting the toxicity (*27*). Both the precursor and the activated toxin possessed the same sedimentation constants of 11.5S and no other physicochemical differences were found between them (*26*). This is an indication that the activation involves a minor structural change of the precursor molecule. On the contrary type E toxin of much smaller molecular size, 1.7S, was obtained by Gerwing et al. (*5*), who found that activation involved the removal of at least 18 amino acid residues from the molecule (*4*). They stated that the 11.5S toxin obtained by Sakaguchi et al. must have been an artifact aggregated during the purification. The arguments between Gerwing's and Sakaguchi's groups lasted for a long time. In the meantime, Sakaguchi, Sakaguchi and Karashimada

(28) demonstrated that the toxin in izushi possessed about the same sedimentation constant as the purified toxin obtained by themselves. Schantz and Spero (32) demonstrated that the sedimentation constants of the toxins of all six types in spent cultures are larger than 14S. From these findings, it can be said that the macromolecular toxins are not the artifact, but represent the natural form of botulinum toxins, even if they represent the aggregates. In fact, the 11.5S toxin was found to consist of two 7S components; one is apparently or potentially toxic, while the other component is nontoxic (13). Details of purification and dissociation of type E toxin will be presented by Dr. G. Sakaguchi.

The case fatality rate from botulism in Hokkaido was about 29 percent until 1959; since then it has dropped down to 3 percent (9). In 1959, type E antitoxin, sent from Dr. C. E. Dolman of the University of British Columbia, was first used (7) and it appeared to be very effective, even applied to the very seriously diseased cases. Therefore, the National Institute of Health, Tokyo, undertook the preparation of type E antitoxin with the aid of Hokkaido local government, from 1960 and onward. Since 1959, as stated before, practically no deaths have resulted from type E botulism.

It is rather unbelievable that the antitoxin rescued botulism cases from death even after development of the symptoms. Iida and his associates of the Hokkaido Institute of Public Health have been working to explain why type E antitoxin therapy is so effective. The paper by Dr. T. Ono on the absorption of type E toxin from the intestine, is one of the series of their studies.

Before the establishment of the International Standards for C. botulinum antitoxins in 1963, Kondo et al. (17) had proposed a method for testing potency of type E antitoxin by determining the relative potency against an arbitrary standard antitoxin. It was found that the slopes of the neutralization curves of botulinum toxins are not 45°, being different from those of diphtheria or tetanus toxins. The toxins and antitoxins must be studied further to explain the difference.

In preparation of the antitoxin, we started to immunize horses with trypsin-activated toxin, but later we found that the precursor was a much better antigen. The antigenicities of the precursor and trypsin-activated toxin will be reported by Dr. H. Kondo. Partially purified precursor materials are now being used to immunize horses and it is not difficult to obtain a serum containing over 1,000 IU/ml. In the treatment of the cases in this country, a dose of 2,600 to 8,400 IU per person has been administered with remarkable success. The production of type E antitoxin is now undertaken by Chiba Kessei Labor-

atories in Chiba prefecture. Two hundred doses are subsidized by the Government every year and these are available at any time in any district in Japan.

Even though people are aware of the danger of izushi, it is still popular in northern parts of Japan and even many of those who once suffered from izushi-borne botulism still cannot abstain from it. Recurrences of type E botulism, therefore, seem to be quite possible, particularly since the individuals may not have acquired immunity by the previous intoxication. Serum sickness is anticipated if one who has received serum should become ill again. Therefore, vaccination with toxoid of the inhabitants of the areas where type E spore distribution is particularly dense and izushi and similar foods are popular has become a matter of interest. Type E toxoid, prepared by Kondo et al., from a highly purified precursor, was administered to a total of 34 human volunteers and satisfactorily high levels of immunity were attained. The results will also be introduced by Dr. H. Kondo. There are, however, considerable difficulties in the practice of vaccinating a large number of people.

Approaches to the prevention of botulism by other methods have been made. Kanzawa and Iida (11) advocated preparing izushi only at cold seasons with extremely fresh fish and minimizing the period of soaking the fish in water, preferably in acidified water. The attempts to irradiate foods to destroy C. botulinum spores made by Dr. Y. Ando and his associates and the preformed toxin by Dr. T. Miura and his associates will be presented. The use of such antibiotics as tetracyclines (29) or tylosine (Iida et al., unpublished data) was attempted. The propaganda for a safe method of preparation by Kanzawa and Iida has undoubtedly worked to a considerable extent, but no other methods have been practiced. Control of botulism should rely upon food sanitation in the first place and antitoxin administration, unfortunately, if cases occur. Those who have received the antitoxin had better be actively immunized.

Spores of C. botulinum are, no doubt, very widely and heavily distributed in this and other countries. Type E spores are particularly associated with seafoods which are, in this country, eaten either fresh or often preserved without any cooking at any steps of processing. Although botulism is a rare disease and deaths from it are very rare as compared, for example, with those from traffic accidents, it will no doubt, continue to threaten people. In recent years, with the development of modern food technology, people will eat foods which they have never encountered before. We can eat anything from any place in the world in frozen, refrigerated or vacuum-packed form that are stored and transported under so-called "the cold-chain system". Botulism may no longer be a mere local disease. I believe that the potential hazard of these and other foods must be reevaluated and the standardization of each item of food must be established. Simple and reliable methods for detecting *C. botulinum* and the toxin in varieties of foods must be established and standardized.

The public health authorities must realize the botulism will go on threatening people as a potential hazard no matter how the life is modernized or food technology industrialized. Some years ago, ladies in Detroit died from type E botulism after eating commercially canned tuna fish manufactured in California. This occurred nearly half a century after the canning industry established the sterilization standard against botulism. This is just an example that a disaster comes when people have forgotten the possible dangers. Many scientists in Japan are interested in work on botulism, but it seems to me that the Government is not as interested. Dr. G. Sakaguchi's and Dr. H. Iida's groups have been supported financially to carry on their work by the U.S. Public Health Service. I hope that this joint conference, in which the participants from the United States and Japan are presenting the most recent findings, will stimulate not only the scientists concerned with botulism projects, but also the governmental authorities concerned with public health. It should stimulate them to realize that research activities on botulism must be further encouraged, in order to prevent disasters which will always be possible when people ignore the problem.

References

(1) BOROFF, D. A., and U. FLECK. 1966. Statistical analysis of a rapid *in vivo* method for the titration of the toxin of *Clostridium botulinum*. J. Bacteriol. *92:* 1580–1581.

(2) DOLMAN, C. E. 1957. Recent observations on type E botulism. Can. J. Publ. Health *48:* 187–198.

(3) DUFF, J. T., G. G. WRIGHT, and A. YARINSKY. 1956. Activation of *Clostridium botulinum* type E toxin by trypsin. J. Bacteriol. *72:* 455–460.

(4) GERWING, J., C. E. DOLMAN, and A. KO. 1965. Mechanism of tryptic activation of *Clostridium botulinum* type E toxin. J. Bacteriol. *89:* 1176–1179.

(5) GERWING, J., C. E. DOLMAN, M. E. REICHMANN, and H. S. BAINS. 1964. Purification and molecular weight determination of *Clostridium botulinum* type E toxin. J. Bacteriol. *88:* 216–219.

(6) IIDA, H. 1963. Recent observation on the growth and toxin production of *Clostridium botulinum* type E. Japan. J. Med. Sci. Biol. *16:* 307–309.

(7) IIDA, H., T. KARASHIMADA, and T. SAITO. 1961. Three outbreaks of izushi-borne type E botulism encountered recently in Hokkaido. Rep. Hokkaido Inst. Publ. Health *12:* 16–20 (text in Japanese).

(8) IIDA, H., and T. KARASHIMADA. 1956. An outbreak of type E botulism due to trout eggs. Spec. Rep. Hokkaido Inst. Publ. Health *5:* 40–41 (text in Japanese).

(9) IIDA, H., K. KANZAWA, Y. NAKAMURA, T. KARASHIMADA, T. ONO, and T. SAITO. 1964. Botulism outbreaks encountered in Hokkaido in 1962: with special reference to the therapeutic value of specific antitoxin. Rep. Hokkaido Inst. Publ. Health *14:* 6–18 (text in Japanese).

(10) KANZAWA, K. 1960. Ecological studies on *Clostridium botulinum* type E, with special reference to the distribution of the spores in soil in Hokkaido. Rep. Hokkaido Inst. Publ. Health *11:* 161–173 (text in Japanese).

(11) KANZAWA, K., and H. IIDA. 1957. Studies on prevention of toxin production by *Clostridium botulinum* type E in izushi. Rep. 2. Rep. Hokkaido Inst. Publ. Health *8:* 33–38 (text in Japanese).

(12) KARASHIMADA, T., and K. INOUE. 1958. Studies on the effects of aerobic bacteria on the growth and toxin production of *Clostridium botulinum* type E. Rep. Hokkaido Inst. Publ. Health *9:* 58–66 (text in Japanese).

(13) KITAMURA, M., S. SAKAGUCHI, and G. SAKAGUCHI. 1967. Dissociation of *Clostridium botulinum* type E toxin. Biochem. Biophys. Res. Commun. *29:* 892–897.

(14) KOBAYASHI, S. 1961. Investigations on the geographical prevalence of *Clostridium botulinum* in the eastern parts of Japan. Hirosakai Med. J. *12:* 682–695 (text in Japanese).

(15) KODAMA, E., S. FUJISAWA, and T. SAKAMOTO. 1964. Epidemiology and ecology of botulism in Akita prefecture. Rep. Akita Inst. Publ. Health *8:* 15–27 (text in Japanese).

(16) KODAMA, E., S. FUJISAWA, T. SAKAMOTO, H. ASANO, and J. ETO. 1963. Uber den *Cl. botulinum* Typus A, der in der Akita Prafektur Gefunden Wurde. Hirosaki Med. J. *14:* 156–164.

(17) KONDO, H., S. KONDO, R. MURATA, and G. SAKAGUCHI. 1963. Potency test and therapeutic effect of type E botulinus antitoxin. Japan. J. Med. Sci. Biol. *16:* 310–311.

(18) NAKAMURA, G., M. TAKEYA, H. KUDO, C. IZUMIYAMA, K. YAMAMOTO, H. ASANO, and M. TAKEYAMA. 1963. Ein Fall von Typus B-Botulismus. Hirosaki Med. J. *14:* 123–127.

(19) NAKAMURA, Y., H. IIDA, and K. SAEKI. 1952. Botulism occurred in Shimano-mura, Iwanai-gun. Spec. Rep. Hokkaido Inst. Publ. Health *1:* 1–18 (text in Japanese).

(20) NAKAMURA, Y., H. IIDA, K. SAEKI, and K. KANZAWA. 1954. Botulism outbreaks occurred in Hokkaido. Spec. Rep. Hokkaido Inst. Publ. Health *3:* 1–37 (text in Japanese).

(21) NAKAMURA, Y., H. IIDA, K. SAEKI, K. KANZAWA, and T. KARASHIMADA. 1956. Type E botulism in Hokkaido, Japan. Japan. J. Med. Sci. Biol. *9:* 45–58.

(22) ONO, T. 1962. Immunological studies on *Clostridium botulinum*. II. Properties of the antigens. Rep. Hokkaido Inst. Publ. Health *13:* 9–20 (text in Japanese).

(23) ONO, T., and K. REI. 1960. Immunological studies on *Clostridium botulinum* type E. I. Preparation of the antigens. Rep. Obihiro Veterinary and Animal Husbandry College *3:* 169–180 (text in Japanese).

(24) SAEKI, K. 1956. A culture medium for toxin production by *Clostridium botulinum* type E. Spec. Rep. Hokkaido Inst. Publ. Health *5:* 28–31 (text in Japanese).

(25) SAKAGUCHI, G., and S. SAKAGUCHI. 1959. Studies on toxin production of *Clostridium botulinum* type E. III. Characterization of toxin precursor. J. Bacteriol. *78:* 1–9.

(26) SAKAGUCHI, G., and S. SAKAGUCHI. 1967. Some observation on activation of *Cl. botulinum* type E toxin by trypsin. *In* Botulism 1966. (M. Ingram & T. A. Roberts, eds.), pp. 267–277, Chapman & Hall, London.

(27) SAKAGUCHI, G., S. SAKAGUCHI, and N. IMAI.

1964. Comparative gel filtration of toxin precursor and trypsin-activated toxin of *Clostridium botulinum* type E. J. Bacteriol. *87:* 401–407.

(*28*) SAKAGUCHI, G., S. SAKAGUCHI, and T. KARA-SHIMADA. 1966. Molecular size of *Clostridium botulinum* type E toxin in "izushi." Japan. J. Med. Sci. Biol. *19:* 201–207.

(*29*) SAKAGUCHI, G., S. SAKAGUCHI, T. KAWABATA, T. NAKAMURA, T. AKANO, and K. SHIROMIZU. 1960. Influence of oxytetracycline upon the toxin production of type E *Cl. botulinum*. Japan. J. Med. Sci. Biol. *13:* 13–22.

(*30*) SAKAGUCHI, G., and Y. TOHYAMA. 1955*a*. Studies on the toxin production of *Clostridium botulinum* type E. I. A strain of genus *Clostridium* having the action to promote type E botulinal toxin production in a mixed culture. Japan. J. Med. Sci. Biol. *8:* 247–253.

(*31*) SAKAGUCHI, G., and Y. TOHYAMA, 1955*b*. Studies on the toxin production of *Clostridium botulinum* type E. II. The mode of action of the contaminant organisms to promote toxin production of type E organisms. Japan. J. Med. Sci. Biol. *8:* 255–262.

(*32*) SCHANTZ, E. J., and L. SPERO. 1967. Molecular size of *Cl. botulinum* toxins. *In* Botulism 1966 (M. Ingram and T. A. Roberts, eds.), pp. 296–301, Chapman & Hall, London.

(*33*) WAKAMATSU, T., and H. DIROKI. 1953. Ecological study of *Clostridia* in Kyushu, especially in its southern part. Kitasato Arch. Expt. Med. *25:* 163–186 (text in Japanese).

(*34*) YAMAGATA, H. 1963. Distribution of pathogenic *Clostridia* (*Cl. welchii, Cl. botulinum*) in soil. Rep. Yamaguchi Prefect. Res. Inst. Publ. Health *1:* 101–106 (text in Japanese).

(*35*) YAMAGATA PREFECTURAL BUREAU OF WEL-FARE. 1959. An outbreak of botulism encountered for the first time in Yamagata Prefecture. Rep. Bureau of Welfare, Yamagata Prefecture. Pg. 14 (text in Japanese).

CRITICAL COMMENT ON RESEARCH NEEDS IN BOTULISM: ECOLOGY, NATURE, AND ACTION OF TOXIN

by CARL LAMANNA
Office of the Chief of Research and Development,
Department of the Army, Washington, D.C. 20310

I welcome the opportunity to present some thoughts on directions for future research in botulism. It is an instructive activity for the investigator to stop on occasion and to look back before he continues ahead. Such a step is an occasion to think critically about what has been done and reported. One should be enabled to unmask past errors, identify important unasked questions, and focus attention on promising opportunities. This I hope to do by examining some aspects of the ecology of botulism, the nature of botulinal toxins, and the mode of action of the toxins.

Action

What is remarkable and unexplained is the unequal distribution around the world of *Clostridium botulinum* and its toxin types. In the last 10 years there has been a spurt in publication of searches for the presence of the organism in previously unexplored regions. To date where the search has been extended the botulinal organism has been found and previous observations of the unequal distribution of types have not been violated. Nonetheless there remain gaps in our knowledge of the geographic distribution of the organism. There have not been reported adequate studies of distribution in the humid tropics. For example, I have not found studies of the water courses of the Amazon, Orinoco, Congo, and the heavy rainfall tropical regions of Central America, Asia (Indonesia and the Philippines, for example), and South Pacific islands. Nor have I found reports on studies of snow, ice, and soil specimens from the Antarctic. In the Arctic environment of Alaska and Canada, epidemics of botulism described by Dr. C. E. Dolman have been associated with marine animals that are migratory. Does this botulism result from introduction of clostridia from non-Arctic sources? To complete the worldwide survey of the distribution of *Clostridium botulinum* the true arctic and humid tropical regions should be surveyed adequately. It would be both a convenience and a stimulus to the investigator if someone will update Meyer's (13) survey of botulism as a worldwide problem by publication of a world map marked correctly as to rainfall, latitude and longitude with points separately identifying areas in which human and animal botulism, and isolations of *C. botulinum* types from soils and bodies of water have been reported.

If *Clostridium botulinum* were adapted to life in the soils of the humid tropics, one would expect botulism to occur in man and other susceptible animals. The standards of living and methods of preserving home-grown foods in the developing nations of the humid tropics should provide ample opportunity for food poisoning. Certainly, food poisoning by microbes other than *C. botulinum* is a common event in the humid tropics. Botulism, a dramatic disease with distinctive neurological signs, can hardly have escaped medical and veterinary notice. So we are presented with a problem. Is the organism absent in the humid tropics? Or is there some peculiarity of human existence, animal husbandry, and the habits of wildlife which prevents the appearance of clinical disease in spite of the presence of the organism in the natural environment? I do not believe that populations in the humid tropics have developed antitoxic immunity by reason of exposure to sublethal doses of toxin. This is based on observation of absence of antitoxin in sera of normal persons both in the United States and from an area of the humid tropics. A normal person in this context would be defined as one not having a history of exposure to toxoid or clinical botulism.

In the United States we have the interesting situation of the occurrence of type C epizootics without report of cases of human type C poisoning. A logical reaction to this realization is to assume man to be immune to type C poisoning. Since all common laboratory experimental animals, including monkeys, do become ill when exposed by any route to a sufficient quantity of type C toxin, it would be necessary to accept the hypothesis by becoming a believer in the uniqueness of man, a prejudice I reject. More important is the recent Russian claim of two cases of type C botulism in man (10). What is required is an intensive investigation of the growth and toxin production habits of type C organism to learn if it cannot grow in some soils man cultivates to grow his foods, or is present in bottom muck of bodies of water so unpalatable as to never be a source of raw drinking water. A final possibility is that concentration of type C toxin in natural waters is so low as to make it impossible for a man to drink enough for visible harm to result. Exploration of the aforementioned possibilities would go a long way in providing understanding or clues as to what combinations of natural events must occur before the threat of type C botulism can become a reality for man.

From a bacteriological point of view we are only superficially acquainted with the factors determining the opportunity for growth and consequent sporulation and persistence of the botulinal organism under natural conditions. This knowledge could be essential for understanding the peculiarities of distribution of the different types. Here the interaction of physical and chemical factors might be of critical importance. If this is so then laboratory studies of temperature limits of growth or other physical agents, would not be helpful unless the laboratory medium duplicated the natural chemical environment. In this context the term natural chemical environment encompasses any contributions made by soil organisms, chiefly microbes. That antagonistic effects of a mixed microflora might explain the absence of types of *C. botulinum* is attested by the recent claim that the type F organism is subject to seasonal inhibition by the fluctuations in the population density of *Bacillus licheniformis* (*B. subtilis*) (*16*). This study is a typical attempt to relate microbial flora to the growth of a particular organism of interest. What is done is to seek correlations between the counts of a particular micro-organism and *C. botulinum* in soil samples. Such studies are suggestive but not definitive. A specific natural event in the complex environment of soil might simultaneously cause an increase in population of one organism and a decrease in population of another kind of organism. Thus the correlations published to date can be viewed as clues to pursue but not as evidence of cause and effect.

Nature of Botulinal Toxin

Ever since the crystallization of type A toxin, it has been the conscious and unconscious wish of some persons that the reported high-molecular weight of the material was false, or if true, was not representative of the size of the true toxin molecule. This thinking results from a number of considerations, some reasonable and others mythological. Prominent is the mythology that to be absorbed an oral poison must have a low-molecular weight. This view is unphysiological since it ignores the fact that the intestinal barrier is penetrable to some degree by molecules of all kinds and all sizes. The barrier to absorption is not absolute in its capacity to deny to any molecule

an escape route through the intestinal wall. Direct proof has been offered for the appearance of botulinal toxin as a full-sized protein in the lymph draining from the intestinal tract (*6*). Thus there should now be laid to rest any further doubts about the large size of botulinal toxin simply because the toxin acts as an oral poison.

Another incentive for the wish that botulinal toxin is a small-molecular-weight protein is the hope to synthesize the toxin in the laboratory. Obviously, the smaller the molecule the easier the task. The wish ignores the universe not organized to suit man's convenience. Hopefully, the increasing skill in analyzing the amino-acid sequence of increasingly larger molecules and improved control of peptide bond formation will quiet the need some people feel to hope the toxin is a small molecular weight protein.

Language can help or victimize us. The word toxiphore has a historic appeal to microbiologists. So it is not unnatural for members of the microbiological fraternity to speak of a toxiphore in the botulinal toxin. From this habit it is easy to go one step further and hope that most of the amino-acid structure of the toxin molecule is outside the toxiphore and superfluous to the property of poisoning. Hence the large-molecular-weight toxin should be reducible to a smaller weight toxiphore which is the true toxin. We should be reminded that our knowledge and appreciation of protein structure has expanded since the simplistic concept of a toxiphore was invented. We might be better advised to drop this term when we are considering the biological activity of a simple (unconjugated) protein molecule as is the case for the botulinal toxins. A molecule composed only of amino acids may have an "active center," if we must borrow a modern term, but a role remains for more amino-acid residues than those composing the active center alone. The fact is that while active centers of simple enzymatic proteins have been identified, these active centers depend for their catalytic (biological) role upon their incorporation within a larger molecule. There is no theoretical or real-life obstacle to believing that a large protein molecule as a whole can act as a poison rather than some smaller piece of it alone.

When it was demonstrated that crystalline botulinal toxin possessed the property of agglutinating erythrocytes, and that this property was resident in a substance separable from a neurotoxic component (*9*), it became reasonable to think of the crystalline toxin as being a complex. The separation of the neurotoxin from the hemagglutinating material results in a toxic molecule of lower molecular weight than the complex. On the other hand the hemagglutinin-free toxin still has the dimensions of a large protein (*11*). That the large molecular size of crystalline and other purified toxin types is not an artifact of the method of purification but is a reflection of the original state of molecular size in the growth culture has been conclusively demonstrated by Schantz (*15*). These facts dictate the necessity to focus attention on the size of hemagglutinin-free toxin. This is the direction future research on the molecular size of toxin should take. Any claim for a molecular size smaller than crystalline toxin or toxin in culture medium should include data on the hemagglutinating activity of the material. Unfortunately this has not been done in most of the publications of claims of isolations of low molecular weight toxin.

An inexcusable defect in most of the published claims for small molecular weight toxin is the lack of precise data on specific activity (LD_{50}/mg. dry weight or mg. N). Either no data are given or the information is sketchy and reported as MLD instead of LD_{50}. A less serious but nonetheless significant defect is that the amount of low molecular weight material isolated is meagre. I suspect in some cases this is the reason for the nonexistent or poor data on specific activity. Apparently so little material is isolated as to make the authors reluctant or unable to use the quantity of material needed to perform well-controlled quantitatively adequate titrations for specific activity.

A significant fact is that, except for claims of isolation of about 150,000 molecular weight toxin (*3, 7*), when specific activity is quoted it is considerably less for the small-sized material than for the 900,000 molecular weight type A toxin or large-sized toxin of other types. If large molecular weight toxin were some kind of aggregate of lower sized toxic particles specific activity for the large molecular weight material should not be greater than for the individually toxic particle (*8*). If it was greater, we must conclude the state of aggregation to confer an intensification, if not a qualitative change, on the biological activity of a particle. In fact the toxicity of small molecular weight toxin when quoted has been so low as to cause one to suspect the probability of inadvertent contamination of the material with active larger sized toxin. Recently Boroff, Dasgupta, and Fleck (*3*) have said contamination is the explanation for the toxicity of the low molecular weight type B material isolated by Canadian workers (*5*).

To assist in the planning of future research on the question of the ultimate size of the toxic particle of botulism, I have prepared in table 1 a list of characteristics that should be studied. Data on these characteristics would tell us what is the true story with

Table 1.—Characteristics to be studied to determine relation of small to large molecular weight botulinal toxin

Step 1. Selective removal of hemagglutinin to yield hemagglutinin-free neurotoxin. Comparison of specific activity of hemagglutinin-free toxin and hemagglutinating toxin.

Step 2. Choice between alternate possible structures of high molecular weight hemagglutinin-free neurotoxin:

Alternate 1
Aggregate organization.

Alternate 2
Molecule with groups of nonessential amino-acid residues.

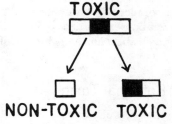

Likely properties:

a. Molecular weight of aggregate is a whole number multiple of a basic unit.

b. Ratio of free amino or carboxyl groups per unit of toxicity (LD_{50}) independent of molecular size.

c. Specific activity per mg. N fixed or decreased by disaggregation.

d. Total weight of large molecular weight toxin should be recoverable as active low-molecular weight toxin.

e. Manipulation of physical environment (pH, ionic activity, temperature, etc.) may result in disassociation of aggregate.

a. Large molecular weight toxic particle is not a whole number multiple of a basic unit. Different fragments of low-molecular weight may have different nonmultiple whole number weights.

b. Ratio of free amino or carboxyl groups per unit of toxicity may differ between different molecular sized toxin.

c. Specific activity greater for low-molecular weight toxin.

d. Only a fractional part of the total weight of large-molecular weight toxin should be isolated as small-molecular weight toxin.

e. More drastic manipulations required to free toxin molecule of amino acids not essential to the property of toxicity.

respect to how large molecular weight toxin is related to smaller weight toxin. The data asked for would tell us definitively if the large hemagglutinin-free toxic molecule is an aggregate of toxic particles or alternatively a compound capable of retaining biological activity in the face of loss of substituent amino acids. In addition, the question of whether the small molecular weight toxin is simply hemagglutinin-free toxin would be settled.

It would greatly assist progress if in the future editors of journals would make two inviolate demands of investigators before accepting papers for publication on the subject of molecular size and amino acid composition of toxin: (1) Clear-cut quantitatively adequate data on specific activity, and (2) proof of presence or absence of hemagglutinating activity.

Action of the Toxins

The evidence is convincing that the basic mode of poisoning by the botulinal toxins is by interference with the release of acetylcholine from the synaptic fibrils of susceptible nerves. What continues to excite interest is the question of sensitivity by all nervous tissues where acetylcholine has been found or is presumed to be present. While there is increasing evidence for the presence of acetylcholine in the mammalian central nervous system, there are conflicting reports on the ability of botulinal toxin to poison central nervous system activity. Since the role of acetylcholine in the different subsystems of the nervous system is not settled, it would be useful to employ botulinal toxin as a tool for learning whether or not acetylcholine acts as a transmitter in particular situations. Unfortunately, lack of poisoning does not have a conclusive meaning. It could be due to lack of penetration to a nerve ending rather than evidence against cholinergic activity. More insight and practical suggestions are needed on how to distinguish a permeability barrier as opposed to lack of receptivity for botulinal toxin by nervous tissue.

Acetylcholine is present in nerve tissue of both invertebrate and vertebrate animals. Its role in invertebrate tissue is imperfectly understood. Most evidence is against the ability of botulinal toxin to affect invertebrates. But, unfortunately, reported observations are few in number. Larvae of flies feeding on carcasses of birds and other animals dead of botulism poisoning do not seem to be affected. Birds eating such larvae can come down with botulism poisoning (2, 14, 17), so there is no doubt of natural exposure of the larvae to the toxin. Prof. C. M. Williams of Harvard University, who has injected type A toxin into female pupal of the moth, *Hyalophora cecropia*, did not observe any interference with development into healthy adults (18). Meyer (12) has quoted old work claiming para-

mecia to be insensitive, while daphnia, copopods, snails and "rain worms" were said to be sensitive. At the time these observations were quoted, purified toxins were not available. It would be worthwhile to employ purified tosins in comprehensive future studies of representative species from all of the phyla of invertebrates.

Based on my own experience I am skeptical of the ability of the toxin to affect invertebrates. In collaboration with Prof. Thomas Symthe, Jr., of the Pennsylvania State University, when crystalline type A toxin was injected into adults of the black blow fly (*Phormia regina*), males of the American cockroach (*Periplaneta americana*), the large milkweed beetle (*Oncopeltus fasciatus*), and yellow mealworms (*Tenebrio molitor*), neither death nor overt signs of illness developed. When with the collaboration of Prof. Ernest Bueding of The Johns Hopkins University, crystalline type A toxin was placed in the aqueous environment of the following species no changes in activity or deaths were noted: the snail *Australorbus glabratus*, the adult stage of the rat worm parasite *Hymenolepis diminuta*, and the miricidia, cercariae and adult stages of *Schistosoma mansoni*. The latter species has been shown to possess an inhibitory cholinergic system (1).

Does the insensitivity to botulinal toxin mean that acetylcholine does not act as a nerve system transmittor in the invertebrates? The lack of effect could be due to an efficient detoxification mechanism. This is doubtful since abdominal fluid taken from symptomless cockroaches 24 hours after they had been injected with crystalline type A toxin was able to kill adult white mice. The mice succumbed with typical signs of botulinal intoxication. Another possibility would be the inability of the toxin to penetrate to sensitive nerve sites. Professor Smythe has measured the endplate potentials of the metathoracic flexor tibiae of the American cockroach exposed 2½ hours to crystalline toxin, and found only normal activity. The same lack of effect was noted for toxin directly bathing giant interneurons of the roach. Nor was any effect observed on the electrical potentials of the desheathed metathoracic ganglion of the cockroach. Mrs. Mary H. Greer, a student of Professor Smythe, has found no effect on the appearance or frequency of either excitatory or miniature end-plate potentials in cockroach muscle during 2-hour exposures. Thus what little work has been done points to an intrinsic insensitivity of invertebrate nervous tissue to botulinal toxin.

Aside from the use of antitoxin, rational specific therapy of botulism depends on knowledge of the events preventing release of acetylcholine from nerve endings by toxin. This knowledge, beyond us today, is a long-term goal we can hope to acquire difficult step by step as neurophysiologists gradually unravel the molecular events accompanying nervous activity. If we are impatient, is there any other approach worth taking while we wait for the revelations of molecular biology? What can be done is to suggest hypotheses for experimental therapeutic tests based on what we already know. Hopefully, the more people who will imaginatively think about what is known the greater the chance someone will stumble on some useful therapeutic measure. History provides many example of usefully ameliorative or curative therapy derived in the absence of knowledge of ultimate cause.

Any hypothesis for countering botulinal poisoning should consider the following observations. Once nerve endings have been exposed the toxin is not easily neutralized by antitoxin. Recovery following poisoning is extraordinarily slow. In mice nerve-muscle activity has been found defective for more than 9 months. The histological picture of the poisoned neuromuscular junction is remarkable in the normality of its appearance. Most unexpectedly the growth of nerve fibers following poisoning is not analogous to regeneration after trauma, and appears to be an overgrowth rather than replacement of fibrils (4).

What can be made of such facts? My own working hypothesis is that botulinal toxin remains tightly bound at the site of poisoning for a long period of time, and by its presence blocks by some physical means the release of acetylcholine. Possibly the large size of botulinal toxin is useful both in providing a large series of bonds for holding tightly to receptor substance, and for physically covering and thus plugging escape routes for acetylcholine. The persistence of tightly bound toxin would account for inactivity of antitoxin, and the long-term paralysis. The peculiar histological features of repair could be due to need for generation of new fibrils since the presence of toxin at blockaded fibrils would not necessarily provide a stimulus for regeneration of the immediate site of poisoning if the toxin did not create a chemical lesion. The observation of a high-temperature coefficient for botulinal poisoning does not necessarily argue against this concept since there are adsorptive and other surface phenomena which do have high-temperature coefficients. The hypothesis does require the assumption that tightly bound foreign protein at the neuromuscular or ganglionic synaptic junction is metabolized or otherwise destroyed at a slow rate. Therapeutically, the hypothesis suggests testing of physical means for release of bound toxin and chemical reactions for destroying the toxin.

A virtue of the hypothesis is that it reinforces and gives a therapeutic emphasis to the desirability for the invention of techniques for pinpointing and marking the presence of toxin at nerve endings by means of some kind of tag. If this tagging can be accomplished and the hypothesis is correct then the toxin should be found to be present at poisoned nerve endings long after the initial exposure. To this point in the life of toxin at nerve endings specific therapy could aim to remove or destroy toxin. Beyond this time, therapy would aim at the repair of whatever damage remained after the toxin disappeared. The concept provides for a wider variety of therapeutic ideas for testing than have been offered in the past.

An objection to the hypothesis could be that it cannot explain the extreme potency of the toxin. This remains to be seen. The number of release points for acetylcholine for any one nerve must be finite as is the number of malfunctioning nerves needed to kill an animal. The multiple of these numbers might be the number of molecules in a lethal dose of toxin. What appears at first glance to be an objection to the hypothesis becomes an incentive to develop some basic quantitative information on the number of sites of acetylcholine release of nerves. Such knowledge would either make the hypothesis more plausible or reinforce thinking of the toxin as a harmful enzyme. To date no proofs for the enzymatic nature of botulinal toxins exist.

References

(1) BARKER, L. R., E. BUEDING, and A. R. TIMMS. 1966. The possible role of acetylcholine in *Schistosoma mansoni*. Brit. J. Pharmacol. Chemother. *26:* 656–665.

(2) BISHOPP, F. C. 1923. Limberneck of fowls produced by fly larvae. J. Parasitol. *9:* 170–173.

(3) BOROFF, D. A., B. R. DASGUPTA, and U. S. FLECK. 1968. Homogeneity and molecular weight of toxin of *Clostridium botulinum* type B. J. Bacteriol. *95:* 1738–1744.

(4) DUCHEN, L. W., and S. J. STRICH. 1968. The effects of botulinum toxin on the pattern of ennervation of skeletal muscle in the mouse. Quart. Journal Exp. Physiol. *53:* 84–89.

(5) GERWING, J., C. E. DOLMAN, D. V. KASON, and J. H. TREMAINE. 1966. Purification and characterization of *Clostridium botulinum* type B toxin. J. Bacteriol. *91:* 484–487.

(6) HECKLY, R. J., G. J. HILDEBRAUD, and C. LAMANNA. 1960. On the size of the toxic particle passing the intestinal barrier in botulism. J. Exp. Med. *111:* 745–759.

(7) KITAMURA, M., S. SAKAGUCHI, and G. SAKAGUCHI. 1967. Dissociation of *Clostridium botulinum* type E toxin. Biochem. Biophys. Res. Comm. *29:* 892–897.

(8) LAMANNA, C., and C. J. CARR. 1967. The botulinal, tetanal, and enterostaphylococcal toxins: a review. Clin. Pharmacol. Therap. *8:* 286–332.

(9) LAMANNA, C., and J. P. LOWENTHAL. 1951. The lack of identity between hemagglutinin and the toxin of type A botulinal organism. J. Bacteriol. *61:* 751–752.

(10) MATVEEV, K. I., N. P. NEFEDJEVA, T. I. BULATOVA, and I. S. SOKOLOV. 1967. Epidemiology of botulism in the U.S.S.R. *In* Botulism 1966. Chapman and Hall Ltd., London, pp. 1–10.

(11) MEYER, E. A., and C. LAMANNA. 1959. Activity of

type A botulinal toxin and hemagglutinin exposed to proteolytic enzyme. J. Bacteriol. *78:* 175–180.

(*12*) MEYER, K. F. 1928. Botulismus. *In* "Handbuch der pathogenen Mikro-organismen." 3d ed., p. 1331.

(*13*) MEYER, K. F. 1956. The status of botulism as a world problem. Bull. World Health Org. *15:* 281–298.

(*14*) SAUNDERS, E. W., S. WISDOM, and T. W. WHITE. 1921. The *Lucilia ceasar* epizootic. J. Missouri State Med. Assoc. *18:* 4–9.

(*15*) SCHANTZ, E. J. 1967. Some chemical and physical properties of *Clostridium botulinum* toxins in culture. Japan. J. Microbiol. *11:* 380–383.

(*16*) WENTZ, M. W., R. A. SCOTT, and J. W. VENNES. 1967. *Clostridium botulinum* type F: seasonal inhibition by *Bacillus licheniformis*. Science *155:* 89–90.

(*17*) WILKINS, S. and R. A. DUTCHER. 1920. Limberneck in poultry. J. Amer. Vet. Med. Assoc. *57:* 653–685.

(*18*) WILLIAMS, C. M. 1967. Personal communication.

THE DETECTION, IDENTIFICATION, AND ISOLATION OF *CLOSTRIDIUM BOTULINUM*

by D. A. Kautter, R. K. Lynt, Jr., H. M. Solomon, T. Lilly, Jr., *and* S. M. Harmon
Division of Microbiology, Food and Drug Administration,
Washington, D.C. 20204

Summary

Enrichment media for *Clostridium botulinum* generally consist of infusions of either cooked meat or liver. Some are supplemented with peptone and glucose and others may contain minced meat particles. For the cultivation of specific types of *C. botulinum*, special media have been employed. A tabulation of many of these is given. Conditions for maximum toxin production are given and advantages and disadvantages of trypsinization pointed out. The usual method of identification is the mouse test by either passive immunization or *in vitro* neutralization. Goldfish and guinea pigs also have been used experimentally. Classification serologically, by agglutination, on the basis of flagellar, somatic, and spore antigens shows promise as an aid to taxonomy and gives evidence of many nontoxigenic variants. Reports of the use of fluorescent antibody give conflicting results. Thus far, our FA work, using somatic antigens, gives results similar to those obtained by agglutination. It is possible to detect toxin and type it by immunodiffusion but this procedure is less sensitive than the mouse test. Discontinuous pH electrophoresis has been used to separate *C. botulinum* proteins, including toxin, from foods. Elimination of nonspore-forming contaminants from enrichment cultures by heat, as is usual, is not satisfactory for type E but has been successful with alcohol. When this is followed by streaking on suitable plating media, typical colonies may be selected. The use of trypsin in enrichment cultures to destroy a bacteriocin produced by certain nontoxigenic variants of type E and certain other problems arising out of the procedures presented above are discussed.

Introduction

Methods of detection, identification, and isolation are basic in establishing the role of *Clostridium botulinum* in an outbreak of botulism or in determining its distribution in nature. This report will briefly review methods and media for enrichment and toxin production of the different types of *C. botulinum*; methods for the identification of both the organism and its toxin, including the experimental techniques of fluorescent antibody and immunodiffusion; methods and media for the isolation of the organism from enrichment cultures and food; and finally, some of the problems associated with the detection of *C. botulinum* in enrichment cultures, especially this of environmental materials.

Enrichment

There are many enrichment media used for the cultivation of the different types of *C. botulinum*. Van Ermengen's original observation that *C. botulinum* grew and produced toxin in a double-strength meat infusion broth supplemented with peptone, sodium chloride, and glucose has given rise to a multiplicity of meat-infusion media for this purpose, and generally the most common enrichment media for all types of *C. botulinum* are infusions of either cooked meat or liver. Dubovsky and Meyer (*10*), in early work, utilized a buffered beef peptic digest veal infusion broth. Some of those most frequently used by other investigators include Robertson's cooked meat medium, Dolman's (*8*) beef infusion medium supplemented with peptone and glucose, and the modification by Eklund et al. (*15*) of Dolman's medium. Johannsen (*22*), on the other hand, recommends adding minced meat particles to an infusion of cardiac muscle.

In addition to media used for the general cultivation of all types of *C. botulinum*, specific media have been utilized by different investigators for the cultivation and toxin production of specific types of *C. botulinum*. Table 1 shows the various types of media that have been employed.

This tabulation is intended to be merely representative and is far from complete. Although not shown in the tables, most of these media contain one or more buffering components and some means of maintaining anaerobic conditions such as sodium thioglycollate, cysteine hydrochloride, or semisolid agar.

The usual temperature for maximum toxin production and enrichment of proteolytic types A, B, and F, types $C\alpha$ and $C\beta$, and type D is 35° to 37° C.

Table 1.—Media employed for enrichment and toxin production of *Clostridium botulinum*

C. botulinum type	Investigator	Media
Type A (proteolytic)	Inukai (21)	Proteose peptone and yeast extract.
	Rice et al. (34)	Casein digest medium.
	Schmidt and Nank (35)	Trypticase and peptone.
	Duff et al. (12)	Pancreatic digest of casein, autolyzed yeast and glucose.
	Bonventre and Kempe (1)	Tryptic digest of casein, yeast extract and glucose.
	Ohye and Scott (31)	Neopeptone, yeast extract and glucose.
	Day (thesis)	Trypticase and thiamine hydrochloride.
Type B (proteolytic)	Rice et al. (34)	Casein digest medium.
	Duff et al. (13)	Trypticase, yeast extract, cysteine hydrochloride, and glucose.
	Bonventre and Kempe (1)	Tryptic digest of casein, yeast extract, and glucose.
	Day (thesis)	Trypticase and thiamine hydrochloride.
	Ohye and Scott (31)	Neopeptone, yeast extract, and glucose.
Type B (nonproteolytic)	Eklund et al. (14)	Dolman's glucose, peptone beef infusion medium (GPBI) modified with the addition of trypticase, starch, and yeast extract (GPTBI).
Type C (nonproteolytic)	Cardella et al. (3)	Proteose peptone, N–Z amine type B, yeast extract, and glucose.
Type D	Schmidt (personal communication)	Trypticase, peptone, and glucose.
	Cardella et al. (4)	Corn steep liquor, glycerol, and calcium carbonate.
Type E (nonproteolytic)	Schmidt et al. (36)	Trypticase, peptone, and glucose.
	Lechowich (personal communication)	Trypticase, peptone, and sucrose.
	Dolman (8)	Glucose, peptone beef infusion medium (GPBI).
	Johannsen (22)	Infusion of cardiac muscle with added minced meat particles.
	Bott et al. (2)	Difco brain heart infusion.
	Eklund (personal communication)	Dolman's glucose, peptone beef infusion medium (GPBI) modified with the addition of trypticase, starch and yeast extract (GPTBI).
Type F (proteolytic)	Møller and Scheibel (29)	Casein, yeast extract, and glucose.
	Dolman (9)	Glucose, peptone beef infusion medium (GPBI).
	Walls (personal communication)	Proteose peptone, N–Z amine type B, yeast extract, and glucose.
Type F (nonproteolytic)	Eklund et al. (15)	Dolman's glucose, peptone beef infusion medium (GPBI) modified with the addition of trypticase, starch, and yeast extract (GPTBI).
	Craig and Pilcher (5)	Trypticase, peptone, and glucose.

for 5 to 7 days. For maximum toxin production by the nonproteolytic types B, E, and F, 25° to 28° C. for 3 to 5 days is generally recommended.

Many investigators trypsinize enrichment cultures for type E (11) and the nonproteolytic types B and F after growth as a means of increasing toxin titers prior to animal testing. Since it has been claimed that in some instances trypsinization after growth will decrease the amount of toxin present in the cultures, we have, in our laboratories, routinely tested them both before and after trypsinization. This procedure has been supplemented by one using a medium containing trypsin for the detection of *C. botulinum* type E in environmental samples. This will be discussed later.

Identification

The generally accepted method of detecting the presence of toxin in food extracts or enrichment cultures is the mouse test. For routine analysis mice are injected intraperitoneally with known quantities of food extracts or culture filtrates and tested for specific toxins by passive immunization with monovalent antiserum. Another method commonly employed is neutralization of the toxin with monovalent antiserum in the test tube prior to injection into the mouse.

Goldfish have been used in place of mice by Crisley (6) and Graikoski (personal communication) and their sensitivity to botulinum toxin seems to be about the same. Although goldfish are not as expensive as mice, not enough work has been done to firmly establish the relative sensitivities of the two animals. In addition, the complications involved in utilizing goldfish, such as the need for tanks or aquariums and the means of giving the toxin, may offset any advantage that they might otherwise have.

The guinea pig also has been utilized for identification of botulinum toxins, but this animal is not as sensitive as the mouse and the cost limits its use to specialized studies.

Many workers have tried to classify either the vegetative cells or the spores of *C. botulinum* without regard to toxin production, on the basis of serological reactions. Investigations dealing with the serological classification of *C. botulinum* with special emphasis on type E have been limited. Gunnison et al. (*18*) found two cultures of type E from Russia to be identical by agglutination and agglutinin absorption tests. Hazen (*19*) found strains from two different sources to be antigenically dissimilar. Nakamura et al. (*30*) classified strains isolated in the vicinity of Hokkaido, Japan, into five serological groups. Ono (*32, 33*), studying strains from the same source, found the heat-labile antigens to have a high degree of group specificity, whereas the heat-stable antigens were common to all.

Investigators in our laboratories (*25*) used *C. botulinum* type E antigens, prepared from either formalin-treated or heat-treated vegetative cells of 18-hour broth cultures, to produce antisera. Whole cell (H–O) antigens were prepared by treatment with 0.4 percent formalin and heat stable (somatic or O) antigens, by heating at 100° C. for 1 hour. New Zealand white rabbits were given six intravenous injections of 1.0 ml. of antigen at 3- to 4-day intervals followed by a 1.0-ml. booster a week later and bleeding in 10 days.

Flagellar agglutination tests were performed in 13 x 100 mm. tubes, using 0.5 ml. quantities each of antigen and diluted antiserum and incubating in a 50° C. waterbath for 2 hours. Somatic agglutination tests used 0.1 ml. quantities each of antigen and serum but at the end of the incubation time 0.5 ml. of saline was added to facilitate reading.

Whole-cell antisera were prepared against eight toxigenic type E strains and three nontoxigenic strains whose morphology and physiology, except for the ability to produce boticin E in two and lack of toxin production in all, were indistinguishable from type E. Somatic antisera were prepared against seven toxigenic type E strains and two nontoxigenic boticin E producing strains.

These sera were tested against 32 toxigenic strains and six nontoxigenic strains of which two were boticin E producers and two differed in their fermentation patterns and hemolytic ability but closely resembled type E in colonial morphology. All antisera had high-antibody titers against the homologous antigen.

By flagellar agglutination, a few small groups of strains were found to be agglutinated by the same H–O serum, but otherwise agglutination was generally confined to the homologous strain and the few additional cross agglutinations which occurred were minimal. These groupings were confirmed by agglutinin absorption tests (table 2). The whole-cell antisera also agglutinated somatic antigens of all strains of type E and nontoxigenic organisms, but absorption with these antigens left the flagellar component unaffected.

Antisera prepared against antigens heated at 100° C. for 1 hour agglutinated all somatic antigens of type E organisms and similar nontoxigenic strains to equal titer. Absorption tests showed the antigens of the toxigenic and nontoxigenic strains to be identical. Neither the somatic nor the whole-cell antisera agglutinated other types of *C. botulinum* or other species of *Clostridium* tested.

One toxigenic strain (066B) regularly gave rise to both toxigenic and nontoxigenic progeny. Toxigenic and nontoxigenic strains derived from the same colony of this strain were found to have identical flagellar and somatic antigens. Other nontoxigenic strains differed from each other and from type E strains in their flagellar antigens but shared common somatic antigens with all. Thus, except for lack of toxigenicity and the ability of some to produce bacteriocins, the nontoxigenic strains differed no more from type than type E strains differed among themselves.

Because of the diversity of the flagellar antigens and the broad spectrum of the somatic antigens, neither could be used to distinguish type E from nontoxigenic strains having similar cultural characteristics. For this reason an investigation of the spore antigens of *C. botulinum* (*37*) was undertaken in our laboratory. Another objective was to ascertain whether spore antigens might be useful in assessing the relationship of type E to other types of *C. botulinum* and other *Clostridium* species.

Strains which, though differing from *C. botulinum* type E in several cultural characteristics, showed closer overall relationship to type E than to other types of *C. botulinum* and other *Clostridium* species were grouped and tentatively designated as nontoxigenic atypical strains. They were included in this investigation because of their persistent presence wherever type E is found, because some of them shared somatic antigens with toxigenic type E and because some were claimed to be nontoxigenic variants of *C. botulinum* type E.

Spore antigens free of vegetative cell components were produced by a combination of techniques. During the first phase of this process vegetative cell components, in a suspension of vegetative cells and spores, were digested with 100 μg./ml. of trypsin plus 200

Table 2.—Summary of results of agglutination tests with vegetative cells and spores of *C. botulinum* type E, nontoxigenic variants, other types of *C. botulinum* and other Clostridia

Antigen		Type E	Boticin +	Boticin −	Type A	Type B
Type E	Flagellar	+, −	−	+, −	---	
	Somatic	+	+	+	---	
	Spore	+	+	+	---	
Boticin +	Flagellar	−	−	−	−	−
	Somatic	+	+	+	---	
	Spore	+	+	+	---	−
Nontoxigenic variants: Boticin	Flagellar	+, −	−	+, −	−	−
	Somatic	+	+	+	---	
	Spore	+	+	+	---	−
Type A	Flagellar	−	−	−	---	
	Somatic	−	−	−	---	
	Spore	−	−	−	−	
Type B (proteolytic)	Flagellar	−	−	−	+	−
	Somatic	−	−	−	---	
	Spore	−	−	−	---	
Type C	Flagellar	−	−	−	−	+
	Somatic	−	−	−	---	
	Spore	−	−	−	---	
Type F (proteolytic)	Flagellar	−	−	−	---	
	Somatic	−	−	−	---	
(Nonproteolytic)	Spore	−	−	−	---	
Other Clostridia	Flagellar	−	−	−	−	−
	Somatic	−	−	−	---	
	Spore	−	−	−	---	−

μg./ml. of lysozyme augmented by 1-minute sonications at hourly intervals during a 6- to 8-hour incubation period at 37° C. In the second phase the spores were separated from the debris by extraction in a two-phase system using polyethylene glycol (PEG) followed by as many washings as necessary to remove the PEG. The pure spore suspensions were diluted to contain 10^6 to 10^7 spores per milliliter, attenuated in 0.5 percent formalin and used to immunize New Zealand white rabbits as described above for the vegetative antigens.

Spore antisera were produced for seven toxigenic type E strains, four nontoxigenic variants—both producers and nonproducers of boticin E—one atypical strain (S9), one type A (62A) strain, one type B (169B) strain and a strain of *C. bifermentans*. These antisera were tested by the tube agglutination procedure against spore antigens of 18 toxigenic type E strains, 11 nontoxigenic variants, seven atypical strains, one strain each of types A, B, C, and F, and one strain each of *C. bifermentans*, *C. sordelli*, *C. perfringens* and *C. sporogenes*.

Agglutination tests showed that spore antigens were distinct and apart from those of the vegetative cell, since neither flagellar nor somatic antigens nor the debris of vegetative cells was agglutinated by these antisera. The nontoxigenic strains whose cultural characteristics are identical with type E were found to have identical spore antigens with the toxigenic strains and, therefore, appear to be true variants of type E.

The nontoxigenic atypical group was found, by agglutination and agglutinin absorption tests, to include strains sharing antigens with toxigenic type E and its nontoxigenic variants to varying degrees, and strains which were not agglutinated at all. Among those which failed to agglutinate was a strain originally described as a TP variant of toxigenic type E and later identified by Holdeman (personal communication) as *C. bifermentans*. This was confirmed by agglutination and agglutinin absorption tests which showed it to share common spore antigens with *C. bifermentans*.

Spore antisera of type E strains and nontoxigenic variants failed to agglutinate the spores of other types of *C. botulinum* or other *Clostridium* species investigated. Likewise, antisera produced against spores of other types of *C. botulinum* and other *Clostridium* species did not agglutinate the spores of type E or its nontoxigenic variants; neither did they share common spore antigens with each other.

The use of fluorescent antibody techniques for studying *C. botulinum* has given a variety of results, notwithstanding the popularity in recent years of such procedures for locating antigens, tracing proteins and identifying bacteria. Theoretically, fluorescent antibody techniques offer a number of advantages over cultural methods of identifying unknown bacteria.

They are rapid, are capable of detecting small numbers of the suspect organism, and can single it out among large numbers of other contaminants.

By the use of FA, Walker and Batty (40) grouped proteolytic types A, B, and F with conjugated type A antiserum, types C and D with conjugated antisera to each other, and found type E to be distinct from the others. Later they (41) found that three nontoxigenic strains stained brilliantly with type E conjugate whereas three OS variants were all negative. Spore antisera did not stain vegetative cells and type E spore antiserum was specific for type E, but that of type A stained spores of both A and B and reacted slightly with those of type E. Georgala and Boothroyd (17) used pasteurized vegetative-cell antigens for immunization and agar or broth cultures for smears. They were unable to get all type E strains to fluoresce with the same anti-E conjugate. Conjugated spore antibody, made specific for spores by adsorbing with vegetative cells, stained 41 out of 51 strains, indicating a broader spectrum for the spore antigen. Evancho et al. (16) also showed spore antigens to be distinct from vegetative antigens, but their spore antisera produced fluorescence with all six types.

Ward et al. (42) surveyed estuarine waters for the presence of *C. botulinum*, using FA in conjunction with culture methods. They found low fluorescence and poor correlation between fluorescence and toxicity. Midura et al. (27) inoculated commercial food products with type E spores and examined them by the direct FA method, using antisera to formalin-killed cells. Later they (28) used the same method to follow the growth of type E in artificially contaminated turkey rolls.

Our work is still in an early stage of development. The indirect method was chosen because a large number of antisera were already on hand and, since they were all prepared in rabbits, one antirabbit conjugate would do for all. Antigens for smears were prepared from overnight broth cultures heated at 100° C. for an hour from which the cells were centrifuged and resuspended in an equal volume of distilled water containing 0.5 percent formalin as a preservative. The sera were prepared by immunizing rabbits with suspensions of cells which had been similarly heat treated. These are what were referred to as somatic antigens and antisera in our agglutination work. While it is still too early to draw conclusions, four type E antisera and antisera produced against two nontoxigenic variants, when tested against a battery of antigens, have produced brilliant fluorescence with all 30 type-E strains used (figs. 1 and 2) with all 11 nontoxigenic variants (fig. 3). They also produced brilliant fluorescence with three of the "atypical" strains but not with four others which are OS or TP variants. A nonproteolytic strain of type F (strain 202 F) also fluoresced brilliantly with these sera (fig. 4) but a proteolytic one (Langeland strain) did not (fig. 5). The somatic antigen of the nonproteolytic strain was also agglutinated by these sera, whereas that of the proteolytic strain was not. Very weak fluorescence or none at all was produced with the proteolytic types A (fig. 6) and B (fig. 7) and with type C. Five commonly encountered additional clostridia were also negative (fig. 8) (*C. sporogenes*). Thus the results so far seem to be analogous to those obtained by somatic agglutination tests.

Immunodiffusion by the Ouchterlony gel diffusion

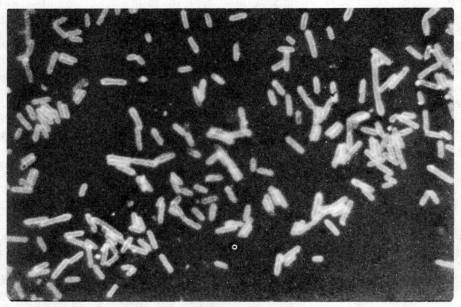

Figure 1.—Toxigenic type E strain 5192 stained with homologous antiserum.

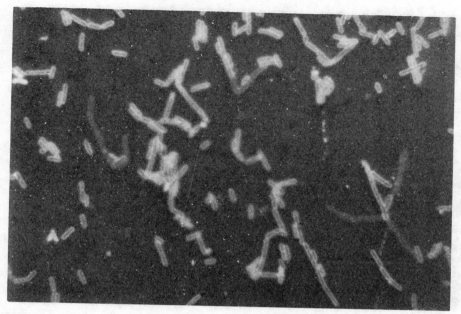

Figure 2.—Toxigenic type E strain 4203 stained with antiserum to type E strain 5192.

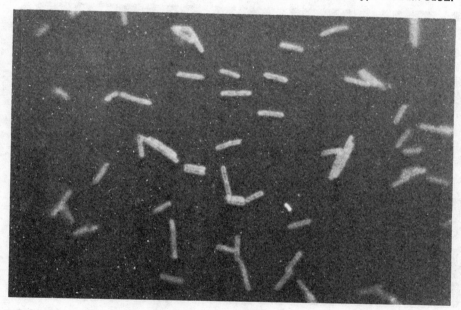

Figure 3.—Nontoxigenic variant strain S5 stained with antiserum to toxigenic type E strain 5192.

plate method for the study of *C. botulinum* toxins was reported by Sugiyama et al. (*38*). All six type-E strains tested gave a single precipitin line when 1 to 2 IU of antitoxin were used. Trypsinization of the toxin showed no increase in the maximum dilution producing a line but there was about a 200-fold increase in the minimum number of LD_{50} which this represented. Vermilyea et al. (*39*) used a slide modification of the Ouchterlony method and found that toxin of types A, B, and E all produced visible lines of precipitation but the mouse test was about 10,000 times as sensitive.

Anderson (personal communication) has developed a technique for concentrating *C. botulinum* proteins, including toxin, from food samples. Discontinuous pH electrophoresis on a modified polyacrylamide gel column, incorporating a liquid buffer trapped between two layers of small pore gel, is utilized to remove proteins from the sample and concentrate them in the trapped buffer. Complete medium in which *C. botulinum* had been grown was subjected to

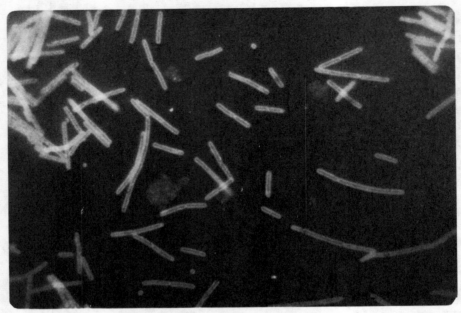

Figure 4.—Nonproteolytic type F strain 202F stained with antiserum to type E strain 5192.

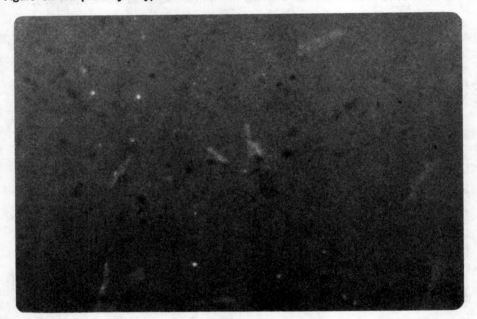

Figure 5.—Proteolytic type F, Langeland strain, treated with antiserum to type E strain 5192.

electrophoresis on a vertical flat polyacrylamide gel electrophoresis unit resulting in separation of the hemagglutinin and toxin of both types A and B into distinct fractions. The hemagglutinin protein bands of types A and B were found to cross react with the National Communicable Disease Center antitoxins for types A and B in double diffusion slide precipitin tests whereas the toxin bands did not.

In addition, analyzing the enzyme patterns of the strains revealed that most of these enzyme systems seem to be useful for distinguishing the types of *C. botulinum* and the nontoxigenic strains.

Isolation

Non-spore-forming contaminants are usually eliminated from enrichment cultures to improve the chances of isolating *C. botulinum* by heating at 80° C. for 30 minutes. This, however, is of little value for type E and nonproteolytic types B and F, since their

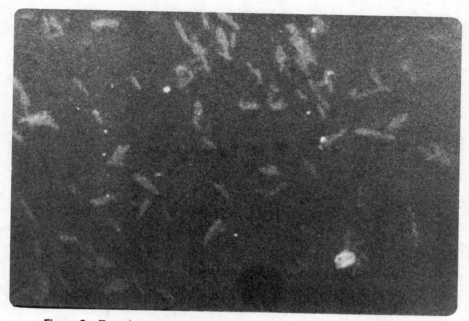

Figure 6.—Type A strain 62A treated with antiserum to type E strain 5192.

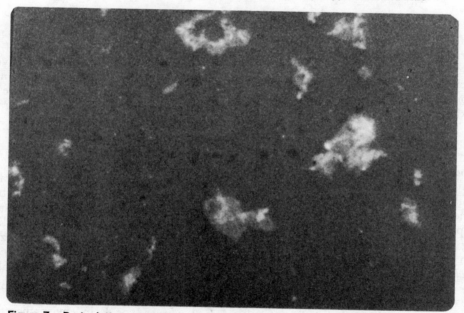

Figure 7.—Proteolytic type B strain 169B treated with antiserum to type E strain 5192.

spores are known to be almost as heat sensitive as the vegetative cells of many of the common contaminants. For this purpose, enrichment cultures have been treated with alcohol (23) successfully when a variety of environmental samples served as the inoculum.

After treatment, the cultures are streaked on plating media for the selection of typical colonies. A variety of media may be used for this purpose. Some of those frequently employed are blood agar, liver veal egg agar, brain heart infusion agar, a variety of bee infusion agars, and a modification of an egg yolk medium orginally proposed by McClung and Toabe (26). Wheaton and Pratt (43) list a variety of additional media which also could be utilized for the isolation of C. botulinum. On agar media containing egg yolk, the production of opalescence in the medium and a layer having an iridescent appearance adjacent to and covering the colonies of C. botulinum has been used as an aid in the selection of this organism. Hobbs et al. (20) caution, however, that the use of liver veal

Figure 8.—*Clostridium sporogenes* treated with antiserum to type E strain 5192.

egg agar, in their experience, does not produce a very marked iridescence or pearly layer with *C. botulinum*. This might also be true of any agar containing glucose to which egg yolk was added. Typical colonies are picked from the plates and subcultured into a satisfactory toxin production medium.

Problems

The isolation of pure cultures from grossly contaminated samples or enrichment cultures from the samples is quite difficult and in many instances impossible. The success of any specific procedure for isolation is dependent upon the type and amount of contaminating microflora. Treatment with alcohol (*23*), although facilitating the isolation of pure cultures of *C. botulinum* from enrichment media, is useful only when the extraneous microflora contain primarily vegetative cells. If the mixed microflora consist primarily of spore formers, this technique is not satisfactory. The predominant types of clostridia in a large number of environmental samples examined for *C. botulinum* type E are nontoxigenic organisms resembling type E. Among the other numerous clostridia which complicate isolation are *C. bifermentans*, *C. novyi*, *C. perfringens*, and *C. sporogenes*. Failure to demonstrate the toxins of *C. botulinum* does not preclude the possibility that the organism may be present in foods or environmental materials such as sediments, soils, clams, oysters, fish viscera, or crabs.

Certain micro-organisms present in grossly contaminated samples may prevent germination and outgrowth of *C. botulinum* while others may destroy the toxins as they are being produced (*7*). It has been shown by our laboratory (*24*) that environmental materials frequently contain nontoxigenic microorganisms resembling type E that produce bacteriocinlike substances which are active against strains of toxigenic type E. One of these bacteriocins, boticin E, was shown to be active against strains of *C. botulinum* type E and non-proteolytic types B and F, but not active against proteolytic types A, B, or F.

This substance is produced by certain nontoxigenic variants of type E. Boticin E is bacteriolytic for vegetative cells and bacteriostatic for spores.

One of the characteristics of this bacteriocin is its extreme sensitivity to proteolytic enzymes. Utilizing this characteristic, a procedure has been developed in our laboratories which incorporates filtered, sterilized trypsin (Difco 1:250) at a concentration of 1 mg./ml. into enrichment medium to improve the detection of *C. botulinum* type E in environmental samples. Preliminary data, a portion of which is given in table 3, show the effect of this procedure. More positives were obtained when samples of sediments, shellfish and crabs were cultured in TPGY containing trypsin than in the trypsin-free medium.

The number of positives is also greater upon trypsinization of cultures following growth in trypsin-free medium, but the trypsin-containing medium is superior. In addition to obtaining a greater number of positives with this medium, the addition of trypsin also potentiates the type E toxin which is formed and produces higher titers than when cultures are tryp-

Table 3.—Effect of incorporating trypsin in culture medium for detecting *Clostridium botulinum* type E

Type of samples	Number of samples	Number of positive samples in 72 hours at 26° C.		
		TPGY containing 1 mg./ml. trypsin	TPGY without trypsin	Trypsinized following growth in TPGY
Sediments_____	227	126 (56)	32 (14)	76 (33)
Shellfish_____	85	24 (28)	13 (15)	13 (15)
Blue crab_____	200	63 (31)	27 (13)	49 (24)

NOTE.—Numbers in parentheses are percentages.

sinized after growth, thus permitting serological typing of the toxin with greater accuracy. Table 4 shows typical examples of toxin titers obtained with sediment samples.

Table 4.—Effect of incorporation of trypsin in culture medium on toxin titers

Sample number	Toxicity[1] produced in 72 hours at 26° C.		
	TPGY containing 1 mg./ml. trypsin	TPGY without trypsin	Trypsinized following growth in TPGY
11_____	>200	3	>4
12_____	>10	1–2	5
24_____	>40	<3	4
34_____	>40	1–2	5

[1]Toxicity expressed as minimum lethal dose per milliliter.

Medium containing trypsin will support outgrowth and toxin production of the other types of *C. botulinum* and potentiate the toxin of nonproteolytic strains of type F as well.

A limited number of experiments has shown that a greater number of positives was obtained from environmental samples inoculated with small number of spores of nonproteolytic types B and F when trypsin was incorporated into the medium than when it was not. Moreover, this medium has the additional advantage that fewer mice are necessary for sample analysis since the need of titrating both the trypsinized and nontrypsinized enrichment cultures is eliminated.

References

(1) BONVENTRE, P. F., and L. L. KEMPE. 1960. Physiology of toxin production by *Clostridium botulinum* types A and B. I. Growth, autolysis, and toxin production. J. Bacteriol. *79:* 18–23.

(2) BOTT, T. L., J. S. DEFFNER, E. McCOY, and E. M. FOSTER. 1966. *Clostridium botulinum* type E in fish from the Great Lakes. J. Bacteriol. *91:* 919–924.

(3) CARDELLA, M. A., J. T. DUFF, C. GOTTFRIED, and J. S. BEGEL. 1958. Studies on immunity to toxins of *Clostridium botulinum*. IV. Production and purification of type C toxin for conversion to toxoid. J. Bacteriol. *75:* 360–365.

(4) CARDELLA, M. A., J. T. DUFF, B. H. WINGFIELD, and C. GOTTFRIED. 1960. Studies on immunity to toxins of *Clostridium botulinum*. VI. Purification and detoxification of type D toxin and the immunological response to toxoid. J. Bacteriol. *79:* 372–378.

(5) CRAIG, J. M., and K. S. PILCHER. 1966. *Clostridium botulinum* type F: isolation from salmon from the Columbia River. Science *153:* 311–312.

(6) CRISLEY, F. D. 1960. Routine method for the goldfish assay of toxin in crude culture centrifugates of *Clostridium botulinum* type A. Appl. Microbiol. *8:* 282–285.

(7) DOLMAN, C. E. 1957. Type E (fish-borne) botulism: a review. Japan. J. Med. Sci. Biol. *10:* 383–395.

(8) DOLMAN, C. E. 1957. Recent observations on type E botulism. Canad. J. Public Health *48:* 187–198.

(9) DOLMAN, C. E., and L. MURAKAMI. 1961. *Clostridium botulinum* type F with recent observations on other types. J. Infect. Diseases *109:* 107–128.

(10) DUBOVSKY, B. J., and K. F. MEYER. 1922. An experimental study of the methods available for the enrichment, demonstration and isolation of *B. botulinus* in specimens of soil and its products, in suspected food, in clinical and in necropsy material. J. Infect. Diseases *31:* 501.

(11) DUFF, J. T., G. G. WRIGHT, and A. YARINSKY. 1956. Activation of *Clostridium botulinum* type E toxin by trypsin. J. Bacteriol. *72:* 455–460.

(12) DUFF, J. T., G. G. WRIGHT, J. KLERER, D. E. MOORE, and R. H. BIBLER. 1957. Studies on immunity to toxins of *Clostridium botulinum*. I. A simplified procedure for isolation of type A toxin. J. Bacteriol. *73:* 42–47.

(13) DUFF, J. T., J. KLERER, R. H. BIBLER, D. E. MOORE, C. GOTTFRIED, and G. G. WRIGHT. 1957. Studies on immunity to toxins of *Clostridium botulinum*. II. Production and purification of type B toxin for toxoid. J. Bacteriol. *73:* 597–601.

(14) EKLUND, M. W., D. I. WIELER, and F. T. POYSKY. 1967. Outgrowth and toxin production of nonproteolytic type B *Clostridium botulinum* at 3.3° to 5.6° C. J. Bacteriol. *93: 1461–1462.*

(15) EKLUND, M. W., F. T. POYSKY, and D. I. WIELER. 1967. Characteristics of *Clostridium botulinum* type F isolated from the Pacific coast of the United States. Appl. Microbiol. *15:* 1316–1323.

(16) EVANCHO, G. M., J. H. KEENE, and D. F. HOLTMAN. 1967. Antigenic relationships between vegetative cells and spores of *Clostridium botulinum* types A–F. Bacteriol. Proc. p. 6.

(17) GEORGALA, D. L., and M. BOOTHROYD. 1966. Fluorescent antibody techniques applied to *C. botulinum* types A, B, and E. *In* Botulism 1966. Proc. Intern. Symp. Food Microbiol. Moscow, pp. 494–502.

(18) GUNNISON, J. B., J. R. CUMMINGS, and K. F. MEYER. 1936. *Clostridium botulinum* type E. Proc. Soc. Exptl. Biol. Med. *35:* 278–280.

(19) HAZEN, E. L. 1942. Differential characters of two strains of *Clostridium botulinum* type E: action of toxin on chickens. Proc. Soc. Exptl. Biol. Med. *50:* 112–114.

(20) HOBBS, G., A. STIEBRS, and M. W. EKLUND. 1967. Egg yolk reaction of *Clostridium botulinum* type E in different basal media. J. Bacteriol. *93:* 1192.

(21) INUKAI, Y. 1962. Effect of carbohydrate on toxin production by *Clostridium botulinum* type A. Japan. J. Vet. Res. *10:* 64–71.

(22) JOHANNSEN, A. 1963. *Clostridium botulinum* in Sweden and the adjacent waters. J. Appl. Bacteriol. *26:* 43–47.

(23) JOHNSTON, R., S. HARMON, and D. KAUTTER. 1964. Method to facilitate the isolation of *Clostridium botulinum* type E. J. Bacteriol. *88:* 1521–1522.

(24) KAUTTER, D. A., HARMON, R. K. LYNT, Jr., and T. LILLY, Jr. 1966. Antagonistic effect on *Clostridium botulinum* type E by organisms resembling it. Appl. Microbiol. *14:* 616–622.

(25) LYNT, R. K., Jr., H. M. SOLOMON, D. A. KAUTTER, and T. LILLY, Jr. 1967. Serological studies of *Clostridium botulinum* type E and related organisms. J. Bacteriol. *93:* 27–35.

(26) McCLUNG, L. S., and R. TOABE. 1947. The egg yolk plate reaction for the presumptive diagnosis of *Clostridium sporogenes* and certain species of the gangrene and botulinum groups. J. Bacteriol. *53:* 139–147.

(27) MIDURA, T. F., Y. INOUYE, and H. L. BODILY. 1967. Use of immunofluorescence to identify *Clostridium botulinum* types A, B, and E. Public Health Rept. (U.S.) *82:* 275–279.

(28) MIDURA, T., C. TACLINDO, Jr., G. S. NYGAARD, H. L. BODILY, and R. M. WOOD. 1968. Use of immunofluorescence and animal tests to detect growth and toxin production by *Clostridium botulinum* type E in food. Appl. Microbiol. *16:* 102–105.

(29) MØLLER, V., and I. SCHEIBEL. 1960. Preliminary report on the isolation of an apparently new type of *C. botulinum*. Acta Pathol. Microbiol. Scand. *48:* 80.

(30) NAKAMURA, Y., H. IIDA, K. SAEKI, K. KANZAWA, and T. KARASHIMADA. 1956. Type E botulism in Hokkaido, Japan. Japan. J. Med. Sci. Biol. *9:* 45–58.

(31) OHYE, D. F., and W. J. SCOTT. 1953. The temperature relations of *Clostridium botulinum* types A and B. Australian J. Biol. Sci. *6:* 178–189.

(32) ONO, T. 1962. Serological studies on *Clostridium botulinum* type E. II. Properties of the antigens. Res. Bull. Hokkaido Provincial Sanit. Res. Center *13:* 9-20.

(33) ONO, T. 1962. Studies on the variation in *Clostridium botulinum* type E. II. Stability and agglutinability of dissociated colonies. Res. Bull. Hokkaido Provincial Sanit. Res. Center *13:* 41–49.

(34) RICE, C. E., L. C. SMITH, E. F. PALLISTER, and G. B. REED. 1947. *Clostridium botulinum* type B toxoids. Canad J. Res. *25:*(Sec. E): 175–180.

(35) SCHMIDT, C. F., and W. K. NANK. 1960. Radiation sterilization of food. I. Procedures for the evaluation of the radiation resistance of spores of *Clostridium botulinum* in food products. Food Res. *25:* 321–327.

(36) SCHMIDT, C. F., W. K. NANK, and R. V. LECHOWICH. 1962. Radiation sterilization of food. II. Some aspects of the growth, sporulation and radiation resistance of spores of *Clostridium botulinum* type E. J. Food Sci. *27:* 77–84.

(37) SOLOMON, H. M., R. K. LYNT, Jr., D. A. KAUTTER, and T. LILLY, Jr. 1968. Serological studies of *Clostridium botulinum* type E and related organisms. II. Serology of spores. Bacteriol. Proc. p. 76.

(38) SUGIYAMA, H., B. VON MAYERUAUSER, G. GOGAT, and R. C. HEIMSCH. 1967. Immunological reactivity of trypsinized *Clostridium botulinum* type E toxin. Proc. Soc. Exptl. Biol. Med. *126:* 690–694.

(39) VERMILYEA, B. L., H. W. WALKER, and J. C. AYRES. 1968. Detection of botulinal toxins by immunodiffusion. Appl. Microbiol. *16:* 21–24.

(40) WALKER, P. D., and I. BATTY. 1964. Fluorescent studies in the genus *Clostridium*. II. A rapid method for differentiating *Clostridium botulinum* types A, B, and F, types C and D, and type E. J. Appl. Bacteriol. *27:* 140–142.

(41) WALKER, P. D., and I. BATTY. 1966. The serology of *C. botulinum* with reference to fluorescent staining. In *Botulism 1966*, Proc. Intern. Symp. Food Microbiol. Moscow, pp. 482–493.

(42) WARD, B. Q., B. J. CARROLL, and E. S. GARRETT. 1967. Presence of *C. botulinum* type E in estuarine waters of the United States Gulf Coast comparing fluorescent detection and mouse-toxin methods. *In* Botulism 1966. Proc. Intern. Symp. Food Microbiol. Moscow, pp. 503–507.

(43) WHEATON, E., and G. B. PRATT. 1961. Comparative studies on media for counting anaerobic bacterial spores. II. J. Food Sci. *26:* 261–268.

TYPING OF *CLOSTRIDIUM BOTULINUM* TYPE E BY AGGLUTINATION*

by Koichi Yamamoto, Heiji Kudo, Hiroshi Asano, Tsutomu Sato, Keiichi Koshida, Shodo Nabeya, Koichi Kasai, *and* Yoji Horiuchi
Department of Bacteriology, Faculty of Medicine of The Hirosaki University, Hirosaki, Japan

Summary

By the application of immune sera prepared against mechanically isolated flagella and extract obtained from bacillary bodies deprived of flagella, an antigen schema for *C. botulinum* type E was established. This schema, though not yet complete, seems to show differences in antigenic structure between the strains of *C. botulinum* type E studied and related clostridia, and a relationship between the strains and their regional or geographical distribution.

Introduction

Since the first description of type E botulism in Japan by Nakamura et al. (7) in 1951, 55 outbreaks involving 315 patients and 81 victims have been recorded in this country. With one exceptional type B case, the outbreaks were all caused by type E. On the other hand, a number of nontoxigenic strains resembling in every way *C. botulinum* type E have been isolated in Japan and other countries, thus causing difficulties and confusion in identification. It would be desirable to establish the antigenic structure of *C. botulinum* and related bacilli. The authors hypothesized that nontoxigenic strains, with cultural and morphological characteristics similar to those of *C. botulinum* type E, are identical with *C. botulinum* type E, because no available technique to prove toxin producing abilities has ever been proposed. For these reasons they undertook to establish the antigenic structure of this genus.

As early as 1925, Schoenholz and Meyer (10) issued the immunological classification of *C. botulinum* type A and B.

Serological dissimilarity between one strain of type E from Germany and another strain of type E from Canada was reported by Hazen (3). Dolman (2) indicated also several strains to be antigenically distinguishable. Nakamura et al. (8) classified 18 strains isolated in Hokkaido into five groups by slide agglutination. According to Ono (9) heat-labile antigen was group specific and heat-stable antigen was common to all. Kudo (5) tried to classify 36 strains of type E with sera prepared against living and heated bacilli but without any appreciable result. Lynt et al. (6) reported that the flagellar antigen (H–O) treated with

formalin was highly strain specific, whereas the somatic antigens (heated) produced cross agglutination. Nontoxigenic strains physiologically and morphologically identical with type E strains cross agglutinated via the somatic antigen. The nontoxigenic strains seemed to have no great antigenic differences from toxigenic type E. The results of the above authors seem only to show the possibility of a classification of *C. botulinum* by agglutination but give no reliable immunological clues for further investigations. Kudo's results (5) being unsatisfactory, the present authors undertook the classification of *C. botulinum* type E from an immunological viewpoint which is different from that introduced first by Weil-Felix and later developed and established by Kauffman and White. That is, this approach is different from the interpretation of H (OH) agglutination between flagellated bacteria and immune serum as well as from that of O agglutination between the so-called nonflagellated or *heated bacteria* and immune serum. As the interpretation and application of H (OH) and O agglutinations to the agglutination of *C. botulinum* type E require exact experimental data, Kudo (4) and Asano (1) made a series of preliminary investigations.

Methods

KUDO'S TEST

Cultivation and preparation of flagella and bacillary bodies deprived of flagella.—Four strains "Aomori," "Tenno," "341," and "211" were cultured on the nutrient agar consisting of ox-liver-infusion, 0.25 percent NaCl, 1 percent peptone, 1 percent beef extract, 1.5 percent agar, and 5 percent goat erythrocytes. The cultured Petri-plates were kept in a tightly closed steel jar under burning phosphorus and incubated for 48 hours at 30° C.; under which conditions spore formation was discouraged. Cultures were suspended in distilled water, vibrated strongly for flagella separation, and then centrifuged at various velocities. This procedure yielded flagella separate from bacillary bodies deprived of flagella (dpf) (fig. 1). The purification of flagella was confirmed with the electron microscope (Hitachi HU11 A special). Rarely seen, fragment-like corpuscles among flagella proved to have no practical immunological significance.

---

*Paper not read at the conference.

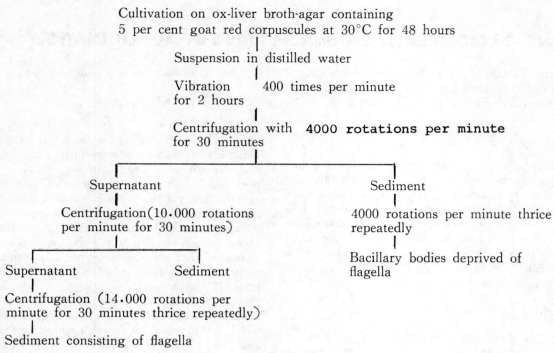

Cultivation on ox-liver broth-agar containing
5 per cent goat red corpuscules at 30°C for 48 hours

Suspension in distilled water

Vibration   400 times per minute
for 2 hours

Centrifugation with   **4000 rotations per minute**
for 30 minutes

Supernatant

Centrifugation(10.000 rotations
per minute for 30 minutes)

Supernatant   Sediment

Centrifugation (14.000 rotations per
minute for 30 minutes thrice repeatedly)

Sediment consisting of flagella

Sediment

4000 rotations per minute thrice
repeatedly

Bacillary bodies deprived of
flagella

Figure 1.

Immunization.—Flagella, lyophilized bacillary bodies dpf, unwashed fresh living bacilli and bacilli heated at 100° C. for 2 hours were used as immunogens. The optical density of the immunogens was adjusted to McFarland No. 2 opacity standard. These were then injected intraperitoneally into rabbits, in doses of 0.5 ml. each several times at 4- to 5-day intervals, then intravenously into the ear vein in increasing doses. The animals were exsanguinated 1 week after the last injection.

Agglutination.—The agglutinogens were suspensions of living bacilli, bacillary bodies dpf, and heated bacilli adjusted to an optical density equivalent to McFarland No. 3 opacity standard. When a bacillary suspension agglutinated spontaneously, it was kept standing at room temperature until the supernatant remained homogenous. Such a supernatant gave satisfactory results as an antigen, as long as the turbidity could be detected by the eye.

Antigens were added into serial dilutions of immune sera in equal proportions (0.5 ml. each), kept in a water-bath for 3 hours at 37° C., then the endpoint titre was determined with a 6X-hand lens. The agglutination tests with the four strains studied showed the following:

(*1*) Flagella serum agglutinated only living bacilli but did not agglutinate bacillary bodies dpf nor heated bacilli (table 1a). The reaction was therefore highly specific, that is, the reaction was H agglutination in its true sense.

(*2*) Serum prepared against living bacilli agglutinated, contrary to the flagella serum, not only living bacilli but also bacillary bodies dpf, both agglutinations showing almost the same titre (table 1b) and in the same manner. Thus the differentiation between flagella and bacillary bodies dpf was masked. Therefore the interpretation that the agglutination of living bacilli is so-called H (OH) agglutination is not correct. This kind of agglutination should be termed only OH agglutination.

(*3*) Living bacilli and bacillary bodies dpf agglutinated alike in the sera against bacillary bodies dpf, so that the differentiation between both agglutinations is impossible (table 1c). Heated bacilli were scarcely agglutinated.

(*4*) Sera prepared against heated bacilli cross-agglutinated living bacilli and bacillary bodies dpf feebly and heated bacilli strongly, so that heat-stable antigens are common to all (table 1d). It is not advisable to use such a nonspecific reaction for bacterial classification. The reason why such a reaction occurs can be easily imagined; heating itself might give rise, partially or mostly, to the degeneration of bacillary components which results in nonspecific reactions.

These four results demonstrate well that, in case of H agglutination, in its true sense, only the agglutination between the living bacilli and the serum against flagella should be adopted.

ASANO'S TEST

Preparation of bacillary extract.—Cultures grown for 48 hours on the same nutrient agar as was used by Kudo were suspended in distilled water, vibrated for 3 hours and centrifuged. The bacillary bodies thus separated from flagella were resuspended in distilled water and disintegrated with an ultrasonic generator (KMS–250–160 Kubota Seisakusho). The suspension was then centrifuged at high velocity and the supernatant was obtained as bacillary extract. The procedure is shown in figure 2. The extract concentration was then adjusted to 1 percent protein content with Hitachi Hand Protein Refractrometer and lyophilized.

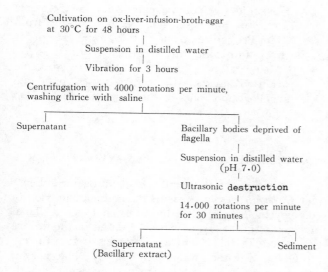

Figure 2.

Immunization.—The inoculations of rabbits were begun at first intraperitoneally with 0.2 cc. of extract and then repeated, with increasing doses, at 4 to 5 days interval for three or four times. Thereafter it was given intravenously by the same schedule. The animals were exsanguinated when the agglutinin titre reached 1:3,200 or higher. In this manner immune sera were prepared against the four kinds of bacillary extracts, "Aomori," "Tenno," "341," and "211."

Bacillary extract or extract as an immunogen was termed *"extract antigen"* by Asano and the serum against the extract *"extract antiserum"* a designation analagous to "O serum" against "O antigen." Therefore the term *"extract agglutination"* denotes "agglutination between bacillary antigen and extract antiserum."

Agglutination.—Cross agglutination tests were made between the strains "Aomori," "Tenno," "341," "211" and the above four immune sera. The method

and the observation were the same as in the flagellar agglutination of Kudo and the results were as follows (table 2):

(1) Each of four living strains were agglutinated specifically by homologous serum; this agglutination being consistent with flagella agglutination.

(2) Contrary to this, the strains heated at 100° C. for 2 hours were influenced by at least two or more sera, that is, this reaction is nonspecific and unfavorable for the classification. Based on these results, the first reaction is substituted for the socalled "O agglutination" widely used in routine work.

Results

Sixty-four toxigenic and 54 nontoxigenic strains were used. Of the toxigenic strains, eight were derived from Canada, three from Alaska and one from America, and one of nontoxigenic strains derived from Canada. Before the serological testing the strains were studied for characteristics such as sugar fermenting abilities, soubleization of coagulated serum and egg-white. They were then tested for agglutinability in the antisera prepared against flagella and bacillary extracts of 27 toxigenic and 17 nontoxigenic strains, respectively. The methods used were those of Kudo and Asano as described above.

Flagellar and extract antiserum agglutinations.—The authors could classify 118 strains into 9 serological groups with both agglutinations, respectively, (tables 3 and 4). It is noteworthy that the groups 1, 2, 3, 4, and 7 of both agglutination types were completely consistent in numbers and kinds of the strains included. All strains in flagella agglutination groups 2, 3, and 4 were agglutinated by the sera prepared against the extracts of 15 toxigenic and nontoxigenic strains (table 4). From these data it is obvious that the antigens of the strains in these groups are widely shared.

Absorption studies.—Because of excessive serum consumption in the previous experiment, seven kinds of sera against toxigenic strains and two kinds of sera against nontoxigenic strains had to be omitted. Twenty-six kinds of absorbed sera and nine sera which did not require absorption were used for further agglutination reactions. So, 35 antiflagella sera and 35 antiextract sera were studied (tables 5 and 6). Flagella serum and extract serum of one and the same strain were labeled with the same arabic cipher so that the combination of cipher of every serum agglutinating one strain represented antigenic structure of the strain concerned (tables 7 and 8). In this way 103 of 118 strains were classified into 13 serological groups (table 8).

Group 1.—Only one strain "Aomori" belongs to this group. It has one flagellar antigen and one extract antigen designated as 1. Strain "VH" deficient in this flagellar antigen was omitted.

Group 2.—All 28 strains of this group, possessing flagellar antigens 6, 7, 8, 9, 10, and extract antigens 6, 7, 8, 9, 10, were from Akita Prefecture. Some strains possess, in addition, the flagellar and/or extract antigens 2 and/or 5. Flagellar and extract antigens of strains "667," "Fish 7," "Honjyo 37," "Haginari 8," "762" were the same. These strains, except for two, were all toxigenic. The above fact indicates the existence of a relationship between antigenic structure of the strains and their regional distribution.

Group 3.—Five toxigenic strains belong to this group. They possess common extract antigens 6, 7, 9, 10, and common flagellar antigens 7, 8, 9, 14. One was isolated in Hokkaido and four in Akita Prefecture, so that the same relationship as in group 2 seems to exist.

Group 4.—Strains of this group, with one exception, possess antigens 14, 15, 16 as both flagellar and extract antigens, and 11 as an extract antigen. All or some of the antigens 6, 7, 8, 9, 10 exist also in both flagella and extract, or in either one of them. Of 12 toxigenic strains, seven were from Hokkaido, only one from Aomori Prefecture, four from Akita Prefecture, and two nontoxigenic strains from Akita Prefecture.

Group 5.—Three toxigenic strains of this group are represented with flagellar antigens 6, 7, 8, 9, and extract antigens 6, 8, 9. Flagellar antigens 14, 15, 16 seem to characterize this group, more or less. Two are from Akita Prefecture and one from Hokkaido.

Group 6.—Only one extract antigen 9, and one flagellar antigen 8, are shared by two toxigenic strains. One strain was isolated in Hokkaido and the other in Aomori Prefecture.

Group 7.—This group includes nine toxigenic and eight nontoxigenic strains. Most of them, irrespective of toxigenicity, possess flagellar antigens 3, 11, 13, 15, 16, 21, and extract antigens 11, 13. The fact that five Canadian strains are included, seems to point toward some geographical distribution.

Group 8.—Two toxigenic strains from Canada and Hokkaido, and six nontoxigenic strains from Akita Prefecture are included. The latter are all lacking in extract antigens, but flagellar antigen 11 is common to all eight strains.

Group 9.—Two toxigenic strains, one from Alaska, one from Canada seem to react with antigen 13 of the nontoxigenic strain "Joryu 74."

Group 10.—All four nontoxigenic strains from Akita Prefecture have in common extract antigen 20 and three of them have flagellar antigens 13 and 20.

Group 11.—All three toxigenic strains from Hokkaido belong here. Very characteristic of this group is that two strains have 17, 22, 24 as both flagellar and extract antigens, and one strain 17, 22, 24 as extract antigens and 17, 23 as flagellar antigens.

Group 12.—One flagellar antigen 8, and one extract antigen 10, characterize two toxigenic strains of this group. They are from Akita Prefecture.

Group 13.—Three toxigenic strains from Hokkaido, five nontoxigenic strains from Aomori Prefecture, and six nontoxigenic strains from Akita Prefecture belong to this group. Except for three nontoxigenic strains "Aomori 783," "Aomori 786," "Fish 9," and one toxigenic strain "Kameda," the others possess only one flagellar and one extract antigen specific to themselves.

Discussion

The authors could establish an antigenic schema for *C. botulinum* type E with methods not previously employed. This schema indicates that, as a whole, toxigenic strains are prone to be found in the groups 1 through 7 while nontoxigenic strains are most likely to be found in the groups 7 through 13. The schema also shows a relationship existing between the antigenic structure of the strains and their regional or geographical distribution; for example, 26 of 38 toxigenic strains from Akita Prefecture belong to group 2, while seven of 18 toxigenic strains from Hokkaido to the group 4, and 5 of seven toxigenic strains from Canada to group 7.

Twelve nontoxigenic strains resemble toxigenic strains antigenically as seen in the groups 2, 4, and 7. Skulberg and Hausken (11) stated that the formation of toxin is a main characteristic of *C. botulinum*, but these data show with great probability that these nontoxigenic strains may be identical with *C. botulinum* type E. The nontoxigenic strains in the group 13 contain only one or two antigens specific to themselves, so that they might clearly be regarded as different from the nontoxigenic strains in groups 3, 4, and 7. That is, they probably are only related clostridia.

The antigenic schema proposed by the authors is not always decisive, because of the impossibility of the fixation of variable antigenic phases appearing

Table 1.—Agglutination of four strains of *Clostridium botulinum* type E with antisera prepared against them (Kudo's test)

Strains \ Immune Sera		Prepared with flagella			
		Aomori	Tenno	341	211
Living	Aomori	6400	—		200
	Tenno	—	6400	—	—
	341	—	—	12800	800
	211	400	—	800	12800
Bacillary bodies deprived of flagella	Aomori	—	—	—	—
	Tenno	—	—	—	—
	341	—	—	—	—
	211	—	—	—	—
Heated at 100°C for 2 hours	Aomori	—	—	—	—
	Tenno	—	—	—	—
	341	—	—	—	—
	211	—	—	—	—

Strains \ Immune Sera		Prepared with living bacilli			
		Aomori	Tenno	341	211
Living	Aomori	6400	—	—	400
	Tenno	—	6400	200	200
	341	—	—	6400	200
	211	400	—	200	6400
Bacillary bodies deprived of flagella	Aomori	6400	—	—	400
	Tenno	—	6400	200	200
	341	—	—	6400	200
	211	—	—	200	6400
Heated at 100°C for 2 hours	Aomori	100	—	—	—
	Tenno	—	—	—	—
	341	—	—	200	—
	211	—	—	100	100

Strains \ Immune Sera		Prepared with bacillary bodies deprived of flagella			
		Aomori	Tenno	341	211
Living	Aomori	3200	100	200	200
	Tenno	—	3200	200	200
	341	—	100	3200	200
	211	—	200	400	3200
Bacillary bodies deprived of flagella	Aomori	3200	100	200	200
	Tenno	—	3200	200	200
	341	—	200	3200	400
	211	—	200	400	6400
Heated at 100°C for 2 hours	Aomori	100	—	—	—
	Tenno	—	—	—	—
	341	—	—	200	—
	211	—	—	—	—

Strains \ Immune Sera		Prepared with bacilli which were heated at 100°C for 2 hours			
		Aomori	Tenno	341	211
Living	Aomori	400	200	100	200
	Tenno	100	200	100	100
	341	200	200	200	100
	211	200	200	200	200
Bacillary bodies deprived of flagella	Aomori	400	100	100	200
	Tenno	100	200	100	100
	341	100	200	200	100
	211	200	200	100	200
Heated at 100°C for 2 hours	Aomori	3200	6400	1600	1600
	Tenno	3200	6400	3200	6400
	341	800	3200	6400	1600
	211	1600	6400	1600	6400

Table 2.—Agglutination of four strains of *Clostridium botulinum* type E with antisera prepared against their bacillary extracts (Asano's test)

Strains \ Immune Sera		Prepared with bacillary extract			
		Aomori	Tenno	341	211
Living	Aomori	3200	----	----	----
	Tenno	----	3200	----	----
	341	----	----	3200	----
	211	----	----	100	3200

Strains \ Immune Sera		Prepared with bacillary extract			
		Aomori	Tenno	341	211
Heated at 100° C. for 2 hours	Aomori	800	---	400	---
	Tenno	400	1600	400	400
	341	100	400	800	200
	211	100	---	---	1600

Table 3.—Flagellar agglutination of 118

Immune Sera		Aomori	Tenno	341	211	Fish 8	667	Jundai 1	Iwanai	Fish 7	Haginari 28	Haginari 9	762	Fish 6	801	777	Yamagata	Hashishita 40	Fish 11	Fish 6H	Bute 7	Jōryu 74
		●	●	●	●	●	●	●	●	●	●	●	●	●	●	●	●	○	●	●	○	○
Group 1																						
Aomori	●	6400	—	—	200	—	—	—	—	—	—	—	—	—	—	—	—	—	—	800	3200	—
VH	●	6400	—	—	200	—	—	—	—	—	—	—	—	—	—	—	—	—	—	400	1600	—
Group 2																						
Tenno	●	100	12800	—	—	1600	1600	6400	3200	3200	1600	1600	3200	12800	12800	1600	800	12800	800	200	—	—
Fish 8	●	100	12800	—	—	3200	3200	3200	1600	3200	1600	3200	6400	6400	3200	1600	800	6400	3200	100	—	—
759	●	—	12800	—	—	1600	800	6400	3200	3200	1600	1600	3200	6400	3200	1600	3200	6400	800	200	—	—
667	●	—	12800	—	—	1600	6400	3200	3200	3200	3200	3200	12800	12800	3200	3200	800	12800	3200	200	—	—
Fish 35	●	—	6400	—	—	1600	6400	6400	3200	3200	3200	3200	6400	12800	3200	1600	800	12800	800	200	—	—
798	●	100	1600	—	—	1600	1600	6400	3200	6400	1600	1600	6400	12800	6400	3200	800	12800	800	200	—	—
800	●	100	1600	—	—	1600	6400	800	3200	6400	3200	1600	6400	12800	3200	1600	400	12800	800	200	—	—
Fish 3	○	100	800	—	—	1600	3200	6400	3200	3200	1600	1600	6400	12800	3200	1600	400	12800	800	200	—	—
Fish 67	●	—	1600	—	—	1600	3200	6400	3200	3200	1600	1600	3200	12800	3200	1600	800	12800	800	200	—	—
Fish 13	●	—	3200	200	—	1600	6400	6400	3200	6400	1600	800	6400	12800	6400	1600	800	12800	1600	—	—	—
761	●	—	3200	—	—	1600	6400	6400	3200	6400	3200	800	12800	12800	6400	3200	12800	12800	3200	—	—	—
Jundai 1	●	—	3200	—	—	1600	6400	6400	6400	3200	3200	3200	6400	12800	3200	6400	6400	12800	3200	—	—	—
760	●	—	1600	—	—	1600	6400	6400	3200	6400	3200	800	12800	12800	12800	3200	12800	12800	3200	—	—	—
Haginari 8	●	100	1600	—	—	1600	1600	6400	1600	6400	1600	1600	6400	6400	3200	1600	800	12800	1600	—	—	—
Iwanai	●	—	1600	—	—	3200	1600	12800	6400	6400	3200	1600	6400	12800	6400	6400	1600	12800	3200	—	—	—
Fish 7	●	100	12800	—	—	1600	12800	6400	3200	6400	3200	3200	12800	12800	6400	800	800	12800	3200	100	—	—
Haginari	●	—	12800	—	—	1600	6400	3200	1600	3200	1600	1600	3200	12800	3200	800	800	12800	800	100	—	—
775	●	—	3200	—	—	800	3200	6400	3200	3200	1600	800	3200	12800	6400	1600	6400	12800	3200	200	—	—
Haginari 28-1	●	—	400	—	—	1600	3200	6400	3200	3200	6400	3200	12800	12800	6400	3200	1600	12800	3200	200	—	—
527	○	100	12800	—	—	1600	3200	3200	800	3200	1600	800	6400	12800	3200	3200	800	12800	1600	200	—	—
Haginari 9	●	100	1600	—	—	1600	6400	6400	3200	6400	3200	3200	12800	12800	6400	1600	800	12800	800	400	100	—
762	●	—	1600	—	—	1600	12800	12800	1600	12800	12800	6400	12800	6400	3200	1600	400	12800	800	100	—	—
Nakahadachi	●	—	1600	—	—	1600	6400	3200	800	3200	6400	3200	12800	6400	3200	1600	3200	6400	1600	200	—	—
Kimoto	●	—	1600	—	—	1600	12800	12800	1600	3200	12800	6400	12800	12800	6400	1600	800	12800	1600	200	—	—
Shinonome 1	●	—	3200	—	—	1600	3200	6400	3200	3200	6400	6400	12800	12800	6400	1600	800	12800	800	400	—	—
Honjō 35	●	—	3200	—	—	1600	12800	12800	1600	6400	6400	6400	12800	12800	6400	1600	800	12800	1600	200	—	—
Honjō 37	●	—	1600	—	—	1600	6400	12800	800	6400	6400	6400	12800	12800	6400	1600	800	12800	800	200	—	—
Fish 14	●	100	1600	—	—	1600	3200	1600	3200	3200	800	800	3200	12800	1600	1600	400	12800	800	200	—	—
Funakawa	●	200	6400	100	—	1600	6400	3200	1600	3200	3200	3200	6400	12800	3200	3200	800	12800	3200	200	—	—
Fish 6	●	—	1600	—	—	800	3200	12800	3200	3200	3200	1600	6400	12800	6400	3200	1600	12800	3200	100	—	—
Kaneura 1-3	●	100	1600	—	—	1600	12800	6400	800	6400	3200	6400	12800	12800	6400	1600	400	12800	800	200	—	—
Futto	●	100	3200	—	—	1600	3200	3200	800	3200	1600	3200	6400	6400	3200	3200	400	6400	1600	200	—	—
801	●	100	1600	—	—	1600	3200	6400	3200	6400	1600	800	6400	12800	12800	3200	800	12800	3200	200	—	—
777	●	—	1600	—	—	1600	1600	12800	1600	6400	1600	1600	6400	12800	12800	3200	12800	12800	3200	3200	—	6400
Yamagata	●	—	6400	800	400	3200	6400	6400	3200	1600	3200	800	6400	12800	3200	3200	6400	12800	800	6400	—	3200
Jundai 4	●	—	800	200	100	3200	800	6400	3200	3200	1600	800	3200	12800	6400	1600	12800	12800	3200	3200	—	6400
Aomori 177	●	—	1600	400	200	1600	1600	6400	3200	6400	1600	1600	3200	12800	6400	1600	12800	12800	3200	1600	—	6400
Hashishita 57	○	400	3200	—	200	1600	3200	6400	1600	3200	1600	800	6400	12800	6400	800	1600	12800	1600	12800	400	12800
Hashishita 40	○	100	1600	—	100	3200	3200	3200	3200	3200	1600	800	3200	12800	1600	800	12800	12800	3200	6400	800	12800
Fish 11	●	—	3200	—	—	3200	3200	6400	1600	3200	1600	800	6400	12800	6400	3200	6400	12800	3200	3200	1600	12800
758	●	100	12800	100	100	1600	6400	6400	1600	6400	1600	1600	6400	12800	3200	1600	800	12800	800	100	—	—
Group 3																						
770	●	—	3200	3200	400	1600	1600	1600	6400	800	800	200	1600	6400	1600	3200	6400	6400	3200	3200	200	6400
Abashiri	●	—	1600	1600	200	1600	1600	1600	6400	800	800	200	1600	6400	1600	1600	6400	6400	3200	3200	200	6400
Jundai 6	●	—	1600	800	800	1600	1600	1600	3200	1600	800	100	1600	6400	3200	1600	6400	6400	3200	1600	200	3200
Jundai 7	●	—	1600	1600	800	1600	1600	1600	1600	1600	800	100	1600	6400	1600	1600	6400	6400	1600	1600	100	3200
Onbetsu	●	—	1600	800	400	1600	1600	800	3200	400	800	100	1600	6400	1600	3200	6400	6400	1600	1600	100	6400
Memanbetsu	●	—	3200	3200	800	1600	1600	1600	3200	1600	800	200	1600	6400	1600	1600	6400	6400	3200	6400	100	6400
Fish 12	○	100	3200	6400	800	1600	800	1600	6400	400	800	100	1600	6400	1600	3200	6400	6400	1600	6400	200	6400
786	●	100	800	1600	400	1600	1600	1600	3200	1600	800	200	3200	6400	1600	3200	6400	6400	3200	3200	200	6400
Daijima	●	100	1600	1600	800	1600	1600	1600	3200	800	400	100	1600	6400	1600	1600	6400	6400	3200	3200	100	6400
804	○	—	1600	800	400	1600	1600	1600	1600	400	800	100	1600	6400	1600	1600	6400	6400	3200	1600	—	1600
802	●	—	1600	800	400	1600	200	1600	1600	400	800	100	200	6400	1600	1600	6400	6400	3200	100	—	—
Group 4																						
Nangai	●	—	—	1600	200	1600	6400	12800	6400	6400	3200	800	12800	12800	6400	3200	3200	12800	1600	1600	—	6400
Nishishynbetsu	●	—	100	1600	100	1600	3200	3200	3200	6400	3200	800	6400	12800	3200	3200	3200	—	1600	1600	—	6400
779	●	—	—	3200	800	1600	6400	12800	6400	6400	3200	1600	12800	12800	6400	6400	12800	12800	3200	1600	—	6400
Jundai 3	●	100	1600	6400	800	1600	6400	12800	6400	6400	6400	800	12800	12800	6400	3200	3200	12800	3200	3200	—	12800
168	●	100	1600	6400	800	1600	6400	12800	6400	6400	3200	1600	12800	12800	6400	6400	12800	12800	3200	800	—	3200
Group 5																						
341	●	100	—	12800	800	—	—	—	6400	—	—	—	—	—	400	—	6400	—	1600	6400	1600	12800
Matsugasaki 156	○	—	—	6400	1600	—	—	—	1600	—	—	—	—	—	200	—	1600	—	1600	6400	800	12800
Eskimo whale	●	200	—	12800	3200	—	—	—	3200	—	—	—	—	—	200	—	6400	—	1600	3200	3200	12800
Fish 6H	●	100	—	3200	6400	—	—	—	—	—	—	—	—	—	—	—	—	—	—	12800	6400	12800
Jōryu 74	○	—	—	6400	3200	—	—	—	6400	—	—	—	—	—	400	—	6400	—	1600	12800	6400	12800
No. 8	●	100	—	12800	1600	—	—	—	6400	—	—	—	—	—	400	—	6400	—	800	12800	6400	12800
Hashishita 96	○	—	—	12800	1600	—	—	—	6400	—	—	—	—	—	400	—	6400	—	1600	12800	3200	12800
Hashishita 62	○	—	—	12800	3200	—	—	—	6400	—	—	—	—	—	400	—	6400	—	800	12800	1600	12800
Hashishita 65	○	—	—	12800	1600	—	—	—	6400	—	—	—	—	—	400	—	6400	—	1600	12800	800	12800
Hashishita 56	○	—	—	12800	3200	—	—	—	6400	—	—	—	—	—	400	—	6400	—	1600	12800	3200	12800
Bute 2	●	—	—	12800	1600	—	—	—	6400	—	—	—	—	—	400	—	6400	—	1600	12800	3200	12800
Funakoshi	○	—	200	12800	1600	—	—	—	6400	—	—	—	—	12800	400	1600	6400	1600	1600	12800	3200	12800
Nanaimo Chicken	●	800	—	12800	1600	—	—	—	6400	—	—	—	—	—	800	—	6400	—	800	12800	6400	12800
Beluga A	●	800	—	12800	3200	—	—	—	6400	—	—	—	—	—	800	—	6400	—	1600	6400	3200	12800
Salmon eggs	●	800	—	12800	1600	—	—	—	6400	—	—	—	—	—	400	—	6400	—	800	12800	6400	12800
Bute 7	○	1600	—	6400	1600	—	—	—	—	—	—	—	—	—	—	—	—	—	—	12800	6400	12800
Group 6																						
Honjō 133	○	—	—	400	1600	—	—	—	3200	—	—	—	—	—	—	200	400	—	800	12800	—	12800
Michikawa 14	○	—	—	400	1600	—	—	—	6400	—	—	—	—	—	—	200	400	—	800	12800	—	12800
Michikawa 15	○	—	—	400	1600	—	—	—	6400	—	—	—	—	—	—	100	400	—	400	12800	—	12800
Honjō 121	○	—	—	400	1600	—	—	—	6400	—	—	—	—	—	—	200	400	—	400	12800	200	12800
Kosagawa 92	○	—	—	400	3200	—	—	—	3200	—	—	—	—	—	—	200	400	—	800	12800	100	12800
211	●	400	200	800	12800	—	—	—	3200	—	—	—	—	—	—	200	3200	—	400	6400	400	12800
Michikawa 10	○	400	—	800	3200	—	—	—	6400	—	—	—	—	—	—	200	400	—	800	12800	200	12800
Matsuzasaki 54	○	—	—	200	1600	—	—	—	6400	—	—	—	—	—	200	200	400	—	800	12800	800	12800
Matsuzasaki 94	○	—	—	400	1600	—	—	—	3200	—	—	—	—	—	400	200	3200	—	800	12800	800	12800
Seal IIIa	●	200	—	200	1600	—	—	—	3200	—	—	—	—	—	200	200	200	—	1600	6400	—	12800
Kaneura 39	○	—	—	100	1600	—	—	—	6400	—	—	—	—	—	400	200	6400	—	1600	3200	—	12800
Jōryu 58	○	100	100	200	800	—	—	200	200	—	400	—	—	1600	—	1600	—	800	100	6400	—	6400
Hashishita 34	○	100	100	—	400	—	—	100	800	—	400	—	—	1600	—	800	—	800	100	6400	—	6400

strains of *Clostridium botulinum* type E

● Toxigenic   ○ Non-toxigenic

	Fish 12 (○)	Meman-betsu (●)	802 (●)	611 (●)	Kisagata 133 (○)	Otaru (○)	Hashi-shita 23 (○)	Pince-Rupert 2 (●)	1314 (●)	Hagina-ri 27 (○)	715 (●)	Fish 5 (●)	Wakino-sawa (○)	Aomori 102 (○)	Aomori 783 (○)	Aomori 786 (○)	Aomori 207 (○)	Hagina-ri 4-22 (○)	Fish 9 (●)	Kameda (●)	Masuke (●)	486 (●)	Hashi-shita 21 (○)
Group 1	—	—	—	—	—	—	—	—	—	—	—	—	—	—	—	—	—	—	—	—	—	—	—
Group 2	200	—	—	—	—	—	—	—	—	—	—	—	—	—	—	—	—	—	—	—	—	—	—
	100	—	—	—	—	—	—	—	—	—	—	—	—	—	—	—	—	—	—	—	—	—	—
	100	—	200	—	—	—	—	—	—	—	—	—	—	—	—	—	—	—	—	—	—	—	—
	—	—	—	—	—	—	—	—	—	—	—	—	—	—	—	—	—	—	—	—	—	—	—
	—	—	—	—	—	—	—	—	—	—	—	—	—	—	—	—	—	—	—	—	—	—	—
	—	—	—	—	—	—	—	—	—	—	—	—	—	—	—	—	—	—	—	—	—	—	—
	—	—	—	—	—	—	—	—	—	—	—	—	—	—	—	—	—	—	—	—	—	—	—
	—	—	—	—	—	—	—	—	—	—	—	—	—	—	—	—	—	—	—	—	—	—	—
	1600	3200	12800	—	—	—	—	—	—	—	—	—	—	—	—	—	—	—	—	—	—	—	—
	3200	1600	12800	—	—	—	—	—	—	—	—	—	—	—	—	—	—	—	—	—	—	—	—
	1600	3200	12800	—	—	—	—	—	—	—	—	—	—	—	—	—	—	—	—	—	—	—	—
	800	1600	6400	—	—	—	—	—	—	—	—	—	—	—	—	—	—	—	—	—	—	—	—
	800	1600	3200	100	—	—	—	—	—	—	—	—	—	—	—	—	—	—	—	—	—	—	—
	—	800	1600	—	—	—	—	—	—	100	—	—	—	—	—	—	—	—	—	—	—	—	—
	—	800	1600	—	—	—	—	—	—	—	—	—	—	—	—	—	—	—	—	—	—	—	—
	—	3200	1600	100	100	—	—	—	—	—	—	—	—	—	—	—	—	—	—	—	—	—	—
	—	800	3200	—	—	—	—	100	—	—	—	—	—	—	—	—	—	—	—	—	—	—	—
	800	3200	6400	—	—	—	—	—	—	100	—	—	—	—	—	—	—	—	—	—	—	—	—
	1600	3200	6400	—	—	—	—	—	—	—	—	—	—	—	—	—	—	—	—	—	—	—	—
	800	3200	6400	—	—	—	—	—	—	—	—	—	—	—	—	—	—	—	—	—	—	—	—
	1600	1600	6400	—	—	—	—	—	—	—	—	—	—	—	—	—	—	—	—	100	—	—	—
	1600	1600	6400	—	—	—	—	—	—	—	—	—	•	—	—	—	—	—	—	—	—	—	—
	800	1600	3200	—	—	—	—	—	—	—	—	—	—	—	—	—	—	—	—	—	—	100	—
	800	1600	3200	—	—	—	—	—	—	—	—	—	—	—	—	—	—	—	—	—	—	100	—
	800	1600	3200	—	—	—	100	—	—	—	—	—	—	—	—	—	—	—	—	—	—	—	—
	200	800	3200	—	—	—	—	—	—	—	—	—	—	—	—	—	—	—	—	—	—	—	—
	200	1600	3200	—	—	—	—	—	—	—	—	—	—	—	—	—	—	—	—	—	—	—	—
	100	1600	1600	—	—	—	—	—	—	—	—	—	—	—	—	—	—	—	—	—	—	—	—
	800	800	1600	—	—	—	—	—	—	—	—	—	—	—	—	—	—	—	—	—	200	100	—
	400	800	1600	—	—	—	—	—	—	—	—	—	—	—	—	—	—	—	—	—	—	—	—
	200	200	400	—	—	—	—	—	—	—	—	—	—	—	—	—	—	—	—	—	—	—	—
	800	6400	1600	—	—	—	—	—	—	—	—	—	—	—	—	—	—	—	—	100	—	—	—
	1600	3200	3200	—	—	—	—	200	—	—	—	—	—	—	—	—	—	—	—	100	—	—	—
	800	3200	1600	—	—	—	—	100	—	—	—	—	—	—	—	—	—	—	—	—	—	—	—
	800	1600	1600	100	—	—	—	100	—	—	—	—	—	—	—	—	—	—	—	100	—	—	—
	200	800	1600	—	—	—	—	—	—	—	—	—	—	—	—	—	—	—	—	—	—	—	—
	800	1600	6400	—	100	—	—	—	—	—	—	—	—	—	—	—	—	—	—	100	100	—	—
	1600	3200	3200	—	—	—	—	100	—	—	—	—	—	—	—	—	—	—	—	—	—	—	—
	100	200	1600	—	—	—	—	200	—	—	—	—	—	—	—	—	—	—	—	100	—	—	—
																				—			
Group 3	1600	1600	6400	—	—	—	—	—	—	—	—	—	—	—	—	—	—	—	—	—	—	—	—
	1600	1600	6400	—	—	—	—	—	—	—	—	—	—	—	—	—	—	—	—	100	—	—	—
	1600	3200	6400	—	—	—	—	—	—	—	—	—	—	—	—	—	—	—	—	—	—	—	—
	800	800	1600	—	—	—	—	—	—	—	—	—	—	—	—	—	—	—	—	—	—	—	—
	1600	1600	3200	—	—	—	—	—	—	—	—	—	—	—	—	—	—	—	—	—	—	—	200
	1600	6400	6400	—	—	—	—	—	—	—	—	—	—	—	—	—	—	—	—	—	—	—	—
	3200	3200	6400	—	—	—	—	—	—	—	—	—	—	—	—	—	—	—	—	—	—	—	—
	800	800	3200	—	—	—	—	—	—	—	—	—	—	—	—	—	—	—	—	—	—	—	—
	1600	3200	3200	—	—	—	—	—	—	—	—	—	—	—	—	—	—	—	—	—	—	—	—
	800	1600	3200	—	—	—	—	—	—	—	—	—	—	—	—	—	—	—	—	—	—	—	—
	1600	3200	6400	—	—	—	—	—	—	—	—	—	—	200	—	—	—	—	—	—	—	—	—
Group 4	800	3200	3200	—	—	—	—	—	—	—	—	—	—	—	—	—	—	—	—	—	—	—	—
	800	3200	1600	—	—	—	—	—	—	—	—	—	—	—	—	—	—	—	—	—	—	—	—
	800	1600	1600	—	—	—	—	—	—	—	—	—	—	—	—	—	—	—	—	—	—	—	—
	1600	3200	6400	—	—	—	—	—	—	—	—	—	—	—	—	—	—	—	—	—	—	—	—
	800	3200	3200	—	—	—	—	—	—	—	—	—	—	—	—	—	—	—	—	—	—	—	—
Group 5	800	12800	6400	—	—	—	—	1600	—	—	—	—	—	—	—	—	—	—	—	—	—	—	—
	800	3200	1600	—	—	—	—	1600	—	—	—	—	—	—	—	—	—	—	—	—	—	—	—
	800	3200	6400	—	—	—	—	—	—	—	—	—	—	—	—	—	—	—	—	100	12800	—	—
	800	6400	1600	—	—	—	—	800	—	—	—	—	—	—	—	—	—	—	—	—	—	—	—
	400	3200	1600	—	100	—	—	1600	—	—	—	—	—	—	—	—	—	—	—	—	—	—	—
	1600	12800	6400	—	200	—	—	800	—	400	—	—	—	—	—	—	—	—	—	—	—	—	—
	800	6400	3200	—	200	—	—	400	—	—	—	—	—	—	—	—	—	—	—	—	—	—	—
	800	6400	1600	—	200	—	—	1600	—	—	—	—	—	—	—	—	—	—	—	—	—	—	—
	1600	12800	6400	—	100	—	—	1600	—	—	—	—	—	—	—	—	—	—	—	—	—	—	—
	800	6400	3200	—	200	—	—	1600	—	—	—	—	—	—	—	—	—	—	—	—	—	—	—
	1600	6400	3200	—	200	—	—	400	—	—	—	—	—	—	—	—	—	—	—	—	—	—	—
	1600	12800	6400	—	400	—	400	—	—	—	—	—	—	—	—	—	—	—	—	—	—	—	—
	1600	3200	6400	—	200	—	—	400	—	—	—	—	—	—	—	800	—	—	—	—	—	—	100
	800	6400	1600	—	200	—	—	—	—	—	—	—	—	—	—	200	—	—	—	—	—	—	—
	400	3200	1600	—	—	—	—	—	—	—	—	—	—	—	—	—	—	—	—	—	—	—	100
Group 6	100	400	400	—	—	—	—	—	—	—	—	—	—	—	—	—	—	—	—	—	—	—	—
	100	400	400	—	—	—	—	—	—	—	—	—	—	—	—	—	—	—	—	—	—	—	—
	100	400	400	—	—	400	200	400	—	—	—	—	—	—	—	—	—	—	—	—	—	—	—
	100	400	400	—	—	—	—	—	—	—	—	—	—	200	—	—	—	—	—	400	—	—	—
	100	800	400	—	—	—	—	—	—	—	—	—	—	—	—	—	—	—	—	400	200	—	—
	—	400	400	—	—	—	—	—	—	—	—	—	—	—	—	—	—	—	—	—	—	—	—
	100	400	400	—	—	—	—	—	—	—	—	—	—	—	—	—	—	—	—	800	—	—	—
	200	1600	400	—	—	—	—	—	—	—	—	—	—	—	—	—	—	—	—	—	—	—	—
	400	1600	800	—	—	—	—	—	—	—	—	—	—	—	—	—	—	—	—	—	—	—	—
	400	800	800	—	800	—	—	—	—	—	—	—	—	—	—	—	—	—	—	—	—	800	100
	200	400	200	—	400	—	—	—	—	—	—	—	—	—	—	—	—	—	—	—	—	—	100
	800	1600	1600	—	1600	—	—	—	—	—	—	—	—	—	—	—	—	—	—	—	—	800	800
	800	1600	1600	—	1600	—	—	—	—	—	—	—	—	—	—	—	—	—	—	100	—	—	1600

Table 3.—Flagellar agglutination of 118 strains

Immune Sera	Aomori ●	Tenno ●	341 ●	211 ●	Fish 8 ●	667 ●	Jundai 1 ●	Iwanai ●	Fish 7 ●	Haginari 28 ●	Haginari 9 ●	762 ●	Fish 6 ●	801 ●	777 ●	Yamagata ●	Hashishita 40 ○	Fish 11 ●	Fish 6H ●	Bute 7 ○	Jōryu 74 ○
Group 7																					
Kisagata 133 ○	200	100	100	—	—	—	—	200	—	—	—	—	—	—	—	—	—	—	—	—	—
Kisagata 64 ○	—	—	—	—	—	—	—	100	—	—	—	—	—	—	—	—	—	—	—	—	—
Kisagata 61 ○	—	—	—	—	—	—	—	100	—	—	—	—	—	—	—	—	—	—	—	—	—
Otaru ○	—	—	—	—	—	—	—	200	—	—	—	—	—	—	—	—	—	—	—	—	—
Group 8																					
Hashishita 21 ○	—	100	—	—	—	—	—	800	—	—	—	1600	—	—	—	—	400	—	6400	—	12800
Hashishita 23 ○	—	—	—	—	—	—	—	400	—	—	—	800	—	—	—	—	800	—	12800	—	12800
Hashishita 32 ○	—	—	200	—	—	—	—	800	—	—	—	400	—	—	—	800	400	—	12800	3200	12800
486 ●	—	—	—	—	—	—	—	—	—	—	100	200	—	—	—	800	400	—	12800	3200	3200
Prince Rupert 2 ●	200	—	800	400	—	1600	1600	1600	1600	800	—	1600	6400	1600	400	1600	6400	800	1600	100	—
Kaochi ●	400	200	200	200	—	—	—	—	—	400	—	—	1600	—	—	100	800	—	—	100	—
611 ●	—	—	—	—	—	—	—	—	—	—	—	—	—	—	—	—	—	—	—	—	—
1314 ●	—	—	—	—	—	400	—	—	—	—	—	—	—	—	—	—	—	—	—	—	—
Haginari 27 ●	—	—	—	—	—	—	—	—	—	—	—	—	12800	—	400	6400	—	1600	12800	12800	12800
36208 ●	100	—	12800	1600	—	—	12800	6400	—	—	—	—	—	—	—	—	—	—	—	—	—
Group 9																					
1304 ●	200	—	6400	400	—	—	—	—	200	—	—	100	—	—	—	200	—	—	—	—	—
Oil H ●	200	—	1600	400	—	—	—	—	—	—	—	—	—	—	—	100	—	—	—	—	—
Fish 9 ○	100	—	100	—	—	—	—	—	—	—	—	—	—	—	—	—	—	—	—	—	—
Aomori 207 ○	100	—	—	—	—	—	—	—	—	—	—	—	—	—	—	—	—	—	—	—	—
Haginari 4-22 ●	200	—	—	100	—	—	—	—	—	—	—	—	—	—	—	—	—	—	—	—	—
Masuke ●	—	—	—	100	—	—	—	—	—	—	—	—	—	—	—	—	—	—	—	—	—
Kameda ●	—	—	—	—	—	—	—	—	—	—	—	—	—	—	—	—	—	—	—	—	—
715 ●	—	—	—	—	—	—	—	—	—	—	—	—	—	—	—	—	—	—	—	—	—
Fish 4 ○	—	—	—	—	—	—	—	—	800	—	—	—	—	—	—	—	—	—	—	—	—
Fish 5 ○	—	—	—	—	—	—	—	—	—	—	—	—	—	—	400	—	—	—	—	—	—
Wakinosawa ○	—	—	—	—	—	—	—	—	—	—	—	—	—	—	—	—	—	—	—	—	—
Maruya ○	—	—	—	—	—	—	—	—	—	—	—	—	—	—	—	100	—	—	—	—	—
Aomori 102 ○	—	—	—	—	—	—	—	—	—	—	—	—	—	—	—	400	—	—	—	—	—
Aomori 103 ○	—	—	—	—	—	100	100	—	—	—	—	—	—	—	—	400	—	—	—	—	—
Aomori 783 ○	—	—	—	—	—	100	100	—	—	—	—	—	—	—	—	100	—	—	—	—	—
Aomori 786 ○	—	—	—	—	—	—	—	—	—	—	—	—	—	—	—	—	—	—	—	—	—

of *Clostridium botulinum* type E—Continued

● : Toxigenic
○ : Non-toxigenic

Fish 12 (○)	Meman-betsu (●)	802 (●)	611 (●)	Kisagata 133 (○)	Otaru (○)	Hashi-shita 23 (○)	Pince-Rupert 2 (●)	1314 (●)	Hagina-ri 27 (○)	715 (●)	Fish 5 (○)	Wakino-sawa (○)	Aomori 102 (○)	Aomori 783 (○)	Aomori 786 (○)	Aomori 207 (○)	Hagina-ri 4-22 (○)	Fish 9 (○)	Kameda (●)	Masuke (●)	486 (●)	Hashi-shita 21 (○)

Group 7

Fish 12	Meman-betsu	802	611	Kisagata 133	Otaru	Hashi-shita 23	Pince-Rupert 2	1314	Hagina-ri 27	715	Fish 5	Wakino-sawa	Aomori 102	Aomori 783	Aomori 786	Aomori 207	Hagina-ri 4-22	Fish 9	Kameda	Masuke	486	Hashi-shita 21
100	—	—	—	6400	800	—	—	—	—	—	—	—	—	—	—	—	—	—	—	—	200	—
—	—	—	100	6400	800	—	—	—	—	—	—	—	—	—	—	—	—	—	100	—	—	—
—	—	—	100	3200	800	—	—	—	—	—	—	—	—	—	—	—	—	—	—	—	—	—
—	—	—	—	3200	12800	—	—	—	—	—	—	—	—	—	—	—	—	—	—	—	—	100

Group 8

Fish 12	Meman-betsu	802	611	Kisagata 133	Otaru	Hashi-shita 23	Pince-Rupert 2	1314	Hagina-ri 27	715	Fish 5	Wakino-sawa	Aomori 102	Aomori 783	Aomori 786	Aomori 207	Hagina-ri 4-22	Fish 9	Kameda	Masuke	486	Hashi-shita 21
400	800	400	—	800	—	1600	—	—	—	—	—	—	—	—	—	—	—	—	—	—	—	12800
400	800	800	—	800	—	3200	—	—	—	—	—	—	—	—	—	—	—	—	—	—	—	3200
400	800	800	—	800	—	400	—	—	—	—	—	—	—	—	—	—	—	—	—	—	—	3200
800	12800	3200	—	100	—	—	—	—	—	—	—	—	—	—	—	—	—	—	—	—	—	—
800	12800	1600	—	200	—	—	3200	—	—	—	—	—	—	—	—	—	—	—	—	—	12800	—
800	1600	3200	—	—	—	—	—	—	—	—	—	—	—	—	—	—	—	—	—	—	100	—
—	—	—	6400	6400	—	—	—	6400	—	—	—	800	—	—	—	—	—	—	—	—	—	—
—	—	—	6400	—	—	—	—	6400	—	—	—	800	—	—	—	—	—	—	—	—	—	—
—	—	—	1600	—	—	—	—	—	800	—	—	—	—	—	—	—	—	—	—	—	—	—
12800	12800	12800	800	3200	—	—	6400	—	—	—	—	—	—	—	—	100	—	—	—	—	—	—

Group 9

Fish 12	Meman-betsu	802	611	Kisagata 133	Otaru	Hashi-shita 23	Pince-Rupert 2	1314	Hagina-ri 27	715	Fish 5	Wakino-sawa	Aomori 102	Aomori 783	Aomori 786	Aomori 207	Hagina-ri 4-22	Fish 9	Kameda	Masuke	486	Hashi-shita 21
—	200	100	6400	—	—	—	—	—	800	—	—	—	—	—	—	—	—	—	—	—	—	200
—	—	—	—	—	—	—	—	—	—	—	—	—	400	—	—	—	—	—	—	—	25600	—
—	—	—	—	—	—	—	—	—	—	—	—	—	—	—	—	—	—	12800	—	—	200	—
—	—	—	100	—	—	—	—	—	—	1600	—	—	—	—	—	—	—	—	—	—	—	—
—	—	—	—	—	—	—	—	—	—	1600	—	—	—	—	—	—	—	—	6400	—	—	—
—	—	—	—	—	—	400	—	—	—	—	—	—	800	—	—	—	—	—	—	6400	—	—
—	—	—	—	—	—	—	—	—	100	—	—	—	1600	—	3200	12800	—	—	—	—	—	—
—	—	—	—	—	—	—	—	—	100	—	—	3200	100	—	—	12800	—	—	—	—	—	—
—	—	—	—	—	—	—	—	—	—	—	—	1600	—	—	—	—	—	—	—	—	—	—
—	—	—	—	—	—	—	—	—	—	—	—	—	—	—	3200	12800	—	—	—	—	—	—
—	—	—	—	—	—	—	—	—	—	—	—	—	—	800	—	25600	—	—	—	—	—	—
—	—	—	—	—	—	400	—	—	—	100	—	—	—	—	3200	—	—	—	—	—	—	—

Table 4.—Agglutination of strains of *Clostridium botulinum*

Immune Sera		● Aomori	● Tenno	● 341	● 211	● Fish 8	● 667	● Jundai 1	● Iwanai	● Fish 7	● Hagina-ri 28 1	● Hagina-ri 9	● 762	● Fish 6	● 801	● 777	● Yama-gata	○ Hashi-shita 40	● Fish 11	● Fish 6H	○ Bute 7	○ Jōryu 74
Group 1																						
Aomori	●	3200	—	—	—	—	—	—	—	—	—	—	—	—	—	—	—	—	—	—	800	—
VH	●	800	—	—	—	—	—	—	—	—	—	—	—	—	—	—	—	—	—	—	200	—
Group 2																						
Tenno	●	—	3200	—	—	3200	1600	800	3200	1600	6400	1600	800	1600	800	800	3200	6400	1600	—	—	—
Fish 8	●	—	1600	—	—	3200	3200	800	3200	3200	3200	1600	400	1600	800	800	3200	6400	1600	—	—	—
759	●	—	1600	—	—	3200	3200	800	3200	1600	3200	1600	800	1600	800	800	3200	6400	1600	—	100	—
667	●	—	3200	—	—	3200	3200	1600	3200	3200	6400	1600	1600	1600	1600	800	3200	6400	1600	—	100	—
Fish 35	●	—	3200	—	100	3200	3200	800	3200	1600	6400	1600	1600	1600	1600	400	3200	6400	1600	—	100	—
798	●	—	1600	—	—	3200	3200	800	3200	1600	6400	800	400	1600	800	800	3200	6400	1600	—	—	—
800	●	—	1600	—	—	6400	1600	800	3200	1600	6400	3200	1600	1600	3200	800	3200	6400	1600	100	200	—
Fish 3	○	—	1600	—	200	3200	3200	800	3200	3200	6400	1600	1600	1600	800	800	3200	6400	1600	—	100	—
Fish 67	●	—	3200	—	100	3200	3200	800	3200	1600	6400	1600	1600	1600	1600	800	3200	6400	1600	—	100	—
Fish 13	●	—	—	—	—	3200	3200	800	3200	1600	6400	1600	1600	3200	1600	1600	3200	6400	1600	—	100	—
761	●	—	3200	—	—	3200	3200	800	3200	1600	6400	1600	800	3200	1600	800	3200	6400	1600	—	—	—
Jundai 1	●	—	—	—	—	3200	3200	800	3200	800	6400	1600	800	1600	1600	1600	3200	6400	3200	—	—	—
760	●	—	—	—	—	3200	3200	800	3200	800	6400	1600	800	3200	1600	1600	3200	6400	1600	—	—	—
Haginari 8	●	—	3200	—	—	3200	3200	800	3200	1600	6400	1600	800	1600	1600	800	3200	6400	1600	—	200	—
Iwanai	●	—	1600	—	—	1600	3200	800	3200	1600	6400	1600	400	1600	800	800	3200	6400	1600	—	100	—
Fish 7	●	—	1600	—	—	3200	3200	800	3200	3200	6400	1600	1600	1600	800	800	3200	6400	1600	—	100	—
Haginari	●	—	3200	—	—	3200	3200	800	3200	1600	6400	1600	1600	1600	800	800	3200	6400	1600	—	—	—
775	●	—	—	—	—	3200	3200	800	3200	800	6400	1600	800	3200	1600	1600	3200	6400	1600	800	—	—
Haginari 28-1	●	—	1600	—	—	3200	3200	800	3200	1600	6400	1600	800	1600	1600	800	3200	6400	1600	—	—	—
527	○	—	1600	—	—	1600	3200	800	3200	1600	6400	400	1600	1600	800	800	3200	6400	1600	—	100	—
Haginari 9	●	—	800	—	—	3200	1600	800	3200	1600	3200	3200	1600	1600	1600	800	3200	6400	1600	—	100	—
762	●	—	1600	—	—	3200	3200	800	3200	3200	3200	1600	1600	1600	1600	800	1600	6400	1600	—	100	—
Nakahadachi	●	100	3200	—	400	3200	1600	800	1600	1600	3200	1600	1600	1600	1600	800	3200	6400	1600	—	—	—
Kimoto	●	—	1600	—	—	3200	3200	800	3200	1600	6400	1600	800	1600	1600	800	3200	6400	1600	—	—	—
Shinonome 1	●	—	3200	—	—	3200	3200	800	3200	1600	6400	3200	1600	1600	3200	800	3200	6400	1600	—	100	—
Honjo 35	●	—	1600	—	—	3200	3200	800	3200	1600	6400	3200	1600	1600	1600	800	3200	6400	1600	—	100	—
Honjo 37	●	—	1600	—	—	3200	3200	800	1600	1600	6400	3200	1600	1600	1600	800	3200	6400	1600	—	—	—
Fish 14	●	—	1600	—	—	3200	3200	800	3200	1600	6400	1600	1600	1600	1600	800	3200	6400	1600	—	100	—
Funakawa	●	—	1600	—	—	3200	1600	800	3200	1600	6400	1600	1600	1600	1600	800	3200	6400	1600	—	200	—
Fish 6	●	—	—	—	—	3200	3200	800	3200	1600	6400	1600	800	3200	1600	1600	3200	6400	1600	—	—	—
Kaneura 1-3	●	—	3200	—	—	1600	1600	800	1600	1600	6400	3200	1600	1600	1600	800	3200	6400	1600	—	200	—
Futto	●	—	1600	—	—	3200	3200	800	3200	800	3200	1600	1600	400	1600	800	3200	6400	1600	100	100	—
801	●	—	3200	—	—	3200	1600	800	3200	1600	6400	1600	1600	3200	1600	800	3200	6400	1600	—	100	—
777	●	—	400	—	—	3200	3200	800	3200	1600	6400	1600	400	1600	800	800	3200	6400	1600	800	—	—
Yamagata	●	—	—	—	—	3200	3200	800	3200	1600	6400	1600	400	1600	800	800	3200	6400	1600	6400	800	—
Jundai 4	●	—	—	—	—	3200	3200	800	3200	1600	6400	1600	400	1600	800	800	3200	6400	1600	100	100	—
Aomori 177	●	—	—	—	—	3200	3200	800	3200	1600	6400	1600	400	1600	800	800	3200	6400	1600	—	—	—
Hashishita 57	○	—	—	—	3200	3200	3200	800	3200	1600	6400	1600	1600	3200	1600	1600	3200	6400	1600	200	100	—
Hashishita 40	○	—	—	—	1600	3200	3200	400	3200	1600	6400	1600	1600	3200	1600	1600	3200	6400	1600	100	—	—
Fish 11	●	—	—	—	—	3200	1600	800	3200	1600	6400	1600	1600	3200	1600	1600	3200	6400	1600	—	—	—
758	●	—	800	—	—	3200	3200	800	3200	3200	6400	1600	1600	1600	800	800	3200	6400	1600	—	—	—
Group 3																						
770	●	—	—	—	—	3200	400	800	3200	400	6400	800	400	1600	800	800	3200	6400	800	6400	—	—
Abashiri	●	—	—	—	—	6400	800	800	3200	400	6400	800	400	1600	800	800	3200	6400	800	6400	—	—
Jundai 6	●	—	—	—	—	6400	800	800	3200	400	6400	800	400	800	800	800	3200	6400	800	3200	—	—
Jundai 7	●	—	—	—	—	3200	800	400	3200	800	6400	800	400	1600	800	800	3200	6400	800	3200	—	—
Onbetsu	●	—	100	—	—	3200	800	800	3200	800	6400	800	800	1600	1600	800	3200	6400	800	6400	—	—
Memanbetsu	●	—	—	—	—	3200	800	800	3200	800	6400	800	400	1600	800	800	3200	6400	800	3200	100	—
Fish 12	○	—	100	—	—	6400	800	400	800	400	1600	800	400	1600	800	800	3200	6400	800	3200	100	—
786	●	—	—	—	—	6400	800	800	3200	800	6400	800	400	1600	800	800	3200	6400	800	3200	—	—
Daijima	●	—	—	—	—	3200	800	800	3200	800	6400	800	800	1600	800	800	3200	6400	800	1600	—	—
804	○	—	—	—	—	3200	800	800	3200	400	6400	800	800	1600	800	800	3200	6400	800	6400	—	—
802	●	—	—	—	—	3200	800	800	3200	400	6400	1600	800	1600	800	800	3200	6400	800	6400	—	—
Group 4																						
Nangai	●	—	—	—	—	3200	3200	800	1600	1600	6400	400	800	100	800	800	3200	6400	1600	1600	—	—
Nishishunbetsu	●	—	—	—	—	3200	3200	800	1600	400	6400	800	800	1600	800	800	3200	—	1600	400	—	—
779	●	100	800	200	400	3200	800	800	1600	1600	6400	1600	800	3200	800	800	3200	6400	1600	1600	—	—
Jundai 3	●	—	—	—	—	3200	3200	800	1600	1600	6400	400	800	100	800	800	3200	6400	800	800	—	—
168	●	—	—	—	—	3200	1600	800	1600	400	6400	800	800	1600	800	800	3200	6400	1600	800	—	—
Group 5																						
341	●	—	—	3200	—	400	—	—	400	—	—	—	—	—	400	—	400	—	200	6400	100	3200
Matsugasaki 156	○	—	—	100	3200	800	—	—	—	—	—	—	—	—	400	—	800	—	200	1600	1600	1600
Eskimo whale	●	—	—	100	200	400	—	—	—	—	—	—	—	—	200	—	800	800	800	3200	800	—
Joryu 74	○	—	—	100	100	200	—	—	—	—	—	—	—	—	400	—	800	1600	400	3200	800	3200
No. 8	●	—	—	—	1600	400	—	—	400	—	—	—	—	—	400	—	800	800	400	6400	—	3200
Hashishita 96	○	—	—	—	—	800	—	—	400	—	—	—	—	—	800	—	800	—	400	6400	—	3200
Hashishita 62	○	—	—	—	3200	800	—	—	800	—	—	—	—	—	800	—	1600	—	400	6400	100	3200
Hashishita 65	○	—	—	1600	1600	400	—	—	—	—	—	—	—	—	800	—	800	—	400	6400	—	3200
Hashishita 56	○	—	—	1600	1600	400	—	—	400	—	—	—	—	—	800	—	400	—	400	6400	200	3200
Bute 2	●	—	—	1600	1600	400	—	—	400	—	—	—	—	—	800	—	800	800	800	6400	—	3200
Funakoshi	○	—	—	—	800	400	—	—	800	—	800	—	—	—	800	—	800	1600	400	6400	—	3200
Nanaimo Chicken	●	100	—	3200	3200	400	—	—	400	—	—	—	—	—	800	—	800	1600	400	6400	—	3200
Beluga A	●	—	—	—	—	800	—	—	400	—	—	—	—	—	800	—	800	1600	800	6400	—	3200
Salmon eggs	●	—	—	800	800	400	—	—	400	—	—	—	—	—	800	—	800	800	800	6400	—	3200
Matsugasaki 54	○	—	—	1600	800	400	—	—	400	—	—	—	—	—	400	—	400	800	200	3200	1600	1600
Matsugasaki 94	○	—	—	400	3200	200	—	—	400	—	—	—	—	—	400	—	800	400	400	3200	400	1600
Seal IIIa	●	—	—	—	1600	800	—	—	200	—	—	—	—	—	200	—	400	1600	200	—	—	—
Kaneura 39	○	—	100	200	1600	400	—	—	400	—	—	—	—	—	400	—	400	1600	400	800	400	—
Joryu 58	○	—	—	—	1600	200	—	—	800	—	—	—	—	—	—	200	400	400	—	—	—	—
Hashishita 34	○	—	—	—	800	—	—	—	800	—	200	—	—	—	—	400	400	400	—	200	—	—
Group 6																						
Honjo 133	○	—	—	100	3200	—	—	—	—	—	—	—	—	—	—	—	—	400	—	800	—	—
Michikawa 14	○	—	—	—	1600	—	—	—	—	—	—	—	—	—	—	—	—	400	—	800	—	—
Michikawa 15	○	—	—	100	3200	—	—	—	—	—	—	—	—	—	—	—	—	400	—	800	—	—
Honjo 121	○	—	—	100	3200	—	—	—	—	—	—	—	—	—	—	—	—	400	—	400	—	—
Kosagawa 92	○	—	—	100	3200	—	—	—	—	—	—	—	—	—	—	—	—	400	—	800	—	—
211	●	—	—	100	3200	—	—	—	—	—	—	—	—	—	—	—	400	800	—	800	—	—
Michikawa 10	○	—	—	100	3200	—	—	—	—	—	—	—	—	—	—	—	200	800	—	400	400	—

with antisera prepared against extract antigen type E

● : Toxigenic
○ : Non-toxigenic

	Fish 12 (○)	Meman-betsu (●)	802 (●)	611 (●)	Kisaga-ta 133 (○)	Otaru (○)	Hashi-shita 23 (○)	Pince Rupert 2 (●)	1314 (●)	Hagina-ri 27 (○)	715 (●)	Fish 5 (○)	Wakino-sawa (○)	Aomori 102 (○)	Aomori 783 (○)	Aomori 786 (○)	Aomori 207 (○)	Hagina-ri 4-22 (○)	Fish 9 (○)	Kameda (●)	Masuke (●)	486 (●)	Hashi-shita 21 (○)

Group 1

—	—	—	—	—	—	—	—	—	—	—	—	—	—	—	—	—	—	—	—	—	—	—

Group 2

Fish 12	Meman-betsu	802	611	Kisagata 133	Otaru	Hashishita 23	Pince Rupert 2	1314	Haginari 27	715	Fish 5	Wakinosawa	Aomori 102	Aomori 783	Aomori 786	Aomori 207	Haginari 4-22	Fish 9	Kameda	Masuke	486	Hashishita 21
400	200	100	—	—	—	—	—	—	—	—	—	—	—	—	—	—	—	—	—	—	—	—
400	800	100	100	—	—	—	—	—	—	—	—	—	—	—	—	—	—	—	—	—	—	—
100	100	100	100	—	—	—	200	—	—	—	—	—	—	—	—	—	—	—	—	—	—	—
400	800	200	200	—	—	—	—	200	—	—	—	—	—	—	—	—	—	—	—	—	—	—
400	800	100	100	—	—	—	—	—	—	—	—	—	—	—	—	—	—	—	200	—	—	—
400	800	200	—	—	—	—	—	—	—	—	—	—	—	—	—	—	—	—	—	—	—	—
400	1600	200	100	—	200	—	—	—	—	—	—	—	—	—	—	—	—	—	—	—	—	—
400	800	400	100	—	—	—	—	—	—	—	—	—	—	—	—	—	—	—	—	—	—	—
400	800	200	100	—	—	—	—	—	—	—	—	—	—	—	—	—	—	—	—	—	—	—
400	800	400	100	—	—	—	—	—	—	—	—	—	—	—	—	—	—	—	—	—	—	—
400	800	400	200	—	—	—	—	—	—	—	—	—	—	—	—	—	—	—	—	—	—	—
400	800	200	200	—	—	—	—	—	—	—	—	—	—	—	—	—	—	—	—	—	—	—
400	800	400	—	—	—	—	—	—	—	—	—	—	—	—	—	—	—	—	100	—	—	—
200	800	400	200	—	—	—	—	—	—	—	—	—	—	—	—	—	100	100	100	—	—	—
400	800	200	100	—	—	—	—	—	—	—	—	—	—	—	—	—	—	—	—	100	—	—
400	1600	200	200	—	—	—	—	—	—	—	—	—	—	—	—	—	—	—	—	—	—	—
400	800	200	100	—	—	—	—	100	—	—	—	—	—	—	—	—	—	—	—	—	—	—
6400	1600	800	—	—	—	—	—	—	—	—	—	—	—	—	—	—	—	—	—	—	—	—
400	800	100	—	—	—	—	—	—	—	—	—	—	—	—	—	—	—	—	—	—	—	—
800	800	200	200	—	—	—	—	200	—	—	—	—	—	—	—	—	—	—	200	—	—	—
800	1600	200	100	—	—	—	—	—	—	—	—	—	—	—	—	—	—	—	—	—	—	—
200	200	100	100	—	—	—	—	—	—	—	—	—	—	—	—	—	100	—	—	—	—	100
400	800	200	100	100	—	—	—	—	—	—	—	—	—	—	—	—	—	—	—	—	—	—
400	400	100	—	—	—	—	—	—	—	—	—	—	—	—	—	—	—	—	—	—	100	—
200	400	100	100	—	—	—	—	—	—	—	—	—	—	—	—	—	—	—	—	—	100	—
200	100	200	200	—	—	—	—	—	—	—	—	—	—	—	—	—	100	—	200	—	100	—
200	800	100	200	—	—	—	—	—	—	—	—	—	—	—	—	—	—	—	—	—	—	—
200	800	400	100	—	—	—	—	100	—	—	—	—	—	—	—	—	100	—	100	100	400	—
400	800	200	100	—	—	100	—	100	—	—	—	—	—	—	—	—	100	—	100	200	—	—
200	400	400	200	—	—	—	—	—	—	—	—	—	—	—	—	—	—	—	200	—	100	—
400	800	200	100	—	—	—	—	—	—	—	—	—	—	—	—	—	—	—	—	—	100	—
400	200	100	200	—	—	—	—	—	—	—	—	—	—	—	—	—	—	—	200	—	—	—
400	800	100	—	—	—	—	—	—	—	—	—	—	—	—	—	—	—	—	200	—	—	—
6400	1600	800	—	—	—	—	—	—	—	—	—	—	—	—	—	—	—	—	200	—	—	—
6400	3200	400	200	—	—	—	100	—	—	—	—	—	—	—	—	—	—	—	—	—	—	—
800	800	800	100	—	—	—	—	—	—	—	—	—	—	—	—	—	—	—	6400	—	—	—
400	800	400	100	—	—	—	—	—	—	—	—	—	—	—	—	—	—	—	100	—	—	—
800	1600	200	400	—	—	—	—	—	—	—	—	—	—	—	—	—	—	—	—	—	—	—
800	800	200	100	—	—	—	—	—	—	—	—	—	—	—	—	—	—	—	—	—	—	—
1600	800	800	100	—	—	—	—	—	—	—	—	—	—	—	—	—	—	—	—	—	—	—
400	800	200	200	—	—	—	—	—	—	—	—	—	—	—	—	—	—	—	200	—	—	—

Group 3

Fish 12	Meman-betsu	802	611	Kisagata 133	Otaru	Hashishita 23	Pince Rupert 2	1314	Haginari 27	715	Fish 5	Wakinosawa	Aomori 102	Aomori 783	Aomori 786	Aomori 207	Haginari 4-22	Fish 9	Kameda	Masuke	486	Hashishita 21
6400	6400	800	200	—	—	—	—	—	—	—	—	—	—	—	—	—	—	—	—	—	—	—
6400	6400	800	200	—	—	—	—	—	—	—	—	—	—	—	—	—	—	—	—	—	—	—
6400	6400	400	200	—	—	—	—	—	—	—	—	—	—	—	—	—	—	—	100	—	—	—
6400	3200	400	200	—	—	—	—	—	—	—	—	—	—	—	—	—	—	—	—	—	—	—
6400	6400	800	200	—	—	—	—	—	—	—	—	—	—	—	—	—	—	—	—	—	—	—
6400	3200	800	200	—	—	—	—	—	—	—	—	—	—	—	—	—	—	—	100	—	—	—
6400	1600	800	200	—	—	—	—	—	—	—	—	—	—	—	—	—	—	—	—	—	—	—
6400	3200	400	200	—	—	—	—	—	—	—	—	—	—	—	—	—	—	—	—	—	—	—
6400	3200	400	200	—	—	—	—	—	—	—	—	—	—	—	—	—	—	—	—	—	—	—
6400	3200	800	200	—	—	—	—	—	—	—	200	—	—	—	—	—	—	—	—	—	—	—
6400	6400	800	200	—	—	—	—	—	—	—	—	—	—	—	—	—	—	—	—	—	—	—

Group 4

Fish 12	Meman-betsu	802	611																			
6400	1600	200	—	—	—	—	—	—	—	—	—	—	—	—	—	—	—	—	—	—	—	—
800	800	100	—	—	—	—	—	—	—	—	—	—	—	—	—	—	—	—	—	—	—	—
6400	1600	400	—	—	—	—	—	—	—	—	—	—	—	—	—	—	—	—	—	—	—	—
3200	800	200	—	—	—	—	—	—	—	—	—	—	—	—	—	—	—	—	—	—	—	—
6400	800	200	—	—	—	—	—	—	—	—	—	—	—	—	—	—	—	—	—	—	—	—

Group 5

Fish 12	Meman-betsu	802	611	Kisagata 133	Otaru	Hashishita 23	Pince Rupert 2	1314	Haginari 27	715	Fish 5	Wakinosawa	Aomori 102	Aomori 783	Aomori 786	Aomori 207	Haginari 4-22	Fish 9	Kameda	Masuke	486	Hashishita 21
3200	800	—	—	—	—	—	—	—	—	—	—	—	—	—	—	—	—	—	—	—	25600	—
3200	200	—	—	—	—	—	—	—	—	—	—	—	—	—	—	—	1600	—	—	—	—	—
—	—	—	—	—	—	—	—	—	—	—	—	—	—	—	—	—	—	—	—	—	—	—
1600	200	—	—	—	—	—	—	—	—	—	—	—	—	—	—	—	—	—	—	—	—	—
3200	1600	—	—	—	—	—	—	—	—	—	—	—	—	—	—	—	1600	—	—	—	—	—
3200	800	—	—	—	—	—	—	—	—	—	—	—	—	—	—	—	—	—	—	—	—	—
3200	800	—	—	—	—	—	—	—	—	—	—	—	—	—	—	—	—	—	—	—	—	—
6400	1600	—	—	—	—	—	—	—	—	—	—	—	—	—	—	—	—	—	—	—	—	—
1600	800	—	—	—	—	—	—	—	—	—	—	—	—	—	—	—	—	200	—	—	—	—
3200	800	—	—	—	—	—	—	—	—	—	—	—	—	—	—	—	—	—	—	—	—	—
3200	800	—	—	—	—	800	—	—	—	—	—	—	—	—	—	—	—	—	—	—	—	—
3200	1600	—	—	—	—	—	—	—	—	—	—	—	—	—	—	—	—	—	—	—	—	800
3200	800	—	—	—	—	—	—	—	—	—	—	—	—	—	—	—	—	—	—	—	—	—
3200	800	—	—	—	—	—	—	—	—	—	—	—	—	—	—	—	—	—	—	—	—	—
1600	800	—	—	—	—	—	—	—	—	—	—	—	—	—	—	—	—	—	—	—	—	—
800	400	—	—	—	—	—	—	—	—	—	—	—	—	—	—	—	—	—	—	—	—	—
3200	—	—	—	—	—	—	—	—	—	—	—	—	—	—	—	—	—	—	—	—	—	—
3200	100	400	—	—	—	—	100	—	—	—	—	—	—	—	—	—	—	—	—	—	—	3200
3200	100	100	200	200	—	—	1600	—	—	—	—	—	—	—	—	—	—	—	400	—	—	800
6400	100	100	200	200	—	—	6400	—	—	—	—	—	—	—	—	—	—	—	200	—	—	200

Group 6

Fish 12	Meman-betsu	802	611	Kisagata 133	Otaru	Hashishita 23	Pince Rupert 2	1314	Haginari 27	715	Fish 5	Wakinosawa	Aomori 102	Aomori 783	Aomori 786	Aomori 207	Haginari 4-22	Fish 9	Kameda	Masuke	486	Hashishita 21
—	—	—	—	—	—	—	—	—	—	—	—	—	—	—	—	—	—	—	—	—	—	—
—	—	—	—	—	—	—	400	400	—	—	—	—	400	100	200	—	—	—	—	—	—	—
—	—	—	—	—	—	—	—	—	—	—	—	—	—	—	—	—	—	—	—	—	—	—
—	—	—	—	—	—	—	—	—	—	—	—	—	—	—	—	—	—	—	200	—	—	—
—	—	200	—	—	—	—	—	—	—	—	—	—	—	—	—	—	—	—	—	—	—	—

Table 4.—Agglutination of strains of *Clostridium botulinum* with

Immune Sera		Aomori ●	Tenno ●	341 ●	211 ●	Fish 8 ●	667 ●	Jundai 1 ●	Iwanai ●	Fish 7 ●	Hagina-ri 28 1 ●	Hagina-ri 9 ●	762 ●	Fish 6 ●	801 ●	777 ●	Yama-gata ●	Hashi-shita 40 ○	Fish 11 ●	Fish 6H ●	Bute 7 ○	Jōryu 74 ○
Group 7																						
Kisagata 133	○	—	—	—	—	—	—	—	400	—	—	—	—	—	—	—	—	—	—	—	400	—
Kisagata 64	○	—	—	—	—	—	—	—	400	—	—	—	—	—	—	—	—	—	—	—	100	—
Kisagata 61	○	—	—	—	—	—	—	—	400	—	—	—	—	—	—	—	—	—	—	—	200	—
Otaru	○	—	—	—	—	—	—	—	200	—	—	—	—	—	—	—	—	—	—	—	—	—
Group 8																						
Hashishita 21	○	—	—	—	—	800	—	—	—	—	—	—	—	—	—	—	100	—	—	100	200	400
Hashishita 23	○	—	—	—	800	400	—	—	—	—	—	—	—	—	—	—	400	—	—	100	100	200
Hashishita 32	○	—	—	—	800	400	—	—	—	—	—	—	—	—	—	—	400	—	—	6400	100	3200
486	●	—	—	—	—	—	—	—	—	—	—	—	—	—	—	—	—	—	—	3200	—	3200
Prince Rupert 2	●	—	—	1600	1600	—	—	800	1600	—	800	800	800	1600	800	800	1600	400	—	3200	—	—
Kacchi	●	—	—	—	—	1600	—	—	—	—	—	—	—	—	—	—	400	400	—	—	200	—
611	●	—	—	—	—	1600	—	—	—	—	—	—	—	—	—	—	—	—	—	—	—	—
1314	●	—	—	—	—	400	—	—	—	—	—	—	—	—	—	—	—	—	—	—	—	—
Haginari 27	○	—	1600	—	—	400	—	—	—	—	—	—	—	—	—	—	—	—	—	3200	800	3200
Fish 6H	●	100	—	100	100	800	—	—	—	—	—	—	—	—	400	—	800	800	—	6400	—	3200
36208	●	100	—	1600	1600	800	—	—	—	—	—	100	—	—	200	—	800	—	—	—	100	—
1304	●	—	—	—	—	800	—	—	—	—	—	—	—	—	—	—	—	—	—	—	—	—
Group 9																						
Fish 9	○	—	—	—	—	—	—	—	—	—	—	—	—	—	—	—	—	200	—	—	200	—
Aomori 207	○	—	100	—	—	400	—	—	—	—	—	—	—	—	—	—	—	—	—	—	100	—
Haginari 4 22	●	—	—	—	—	400	—	—	—	—	—	100	—	—	—	—	—	—	—	—	100	—
Masuke	●	—	—	—	—	400	—	—	—	—	—	—	—	—	—	—	—	—	—	—	—	—
Kameda	●	—	—	—	—	—	—	—	—	—	—	—	—	—	—	—	—	—	—	—	400	200
715	●	—	—	—	—	—	—	—	—	—	—	—	—	—	—	—	—	—	—	—	100	800
Fish 4	○	—	—	—	—	—	—	—	—	—	—	—	—	—	—	—	—	—	—	—	—	—
Fish 5	○	—	—	—	—	—	—	—	—	—	—	—	—	—	—	—	—	—	—	—	—	—
Wakinosawa	○	—	—	—	—	—	—	—	—	100	—	—	—	—	—	—	—	—	—	—	200	—
Maruya	○	—	—	—	—	—	—	—	—	—	—	—	—	—	—	—	—	—	—	—	—	—
Aomori 102	○	—	—	—	—	—	—	—	—	—	—	—	—	—	—	—	—	—	—	400	400	400
Aomori 103	○	—	—	—	—	—	—	—	—	—	—	—	—	—	—	—	—	—	—	—	100	—
Aomori 783	○	—	—	—	—	400	—	—	—	—	—	—	—	—	—	—	—	—	—	400	—	—
Aomori 786	○	—	—	—	—	400	—	—	—	400	—	—	—	—	—	—	—	—	—	3200	800	—
Bute 7	●	100	200	400	100	—	—	—	—	400	—	100	—	—	—	—	—	—	—	—	—	—
Oil H	●	1600	—	3200	—	—	—	—	—	—	—	—	—	—	—	—	—	—	—	—	—	—

antisera prepared against extract antigen type E—Continued

● : Toxigenic
○ : Non-toxigenic

Fish 12 ○	Meman-betsu ●	802 ●	611 ●	Kisaga-ta 133 ○	Otaru ○	Hashi-shita 23 ○	Pince Rupert 2 ●	1314 ●	Hagina-ri 27 ○	715 ●	Fish 5 ○	Wakino-sawa ○	Aomori 102 ○	Aomori 783 ○	Aomori 786 ○	Aomori 207 ○	Hagina-ri 4-22 ○	Fish 9 ○	Kameda ●	Masuke ●	486 ●	Hashi-shita 21 ○

Group 7

Fish 12	Meman-betsu	802	611	Kisaga-ta 133	Otaru	Hashi-shita 23	Pince Rupert 2	1314	Hagina-ri 27	715	Fish 5	Wakino-sawa	Aomori 102	Aomori 783	Aomori 786	Aomori 207	Hagina-ri 4-22	Fish 9	Kameda	Masuke	486	Hashi-shita 21
—	—	100	200	3200	400	—	—	200	—	800	—	—	—	—	100	—	—	—	1600	—	—	100
—	—	100	00	6400	1600	—	—	400	—	—	—	—	200	—	—	—	—	—	200	-	—	—
—	—	400	400	3200	3200	—	—	—	—	—	—	—	—	—	—	—	—	—	—	—	—	—
—	—	—	—	100	6400	—	—	—	—	—	—	—	—	—	—	—	—	—	—	—	—	—

Group 8

Fish 12	Meman-betsu	802	611	Kisaga-ta 133	Otaru	Hashi-shita 23	Pince Rupert 2	1314	Hagina-ri 27	715	Fish 5	Wakino-sawa	Aomori 102	Aomori 783	Aomori 786	Aomori 207	Hagina-ri 4-22	Fish 9	Kameda	Masuke	486	Hashi-shita 21
1600	200	—	—	—	—	3200	—	—	—	—	—	—	—	—	—	—	—	—	—	—	—	6400
800	100	—	—	100	—	1600	—	—	—	—	—	—	—	—	—	—	—	—	—	—	—	1600
800	—	—	—	100	—	800	—	—	—	800	—	—	—	—	—	—	—	—	—	—	—	1600
3200	800	—	—	—	—	—	100	—	—	—	—	—	—	—	—	—	—	—	—	—	3200	—
1600	100	—	—	—	—	—	400	—	—	—	—	—	—	—	—	—	—	—	—	—	—	—
6400	6400	1600	200	200	—	—	—	—	—	—	—	—	—	—	—	—	—	100	—	—	—	—
		100	3200	100	—	—	—	—	—	1600	—	—	—	—	—	—	—	—	—	—	—	—
		—	1600	—	—	—	—	1600	—	1600	—	—	—	—	—	—	—	—	—	—	—	—
100	100	—	—	—	—	—	—	—	1600	—	—	—	—	—	—	—	—	—	—	—	—	—
3200	200	—	—	—	—	—	—	—	—	—	—	—	—	—	—	—	—	—	—	—	—	—
3200	800	—	3200	—	—	—	—	—	—	—	—	—	—	—	—	—	—	—	—	—	—	—
—	—	—	—	—	—	—	—	3200	—	3200	—	—	—	—	—	—	—	—	—	—	—	—

Group 9

Fish 12	Meman-betsu	802	611	Kisaga-ta 133	Otaru	Hashi-shita 23	Pince Rupert 2	1314	Hagina-ri 27	715	Fish 5	Wakino-sawa	Aomori 102	Aomori 783	Aomori 786	Aomori 207	Hagina-ri 4-22	Fish 9	Kameda	Masuke	486	Hashi-shita 21
1600	—	—	—	—	—	—	—	—	1600	—	—	—	—	—	400	—	3200	—	—	—	—	—
—	—	—	—	—	—	—	—	—	—	—	—	—	—	—	3200	—	—	—	—	—	—	—
—	—	100	—	100	—	—	—	—	—	—	—	—	—	—	—	6400	—	—	6400	—	—	—
—	—	—	—	—	—	—	—	—	1600	—	—	—	—	—	—	—	—	6400	12800	—	—	—
400	200	800	—	100	—	—	—	—	1600	3200	—	—	—	—	—	—	—	—	100	—	—	—
200	400	—	—	—	—	100	—	—	—	—	—	—	—	—	—	—	—	—	—	—	—	—
200	200	—	—	400	—	200	—	—	—	200	—	400	—	3200	25600	—	—	—	—	—	—	—
100	—	100	200	100	—	—	—	—	—	—	—	6400	—	—	—	—	—	—	—	—	—	—
400	200	400	200	200	—	—	—	—	—	—	—	—	400	—	—	—	—	—	—	—	—	—
—	—	—	—	200	—	—	—	—	—	—	—	—	—	1600	25600	—	—	—	—	—	—	—
100	—	100	200	200	—	—	—	—	—	—	—	—	—	1600	25600	—	—	—	—	—	—	—
—	—	—	—	—	—	—	—	—	—	—	—	—	—	—	—	—	—	—	—	—	—	—

Table 5.—Flagellar agglutination of strains of

Immune Sera	Aomori	Tenno	341	211	667	Iwanai	Fish 6	801	777	Fish 11	Fish 6H	Bute 7	Jōryu 74	Fish 12	Memanbetsu	802
Before Absorption	6400	6400	12800	12800	12800	1600	25600	6400	12800	12800	6400	6400	12800	3200	6400	6400
Absorption with	VH /	Iwanai /	Nangai /	Seal IIIa Michikawa 10 /	Fish 12 /	Otaru /	Nishishunbetsu /	Kaneura 39 /	Jōryu 58 /	Seal IIIa /	Nangai 786	Hashishita 65 /	Bute 7 168	Bute 7 Funakoshi Iwanai /	Iwanai /	Haginari ri /

Group 1

Strain	Aomori	Tenno	341	211	667	Iwanai	Fish 6	801	777	Fish 11	Fish 6H	Bute 7	Jōryu 74	Fish 12	Memanbetsu	802
Aomori	800	—	—	—	—	—	—	—	—	—	—	—	—	—	—	—
VH	—	—	—	—	—	—	—	—	—	—	—	—	—	—	—	—

Group 2

Strain	Aomori	Tenno	341	211	667	Iwanai	Fish 6	801	777	Fish 11	Fish 6H	Bute 7	Jōryu 74	Fish 12	Memanbetsu	802
Tenno	—	1600	—	—	200	—	—	800	—	—	—	—	—	—	—	—
Fish 8	—	1600	—	—	—	400	3200	400	1600	—	—	—	—	—	—	—
759	—	1600	—	—	—	400	3200	800	800	400	—	—	—	—	—	—
667	—	1600	—	—	200	800	3200	800	800	800	—	—	—	—	—	—
Fish 35	—	1600	—	—	—	800	3200	1600	800	800	—	—	—	—	—	—
798	—	—	—	—	—	400	3200	1600	800	—	—	—	—	—	—	—
800	—	—	—	—	—	400	3200	400	1600	800	—	—	—	—	—	—
Fish 3	—	—	—	—	—	400	3200	400	1600	800	—	—	—	—	—	—
Fish 67	—	—	—	—	—	400	3200	400	800	800	—	—	—	—	—	—
Fish 13	—	1600	—	—	—	400	3200	400	800	800	—	—	—	100	—	1600
761	—	—	—	—	—	400	3200	800	1600	400	—	—	—	400	1600	1600
Jundai 1	—	—	—	—	—	400	3200	800	1600	800	—	—	—	400	—	—
760	—	—	—	—	—	800	6400	800	800	800	—	—	—	—	—	—
Haginari 8	—	—	—	—	—	800	6400	800	800	800	—	—	—	200	—	—
Iwanai	—	—	—	—	—	800	3200	800	1600	—	—	—	—	—	—	—
Fish 7	—	1600	—	—	—	800	6400	400	1600	800	—	—	—	—	—	—
Haginari	—	1600	—	—	—	800	6400	400	1600	800	—	—	—	—	—	—
775	—	—	—	—	100	800	6400	800	1600	800	—	—	—	—	—	—
527	—	1600	—	—	—	800	6400	400	1600	800	—	—	—	—	—	—
Haginari 28-1	—	—	—	—	—	800	6400	800	800	400	—	—	—	—	—	—
Haginari 9	—	—	—	—	—	400	6400	400	800	400	—	—	—	—	—	—
762	—	—	—	—	—	400	3200	400	800	400	—	—	—	—	—	—
Nakahadachi	—	—	—	—	—	400	3200	400	1600	800	—	—	—	—	—	—
Kimoto	—	—	—	—	400	800	3200	400	800	800	—	—	—	—	—	—
Shinonome 1	—	1600	—	—	200	800	3200	400	800	800	—	—	—	—	—	—
Honjō 35	—	1600	—	—	200	800	1600	400	800	1600	—	—	—	—	—	—
Honjō 37	—	—	—	—	200	800	6400	400	800	800	—	—	—	—	—	—
Fish 14	—	—	—	—	100	800	6400	800	800	800	—	—	—	—	—	—
Funakawa	—	1600	—	—	200	—	3200	800	800	1600	—	—	—	400	—	—
Fish 6	—	—	—	—	—	—	3200	800	800	800	—	—	—	—	—	—
Kaneura 1-3	—	—	—	—	200	800	3200	800	800	800	—	—	—	—	—	—
Futto	—	1600	—	—	200	400	3200	800	800	800	—	—	—	—	—	—
801	—	—	—	—	200	400	3200	800	800	800	—	—	—	400	—	—
777	—	—	—	—	100	—	3200	800	800	800	—	—	—	400	1600	1600
Jundai 4	—	—	—	—	—	—	3200	800	1600	1600	—	—	—	800	1600	1600
Aomori 177	—	—	—	—	100	—	3200	800	800	400	—	—	—	200	1600	1600
Fish 11	—	—	—	—	—	—	3200	800	800	800	—	—	—	—	—	—
758	—	1600	—	—	—	800	3200	800	800	800	—	—	—	—	—	—

Group 3

Strain	Aomori	Tenno	341	211	667	Iwanai	Fish 6	801	777	Fish 11	Fish 6H	Bute 7	Jōryu 74	Fish 12	Memanbetsu	802
770	—	—	—	—	—	1600	3200	800	1600	800	—	—	—	400	3200	1600
Abashiri	—	—	—	—	—	400	—	—	—	1600	—	—	—	400	1600	1600
Jundai 6	—	—	—	—	—	—	—	—	—	400	—	—	—	400	1600	1600
Jundai 7	—	—	—	—	—	800	3200	400	1600	800	—	—	—	400	3200	1600
Onbetsu	—	—	—	—	—	800	—	400	—	800	—	—	—	400	1600	3200
Memanbetsu	—	—	—	—	—	800	3200	800	800	1600	—	—	—	400	1600	1600
Fish 12	—	—	—	—	—	800	800	400	—	400	—	—	—	400	3200	1600
786	—	—	—	—	—	—	—	400	—	1600	—	—	—	400	3200	3200
Daijima	—	—	—	—	—	800	800	800	800	1600	—	—	—	400	3200	1600
804	—	—	—	—	—	—	—	—	—	—	—	—	—	400	3200	1600
802	—	—	—	—	—	—	—	—	—	—	—	—	—	—	—	—

Group 4

Strain	Aomori	Tenno	341	211	667	Iwanai	Fish 6	801	777	Fish 11	Fish 6H	Bute 7	Jōryu 74	Fish 12	Memanbetsu	802
Nangai	—	—	—	—	—	800	3200	800	800	400	—	—	—	200	1600	200
Nishishunbetsu	—	—	—	—	—	—	—	400	—	—	—	—	—	—	1600	—
779	—	—	—	—	—	—	—	400	—	—	—	—	—	400	1600	200
Jundai 3	—	—	—	—	—	800	3200	800	800	—	—	—	—	—	400	200
168	—	—	—	—	—	800	6400	800	1600	—	—	—	—	200	—	—

Group 5

Strain	Aomori	Tenno	341	211	667	Iwanai	Fish 6	801	777	Fish 11	Fish 6H	Bute 7	Jōryu 74	Fish 12	Memanbetsu	802
341	—	—	1600	—	—	—	—	—	—	400	—	3200	—	—	800	200
Matsugasaki 156	—	—	—	—	—	—	—	—	—	800	—	6400	—	—	1600	200
Eskimo whale	—	—	—	—	—	—	—	—	—	400	400	1600	—	—	400	—
Fish 6H	—	—	—	—	—	—	—	—	—	400	—	1600	—	—	800	200
Jōryu 74	—	—	—	—	—	—	—	—	—	800	—	3200	—	—	400	200
No. 8	—	—	1600	—	—	—	—	—	—	—	—	—	—	—	—	—
Hashishita 96	—	—	1600	—	—	—	—	—	—	800	—	6400	—	—	1600	200
Hashishita 62	—	—	1600	—	—	—	—	—	—	400	—	6400	—	—	1600	200
Hashishita 65	—	—	1600	—	—	—	—	—	—	800	—	6400	—	—	1600	200
Hashishita 56	—	—	1600	—	—	—	—	—	—	400	—	6400	—	—	1600	200
Bute 2	—	—	1600	—	—	—	—	—	—	400	—	6400	—	—	1600	200
Funakoshi	—	—	1600	—	—	—	—	—	—	800	—	6400	—	—	1600	200
Nanaimo Chicken	—	—	1600	—	—	—	—	—	—	400	—	6400	—	—	1600	200
Beluga A	—	—	1600	—	—	—	—	—	—	—	—	—	—	—	—	—
Alaska	—	—	1600	—	—	—	—	—	—	—	—	—	—	—	—	—
Bute 7	—	—	—	—	—	—	—	—	—	400	400	—	—	—	1600	—

Clostridium botulinum type E with absorbed antisera

●: Toxigenic
○: Non-toxigenic

●	○	○	○	●	●	○	●	○	○	○	○	○	○	○	●	●	●	○
611	Kisaga-ta 133	Otaru	Hashi-shita 23	Prince Rupert 2	1314	Hagina-ri 27	715	Fish 5	Wakino-sawa	Aomori 102	Aomori 783	Aomori 786	Hagina-ri 4-22	Fish 9	Kameda	Masuke	486	Hashi-shita 21
6400	6400	12800	3200	3200	6400	800	1600	1600	3200	1600	1600	3200	12800	12800	6400	6400	12800	12800
Hagina-ri 27	Seal IIIa	Michika-wa 15	Funako-shi	Michika-wa 15	/	F 5	/	/	/	/	/	/	/	/	211	Funaka-wa	Kaneura 39	Hashi-shita 23
/	Otaru	/	/	/	/	/	/	/	/	/	/	/	/	/	/	/	Kisaga-ta 133	/
/	/	/	/	/	/	/	/	/	/	/	/	/	/	/	/	/	/	/

Group 1

−	−	−	−	−	−	−	−	−	−	−	−	−	−	−	−	−	−	−

Group 2

(All reactions negative: − across all columns for each row.)

Group 3

(All reactions negative: − across all columns for each row.)

Group 4

(All reactions negative: − across all columns for each row.)

Group 5

−	−	−	−	3200	−	−	−	−	−	−	−	−	−	−	−	−	200	−
−	−	−	−	−	−	−	−	−	−	−	−	−	−	−	−	−	−	−
−	−	−	−	1600	−	−	−	−	−	−	−	−	−	−	−	−	−	−
−	−	−	−	1600	−	−	−	−	−	−	−	−	−	−	−	−	−	−
−	−	−	−	1600	−	−	−	−	−	−	−	−	−	−	−	−	−	−
−	−	−	−	1600	−	−	−	−	−	−	−	−	−	−	−	−	−	−
−	−	−	−	1600	−	−	−	−	−	−	−	−	−	−	−	−	−	−
−	−	−	−	3200	−	−	−	−	−	−	−	−	−	−	−	−	−	−
−	−	−	−	3200	−	−	−	−	−	−	−	−	−	−	−	−	−	−
−	−	−	−	−	−	−	−	−	−	−	−	−	−	−	−	−	−	−
−	−	−	−	1600	−	−	−	−	−	−	−	−	−	−	−	−	−	−
−	−	−	−	−	−	−	−	−	−	−	−	−	−	−	−	−	−	−

Table 5.—Flagellar agglutination of strains of Clostridium

Immune Sera	mark	Aomori	Tenno	341	211	667	Iwanai	Fish 6	801	777	Fish 11	Fish 6H	Bute 7	Jōryu 74	Fish 12	Memanbetsu	802
(symbol)		●	●	●	●	●	●	●	●	●	●	●	●	○	○	○	●
Before Absorption		6400	6400	12800	12800	12800	1600	25600	6400	12800	12800	6400	6400	12800	3200	6400	6400
Absorption with		VH	Iwanai	Nangai	Seal IIIa / Michikawa 10	Fish 12	Otaru	Nishi-shunbetsu	Kaneura 39	Jōryu 58	Seal IIIa	Nangai 786	Hashishita 65	Bute 7 168	Bute 7 / Funakoshi Iwanai	Iwanai	Haginari
Group 6																	
Honjō 133	○	—	—	—	—	—	—	—	—	—	—	400	—	—	—	—	—
Michikawa 14	○	—	—	—	—	—	—	—	—	—	—	400	—	—	—	—	—
Honjō 121	○	—	—	—	—	—	—	—	—	—	—	400	—	—	—	—	—
Kosagawa 92	●	—	—	—	—	—	—	—	—	—	—	800	—	—	—	—	—
211	●	—	—	—	1600	—	—	—	—	—	—	400	—	3200	—	—	—
Matsugasaki 54	○	—	—	—	—	—	—	—	—	—	—	400	—	3200	—	—	—
Matsugasaki 94	○	—	—	—	—	—	—	—	—	—	—	400	—	3200	—	—	—
Seal IIIa	●	—	—	—	—	—	—	—	—	—	—	400	—	3200	—	—	—
Kaneura 39	●	—	—	—	—	—	—	1600	—	—	—	400	—	3200	—	—	—
Jōryu 58	○	—	—	—	—	—	—	—	—	—	—	400	—	—	—	—	—
Hashishita 34	○	—	—	—	—	—	—	—	—	—	—	—	—	—	—	—	—
Group 7																	
Kisagata 133	○	—	—	—	—	—	—	—	—	—	—	—	—	—	—	—	—
Kisagata 64	○	—	—	—	—	—	—	—	—	—	—	—	—	—	—	—	—
Kisagata 61	○	—	—	—	—	—	—	—	—	—	—	—	—	—	—	—	—
Otaru	○	—	—	—	—	—	—	—	—	—	—	—	—	—	—	—	—
Group 8																	
Hashishita 21	○	—	—	—	—	—	—	—	—	—	—	—	3200	—	—	-	—
Hashishita 23	○	—	—	—	—	—	—	—	—	—	—	—	3200	—	—	—	—
Hashishita 32	○	—	—	—	—	—	—	—	—	—	—	200	3200	—	—	—	—
486	○	—	—	—	—	—	—	—	—	—	—	—	3200	—	—	—	—
Prince Rupert 2	●	—	—	—	—	—	—	—	—	—	—	—	—	—	400	—	—
Kacchi	●	—	—	—	—	—	—	6400	800	—	800	400	6400	—	—	—	—
36208	●	—	—	1600	—	—	—	—	—	—	—	—	6400	—	—	1600	200
611	●	—	—	—	—	—	—	—	—	—	—	—	—	—	—	—	—
1314	●	—	—	—	—	—	—	—	—	—	—	—	—	—	—	—	—
Haginari 27	○	—	—	—	—	—	—	—	—	—	—	—	—	—	—	—	—
Group 9																	
1304	●	—	—	—	—	—	—	—	—	—	—	—	—	—	—	—	—
Oil H	●	—	—	—	—	—	—	—	—	—	—	—	—	—	—	—	—
Fish-9	○	—	—	—	—	—	—	—	—	—	—	—	—	—	—	—	—
Aomori 207	○	—	—	—	—	—	—	—	—	—	—	—	—	—	—	—	—
Haginari 4-22	○	—	—	—	—	—	—	—	—	—	—	—	—	—	—	—	—
Masuke	●	—	—	—	—	—	—	—	—	—	—	—	—	—	—	—	—
Kameda	●	—	—	—	—	—	—	—	—	—	—	—	—	—	—	—	—
715	●	—	—	—	—	—	—	—	—	—	—	—	—	—	—	—	—
Fish 4	○	—	—	—	—	—	—	—	—	—	—	—	—	—	—	—	—
Fish 5	○	—	—	—	—	—	—	—	—	—	—	—	—	—	—	—	—
Wakinosawa	○	—	—	—	—	—	—	—	—	—	—	—	—	—	—	—	—
Maruya	○	—	—	—	—	—	—	—	—	—	—	—	—	—	—	—	—
Aomori 102	○	—	—	—	—	—	—	—	—	—	—	—	—	—	—	—	—
Aomori 783	○	—	—	—	—	—	—	—	—	—	—	—	—	—	—	—	—
Aomori 786	○	—	—	—	—	—	—	—	—	—	—	—	—	—	—	—	—

botulinum type E with absorbed antisera—Continued

● : Toxigenic
○ : Non-toxigenic

●	○	○	○	●	●	○	●	○	○	○	○	○	○	○	●	●	●	○
611	Kisagata 133	Otaru	Hashishita 23	Prince Rupert 2	1314	Haginari 27	715	Fish 5	Wakinosawa	Aomori 102	Aomori 783	Aomori 786	Haginari 4-22	Fish 9	Kameda	Masuke	486	Hashishita 21
6400	6400	12800	3200	3200	6400	800	1600	1600	3200	1600	1600	3200	12800	12800	6400	6400	12800	12800
Haginari 27	Seal IIIa	Michikawa 15	Funakoshi	Michikawa 15	/	F 5	/	/	/	/	/	/	/	/	211	Funakawa	Kaneura 39	Hashishita 23
/	Otaru	/	/	/	/	/	/	/	/	/	/	/	/	/	/	/	Kisagata 133	/
/	/	/	/	/	/	/	/	/	/	/	/	/	/	/	/	/	/	/

Group 6

(all values —)

Group 7

—	3200	—	—	—	—	—	—	—	—	—	—	—	—	—	—	—	—	—
—	3200	—	—	—	—	—	—	—	—	—	—	—	—	—	—	—	—	—
—	1600	—	—	—	—	—	—	—	—	—	—	—	—	—	—	—	—	—
—	—	—	400	—	—	—	—	—	—	—	—	—	—	—	—	—	—	—

Group 8

—	—	—	100	—	—	—	—	—	—	—	—	—	—	—	—	—	—	200
—	—	—	100	—	—	—	—	—	—	—	—	—	—	—	—	—	—	—
—	—	—	100	—	—	—	—	—	—	—	—	—	—	—	—	—	—	—
—	—	—	200	—	—	—	—	—	—	—	—	—	—	—	—	400	—	—
—	—	—	—	3200	—	—	—	—	—	—	—	—	—	—	—	—	—	—
—	—	—	—	1600	—	—	—	—	—	—	—	—	—	—	—	—	—	—
1600	—	—	—	—	6400	800	—	—	—	—	—	—	—	—	—	—	—	—
1600	—	—	—	—	6400	800	—	—	—	—	—	—	—	—	—	—	—	—
—	—	—	—	—	800	—	—	—	—	—	—	—	—	—	—	—	—	—

Group 9

1600	—	—	—	—	800	—	—	—	—	—	—	—	—	12800	—	—	400	—
—	—	—	—	—	—	1600	—	—	—	—	—	3200	12800	—	3200	400	—	—
—	—	—	—	—	—	1600	800	—	—	—	—	—	—	—	—	—	—	—
—	—	—	—	—	—	—	1600	3200	—	—	3200	—	—	—	—	—	—	—
—	—	—	—	—	—	—	—	—	1600	1600	800	—	—	—	—	—	—	—
—	—	—	—	—	—	—	—	—	—	—	3200	—	—	—	—	—	—	—

Table 6.—Agglutination of strains of *Clostridium botulinum* type E with

Immune Sera	Aomori	Tenno	341	211	667	Iwanai	Fish 6	801	777	Fish 11	Fish 6H	Bute 7	Jōryu 74	Fish 12	Memanbetsu	802
Before Absorption	3200	3200	3200	3200	3200	3200	3200	1600	800	1600	3200	800	3200	6400	3200	800
Absorption with	VH	777	Bute 7	Nakaha-dachi	802 / 761 / Tenno	Seal IIIa / Nishi-shunbetsu / Nangai	802	Seal IIIa / F 11 / 804	Jōryu 58	Seal IIIa	Nishi-shunbetsu	Hashi-shita 34	Hashi-shita 23	Kimoto / Jōryu 74 / Iwanai	Iwanai	Hagina-ri

Group 1

Strain	Aomori	Tenno	341	211	667	Iwanai	Fish 6	801	777	Fish 11	Fish 6H	Bute 7	Jōryu 74	Fish 12	Memanbetsu	802
Aomori / VH	400	—	—	—	—	—	—	—	—	—	—	—	—	—	—	—

Group 2

Strain	Aomori	Tenno	341	211	667	Iwanai	Fish 6	801	777	Fish 11	Fish 6H	Bute 7	Jōryu 74	Fish 12	Memanbetsu	802
Tenno	—	400	—	—	—	200	—	800	—	400	—	—	—	—	—	—
Fish 8	—	—	—	—	200	400	—	800	800	800	—	—	—	—	—	—
759	—	200	—	—	400	400	400	800	400	400	—	—	—	—	—	—
667	—	200	—	—	400	400	400	1600	800	400	—	—	—	—	—	—
Fish 35	—	—	—	—	200	400	400	1600	400	800	—	—	—	—	—	—
798	—	—	—	—	200	400	400	800	800	800	—	—	—	—	—	—
800	—	—	—	—	400	400	400	1600	800	800	—	—	—	—	—	—
Fish 3	—	—	—	—	200	400	400	800	800	800	—	—	—	—	—	—
Fish 67	—	—	—	—	200	400	400	800	400	400	—	—	—	—	—	—
Fish 13	—	—	—	—	400	400	—	1600	400	400	—	—	—	—	—	—
761	—	—	—	—	—	200	—	1600	400	400	—	—	—	3200	—	200
Jundai 1	—	—	—	—	400	400	200	1600	400	400	—	—	—	—	—	—
760	—	—	—	—	—	400	200	1600	800	400	—	—	—	—	—	—
Haginari 8	—	—	—	—	—	400	400	1600	800	400	—	—	—	—	—	—
Iwanai	—	—	—	—	—	400	800	800	800	800	—	—	±	—	—	—
Fish 7	—	200	—	—	—	400	400	800	400	800	—	—	—	—	—	—
Haginari	—	—	—	—	200	400	200	800	400	400	—	—	—	—	—	—
775	—	—	—	—	200	400	200	1600	400	800	—	—	—	—	—	—
Haginari 28-1	—	200	—	—	200	400	400	1600	400	400	—	—	—	—	—	—
527	—	400	—	—	200	400	400	1600	400	400	—	—	—	—	—	—
Haginari 9	—	200	—	—	—	400	400	1600	400	400	—	—	—	—	—	—
762	—	—	—	—	—	200	400	400	400	400	—	—	—	—	—	—
Nakahadachi	—	400	—	—	—	200	400	1600	800	400	—	—	—	—	—	—
Kimoto	—	400	—	—	—	200	400	800	800	400	—	—	—	—	—	—
Shinonome 1	—	400	—	—	—	200	200	800	400	400	—	—	—	—	—	—
Honjō 35	—	—	—	—	—	200	200	1600	400	400	—	—	—	—	—	—
Honjō 37	—	—	—	—	200	200	200	1600	400	400	—	—	—	—	—	—
Fish 14	—	200	—	—	—	200	200	1600	400	400	—	—	—	—	—	—
Funakawa	—	400	—	—	200	200	200	1600	800	400	—	—	—	—	—	—
Fish 6	—	—	—	—	—	200	200	1600	400	400	—	—	—	—	—	—
Kaneura 1-3	—	200	—	—	—	200	200	1600	400	400	—	—	—	—	—	—
Futto	—	200	—	—	—	200	400	800	800	400	—	—	—	—	—	—
801	—	200	—	—	—	200	400	1600	400	400	—	—	—	—	—	—
777	—	400	—	—	—	200	400	—	800	400	—	—	—	—	—	—
Yamagata	—	—	—	—	—	200	400	800	800	400	800	—	—	3200	400	400
Jundai 4	—	—	—	—	—	200	400	800	400	400	800	—	—	3200	400	200
Aomori 177	—	—	—	—	—	—	—	—	—	—	—	—	—	—	—	—
Hashishita 57	—	—	—	—	—	—	—	—	—	—	—	—	—	—	—	—
Hashishita 40	—	—	—	—	—	—	—	—	—	—	—	—	—	—	—	—
Fish 11	—	—	—	—	—	400	200	—	400	800	—	—	—	—	—	—
758	—	—	—	—	—	400	200	800	400	400	—	—	—	—	—	—

Group 3

Strain	Aomori	Tenno	341	211	667	Iwanai	Fish 6	801	777	Fish 11	Fish 6H	Bute 7	Jōryu 74	Fish 12	Memanbetsu	802
770	—	—	—	—	—	200	200	800	400	400	800	—	—	3200	800	200
Abashiri	—	—	—	—	—	400	400	—	400	400	800	—	—	3200	400	200
Jundai 6	—	—	—	—	—	400	—	—	—	—	800	—	—	3200	400	200
Jundai 7	—	—	—	—	—	400	—	1600	400	400	800	—	—	3200	400	200
Onbetsu	—	—	—	—	—	—	—	—	400	—	800	—	—	3200	800	200
Memanbetsu	—	—	—	—	—	400	200	800	400	400	800	—	—	3200	800	200
Fish 12	—	—	—	—	—	200	—	—	—	—	800	—	—	3200	400	200
786	—	—	—	—	—	400	200	800	—	800	800	—	—	3200	400	200
Daijima	—	—	—	—	—	—	400	—	—	—	800	—	—	3200	800	200
804	—	—	—	—	—	—	—	—	400	400	800	—	—	3200	800	200
802	—	—	—	—	—	—	—	—	—	—	800	—	—	3200	400	200

Group 4

Strain	Aomori	Tenno	341	211	667	Iwanai	Fish 6	801	777	Fish 11	Fish 6H	Bute 7	Jōryu 74	Fish 12	Memanbetsu	802
Nangai	—	—	—	—	—	200	—	800	400	—	—	—	—	800	—	—
Nishishunbetsu	—	—	—	—	—	—	—	—	400	—	—	—	—	—	—	—
779	—	—	—	—	—	—	—	—	400	—	—	—	—	800	—	—
Jundai 3	—	—	—	—	—	400	—	800	400	—	—	—	—	—	—	—
168	—	—	—	—	—	400	100	800	400	—	—	—	—	—	—	—

Group 5

Strain	Aomori	Tenno	341	211	667	Iwanai	Fish 6	801	777	Fish 11	Fish 6H	Bute 7	Jōryu 74	Fish 12	Memanbetsu	802
341	—	—	—	—	—	—	—	—	—	—	400	—	400	—	—	—
Matsugasaki 156	—	—	—	800	—	—	—	—	—	—	400	—	400	—	—	—
Eskimo whale	—	—	—	—	—	—	—	—	—	—	200	200	—	—	—	—
Jōryu 74	—	—	—	—	—	—	—	—	—	—	200	—	400	—	—	—
No. 8	—	—	—	—	—	—	—	—	—	—	200	—	400	—	—	—
Hashishita 96	—	—	—	—	—	—	—	—	—	—	200	—	400	—	—	—
Hashishita 62	—	—	—	—	—	—	—	—	—	—	200	—	400	—	—	—
Hashishita 65	—	—	—	—	—	—	—	—	—	—	200	—	400	—	—	—
Hashishita 56	—	—	—	—	—	—	—	—	—	—	200	—	400	—	—	—
Bute 2	—	—	—	—	—	—	—	—	—	—	400	—	200	—	—	—
Funakoshi	—	—	—	—	—	—	—	—	—	—	—	—	200	—	—	—
Nanaimo Chicken	—	—	—	—	—	—	—	—	—	—	—	—	200	—	—	—
Beluga A	—	—	—	—	—	—	—	—	—	—	—	—	200	—	—	—
Salmon eggs	—	—	—	—	—	—	—	—	—	—	—	—	200	—	—	—
Matsugasaki 54	—	—	—	—	—	—	—	—	—	—	—	—	200	—	—	—
Matsugasaki 94	—	—	—	—	—	—	—	—	—	—	200	400	200	—	—	—
Seal IIIa	—	—	—	—	—	—	—	—	—	—	200	400	200	—	—	—
Kaneura 39	—	—	—	—	—	—	—	—	—	—	—	—	—	—	—	—
Jōryu 58	—	—	—	—	—	—	—	—	—	—	—	—	—	—	—	—
Hashishita 34	—	—	—	—	—	—	—	—	—	—	—	—	—	—	—	—

antisera prepared against extract antigen and absorbed with various strains

● : Toxigenic
○ : Non-toxigenic

●	○	○	○	●	●	○	●	○	○	○	○	○	○	○	●	●	●	○
611	Kisagata 133	Otaru	Hashishita 23	Prince Rupert 2	1314	Hagina-ri 27	715	Fish 5	Wakino-sawa	Aomori 102	Aomori 783	Aomori 786	Hagina-ri 4-22	Fish 9	Kameda	Masuke	486	Hashishita 21
3200	3200	6400	1600	400	1600	1600	1600	3200	200	6400	400	1600	6400	3200	6400	6400	3200	6400
761	Seal IIIa	Kisagata 133	Aomori 783	486	Wakino-sawa	/	/	/	/	Michika-wa 15	/	Michika-wa 15	Jōryu 74	/	Kisagata 133	/	Honjō 36	Jōryu 58
Hagina-ri 27	Otaru	/	/	/	/	/	/	/	/	/	/	/	/	/	Jōryu 58	/	/	Hashishita 34
/	/	/	/	/	/	/	/	/	/	/	/	/	/	/	/	/	/	/

Group 1

(all entries: —)

Group 2

(all entries: —)

Group 3

(all entries: —)

Group 4

(all entries: —)

Group 5

(all entries: —, except "800" in the 486 column and "100" in the Prince Rupert 2 column)

Table 6.—Agglutination of strains of *Clostridium botulinum* type E with antisera

Immune Sera	Aomori	Tenno	341	211	667	Iwanai	Fish 6	801	777	Fish 11	Fish 6H	Bute 7	Jōryu 74	Fish 12	Memanbetsu	802
	●	●	●	●	●	●	●	●	●	●	●	○	○	○	●	●
Before Absorption	3200	3200	3200	3200	3200	3200	3200	1600	800	1600	3200	800	3200	6400	3200	800
Absorption with	VH	777	Bute 7	Nakahadachi	802 / 761 / Tenno	Seal IIIa / Nishi-shunbetsu / Nangai	802	Seal IIIa / F 11 / 804	Jōryu 58	Seal IIIa	Nishi-shunbetsu	Hashishita 34	Hashishita 23	Kimoto / Jōryu 74 / Iwanai	Iwanai	Haginari

Group 6

Strain		Aomori	Tenno	341	211	667	Iwanai	Fish 6	801	777	Fish 11	Fish 6H	Bute 7	Jōryu 74	Fish 12	Memanbetsu	802
Honjō 133	○	—	—	—	—	—	—	—	—	—	—	—	—	—	—	—	—
Michikawa 14	○	—	—	—	—	—	—	—	—	—	—	—	—	—	—	—	—
Michikawa 15	○	—	—	—	—	—	—	—	—	—	—	—	—	—	—	—	—
Honjō 121	○	—	—	—	—	—	—	—	—	—	—	—	—	—	—	—	—
Kosagawa 92	○	—	—	—	—	200	—	—	—	—	—	200	—	—	—	—	—
211	●	—	—	—	—	200	—	—	—	—	—	—	—	—	—	—	—
Michikawa 10	○	—	—	—	—	—	—	—	—	—	—	—	—	—	—	—	—

Group 7

Strain		Aomori	Tenno	341	211	667	Iwanai	Fish 6	801	777	Fish 11	Fish 6H	Bute 7	Jōryu 74	Fish 12	Memanbetsu	802
Kisagata 133	○	—	—	—	—	—	—	—	—	—	—	—	—	—	—	—	—
Kisagata 64	○	—	—	—	—	—	—	—	—	—	—	—	—	—	—	—	—
Kisagata 61	○	—	—	—	—	—	—	—	—	—	—	—	—	—	—	—	—
Otaru	○	—	—	—	—	—	—	—	—	—	—	—	—	—	—	—	—

Group 8

Strain		Aomori	Tenno	341	211	667	Iwanai	Fish 6	801	777	Fish 11	Fish 6H	Bute 7	Jōryu 74	Fish 12	Memanbetsu	802
Hashishita 21	○	—	—	—	—	—	—	—	—	—	—	—	—	—	—	—	—
Hashishita 23	○	—	—	—	—	—	—	—	—	—	—	—	200	—	200	—	—
Hashishita 32	○	—	—	—	—	—	—	—	—	—	—	—	200	—	200	—	—
486	●	—	—	—	—	—	—	—	—	—	—	—	—	—	—	—	—
Prince Rupert 2	●	—	—	—	—	—	—	—	—	800	—	—	—	—	—	—	—
Kacchi	●	—	—	—	—	—	—	—	—	—	—	—	—	—	—	—	—
611	●	—	—	—	—	—	—	—	—	—	—	—	—	—	—	—	—
1314	●	—	—	—	—	—	—	—	—	—	—	—	—	—	—	—	—
Haginari 27	○	—	—	—	—	—	—	—	—	—	—	—	200	—	—	—	—
Fish 6H	●	—	—	—	—	—	—	—	—	—	—	—	200	—	—	—	—
36208	●	—	—	—	—	—	—	—	—	—	—	—	—	—	—	—	—
1304	●	—	—	—	—	—	—	—	—	—	—	—	—	—	—	—	—

Group 9

Strain		Aomori	Tenno	341	211	667	Iwanai	Fish 6	801	777	Fish 11	Fish 6H	Bute 7	Jōryu 74	Fish 12	Memanbetsu	802
Fish-9	○	—	—	—	—	—	—	—	—	—	—	—	—	—	—	—	—
Aomori 207	○	—	—	—	—	—	—	—	—	—	—	—	—	—	—	—	—
Haginari 4-22	○	—	—	—	—	—	—	—	—	—	—	—	—	—	—	—	—
Masuke	●	—	—	—	—	—	—	—	—	—	—	—	—	—	—	—	—
Kameda	●	—	—	—	—	—	—	—	—	—	—	—	—	—	—	—	—
715	○	—	—	—	—	—	—	—	—	—	—	—	—	—	—	—	—
Fish 4	○	—	—	—	—	—	—	—	—	—	—	—	—	—	—	—	—
Fish 5	○	—	—	—	—	—	—	—	—	—	—	—	—	—	—	—	—
Wakinosawa	○	—	—	—	—	—	—	—	—	—	—	—	—	—	—	—	—
Maruya	○	—	—	—	—	—	—	—	—	—	—	—	—	—	—	—	—
Aomori 102	○	—	—	—	—	—	—	—	—	—	—	—	—	—	—	—	—
Aomori 103	○	—	—	—	—	—	—	—	—	—	—	—	—	—	—	—	—
Aomori 783	○	—	—	—	—	—	—	—	—	—	—	—	200	—	200	—	—
Aomori 786	○	—	—	—	—	—	—	—	—	—	—	—	—	—	—	—	—
Bute 7	○	—	—	—	—	—	—	—	—	—	—	—	—	—	—	—	—
Oil H	●	—	—	1600	—	—	—	—	—	—	—	—	—	—	—	—	—

prepared against extract antigen and absorbed with various strains—Continued

● : Toxigenic
○ : Non-toxigenic

● 611	○ Kisagata 133	○ Otaru	○ Hashishita 23	● Prince Rupert 2	● 1314	○ Haginari 27	● 715	○ Fish 5	○ Wakinosawa	○ Aomori 102	○ Aomori 783	○ Aomori 786	○ Haginari 4-22	○ Fish 9	● Kameda	● Masuke	● 486	○ Hashishita 21
3200	3200	6400	1600	400	1600	1600	1600	3200	200	6400	400	1600	6400	3200	6400	6400	3200	6400
761 / Haginari 27 /	Seal IIIa / Otaru /	Kisagata 133 / /	Aomori 783 / /	486 / /	Wakinosawa / /	/ /	/ /	/ /	/ /	Michikawa 15 / /	/ /	Michikawa 15 / /	Jōryu 74 / /	/ /	Kisagata 133 / Jōryu 58	/ /	Honjō36 / /	Jōryu 58 / Hashishita 34 /

Group 6

611	Kisagata 133	Otaru	Hashishita 23	Prince Rupert 2	1314	Haginari 27	715	Fish 5	Wakinosawa	Aomori 102	Aomori 783	Aomori 786	Haginari 4-22	Fish 9	Kameda	Masuke	486	Hashishita 21
—	—	—	—	—	—	—	—	—	—	—	—	—	—	—	—	—	—	—
—	—	—	—	—	—	—	—	—	—	—	—	—	—	—	—	—	—	—
—	—	—	—	—	—	—	—	—	—	—	—	—	—	—	—	—	—	—
—	—	—	—	—	—	—	—	—	—	—	—	—	—	—	—	—	—	—

Group 7

611	Kisagata 133	Otaru	Hashishita 23	Prince Rupert 2	1314	Haginari 27	715	Fish 5	Wakinosawa	Aomori 102	Aomori 783	Aomori 786	Haginari 4-22	Fish 9	Kameda	Masuke	486	Hashishita 21
—	3200	—	—	—	—	—	—	—	—	—	—	—	—	—	—	—	—	—
—	6400	—	—	—	—	—	800	—	—	—	—	—	—	—	—	—	—	—
—	3200	—	—	—	—	—	—	—	—	—	—	—	—	—	—	—	—	—
—	—	400	—	—	—	—	—	—	—	—	—	—	—	—	—	—	—	—

Group 8

611	Kisagata 133	Otaru	Hashishita 23	Prince Rupert 2	1314	Haginari 27	715	Fish 5	Wakinosawa	Aomori 102	Aomori 783	Aomori 786	Haginari 4-22	Fish 9	Kameda	Masuke	486	Hashishita 21
—	—	—	100	—	—	—	—	—	—	—	—	—	—	—	—	—	—	800
—	—	—	100	—	—	—	—	—	—	—	—	—	—	—	—	—	—	—
—	—	—	100	—	—	—	800	—	—	—	—	—	—	—	—	—	—	—
—	—	—	—	200	—	—	—	—	—	—	—	—	—	—	—	800	—	—
1600	—	—	—	—	1600	—	1600	—	—	—	—	—	—	—	—	—	—	—
3200	—	—	—	—	1600	—	1600	—	—	—	—	—	—	—	—	—	—	—
—	—	—	—	—	1600	—	—	—	—	—	—	—	—	—	—	—	—	—
3200	—	—	—	—	1600	—	3200	—	—	—	—	—	—	—	—	—	—	—

Group 9

611	Kisagata 133	Otaru	Hashishita 23	Prince Rupert 2	1314	Haginari 27	715	Fish 5	Wakinosawa	Aomori 102	Aomori 783	Aomori 786	Haginari 4-22	Fish 9	Kameda	Masuke	486	Hashishita 21
—	—	—	—	—	—	—	1600	—	—	—	—	—	—	3200	—	—	—	—
—	—	—	—	—	—	—	—	—	—	—	—	—	1600	—	—	—	—	—
—	—	—	—	—	1600	—	—	—	—	—	—	—	—	—	6400	6400	—	—
—	—	—	—	—	1600	—	3200	—	—	—	—	—	—	—	—	12800	—	—
—	—	—	—	—	—	—	—	—	200	—	—	—	—	—	—	—	—	—
—	—	—	—	—	—	—	—	—	—	3200	—	—	—	—	—	—	—	—
—	—	—	—	—	—	—	—	—	—	—	400	—	—	—	—	—	—	—
—	—	—	—	—	—	—	—	—	—	—	—	800	—	—	—	—	—	—

Table 7.—Numbering system of the antigens of the strains of *Clostridium botulinum* type E employed in the antigenic schema

Antigen Number of the strains	Strains	Toxignicity	Antigen Number of the strains	Strains	Toxigenicity
1	Aomori	●	19	Otaru	○
2	Tenno	●	20	Hashishita 23	○
3	341	●	21	Prince Rupert-2	●
4	211	●	22	1314	●
5	667	●	23	Haginari 27	○
6	Iwanai	●	24	715	●
7	Fish 6	●	25	Fish 5	○
8	801	●	26	Wakinosawa	○
9	777	●	27	Aomori 102	○
10	Fish 11	●	28	Aomori 783	○
11	Fish 6H	●	29	Aomori 786	○
12	Bute 7	○	30	Haginari4-22	○
13	Jōryu 74	○	31	Fish 9	○
14	Fish 12	○	32	Kameda	●
15	Memanbetsu	●	33	Masuke	●
16	802	●	34	486	●
17	611	●	35	Hashishita 21	○
18	Kisagata 133	○			

● Toxigenic   ○ Non-toxigenic

Table 8.—The antigenic schema for distinguishing strains of *Clostridium botulinum* type E

Strains	Isolation places	Toxigenicity	Extract Antigens	Flagella Antigens
Group 1				
Aomori	Aomori Prefecture	●	1	1
Group 2				
667	Akita Prefecture	●	2, 5, 6, 7, 8, 9, 10	2, 5, 6, 7, 8, 9, 10
759	Akita Prefecture	●	2, 5, 6, 7, 8, 9, 10	2, 6, 7, 8, 9, 10
527	Akita Prefecture	○	2, 5, 6, 7, 8, 9, 10	2, 6, 7, 8, 9, 10
Haginari 28-1	Akita Prefecture	●	2, 5, 6, 7, 8, 9, 10	6, 7, 8, 9, 10
Shinonome	Akita Prefecture	●	2, 6, 7, 8, 9, 10	2, 5, 6, 7, 8, 9, 10
Funakawa	Akita Prefecture	●	2, 6, 7, 8, 9, 10	2, 5, 6, 7, 8, 9, 10
Futto	Akita Prefecture	●	2, 6, 7, 8, 9, 10	2, 5, 6, 7, 8, 9, 10
Fish 7	Akita Prefecture	●	2, 6, 7, 8, 9, 10	2, 6, 7, 8, 9, 10
Kimoto	Akita Prefecture	●	2, 6, 7, 8, 9, 10	5, 6, 7, 8, 9, 10
Fish 14	Akita Prefecture	●	2, 6, 7, 8, 9, 10	5, 6, 7, 8, 9, 10
Kaneura 1	Akita Prefecture	●	2, 6, 7, 8, 9, 10	5, 6, 7, 8, 9, 10
801	Akita Prefecture	●	2, 6, 7, 8, 9, 10	5, 6, 7, 8, 9, 10
Haginari 9	Akita Prefecture	●	2, 6, 7, 8, 9, 10	6, 7, 8, 9, 10
Nakahadachi	Akita Prefecture	●	2, 6, 7, 8, 9, 10	6, 7, 8, 9, 10
Fish 35	Akita Prefecture	●	5, 6, 7, 8, 9, 10	2, 6, 7, 8, 9, 10
Haginari	Akita Prefecture	●	5, 6, 7, 8, 9, 10	2, 6, 7, 8, 9, 10
798	Akita Prefecture	●	5, 6, 7, 8, 9, 10	6, 7, 8, 9, 10
800	Akita Prefecture	●	5, 6, 7, 8, 9, 10	6, 7, 8, 9, 10
Fish 3	Akita Prefecture	○	5, 6, 7, 8, 9, 10	6, 7, 8, 9, 10
Fish 67	Akita Prefecture	●	5, 6, 7, 8, 9, 10	6, 7, 8, 9, 10
Honjō 37	Akita Prefecture	●	5, 6, 7, 8, 9, 10	5, 6, 7, 8, 9, 10
775	Akita Prefecture	●	5, 6, 7, 8, 9, 10	2, 6, 7, 8, 9, 10
Fish 13	Akita Prefecture	●	5, 6, 7, 8, 9, 10	2, 6, 7, 8, 9, 10
Fish 8	Akita Prefecture	●	5, 6, 8, 9, 10	2, 6, 7, 8, 9, 10
Honjō 35	Akita Prefecture	●	6, 7, 8, 9, 10	2, 5, 6, 7, 8, 9, 10
758	Akita Prefecture	●	6, 7, 8, 9, 10	2, 6, 7, 8, 9, 10
Haginari 8	Akita Prefecture	●	6, 7, 8, 9, 10	6, 7, 8, 9, 10
762	Akita Prefecture	●	6, 7, 8, 9, 10	6, 7, 8, 9, 10
Group 3				
Iwanai	Hokkaido	●	6, 7, 8, 9, 10	6, 7, 8, 9, 14
768	Akita Prefecture	●	6, 7, 8, 9, 10	6, 7, 8, 9, 10, 14
Fish 6	Akita Prefecture	●	6, 7, 8, 9, 10	7, 8, 9, 10, 14
777	Akita Prefecture	●	6, 7, 9, 10	5, 7, 8, 9, 10, 14
Fish 11	Akita Prefecture	●	6, 7, 9, 10	7, 8, 9, 10, 14
Group 4				
Jundai 1	Hokkaido	●	5, 6, 7, 8, 9, 10	6, 7, 8, 9, 10, 14, 15, 16
Jundai 4	Hokkaido	●	6, 7, 8, 9, 10, 11, 14, 15, 16	7, 8, 9, 10, 14, 15, 16
Aomori 177	Aomori Prefecture	●	6, 7, 8, 9, 10, 11, 14, 15, 16	5, 7, 8, 9, 10, 14, 15, 16
770	Akita Prefecture	●	6, 7, 8, 9, 10, 11, 14, 15, 16	6, 7, 8, 9, 10, 14, 15, 16
Memanbetsu	Hokkaido	●	6, 7, 8, 9, 10, 11, 14, 15, 16	6, 7, 8, 9, 10, 14, 15, 16
786	Akita Prefecture	●	6, 7, 8, 10, 11, 14, 15, 16	6, 7, 8, 9, 10, 14, 15, 16
Abashiri	Hokkaido	●	6, 7, 9, 10, 11, 14, 15, 16	6, 10, 14, 15, 16
Jundai 7	Hokkaido	●	6, 8, 10, 11, 14, 15, 16	6, 7, 8, 9, 10, 14, 15, 16
Jundai 6	Hokkaido	●	6, 11, 14, 15, 16	10, 14, 15, 16
Fish 12	Akita Prefecture	○	6, 11, 14, 15, 16	6, 7, 8, 10, 14, 15, 16
Daijima	Akita Prefecture	●	7, 11, 14, 15, 16	8, 10, 14, 15, 16
Onbetsu	Hokkaido	●	9, 11, 14, 15, 16	6, 8, 10, 14, 15, 16
804	Akita Prefecture	○	10, 11, 14, 15, 16	6, 7, 8, 9, 10, 14, 15, 16
802	Akita Prefecture	●	11, 14, 15, 16	14, 15, 16

Table 8.—The antigenic schema for distinguishing strains of *Clostridium botulinum* type E—Continued

Strains	Isolation places	Toxigenicity	Extract Antigens	Flagella Antigens
Group 5				
Nangai	Akita Prefecture	●	6, 8,9, 14	6,7,8,9,10,14,15,16
Jundai 3	Hokkaido	●	6, 8,9	6,7,8,9, 15,16
168	Akita Prefecture	●	6,7,8,9	6,7,8,9, 14
Group 6				
Nishishyunbetsu	Hokkaido	●	9	8, 15
Kacchi	Aomori Prefecture	●	9	7,8, 10,14
Group 7				
341	Hokkaido	●	3 11 13 34	3 11,13,15,16 21 34
Oil H	Canada	●	3	11,13,15,16 21
Fish 6H	Canada	●	3	11,12,15
Hashishita 56	Akita Prefecture	○	11 13	3 11,13,15,16 21
Hashishita 62	Akita Prefecture	○	11 13	3 11,13,15,16 21
Hashishita 65	Akita Prefecture	○	11 13	3 11,13,15,16 21
Hashishita 96	Akita Prefecture	○	11 13	3 11,13,15,16 21
36208	America	●	11	3 11,13,15,16 21
Nanaimo Chicken	Canada	●	13	3 11,13,15,16
Bute 2	Canada	●	11 13	3 11,13,15,16
Funakoshi	Akita Prefecture	●	13	3 11,13,15,16
Matsugasaki156	Akita Prefecture	○	11 13	3 11,13,15,16
486	Hokkaido	●	11 13	11,13,
Matsugasaki 54	Akita Prefecture	○	11,12,13	11,13, 20 34
Matsugasaki 94	Akita Prefecture	●	11,12,13	11,13
No. 8	Canada	○	11 13	3 11,13 21
Bute 7	Canada	○	11,12	11,12,15
Group 8				
211	Hokkaido	●	4 11	4 11
Seal Ⅲa	Canada	●		11,13
Kaneura 39	Akita Prefecture	○		11,13
Jōryu 58	Akita Prefecture	○		11,13
Honjō 121	Akita Prefecture	○		11
Honjō 133	Akita Prefecture	○		11
Michikawa 14	Akita Prefecture	○		11
Kosagawa 92	Akita Prefecture	○		11
Group 9				
Salmon eggs-A	Alasca	●	13	3 13 21
Prince Rupert-2	Canada	●	21	
Group 10				
Hashishita 34	Akita Prefecture	○	20	
Hashishita 23	Akita Prefecture	○	20	
Hashishita 32	Akita Prefecture	○	20, 24	13 20
Hashishita 21	Akita Prefecture	○	20 35	13 20 35
Group 11				
611	Hokkaido	●	17 22 24	17 22 24
1314	Hokkaido	●	17 22 24	17 22 24
1304	Hokkaido	●	17 22 24	17 23
Group 12				
Tenno	Akita Prefecture	●	2 6 10	2,5 8
779	Akita Prefecture	●	9,10	8 14,15,16
Group 13				
Haginari 27	Akita Prefecture	○	23	23
715	Hokkaido	○	24	24
Fish 4	Akita Prefecture	○	24	
Fish 5	Akita Prefecture	○	25	25
Fish 9	Akita Prefecture	○	25 31	25
Wakinosawa	Aomori Prefecture	○	26	26 31
Aomori 102	Aomori Prefecture	○	27	27
Aomori 783	Aomori Prefecture	○	28	28,29
Aomori 786	Aomori Prefecture	○	29	29,30
Aomori 207	Aomori Prefecture	○		29
Maruya	Akita Prefecture	○		29
Haginari 4-22	Akita Prefecture	○	30	30
Kameda	Hokkaido	●	32, 33	32
Masuke	Hokkaido	●	33	33

ordinarily in routine work. However, the authors believe that the schema will come nearer and nearer to a complete form as antigenic phase fixation is better understood.

Acknowledgment

The authors wish to express their grateful thanks to Dr. Dolman of the British Columbia University, Dr. Nakamura of the Hokkaido Institute of Public Health and Dr. Kodama of the Akita Institute of Public Health for their invaluable help in sending of strains.

References

(1) ASANO, H. Unpublished data.

(2) DOLMAN, C. E. 1956. Cited from Special Report 6 of the Hokkaido Institute of Public Health.

(3) HAZEN, E. L. 1942. Differential characteristics of two strains of *Clostridium botulinum* type E: action of toxin on chickens. Proc. Soc. Exp. Biol. Med. *50*: 112–114.

(4) KUDO, H. Unpublished data.

(5) KUDO, Y. 1962. Immunisatorische Studien uber *C. botulinum* Typus E. Hirosaki Med. J. *14:* 75–88.

(6) LYNT, R. K., H. M. SOLOMON, D. A. KAUTTER, and T. LILLY. 1967. Serological studies of *Clostridium botulinum* type E and related organisms. J. Bacteriol. *93:* 27–35.

(7) NAKAMURA, Y., H. IIDA, and K. SAHEKI. 1952. Special Report of the Hokkaido Institute of Public Health.

(8) NAKAMURA, Y., and H. IIDA. 1956. Special Report 5 of the Hokkaido Institute of Public Health.

(9) ONO, T. 1962. Serological studies on *Clostridium botulinum* type E. II. Stability and agglutinability of dissociated colonies. Research Bulletin of Obihiro *3:* 30–31.

(10) SCHOENHOLZ, P., and K. F. MEYER. 1925. Studies on the serologic classification of *B. botulinus*. II. Agglutination. J. Immunol. *10:* 1–53.

(11) SKULBERG, A., and O. W. HAUSKEN. 1965. The differentiation of various strains of *Clostridium botulinum* and transformation experiments with type E. J. Appl. Bacteriol. *28*: 83–89.

DISTRIBUTION OF *CLOSTRIDIUM BOTULINUM* IN THE ECOSYSTEM OF THE GREAT LAKES

by J. T. GRAIKOSKI, E. W. BOWMAN, R. A. ROBOHM, *and* R. A. KOCH
U.S. Bureau of Commercial Fisheries, Ann Arbor, Mich. 48107

Introduction

The particular circumstances surrounding the type E outbreaks in fish in the United States the past several years centered the problem around the Great Lakes. In 1960 and 1963, eight outbreaks of type E botulism involving 21 cases and nine deaths were attributed to smoked fish of the *Coregonus* sp. which were harvested and smoke processed in the Great Lakes region. An additional type E outbreak, although not involving Great Lakes fish, occurred in Detroit, Mich., in 1963 from canned tuna. A most recent outbreak of one case and one death occurred in Chicago, Ill., in 1967, from home-processed gefilte fish prepared from whitefish (*Coregonus clupeaformis*), presumably harvested from the Great Lakes area.

Another phenomenon relating botulism to waterfowl occurred in the fall and early winter of 1963 and 1964. Lake Michigan was the scene of extensive mortalities of water birds, principally gulls (*Lauis argentatus*, *L. delewarensis*) and loons (*Gavia insmer*). Approximately 12,000 birds were estimated by Fay, Kaufman, and Ryel (4) to be involved in these mortalities. Tests made by Kaufman and Fay (10) from the blood of morbid and dead birds from these mortalities indicated that *C. botulinum* type E toxin was present. Mortalities among waterfowl had been observed previously in the Great Lakes region, and had been attributed to type C toxin. However, extensive mortalities, as observed in 1963 and 1964, have not been previously reported. Prior to this time, there have been no published reports associating type E toxin with mortalities in wild birds.

Another phenomenon, although not related to botulism, which has been of considerable interest in the Great Lakes is the continued mortalities of alewife (*Alosa pseudoharengus*), which have been observed to occur annually. The usual situation has been localized mortalities around river mouths during late spring and early summer of the spawning season. However, extensive mortalities occurred over Lake Michigan proper in the summer of 1967. Several million pounds of fish were involved in these mortalities. No specific cause can be attributed to the mortalities of the alewives.

Although type E was first described by Gunnison, Cummings, and Meyer in 1936 (6), an extensive search for the presence of this organism had not been carried out in the United States prior to the 1963 type E outbreaks. Studies in France by Prevot and Huet (14), Johannsen (8) in Sweden, Kanzawa (9) and Nakamura (12) in Japan, and Pederson (13) demonstrated the association of type E with the aquatic environment.

Preliminary studies in 1963 showed that type E was present in fish harvested from Lake Michigan. Studies by Foster, et al. (5) and Bott, et al. (1), at the University of Wisconsin, on 3,000 fish collected from four of the Great Lakes demonstrated the wide distribution of the organism in several species of fish, with an overall incidence of 1 to 9 percent.

The objective of our ecological study was initially to determine the incidence of *C. botulinum* in various elements of the Great Lakes, in order to establish a base line for a continuing monitoring program to determine the persistence of the organism in the environment. The information obtained would be of importance in evaluating the potential botulism hazard from fish harvested from the Great Lakes. Additional objectives were: (1) To determine possible reservoirs of the organism in the environment, (2) mode of transmission to the fisheries, and (3) the relationship, if any, the fish mortalities contribute to the incidence of the organism and waterfowl deaths.

Materials and Methods

Much of the work reported in this study was performed on board the U.S. Bureau of Commercial Fisheries R/V CISCO. For the initial survey, samples were collected from areas of the commercial fisheries on the Great Lakes. Monitoring stations for yearly samplings were established at a transect between Ludington, Mich., and Sturgeon Bay and Green Bay, Wisc., on Lake Michigan. A monitoring station was also established on Lake Huron in the Saginaw Bay area. This area was selected for sampling since periodic fish and waterfowl mortalities has occurred there.

Samples collected for this study were fish, bottom sediments, water, invertebrates, plankton, and waterfowl. Fish were obtained by means of a bottom trawl. Samples of the various species obtained in the trawl were aseptically opened and the entire intestinal tract subcultured into enrichment media. Bottom sediments were obtained with a Pedersen dredge. A sample was obtained just below the surface of the sediment by means of a sterile tongue depressor and transferred to a sterile jar. This was done to minimize any possible contamination from the dredge. The dredge was thoroughly washed between samplings. For an inoculum, approximately 1 g. of sediment was employed. Water was obtained in sterile Cobet water samplers. Approximately 100 to 200 ml. were collected at each station. Water was filtered through a 2-inch Gelman metricel filter (0.2μ pore size), and the membrane subcultured into enrichment media. Invertebrates were screened from the bottom sediments, washed several times in sterile saline, and directly subcultured into the enrichment media. Plankton obtained by a vertical tow with one-half meter net, was concentrated by settling in a sterile bottle and 5 ml. subcultured into the media.

The beef infusion media used for our primary enrichment cultures was developed for studies on type E. The composition of the beef infusion broth (BI medium) was as follows: Beef infusion 1 liter (1 pound of ground beef per liter distilled water, boiled for one-half hour, chilled overnight and filtered), Bacto-peptone 10 g., disodium phosphate 2 g., glucose 2 g., soluble starch 1 g., sodium chloride 5 g., sodium thioglycollate 1 g., dried meat particles 10 percent, final pH 7.2–7.4.

For enrichment cultures, approximately 60 ml. in square bottles were employed. The enrichment cultures were incubated at 20° C. for 10–14 days before assays for toxin were made.

The beef infusion media was compared with the TPG (trypticase-peptone-glucose) media commonly employed for producing type E cultures (*14*). Better recovery of the organism from bottom sediments occurred in the BI media than in the TPG media (tables 1 and 2).

After incubation the cultures were centrifuged in the cold at 5,000 r.p.m. for 30 minutes. Initially, in our studies, 0.5 ml. of the supernatant fluid was injected intraperitoneally in three 20g. albino mice to detect toxin. However, nonspecific deaths occurred in the mice on occasions when this amount was injected. Some of the nonspecific deaths were minimized by injecting 0.3 ml. into the mice. The mice were observed for symptoms of botulism, especially during the early stages after injection. If cultures contained type E toxin, death usually occurred within 12 hours after injection. Mice were observed for 48 hours before disposal. Supernatants which caused deaths in mice were neutralized with specific type E antitoxin (Pasteur Institute). For the *in vitro* neutralization test, 0.1

Table 1.—Relative effectiveness of 3 media in producing toxic outgrowth of naturally occurring *C. botulinum* type E from Lake Michigan sediments[1]

Type of sediment	Number of samples tested	Number of culture supernatants containing type E toxin		
		BI	BI + YE	TPG
Mud_____	9	8	8	5
Sand_____	5	5	5	5
Gravel_____	1	1	--	0
Total_____	15	14	13	10

[1]The 3 media compared consisted of a trypticase-peptone glucose medium. Media were inoculated with approximately 1.0 g. of sediment and incubated at 20° C. for 22 days before testing for toxin.

Table 2.—Relative effectiveness of 2 media in producing toxic outgrowth[1] of naturally occurring *C. botulinum* type E spores from lake sediments[2] stored at 0° to 4° C. for 6 to 12 months

Type of sediment	Number tested	Number of culture supernatants containing type E			
		20° C. incubation		30° C. incubation	
		TPG	BI	TPG	BI
Sand_____	8	3	4	2	4
Mud_____	7	5	7	5	7
Clay_____	2	0	0	1	1
Sand-mud____	1	0	1	0	0
Gravel_____	1	1	0	1	1
Total__	19	9	12	9	13

[1]Media were inoculated with approximately 1.0 g. of sediment and incubated at 20° C. for 10 days or 30° C. for 3 days before testing for toxin.

[2]Sediments were taken from Lake Superior, Lake Charlevoix, Lake Michigan (Traverse Bay, Green Bay, and main body of the lake), and Lake Huron.

ml. of antitoxin (enough to neutralize 2,000 MLD of homologous toxin) was allowed to combine with 0.9 ml. of the culture supernatant in the cold for at least 2 hours; 0.3 ml. of this mixture was then injected into three mice. Other mice were also injected with the nonneutralized toxin, in order to ascertain that toxin loss did not occur. Some toxin loss did occur, however, from cultures produced from highly contaminated samples. Cultures were considered positive if typical botulism symptoms were observed in the mice, and if they were neutralized with specific homologous antitoxin.

Results

The map below shows the areas of the Great Lakes where the various samples were obtained on our initial survey in 1965. Stations located on the transect be-

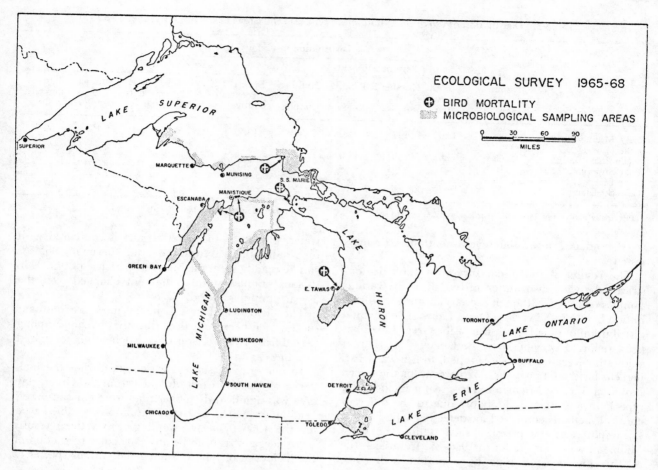

ECOLOGICAL SURVEY 1965-68
⊕ BIRD MORTALITY
☐ MICROBIOLOGICAL SAMPLING AREAS
0   30   60   90
MILES

tween Ludington, Mich., and Green Bay, Wis., were sampled several times during that year, as well as at yearly intervals. The crosses point to the areas where we observed waterfowl mortalities in 1965. The extensive waterfowl mortalities observed in 1963 and 1964 were also in the general areas marked, as well as on the lower, eastern shore of Lake Michigan. Sea gull and fish mortalities were observed in the area near East Tawas, Mich., on Lake Huron. This area was also selected for yearly observations.

Samples of bottom sediments were collected in 1964 from Lake Ontario. However, the samples were stored for some time prior to examination and a large number of cultures gave nonspecific toxicities in mice, so no judgment can be made on whether type E was present in these samples.

The results presented in table 3 summarize the incidence of type E in cultures prepared from the various elements of the Great Lakes collected in 1965. The highest occurrence of type E was from samples collected from Saginaw Bay of Lake Huron. Of the cultures produced from fish, 5.29 percent were positive for type E. The bottom sediments yielded 45 percent positive cultures.

The next highest incidence of positive type E cultures was obtained from samples collected from Lake Michigan. The total number of samples from various elements presented in the table are those which were collected several times during the year at the established monitoring stations, as well as from other selected areas in Lake Michigan. The fish samples include those obtained from Green Bay and those from Lake Michigan proper. Of the 281 fish intestines subcultured, 37 percent were positive for type E. Bottom sediments produced 37 positive cultures, and water, invertebrates, and plankton yielded 1.29, 17.1, and 30.7 percent type E cultures, respectively. One culture from a fish (*Catostomus* sp.) contained both B and E toxin. The results show that the type E is well distributed in all the elements cultured.

Fish examined from Lake Superior and Lake Erie had a very low incidence, only 2 percent of the cultures were positive for type E. Bottom sediments from Lake Superior, but not Lake Erie, yielded positive type E cultures, although these had a significantly lower incidence than those from Lake Michigan.

Of the 35 fish examined from Lake St. Clair, 14.2 percent yielded positive cultures. No positive cultures

Table 3.—Distribution of *Clostridium botulinum* type E in the Great Lakes April–October 1965

| | Distribution in various elements | | | | | | | | | |
| | Fish | | Bottom sediments | | Water | | Invertebrates[1] | | Plankton | |
Area	Number of samples	Type E percent positive	Number of samples	Type E percent positive	Number of samples	Type E percent positive	Number of samples	Type E percent positive	Number of samples	Type E percent positive
Lake Michigan	281	[2]37.0	147	34.0	108	12.9	64	17.1	13	30.7
Lake Huron (Saginaw Bay)	68	52.9	9	45.0	---------	---------	---------	---------	---------	---------
Lake Superior	110	2.7	15	20.0	18	5.5	10	---------	---------	---------
Lake Erie	45	2.2	7	---------	15	---------	6	---------	---------	---------
Lake St. Clair	35	14.2	8	---------	2	---------	4	---------	---------	---------

[1]Principally *Pontoporeia affinis, Mysis relicta,* and *Chironomus* ssp.   [2]1 fish culture neutralized by both E and B antitoxin.

were produced from the several bottom sediments tested.

The results of the initial survey in 1965 demonstrated the wide distribution of type E in the various samples collected, although there is an unequal distribution between the various Great Lakes. The unequal distribution of type E from fish of the Great Lakes has been reported previously by Bott et al. (2). In that study, the overall incidence of type E in fish was 1 to 9 percent for the Great Lakes; 57 percent for the Green Bay area of Lake Michigan. The greater incidence of type E in our study is probably due to the different cultural methods employed for detecting type E.

Samplings at the preestablished stations on Lake Michigan were carried out in 1966–67. In table 4, the relative incidence of type E in bottom sediments,

water, plankton, and invertebrates is compared with the results obtained from the initial survey in 1965. As can be readily seen, the relative incidence of type E in various samples cultured has not changed over the 3-year sampling period.

The incidence of type E in the most predominant species of fish examined during the 3-year sampling period from two areas on Lake Michigan is compared in tables 5 and 6.

In our original survey, we observed that the incidence of type E in fish obtained from the Green Bay area was significantly higher than from our station off Ludington, Mich. The same situation remained true for the 1966–67 year sampling. From these results there does not seem to be any particular restriction of the incidence of type E among the various species of

Table 4.—Distribution of *Clostridium botulinum* type E in Lake Michigan

| | Sampling year | | | | | |
| | 1967 | | 1966 | | 1965 | |
Sample	Number	Type E percent positive	Number	Type E percent positive	Number	Type E percent positive
Bottom sediment	45	75.6	24	87.8	147	34.0
Water	12	2.0	57	3.5	108	12.9
Plankton	17	10.0	32	75.0	13	30.7
Invertebrates	18	6.0	53	33.6	64	17.1

Table 5.—Incidence of *C. botulinum* type E in Lake Michigan fish—Ludington area

| | 1967 | | 1966 | | 1965 | |
Species	Number sampled	Percent type E	Number sampled	Percent type E	Number sampled	Percent type E
Chub (*Coregonus* sp.)	13	84.6	40	50.0	61	62.2
Alewife (*Alosa* sp.)	30	23.3	10	30.0	2	--------
Smelt (*Osmerus* sp.)	3	--------	10	10.0	3	--------
Sculpin (*Cottus* sp.)	7	14.3	90	10.0	1	100.0
Total	43	44.2	70	47.1	67	48.2

Table 6.—Incidence of *C. botulinum* type E in Lake Michigan fish—Green Bay area

Species	1967		1966		1965	
	Number tested	Type E percent	Number tested	Type E percent	Number tested	Type E percent
Perch (*Perca* sp.)	14	85.8	10	60.0	20	55.0
Sucker (*Catostomus*)	2	100.0	15	93.6	20	90.0
Spottails (*Notropis* sp.)					11/19	57.8
Alewife (*Alosa* sp.)	11	81.6				
Burbot (*Lota* sp.)	2	100.0				
Total	29	86.2	25	80.0	59	66.9

fish tested. Although the incidence seems to be consistently higher in the sucker (*Catostomus* sp.), a predominantly bottom feeding fish.

Limited samplings of fish and bottom sediments from Lake Michigan have been carried out this year. The results to date show that evidence of type E is similar to that observed in previous years.

In our studies on Lake Huron in July 1965, we observed a large number of sea gull mortalities on the beaches of Saginaw Bay near East Tawas, Mich. (Tawas Point). Several hundred sea gulls were observed on the beaches of the peninsula. In June of that year, a large die-off of alewife also occurred in this area. Fish and waterfowl mortalities continued to occur (at a lesser extent) periodically until early falls Enrichment cultures produced from nine shore sand. obtained from the area where the mortalities occurred were all toxic for mice. Of these toxic cultures, five were positive for type E toxin. Also, cultures prepared from the organs of several dead birds were positive for type E.

The same area was under observation and extensively surveyed in 1966, in order to determine the relative incidence of type E in the environment. Also under surveillance were two small islands (Charity and Dredging) in the Saginaw Bay area. These uninhabited islands are nesting sites for sea gulls in the spring of the year. Table 7 shows the results of some of the data collected during that year. The results indicate that the incidence of type E in sand, water, and fish from the Tawas Point area was quite high.

In four of the cultures produced from sand, type C toxin was demonstrated and one culture indicated the presence of type A toxin. All 12 samples of cultures produced from soil collected from Charity Island (a highly contaminated area) were toxic for mice. Two cultures contained type E toxin and six cultures type C toxin. Samples from this area produced a large number of cultures which caused nonspecific deaths in mice, thus making it difficult to obtain a true picture of the incidence of the organism in various samples tested. The presence of type C in the environment of

this area was not surprising. The small peninsula under observation has been used by waterfowl as a resting area during migration for a number of years. Although documentation is lacking, mortalities have been observed in migratory birds in this area in the past due to type C toxin.

Cultures produced from various organs of recently dead and dying gulls were positive for type E, but here again, a number of cultures were toxic for mice that could not be typed with specific botulinum antitoxin (table 8).

Although attempts to demonstrate preformed toxin in the blood of morbid or dead birds were to a large

Table 7.—Distribution of *Clostridium botulinum* in the Great Lakes, Lake Huron—Saginaw Bay

Sample	Number tested	Number toxic	Number type E	Percent type E	Other types
Tawas Point:					
Sand	76	39	25	64.1	4C, 1A
Water	14	6	4	66.7	
Fish	55	29	13	44.7	
Charity Island:					
Soil	12	12	2	16.7	6C

Table 8.—Toxicity of cultures produced from the organs of morbid and dead sea gulls (*Lauis* sp.)

Specimen	Samples cultured	Number toxic for mice	Type E
Liver	10	5	3
Heart	5	0	0
Blood	6	2	1
Feces	2	2	1
Intestine	8	4	2
Stomach contents	2	0	0
Intestine + stomach	4	3	2
Total	37	[1]16	[2]9

[1]43 percent.
[2]24 percent.

extent unsuccessful, positive demonstration of type E toxin in the blood of dying waterfowl from one mortality was accomplished. Similarly, attempts at demonstrating preformed toxin were quite unsuccessful in dead fish from the field, because of the many non-specific deaths which occurred when extracts of dead fish were injected into mice. However, type E toxin was demonstrated in several fish obtained from the beach areas. In both cases, the level of toxin detected was quite low; somewhat less than 100 MLD.

Discussion

With the few exceptions noted, type E was the predominant botulinum type demonstrated in all of the samples from the Great Lakes. These results were not surprising, because of the relative ease in which type E was demonstrated in fish in some of the early studies. The Great Lakes receive drainage from many rivers and soil from contingent land masses. These are deposited around the mouths of the rivers. If types A and B are endogenous to soil, then one would expect demonstrations of these types in the aquatic environs in certain areas of the Great Lakes with a greater frequency. However, this was not the case. One would suspect that the cultural methods employed, particularly the lower incubation temperature, might be selective for type E. However, the several exceptions noted in this study and other studies would indicate that botulinum types, if present, could be detected under the cultural conditions employed.

Fish mortalities would contribute to the high incidence of type E in the areas studied. Contaminated fish would release the organism into the environment on decomposing. Considering the large number of fish involved in the mortalities and the incidence of the organism in the fish, this would contribute significantly to the incidence in the environment. Multiplication of type E in Green Bay has been suggested for the high incidence observed in that area (2). Conditions for growth in regard to temperature and nutrients in the bay, as well as other bays, are conducive to the growth of type E. The demonstration of low levels of type E toxin in dead fish is an indication that type E organisms can proliferate under natural environmental conditions. The unusually high incidence of the organism in the bays can be explained by the physical characteristics of the environment. Less water exchange with the open lakes occurs in the shallower bays, hence the organism would not be disseminated readily. The low-water levels of the Great Lakes of the past few years would also be important in the maintenance of the type E organism. The extended shorelines as a consequence of the low-water levels provide small catchment basins for the dead fish along the shoreline, creating foci of contamination.

Invertebrates, plankton, and water, which were shown by this study to harbor the organism, are means by which fish become contaminated during their feeding. This is confirmed by our observation and others (2) that the incidence of type E is higher in fish containing food.

The observations on Lake Huron would indicate that fish and waterfowl mortalities are related. However, the demonstration of this relation is not simple. The amount of preformed type E toxin which is necessary to induce botulism symptoms in gulls (in the laboratory) is in the order of 20,000 MLD's (11). One, therefore, would expect to demonstrate toxin in field samples more readily than has been so far possible. Considering the transitory nature of botulinum toxin as produced under natural conditions in contaminated material, obtaining samples with high titres of toxin would indeed be quite fortunate.

Type E botulinum intoxications occurring in waterfowl under natural conditions may not require the level of toxin needed as observed in laboratory experiments. As was shown by Jensen and Gritman (7), lower levels of type E toxins when injected with type C toxin can induce symptoms in waterfowl. Since type C has been demonstrated in the environs where waterfowl mortalities have been observed, this could very likely be the situation. The relationship of type E to the large waterfowl mortalities which occurred in 1963–64 is difficult to explain. These mortalities occurred in the fall of the year, a time when fish mortalities do not occur. Unfortunately, specific observations on the environment where these mortalities occurred is not available.

Although our observations and studies on the distribution of type E in the ecosystem have been fairly extensive these past few years, they still can be considered quite limited when one considers the large number of samples to be tested in order for specific conclusions to be reached. They do, however, indicate the relationships which the various elements studied have, in contributing to the incidence and maintenance of type E in the environs of the Great Lakes region.

References

(1) BOTT, T. L., J. DEFFNER, E. McCOY, and E. M. FOSTER. 1966. *Clostridium botulinum* type E in fish from the Great Lakes. J. Bacteriol. *91:* 919–924.
(2) BOTT, T. L., J. JOHNSON, JR., E. M. FOSTER, and H. SUGIYAMA. 1968. Possible origin of the high incidence of *Clostridium botulinum* type E on Inland Bay (Green Bay of Lake Michigan). J. Bacteriol. *95:* 1542–1547.
(3) DOLMAN, C. E. 1957. Recent observations on type E botulism: A review. Can. J. Public Health *48:* 187–198.

(4) FAY, L. D., O. W. KAUFMAN, and L. A. RYEL. 1965. Field observations and laboratory investigations concerning recent Lake Michigan bird mortalities. Eighth Conference on Great Lakes Research, Ann Arbor, Mich.

(5) FOSTER, E. M., J. S. DEFFNER, T. L. BOTT, and E. McCOY. 1965. *Clostridium botulinum* food poisoning. J. Milk Food Technol. *28:* 86–91.

(6) GUNNISON, J. B., J. R. CUMMINGS, and K. F. MEYER. 1936. *Clostridium botulinum* type E. Proc. Soc. Exptl. Biol. Med. *35:* 278–279.

(7) JENSEN, W. I., and R. B. GRITMAN. 1967. *In* Botulism 1966. Chapman and Hall, Ltd., London, 1967. Eds. M. Ingram and T. P. Roberts, 407–413.

(8) JOHANNSEN, A. 1963. *Clostridium botulinum* in Sweden and the adjacent waters. J. Appl. Bacteriol. *26:* 43–47.

(9) KANZAWA, K. 1960. Ecological studies on *Clostridium botulinum* type E: Distribution of this organism in the soil of Hokkaido. Rept. Hokkaido Inst. Public Health *11:* 161–173.

(10) KAUFMAN, O. W., and L. D. FAY. 1964. *Clostridium botulinum* type E toxin in tissues of dead loons and gulls. Quart. Bull. Mich. Agric. Expt. Sta. *47:* 236–242.

(11) KAUFMAN, O. W., H. M. SOLOMON, R. H. MONHEIMER. 1967. Experimentally induced type E botulism in gulls hatched under natural field conditions and reared in captivity. *In* Botulism 1966. Chapman & Hall, Ltd., London. Eds. M. Ingram and T. A. Roberts.

(12) NAKAMURA, Y., H. IIDA, K. SACKI, K. KANZAWA, and T. KARASHIMADA. 1956. Type E botulism in Hokkaido, Japan. Japan J. Med. Sci. Biol. *9:* 45–58.

(13) PEDERSON, H. O. 1955. On type E botulism. J. Appl. Bacteriol. *18:* 619–628.

(14) PRÉVOT, A. R., and M. HUET. 1951. Existence en France du botulisme humain d'origine pisciaire et de *C. botulinum* E. Bull. Acad. Natl. Med. Paris *135:* 432–435.

(15) SCHMIDT, C. F., W. F. NANK, and R. V. LECHOWICH. 1962. Radiation Sterilization of Foods. Some Aspects of the Growth, Sporulation and Radiation Resistance of Spores of *Clostridium* Type E. J. Food Sci., *27*(1): 77–84.

VARIATION AMONG STRAINS OF *CLOSTRIDIUM BOTULINUM* AND RELATED CLOSTRIDIA

by Lillian V. Holdeman *and* John B. Brooks
Anaerobe Laboratory, Department of Veterinary Science,
Research Division, Virginia Polytechnic Institute, Blacksburg, Va. 24061

Summary

Three distinct physiological groups of *Clostridium botulinum* can be differentiated on the basis of reactions on 58 substrates, acid and alcohol products, and limited studies of protein metabolism. Some other species of clostridia also have similar characteristics.

    Group I.—*C. botulinum* type A, proteolytic strains of *C. botulinum* types B and F, and *C. sporogenes*.

    Group II.—*C. botulinum* types C and D and *C. novyi* type A.

    Group III.—Nonproteolytic strains of *C. botulinum* types B and F, type E, and culturally similar organisms that are nontoxic.

Characteristics of the groups and variation within the groups are presented and indicate that the three cultural groups cannot be reliably subdivided on the basis of cultural reactions, morphological characteristics, or metabolic products other than toxins.

Introduction

The most outstanding characteristic of a strain of *Clostridium botulinum* is the toxin that it produces. On the basis of the antigenic specificity of the toxins, the species has been divided into six types, A through F, with the type C having two antigenic subgroups, Cα and Cβ. In most cases the cultural characteristics of the strains producing the toxin are only of secondary interest. A strain producing a toxin antigenically and pharmacologically similar to another *C. botulinum* toxin is a strain of *C. botulinum*, no matter what other characteristics it exhibits, assuming of course that it is an anaerobic, sporeforming bacillus. Nevertheless, strains within types or groups share certain cultural and biochemical characteristics. The purpose of this paper is to report the cultural and biochemical variations and similarities that we have observed among different strains of the types and among strains of organisms that are culturally similar to toxigenic strains.

Cultures

Unless it is otherwise stated, the strains originally were identified in our laboratory. All labeled strains included in this study were also tested for toxicity and typed in our laboratory, using antitoxin obtained from the National Communicable Disease Center.

    Labeled strains in group I.—*C. botulinum* type A, Prévot 146. *C. botulinum* type B (proteolytic), strains ATCC 7949 (NCA 213B), Prévot 24 NCASE, and Smith A–116. *C. botulinum* type F (proteolytic), strains Giménez 160 and Langeland. *C. sporogenes* (rhizoid colony), strains ATCC 7905 and Smith M–154. *C. sporogenes* (nonrhizoid colony), strains ATCC 7955 (NCA 3679) and ATCC 3584. *C. sporogenes* strain designated "ocean sediment" and Smith 09 (See reference (7)).

    Strains in group II.—*C. botulinum* type C (toxic). Smith strains α and β. One of the two nontoxic strains had previously been toxic when we tested it. *C. botulinum* type D: the one toxic strain was obtained from Smith; of the two nontoxic strains, one had been toxic when we tested it previously and one was ATCC 9633 (South African strain). *C. novyi* type A, strains ATCC 3540, ATCC 17861, Prévot 669, and Smith "Prac B." *Related clostridia:* three of these four nontoxic strains were received labeled as *C. botulinum* type C; one had been sent to us for identification.

    Strains in group III.—*C. botulinum* type B (nonproteolytic), strains Eklund 17B and Prévot 59. *C. botulinum* type F (nonproteolytic), strains Eklund 83F, Eklund 202F, and one identified by Smith. *C. botulinum* type E, strains ATCC 9564, "Tenno" strain from Hobbs, "Beluga" strain from Hobbs; Hobbs FT–18, Johannsen 1084, and Kautter 066B TOX.

    Related clostridia.—Strains labeled "typical" had cultural reactions similar to *C. botulinum* type E, but were nontoxic and include Hobbs strains 18E, 14G, 14D, and Kautter strains 066B NT (nontoxic), S–5, 28–2, 810; strains PM–15 and S–9 also were obtained from Kautter, but were more different, culturally, from the toxic strains in this group than are the strains labeled "typical."

Methods

    General methods.—Cultures were grown by the anaerobic culture methods described by Moore (4) and characterized using the tests described by Holdeman et al. (1). Cultures were incubated in an atmosphere of 97 to 100 percent oxygen-free CO_2 for 5 days or 3 weeks. Cultural results were essentially the same at 5 days as at 3 weeks.

The pH in glucose broth cultures was determined with a pH meter after cultures had been incubated for 1, 3, and 5 or 7 days and also at 14 and 21 days, for those cultures incubated for 3 weeks. In comparing our results with those obtained by other investigators on the same strain, we have noted that we often detected complete liquefaction of gelatin when others do not and that we failed to detect fermentation of adonitol by strains which others found do ferment adonitol.

The major products detected from growth in glucose medium, presented in table 4, were determined by the methods described by Moore et al. (5).

Detection of amines, long-chain fatty acids, and neutral compounds.—Cultures were inoculated into 6 ml. chopped meat-glucose medium and incubated for 7 days.

Culture extracts and derivatives were prepared as described in figure 1 and were chromatographed on a Beckman GC-4[1] gas chromatograph using dual flame detectors, dual stainless steel columns, with helium as the carrier gas at a flow rate of 48cc/min. Columns, 20 feet long and one-eighth inch in diameter, were packed with Chromosorb W, 80/100 mesh (AW-DMCS)HP[2]. Samples were run for 25 minutes; temperature was programmed from 80° to 255°C.

More details of the method and results with additional strains and species will be reported by one of us (JBB) in a doctoral dissertation.

Results and Discussion

The strains of *C. botulinum* types A through F form three major groups according to their cultural characteristics and metabolic products. Clostridia that have characteristics similar to those of *C. botulinum* also have been included in this grouping.

Group I. *C. botulinum* type A, proteolytic strains of *C. botulinum* types B and F and *C. sporogenes*.—Characteristics of these strains are presented in tables 1 and 4. No cultural or morphological characteristic that can be used to reliably separate the toxic from the nontoxic strains is known. One of the type B strains had rhizoid, "sporogenes-like" colonies when originally tested and again 1 year later when this culture was reexamined after lyophilization. One of the type A strains was nonhemolytic on agar containing horse blood and also produced no reaction on egg yolk agar. Although these cultures no doubt

[1]Use of trade names does not constitute endorsement.
[2]Chromosorb W, 80/100 mesh, acid washed, dimethyl-dichloro-silane; Applied Science Laboratories, Post Office Box 440, State College, Pennsylvania, U.S.A.

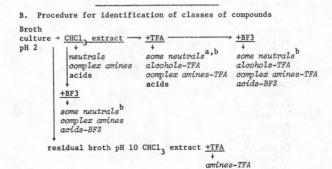

A. Procedure for identification of fatty acids and amines

B. Procedure for identification of classes of compounds

Note: Compounds in italics will chromatograph.

BF3 = boron trifluoride methanol.

TFA = trifluoroacetic anhydride.

[a] Some neutral compounds form TFA derivatives; some do not.

[b] Some neutral compounds may be lost by dilution or evaporation during acylation or methylation procedures.

Figure 1.—Methods for analysis of soluble compounds in culture fluids.

represent rare exceptions to the general rule that all strains of *C. botulinum* and *C. sporogenes* produce lipase on egg yolk agar and that rhizoid colonies are *C. sporogenes* rather than *C. botulinum*, these types of variation do occur occasionally.

At first we did not detect, with some of the organisms in group I, the marked fermentation of glucose and maltose that usually is so characteristic of organisms in this group. However, when the concentration of peptone in the basal medium was lowered from 2 g./100 ml. to 0.5 g./100 ml. weak acid production could be detected from both glucose and maltose.

In the medium containing 2 percent peptone, cultures produced as much total acid, quantitatively determined, in media without glucose as in media with glucose, indicating that little fermentation of glucose occurred. The total quantity of acids produced by the cultures in basal peptone-yeast medium was large (8 to 10 meq./100 ml.).

In glucose cultures of the "ocean sediment" strain of *C. sporogenes*, the glucose was actively fermented and major amounts of lactic acid accumulated. This accumulation of lactic acid probably was responsible for the lower pH obtained with this strain in media with a fermentable carbohydrate (table 1).

Group II. *C. botulinum* types C and D and *C. novyi* type A.—Characteristics of strains in this group are given in tables 2 and 4. Adequate study

Table 1.—Reactions of some strains of *C. sporogenes* and proteolytic strains of *C. botulinum* types A, B, F (cultural group I)

Characteristic	*C. botulinum*			*C. sporogenes*		
	Type A	Type B	Type F	Rhizoid	Not rhizoid	Ocean sediment
	7[1]	5	2	17	2	1
Toxicity	[2]+	+	+	−	−	−
Digestion of:						
Gelatin	+	+	+	+	+	+
Milk	6/7	4/5	1/2	14/17	+	+
Meat	+	+	+	+	1/2	
Lowest pH (glucose)	5.4–6.0	5.8–6.1	5.93	5.5–6.2	5.9–6.0	4.95
Acid in media with:						
Glucose	+	3/5	+	14/17	+	+
Fructose	4/7	1/5	−	5/15	−	−
D (+)-maltose	1/7	1/5	−	−	−	+
Sucrose	−	−	−	−	−	−
Cellobiose	−	−	−	1/17	−	−
Glycogen	1/7	−	−	1/17	−	−
D (+)-mannose	1/7	−	−	−	−	+
Pectin	−	−	−	1/17	−	−
D-sorbitol	2/7	1/5	−	−	−	−
H$_2$S production	5/7	4/5	+	15/17	+	−
Hydrolysis of:						
Esculin	+	+	+	+	+	+
Starch	−	−	−	1/17	−	+
6.5 percent NaCl. grains	3/7	4/5	1/2	12/17	1/2	+
Hemolysis[3]	[5]6/7	+	+	+	+	+
Lipase[4]	[5]6/7	+	+	[6]+	+	+
Rhizoid colonies	−	1/5	−	+	−	+
Motile	5/7	+	+	15/17	+	+

[1]Number of strains.

[2]+ = positive for all strains; − = negative for all strains; #/# = strains positive/strains tested.

[3]Horse red blood cells.

[4]Egg yolk agar.

[5]The same culture that does not lyse horse red blood cells also does not produce lipase.

[6]Both lipase positive and lipase negative variants consistently were observed in one culture. Subcultures from lipase positive colonies also contained variants that did not produce detectable lipase.

NOTES.—All strains produce NH₃, are anaerobic, and produce gas in glucose agar deeps.

No strain produces acid from adonitol, amygdalin, L-arabinose, dextrin, dulcitol, DL-erythritol, esculin, D-galactose, glycerol, inositol, inulin, lactose, D-mannitol, melezitose, melibiose, raffinose, rhamnose, D(−)-ribose, salicin, L-sorbose, starch, trehalose, D-xylose.

Except where indicated, unusual reactions were not associated with any 1 strain.

of this group of *C. botulinum* was not possible because there were so few toxic strains available for examination.

We became aware of the similarity between strains of *C. botulinum* type C and *C. novyi* type A when we were examining some nontoxic strains labeled *C. botulinum* type C (designated "related clostridia" in table 2). When these cultures were grown in egg yolk agar, we noted an opaque zone (presumably due to lecithinase activity) in the agar around the colonies. This opaque zone extended far beyond the pearly zone that was over and immediately around the colonies and, except for intensity, was similar to the reaction on egg yolk agar exhibited by *C. novyi* type A strains. The opaque zone produced by these "related strains" was much lighter than that produced by *C. novyi* type A strains, but it was nonetheless present. We have not determined whether these are nontoxic variants of *C. botulinum* type C (as labeled) or nontoxic strains of *C. novyi* type A that do not produce much lecithinase. There was no characteristic

colonial or cellular morphology by which species of cultural group II might be differentiated.

Fermentation acids produced by the various strains in this group (table 4) were similar. Acetic, propionic, and butyric acids were the major products from fermentation of glucose and lactate; acetic and butyric acids were produced from pyruvate. These acids were produced in different ratios from the different substrates (table 5).

Thus, a greater amount of acid and more propionic acid were produced from lactate than from glucose or pyruvate. We have found very few other species of anaerobic bacteria, either spore-formers or non-spore-formers that, in our test system, produce appreciably larger amounts of propionate from lactate than from glucose.

Group III. *C. botulinum* type E, nonproteolytic strains of types B and F, and related organisms.— Characteristics of strains in this group are given in tables 3 and 4. A few of the toxic type E strains decreased the pH in basal peptone-yeast media so

Table 2.—Reactions of some strains of C. *botulinum* types C and D, C. *novyi* type A, and related clostridia (cultural group II)

Characteristic	C. botulinum Type D [1]2	C. botulinum Type D 1	C. botulinum Type C 2	C. botulinum Type C 2	Related clostridia 4	C. novyi Type A 4
Toxicity	[2]−	+	−	+	−	+
Digestion of:						
Gelatin	+	+	+	+	+	+
Milk	1/2	+	1/2	−	1/4	−
Meat	−	−	−	−	1/4	−
Lowest pH (glucose)	5.2–5.4	5.2	5.1–5.2	5.2–5.7	4.9–5.3	5.5–5.6
Acid from:						
Glucose	+	+	+	+	+	+
D-fructose	−	−	+	1/2	3/4	−
D-galactose	−	−	+	+	2/4	−
Glycerol	+	−	+	−	2/4	2/3
Inositol	+	+	+	+	+	1/4
D (+)-maltose	+	−	+	1/2	2/4	+
D (+)-mannose	+	−	+	+	+	2/4
Melibiose	−	+	1/2	+	2/4	1/4
Pectin	−	+	+	+	3/3	3/4
D (−)-ribose	+	−	+	−	+	1/4
Adonitol	−	−	−	−	3/4	−
L-arabinose	−	−	+	−	2/4	−
Cellobiose	−	−	1/2	−	1/4	−
Dextrin	−	−	−	−	2/4	−
DL-erythritol	−	−	−	−	1/4	−
Esculin	−	−	−	−	1/4	−
Glycogen	−	−	1/2	−	1/4	−
Inulin	−	−	−	−	2/4	−
Raffinose	−	−	−	−	3/4	1/4
Rhamnose	−	−	−	−	1/4	1/4
Salicin	−	−	−	−	2/4	1/4
D-sorbitol	−	−	−	−	2/4	−
L-sorbose	−	−	−	−	2/4	−
Starch	−	−	−	−	3/4	−
Sucrose	−	−	1/2	−	2/4	1/4
Trehalose	−	−	−	−	2/4	−
Indol production	−	−	−	1/2	−	−
6.5 percent NaCl, grain	−	−	−	−	−	−
Hemolysis[3]	+	+	2/3	+	+	+
Lecithinase[4]	−	−	−	−	weak	+
Lipase[4]	+	+	+	+	+	+
Rhizoid colony	−	−	−	+	+	+

[1]Number of strains tested.

[2]+ = positive for all strains; − = negative for all strains; #/# = strains positive/strains tested.

[3]Horse blood cells.

[4]Egg yolk agar.

NOTES.—All strains are anaerobic and produce gas in glucose agar deeps.

No strain produces H_2S or hydrolyzes esculin or starch.

No strain produces acid from amygdalin, dulcitol, lactose, mannitol, melezitose, xylose.

Except where indicated, unusual reactions were not associated with any 1 strain.

much that determination of acid production from carbohydrate was difficult. Results designated positive for acid production in table 3 represent pH values at least 0.5 unit lower than that found in the basal medium.

In the group of nontoxic organisms that might be related to these nonproteolytic strains of *C. botulinum*, we included strains (designated "typical" in table 3) that had cultural reactions similar to the toxic strains in group III and two strains (PM–15 and S–9) that were different culturally but had been found to be serologically related to toxic type E strains (*6*).

In an effort to determine whether in the past we had examined other strains of clostridia that should be included in this group, we coded many of the characteristics that were uniformly positive and some that were uniformly negative for toxic type E strains. Then by computer we compared about 400 clostridia to select the strains that were identical in 21 of the 22 characteristics indicated.

To allow for a coding error or strain variation, absolute agreement was not requested. Positive characteristics coded were: gram-positive, motile, anaerobic, rods, forming gas from glucose, producing moderate or greater amounts of butyric and acetic acids, and fermenting glucose, fructose, maltose, mannose, sucrose. Negative characteristics coded were: no fermentation of lactose, no production of

Table 3.—Reactions of strains of *C. botulinum* type E, nonproteolytic strains of types B and F, and of related organisms (cultural group III)

Characteristic	*C. botulinum* types				Related clostridia	
	B [1][2]	F [3]	E [6]	Typical [8]	PM–15	S–9
Toxicity	[2]+	+	+	−	−	−
Hemolysis[3]	+	+	+	+	+	+
Lipase[4]	+	+	+	+	+	+
Lecithinase[4]	−	−	−	−	−	−
Rhizoid colony	−	−	−	−	−	−
Digestion of:						
Gelatin	+	+	5/6	7/8	+	+
Milk and meat	−	−	−	−		
Lowest pH (glucose)	5.3–5.6	5.0–5.4	5.0–5.5	5.0–5.5	5.2	5.45
Acid from:						
Glucose	+	+	+	+	+	+
Amygdalin	−	2/3	−	3/8	v	−
L-arabinose	−	−	−	1/8	−	−
Cellobiose	−	−	−	−	+	−
Dextrin	1/2	1/3	−	−	+	−
Esculin	1/2	2/3	−	−	+	−
D-fructose	+	+	+	+	+	+
D-galactose	1/2	−	−	−	−	−
Glycogen	+	−	−	−	−	−
Inositol	−	+	−	1/8	−	−
D (+)-maltose	1/2	+	+	+	+	−
D-mannitol	−	+	−	−	+	−
D (+)-mannose	+	+	+	+	+	−
Melezitose	−	−	+	4/8	−	−
Pectin	1/2	1/3	5/6	7/8	+	+
D (−)-ribose	1/2	+		6/8	v	−
Salicin	−	−	−	−	+	−
D-sorbitol	+	2/2	5/6	7/8	+	+
Starch	1/2	+	4/6	6/8	+	+
Sucrose	+	+	+	+	v	−
Trehalose	+	+	5/6	7/8	−	−
D-xylose	−	−	−	1/8	−	−
Hydrol. of:						
Esculin	−	−	1/6	−	+	−
Starch	−	+	4/6	6/8	−	+
6.5 percent NaCl, grain	−	−	−	−	−	−
"Boticin" production[5]				3/4	−	−
Serologically related to E[5]			2/2	4/4	+	±

[1] Number of strains tested.

[2] + = all strains positive; − = all strains negative; /strains positive/strains tested; v = variable results on replicate tests.

[3] Horse red blood cells.

[4] Egg yolk agar.

[5] As reported by Kautter et al. (1966), Lynt et al. (1967), and Solomon et al. (1968).

NOTES.—All strains are anaerobic, gram-positive, motile bacilli that form oval, subterminal spores. All strains produce gas in glucose agar deeps. No strain produces H_2S, indol; nitrates not reduced.

No strain produces acid from adonitol (see discussion), dulcitol, erythritol, glycerol, inulin, lactose, melibiose, raffinose, rhamnose, sorbose.

Except where indicated, unusual reactions were not associated with any 1 strain.

indol, no major amount of lactic acid from glucose, and no moderate or greater amounts of caprylic, heptanoic, caproic, valeric, isovaleric, isobutyric, or propionic acids from glucose. Production of toxin, hemolysin, lipase, or spores was not included in the comparison.

Because we required agreement of only 21 of the 22 characteristics listed, strains of *C. chauvoei* and of *C. butyricum* (both of which ferment lactose) were selected, as were two strains of non-spore-forming anaerobes and PM–15. With these exceptions, no other organism similar to the toxic organisms in group III was selected. Labeled *Clostridium* strains bearing more than 80 different species names and many unidentified clostridia were represented in the collection subjected to analysis. The S–9 strain was not selected because it ferments neither maltose, mannose, nor sucrose. Both S–9 and PM–15 appear to be more closely related to the toxic strains in group III than to any of the other clostridia that we can now recognize.

Amines long-chain fatty acids, and neutral compounds produced by strains of *C. botulinum* and related organisms.—The following portion of this report, concerning these soluble compounds present in culture fluids, should be considered preliminary because we have studied only a few strains. Nevertheless, the general types of compounds that have been detected are of interest and are pertinent.

By using combinations of extraction methods and treatment with trifluoroacetic anhydride (TFA) or

Table 4.—Major products of *C. botulinum* and related clostridial groups in glucose media

Group I[1]		Group II		Group III	
ACETIC	3.0–4.0.	ACETIC	0.0–1.0.	ACETIC	1.0–1.5.
propionic	0.2–0.3.	PROPRIONIC	1.5–2.5.		
ISOBUTYRIC					
BUTYRIC[2]		BUTYRIC		BUTYRIC	1.5–2.0.
ISOVALERIC }	3.0–4.0.	}	1.5–3.0.		
valeric		valeric			
isocaproic					
lactic[3]	0.0–tr.	lactic	tr–mod.	lactic	tr–mod.
succinic	0.0–tr.	succinic	tr–mod.	succinic	tr–mod.
alcohols	mod.	formic	0.0–tr.	formic	tr–mod.

[1]Group I: *C. botulinum* type A, proteolytic strains of types B and F, and *C. sporogenes*. Group II: *C. botulinum* type E, nonproteolytic strains of types B and F, and related nontoxic clostridia. Group III: *C. botulinum* type C and D and *C. novyi* type A.

[2]One strain of *C. botulinum* type A is unusual in that very little butyric acid is produced. The other products of this strain are similar to those of the other organisms in this group.

[3]In cultures of 1 strain of *C. sporogenes* (labeled ocean sediment) major quantities of lactic acid accumulate. The other acids produced by this strain are similar to those produced by the other organisms in this group.

NOTE.—Upper case letters, underlined = products present in major amounts (> 1.0 meq./100 ml.). Upper case letters = products present in moderate amounts (0.25 to 1.0 meq./100 ml.). Lower case letters = products present in minor amounts (<0.25 meq./100 ml.). Numerals = approximate concentrations in milliequivalents per 100 ml.; tr = trace; mod = moderate.

Table 5.—Major products of fermentation of group II clostridia acting on different substrates

Substrate	Total[1] acids	Ratio		
		Acetic	Propionic	Butyric
Peptone-yeast (PY)	1.0	1	2.0	2.0
PY-glucose	4.7	1	4.0	5.0
PY-lactate	8.5	1	5.0	2.5
PY-pyruvate	4.8	1	.5	1.8

[1]Total milliequivalent per 100 ml. acetic, propionic, and butyric acids or salts thereof.

boron trifluoride methanol (BF3), we have been able to identify classes of compounds as well as a variety of individual compounds (fig. 1). By comparing the retention times of peaks from treated culture extracts with those of known compounds similarly treated, we have tentatively identified 18 amines and 23 fatty acids. Identification was further substantiated by using several conditions of operation; e.g., different temperature programs, carrier gas flow rates, and column packings.

Unless present in very high concentrations, natural (neither methylated nor acylated) acids and most alcohols and amines do not elute from the Chromosorb W packing material; even then, resolution is poor and peaks are small and not well defined. To reduce their affinity for the packing material and permit elution of these compounds from the column, charged groups can be acylated (amino and hydroxyl groups) with TFA or methylated (carboxyl groups) with BF3. Natural aldehydes, ketones, and tertiary alcohols and amines will elute from the Chromosorb W.

An example of the differentiation of classes of com-

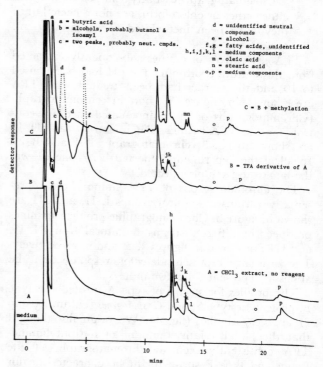

a = butyric acid
b = alcohols, probably butanol & isoamyl
c = two peaks, probably neut. cmpds.
d = unidentified neutral compounds
e = alcohol
f,g = fatty acids, unidentified
h,i,j,k,l = medium components
m = oleic acid
n = stearic acid
o,p = medium components

C = B + methylation
B = TFA derivative of A
A = CHCl₃ extract, no reagent

Figure 2.—Differentiation of neutral compounds, fatty acids, and alcohols by formation of TFA derivatives followed by methylation. CHCl₃ extracts of acidified whole cultures, *C. botulinum* type C.

pounds present in one culture fluid is presented in figure 2.

Bottom chromatograph, "medium": Compounds represented by peaks h, i, j, k, l, o, and p are present in CHCL₃ extracts of the acidified uninoculated medium and still are detected after acylation and methylation (chromatographs B and C).

Chromatograph A: Compounds extracted at pH 2 from the broth culture are represented by peaks c and d. These probably are aldehydes or ketones. Such compounds may be partially or completely lost during acylation or methylation procedures, possibly from boiling, evaporation, or dilution (see peaks c and d, chromatograph B and peak d, chromatograph A).

Chromatograph B: After the CHCl₃ extract of acidified culture was treated with TFA, the TFA-alcohols (peaks b and e) are chromatographed. The TFA derivatives represented by peaks b and e were not stable when acidified (1 percent HCl, final concentration) and heated; TFA-amine compounds are stable to such treatment, TFA-alcohol compounds are not and are lost during methylation procedures (see chromatograph C).

Chromatograph C: Fatty acids, extracted with either ether or chloroform, are not detected until they have been methylated (peaks a, f, g, m, and n).

TFA derivatives of amines subsequently extracted from this culture broth after the pH had been raised to 10 and the extract had been treated with TFA are shown in figure 3, bottom chromatograph. (Chromatographs of the uninoculated medium controls for the TFA-treated CHCl₃ extracts at pH 10 are shown in fig. 8 (chromatographs B–1 and B–2). In all of the experiments reported here, one μl was the largest test sample injected.)

The chromatographs of TFA-amines from representative strains of cultural groups I, II, and III are shown in figure 3. Chromatographic profiles of amines produced by different strains in cultural groups I, II, and III are shown in figures 4, 5, and 6, respectively. The ordinates represent detector response and the abscissas represent 0 to 25 minutes.

The profiles for strains of type A, proteolytic type B, proteolytic type F, and *C. sporogenes* (cultural group I) are very similar (fig. 4). We originally thought that the larger relative amount of n-dibutylamine-TFA consistently seen in chromatographs of the Langeland type F strain might be characteristic for all proteolytic strains of type F, but this is not true. The Giménez strain of type F, like other strains in cultural group I, has the lesser relative amount of n-dibutylamine.

In the chromatograph of the *C. sporogenes* cultural extract, the notch on peak c and the two notches on the preceding peak appear to constitute a difference between *C. sporogenes* and the toxic strains. In other preparations from *C. sporogenes* cultures, these peaks are much smaller. Compounds eluted in 12 to 15 minutes have retention times similar to those of substances obtained from the uninoculated medium (fig.

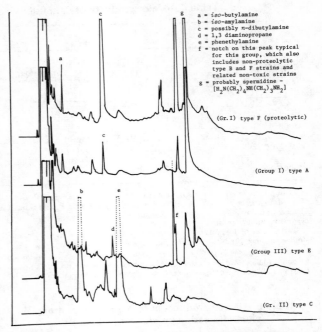

a = *iso*-butylamine
b = *iso*-amylamine
c = possibly *n*–dibutylamine
d = 1,3 diaminopropane
e = phenethylamine
f = notch on this peak typical for this group, which also includes non-proteolytic type B and F strains and related non-toxic strains
g = probably spermidine – [H₂N(CH₂)₄NH(CH₂)₃NH₂]

(Gr. I) type F (proteolytic)

(Group I) type A

(Group III) type E

(Gr. II) type C

Figure 3.—Chromatographs: TFA derivatives of CHCl₃ extracts of alkaline whole cultures of *C. botulinum*.

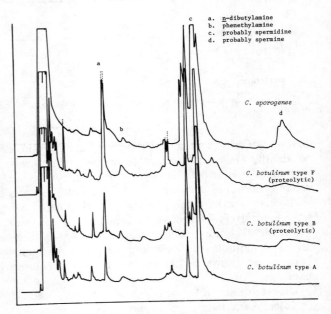

a. *n*–dibutylamine
b. phenethylamine
c. probably spermidine
d. probably spermine

C. sporogenes

C. botulinum type F (proteolytic)

C. botulinum type B (proteolytic)

C. botulinum type A

Figure 4.—Chromatographs: TFA derivatives of CHCl₃ extracts of alkaline whole cultures of *C. sporogenes* and proteolytic *C. botulinum* strains, group I.

8, chromatograph B–2). In this area of the chromatographs, differences in peak heights may not be very reliable.

In interpreting these chromatographs, presence or absence of peaks and relative ratios of peak areas are more important than individual peak height. When the amount of sample is increased only a few hundredths of a microliter, some peaks may be completely obscured by the increased size of neighboring peaks; also, isolated smaller peaks may be greatly increased in height.

Strains of *C. botulinum* types C and D (toxic strains) and *C. novyi* type A (cultural group II) characteristically produce large quantities of *iso*-amylamine and phenethylamine (figs. 3, 5).

The chromatographs of the amines produced by the nonproteolytic strains of types B and F and type E (cultural group III) are remarkably similar (fig. 6). Note in particular the notched peak (fig. 3, peak figure 6, preceding peak d), which has appeared in chromatographs of all of the strains in this group which we have examined, including some of the related clostridia (strains 810, S–9, and 28–2).

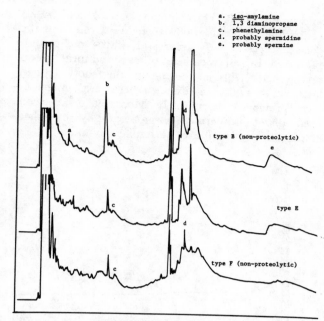

a. *iso*-amylamine
b. 1,3 diaminopropane
c. phenethylamine
d. probably spermidine
e. probably spermine

Figure 6.—Chromatographs: TFA derivatives of CHCl₃ extracts of alkaline whole culture of nonproteolytic *C. botulinum* strains, group III.

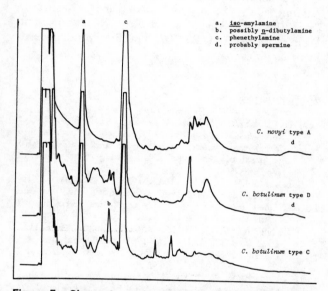

a. *iso*-amylamine
b. possibly *n*-dibutylamine
c. phenethylamine
d. probably spermine

Figure 5.—Chromatographs: TFA derivatives of CHCl₃ extracts of alkaline broth cultures of *C. botulinum* types C and D and *C. novyi* type A group II.

Except for the three nontoxic organisms mentioned, only toxic strains of *C. botulinum* have been examined for amines. We have studied at least three strains of each subgroup (or all of the strains available) and three strains each of *C. sporogenes* and *C. novyi* type A.

Amines produced by strains within each of the three cultural groups (as previously defined) were very similar and we have been unable to use this analysis to differentiate with certainty among strains within each group. Analysis of amines produced by these organisms extends and further confirms the previous observations that organisms within the groups are metabolically similar.

Chromatographic patterns of methylated ether extracts of whole cultures are shown in figure 7. (Chromatographs of the uninoculated medium controls for these methylated ether extracts at pH 2 are

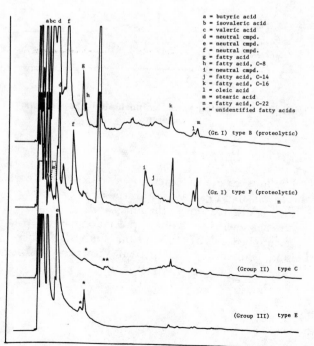

a = butyric acid
b = isovaleric acid
c = valeric acid
d = neutral cmpd.
e = neutral cmpd.
f = neutral cmpd.
g = fatty acid
h = fatty acid, C-8
i = neutral cmpd.
j = fatty acid, C-14
k = fatty acid, C-16
l = oleic acid
m = stearic acid
n = fatty acid, C-22
* = unidentified fatty acids

Figure 7.—Chromatographs: methylated ether extracts of acidified whole cultures of *C. botulinum*.

shown in fig. 8, chromatographs A–1 and A–2.) Individual chromatographs in figure 7 represent the general types of fatty acids and neutral compounds produced by all members of each cultural group represented. Differences among the short-chained fatty acids, not so easily seen here, are similar to those previously described by Moore et al. (5), who used direct isothermal chromatography of ether extracts of whole cultures on resoflex columns.

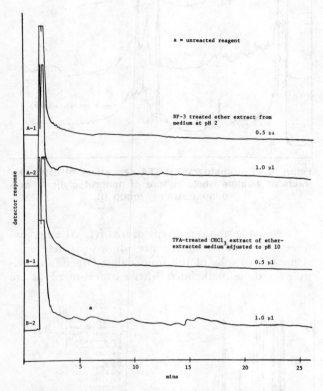

Figure 8.—Chromatographs: uninoculated chopped meat medium.

Acknowledgments

The authors are indebted to Dr. W. E. C. Moore and to Elizabeth P. Cato for assistance in preparation of the manuscript and in the analysis of the data.

We acknowledge, with appreciation, those who have supplied cultures used in this study: Dr. M. W. Eklund, Bureau of Commercial Fisheries, Seattle, Wash.; Dr. Domingo Giménez, Ciencias Médicas, Mendoza, Argentina; Dr. A. Johannsen, The Public Health Authority's Laboratory, Lund, Sweden; Mr. D. A. Kautter, Food and Drug Administration, Washington, D. C.; Dr. Geoffrey Hobbs, Torry Research Station, Aberdeen, Scotland; Dr. Erwin Lessel, American Type Cultural Collection; and Dr. A. R. Prévot, Pasteur Institute, Paris, France. We also wish to express our appreciation to Dr. Knox Harrell, National Communicable Disease Center, Atlanta, Ga., who provided the antitoxin used in typing the toxic strains of *C. botulinum*.

This research was supported, in part, by the Institute of General Medical Science, National Institutes of Health, Grant GM–14604. Mr. Brooks is an employee of the National Communicable Disease Center, Health Services and Mental Health Administration, U.S. Department of Health, Education, and Welfare, Atlanta, Ga., U.S.A., and acknowledges assistance from the Department of Health, Education, and Welfare, Public Law 85–507, Training in nongovernment facilities.

References

(1) HOLDEMAN, LILLIAN V., ELIZABETH P. CATO, and W. E. C. MOORE. 1967. Amended description of *Ramibacterium alactolyticum* Prevot and Taffanel with proposal of a neotype strain. Int. J. Syst. Bacteriol. *17:* 323–341.

(2) KAUTTER, D. A., S. HARMON, R. K. LYNT, Jr., and T. LILLY, Jr. 1966. Antagonistic effect on *Clostridium botulinum* type E by organisms resembling it. Appl. Microbiol. *14:* 616–622.

(3) LYNT, R. K., Jr., H. M. SOLOMON, D. A. KAUTTER, and T. LILLY, Jr. 1967. Serological studies of *Clostridium botulinum* type E and related organisms. J. Bacteriol. *93:* 27–35.

(4) MOORE, W. E. C. 1966. Techniques for routine culture of fastidious anaerobes. Int. J. Syst. Bacteriol. *16:* 173–190.

(5) MOORE, W. E. C., ELIZABETH P. CATO, and LILLIAN V. HOLDEMAN. 1966. Fermentation patterns of some *Clostridium* species. Int. J. Syst. Bacteriol. *16:* 383–415.

(6) SOLOMON, H. M., R. K. LYNT, Jr., D. A. KAUTTER, and T. LILLY, Jr. 1968. Serological studies of *Clostridium botulinum* type E and related organisms. II. Serology of spores. Bacteriol. Proc. 76.

(7) SMITH, L. DS. 1968. The clostridial flora of marine sediments from a productive and from a nonproductive area. Can. J. Microbiol. In press.

CLOSTRIDIUM BOTULINUM TYPE E IN AN INLAND BAY (GREEN BAY OF LAKE MICHIGAN)

by H. Sugiyama, Thomas L. Bott, *and* E. M. Foster
Food Research Institute and the Department of Bacteriology,
University of Wisconsin, Madison, Wis. 53706

Beginning in 1960 a series of six type E botulism outbreaks have occurred in the United States (*1, 2*). Half of these were due to a single product: whitefish chub or cisco caught in the Great Lakes and smoked by commercial operators. Although any outbreak of botulism is important, one in 1963, involving 17 cases with five deaths, emphasized the magnitude of the problem posed by the fish in these lakes. Since that time work has been going on at the University of Wisconsin, currently in the Food Research Institute, on the presence of *Clostridium botulinum* type E in the Great Lakes with the hopes of explaining the high concentration of the organism in some of these lakes.

The source of the *C. botulinum* type E on the smoked fish responsible for the outbreaks was soon shown to be the fish themselves. Type E organism was found in the intestinal contents of fish from all these lakes (Lake Ontario not studied) although the percentages of fish carrying the organism varied with the lakes and within a given lake (table 1), These figures represent the totals for all species of fish and for all times of the year, since these factors did not appreciably affect the incidence figures.

Of particular interest was the unusually high 56 percent incidence for fish of Green Bay. The bay is an arm of Lake Michigan and is approximately 125 miles long by less than 20 miles wide with a maximal depth of 20 fathoms. Figure 1 is an outline map of Green Bay; the locations of the numbers indicate the general areas where groups of fish were caught for

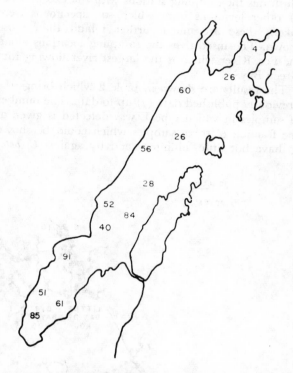

Figure 1.—Incidence of *C. botulinum* type E in fish from different parts of Green Bay. Numbers are percentages positive; location of numbers indicates general area where fish were caught.

testing and the numbers represent the percentages among the 50 or more fish per location which were positive for type E. Except for one location having a 4-percent incidence, at least 25 percent of the fish of all parts of the bay had the organism (*4*). Because of the proximity of Green Bay to our laboratory, most of the subsequent work has been focused on this area, although fish from certain areas of Lake Michigan proper have a similar carrier rate of type E (Graikoski, personal communication).

Since *C. botulinum* type E was common in the fish of Green Bay, its occurrence in the free environment of the bay was studied. Mud, sand, soil, etc., were collected from representative areas of the Bay, its tributary rivers and from land areas around these

Table 1.—Incidence of *C. botulinum* type E in the intestinal contents of fish from the Great Lakes[1]

Location	Number of fish tested	Percent with type E
Erie	363	2
Sandusky Bay	289	4
Huron	224	3
Saginaw Bay	240	3
Superior	681	<1
Duluth Harbor and Chequamegon Bay	213	12
Michigan	1,037	8
Green Bay	855	56

[1]From reference (*3*).

waters. Samples identified as bottom deposits were mud and sand from the deepest part to near the shore while similar materials obtained within a foot of the water's edge were classified as shoreline specimens; both types are under water and hence wet specimens. Shore specimens were dry earth taken at locations 20 to 150 feet inland from bay or lakes or 6 to 20 feet from rivers. Soil samples were those obtained from gardens, fields, woods, etc., at least half a mile or more from any permanent body of water. Figure 2 illustrates the sampling stations with the exception of 31 other locations from which soil specimens were taken; these are much further inland than those shown. The inset gives the sampling locations along the Fox River which is the largest river flowing into Green Bay.

The results are shown in table 2 which brings the previously published data (5) up to date. The number of samples in which type E was detected is given as the fraction of those samples which could be shown to have but little inhibitory activity against *C. botu-*

linum type E. The latter was determined in a control culture in which a duplicate enrichment culture of the test sample was inoculated with approximately 100 type-E spores. Failure to detect type E toxin after incubation of such a culture showed that the sample contained factors which could mask the presence of the type E organism. These specimens are given as samples with negative controls and are omitted from the incidence figures since they could include false negative results.

C. botulinum type E was present in over 90 percent of the wet samples obtained from the main body of Green Bay and Little Bay de Noc with a lower incidence 68 percent of those from Big Bay de Noc. The high percentage of type E positive wet samples collected just outside of Green Bay in Lake Michigan was not surprising, since the flow from Green Bay into Lake Michigan would be expected to disseminate the organism. It is evident that the incidence of type E was significantly lower in the shore (i.e., dry) specimens taken adjacent to the locations whose wet

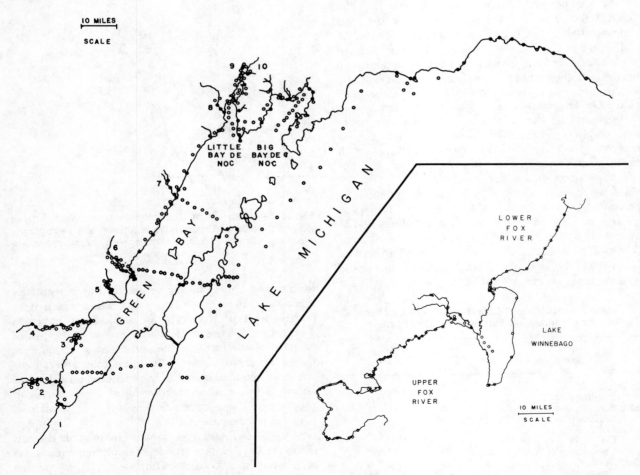

Figure 2.—Sampling locations of bottom, shoreline, shore and soil samples in Lake Michigan, Green Bay, and its tributary rivers and drainage basin.

Table 2.—Occurrence of *C. botulinum* type E in bottom, shoreline, shore and soil samples from Lake Michigan, Green Bay, Little Bay de Noc, Big Bay de Noc, and the Green Bay watershed

Location and sample	Number of samples with negative control	For samples with positive control	
		Number of type E/ number of samples	Percent
Lake Michigan:			
Bottom and shoreline	0	49/54	91
Shore	0	10/18	56
Green Bay:			
Bottom and shoreline	2	62/64	97
Shore	0	8/22	36
Little Bay de Noc:			
Bottom and shoreline	0	24/26	92
Shore	0	2/8	25
Big Bay de Noc:			
Bottom and shoreline	3	17/25	68
Shore	0	0/9	0
Fox River system:			
Bottom and shoreline	36	5/130	4
Shore	3	1/75	1
Other rivers and lakes:			
Bottom and shoreline	14	33/85	39
Shore	3	4/53	8
Soils	0	5/109	5

samples contained the organism. Furthermore, the organism could be detected in only 5 percent of the soil specimens representing the land mass in which the water supply of Green Bay originates.

These results have been used to suggest the possible origin of the high incidence of *C. botulinum* type E in Green Bay (5). Two possibilities could explain the consistent findings of *C. botulinum* type E in Green Bay bottom deposits. The first would be the catchment basin concept which has been proposed to explain the foci of high concentrations of this organism in marine areas off northern Japan (6, 7), British Columbia (8), and in the Baltic Sea (9). According to this theory, *C. botulinum* type E is of terrestrial origin and is carried by the runoff water to the sea where it is concentrated. The other possibility would consider active multiplication of the organism in the area of high incidence as more important than the passive accumulation. In the case of Green Bay, both may be operative but the latter seems the more important and could, of itself, account for the following observations:

The findings for the wet (bottom deposit) specimens of the rivers exclusive of the Fox River present an interesting pattern when the sampling sites are related to the distance from the mouth of the rivers (table 3). Type E was present at approximately one-half of the 61 locations within 7 miles of Green Bay but in only one of 21 specimens collected further upstream. It would seem that if the major source of *C. botulinum* type E in Green Bay is the organisms being washed down from the surrounding land areas, a more even distribution of the organism

Table 3.—Decreasing incidence of *C. botulinum* type E in riverbottom and shoreline samples with increasing distance from Green Bay

Distance from Green Bay (miles)	Number of samples with type E/number of samples with positive control
<2.0	14/25
2.0 to 3.9	5/12
4.0 to 6.9	12/24
7.0 to 9.9	0/8
10.0 to 14.9	1/9
>15.0	0/4

along the entire length of the rivers would have been found.

The catchment basin theory does not hold for the Fox River system in which the upper Fox is separated from the lower Fox River by Lake Winnebago. With 5 percent (three of 66) of the wet samples of the upper Fox positive for type E, the theory would predict a high level of botulinal organism in Lake Winnebago. This is not the case; the organism was found in only one of 30 samples taken from this lake.

The numbers of type E in the wet samples of Green Bay and the rivers are of different magnitudes. Whereas Green Bay materials usually have from 100 to over 1,000 type E per g., with a high of 36,000/g., those from the rivers seldom exceed 10 per gram.

The affinity of type E for the aquatic environment is shown when the locations of soil specimens of the drainage basin (table 2) which are positive for type

E are considered. Of the five locations at which type E was found, three were sites less than 0.5 miles from Green Bay. Enumeration of type E in specimens taken at various distances on a transect heading inland from the bay (table 4) emphasized the difference between the water and the land, *C. botulinum* type E disappearing within a short distance from the waterline. The different shorelines at the GB8 location at two different times suggest that the maximum counts found are probably due to previous high-water levels.

Table 4.—Most probable numbers (5 tubes/dilution) of *C. botulinum* type E per gram of samples collected on transects heading inland from the Green Bay shoreline

Feet inland from shoreline	Location and date of sampling			
	GB4 Apr. 7, 1967	GB8 Apr. 7, 1967	GB8 June 22, 1967	GB7 June 22, 1967
Under water	5		24	
Shoreline	17	620		140
25	18	470	490	
50	4	1,800	240	280
75	1	620	240	<1
100	35	35	490	2
125	330	18	35	0
150	0	6	35	0
175	0	0	[1]<1	0
200	0	1	0	0
225	<1			
250			0	
275			0	
300			<1	

[1]New shoreline at time of collection; all locations toward bay under 2–5 in. of water

The above considerations suggest that *C. botulinum* type E is multiplying in Green Bay. However, we have not, as yet, been able to demonstrate growth of the organism in bottom deposit samples held in the laboratory without the addition of culture mediums. This is not necessarily from lack of nutrients, since a hundred- to thousand-fold increase of the type E inoculums of either vegetative cells or spores takes

place in similar samples which have been autoclaved previously. It may be that transferring the specimens from the field to the laboratory alters the samples so that the chances of multiplication of *C. botulinum* in the presence of the other microflora are minimized.

It is not suggested that multiplication of type E could occur in bottom deposits of all areas. Of the 47 wet samples taken along the lower Fox River, 21 gave negative control cultures. The inhibition of type E growth in enrichment cultures of these specimens probably has a microbial basis since extracts of the muds are not inhibitory to type E growth and the inhibition disappears when the specimens are autoclaved. With some of the Fox River samples, type E inoculums of up to a million spores must be added to 1 g. of mud before type E toxin can be produced in the enrichment culture. It seems significant that samples of bottom deposits from Green Bay very seldom gave evidence of inhibition; i.e., negative control cultures (table 2).

C. botulinum type E does not multiply in or on the living fish. Fish maintained in aquariums were fed an estimated 1,000 type E spores. Groups of fish were sacrificed at daily intervals and the presence of the organism determined in decimal dilutions of the contents of the digestive tract (table 5). In this particular experiment, the organism was not found in the five fish examined on the second day after the force-feeding of the spores. In other tests, the disappearance of the spores was more gradual but by the sixth day almost all were no longer carrying type E. The same pattern occurred following the feeding of vegetative cells and when spores were inoculated on the surface of the fish. The high percentage of fish of Green Bay which have *C. botulinum* type E is, therefore, a reflection of the high contamination of the environment with the organism. The likelihood of finding type E in the digestive tract is related to the amount of food in the alimentary tract at the time of testing (4).

Although type E does not multiply in or on the living fish, fish must spread the organism in their travels. Upon death of these carriers, type E multiplies actively in the carcass in spite of the competition

Table 5.—Disappearance of *C. botulinum* type E spores from digestive tract. 10³ spores per os to each fish. Food force-fed every other day

Days	Number of fish tested	Number of fish positive for type E Dilutions of intestinal tract having organism				
		−1	−2	−3	−4	−5
0	5	4	5	1	1	1
1	5	4	1	0	0	0
2	5	0	0	0	0	0
3	5	0	0	0	0	0
4	5	0	0	0	0	0
5	5	0	0	0	0	0
6	3	1	0	0	0	0

from other microflora. Thus, dead fish and other animal life undoubtedly contribute to the maintenance of *C. botulinum* type E in nature. However, other sources of the organism seem necessary to explain the high numbers of the organism in Green Bay and at present the most likely explanation would be the active growth of the species in the bottom deposits of the Bay.

Acknowledgments

Supported by U.S. Public Health Service, Urban and Industrial Health grant UI 00165 and by contracts 64–44 (Neg.) and 68–4 (Neg.) with the Food and Drug Administration.

Published with permission of the Director, Wisconsin Agricultural Experiment Station.

References

(1) MEYER, K. F., and B. EDDIE. 1965. Sixty-five years of human botulism in the United States and Canada. George Williams Hooper Foundation, University of California, San Francisco Medical Center, 78 pp.

(2) National Communicable Disease Center, Morbidity and Mortality Report. 1967. *16:* 193–194.

(3) BOTT, T. L., J. S. DEFFNER, and E. M. FOSTER. 1967. Occurrence of *Cl. botulinum* type E in fish from the Great Lakes, with special reference to certain large bays. *In* Botulism 1966, pp. 25–33. Chapman & Hall, Ltd.

(4) BOTT, T. L., J. S. DEFFNER, E. McCOY, and E. M. FOSTER. 1966. *Clostridium botulinum* type E in fish from the Great Lakes. J. Bacteriol. *91:* 919–924.

(5) BOTT, T. L., J. JOHNSON, E. M. FOSTER, and H. SUGIYAMA. 1968. Possible origin of the high incidence of *Clostridium botulinum* type E in an inland bay (Green Bay of Lake Michigan). J. Bacteriol. *95:* 1542–1547.

(6) KANZAWA, K. 1960. Ecological studies on *Clostridium botulinum* type E. Distribution of the organism in the soil of Hokkaido. Rept. Hokkaido Inst. Public Health *11:* 161–173.

(7) NAKAMURA, Y., H. IIDA, S. SAEKI, K. KANZAWA, and T. KARASHIMADA. 1956. Type E botulism in Hokkaido, Japan. Japan J. Med. Sci. Biol. *9:* 45–59.

(8) DOLMAN, C. E., and H. IIDA. 1963. Type E botulism: its epidemiology, prevention, and specific treatment. Can. J. Public Health *54:* 293–308.

CLOSTRIDIUM BOTULINUM ALONG THE EASTERN COASTS OF AMERICA SOUTH OF STATEN ISLAND, N.Y.

by B. Q. WARD
Institute of Marine Sciences, University of Miami, Miami, Fla.

Summary

Packs of penaeid shrimp inoculated with 0, 10^2, 10^4, or 10^6 spores of *Clostridium botulinum* type E (Beluga strain) per gram of shrimp, and subsequently irradiated at levels of 0, 100, or 200 Krad were incubated at temperatures of 38°, 42°, 50°, or 72° F. The day of total consumer rejection, as determined by an informal panel of nonexperts, was noted for each permutation, and total plate counts were determined for each on the day of rejection. The time required for the development of toxicity in each permutation, and the type of botulism involved, was determined by mouse protection testing.

Increased radiation levels always resulted in lowered total counts. At all temperatures except 72° F., consumer rejection preceded botulinum toxin development with some margin of safety. At 72° F., botulinum toxin was occasionally detected on the day of rejection in pink shrimp (*Penaeus duorarum*). Such early toxicity was found to be of type A or C. The tropical location of the pink shrimp grounds may explain similarities between these results and earlier reports of the high incidence of *C. botulinum* types A and C in tropical Latin American waters. In brown shrimp (*P. aztecus*) botulinum toxin never appeared as early as the day of rejection, and toxins which were eventually developed were of types A, B, and E. Irradiation at a level of 200 Krads seemed adequate in all cases. The advisability of experimental designs, predicated upon botulism survey results in future inoculated pack studies is discussed.

Introduction

Studies of the incidence of *C. botulinum* of all types from the southern inshore waters of eastern North America have been reported by Carroll et al. (*2*) and Ward et al. (*10–13*). The areas encompassed by these reports are the U.S. Atlantic coast from New York City to the tip of Florida, the U.S. gulf coast from Florida to Texas, and (incompletely) Latin America from northern Brazil to Honduras. Among 717 Atlantic coast samples, only 15 were positive for botulism (types A-1, B-3, C-3, D-3, and E-5), but this favorable picture was marred by the observation that a dis-

proportionate share of these positive indications were obtained from a limited number of areas of high-human population. From the U.S. gulf coast, 58 of 1,414 samples tested were positive for botulism, 36 of these being type E. Other types and numbers were: A-3, B-3, C-9, D-6, and F-1. It might be noted that five of the nine type-C reports originated in south Florida specimens. From brown shrimp (*P. aztecus*) and a limited number of finfish taken in the Gulf of Venezuela and the Gulf of Darien, a preponderance of types A and C was detected (types A-4, C-3, A and C-3, B-1, and type E-1). Later testing of a limited number of sediment samples from the state of Ceara, Brazil, and of assorted animals, mostly finfish, captured off Nicaragua and Honduras showed dominance similar to the Venezuela-Darien results: From 82 fish, two tests for botulism were positive, both being type C; from only 26 sediment samples, five tests were positive (types A-1, C-1, B-2, and F-1).

At present, a study is being conducted of shrimp inoculated with *C. botulinum* type E (Beluga strain), irradiated at low dosage, incubated at several temperatures, and tested periodically for both spoilage and the appearance of botulinum toxin. In recent years similar research efforts have been directed toward the demonstration of both the feasibility and the safety of the irradiation pasteurization process as applied to seafoods, primarily to finfish, especially to northern species such as cod and haddock. A description of this kind of research may be obtained from reports of the annual food irradiation contractor's meetings, compiled and published by the USAEC (*7, 8, 9*).

In 1966, the use by individual workers of different strains and procedural details made the establishment of an ad hoc committee on standardization necessary. It was felt that, if the full weight of all research efforts were to be marshalled in the preparation of petitions for FDA approval of radiation-pasteurization of seafoods, all reports would have to be easily correlated. Procedures here reported are in general accordance with those agreed upon by all concerned with fishery products under the radiation pasteurization of foods program of the USAEC.

Materials and Methods

The shrimp used in these tests are obtained from commercial sources by the Technological Laboratory, Bureau of Commercial Fisheries, Gloucester, Mass. The shrimp are always fresh (a matter of hours in most cases), and the exact position of capture is known. The freshness of the headed shrimp is evaluated by Gloucester personnel, after which they are iced and delivered to the Institute of Marine Sciences of the University of Miami within a few additional hours. At the laboratory, the shrimp are packed in No. 300 "C" enamel cans, 12 ounces (340.2 g.) to the can; this weight provides a full but not crushed pack.

Cans are separated into four groups, each receiving one of the following treatments: (1) 10^6 spores of *C. botulinum* type E per gram of shrimp; (2) 10^4 spores per gram; (3) 10^2 spores per gram; (4) 0 spores per gram. Spore dilutions are so prepared that 1 ml. of fluid contains the requisite number of spores. Spores are produced at 28° C., purified in polyethylene glycol 4,000 by the method of Sacks and Alderton (6), and enumerated in duplicate trypticase-phytone-yeast extract (TPY) agar plates (30° C., 2 to 4 days, in Case anaerobe jars). The Beluga strain is used exclusively. Spores are not heat shocked. Cans are inoculated by dripping the inoculum over the surface at the open end of the can. Cans are then sealed, packed 22 to a tin, and the tins are iced. Iced tins are flown to Gloucester, Mass. for irradiation, where one-third of the cans of each inoculation level receive a 200-,100-, or 0-Krad dose in the Bureau of Commercial Fisheries' Marine Products Development irradiator. The geometry and dosimetry of this machine are described in an AEC bulletin by Ronsivalli et al. (5). Following irradiation, the iced shrimp are returned to Miami by air. The Miami-Gloucester-Miami operation usually requires 2 to 3 days, but with pink shrimp transport was unavoidably extended to a total of 8 days by scheduling difficulties.

At the Miami laboratory each of the 12 groups of cans (four levels of inoculation, three levels of irradiation) are further divided, one-quarter being placed at each of four incubation temperatures: 38° F. (3.3° C.), 42° F. (5.6° C.), 50° F. (10° C.), or 72° F. (27.8° C.). Cans are opened periodically (e.g., daily for 72° F. cans, weekly for 38° F. cans) and the odors are evaluated by students, faculty, or staff of the Division of Fishery Sciences of the Institute of Marine Sciences, who constitute an informal panel of non-experts. Evaluations are sought on untreated, washed, and cooked shrimp of each can until rejection is total. At the time of total rejection, total aerobic plate counts are made in duplicate, using 50 g. of shrimp homogenized for 2 minutes in 450 ml. Delafield buffer, TPY agar (trypticase-15 g., phytone-5 g., yeast extract-5 g., NaCl-5 g., glucose-1 g., agar-15 g., H_2O-1,000 ml., pH 7.2) and an incubation temperature of 30° C. for 48 hours. Free liquid in cans (drip, moisture adherent to shrimp at packing, suspending fluid of inoculum, etc.) is periodically injected into mice (e.g., twice weekly with 72° F. material, weekly with 38° F. material, etc.) until toxicity develops. The procedure employed is to use 0.2 ml. of test fluid +0.2 ml. of gelatin-phosphate buffer +0.1 ml. of a specific antiserum (where applicable) providing a complete set of eight mice for each test material. Each material is injected as untreated (or raw) fluid, fluid heated for 10 minutes at 100° C., and fluid mixed with one of the six specific antisera (A through F) and allowed to react for at least 30 minutes before injection. Duplicate sets of mice are used. Trypsinization is not used. Mouse deaths are recorded for 96 hours. Incidental deaths giving no clear-cut indication of botulism are recorded if noted in either of duplicate sets of mice, but positive typing has been based only upon complete evidence in both sets.

Results

Results are presented in tables 1 through 5. In tables 3 and 4, only the results of mouse testing with 72° F. materials are recorded. Only positive results are recorded in table 5, all "dead-none, live-all" (no deaths, or negative) instances being omitted.

With pink shrimp, mouse death occurred 39 days after catch with 38° F. and 42° F. materials, and in no case was death attributable to botulism. The toxic agent was heat stable or manifested itself in only a few of the eight mice in any given set. With 50° F. material, some deaths occurred on the 21st day with 0 and 100 Krad materials, but not with 200 Krad material. Again, deaths could not be attributed to botulism because the toxic agent was heat stable, and entire sets (raw, heated, A through F) of mice died. With 200 Krad material, death was noted only on the 39th day, and then in only one mouse of a set of eight injected with 0-spore material. All efforts to increase the toxicity of the fluids responsible for occasional deaths failed. After removal of tubes from frozen storage and trypsinization, all toxicity disappeared.

With brown shrimp held at 38° F., some deaths were noted as early as the 19th day (15 days of incubation, and 8 days after rejection). Through the 33d day, however, the presence of botulinum toxin was never conclusively demonstrated, and no deaths occurred from injection of 200 Krad materials. In 42° F. materials, results were generally similar. However, nonbotulinic deaths were noted following injec-

Table 1.—Total aerobic plate counts of pink shrimp on last day of acceptability

Can designation		Temperature (degrees F.)	Days of incubation[1]	Total aerobic plate count (average)
Spores per gram	Krad			
0	0	38	7	330 x 10⁶
10²	0	38	7	305 x 10⁶
10⁴	0	38	7	250 x 10⁶
10⁶	0	38	7	260 x 10⁶
0	100	38	7	7.6 x 10⁶
10²	100	38	7	18.8 x 10⁶
10⁴	100	38	7	29 x 10⁶
10⁶	100	38	7	35 x 10⁶
0	200	38	7	19.6 x 10⁶
10²	200	38	7	16.8 x 10⁶
10⁴	200	38	7	4.6 x 10⁶
10⁶	200	38	7	3.6 x 10⁶
0	0	42	4	535 x 10⁶
10²	0	42	4	165 x 10⁶
10⁴	0	42	4	235 x 10⁶
10⁶	0	42	4	265 x 10⁶
0	100	42	4	7.6 x 10⁶
10²	100	42	4	17 x 10⁶
10⁴	100	42	4	9 x 10⁶
10⁶	100	42	4	15.8 x 10⁶
0	200	42	4	0.85 x 10⁶
10²	200	42	4	1.05 x 10⁶
10⁴	200	42	4	0.9 x 10⁶
10⁶	200	42	4	5.45 x 10⁶
0	0	50	3	TNC @ 10⁻⁷
10²	0	50	3	42.8 x 10⁶
10⁴	0	50	3	200 x 10⁶
10⁶	0	50	3	95 x 10⁶
0	100	50	3	7.45 x 10⁶
10²	100	50	3	13 x 10⁶
10⁴	100	50	3	9.8 x 10⁶
10⁶	100	50	3	5.7 x 10⁶
0	200	50	3	1.5 x 10⁶
10²	200	50	3	1 x 10⁶
10⁴	200	50	3	0.29 x 10⁶
10⁶	200	50	3	1.2 x 10⁶
0	0	72	2	1.24 x 10⁹
10²	0	72	2	1.07 x 10⁹
10⁴	0	72	2	895 x 10⁶
10⁶	0	72	2	1.39 x 10⁹
0	100	72	2	1.43 x 10⁹
10²	100	72	2	975 x 10⁶
10⁴	100	72	2	1.25 x 10⁹
10⁶	100	72	2	1.52 x 10⁹
0	200	72	2	33.6 x 10⁶
10²	200	72	2	285 x 10⁶
10⁴	200	72	2	195 x 10⁶
10⁶	200	72	2	195 x 10⁶

[1]Experimental incubation begun after 8 days of handling, during which shrimp were iced at all times except during initial vessel handling, the canning operation, 2 overnight periods at 38° F., and a final (8th-day) period of 24 hours at 38° F.

Table 2.—Total aerobic plate counts of brown shrimp on last day of acceptability

Can designation		Temperature (degrees F.)	Days of incubation[1]	Total aerobic plate count (average)
Spores per gram	Krad			
0	0	38	7	310 x 10⁶
10²	0	38	7	335 x 10⁶
10⁴	0	38	7	365 x 10⁶
10⁶	0	38	7	355 x 10⁶
0	100	38	7	25.3 x 10⁶
10²	100	38	7	28.5 x 10⁶
10⁴	100	38	7	32 x 10⁶
10⁶	100	38	7	26.7 x 10⁶
0	200	38	7	8.9 x 10⁶
10²	200	38	7	6.6 x 10⁶
10⁴	200	38	7	11.3 x 10⁶
10⁶	200	38	7	10.6 x 10⁶
0	0	42	5	245 x 10⁶
10²	0	42	5	285 x 10⁶
10⁴	0	42	5	320 x 10⁶
10⁶	0	42	5	480 x 10⁶
0	100	42	6	405 x 10⁶
10²	100	42	6	465 x 10⁶
10⁴	100	42	6	360 x 10⁶
10⁶	100	42	6	500 x 10⁶
0	200	42	6	9.15 x 10⁶
10²	200	42	6	9.1 x 10⁶
10⁴	200	42	6	10.65 x 10⁶
10⁶	200	42	6	10.65 x 10⁶
0	0	50	5	37.6 x 10⁶
10²	0	50	5	37.7 x 10⁶
10⁴	0	50	5	35 x 10⁶
10⁶	0	50	5	42 x 10⁶
0	100	50	5	15 x 10⁶
10²	100	50	5	13.3 x 10⁶
10⁴	100	50	5	16 x 10⁶
10⁶	100	50	5	13.3 x 10⁶
0	200	50	5	365 x 10³
10²	200	50	5	308 x 10³
10⁴	200	50	5	344 x 10³
10⁶	200	50	5	1.35 x 10⁶
0	0	72	2	1.29 x 10⁹
10²	0	72	2	1.26 x 10⁹
10⁴	0	72	2	1.24 x 10⁹
10⁶	0	72	2	1.23 x 10⁹
0	100	72	3	0.98 x 10⁹
10²	100	72	3	4.13 x 10⁹
10⁴	100	72	3	0.94 x 10⁹
10⁶	100	72	3	0.91 x 10⁹
0	200	72	3	297 x 10⁶
10²	200	72	3	285 x 10⁶
10⁴	200	72	3	300 x 10⁶
10⁶	200	72	3	348 x 10⁶

[1]Experimental incubation begun after 4 days of handling, during which shrimp were iced at all times except during initial vessel handling, the canning operation, and 1 overnight period at 38° F.

tion of 33-day 200 Krad material, and type A botulinum toxin was detected in unirradiated material on the 19th day (15 days of incubation, and 10 days after rejection). In 50° F. materials, deaths did not follow injection until the 26th day, and no deaths were caused by irradiated materials. As with pink shrimp, trypsinization of fluids giving incomplete results rendered them nontoxic.

Discussion

Attempts to minimize nonbotulinic deaths through use of antibiotics met with little success and these have been abandoned. Cans have been used instead of plastic containers because shrimp spines puncture the latter. At first, cans which had been opened were retained, the open tops being covered with aluminum foil, or the puncture holes plugged with cotton. It had been hoped in this way to approximate

Table 3.—Mouse test results following injection of pink shrimp fluids incubated at 72° F.

Spores per gram	Krad	Days of incubation[1]	Dead mice	Live mice	Botulism type
0	0	2	Raw, A, B, D, E, F	C, heated	C.
0	0	7	Raw, A, B, D, E, F	C, heated	C.
0	0	10	Raw, A, B, C, D, E, F	C and E, heated	C and E.
10^2	0	2	Raw, A, D, E, heated	B, C, F	
10^2	0	7	Raw, heated	A, B, C, D, E, F	
10^2	0	10	Raw, heated, A, F	B, C, D, E	
10^4	0	2	Raw, B, C, D, E, F	A, heated	
10^4	0	7	Raw, B, C, D, E, F	A, heated	A.
10^4	0	10	Raw, A, B, C, D, E, F; C and E	A and E, heated	A and E.
10^6	0	2	Raw, B, C, D, E, F	A, heated	A.
10^6	0	7	Raw, B, C, D, E, F	A, heated	A.
10^6	0	10	Raw, B, C, D, E, F	A, heated	A.
0	100	2	Raw, A, B, C, D, E, F, heated	None	
0	100	7	Raw, A, B, C, D, E, F, heated	None	
0	100	10	Raw, D, E, heated	A, B, C, F	
10^2	100	2	None	All	
10^2	100	7	None	All	
10^2	100	10	Raw, B, C, F, heated	A, D, E	
10^4	100	2	Raw, D, E	A, B, C, F, heated	
10^4	100	7	None	All	
10^4	100	10	None	All	
10^6	100	2	None	All	
10^6	100	7	None	All	
10^6	100	10	Raw, A, B, C, E, heated	D, F	
0	200	2	None	All	
0	200	7	None	All	
0	200	10	Raw, A, B, C, D, E, F	Heated, A and C	A and C.
10^2	200	2	None	All	
10^2	200	7	None	All	
10^2	200	10	All	None	
10^4	200	2	None	All	
10^4	200	7	None	All	
10^4	200	10	Raw, B, D, F	Heated, A, C, E	
10^6	200	2	None	All	
10^6	200	7	None	All	
10^6	200	10	Raw, A, B, C, D, F	Heated, E	E.

[1]Following 8 days of handling.

"breather" (polyethylene) plastics used in the fillet experiments of other investigators. Since no appreciable differences were detected in results of the two systems, the use of open cans was discontinued. Methylene blue solution dropped on the surfaces of even the freshest shrimp passes under the carapace where it is decolorized, sometimes within half an hour, even in open air. From this it is assumed that if the flesh is essentially anaerobic, observable differences between sealed and opened cans would be only a reflection of the activities of aerobic forms, which would exert slight influence on developments beneath the exoskeleton.

The results of tables 3 and 4 are disturbing. In shrimp subjected to 200 Krad doses, type E botulism is controlled at all temperatures except 72° F.; toxicity, where it develops, invariably follows and never precedes or parallels rejection. At the latter temperature botulism was detected on the same day the evaluation panel rejected the shrimp as unfit. Admittedly a 72° F. holding temperature would rarely be encountered in commercial practice, but it may not be uncommon for brief periods when refrigeration fails or when frozen packs are carelessly handled. The effects of short or intermittent breaks are not known and errors should be on the side of safety. Some method of guaranteeing uninterrupted refrigeration, perhaps by incorporating temperature-sensitive color bands into packaging, would be profitably pursued.

In the light of earlier survey reports by Ward (10, 11, 12, 13) the present results are disturbing for another reason. The Florida Keys, south Florida and the Tortugas area, the origin of pink shrimp, are extensions of the tropics, unrelated to any other area of the Eastern or gulf coast United States. Hence, it is hardly surprising that types A and C botulism should occur, as they do in Venezuela, Columbia, and Honduras. It is less easily understood why these few indigenous bacteria should emerge before even 10^6 spores of type E per gram, but types A and C may have existed in the vegetative state. Conceivably, type E may be less competent in a pink shrimp sub-

Table 4.—Mouse test results following injection of brown shrimp fluids incubated at 72° F.

Can designation		Days of incubation[1]	Dead mice	Live mice	Botulism type
Spores per gram	Krad				
0	0	2	None	All	
0	0	5	All	None	
10^2	0	2	None	All	
10^2	0	5	All	None	
10^4	0	2	None	All	
10^4	0	5	None	All	
10^6	0	2	None	All	
10^6	0	5	All	None	
0	100	3	None	All	
0	100	5	All	None	
10^2	100	3	None	All	
10^2	100	5	Raw, B, C, D, Heated	A, E, F,	
10^4	100	3	None	All	
10^4	100	5	Raw, A, D, F, Heated	B, C, E	
10^6	100	3	None	All	
10^6	100	5	Raw, A, C, D, E, F	Heated, B	B
0	200	3	None	All	
0	200	5	None	All	
10^2	200	3	None	All	
10^2	200	5	None	All	
10^4	200	3	None	All	
10^4	200	5	Raw, Heated	A, B, C, D, E, F	
10^6	200	3	None	All	
10^6	200	5	Raw, A, B, C, D, F	Heated, E	E

[1]Following 4 days of handling.

strate, or types A and C somewhat better adapted to the higher temperature.

The study of brown shrimp from north Florida (which region is a part of the U.S. Coastal Plain extending into Georgia and the Carolinas) has produced no comparable result to date. If a strongly A to C tropical zone does exist, its northern limits should be determined. If we are someday permitted to irradiate U.S. gulf and Atlantic coast fishery products because they seem to harbor the oft-studied type E predominantly, will we also be allowed to irradiate such products when they are imported from the tropics? Would acceptance or proscription be based upon geographic or species considerations? Is the administration of such regulation feasible? It is doubtful that we can ever devise, as an alternative, radiation-pasteurization protocols for seafoods which will be universally applicable. In our selection of *C. botulinum* as a test organism, we have, in effect, arbitrarily relegated other potentially troublesome organisms (especially other spore-forming pathogens) to some sort of limbo. On the basis of morbidity reports from Japan, Canada, and the United States, it must be assumed that our past efforts have been properly directed toward the control of the dominant type E. From Latin America and the tropics, however, there is no comparable body of statistical morbidity information upon which to base such an assumption. Surveys to uncover the presence of *C. botulinum* (which have fallen into some disrepute fol-

lowing a general acceptance of the ubiquity of all types) should be resumed. The results of such surveys should guide the experimental design of future inoculated pack studies unless the area of the fishery in question is known to be type E dominated.

As an alternative we might hope to demonstrate for type E a radiation resistance superior to that o all other types. Such superiority has not been demonstrated, and in most cases, demonstration has not been attempted. These results, as well as some of the experiences with type F, recently reported to the Interagency Botulism Research Coordinating Committee by Dr. Nancy Walls of the Georgia Institute of Technology, should reduce the attractiveness of such an approach.

There remain but two other alternatives: We must study all six types in every instance, or, as we have done with the northern U.S. fisheries, we must concentrate upon the types which figure most prominently in survey and/or morbidity reports.

We cannot question the logic of the ad hoc committee in its selection of *C. botulinum* type E as a test organism, nor in its choice of the resistant Beluga strain. In northern waters and species heretofore under investigation, type E has been found to overwhelmingly dominate all testing efforts, as it has also dominated morbidity reports; e.g., USAEC reports (7, 8, 9), Ingram and Roberts (4), Bott et al. (1), Craig et al. (3).

Accepting the imperfectability of any system (e.g.,

Table 5.—Positive mouse test results following injection of shrimp fluids incubated at 38°, 42°, or 50° F.

Can designation			Species of shrimp	Days of incubation[1]	Dead mice	Live mice	Botulism type
Spores per gram	Krad	Degrees F.					
0 0		50	Pink	13	All	None	
10² 0		50	Pink	13	All	None	
10⁴ 0		50	Pink	13	All	None	
10⁶ 0		50	Pink	13	All	None	
0 100		50	Pink	13	All	None	
10² 100		50	Pink	13	All	None	
10⁶ 100		50	Pink	13	All	None	
0–10⁶ 0–200		38	Pink	31	All raw, heated	No tests	
0–10⁶ 0		42	Pink	31	All	None	
10² 100		42	Pink	31	Raw	A, F, Heated	
10⁴ 100		42	Pink	31	Raw, B, C, D, F, heated	E, A	
10⁶ 100		42	Pink	31	Raw, F	A–E, heated	
10² 200		42	Pink	31	Raw, C, E, heated	A, B, D, F	
10⁶ 200		42	Pink	31	Raw	Heated, A–F	
0 200		50	Pink	31	Raw	Heated, A–F	
10² 0		38	Brown	15	All	None	
10⁴ 0		38	Brown	15	All	None	
0 100		38	Brown	15	Raw, D	Heated, A, B, C, E, F	
0 0		42	Brown	15	Raw, heated, B, C, D, F	A, E	
10⁴ 0		42	Brown	15	Raw, B–F	Heated, A	
10⁶ 0		42	Brown	15	Raw, A, B, E	C, D, F, heated	A
10² 100		42	Brown	15	Raw, A, C	Heated, B, D–F	
10⁶ 100		38	Brown	22	Raw, heated, B	A, C–F	
0 0		42	Brown	22	Raw, heated, D	A–C, E, F	
10⁴ 0		42	Brown	22	Raw, A, E	Heated, B–D, F	
0 0		50	Brown	22	Raw, heated, A, C, E, F	B, D	
10² 0		50	Brown	22	Raw, A, B, E	Heated, C, D, F	
10⁴ 0		50	Brown	22	Raw	Heated, A–F	
10⁴ 100		38	Brown	29	Raw, D–F	Heated, A–C	
0 100		42	Brown	29	Raw, E	Heated, A–D, F	
10⁴ 100		42	Brown	29	Raw, C, F	Heated, A, B, D, E	
10⁶ 100		42	Brown	29	Raw, A, F	Heated, B–E	
10² 200		42	Brown	29	Raw, A, D	Heated, B, C, E, F	
10⁴ 0		50	Brown	29	All	None	

[1] Following 8 days of handling for pink shrimp, and 4 days for brown.

cans, water supplies, milk, etc., continue to figure in morbidity reports despite a voluminous literature and the practical experience of many decades), we then might ask only, "to what extent need we pursue such studies before radiation-pasteurization of a given item is considered worthy of a place in modern technology?" It is in this area that we must attain some mutually satisfactory integration of the divergent viewpoints of the health-oriented and the industrial scientists. In the United States, for cod and haddock, we may be approaching some mutually acceptable irradiation-pasteurization code, but it is to be expected that for some time all such agreements can be made only after extensive product-by-product investigation.

We have made progress in this field within the last few years, and we are still progressing along both theoretical and applied lines, but problems continue to exist. Type shifts from E to A, B and C, similar to those of our own reports, have been observed on the United States Pacific coast by Eklund and Poysky (in USAEC report (7)) and by Ingram and Roberts (4).

In the United States today (with the exception of a very few laboratories investigating type F, and some individuals who study, as time permits, types B, C, or D) the potentials of types other than E as contaminants of seafoods have received too little attention. These are areas of urgency. Opinions regarding our present status are varied. Some feel that we in the United States may have the empirical control of type E botulism almost within our grasp. Others would remind us that in the late 1920's there were those who felt they were quite close to a solution of the type A problem, but it is with us still. Lest we become too optimistic, I might conclude with the observation that, in a recent telephone conversation, a colleague passed along the latest rumor of type G. Perhaps when we, at Miami, have completed our next phase, an examination of white shrimp from the western gulf, we will be able to definitely call ourselves either optimistic or pessimistic about the outlook for approval of pasteurization of shrimp.

Acknowledgments

This work is supported by the Division of Biology and Medicine, U.S. Atomic Energy Commission. (Contract AT(40–1)–3648.)

References

(1) BOTT, T. L., J. S. DEFFNER, E. McCOY, and E. M. FOSTER. 1966. *Clostridium botulinum* type E in fish from the Great Lakes. J. Bacteriol. *91:* 919–24.

(2) CARROLL, BOBBY JOE, E. S. GARRETT, G. B. REESE, and B. Q. WARD. 1966. Presence of *Clostridium botulinum* in the Gulf of Venezuela and the Gulf of Darien. Appl. Microbiol. *14:* 837–8.

(3) CRAIG, J. M., S. HAYES, and K. S. PILCHER. 1968. Incidence of *Clostridium botulinum* type E in salmon and other marine fish in the Pacific Northwest. Appl. Microbiol. *16:* 553–7.

(4) INGRAM, M., and T. A. ROBERTS. 1967. *In* Botulism 1966. Proceedings of the Fifth International Symposium on Food Microbiology, Moscow, July 1966. Chapman & Hall, Ltd., London.

(5) RONSIVALLI, L. J., J. H. CARVER, J. D. KAYLOR, J. B. HUFF, and E. J. MURPHY. 1966. Study of Irradiated-Pasteurized Fishery Products and Operational Guide for MPDI, TID-24016. Clearinghouse for Federal Scientific and Technical Information, National Bureau of Standards, U.S. Dept. of Commerce, Springfield, Va. 22151.

(6) SACKS, L. E., and G. ALDERTON. 1961. Behavior of bacterial spores in aqueous polymer two-phase systems. J. Bacteriol. *82:* 331–341.

(7) U.S. Atomic Energy Commission. 1965. Radiation Pasteurization of Foods: Summaries of Accomplishments. Conf. 651024. Clearinghouse for Federal Scientific and Technical Information, National Bureau of Standards, U.S. Department of Commerce, Springfield, Va. 22151.

(8) U. S. Atomic Energy Commission. 1966. Sixth Annual AEC Food Irradiation Contractors Meeting. Conf. 661017. Clearinghouse for Federal Scientific and Technical Information, National Bureau of Standards, U.S. Department of Commerce, Springfield, Va. 22151.

(9) U.S. Atomic Energy Commission. 1967. Seventh Annual AEC Food Irradiation Contractors Meeting. Conf. 670945. Clearinghouse for Federal Scientific and Technical Information, National Bureau of Standards, U.S. Department of Commerce, Springfield, Va. 22151.

(10) WARD, B. Q., and B. J. CARROLL. 1965. Presence of *Clostridium botulinum* type E in estuarine waters of the Gulf of Mexico. Appl. Microbiol. *13:* 502.

(11) WARD, B. Q., B. J. CARROLL, E. S. GARRETT, and G. B. REESE. 1967a. Survey of the U.S. Gulf Coast for the presence of *Clostridium botulinum*. Appl. Microbiol. *15:* 629–36.

(12) WARD, B. Q., B. J. CARROLL, E. S. GARRETT, and G. B. REESE. 1967b. Survey of the U.S. Atlantic coast and estuaries from Key Largo to Staten Island for the presence of *Clostridium botulinum*. Appl. Microbiol. *15:* 964–5.

(13) WARD, B. Q., E. S. GARRETT, and G. B. REESE. 1967c. Further indications of *Clostridium botulinum* in Latin American waters. Appl. Microbiol. *15:* 1509.

DISTRIBUTION OF *CLOSTRIDIUM BOTULINUM* TYPE E IN HOKKAIDO, JAPAN

by KENZO KANZAWA, TEIJI ONO, TAKASHI KARASHIMADA, *and* HIROO IIDA*
Hokkaido Institute of Public Health, South 2, West 15, Sapporo, Japan

Summary

Sand or mud samples were collected at 30 places along the coastal line and 30 places along the rivers or lakes in Hokkaido, Japan, between 1965 and 1966. Thirty samples were collected at each of these 60 places and the demonstration of *C. botulinum* was carried out on these samples.

Out of 900 sand samples obtained at coastal areas, 118 (13.1 percent) were positive with type E organisms and/or type E toxin. Out of 900 mud samples collected at river or lakesides, 168 (18.8 percent) were positive with type E toxin. However, none of 260 soil samples collected at inland afforestation places were positive. *C. botulinum* other than type E was not demonstrated throughout the survey.

Introduction

Since *C. botulinum* type E was first identified by Gunnison, Cummings, and Meyer (6) in 1936, botulism outbreaks due to this type have occurred in Japan, the United States, Canada, north European countries and U.S.S.R. A systematic investigation on the distribution of spores of this type, however, has been undertaken only recently.

In 1944, Dolman and Kerr (3) reported an outbreak of type E botulism due to home-canned salmon which took place in Nanaimo, British Columbia, Canada. During the investigation of this outbreak, they isolated *C. botulinum* type E strains from soil samples collected at the chicken run belonging to this particular house.

Dolman (4) also isolated type E organisms from mud samples and the intestinal contents of fish collected at littoral areas in British Columbia, and he assumed that *C. botulinum* type E spores are distributed widely in the soil of the northern hemisphere, transported by rivers or underground waters to the oceans and disseminated to several parts of the continents, especially to the northern parts of Pacific coasts where type E outbreaks have frequently been reported (5).

Also in the northern European countries, there have been several outbreaks of type E botulism, and

Pedersen (11) reported the demonstration of *C. botulinum* type E in soil samples collected from fish markets and the sea bottom of the harbor of Copenhagen. Johannsen (7) also reported the very high frequency with which type E is isolated from mud samples of the sea near Sweden, especially of Baltic Sea.

In the United States, type E outbreaks occurred by the consumption of smoked fish commercially prepared on Lake Michigan in 1963. An extensive survey for type E organisms was carried out by Bott et al. (1) on soil and fish samples collected at the Great Lakes, and it was demonstrated that type E spores are widely disseminated in these lakes. Craig and Pilchen (2) also isolated type E from mud and fish samples collected at the coastal areas in Oregon and Washington. Ward et al. (12) reported the existence of type E in mud and small animal specimens collected at the coast of Texas and Florida, thus proving that the distribution of type E extends to areas more southern than 40° N.

In Japan, *C. botulinum* type E was first isolated by the authors from soil samples collected at the lakeside of Abashiri, Hokkaido, in 1953 (10). Since then several surveys for type E have been carried out by the authors on soil samples collected from various parts of Hokkaido. For example, Kanzawa (8) examined soil samples collected along the Ishikari River and found type E toxin in 40 out of 375 cultures (10.7 percent) and he assumed that the origin of type E organisms should be from land areas.

The results of surveys for type E performed in Tohoku district are omitted here because another paper deals with this problem.

Summing up, spores of *C. botulinum* type E seem to be disseminated widely in the soil of various countries in the northern hemisphere and cause human outbreaks of botulism where the inhabitants prepare potentially dangerous foodstuff.

We had a chance to reinvestigate the distribution of spores of *C. botulinum* in soil samples in Hokkaido as a member of joint IAEA/FAO research project group. The present paper deals with the results obtained on soil samples collected at coastal and inland places in Hokkaido, Japan, during 1965 and 1966.

---

*Paper read by H. Iida.

Materials and Methods

Collection and treatment of samples.—About 50 g. of soil samples was obtained at one sampling location. This was put into a sterilized test tube, shaken with 50 ml. phosphate buffer, pH 7.0, allowed to stand for a few minutes and the free liquid was recovered. This was centrifuged at 3,000 r.p.m. for 30 minutes and the supernatant was discarded. The sediment was resuspended in 1.5 ml. of phosphate buffer, pH 7.0.

Initial culture and toxicity test.—The suspension thus obtained was inoculated into cooked meat medium, heated at 60° C. for 1 hour and incubated at 30° C. for 2 days. The supernatant of each of the initial cultures was injected intraperitoneally (0.25 ml.) into each of two mice. When mice died within 48 hours, an equal amount of type E antitoxin (10 IU per milliliter) was mixed with the toxic supernatant and the mixture was injected into two mice. As a control, an equal amount of phosphate buffer, pH 6.0, was mixed with the supernatant. When control mice died, and mice which were injected with the mixture of toxic supernatant and type E antitoxin survived, the toxin in the supernatant was determined as botulinum toxin type E.

Toxic supernatants which were not neutralized by type E antitoxin were tested again with polyvalent antitoxin of types A, B, and C by the method as described above.

Isolation of *C. botulinum* type E.—Brain heart infusion agar with 5 percent calf serum and 0.075 percent cysteine-HCl was used as an isolation medium and the plates were streaked with a small amount of sediment meat of each tube. The plates were incubated at 30° C. for 24 hours anaerobically by Rosenthal's method. Colonies suspicious of *C. botulinum* were picked up, transferred into 0.5 percent glucose cooked meat tubes and incubated at 30° C. Supernatants of cultures which showed marked gas production were injected intraperitoneally into two mice. Neutralization tests were carried out on toxic cultures with monovalent type E and polyvalent types A, B, and C antitoxic sera.

Results

SURVEY ON SAMPLES OF SAND COLLECTED ALONG THE COASTAL LINE OF HOKKAIDO

Place and date of sampling.—The sampling was carried out at 30 places along the coastal line of Hokkaido between April to October, 1965. Thirty samples of sand were collected at a distance of 2 m. from the edge of the water at each sampling place. Each sample of approximately 50 g. of sand was obtained at intervals of 2 m. from a depth of about 10 cm. The samples were brought back to the authors' laboratory where they were kept at 4° C. until use. The sampling places are shown in figure 1.

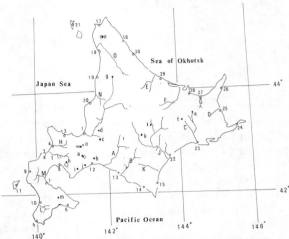

Figure 1.—Sampling spots for sand and soil samples.

At each sampling place, samples of sea water were also collected, on which the temperature, pH, NaCl-content and chemical oxygen demand (COD) were estimated.

The results obtained on 900 sand samples collected as above are shown in table 1. Of these 900 samples, 177 (19.9 percent) were found to be toxic in the initial cooked meat culture. Neutralization tests carried out on these toxic cultures revealed that 85 (9.4 percent) contained *C. botulinum* type E toxin. Toxin of the other types of *C. botulinum* was not demonstrated.

Regardless of the toxicity of the initial culture, isolation of *C. botulinum* was attempted from these cooked meat cultures. As indicated in table 1, type E organisms were often isolated from cultures in which type E toxin was not demonstrated. On the other hand, type E organisms were not always isolated from cultures in which type E toxin was demonstrated. Out of 900 samples, type E toxin was demonstrated in 85 and type E organisms were isolated in 56. In 23 samples, both type E toxin and organisms were demonstrated.

It is obvious from these results that spores of *C. botulinum* type E are widely disseminated along the coastal line of Hokkaido though the positive rate of the 30 sand samples differs from place to place. Generally speaking, the positive rate is relatively high at the northern coast of the Sea of Japan and low at the southern coast except a conspicuously high rate at Okushiri Island. No significant difference was observed among the positive rates at the western and eastern coasts of the Pacific Ocean and the coast of

Table 1.—Distribution of *C. botulinum* in sand samples from coastal areas in Hokkaido

Place[1]	Type E toxin positive	Type E organisms isolated	Both type E toxin and organisms positive	Total type E positive[2]	Percentage of type E positive
Ishikari	2	4	0	6	20.00
Suttsu	3	2	0	5	16.67
Yoichi	2	0	0	2	6.67
Iwanai	0	0	0	0	0
Matsumae	1	0	0	1	3.33
Zenikamezawa	0	0	0	0	0
Yakumo	0	0	0	0	0
Toyoura	0	0	0	0	0
Setana	0	0	0	0	0
Esashi	0	0	0	0	0
Okushiri	18	17	11	24	80.00
Tomakomai	1	0	0	1	3.33
Shizunai	4	0	0	4	13.33
Samani	1	0	0	1	3.33
Biroo	0	0	0	0	0
Hamatonbetsu	1	2	0	3	10.00
Wakkanai	0	2	0	2	6.67
Teshio	7	5	1	11	36.67
Haboro	18	8	5	21	70.00
Mashike	14	10	6	18	60.00
Rebun	1	1	0	2	6.67
Atsunai	0	1	0	1	3.33
Kushiro	7	4	0	11	36.67
Nemuro	1	0	0	1	3.33
Shibetsu	0	0	0	0	0
Rausu	0	0	0	0	0
Shari	0	0	0	0	0
Abashiri	2	0	0	2	6.67
Monbetsu	2	0	0	2	6.67
Ohmu	0	0	0	0	0
Total	85	56	23	118	[3]13.08

[1]30 samples were collected at each place.
[2]None were positive for types A, B, or C.
[3]Average.

the Sea of Okhotsk. The results are diagramed in figure 2.

There were no relationships between the positive rates of *C. botulinum* type E and the values of pH, NaCl-content and COD of the water samples.

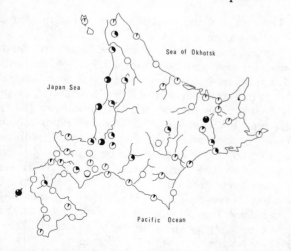

Figure 2.—Distribution of *C. botulinum* type E in Hokkaido (1965–66).

SURVEY ON SAMPLES OF MUD COLLECTED AT THE LAKE AND RIVER SIDE IN HOKKAIDO

Place and date of sampling.—As shown in figure 1, 15 rivers and 15 lakes were selected for sampling of mud. The sampling was carried out between May to August 1966. Sampling of riverside mud was carried out at the upper, middle, and lower reaches of each river, each location giving 10 samples. Sampling of lakeside mud was performed at three sampling locations around each lake, each location giving 10 samples. The samples were obtained by the same procedure as described above, brought to the laboratory and stored at 4° C. until use. Samples of river and lake water were also obtained at each sampling place. The temperature and pH were determined on these water samples and COD was estimated as the amount of oxygen consumption per gram of dried materials.

The results obtained are summarized in table 2 and diagramed in figure 2. Isolation of *C. botulinum* was not performed on these samples. Of 900 mud samples tested, 444 (49.3 percent) were found to be toxic to mice with the initial cooked meat culture. Neutralization tests carried out on these toxic cultures

Table 2.—Distribution of *C. botulinum* in mud samples from river or lake side areas in Hokkaido

Place[1]	Toxicity of initial culture	Type E toxin positive[2]	Percentage of type E toxin positive
RIVER			
Mu	14	9	30.00
Shizunai	3	0	0
Kushiro	23	8	26.67
Shibetsu	7	1	3.33
Shokotsu	16	4	13.33
Tokoro	25	8	26.67
Shari	11	1	3.33
Horikappu	26	7	23.33
Shiribetsu	22	6	20.00
Tokachi	22	10	33.33
Rekishu	10	5	16.67
Amano	3	0	0
Yurappu	21	9	30.00
Rumoe	24	8	26.67
Teshio	0	0	0
LAKE			
Shikotsu	2	1	3.33
Utonai	11	1	3.33
Shuparo	16	6	20.00
Katsurazawa	16	13	43.33
Kussharo	28	23	76.67
Akan	20	7	23.33
Shumarinai	12	8	26.67
Tohya	18	8	26.67
Kuttara	11	0	0
Poroto	14	0	0
Shikaribetsu	13	0	0
Nukabira	14	8	26.67
Ohnuma	16	4	13.33
Kabuto	19	14	46.67
Soranuma	7	0	0
Total	444	169	[3]18.78

[1]30 samples were collected at each place.
[2]None were positive for types A, B, or C.
[3]Average.

revealed that 169 (18.8 percent) contained *C. botulinum* type E toxin. Toxin of the other types of *C. botulinum* was not demonstrated.

No significant difference was observed among the positive rates of type E toxin at the upper, middle, and lower reaches of the rivers. In general, type E spores seem to be disseminated at any reach in a river where they were found in a high rate.

There were no relationships between the positive rate of type E toxin and the values of pH and COD of the water samples.

SURVEY ON SAMPLES OF SOIL COLLECTED AT INLAND LOCATIONS

Further survey for *C. botulinum* was made on 260 soil samples collected at 26 inland places where trees had been planted for afforestation. Though the initial cooked meat culture of 124 (47.7 percent) samples were found to be toxic for mice, none was proved to contain *C. botulinum* toxin including type E.

Discussion

The results of the present survey are of interest in the following three ways.

First, although *C. botulinum* type E was frequently found in sand and mud samples in Hokkaido, the other types have never been detected in such samples. This is in agreement with the results obtained by the previous surveys carried out by the authors (8, 10) that type E spores are dominant and ubiquitous in the soil of Hokkaido. Also this is in accord with the fact that all human outbreaks of botulism encountered in Hokkaido have been exclusively of type E. It was, however, reported that at least two outbreaks of botulism in ranch minks in Hokkaido were caused by *C. botulinum* type C (9). Though this suggests that type C spores may also exist in the soil of Hokkaido, the authors have not yet succeeded in demonstrating type C organisms in soil samples of Hokkaido.

Secondly, it is of interest that type E spores are

found more frequently in inland areas as compared with coastal areas. This may support the view that type E spores are terrestrial in origin and transported by rivers and subterranean waters to the oceans where they are disseminated widely by the ocean currents.

Thirdly, is the fact that type E was not demonstrated in soil samples collected at afforestation places far from rivers and lakes. This might suggest that though type E spores are terrestrial in origin, water should be closely related with their proliferation and dissemination in nature. This seems to be one of the ecological characteristics of *C. botulinum* type E as compared with type A or B.

Acknowledgment

We wish to express our thanks to Mr. K. Kameyama and Mr. A. Sato for much assistance. This investigation was supported by Research Grant No. 315/RB from the International Atomic Energy Agency in Vienna, Austria.

References

(1) BOTT, T. L., J. S. DEFFNER, E. McCOY, and E. M. FOSTER. 1966. *Clostridium botulinum* type E in fish from the Great Lakes. J. Bacteriol. *91:* 919–924.
(2) CRAIG, J. M., and K. S. PILCHER. 1967. The natural distribution of *Clostridium botulinum* type E in the Pacific coast areas of the United States. *In* Botulism 1966, M. Ingram and T. A. Roberts, ed., Chapman & Hall, London. p. 56–61.
(3) DOLMAN, C. E., and D. E. KERR. 1947. Botulism in Canada, with report of a type E outbreak at Nanaimo, B.C. Canad. J. Pub. Health *38:* 48–57.
(4) DOLMAN, C. E. 1957. Type E (fish-borne) botulism. A review. Japan. J. Med. Sci. Biol. *10:* 383–395.
(5) DOLMAN, C. E. 1960. Type E botulism: A hazard of the North. Arctic. *13:* 230–256.
(6) GUNNISON, J. B., J. R. CUMMINGS, and K. F. MEYER. 1936. *Clostridium botulinum* type E. Proc. Soc. Exp. Biol. Med. *35:* 278–280.
(7) JOHANNSEN, A. 1963. *Clostridium botulinum* in Sweden and the adjacent waters. J. Appl. Bacteriol. *26:* 43–47.
(8) KANZAWA, K. 1960. Ecological studies on *Cl. botulinum* Type E. Rep. Hokkaido Inst. Pub. Health *11:* 161–172 (in Japanese).
(9) KARASHIMADA, T., T. ONO, H. IIDA, Y. ANDO, G. SAKAGUCHI, S. SAKAGUCHI, and K. KAGOTA. 1965. Botulism in minks. Report of Hokkaido Institute of Public Health. *15:* 17–23 (in Japanese).
(10) NAKAMURA, Y., H. IIDA, K. SAEKI, and K. KANZAWA. 1954. Botulism outbreaks encountered in Hokkaido, Japan. Rep. Hokkaido Inst. Pub. Health. Special Report *3:* 1–37 (in Japanese).
(11) PEDERSEN, H. O. 1955. On type E botulism. J. Appl. Bacteriol. *18:* 619–628.
(12) WARD, B. Q., B. J. CARROLL, E. S. GARRETT, and G. B. REESE. 1967. Survey of the U.S. gulf coast for the presence of *Clostridium botulinum*. Appl. Microbiol. *15:* 629–639.

DISTRIBUTION OF *CLOSTRIDIUM BOTULINUM* ON THE PACIFIC COAST OF THE UNITED STATES

by M. W. EKLUND *and* F. T. POYSKY
Bureau of Commercial Fisheries, Technological Laboratory, Seattle, Wash. 98102

Summary

C. botulinum type E was shown to be prevalent in fresh water and marine sediments and in crab from the areas of Alaska to northern California. The incidence decreased south of this point to the Mexican border. Type E was detectable south only to 36° N. latitude. Only types A, B, and F were found in southern California. The types B and F cultures were nonproteolytic and resembled type E in physiological and biochemical characteristics including the ability to grow and produce toxin at refrigeration temperatures as low as 38° F. (*1, 2*).

Introduction

Clostridium botulinum type E was first isolated in Russia from the intestines of a sturgeon and identified as such in 1936 by Gunnison et al. (*4*). Since this original isolation, small outbreaks of type E botulism have occured in North America. In 1963, a surge of interest in *C. botulinum* followed the human botulism outbreaks from canned fish from the Pacific coast and smoked fish from the Great Lakes region of the United States. These 1963 botulism outbreaks emphasized the lack of information concerning the prevalence of *C. botulinum* type E in the marine and fresh water environments. Accordingly, one of the phases of our studies was to determine the incidence of *C. botulinum* in marine and fresh water sediments and crab collected from these environments on the Pacific coast of the United States.

Methods

Because of the sensitivity of *C. botulinum* type E spores to heat, no attempt was made to eliminate the other non-spore-forming bacteria in fear that type E itself might be destroyed. Therefore, samples to be analyzed were inoculated directly into cooked meat medium and incubated anaerobically in an atmosphere of 95 percent nitrogen and 5 percent carbon dioxide.

After 3 days of incubation at 30° C. or 5 days of incubation at 25° C., an aliquant of the enrichment culture was centrifuged in a refrigerated centrifuge (5° C.) at 10,000 r.p.m. for 10 minutes and the supernatant was assayed for botulinum toxin by intraperitoneal injection of 0.4 ml. of the supernatant into each of a pair of white mice (15 to 22 g. in weight). In some cases, the injection of this dilution gave rise to a shock condition which was lethal to mice within 10 to 15 minutes after injection. If this occurred, a dilution of 1:4 was usually sufficient to overcome the lethal factor. In the early phases of our studies, the supernatant of each sample was tested for botulinus toxin in both the trypsinized and untrypsinized states. From these studies, it was concluded that the majority of the samples that were positive in the trypsinized state were also positive in the untrypsinized state. Therefore, in later studies, all of the sample supernatants were tested for toxin in the untrypsinized state. Any of the samples which were not lethal to mice within 18 hours after injection of the untrypsinized samples were then checked using a trypsinized sample. The sample supernatant was held at 40° F. during the interim.

Trypsinization procedures were those of Duff et al. (*3*) using a final concentration of 0.25 percent trypsin.

Mice were observed closely for the first 8 to 10 hours after injection for characteristic symptoms of botulism and the death time of the mice was recorded. All mice were observed for at least 4 days.

In cases where diagnostic studies were necessary to identify the lethal toxin, a ratio of 0.4 ml. of supernatant or dilution thereof was mixed *in vitro* with 0.1 ml. of a monovalent antitoxin of types A, B, E, or F. The mixture was allowed to stand for 1 hour at 25° C. and 0.5 ml. of this mixture was injected intraperitoneally into mice. If antitoxins type A, B, E, or F failed to neutralize the toxin, the toxic broth (0.4 ml.) was mixed *in vitro* with a polyvalent antitoxin (0.1 ml.) containing equal volumes of types A, B, C, D, E, and F. If the mice receiving the polyvalent antitoxin survived, the sample was further analyzed to determine whether C and D were present or mixtures of toxins were present. In the beginning of our studies, each sample containing toxic factors was tested for the heat lability of the toxin; however, this procedure was used infrequently in later studies.

Incidence of *C. botulinum* in crab.—Live crabs were collected by our personnel aboard commercial or research vessels. These crabs were taken at points from Ketchikan, Alaska, to San Francisco, Calif. Each crab was dissected aseptically and the gills, intestinal tract, and underside of the carapace were inoculated into CM enrichment medium. The enrichments were incubated for 3 days at 30° C. and then assayed for botulinum toxins.

Incidence of *C. botulinum* in crab processing plants.—Surface of processing equipment.—Sterile cotton swabs were used for this sampling. An area of approximately 4 square inches was swabbed with 4 to 6 different swabs. These swabs were then transferred into tubes of medium, breaking the swabs below the point of handling by inserting the swab inside the mouth of the tube and applying pressure to the stick against the inside wall of the tube.

Sodium chloride flotation tanks.—Since the sodium chloride brine is a saturated solution which would be inhibitory to the outgrowth of *C. botulinum* and also because the spores might be present in small numbers, an attempt was made to lower the sodium chloride content and at the same time to concentrate the spores, if possible. The brine solution contains a large amount of proteinaceous material which prevents its filtration. Therefore the procedure finally adopted was to centrifuge the brine solution in 50-ml. sterile polycarbonate centrifuge tubes fitted with stoppers. After centrifugation, the supernatant was pipetted off and the precipitate resuspended in sterile peptone water (0.1 percent peptone) and again centrifuged. This procedure was repeated three times and the final precipitate was resuspended in CM broth and in turn was transferred to a tube of CM medium. With this procedure, the sodium chloride was diluted to a point where it does not inhibit *C. botulinum* type E. The precipitate from approximately 250 ml. of brine was thus added to each tube.

Picked crabmeat.—Approximately 100 g. of picked crabmeat was collected from each "shaker." Samples were collected throughout the working day of the processing plant. The meat was then held on ice and transported to the laboratory and inoculated into bottles of CM medium. The bottles were incubated anaerobically at 30° C. for 3 days and toxin assays made.

Incidence of *C. botulinum* in marine and fresh water sediments.—Mud samples were collected with the aid of a gravity corer. As an extra precaution to avoid cross-contamination from sample to sample, the bottom of the corer and plastic inserts were immersed in 1,000 p.p.m. sodium hypochlorite solution and allowed to stand for 20 minutes. Rinsing of the core tip was accomplished by the sea water which flowed through it as it dropped to the bottom. The sediment samples were taken to the laboratory and 5 g. of each sample were inoculated into CM medium and incubated at 25° C. for 5 days prior to assaying for botulinus toxins.

Incidence of *C. botulinum* at different depths of marine and fresh water sediments.—Mud samples were collected from Lake Washington and Puget Sound with the use of a gravity corer fitted with plastic inserts. The core samples were stoppered on both ends with sterile rubber stoppers and returned to the laboratory. The exterior of the plastic insert was washed with 1,000 p.p.m. chlorine, rinsed with sterile water, and dried with sterile cotton. The cores were then cut into 1.5-inch sections with sterile hacksaw blades. Both ends of the 1.5-inch sections were flaked away with sterile cotton swabs. The center of the 1.5-inch core was then removed using an 0.5-inch sterile cork borer. Each sample was inoculated into cooked meat medium and incubated at 25° C. for 5 days and assayed for botulinum toxin.

Results and Discussion

Incidence of *C. botulinum* in crab.—A total of 919 crab body sections (gills, intestinal tracts, and shells) representing 369 live crabs from the coastal areas of Alaska, Washington, Oregon, and California have been examined for the presence of *C. botulinum*.

The results of the occurrence of *C. botulinum* in live crabs taken from the different areas are summarized in table 1. The incidence of *C. botulinum* in crab was as follows: 57 percent from Ketchikan, Alaska; 61 to 75 percent from Bellingham Bay, Wash.; 75 percent from Grays Harbor, Wash.; and 87 percent in the area of the Columbia River off the coast of Oregon. As one proceeds south, the incidence of *C. botulinum* type E is less: 14 percent in Eureka area; 30 percent in Fort Bragg; and 12 percent in San Francisco, Calif.

The types of *C. botulinum* found in the crab samples were mainly *C. botulinum* type E. The types of *C. botulinum* from the different regions are also shown in table 1. One culture of *C. botulinum* nonproteolytic

Table 1.—Occurrence of *C. botulinum* in crab from the Pacific coast of the United States

Area where collected	Number of crabs	Crab positive (percent)	*C. botulinum* type
Ketchikan, Alaska	21	57	E
Bellingham, Wash.	18	61	B, E
	6	66	E
	32	75	E
Grays Harbor, Wash.	40	75	A, E
Columbia River	20	87	E
Eureka, Calif.	50	14	E
Fort Bragg, Calif.	43	30	A, B, E
San Francisco, Calif.	50	12	B, C, E

type B was demonstrated in the Bellingham Bay area. One culture of type A was demonstrated in a crab sample taken from Grays Harbor, Wash., and a type C culture was found in crab taken from San Francisco, Calif.

It is interesting to note that in one sampling from the area of Bellingham Bay (data not shown) samples were collected approximately 1 mile from a pulpmill and away from the pulpmill to a final distance of approximately 5 miles. This sampling track was designed to determine whether the incidence may have had any relationship to the wastes of the pulpmill. The incidence, however, was uniformly high on samples taken at the different distances from the pulpmill. Crab taken closest to the mill definitely had a different color due to the wastes from the mill. As one proceeded away from the mill, the color of the crab became more natural.

A comparison of the death times of mice injected with supernatant containing toxin of *C. botulinum* type E is shown in figure 1. The majority of the positive samples proved to be lethal within 24 hours after injection. This is in agreement with other researchers who have reported that if the toxin of type E is present, it will be lethal to mice within 24 hours. We have found in the majority of cases that, if mice do not die within 24 hours during the initial screening, the lethal levels of toxin are no longer detectable during the neutralization tests.

Incidence of *C. botulinum* in crab processing plants.—Three areas within the processing plants were sampled: (1) The equipment and tables where the crab is picked, (2) the brine from the flotation tanks, and (3) the picked crabmeat before it passes into the brine flotation tanks. All of these areas sampled were beyond the boiling tanks within the plant.

The incidence of *C. botulinum* from plant equipment, brine solutions, and crabmeat is summarized in table 2. Ninety-four surfaces of plant equipment, four brine solutions, and 66 samples of picked crabmeat have been examined from two different processing plants. All of these samples failed to yield the botulinus toxin under the conditions of these experiments. One sample of picked crabmeat yielded a toxin which was lethal to mice 23 to 28 hours after injection. However, when neutralization tests were made, the toxic factor was no longer present.

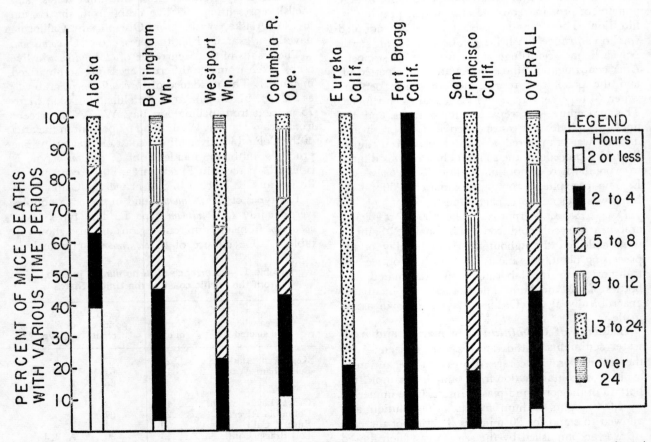

Figure 1.—A comparison of the death times of mice injected with the supernatant of incubated crab samples confirmed as containing the toxin of *Clostridium botulinum* type E.

Table 2.—Incidence of *Clostridium botulinum* in crab processing plants[1]

Samples tested	Number of samples	Number of samples containing *C. botulinum*
Swabs of equipment	94	0.
Brine solutions	4	0.
Picked crab meat	66	1 sample?

[1]All samples taken beyond boiling tanks in the processing plants.

Table 3.—Occurrence of *Clostridium botulinum* in whole crab before and after boiling tanks

Sample	Number of samples	Samples contaminated with type E (percent)
Uncooked:		
Gills	18	28
Shell	18	44
Cooked:		
Gills	18	0
Shell	18	0
Intestine	14	0

It has been shown in earlier sections of this report that a high percentage of the live crab are contaminated with *C. botulinum* type E. The question arises as to where in the processing plant can the organism be destroyed or how can we prevent the entrance of type E into the final product. Because of the sensitivity of type E to heat, the most likely point in the plant to destroy type E would be the boiling tanks. The objective of this experiment was to compare the incidence of type E in live crabs as they enter the processing plant and the incidence in whole cooked crabs. The crabs used for the picked meat are butchered before being cooked, in which case the body cavity is directly exposed to the boiling water. However, the whole crab are also boiled and sold on the fresh market in the shell. Therefore the product offering the greatest amount of protection to type E would be the whole crab. If insufficient cooking resulted, it is foreseeable that the cooling tanks could become contaminated and in turn contaminate the butchered crab to be used for the picked crabmeat.

Results from these studies are summarized in table 3. Twenty-eight percent of the gill samples and 44 percent of the shell samples obtained from the uncooked crab were confirmed as being contaminated with type E. Type E could not be detected in any of the cooked crab.

Incidence of *C. botulinum* in marine and fresh water sediments.—Samples were collected from Lake Washington and along the west coast of the United States to the Mexican border. The occurrence of *C. botulinum* in individual core mud samples from the coastal areas of Washington, Oregon, and California is presented in table 4. Type E was demonstrated in marine sediments collected along the Pacific coast of the United States from 49° to 36° N. latitude. However, only types A, B, and F were found south of 36° N. latitude. The type B demonstrations all required trypsin activation to obtain lethal levels of toxin (samples incubated 5 days at 25° C. before being assayed for toxin). These type B cultures have now been separated into pure cultures. All of these type B cultures are nonproteolytic and trypsin treatment markedly increases the toxin titer.

Type F has been demonstrated on four occasions from marine sediments collected off the coasts of Oregon and California and pure cultures have been obtained from the enrichments. Two of the type F demonstrations came from sediments collected at a depth of 1,646 meters, the third from a depth of 1,326 meters, and the fourth from a depth of 235 meters.

The incidence of *C. botulinum* was also very high in fresh water sediments collected in the State of Washington. In fact, 100 percent of the sediments collected in the Columbia River 200 miles from the Pacific Ocean contained type E or type A.

Marine and fresh water sediments have also been inoculated into CM medium on a "Most Probable Number" (MPN) basis. From the marine sediments of Bellingham Bay, Wash., the MPN varied from 54 to 3,200 type E cells per 100 g. of sediment. From the

Table 4.—Occurrence of *C. botulinum* in marine and fresh water sediments collected on the Pacific coast of the United States

Area where collected	Depth (fathoms)	Number positive/ number tested	Number positive for indicated *C. botulinum* type
Washington:			
Bay	7–35	91/98	1A, 90E
Ocean	25–850	51/101	4B, 47E
Fresh water		50/55	50E
Oregon	61–1,070	32/92	10A, 1B, 18E, 3F
California:			
To 36° N. latitude	38–700	19/128	1B, 18E
Shore, 41° N. latitude		2/28	1A, 1E
36°–32° N. latitude	45–580	15/160	6A, 8B, 1F

fresh water sediments of Lake Washington (adjacent to Seattle), the MPN varied from 1,840 to 3,500 type E cells per 100 g. of sediment.

Comparison of the incidence of type E in crab, mud, and/or fish taken from the same area.—On several occasions, we have had the opportunity to collect fish, mud, and crab from the same area. It is therefore of interest to know what the incidence of type E is in the fish and crab in relation to their environment. A summary of the incidence of type E in these different samples is shown in table 5.

untrypsinized states, whereas type B toxin was detected only after trypsin activation. This is interesting in that type E toxin was activated in the enrichment culture, whereas the toxin of the type B culture was detectable only after trypsin activation, indicating that the type B toxin was present only in the protoxin state.

In the fresh water sediment cores, type E was found at all depths of the core. In one of the cores, a mixture of types E and C was found. This mixture of types was consistent in each of the 1.5-inch sections

Table 5.—A comparison of the incidence of _C. botulinum_ from mud samples with the incidence in crab and fish collected from the same area

Area where collected	Sample	Depth taken	Samples positive (percent)
Columbia River	Mud	50 fathoms	67
	Crab	do	42
	Fish	do	83
Grays Harbor, Wash.	Mud	32 fathoms	75
	Crab	do	75
Puget Sound	Mud	30 fathoms	86
	Fish	do	3
Eureka, Calif.	Mud	15 fathoms	7
	Crab	do	14

From the area southwest of the mouth of the Columbia River, crab, mud, and fish were taken at a depth of 50 fathoms. All samples were heavily contaminated with type E (one culture of type B). A similar trend is observed when the crab and mud samples were collected in the Grays Harbor area in that both mud and crab were heavily contaminated with type E.

From the Puget Sound area, mud and fish were collected at a depth of 30 fathoms. In this experiment, the mud was heavily contaminated with type E but only 3 percent of the fish contained type E.

From the Eureka, Calif., area, mud samples were gathered aboard fishing vessels from the bottoms of crab traps and crab were taken from the inside of the traps. Fourteen percent of the crab taken during the study were contaminated with type E and 7 percent of the mud samples contained type E (one sample yielded type A).

Incidence of _C. botulinum_ at different depths of marine and fresh water sediments.—The next study was undertaken to determine the depth of occurrence of _C. botulinum_ spores in undisturbed fresh water and marine sediments.

One of the mud cores collected from the Puget Sound area contained type E only in the top 1.5-inch section of the core. The other two cores collected from the marine areas contained type E in each of the 1.5-inch sections to a depth of 12 inches (the greatest depth of sample core). In one of the 1.5-inch core sections, types B and E toxin were detected. Type E toxin was detectable in the trypsinized and

to a depth of 12 inches. This is the first time that we have detected type C in areas north of the Columbia River.

Of the different samples analyzed during the survey, all of the nonproteolytic type B cultures, one culture of type A, and 29 cultures of type E required trypsin activation in order to detect lethal levels of toxin in the enrichment culture.

We have also examined 12 samples of Kona crab and the gills and intestines of six Bigeye scad collected from the waters of the Hawaiian Islands for the incidence of _C. botulinum_. None of these enrichment samples contained botulinum toxin after 5 days of incubation at 25° C. Admittedly, one cannot draw any conclusions from such a limited sampling, but it indicates that the incidence is probably low.

References

(1) EKLUND, M. W., D. I. WIELER, and F. T. POYSKY. 1967. Outgrowth and toxin production of nonproteolytic type B _Clostridium botulinum_ at 3.3° to 5.6° C. J. Bacteriol. _93_: 1461–1462.

(2) EKLUND, M. W., F. T. POYSKY, and D. I. WIELER. 1967. Characteristics of _Clostridium botulinum_ type F isolated from the Pacific coast of the United States. Appl. Microbiol. _15_: 1316–1323.

(3) DUFF, J. T., G. WRIGHT, and A. YARINSKY. 1956. Activation of _Clostridium botulinum_ type E toxin by trypsin. J. Bacteriol. _72_: 455–460.

(4) GUNNISON, J. B., J. R. CUMMINGS, and K. F. MEYER. 1936. _Clostridium botulinum_ type E. Proc. Soc. Exp. Biol. Med. _35_: 278–280.

EPIDEMIOLOGICAL OBSERVATIONS ON BOTULISM IN JAPAN, ESPECIALLY ON THE PRESENT STATUS IN THE AKITA PREFECTURE

by Eiichiro Kodama
The Akita Prefectural Institute of Public Health, Akita-shi, Japan

Summary

The presence of botulism in Japan was reviewed from the first incidence at Hokkaido in 1951 to date, comprising 57 outbreaks, including 319 patients and 83 deaths. A summary of the epidemiological observations revealed the following:

The outbreaks of botulism were limited to the areas: Hokkaido, and four prefectures of the northeastern part of Japan. The average morbidity of botulism was 57.4 percent and the average mortality was 26.0 percent.

The toxigenic food was "izushi" of raw fish or analogous food, so-called "kirikomi" or "kayuzushi." One case was due to "sujiko" (salted salmon egg or hard roe), and one case due to canned fish (mackerel). No cases were caused by animal meat or shellfish, nor vegetable izushi. Twenty-two kinds of fish were implicated as the cause of izushi poisoning. Flatfish was most frequent; other fish involved were hatahata, mackerel, pike, and saurel.

Among the botulinal patients, 74 were male and 91 female. By age classification, most patients were in the young adult and middle age groups with few patients in the young or very old, but there were nine children under 9 years of age. The incidence of botulism was frequently seasonal in spring and autumn, especially in autumn. The incubation time reported was 18.9 hours on the average, and the interval from the onset of botulism to death averaged 21.0 hours.

Among the clinical signs and symptoms, the gastrointestinal preceded the neurological in most cases. The most frequent were as follows, in order: nausea and vomiting (85.3 percent), amblyopia (78.4 percent), thirst (73.6 percent), abdominal swelling or meteorism (61.2 percent), numbness of extremities (57.3 percent), midriasis (52.6 percent), double vision (44.3 percent), hoarseness (42.6 percent), abdominal pain (41.9 percent), dyspnea (38.0 percent), and other of lesser frequencies.

The distribution of *Clostridium botulinum* in the Akita Prefecture is heavy in the soil on the perimeter of Lake Hachiro, especially in the southern part, and also in the soil of Oga Peninsula. Twenty-four strains of *C. botulinum* were isolated and all were of type E with exception of four strains of type A. Type B has not been isolated from soil. Botulism due to type A or B has not occurred as yet in the Akita Prefecture. *C. botulinum* type E was also isolated in high frequency from the fish of Lake Hachiro but few isolations were made from the homemade izushi or from the izushi at the markets.

Clostridium botulinum type E was found to be excreted gradually after the ingestion of botulinal izushi and its excretion was occasionally prolonged to approximately 2 weeks.

Introduction

It is difficult to find, historically, the presence of botulism in the Japanese literature. But it is not so recent as to have been introduced from foreign countries.

In 1850, Kuwata Shoan had translated into Japanese, a book on toxicology written by a German doctor, named Sacks, which made mention of botulism. Since then, the term was mentioned at times in Japanese journals or books, but there had been no report of outbreaks of botulism in Japan until relatively recently.

In 1951, Nakamura, Iida, and others, certified the presence of *C. botulinum* in Japan, for the first time, on the occasion of the izushi-poisoning at Iwanai in Hokkaido (*1, 2*). Since then the number of outbreaks of botulism in Japan has gradually increased, 57 having been reported to date. It seems that other outbreaks of botulism must have occurred somewhere in the past, but none had been reported.

I have studied epidemiological observations on botulism in Japan from the documentation on reported cases, and I wish to review those observations together with the present status of botulism in the Akita Prefecture.

The Present Status of Botulism in Japan

The incidence of botulism in Japan is now limited to Hokkaido and four prefectures in the northeastern part of Honshu (Aomori, Akita, Iwate, and Yamagata). As shown in table 1 and figure 1, there were 35 outbreaks in Hokkaido, and 22 outbreaks in four

Table 1.—Incidence, morbidity and mortality of botulism in Japan, 1951–68

Place of incident	Number of outbreaks	Persons who ate izushi	Number of patients	Number of deaths	Morbidity (percent)	Mortality (percent)
Hokkaido	35	432	231	43	53.5	18.6
Akita Prefecture	13	75	60	24	80.0	40.0
Aomori Prefecture	6	31	17	8	54.8	47.1
Iwate Prefecture	2	15	8	5	53.3	62.5
Yamagata Prefecture	1	3	3	3	100.0	100.0
Total	57	556	319	83	[1]57.4	[1]26.0

[1]Average.

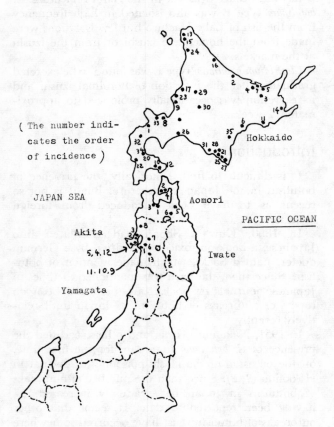

(The number indicates the order of incidence)

JAPAN SEA

Hokkaido

Aomori

PACIFIC OCEAN

Akita

Iwate

Yamagata

Figure 1.—Outbreaks of botulism in Japan.

prefectures of Honshu, a total of 57. These included 556 persons who had eaten botulinal food; 319 became ill and 83 died. Therefore, the average morbidity was 57.4 percent, but in different outbreaks morbidity ranged from 53.3 to 100 percent. Incidence of mortality was 26.0 percent, but it also varied from 18.6 to 100 percent.

Some suspected cases of botulism, occurring primarily before 1951, whose cause of death had been reported as unknown, are listed in table 2. There were two such cases in Hokkaido, one in Aomori,

and eight in the Akita Prefecture (*14*). We searched for such cases which occurred from 1930 to 1952, in areas around Lake Hachiro. In these cases, some kind of fish was eaten as izushi, and the clinical symptoms and signs, such as abdominal pain, nausea and vomiting, headache, thirst, hoarse voice, numbness of whole body, ptosis palpebrae, and dyspnea, had been described.

The majority of the cases of botulism in Japan are caused by type E, with one exception of type B in Aomori (*2*). No case caused by type A has been reported.

On the Food Incriminated

Izushi of various fishes is the incriminated food in most cases of botulism in Japan. In addition to izushi-poisoning, four cases due to the kirikomi of some fish were reported (Hokkaido). One case was caused by kayuzushi of some fish (Iwate), but these are similar in quality to izushi. There was also one case reported as due to sujiko (salted salmon egg) and also one case was reported as due to canned mackerel.

Many kinds of fish are used to prepare izushi. We find 22 kinds of fishes incriminated in botulinal cases. Eighteen cases were caused by flatfish, 10 cases by hatahata, four cases by saury, three cases by mackrel and saurel, two cases by herring, sardine, and trout, respectively, one case each by dace, salmon, young trout, codfish, *Lotella phycis*, *Hexagrammos octogrammus* (Pallas), *Pleurogrammus monopterygius* (Pallas), oonago, sea bream, *Pygosteus sinensis* (Guichenot), *Chloea sarchynnis*, carp, *Sebastodes flammeus* (?) and halfbreak.

The vegetables employed in botulinal-izushi included carrot, cabbage, beefsteak plant, radish, ginger, eggplant, turnip, chrysanthemum. As condiments, salt, vinegar, acetic acid, sake, sugar, rice malt, mirin, and redpepper, were used in one or more kinds of izushi. The izushi is generally eaten in the raw state, but it may be eaten occasionally with miso or shoyu, after boiling. Until now such cooked izushi has not caused poisoning.

Table 2.—Suspected outbreaks of botulism in Japan reported from 1930–55

Date of outbreak	Location of outbreak	Persons who ate izushi	Patients	Deaths	Causal food (kind of izushi)
HOKKAIDO					
June 1945	Tomamae-cho	?	8	3	Herring.
Sept. 1950	Monbetsu-gun	?	6	2	Flatfish.
Total			14	5	
AKITA PREFECTURE					
Oct. 1930	Oga-shi	?	3	1	Konosirus.
Oct. 1934	Tenno-machi	?	6	1	Mackerel.
Dec. 1940	Tenno-machi	?	6	2	Halfbreak.
May 1948	Katanishi-mura	?	4	2	Carp and flatfish.
Nov. 1950	Tenno-machi	?	1	1	Halfbreak.
Oct. 1951	Kotohama-mura	4	4	2	Goby.
June 1952	Hitoichi-machi	10	7	1	Flatfish.
Sept. 1955	Tenno-machi	1	1	0	Mullet.
Total			32	10	
AOMORI PREFECTURE					
Oct. 1950	Imabetsu-machi	4	4	3	Mackerel.

Clinical Symptoms and Signs of Botulism in Japan

There has been a belief among the people residing near Lake Hachiro that, when a poisoning due to izushi-eating has occurred, one must loose his life. This leads one to suspect botulinal poisoning. From this folk belief, it is apparent that the mortality from izushi-poisoning is very high.

Out of the reports on the 319 botulinal patients since 1951, I have selected findings of cases whose clinical descriptions were relatively detailed. From these reports, the following summary was extracted:

Morbidity.—As shown in table 1, the average morbidity was 57.4 percent, but regional difference ranging from 53.5 percent (Hokkaido) to 100 percent (Yamagata) are evident.

Mortality.—Differences appear in regard to mortality among outbreaks in different regions, from 18.5 percent in Hokkaido to 100 percent in Yamagata. The mortality in Hokkaido is lowest of all, perhaps because of the availability of antiserum therapy (4).

Incubation period.—As shown in table 3, the longest incubation period (average) occurred in Hokkaido 20.2 hours, and the shortest reported 15.3 hours in Iwate, and the overall average was 18.9 hours.

Sex and age of patients.—Among 165 cases of botulism, 74 were male and 91 were female. There is no explanation for the higher incidence in females. According to the classification by age (table 4), patients were primarily in the young adult and middle age groups, and fewer in the very young and in the very old. But it is evident that there were some young patients. Nine patients were under 9 years of

Table 3.—The period of incubation of botulism in Japanese cases

Location of outbreaks	Number of cases	Average period of incubation (hours)
Hokkaido	70	20.2
Akita Prefecture	59	17.5
Aomori Prefecture	10	19.7
Iwate Prefecture	3	15.3
Yamagata Prefecture	3	17.3
Total	145	[1]18.9

[1]Average.

age, especially one boy and one girl, both of whom were 4 years old.

Seasonal incidence.—In ancient times izushi was usually processed in winter, and at that time izushi had a meaning of "winter food", but in recent times, with the greater abundance of foodstuff, izushi is processed in other seasons and has acquired a connotation of a subsidiary item of the diet. The seasonal incidence of botulism is recorded in table 5; seven cases occurred in spring, eleven cases in summer, thirty-one cases in autumn, and eight in winter. Botulism is most frequent in autumn. Most of the farmers in Japan plow their rice fields in late spring or early summer and autumn. Botulinal poisoning is apt to happen in such busy seasons, because farmers willingly eat izushi in order to save time in the kitchen.

The interval from onset to death.—The time, from the beginning of signs and symptoms to death, varied somewhat in different areas (see table 6). The shortest interval reported was 8 hours (Iwate), and the longest

Table 4.—Botulinal patients in Japan, by sex and age

Location of outbreaks	Sex	Age (years)								Total
		0 to 9	10 to 19	20 to 29	30 to 39	40 to 49	50 to 59	60 to 69	70 to	
Hokkaido	M	0	3	8	8	4	6	4	0	33
	F	3	5	10	7	8	5	4	0	42
Akita	M	0	4	5	2	3	9	3	1	27
	F	2	2	3	8	7	7	2	1	32
Aomori / Iwate / Yamagata	M	1	0	1	6	1	1	4	0	14
	F	3	0	3	3	2	3	3	0	17
Total:										
Male		1	7	14	16	8	16	11	1	74
Female		8	7	16	18	17	15	9	1	91
Grand total male and female		9	14	30	34	25	31	20	2	265

Table 5.—The seasonal incidence of botulism in Japan

Area	Months												Total
	Spring			Summer			Autumn			Winter			
	Mar.	Apr.	May	June	July	Aug.	Sept.	Oct.	Nov.	Dec.	Jan.	Feb.	
Hokkaido	2	0	3	2	3	1	3	7	6	5	2	1	35
Akita Prefecture	0	0	1	4	0	0	2	5	1	0	0	0	13
Aomori Prefecture	0	0	0	0	0	0	2	3	1	0	0	0	6
Iwate Prefecture	0	0	1	0	0	0	0	1	0	0	0	0	2
Yamagata Prefecture	0	0	0	0	0	1	0	0	0	0	0	0	1
Total	2	0	5	6	3	2	7	16	8	5	2	1	57

Table 6.—The interval from onset to death in cases of botulism in Japan

Location of outbreaks	Number of deaths	Average interval from onset of symptoms to death (hours)
Hokkaido	25	22.0
Akita Prefecture	23	20.5
Aomori Prefecture	7	27.9
Iwate Prefecture	3	8.0
Yamagata Prefecture	3	14.0
Total	61	[1]21.0

[1]Average.

was 27.9 hours (Aomori). The overall average time was 21 hours.

Clinical signs and symptoms.—While there is always some fear that some symptoms, of which patients did not complain, might have been missed, the following are, in order of their frequency, both the symptoms and signs among 129 botulinal cases:

	Percent	Cases
Eye disorder	87.6	113
Nausea and vomiting	85.3	110
Thirst	73.6	95
Abdominal meteorism	61.2	79
Numbness of extremities	57.3	74
Hoarseness	42.6	55
Bellyache	41.9	54
Dyspnea	38.0	49
Dysarthria	34.1	44
Languor of whole body	32.6	42
Obstipation	23.3	30
Diarrhea	19.4	25
Headache and dull head	17.8	23
Retentio urinae	14.7	19
Chill and shivering	10.9	14
Vertigo	9.3	12
Low blood pressure	7.8	10
Fever	6.2	8
Distress in thorax	3.1	4
Convulsion	2.3	3
Abdominal distress	2.3	3
Eruption	1.5	2
Aches in joints	0.8	1
Weak tendon reflex	0.8	1
Dry cornea	0.8	1

Eye disorder was the principal sign or sympton of botulis, but the simple expression "eye disorder" or "eye symptom and sign" is not proper because such an expression does not distinguish between the signs of the outer or inner eye. Fortunately, the clinical reports of 97 cases out of the 129 were written in sufficient detail, yielding the following frequencies:

	Percent	Cases
Amblyopia	78.4	76
Midriasis	52.6	51
Double vision	44.3	43
Ptosis palpebrae	40.2	39
Pupil reflex disturbance	19.6	19
Nystagmus	1.0	1

Gastrointestinal symptoms and signs were first to appear, then the neurological signs generally appeared, but at times gastrointestinal symptoms and signs were missing or both appeared simultaneously.

Chill and shivering were not frequent (10.9 percent) and fever did not always occur. Fever occurred in only eight cases (6.2 percent), the temperature ranging from 37 to 42° C. (3), rarely passing 38° C.

Convulsion appeared in three cases in Akita (2.3 percent), and in four cases in Hamamasu (44 percent) (4), however, the clinical state was not given in sufficient detail. The patients in the Akita outbreak were adults, two were male, 63 and 26 years old, respectively, and the other was a female, 57 years old.

As mentioned above, most patients complained initially of their severe pains and the physicians also observed the noteworthy signs and symptoms at the time of emergency. Therefore, mild cases were often overlooked. For instance, no patient complained of dysosmia or anosmia due to the benumbed N. olfactorius. There was no report that N. olfactorius was affected by botulinal toxin.

The affection of N. opticus led to amblyopia or mist sight (78.4 percent), but there was no amaurotic case. There was the affection of N. abducens, N. trochlearis, and double vision occurred in 44.3 percent of cases. The affection of M. sphincter pupillae provoked midriasis (52.6 percent), but there was no case which showed myopia nor stiffness of pupils among 129 cases. I believe there can be myopia, be it of transient nature. There were seven cases of anisocolia (29.2 percent) among 24 cases of the incident at Toyotomi (4). Ptosis palpebrae was seen in 39 cases (40.2 percent) and nystagmus was seen in only one case (male, 41 years old), but no detailed report (5) was available. There was no report on affection of taste, chewing, hearing, or of facial palsy. Vertigo was seen, its frequency being 9.3 percent.

The affection of N. glossopharyngeus (VII), and of N. hypoglossus (IX), caused difficulty of swallowing and motoric dysarthria. When the numbness of N. vagus (VIII) was associated, causing a numbness of vocal cords, it led to difficulty of utterance, and at the last stage inspiratory dyspnea (38 percent).

The numbness of N. trigeminus provoked the low-lachrymal secretion and finally a dry cornea (5) (1 percent), and also nose obstruction (54.2 percent) in the Toyotomi outbreak (4).

The numbness of the vagal nerve, accompanied by affection of spinal sympathicus, caused the suppression of oesophageal motion and dilatation of oesophagus and with the numbness of N. glosso-pharyngeus and N. hypoglossus caused the difficulty in swallowing (45 percent). The oesophageal dilatation was verified in one case in the Ashizawa outbreak (56-year-old male), and this case was accompanied by elevation of the diaphragm (fig. 2).

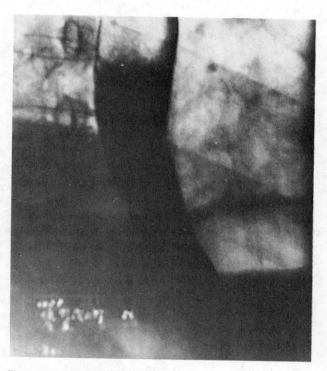

Figure 2.—The dilatation of oesophagus and the elevation of diaphragm.

Swelled abdomen was seen in 79 cases (61.2 percent) due to the numbness of N. parasympathicus and the weakened peristaltic motion provoking persistent obstipation (23.3 percent).

Unconsciousness was not seen except at the agonal stage.

Suppuration of the gingiva and pharynx, glottitis, and sometimes urticaria-like eruptions were recorded (Esashi case) (6) as complications.

After the patients had recovered some symptoms lasted relatively long periods of time; e.g., thirst, weakness of whole body, abdominal swelling or meteorism, soreness of the pharynx, midriasis, and amblyopia, but they faded away gradually.

Of course at the onset of botulism, one must differentiate botulism from other diseases, for instance, from stroke, acute bulbar paralysis, appendicitis, obstruction of intestine, and laparatomies were actually reported.

The Distribution of *Clostridium botulinum* in Soil

Since the first outbreak of botulism in 1951, investigations of the soil in Hokkaido were made by Y. Nakamura, H. Iida, K. Kanzawa et al., with the purpose of isolating *C. botulinum*. Thereafter, Ono (7), Kanzawa (8), Takeuchi et al. (9), investigated the distribution of botulinal spores in Hokkaido. When the first cases of botulism appeared in 1955, in Aomori (10, 11), and in 1956 in Yamagata (12, 13), investigations for *C. botulinum* in soil were carried out by each of the authorities.

In 1953, the first outbreak of botulism occurred in Akita, in a small village near Lake Hachiro (14). Since then we have investigated the soil of the Oga Peninsula and of Lake Hachiro. Next we enlarged the survey to other areas in Akita Prefecture, mainly along the seacoast, rivers, and around lakes (15).

We isolated 24 strains (isolation rate 0.4 percent) out of 6,883 samples. The places or districts where we could isolate *C. botulinum* are shown in figure 3, and among the 24 strains of *C. botulinum*, 20 strains were type E, and four strains were type A (16, 17). Two strains of type A were isolated at Kitaura district of Oga Peninsula.

There was some difference in the distribution among the areas in Akita Prefecture, e.g., on the outskirts of Lake Hachiro and at the Oga Peninsula 22 strains (including four strains of type A) were isolated out of 1,460 samples (1.5 percent), but at the Uri seacoast only two strains were isolated out of 1,600 samples (0.1 percent). At the inland or the mountainous areas only one strain was isolated from 2,873 samples. When an outbreak of botulism occurred in a village of the mountainous district (Haginari), four strains (isolation rate 0.5 percent

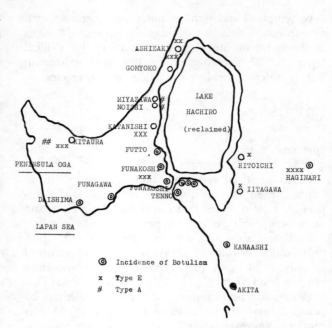

Figure 3.—The isolation of *Clostridium botulinum*.

of *C. botulinum* type E were isolated from soil.

In addition to the above studies, soil investigations in Japan intending to isolate clostridia, made by other authorities, were performed with no relation to botulism. Wakamatsu, Hiroki, et al. (18) isolated one strain of *C. botulinum* type A in the southern parts of Kyushu, and Yamagata (19) also isolated three strains of *C. botulinum* type E from the seashore sand of the Yamaguchi Prefecture (isolation rate 1.3 percent). Uryu, et al. (20) examined the soil of Kannagawa Prefecture and Takagi et al. (21) have investigated the Tokai district, but no isolations were made.

The Relationship Between *C. botulinum* and Fish

K. F. Meyer (22) and other authorities have already reported on the relationship between *C. botulinum* type E and fish. The designation, "fish-borne botulism,"

Table 7.—Isolation of *Clostridium botulinum* from fish of Lake Hachiro

Condition of fish	Kinds of fish	Number of samples	Positive culture	Isolation rate (percent)
Dead fish floating on the water surface.	Halfbreak	3	2	67.0
	Dace	7	7	100.0
	Goby	2	2	100.0
Live fish, freshly caught.	Flatfish	200	1	.5
	Pondsmelt	200	1	.5
	Nikuhaze	100	0	.0
Total		512	13	

Table 8.—The toxicity for mice of feces and vomitus and their cultures, obtained from botulinal patients

Number	Age and sex	Date of incidence	Vomited article			Feces								
			pH	As it is	Incubated 35° C., 3 days	Date of sampling October								
						20	21	22	23	24	26	27	28	29
1	61, F	Oct. 17	n.	n.	n.	+	+	+	–	–	–	–	n.	n.
2	18, M	do	5.5	+ +	+ +	–	–	+	+	+	–	+	+	+
3	26, M	do	5.4	+ –	– +	+	–	+	–	–	–	–	+	+
4	15, M	do	5.0	– –	– –	+	–	+	–	–	n.	n.	n.	n.
5	58, M	Oct. 18	n.	n.	n.	–	+	n.	n.	n.	n.	n.	n.	n.
6	43, F	do	n.	n.	n.	+	+	n.	n.	n.	n.	n.	n.	n.
7	15, M	do	n.	n.	n.	+	n.	n.	n.	n.	n.	n.	n.	n.
8	55, F	do	n.	n.	n.	–	+	n.	n.	n.	n.	n.	n.	n.
9	61, F	do	n.	n.	n.	–	+	n.	n.	n.	n.	n.	n.	n.

NOTE.— + = mouse died; — = mouse alive; n. = no data.

coined by E. C. Dolman, is a most proper expression, in my opinion.

In 1963, Johansen (23) isolated type E from fish in 55 to 100 percent of attempts, and in 1966 Bott et al. (24) isolated *C. botulinum* type E from the fish of the Great Lakes in about the same frequency.

The results of our investigations of the fish of Lake Hachiro are shown in the table 7. The isolation rate from the dead fish, floating over the lake water, was very high (67 to 100 percent), but it was quite low (0 to 0.5 percent) from freshly caught fishes (flatfish, pond smelt, nikuhaze) (25). In 1962, we examined fish at market. Two strains were isolated from 1,205 samples (isolation rate 0.1 percent).

C. botulinum type E was isolated from the incriminated izushi samples which were the cause of botulism in almost all cases. Three strains of *C. botulinum* type E were isolated from 14 homemade izushi samples (at Futto, Yashima, Iwaki, Tenno), having no relation to food poisoning at that time. One strain was isolated from the 19 samples of izushi at the markets (at Konoura, Hirasawa, Araya, Kisagata). Thus, the isolation rate was 21.3 percent in the former, and 5.3 percent in the latter.

The Fate of *C. botulinum* in the Human Digestive Tract

From the literature we know that *C. botulinum* is detectable in the feces of animals. Burke (1919) isolated the micro-organisms from the feces of horse, pig, and chicken, and Kempner (1897) isolated *C. botulinum* from healthy pigs.

In October of 1957, an outbreak of botulism, due to izushi (kanagi), occurred. All nine patients were admitted to the hospital, giving us the opportunity to examine the feces daily with the lapse of time (25). It seemed that there was a tendency for a gradual elimination from the human digestive tract with time, but

in two cases the organism was present in feces even as late as 13 days from the onset of disease (table 8). A possibility of contaminating a virgin soil exists when clostridia are excreted from the human intestine for a long period of time.

References

(1) NAKAMURA, Y., H. IIDA, K. SAEKI, and K. KANZAWA. 1954. On the botulinal food poisonings in several areas of Hokkaido. Report Hokkaido Inst. Public Health (special report).

(2) YAMAMOTA, K., G. NAKAMURA, and H. ASANO. 1962, April. On the izushi, poisoning due to *Clostridium botulinum* type B, which occurred for the first time in our country. The 35th General Meeting of Bacteriology (Nagoya).

(3) SAITO, T., T. KARASHIMADA, and H. IIDA. 1964. Three outbreaks of food poisoning due to izushi encountered in Hokkaido in 1961. Report of the Hokkaido Institute of Public Health. *13:* 26.

(4) IIDA, H., K. KANZAWA, Y. NAKAMURA, T. KARASHIMADA, T. ONO, and T. SAITO. 1964. On the botulism which occurred in Hokkaido in 1962; especially on the effect of antiserum. Report Hokkaido Institute of Public Health. *14:* 6.

(5) IIDA, H., T. KARASHIMADA, I. NAKAGAWA, M. NAKANE, and T. SATO. 1958. Four outbreaks of izushi-borne type E botulism encountered in Hokkaido in 1957. Report of the Hokkaido Institute of Public Health *10:* 19.

(6) OGSAWARA, K., and N. MITSUI. 1958. On the food poisoning associated with putrefaction of izushi. Report of the Hokkaido Institute of Public Health *10:* 44.

(7) ONO, T., T. KARASHIMADA, K. KAMEYAMA, A. SATO, K. KANZAWA, and H. IIDA. 1967. A study on the distribution of *Clostridium botulinum* type E in Hokkaido. Report of the Hokkaido Institute of Public Health *7:* 1.

(8) KANZAWA, K. 1960. Ecological studies on *Clostridium botulinum* type E. Report of the Hokkaido Institute of Public Health *11:* 161.

(9) TAKEUCHI, K. 1960. Epidemiological studies on the outbreaks of botulism in Hokkaido. Report of the Hokkaido Institute of Public Health. Japan. J. Public Health *8:* 573.

(10) The Section of Hygiene of Aomori Prefectural Govern-

ment. On the botulism in Aomori Prefecture. Monograph, 1957.

(11) The Section of Hygiene, Public Welfare and Labour of the Aomori Prefectural Government. An investigation on Botulism in Aomori Prefecture (pt. I). Monograph, 1959.

(12) TOHYAMA, Y., K. MATANO, and S. SAKAGUCHI. 1956. On the botulism-like food-poisoning report.

(13) The Section of Public Welfare of Yamagata Prefectural Government. 1956. Data for the study on the botulism which occurred in Nukanome, Takashima-machi, Ikitama-gun, Yamagata Prefecture.

(14) SAITO, S., S. FUJISAWA, A. WADA, Y. TOHYAMA, and G. SAKAGUCHI. 1953. On the botulinal poisoning due to izushi in Akita Prefecture. J. Akita-Prefecture Med. Assoc. 6: 26–36.

(15) KODAMA, E., S. FUJISAWA, and A. SAKAMOTO. 1964. An epidemiological study of botulism in Akita Prefecture; and on the result of examination of soil. Report Akita Prefectural Institute of Public Health 8: 15.

(16) KODAMA, E., S. FUJISAWA, A. SAKAMOTO, and H. ASANO. 1962. On the Clostridium botulinum type A isolated from the soil of Akita Prefecture. Report Akita Prefectural Institute of Public Health 6: 64.

(17) KODAMA, E., S. FUJISAWA, A. SAKAMOTO, H. ASANO, and J. ETO. 1963. Ueber den Clostridium botulinum typus A, der in der ta Praefecture gefunden wurde. Hirosaki Med. J. 14: 156–164.

(18) WAKAMATSU, T., ET AL. 1953. Ecological study of clostridia in Kyushu; especially in its southern part. Kitasato Arch. Exper. Med. 25: 163–186.

(19) YAMAGATA, H. 1959. On the distribution of clostridia which cause food poisoning. Report Yamaguchi Prefectural Institute of Public Health 2: 34.

(20) URYU, I., ET AL. 1961. A study on clostridia; especially the result of examination of soil in Kannagawa Prefecture. Japan. J. Public Health 8: 721.

(21) TAKAGI, T., S. SUZUKI, K. NAKANO, and U. KURIMOTO. 1961. A study on the clostridia in soil. Japan. J. Bacteriol. 16: 77.

(22) MEYER, K. F. 1956. The status of botulism as a world health problem. Bull. W.H.O. 15: 281–298.

(23) JOHANSEN, A. 1963. Clostridium botulinum in Sweden and in the adjacent waters. J. Bacteriol. 26: 43.

(24) BOTT, T. L., J. S. DEFFNER, E. McCOY, and E. M. FOSTER. 1966. Clostridium botulinum type E in fish from the Great Lakes. J. Bacteriol. 91: 919.

(25) KODAMA, E. 1966. The epidemiology of botulism in Japan. The Colony of Tohoku. No. 14.

PRODUCTION OF *CLOSTRIDIUM BOTULINUM* SPORES TYPES A AND B

by Abe Anellis *and* D. B. Rowley
Microbiology Division, Food Laboratory,
U.S. Army Natick Laboratories, Natick, Mass. 01760

Summary

"Conventional," dialysis membrane, and biphasic cultural procedures were described and illustrated for the preparation of spores of *Clostridium botulinum* types A and B, including the cleaning of the harvested spore crops. Fortification of the sporogenic medium with yeast extract (0.1 percent) significantly enhanced the spore yield, whereas the addition of $NaHCO_3$ (0.1 percent) substantially increased spore germination and outgrowth. The first two techniques produced 10^8 to 10^9 spores per ml. in the washed stock suspensions, while the biphasic method yielded only 10^7 per ml. for strain 62A, the only organism tested. The addition of arginine or $MnCl_2$ in the liquid phase of the latter method did not augment sporogenesis, but the addition of thiamine-HCl (0.001 mg./ml.) increased spore production by some 25 percent over the aqueous control. The radiation resistance of the spore crops was affected by the method used for producing spores and their heat resistance was influenced by the sporulation medium.

Introduction

Considerable literature has accumulated on the physiology of spore production of the genus *Bacillus*. In contrast, comparatively little has been reported on this subject concerning *Clostridium*. Apparently, many investigators have been reluctant to work with organisms which require more complex conditions for growth and sporulation.

Perkins (*45*) has recently provided an excellent review of the requirements and techniques used for producing clostridial spores, including *C. botulinum*. Usually, microbiologists have utilized cooked or uncooked infusions or enzymic digests of fresh animal or plant tissues, with or without the addition of tissue particles, and usually fortified with dehydrated animal or plant protein hydrolysates. Examples of such tissue media include beef infusion (*7*), pea infusion digest, veal infusion digest, brain medium (*17*), nutrient broth-liver tissue (*42*), pork infusion (*49*), beef-heart infusion (*61*), liver infusion (*62*), or digest (*63*).

Such complex media are difficult and time consuming to prepare; when used with tissue particles, harvesting the resulting spore crop becomes inefficient, and cleaning the spores is an even more troublesome chore. Furthermore, it is not certain that these homemade brews are superior to simpler, readily available media.

Sporogenesis of anaerobes has been obtained with commercially available peptones, usually supplemented with other constituents. For example, *C. botulinum* spores were successfully produced in beef extract-peptone (*38*), blood agar, and tryptone-meat extract-yeast extract (*51*), trypticase-peptone-yeast extract (*52*), trypticase-peptone (*56*), casitone-peptone (*60*), basamin, phytone, polypeptone, thiotone, yeast extract, and beef-heart casein (*64*), trypticase (*68*), and brain-heart infusion (*72*). The value of these relatively simple solutions of the dehydrated products were discussed by Perkins (*45*). The latter also reviewed the role of pH, temperature, minerals, growth factors, and glucose on clostridial sporulation.

A number of investigators have attempted to elucidate the growth requirements of *C. botulinum* in chemically defined media (*7, 8, 9, 12, 13, 16, 18, 34, 35, 36, 40, 46, 53, 71*). Only Williams and Blair (*71*) reported sporulation in their medium. Perkins and Tsuji (*46*), however, could not duplicate their findings with strain 62A. They succeeded in making the medium sporogenic by modifying its composition. A solution of 17 amino acids, three vitamins, glucose, and seven salts gave excellent growth but negligible spore yields. But when the arginine content of the medium was increased sevenfold, 70 percent sporulation occurred after 7 days of incubation at 30° C.

Our involvement in the radiation food program necessitates our utilization of *C. botulinum* spores as an index of radiation efficiency. Hence, this communication reviews some of our experiences in the production of types A and B spores.

Materials and Methods

Test organisms.—Five type A and five type B strains of *C. botulinum* were selected from a total of 102 strains screened for radioresistance (*2*). These strains represented groups of the most tolerant (33A, 36A, 40B, 41B, 53B), least tolerant (51B), and of intermediate

(62A, 77A, 12885A, 9B) tolerance to gamma radiation in a model system.

Spore preparation: Conventional methods.— Prior to the preparation of spore crops for use in our irradiated inoculated packs, four liquid media were tested for their capability of producing large numbers of spores from strains 33A, 62A, 12885A, 9B, 40B, and 41B. The media were those of Schmidt and Nank (56), 5 percent BBL trypticase, 0.5 percent Difco peptone, 0.05 percent sodium thioglycolate, pH 7.2; Brown et al. (5), 10 percent trypticase, 0.1 percent sodium thioglycolate, pH 7.2; Kempe et al. (33), 10 percent Difco casitone, 0.5 percent Difco beef extract, 0.5 percent Na_2HPO_4; Gibbs and Hirsch (26), 0.3 percent BBL yeast extract, 1.0 percent peptone, 1.0 percent beef extract, 1 percent ascorbic acid, 0.5 percent sodium acetate, 0.05 percent cysteine, 0.1 percent soluble starch.

Each broth was tested in 40 ml. volume, contained in 25 x 200 mm. tubes, inoculated with 2 ml. of a heat shocked (80° C. for 10 min.), cooled (to about 30° C.) stock spore suspension. The cultures were incubated at 30° C. in a desiccator made anaerobic with pyrogallol and Na_2CO_3 (1 g. of each compound per 100 ml. of air space dissolved in warm tapwater). A culture of each strain was harvested by centrifugation after 3, 10, and 17 days of incubation; the pellets were suspended in 5 ml. of distilled water, smears were prepared over an area of 1 cm^2, and stained with Snyder's technique (58). On the basis of qualitative microscopic examination of 20 random fields per smear, the trypticase-peptone (TP) broth of Schmidt and Nank (56) yielded the highest number of spores with four of the six strains (33A, 62A, 12885A, 40B). Three days of incubation gave the least satisfactory results, whereas incubation for 10 or 17 days yielded equivalent, maximum spore populations.

Based upon the above observations, the following method was used for producing large spore crops of each of the 10 strains. The TP broth was distributed in quantities of 20 ml. in 20 x 150 mm. tubes, 130 ml. in 150-ml. bottles, 450 ml. in 500-ml. flasks and 190 ml. in 250-ml. polypropylene centrifuge bottles containing a teaspoonful of glass beads. Only screwcap containers were used. They were steamed and quickly cooled to about 30° C. immediately before inoculation in order to drive off dissolved oxygen.

A 2-ml. heat-shocked and cooled stock spore suspension was inoculated into a tube of broth and was incubated for 24 hours. Daily transfers (2 ml.) for 2 additional days produced vigorous growth of all strains. On the next transfer, 12 ml. were added to the bottle and incubated for 24 hours. Successive transfers were continued at the 10 percent (v/v) level at 24-hour intervals, thus ensuring rapid and heavy growth with a minimum of headspace for the maintenance of anaerobiosis. No additional anaerobic precautions were necessary. The centrifuge bottles were incubated for 7 to 12 days, depending on the experience accumulated over the years with each of the 10 strains (table 1). The number of centrifuge bottles required per strain also varied, as indicated in table 1, by the total quantities of TP broth used. It was easier, more productive, and less hazardous to distribute the sporulation medium in a large number of centrifuge bottles rather than handle a large volume of broth in a single container. The use of sporogenic media in carboy-size quantities has been anomalous; spore yields were usually lower. Apparently, it is more difficult to maintain anaerobic conditions throughout the large quantity of medium, even when a mixture of 95 percent N_2 and 5 percent CO_2 is bubbled into the broth. More frequent contamination problems were also encountered in carboy cultures.

In addition to our studies on the use of botulinal spores as an indicator of radiation effectiveness in inoculated packs, we also conducted fundamental investigations on the organism. For this purpose, the above procedure was recently modified to utilize, as nearly as possible, a "synchronous" vegetative cell inoculum for sporulation.

The modified method followed the suggestion of Halvorson (30) that the vegetative cells of the final inoculum should be of the same physiological age to ensure nearly complete sporulation. Three media were used: (a) 3.0 percent BBL thiotone, 0.05 percent sodium thioglycolate, 0.1 percent $NaHCO_3$, pH 7.0 (buffered with 0.1 M N-tris (hydroxymethyl)) methyl-2-amino enthanesulfonic acid), and contained in 20-ml. amounts of 20 x 150 mm. screwcap tubes; (b) 5.0 percent trypticase, 0.5 percent peptone, 0.125 percent K_2HPO_4, pH 7.5 (adjusted with 5.5 N-KOH) and distributed in 130-ml. lots in screwcap milk dilution bottles; and (c) the latter medium supplemented with 0.5 percent BBL yeast extract and contained in 170-ml. volumes in 250-ml. screwcap centrifuge bottles. All the media were steamed to drive off dissolved oxygen, cooled rapidly to about 37° C., inoculated in 10 percent (v/v) amounts, and incubated at 37° C. This temperature was chosen because the rate of spore germination of strain 62A was more rapid at 37° C. than at 30° C.; 80 percent of the spores germinated (stained with 0.5 percent methylene blue) within 2 hours at 37° C., whereas only 50 percent of the spores germinated at 30° C.

The initial inoculum consisted of a heat-shocked and cooled spore suspension of strain 62A, inoculated into medium (a) and incubated for 8 hours. This young culture is transferred to the same medium, incubated for 4 hours, then transferred to medium (b). After 4 hours of incubation, it was finally inoculated into centrifuge bottles of sporulating medium (c), and incubated for 6 days.

Dialysis membrane technique.—Dialysis sacs immersed in nutrient media have been used successfully for the production of bacterial vegetative cells (21, 22, 23, 24, 28, 31, 39, 42, 50), toxins (3, 10, 19, 25, 27, 37, 41, 47, 55, 59, 67, 69, 70) and enzymes (32, 54), mammalian cells (15), and for studies on microbial antibiosis (20, 55) and symbiosis (43, 44). A chance observation on the propagation pattern of a botulinal vegetative-cell inoculum in a cellophane tube, disclosed the presence of spores in smears made from the confined contents. A closer investigation of this phenomenon led to the following procedure for the preparation of large populations of C. botulinum spores.

The culture apparatus and the technique were described and illustrated in detail elsewhere (57). It consisted, essentially, of an intussuscepted cellophane tube (of pore size 0.0024 to 0.003μ) containing a vegetative-cell inoculum suspended in saline, and immersed in a large glass container of the sporogenic broth. The test organisms used were strains 33A, 41B and 51B, and the five media studied included TP broth. Incubations were carried out at 30° C.

A 30-ml. dense culture of the organism, obtained from a heat-shocked and cooled spore suspension, was transferred at 2-hour intervals for three consecutive periods into 300 ml. of sporogenic broth. The final inoculum was incubated for 5 to 6 hours, centrifuged, resuspended in 50 ml. of saline, and the entire contents transferred into the dialysis sac. The sac was placed in 350 ml. of appropriate sporulation medium. Just before inoculation the apparatus and its contents were steamed for 20 minutes and cooled; immediately after seeding, sterile 95 percent N_2–5 percent CO_2 was bubbled through the broth for 10 minutes. Sporulation was checked periodically by the most probable number technique.

Biphasic culture technique.—Currently, we are investigating the effectiveness of producing botulinal spores by the biphasic culture method. This is a special case of the above dialysis system whereby nutrients migrate across a solid-liquid interface. The procedure consists of a layer of nutrient agar completely covered with a smaller volume of liquid containing the inoculum. This technic was first reported by Hestrin et al. (32), for the production of levan by *Aerobacter levanicum*. It was then used for growing large numbers of bacterial vegetative cells (4, 24, 65) and spores of *C. botulinum* type E (6).

Our method was as follows. A 2500-ml. Fernbach flask containing 1,000 ml. of sporogenic agar (5 percent BBL trypticase, 0.5 percent Difco peptone, 0.1 percent BBL yeast extract, 0.125 percent K_2HPO_4, 3 percent agar, pH 7.5) was overlaid with 500 ml. of distilled water containing 0.1 percent of sodium thioglycolate and seeded with 50 ml. of a vigorously growing culture of strain 62A. No additional anaerobic precautions were taken. The inoculum was prepared from a heat-shocked spore suspension, grown 8 hours and subsequently subcultured twice at 4-hour intervals. Incubation was at 37° C. up to 5 days. For comparison, the water phase was supplemented with thiamine-HCl (14), $MnCl_2$ (11), K_2HPO_4 (38), or arginine (46), and spore development was followed periodically.

Cleaning of spore crops.—The most efficient sporogenic procedures still produce mixtures of spores in various stages of development, vegetative cells, and debris. Depending on the need, a number of cleaning technics of varying degrees of complexity have been developed. In addition to the methods reviewed by Grecz et al. (29) other methods have been described. Uehara et al. (66) used preliminary filtration through paper and millipore membranes followed by repeated prolonged cold storage and pipette separation of layers of centrifuged pellets. Powers (48) successfully used lysozyme with shaking (only 60 min. at 3° C.) which caused vegetative cells to clump, followed by filtration through a millipore membrane and centrifugation; no further washing was required to obtain practically 100 percent free refractile spores.

Our inoculated pack studies do not require spore inocula of a high degree of purity, since they are contained in a "dirty" (food) environment. Hence, the spore crop was harvested by centrifugation at 3,000 r.p.m. for 20 minutes at 2° to 5° C., the pellets pooled into two to three centrifuge bottles, washed twice by alternate centrifugation and resuspension in sterile distilled water, and finally deposited in a screwcap milk dilution bottle containing a teaspoonful of glass beads. The stock spore suspension was concentrated in a volume of 100 to 110 ml. of water and stored at 2° to 5° C.

For physiological studies, the spore culture was centrifuged at 2° to 5° C., and then washed by four to five repeated cycles of resuspension and centrifugation in glass-distilled water. To eliminate vegetative cells and debris, the washed pellet was mixed with an enzyme mixture consisting of trypsin (50 $\mu g./ml.$) and lysozyme (100 $\mu g./ml.$) in 0.05 M K_2HPO_4, pH 8.1. The mixture was incubated at 45° C. for 60 minutes and washed again as above for 10 to 12 more cycles. Clean spores were suspended in distilled water to approximately $10^9/ml.$ and stored at 2° to 5° C.

Results and Discussions

"Conventional" sporulation methods.—The conventional method for producing spores yields, in a typical preparation, approximately 10^9 spores/ml.

Table 1.—Spore populations of *Clostridium botulinum* types A and B produced by conventional culture

Strain number	Volume (milliliter) of sporogenic medium[1]	Days of incubation at 30° to 32° C.	Final volume (milliliter) of harvested suspension[2]	Harvested spore population per milliliter[3]		Percent viable spores
				Unheated	Heated[4]	
33A	5,600	7	109	7.6×10^8	1.2×10^9	158.0
36A	9,000	12	104	5.0×10^9	2.0×10^9	40.0
62A	4,600	7	105	1.7×10^9	1.0×10^9	58.8
77A	3,400	7	105	5.6×10^9	2.9×10^9	51.8
12885A	4,800	7	105	1.6×10^9	1.7×10^9	106.3
9B	7,600	11	106	2.4×10^9	1.3×10^9	54.2
40B	5,600	7	105	2.0×10^9	2.0×10^9	100.0
41B	8,400	11	105	2.2×10^8	9.0×10^8	409.0
51B	5,400	7	105	2.3×10^8	1.2×10^8	52.2
53B	5,400	10	105	2.0×10^8	2.9×10^8	145.0

[1]TP broth: BBL trypticase 5.0 percent, Difco peptone 0.5 percent, sodium thioglycolate 0.05 percent, pH 7.2.

[2]Spores suspended in distilled water.

[3]Colony counts were made in 12 x 200 mm. tubes with TPY agar: BBL trypticase 5.0 percent, Difco peptone 0.5 percent, yeast extract 0.5 percent, soluble starch 0.1 percent, glucose 0.01 percent, K_2HPO_4 0.125 percent, sodium thioglycolate 0.05 percent, agar 1.5 percent, pH 7.2; 0.3 ml. of 5 percent millipore-filtered $NaHCO_3$ was added to each culture tube before inoculation. Quintuplicate tubes of the proper dilutions were incubated at 30° to 32° C. for 48 hours, and the colonies averaged.

[4]An aliquot of the crop was heated at 80° C. for 10 minutes and cooled.

of stock suspension for eight of the 10 strains tested, or 10^{11} total spores per culture (table 1). Strains 51B and 53B yielded approximately 10^8 spores/ml., or a total of 10^{10} spores per culture. Six of the strains required 7 days of incubation and the remainder of the organisms required 10 to 12 days to attain equivalent spore densities. Using volume of sporogenic medium as a criterion, it appears that strains 62A, 77A, and 12885A formed spores most readily, followed by strains 33A and 40B; the rest of the strains sporulated with more difficulty.

Five of the strains formed about 50 percent viable spores, while the remainder of the cultures (33A, 12885A, 40B, 41B, 53B) consisted primarily of 100-percent heat-resistant spores. Presumably, nonsporulating vegetative cells of the latter five crops were nonviable or had lysed in the process of handling. Spores of strain 41B, which increased by 409 percent after heat shock, may have required, in this instance, a heat-activation treatment for germination and outgrowth, or the finding may merely reflect an unforseen counting error. Examination of other harvested spore crops of strain 41B did not duplicate the exceptionally high percentage yield of viable spores (table 2). But eight of the nine additional harvests did produce 100 percent heat-resistant spores.

The "synchronous" vegetative-cell inoculum method for producing spores of strain 62A was followed by microscopic examination of the cultures and total viable and heat-resistant (survival at 80° C. for 10 min.) colony counts. After 2 hours of incubation, 99 percent of the initial spore inoculum became heat sensitive, 83 percent became stainable, and the culture lost 57 percent of its original optical density. Elongated cells first appeared at 2 hours, and progressed into dividing vegetative cells by 6 hours. In 8 hours the culture contained 0.116 percent spores

(table 3). At the second transfer the spore population was 0.003 percent within 4 hours of incubation and at the third transfer the trypticase-peptone culture consisted mainly of actively dividing vegetative cells (0.00009 percent spores). Yeast extract was omitted from the latter medium, since we have demonstrated that it enhances sporulation (table 6). At this stage we desired a minimum of spores. The vigorously growing culture was inoculated into the sporogenic medium. After 6 days of incubation 86 percent heat-resistant spores were obtained. Daily microscopic examinations and pH determinations were used to follow changes in the sporulating culture (table 4). The number of refractile spores continued to increase up to 6 days of incubation, while the pH of the medium decreased slightly in 24 hours, remained constant for 4 days, and slowly began to rise.

That $NaHCO_3$ enhanced the germination rate of strain 62A is indicated in table 5. Thus, the incorporation of $NaHCO_3$ enabled more of the population to

Table 2.—Spore populations of *Clostridium botulinum* strain 41B produced by conventional culture

Spore crop	Harvested spore population per milliliter (x 10^{-8})[1]		Percent viable spores
	Unheated	Heated[2]	
1	3.8	3.3	87.6
2	3.0	4.3	143.3
3	6.0	7.6	126.7
4	4.4	5.0	113.6
5	4.5	4.9	108.9
6	3.7	4.1	110.8
7	7.2	8.0	111.1
8	6.1	6.9	113.1
9	1.9	2.0	105.3

[1]See table 1, footnote 3.

[2]80° C. for 10 minutes.

Table 3.—Spore population of *Clostridium botulinum* strain 62A produced from a synchronous vegetative inoculum

Hours of incubation at 37° C.	Total viable count[1] (x 10⁷) at transfer Number			
	1[2]	2[2]	3[3]	4[4]
0	1.1	1.0	0.57	0.64
4	----------	5.7	7.0	----------
			[5](0.003)	[5](0.00009)
8	11.0	--		
	[5](0.116)			
144	--			14.2
				[5](86)

[1]Colony counts were made in 12 x 200 mm. tubes with thiotone agar: 3. percent BBL thiotone, 0.05 percent sodium thioglycolate, 0.85 percent ionagar, 0.3 ml./tube of millipore-filtered 5 percent NaHCO₃, pH 7.0.

[2]3.0 percent thiotone, 0.05 percent sodium thioglycolate, 0.1 percent NaHCO₃, pH 7.0 buffered with 0.1 M "tris".

[3]5.0 percent trypticase, 0.5 percent peptone, 0.125 percent K₂HPO₄, pH 7.5 adjusted with 5.5 N KOH.

[4]Identical to "footnote 3" and supplemented with 0.5 percent yeast extract.

[5]Percent spores; samples were heat-shocked at 80° C. for 10 min. prior to making colony counts in thiotone agar.

Table 4.—Rate of sporulation of *Clostridium botulinum* strain 62A grown from a synchronous vegetative inoculum

Days of incubation at 37° C.	Refractile spores percent	pH of sporulating culture
0	0	7.4
1	18	7.1
2	42	7.1
3	65	7.1
4	70	7.1
5	75	7.2
6	84	7.3

Table 5.—Effect of NaHCO₃ in growth medium on germination of spores of *Clostridium botulinum* strain 62A

Medium[1]	Constituents	Percent (W/V)	Germination[2]
A	Trypticase	5.0	9
	Peptone	0.5	
	Yeast extract	do	
	K₂HPO₄	0.125	
B	A	As above	73
	NaHCO₃	0.1	
C	Thiotone	3.0	6
	Sodium thioglycolate	0.05	
D	C	As above	86
	NaHCO₃	0.1	

[1]Initial pH 7.0.
[2]Percent cells stainable with 0.5 percent methylene blue in 2 hours at 37° C.

a low of 6 to 86 percent merely by supplementation with 0.1 percent of NaHCO₃ (medium D). This observation is in agreement with the findings of Andersen (*1*) and Wynne et al. (*73*) that supplementation of a medium with NaHCO₃ produced more rapid outgrowth of botulinal spores.

The fortification of medium A with yeast extract significantly increased the sporogenic capability of this medium (table 6). The addition of 0.1 percent of yeast extract increased the spore yield from 4 to 56 percent in 3 days and from 23 to 86 percent in 6 days. Increasing the yeast extract concentration to 0.5 percent did not improve the sporulation potential of the broth.

Dialysis membrane sporulation method.—Unlike other sporogenesis methods, harvesting the dense growth from the dialysis sac was very easy; only one centrifuge bottle was required. The resulting harvested and washed crop contained about 10⁸ spores/ml., or a total of 10¹⁰ spores, after 10 days of incubation (table 7). Repeated studies indicated that

Table 6.—Effect of yeast extract on sporogenesis of *Clostridium botulinum* strain 62A

Medium	Constituents	Percent (W/V)	Percent refractile spores in	
			3 days	6 days
A	Trypticase	5.0	4	23
	Peptone	0.5		
	K₂HPO₄	0.125		
	pH 7.0			
B	A	As above	56	86
	Yeast extract	0.1		
C	A	As above	60	82
	Yeast extract	0.5		

Table 7.—Spore populations of *Clostridium botulinum* types A and B produced in an intussuscepted dialysis sac[12]

Strain Number	Days of incubation at 30° to 32° C.	Harvested spore population per milliliter[3]
33A	10	7.4 x 10⁸
	10	4.5 x 10⁸
41B	3	2.7 x 10⁷
	4	2.7 x 10⁶
	10	1.7 x 10⁸
	19	7.4 x 10⁷
51B	3	7.4 x 10⁵
	7	7.4 x 10⁷
	10	2.8 x 10⁸

[1]Data obtained from Schneider et al. (*57*).
[2]The sac was immersed in TP broth (see table 1, footnote 1, for composition).
[3]Spore volume was 100 ml. Counts were made by the most probable number technique on heat-shocked (80° C. for 10 min.) aliquots. Quintuplicate tubes of Wynne's broth (*73*) were inoculated with 1.0 ml. of ten-fold dilutions and incubated at 30° to 32° C. for 6 weeks. Maximum growth usually occurred within 2 weeks.

start growing at the same time. The trypticase medium A, without NaHCO₃, had only 9 percent spore germination in 2 hours of incubation whereas the addition of 0.1 percent NaHCO₃ (medium B) produced 73 percent germination in the same time period. In medium C, the germination increased from

incubation for longer or shorter periods in TP broth produced fewer spores.

The morphology of these spores appeared unusual, including such characteristics as enlarged size, dumbbell-shaped sporangia, and semistainable zones at their surfaces (57). Radiation resistance studies were conducted on these spore crops by the method of Anellis and Koch (2) and compared with the resistance of conventionally produced spores. Using strain 33A as a representative of type A, the radiation D value of the "dialysis" spores was 84 percent of the resistance of the "conventional" spores for the first crop produced, and 64 percent of the resistance for the second crop (table 8). Strain 41B provided a

Table 8.—Comparative radiation resistance of *Clostridium botulinum* spores produced conventionally and in dialysis sacs[1]

| Strain Number | Spore crop | Radiation D values (Mrad)[2] | | Ratio (percent) B/A |
		Conventional (A)	Dialysis sac (B)	
33A	1	0.338	0.283	83.7
	2	.330	.212	64.2
41B	1	.301	.266	88.4
	2	.334	.256	76.6

[1]Data obtained from Schneider et al. (57).
[2]Procedure followed was that of Anellis and Koch (2).

similar situation; the "first dialysis" crop was 88 percent as resistant and the second crop was 77 percent as resistant as the "conventional" spores.

Due to the apparent lower radioresistance of "dialysis" spores, the method has been abandoned for the production of such spores for inoculated pack studies. However, it promises to be a fruitful technic for nutritional, morphological, physiological, and toxicological investigations of *C. botulinum* and other micro-organisms.

Biphasic culture sporulation method.—Various liquid phases were compared for their sporogenic properties when used with the trypticase-peptone-yeast extract agar solid phase (table 9). Arginine yielded the smallest quantity (34.2 percent) of strain 62A spores; $MnCl_2$ gave higher numbers of spores (56 percent), and was identical with the concentration provided by water alone; and thiamine-HCl produced 76 percent spores after 5 days at 37° C. The use of K_2HPO_4 (8.71 mg./ml.) as the liquid overlay resulted in so many clumps of spores and vegetative cells that counts were not attempted.

A closer examination of the sporulation process was conducted with the aqueous thiamine-HCl liquid phase. Maximum sporogenesis developed within 3 days (table 10). On the third day refractile spores numbered 78 percent, and on the fifth day, 80 percent. The heat-resistant (80° C. for 10 min.) spore population was 76 percent of the total (unheated) count. Bruch et al. (6), using *C. botulinum* type E strains, reported 95 percent sporulation in their biphasic culture system, with spore crops from 10^7 to 5×10^8/ml.

The biphasic system is attractive in its simplicity, hence, it is being actively investigated in our laboratory. If the radiation resistance of the spores produced by this method is equivalent to those obtained by the

Table 10.—Rate of sporulation of *Clostridium botulinum* strain 62A in biphasic culture

| Days of incubation at 37° C. | Refractile spores percent | Harvested spore population per milliliter (x 10^7)[1] | | |
		Unheated	Heated[2]	Percent viable spores
0	0			
2	57			
3	78			
5	80	8.7	6.6	76

[1]See table 3, footnote 1.
[2]80° C. for 10 minutes.

Table 9.—Spore population of *Clostridium botulinum* strain 62A produced in biphasic culture[1]

| Liquid phase[2] | Aqueous concentration milligram per milliliter | Harvested spore population per milliliter (x 10^7)[3] | | |
		Unheated	Heated[4]	Percent viable spores
Water		7.25	3.9	53.7
Thiamine-HCL	0.001	8.75	6.63	75.8
$MnCl_2$	.002	9.25	5.18	56.0
Arginine	11.67	2.85	.98	34.2
K_2HPO_4	8.71	([5])		

[1]Solid phase: 5 percent BBL trypticase, 0.5 percent Difco peptone, 0.1 percent BBL yeast extract, 0.125 percent K_2HPO_4, 3.0 percent agar, pH 7.5.
[2]Total volume is 500 ml. +50 ml. inoculum.
[3]See table 3, footnote 1.
[4]80° C. for 10 min.
[5]No counts were made since microscopic examination showed that spores and vegetative cells were badly clumped.

conventional technic, we shall attempt to improve the spore yields with this newer process.

Resistance of spores to the environment can be affected both by the sporogenic procedure used and by the sporulation medium. Table 8 indicates a change in radioresistance due to a change in the method for producing spores in the same medium; we did not determine the heat resistance of the two types of spores. However, Tsuji and Perkins (64), among others, showed a dramatic effect on thermal sensitivity merely by producing spores in different media with the same "conventional" method (table 11). Hence, one must bear in mind the purpose for which the spores are intended before indiscriminately selecting a procedure and medium for sporogenesis.

Table 11.—Effect of sporulation medium on heat resistance of *Clostridium botulinum* strain 62A spores[1]

Sporulation medium	D_{240} value (minutes at 240° F.)
Basamin	0.46
Beef heart casein	.57
Phytone	.34
Thiotone	.42
Polypeptone	.77
Trypticase	.30
Yeast extract	.32

[1]Data obtained from Tsuji and Perkins (64).

References

(1) ANDERSEN, A. A. 1951. A rapid plate method of counting spores of *Clostridium botulinum*. J. Bateriol. 62: 425–432.

(2) ANELLIS, A., and R. B. KOCH. 1962. Comparative resistance of strains of *Clostridium botulinum* to gamma rays. Appl. Microbiol. 10: 326–330.

(3) BARRON, A. L., and G. B. REED. 1954. *Clostridium botulinum* type E toxin and toxoid. Can. J. Microbiol. 1: 108–117.

(4) BIRCH-HIRSCHFELD, L. 1934. The activity of extracts of staphylococci grown on cellophane-covered agar. Z. Immunitatsforsch. 81: 260–285.

(5) BROWN, W. L., Z. J. ORDAL, and H. O. HALVORSON. 1957. Production and cleaning of spores of putrefactive anaerobe 3679. Appl. Microbiol. 5: 156–159.

(6) BRUCH, M. K., C. W. BOHRER, and C. B. DENNY. 1967. Adaptation of biphasic culture technique to the sporulation of *Clostridium botulinum* type E. J. Food Science 33: 108–109.

(7) BURROWS, W. 1932. Growth of *Clostridium botulinum* on casein hydrolysate and on hydrolysate preparations. J. Inf. Dis. 51: 293–308.

(8) BURROWS, W. 1933. Growth of *Clostridium botulinum* on synthetic mediums. J. Inf. Dis. 52: 126–137.

(9) BURROWS, W. 1934. Growth stimulating properties of cystine and tryptophane. J. Inf. Dis. 54: 164–170.

(10) CARNOT, P., and L. FOURNIER. 1900. Recherches sur le pneumocoque et ses toxines. Arch. Med. Exptl. 12: 357–378

(11) CHARNEY, J., W. P. FISHER, and C. P. HEGARTY. 1951. Manganese as an essential element for sporulation in the genus *Bacillus*. J. Bacteriol. 62: 145–148.

(12) CLIFTON, C. E. 1939. Utilization of amino acids by *Clostridium botulinum*. Proc. Soc. Exptl. Biol. Med. 40: 338–340.

(13) CLIFTON, C. E. 1940. The utilization of amino acids and of glucose by *Clostridium botulinum*. J. Bacteriol. 39: 485–497.

(14) DAY, L. E., and R. N. COSTILOW. 1964. Physiology of the sporulation process in *Clostridium botulinum*. I. Correlation of morphological changes with catabolic activities, synthesis of dipicolinic acid, and development of heat resistance. 88: 690–694.

(15) EAGLE, H. 1960. The sustained growth of human and animal cells in a protein-free environment. Proc. Natl. Acad. Sci. U.S. 46: 427–432.

(16) ELBERG, S. S., and K. F. MEYER. 1939. The nutritional requirements of *Clostridium parabotulinum* A. J. Bacteriol. 37: 429–445.

(17) ESTY, J. R., and K. F. MEYER. 1922. The heat resistance of the spores of B. botulinus and allied anaerobes. XI. J. Inf. Dis. 31: 650–663.

(18) FILDES, P. 1935. Tryptophane and sporogenes vitamin requirements of B. botulinus. Brit. J. Exptl. Pathol. 16: 309–314.

(19) FREDETTE, V., and G. VINET. 1952. Production en sac de cellophane de toxines tetaniques renfermant au moins 600,000 doses mortelles (cobaye) par millilitre. Can. J. Med. Science 30: 155–56.

(20) FROST, W. D. 1904. The antagonism exhibited by certain saprophytic bacteria against the *Bacillus typhosa*, Gaffky. J. Inf. Dis. 1: 599–640.

(21) GALLUP, D. M., and P. GERHARDT. 1961. Concentrated culture of bacteria in dialysis flasks and fermentor systems. Bacteriol. Proc. p. 52.

(22) GALLUP, D. M., and P. GERHARDT. 1963. Dialysis fermentor systems for concentrated culture of microorganisms. Appl. Microbiol. 11: 506–512.

(23) GERHARDT, P., and D. M. GALLUP. 1963. Dialysis flask for concentrated culture of microorganisms. J. Bacteriol. 86: 919–929.

(24) GERHARDT, P., and C. G. HEDEN. 1960. Concentrated culture of gonococci in clear medium. Proc. Soc. Exptl. Biol. Med. 105: 49–51.

(25) GERWING, J., C. E. DOLMAN, and D. A. ARNOTT. 1961. Purification and activation of *Clostridium botulinum* type E toxin. J. Bacteriol. 81: 819–822.

(26) GIBBS, B. M., and A. HIRSH. 1956. Spore formation by *Clostridium* species in an artificial medium. J. Appl. Bacteriol. 19: 129–141.

(27) GLADSTONE, G. P. 1948. Immunity to anthrax. Production of the cell-free protective antigen in cellophane sacs. Brit. J. Exptl. Pathol. 29: 379–389.

(28) GORELICK, A. N., D. D. MEAD, and E. H. KELLY. 1951. The growth of bacteria in a charcoal cellophane system. J. Bacteriol. 61: 507–513.

(29) GRECZ, N., A. ANELLIS, and M. D. SCHNEIDER. 1962. Procedure for cleaning of *Clostridium botulinum* spores. J. Bacteriol. 84: 552–558.

(30) HALVORSON, H. O. 1957. Rapid and simultaneous sporulation. J. Appl. Bacteriol. 20: 305–314.

(31) HARMSEN, G. W., and W. J. KOLFF. 1947. Cultivation of microorganisms with the aid of cellophane membranes. Science 105: 582–583.

(32) HESTRIN, S., S. AVINERI-SHAPIRO, and M. ASCHNER. 1943. The enzymic production of levan. Biochem. J. 37: 450–456.

(33) KEMPE, L. L., J. T. GRAIKOSKI, and R. A. GILLIES. 1954. Gamma ray sterilization of canned meat previously inoculated with anaerobic spores. Appl. Microbiol. 2: 330–332.

(34) KINDLER, S. H., and J. MAGER. 1956. Nutritional studies with the Clostridium botulinum group. J. Gen. Microbiol. 15: 386–393.

(35) KINDLER, S. H., J. MAGER, and N. GROSSOWICZ. 1955. Production of toxin by resting cells of C. parabotulinum type A. Science 122: 926–927.

(36) KINDLER, S. H., J. MAGER, and N. GROSSOWICZ. 1956. Toxin production by Clostridium parabotulinum type A. J. Gen. Microbiol. 15: 394–403.

(37) KOCH, W., and D. KAPLAN. 1953. A simple method for obtaining highly potent tetanus toxin. J. Immunol. 70: 1–5.

(38) LEIFSON, E. 1931. Bacterial spores. J. Bacteriol. 21: 331–356.

(39) LEWIS, R. W., and E. H. LUCAS. 1945. Apparatus for growing microorganisms on a flowing medium. Science 101: 364–365.

(40) MAGER, J., S. H. KINDLER, and N. GROSSOWICZ. 1954. Nutritional studies with Clostridium parabotulinum type A. J. Gen. Microbiol. 10: 130–141.

(41) McCLEAN, D. 1937. Staphylococcus toxin: factors which control its production in a fluid medium. J. Pathol. Bacteriol. 44: 47–70.

(42) M'EWEN, A. D. 1926. Quarter-evil and braxy: Studies regarding immunity. J. Comp. Pathol. Therap. 39: 253–283.

(43) NURMIKKO, V. 1955. The dialysis technique in the study of the vitamins and amino acids affecting associations of microorganisms. Acta Chem. Scand. 9: 1317–1322.

(44) NURMIKKO, V. 1957. Microbiological determination of vitamins and amino acids produced by microorganisms, using the dialysis cell. Appl. Microbiol. 5: 160–165.

(45) PERKINS, W. E. 1965. Production of clostridial spores. J. Appl. Bacteriol. 28: 1–16.

(46) PERKINS, W. E., and K. TSUJI. 1962. Sporulation of Clostridium botulinum. II. Effect of arginine and its degradation products on sporulation in a synthetic medium. J. Bacteriol. 84: 86–94.

(47) POLSON, A., and M. STERNE. 1946. Production of potent botulinum toxins and formol-toxoids. Nature 158: 238–239.

(48) POWERS, E. M. 1968. Method for obtaining free bacterial spores of Bacillus subtilis var niger. Appl. Microbiol. 16: 180–181.

(49) REED, J. M., C. W. BOHRER, and E. J. CAMERON. 1951. Spore destruction rate studies on organisms of significance in the processing of canned foods. Food Res. 16: 383–408.

(50) RITTER, H. 1949. A method for cultivating Hemophilus influenzae. J. Bacteriol. 57: 474–475.

(51) ROBERTS, T. A. 1967. Sporulation of mesophilic clostridia. J. Appl. Bacteriol. 30: 430–443.

(52) ROBERTS, T. A., and M. INGRAM. 1967. The effect of sporulation medium on heat activation of spores of Cl. botulinum type B. In Botulism 1966: Proc. 5th Intern. Symp. Food Microbiol. Moscow, USSR. Ingram, M., and T. A. Roberts: eds. Chapman & Hall, Ltd., London, pp. 169–175.

(53) ROESSLER, W. G., and C. R. BREWER. 1946. Nutritional studies with Clostridium botulinum toxin types A and B. J. Bacteriol. 51: 571–572.

(54) ROGERS, H. J. 1948. The complexicity of the hyaluronidases produced by microorganisms. Biochem. J. 42: 633–640.

(55) RUFFER, M. A., and M. CRENDIROPOULO. 1900. Contribution to the technique of bacteriology. Brit. Med. J. 2: 1305–1306.

(56) SCHMIDT, C. F., and W. K. NANK. 1960. Radiation sterilization of food. 1. Procedures for the evaluation of the radiation resistance of spores of Clostridium botulinum in food products. Food Res. 25: 321–327.

(57) SCHNEIDER, M. D., N. GRECZ, and A. ANELLIS. 1963. Sporulation of Clostridium botulinum types A, B, and E, Clostridium perfringens, and putrefactive anaerobe 3679, in dialysis sacs. J. Bacteriol. 85: 126–133.

(58) SNYDER, M. A. 1934. A modification of the Dormer spore stain. Stain Technol. 9: 71.

(59) STERNE, M., and L. M. WENTZEL. 1950. A new method for the large-scale production of high titre botulinum formal-toxoid types C and D. J. Immunol. 65: 175–183.

(60) SUGIYAMA, H. 1951. Studies on factors affecting the heat resistance of spores of Clostridium botulinum. J. Bacteriol. 62: 81–96.

(61) TORREY, J. C., N. C. KAHN, and M. H. SALINGER. 1930. The influence of H-ion concentration on the sporulation of B. welchii. J. Bacteriol. 20: 85–98.

(62) TOWNSEND, C. T. 1939. Sporeforming anaerobes causing spoilage in acid-canned foods. Food Res. 4: 231–237.

(63) TOWNSEND, C. T., J. R. ESTY, and F. C. BASELT. 1938. Heat resistance studies on spores of putrefactive anaerobes in relation to determination of safe processes for canned foods. Food Res. 3: 323–346.

(64) TSUJI, K., and W. E. PERKINS. 1962. Sporulation of Clostridium botulinum. I. Selection of an aparticulate sporulation medium. J. Bacteriol. 84: 81–85.

(65) TYRRELL, E. A., R. A. MacDONALD, and P. GERHARDT. 1958. Biphasic systems for growing bacteria in concentrated culture. J. Bacteriol. 75: 1–4.

(66) UEHARA, M., R. S. FUJIOKA, and H. A. FRANK. 1965. Method for obtaining cleaned putrefactive anaerobes 3679 spores. J. Bacteriol. 89: 929–930.

(67) VINET, G., and V. FREDETTE. 1951. Apparatus for the culture of bacteria in cellophane tubes. Science 114: 549–550.

(68) WAGENAAR, R. O., and G. M. DACK. 1958. Factors influencing growth and toxin production in cheese inoculated with spores of Clostridium botulinum types A and B. I. Studies with surface-ripened cheese type I. J. Dairy Sci. 41: 1182–1190.

(69) WENTZEL, L. M., and M. STERNE. 1949. A simple double-surface dialyzing membrane. Science 110: 259.

(70) WENTZEL, L. M., M. STERNE, and A. POLSON. 1950. High toxicity of pure botulinum type D toxin. Nature 166: 739–740.

(71) WILLIAMS, O. B., and E. BLAIR. 1950. Spore formation in synthetic media by Clostridium botulinum. Bacteriol. Proc. pp. 62–63.

(72) WYNNE, E. S. 1948. Physiological studies on spore formation in Clostridium botulinum. J. Inf. Dis. 83: 243–249.

(73) WYNNE, E. S., W. R. SCHMIEDING, and G. T. DAYE, Jr. 1955. A simplified medium for counting Clostridium spores. Food Res. 20: 9–12.

SEROLOGICAL SPECIFICITY OF BOTULINAL TOXINS

by Howard M. Johnson, Bennett G. Smith, Kristen Brenner, Herbert E. Hall, *and* Keith H. Lewis
U.S. Department of Health, Education, and Welfare, Cincinnati, Ohio

Summary

Botulinal antitoxins A, B, and E obtained from several sources were compared by passive hemagglutination (HA), hemagglutination inhibition (HI), and gel diffusion. The serological specificity of each toxin-antitoxin system was demonstrated, although types A and B exhibited considerable cross-reactivity because of the hemagglutinin. Attempts were made to ascertain the relationship between *in vitro* reactions and toxin neutralization in animals. The *in vitro* specificity of type A toxin-antitoxin did not involve neutralizing antibodies. The type B system may involve neutralizing antibodies to some extent, but the lack of a quantitative correlation of HI with toxicity suggested that other factors may be involved. The type E system may involve neutralizing antibodies. Toxic type E cultures were effective, qualitatively and quantitatively, in HI, wheras two atoxic variants were noninhibitory and did not react strongly in gel diffusions.

Introduction

The classification of botulinal toxins into antigenic types is based on animal neutralization tests (2). Neutralization tests, however, do not shed much light on elucidating the complexity of the botulinal system. Biochemical procedures (5) and *in vitro* serological tests (7, 8, 10), for example, suggest that botulinal toxins may be composed of toxic and nontoxic moieties. The various facets of these toxins must be considered in the development of suitable *in vitro* tests. This paper presents some of the *in vitro* serological properties of botulinal toxins types A, B, and E.

Materials and Methods

Toxoid.—Purified botulinal toxoids types A, B, and E were obtained from the U.S. Army Biological Laboratories. Types A and B toxoids were dialyzed against phosphate-buffered saline (PBS), pH 7.2, before use in serological tests.

Antitoxins.—Equine antitoxins to the toxins and toxoids were obtained from the National Communicable Disease Center (NCDC), Atlanta, Ga., and from the Statens Seruminstitut, World Health Organization, Copenhagen, Denmark. Rabbit antitoxins were produced by numerous subcutaneous and intramuscular injections of A, B, and E toxoids contained in complete Freund's adjuvant.

Toxic cultures.—Toxic cultures were obtained originally from NCDC and the U.S. Army Biological Laboratories. Two nontoxigenic variants (810 and 066BNT) of *C. botulinum* type E were obtained from Donald Kautter, Food and Drug Administration. Cultures of types A and B were grown as previously described (8). Type E cultures and type A culture 1168 were grown according to the method of Gordon et al. (4). The type E culture, along with 1168, was grown in cellophane sacs as described previously (1). All culture supernatant fluids were absorbed with formalinized sheep cells prior to use in hemagglutination inhibition tests.

Hemagglutination.—Hemagglutinations (HA) were performed as previously described (7). Briefly, toxoids or toxins were coupled to formalinized sheep red blood cells (SRBC) by bisdiazotized benzidine. The sensitized cells were washed and suspended in a rabbit serum albumin-dextrose-ethylene diaminetetraacetic acid solution (RSA-dex-EDTA) that was prepared as described elsewhere (9). Heat inactivated sera were absorbed with SRBC and serially diluted in RSA-dex-EDTA. Sensitized cells were added to the sera, and hemagglutinations were performed.

Hemagglutination inhibition.—Hemagglutination inhibition (HI) was performed as described by Johnson et al. (8). To 0.25 ml. of twofold serially diluted antitoxin, 0.25 ml. of supernatant botulinal culture fluids, diluted to the appropriate concentration in RSA-dex-EDTA, was added. The antitoxin dilution was based on a final volume of 0.5 ml. Following incubation for 20 minutes at room temperature, HA were carried out. Eightfold or greater reductions in titer by the culture fluids over that of the control were considered as significant inhibitions.

Gel diffusion.—Micro-Ouchterlony gel diffusions were performed with types A and B toxins and antitoxins as previously described (8). Two-by-two lantern slides (2″ x 2″) were used in type E toxin-antitoxin gel diffusion as described by Johnson (6).

Chromatography.—Diethylaminoethycellulose (DEAE-cellulose) chromatography was carried out as described by Gerwing et al. (3), using the 0.067 M citrate phosphate buffer (pH 5.6) containing 0.1 M guanidine acetate.

Gel filtration with Sephadex* G–200 (3 x 50 cm. column) was carried out on a refrigerated (4° C.) Buchler fraction collector. The buffer system was the same as for DEAE-cellulose except that 0.1 M guanidine-HCl replaced guanidine acetate. The flow rate was approximately 20 ml./hr.

Results

Data on comparative hemagglutinations with types A and B botulinal toxoids by corresponding antitoxins from three sources are presented in table 1. In all systems, the homologous reactions were stronger than the heterologous. Cross-reactions with E antitoxins were negligible. The degree of comparative cross-reactivity for the A and B systems is illustrated by the ratio of the homologous to heterologous titers (table 2). In all systems, the ratio of the homologous to heterologous reaction was much greater than 1, demonstrating the specificity of the HA. The degree of cross-reactivity was similar for the different antitoxin systems. The cross-reactivity of type A toxoid-SRBC and type B antitoxin was much greater than the reciprocal cross-reaction.

Data on HA with two ammonium-sulfate-precipitated type E toxins (8E and Beluga) and rabbit and

International equine antitoxins are presented in table 3. The titers were the same for the two toxins. Specific toxicity of Beluga was slightly lower than that of 8E. Cross-reactions with types A and B antitoxins were negligible.

Table 2.—Ratio of homologous to heterologous hemagglutination (HA) titers with types A and B botulinal antitoxins

Antitoxin source	Toxoid	HA titer, homologous/ heterologous
A, rabbit	A/B	1024
B, rabbit	B/A	16
A, NCDC	A/B	>256
B, NCDC	B/A	16
A, international	A/B	512
B, international	B/A	8

HI data with types A and B botulinal cultures and the three sources of antitoxins are presented in table 4. The patterns of inhibition for the different antitoxins were quite similar. Four type A cultures (1168, Hall, CAA, 33), for example, specifically inhibited HA with A antitoxins, although the results with CAA and rabbit anti-type B were equivocal. The degree of inhibition, however, cannot be equated with the degree of toxicity of the culture. Cultures 297 and 1156, although toxic, failed to inhibit HA with the three type A antitoxins. All type B cultures with sufficient toxicity (Beans, 770, 1541) gave significant and specific inhibitions with type B antitoxins. As with type A toxins, however, the degree of inhibition did not appear to be closely related to the degree of toxicity. Culture 41, which was of extremely low toxicity, did not inhibit either the A or B systems. This is in agreement with the limits of sensitivity of inhibition that were established previously (7). Four type E cultures (8E, Beluga, Alaska, Tenno) had no inhibitory effect on the A and B antitoxins.

HI data with type E botulinal cultures and the rabbit and International antitoxins are presented in table 5. Only the toxic cultures inhibited the HA

Table 1.—Passive hemagglutination with types A and B botulinal antitoxins

Toxoid	Antitoxin source	Antitoxin,[1] reciprocal of dilution	
		A	B
A	Rabbit	67,000,000	524,000
B		65,500	8,400,000
A	NCDC, equine	25,600 (0.0004)	3,200 (0.003)
B		<100 (>0.1)	51,200 (0.0002)
A	International Standard, equine	1,640,000 (0.00006)	102,400 (0.001)
B		3,200 (0.03)	820,000 (0.00012)

[1]Values in parentheses indicate the units of antitoxin per milliliter in the end-point tubes. The neutralizing capacities of the rabbit antitoxins were not quantitated.

Table 3.—Passive hemagglutination with type E botulinal toxins and antitoxins

Toxin	LD$_{50}$ per milligram protein	Protein, milligram per milliliter	Antitoxin source	Titer[1]
8E	5.5 x 10^5	0.275	Rabbit	65,500
			International equine	65,500 (0.0015)
Beluga	4.2 x 10^5	.350	Rabbit	65,500
			International equine	65,500 (0.0015)

[1]Values in parentheses indicate the units of antitoxin per milliliter in the end-point tubes. The neutralizing capacity of the rabbit antitoxin was not determined.

*Mention of commercial products does not imply endorsement by the U.S. Department of Health, Education, and Welfare.

Table 4.—Hemagglutination inhibitions with botulinal cultures type A and B

| Culture, type | LD_{50} per 0.25 ml. | Fold reduction in titer[1] | | | | | |
| | | Rabbit antitoxin | | NCDC equine antitoxin | | International equine antitoxin | |
		A	B	A	B	A	B
1168, A_____	600,000	16	4	64	2	128	2
Hall, A[2]_____	14,000	>512	2	>512	2	>512	2
CAA, A_____	6,000	64–128	4–8	32	2–4	32–64	2–4
33, A_____	6,000	32–64	4	16–32	2	64–128	0–4
297, A_____	6,000	2	4	0–2	2	0–2	0–4
1156, A_____	535	0	2–4	0	0–2	0	0
Beans, B[2]____	6,000	0	>512	0	>512	0	>512
770, B_____	10,000	2–4	128–512	2	128	2–4	128–512
1541, B_____	790	0	256	0	256	0	64
41, B_____	6	2–4	2–4	2–4	0–2	0–4	0–2

[1]Eightfold or greater reduction in titer is considered as specific inhibition.　　[2]Strains employed in previous hemagglutinations (4).

Table 5.—Hemagglutination inhibitions with type E botulinal cultures

| Inhibitor | LD_{50}/0.25 ml. | Antigen | Fold reduction in titer | |
			Rabbit antitoxin	International antitoxin
8E_____	80,000	8E_____	4096	>1024
Alaska_____	80,000	_____	>2048	>1024
Beluga_____	80,000	_____	1024	>1024
Tenno_____	250	_____	256	64
810_____	<10	_____	0	0
066BNT_____	<10	_____	0	0
8E_____	80,000	Beluga_____	4096	>1024
Alaska_____	80,000	_____	512	>1024
Beluga_____	80,000	_____	4096	>1024
Tenno_____	250	_____	512	64
810_____	<10	_____	0	0
066BNT_____	<10	_____	0	0

reactions with both 8E and Beluga SRBC antigens. The highly toxic type E cultures, 8E, Alaska and Beluga, inhibited to roughly the same extent, except that Alaska was not as effective against the Beluga-SRBC antigen and rabbit antitoxin. Strain Tenno, which was considerably less toxic, inhibited but to a lesser extent. This does suggest that the degree of inhibition is related roughly to toxicity. The two non-toxigenic variants, 810 and 066BNT, were noninhibitory.

Specificities and serological relationships among types A and B toxins and antitoxins were further studied by micro-Ouchterlony gel diffusions. Figure 1 presents gel diffusion patterns obtained with rabbit types A and B antitoxins and A and B toxoids. The toxoids were from the same lot used in HA. Type A antitoxin produced two lines with its homologous toxoid, the innermost of which showed identity with B toxoid. Type B antitoxin, on the other hand, produced three lines with its homologous toxoid. The middle line showed identity with A toxoid. The inner-

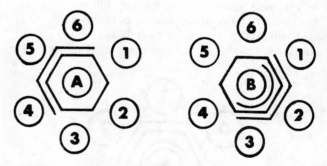

Figure 1.—Diagrammatic representation of gel diffusion reactions of types A and B rabbit antitoxins and their corresponding toxoids. A, rabbit A antitoxin; B, rabbit B antitoxin; 1, 2, 3, B toxoid; 4, 5, 6, A toxoid.

most line was quite weak and could not be reproduced with consistency. The line of identity between the heterologous systems is probably due to the hemagglutinin referred to by Lamanna and Lowenthal (10). NCDC and International antitoxins gave reactions similar to those of rabbit antitoxins, although they were weaker. The innermost line with rabbit type B antitoxin could not be produced with the NCDC and International antitoxins.

Supernatant fluids from the type A cultures employed in the inhibitions in table 4 were also examined by micro-Ouchterlony gel diffusion against rabbit type A antitoxin (fig. 2). The A toxoid as well as strains

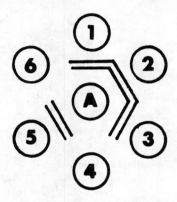

Figure 2.—Diagrammatic representation of gel diffusion reactions of type A rabbit antitoxin and type A botulinal culture fluids. A, rabbit A antitoxin; 1, culture CAA; 2, 5, A toxoid; 3, culture 33; 4, culture 1156; 6, culture 297.

CAA and 33 gave identical reactions. No lines were observed with cultures 297 and 1156 even after numerous ratios of culture and antitoxin were tested. The precipitin reactions, then, are in agreement with the HI data for these cultures. Although not shown, the Hall and 1168 strains produced results identical to A toxoid.

Rabbit type B antitoxin and type B cultures used in HI were also examined by gel diffusion (fig. 3). Culture 770 gave three bands, a reaction identical with that of B toxoid. Although not shown, Bean strain also gave this type of reaction. Culture 1541

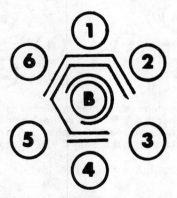

Figure 3.—Diagrammatic representation of gel diffusion reactions of type B rabbit antitoxin and type B botulinal culture fluids. B, rabbit B antitoxin; 1, culture 770; 2, 4, 6, B toxoid; 3, culture 1541; 5, culture 41.

produced only one band, the innermost, with type B antitoxin. It is possible that this is the system involved in HA and HI, since 1541 was an effective inhibitor of HA. Culture 41, which was virtually nontoxic and noninhibitory, produced one precipitin band, which corresponded to the hemagglutinin-antihemagglutinin.

Ouchterlony tests on lantern slides were performed with type E toxins and antitoxins. Figure 4 demon-

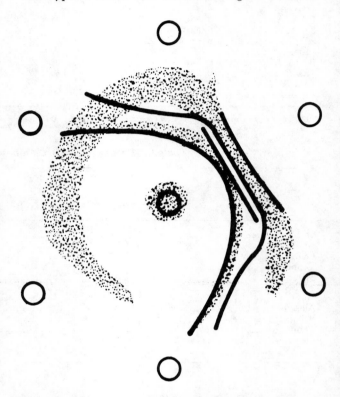

Figure 4.—Diagrammatic representation of gel diffusion reactions of type E rabbit antitoxin and type E botulinal culture fluids. Center well contains antitoxin. Culture fluids in peripheral wells, starting at 12 o'clock, are 8E, Alaska, Beluga, Tenno, 810, and 066BNT.

strates the precipitin patterns with types 8E, Alaska, Beluga, Tenno, 810, and 066BNT cultures against rabbit antitoxin. Four distinct bands were formed with Alaska. Two of the bands showed identity with cultures 8E and Beluga. A diffuse, indistinct band was shared by all of the cultures except Tenno. This band probably plays no significant role in HA and HI since Tenno was inhibitory, whereas 810 and 066BNT were not. A zone of precipitation in the area of the antitoxin well was produced by all of the cultures. This band is probably of no significance to HA and HI. The apparent lack of any observable lines of identity of the Tenno culture with the other three toxic cultures may be attributable to the small amount of antigen present in the Tenno culture.

Ouchterlony tests on lantern slides with International antitoxin and the same cultures used in figure 4 shed further light on the precipitin system (fig. 5).

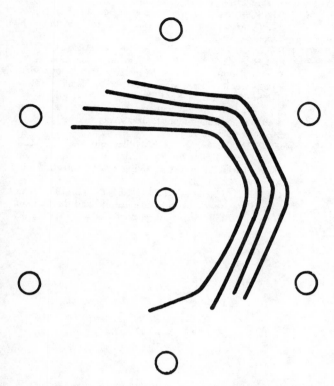

Figure 5.—Diagrammatic representation of gel diffusion reactions of type E International equine antitoxin and type E botulinal culture fluids. Center well contains antitoxin. Culture fluids in peripheral wells, starting at 12 o'clock, are 8E, Alaska, Beluga, Tenno, 810, and 066BNT.

Strains 8E, Alaska, and Beluga showed identity with four precipitin lines. The innermost line also appears with Tenno. The diffuse band, shared by all except Tenno (fig. 4), is not present in this system. Also, the zone in the immediate area of the antitoxin was not observed with the International antitoxin.

Ammonium-sulfate-precipitated sac cultures of type A 1168 and type E Beluga were purified on DEAE-cellulose. A frontal peak similar to that of Gerwing et al. (3) was obtained and was compared with the stock cultures for specific toxicity and serological specificity. Specific toxicities of the two toxins were not significantly different from that of their stocks. The same was also true of their behavior in the the HI tests in which the stock and DEAE-cellulose fractions were used both as antigens and as inhibitors. It is concluded that, from a serological point of view, the DEAE-cellulose chromatographed toxins are not a great deal more purified than those salt-precipitated from sac cultures.

Sephadex (G–200) gel filtration patterns with ammonium-sulfate-precipitated toxin from type A culture 1168 produced several peaks. The bulk of the toxicity was associated with the first peak. Accordingly, the fractions making up this peak were pooled and compared with the stock in terms of specific toxicity and serological specificity in HI tests. The pooled fractions were purified twofold according to specific toxicity. The serological specificities were essentially the same in HI tests in which the pooled fractions and stock were used both as antigens and inhibitors. Thus, neither marked increases in purification nor variation in serological specificities were observed in chromatographically purified toxins.

Discussion

Marked differences in serological specificity were not observed with botulinal antitoxins of a given type. Small variations in HI and gel diffusions were observed, but gross differences in specificity were not observed. The cross-reactions of the types A and B toxins and antitoxins in HA and gel diffusions were probably attributable to the antigenically similar hemagglutinins. Two observations with type A toxin suggested that the HI system was not associated with neutralizing antibodies. First, some toxic cultures did not react in gel diffusions or HA; second, the degree of inhibition of HA by toxic cultures did not appear to be proportional to the toxicity of the cultures.

HI with type B toxic cultures did not unequivocally eliminate the possibility that neutralizing antibodies played a significant role in the HA reaction, since HI was obtained with all of the moderately to highly toxic cultures, but not with strain 41, which was of extremely low toxicity. There seems to be, however, a lack of correlation between the amount of toxicity and inhibitory power. This suggests that substances other than toxin may play a role in the serological specificity of type B toxin. It is possible that the innermost line in gel diffusion with type B cultures may represent the HA system, since all of the cultures that formed it were effective in HI.

HI data with type E toxin correlated roughly with both toxicity and the degree of toxicity and suggest that neutralizing antibodies may play a significant role in serological specificity. It is difficult to compare the HI and gel diffusion data, but the two innermost lines seen in the rabbit antitoxin system (fig. 4) may play a significant role. Tenno did not react with either line in the rabbit system but did show a band with the innermost line in the equine antitoxin system (fig. 5). The apparent lack of a line with Tenno may be attributable to low concentrations of antigen. This culture reacted to a lesser extent than 8E, Alaska, and Beluga in the HI test.

The preliminary data on purification by chromatographic procedures have not shed much light on the nature of serological specificity of the botulinal toxins. Studies along the line of purification and isolation of toxic moieties are continuing.

References

(1) BOROFF, D. A. 1955. Study of toxins of *Clostridium botulinum*. III. Relation of autolysis to toxin production. J. Bacteriol. *70*: 363–367.

(2) DOLMAN, C. E. 1964. Botulism as a world health problem. U.S. Public Health Service Publ. No. 999–FP-1, pp. 5–32.

(3) GERWING, J., C. E. DOLMAN, D. V. KASON, and J. H. TREMAINE. 1966. Purification and characterization of *Clostridium botulinum* type B toxin. J. Bacteriol. *91*: 484–487.

(4) GORDON, M., M. A. FIOCK, A. YARINSKY, and J. T. DUFF. 1957. Studies on immunity to toxins of *Clostridium botulinum*. III. Preparation, purification, and detoxification of type E toxin. J. Bacteriol. *74*: 533–538.

(5) INGRAM, M., and T. A. ROBERTS. 1967. *In* Botulism 1966. Proceedings of the Fifth International Symposium on Food Microbiology: Moscow, July 1966. Chapman & Hall Ltd., London, England.

(6) JOHNSON, A. E. 1967. Microdiffusion agar precipitin technique convenient for viewing and recording. J. Bacteriol. *93*: 1476–1477.

(7) JOHNSON, H. M., K. BRENNER, R. ANGELOTTI, and H. E. HALL. 1966. Serological studies of types A, B, and E botulinal toxins by passive hemagglutination and bentonite flocculation. J. Bacteriol. *91*: 967–974.

(8) JOHNSON, H. M., B. SMITH, H. E. HALL, and K. H. LEWIS. 1967. Serological specificity of types A and B botulinal toxins and antitoxins. Proc. Soc. Exp. Biol. Med. *126*: 856–861.

(9) JOHNSON, H. M., B. G. SMITH, and H. E. HALL. 1968. Carbodiimide hemagglutination: A study of some of the variables of the coupling reaction. Int. Arch. Allergy. *33*: 511–520.

(10) LAMANNA, C., and J. P. LOWENTHAL. 1951. The lack of identity between hemagglutinin and the toxin of type A botulinal organism. J. Bacteriol. *61*: 751–752.

RAPID BIOASSAY FOR *CLOSTRIDIUM BOTULINUM* TYPE E TOXINS BY INTRAVENOUS INJECTION INTO MICE

by Genji Sakaguchi, Sumiko Sakaguchi, *and* Hisashi Kondo
Department of Food Research and Second Department of Bacteriology, National Institute of Health, Tokyo

Summary

A bioassay method for *Clostridium botulinum* type E toxins is proposed. The method consists of intravenous injections into mice with serial dilutions of toxin samples and a reference toxin, determination of the time in minutes from injection to death of each mouse, conversion of the time to the corresponding score, and calculation of the values relative to that of the reference toxin by the parallel-line-assay method. When five mice were used, for each of three twofold serial dilutions, the precision of the assay method was about ±27 percent. By this method, the toxicity could be determined in an hour or two, and the relative values against a reference toxin were highly reproducible. The present scoring system is applicable to undissociated and dissociated activated type E toxins containing about 1,000 intraperitoneal $LD_{50}/0.1$ ml. or higher toxicity.

Introduction

Cl. botulinum toxin is assayed generally by intraperitoneal injections into mice with serial dilutions. The mice are observed for deaths for four days to calculate MLD or LD_{50}.

A much more rapid method was introduced, in which the time from the intraperitoneal injection into mice to death was taken as a measure of the toxicity (*11*). To keep the error on a low level, however, this method was found to require a larger number of mice than the usual method. Boroff and Fleck (*1*) described a similar method in which type A toxin was injected intravenously instead of intraperitoneally. The time to kill the mice ranged from about 30 to 70 minutes depending upon the toxicity from about 5,000 to 500,000 intraperitoneal $LD_{50}/0.1$ ml. They stated that the precision of the method was ±14 percent by using only three mice per dilution.

We applied the intravenous injection method to type E toxin and attempted to establish a rapid and reproducible bioassay method by means of the parallel-line-assay method and by expressing the toxicity as a relative value against a reference toxin.

Type E toxin is obtainable in four different forms, unactivated 12S and 7S and activated 12S and 7S

(*6*). The log-dose-response lines of all forms of the toxin were linear and parallel from one to another, but the ratios of the intraperitoneal LD_{50}, actually determined, to those estimated from the intravenous method were different between the unactivated and the activated toxins.

Materials and Methods

Mice.—Commercially raised white mice of the ddS strain of both sexes weighing 15 to 25 g. were used.

Toxins.—Materials taken at different steps of purification of type E toxin at different periods were used. The 7S toxins were obtained chromatographically on DEAE-Sephadex at pH 8 (unpublished work) from either of the 12S toxins. The dissociation was proved by the single precipitation band in agar-gel-diffusion test (*6*). The materials used and their properties are shown in Table 1.

Mouse inoculation.—The undissociated toxins were diluted in 0.05 M acetate buffer, pH 6.0; the 7S toxins in 0.05 M phosphate buffer, pH 6.0, containing gelatin at 0.2 percent to protect the highly diluted materials from loss of toxicity.

With the half milliliter "Luetin" syringe calibrated with 0.01-ml. interval, 0.1-ml. portions were injected

Table 1.—Type-E toxin materials used in the present investigation

Toxin Number	Specification	Intraperitoneal LD_{50}/ml.	Milligram protein per milliliter	LD_{50}/ mg. N
1	Precursor, undissociated	18,000	1.05	1.07×10^5
2	do	30,200	3.12	6.05×10^4
3	do	25,900	7.01	2.31×10^4
4	do	11,200	4.00	1.75×10^4
5	Precursor, dissociated	13,500	1.95	4.32×10^4
6[1]	Activated toxin, undissociated	13,200,000	3.12	2.64×10^7
7[1]	do	2,860,000	2.42	7.39×10^6
8[1]	Activated toxin, dissociated	372,000	0.035	6.55×10^7

[1]Toxin Nos. 6 and 7 contained trypsin; toxin No. 8 contained no trypsin.

into the tail vein of mice. The inoculated mice were observed continuously for deaths.

The intraperitoneal LD$_{50}$ was determined by the method described elsewhere (*10*).

Results

An assumed scoring system.—A dilution of the toxin No. 7 containing 5,000 LD$_{50}$/0.1 ml. was injected into a total of 101 mice. The time in minutes from injection to death of each mouse was categorized as shown in table 2. The scoring system was set up from the graded death times to obtain a linear relation between the score and the integrated percentage frequency when the integrated frequency distribution was plotted on a normal probability paper (fig. 1).

Table 2.—Death time of the mice injected with a trypsin-activated type E toxin containing 5,000 intraperitoneal LD$_{50}$/0.1 ml. and the assumed scoring system

Score	Time from challenge to death (in minutes)	Frequency Experiment 1	Frequency Experiment 2	Total	Integrated Frequency	Integrated Percentage frequency
0	<35	1	0	1	1	1.0
1	36–41	2	0	2	2	2.0
2	42–45	14	1	15	18	17.8
3	46–50	15	9	24	42	41.6
4	51–54	17	20	37	79	78.2
5	55–60	10	7	17	96	95.0
6	61–73	1	3	4	100	99.0
8	>74	1	0	1	101	100.0

From the scores applied on the results in table 2, a mean score of 3.65 was obtained (table 3).

Parallelism and slope of the log-dose-response lines.—The parallelism and the linearity of the log-dose-response lines obtained with five unactivated and

Table 3.—Calculation of the mean score of the mice injected with 5,000 intraperitoneal LD$_{50}$

Score	Frequency	Sum of scores
0	1	0
1	2	2
2	15	30
3	24	72
4	37	148
5	17	85
6	4	24
8	1	8
Total	101	369
Mean score		369/101 = 3.65

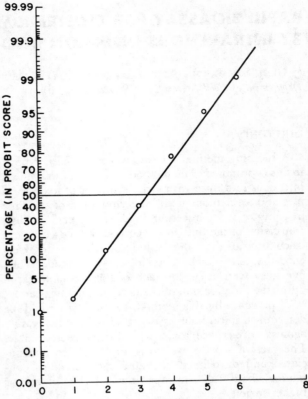

Figure 1.—Integrated percentage frequency and the score.

three activated toxins were examined. Each toxin sample was diluted twofold, serially into three to four levels. Each dilution was injected into five mice. The death time of each mouse was converted into the corresponding score as shown in table 2. The results given in table 4 were analyzed statistically (table 5).

The nonparallelism of the log-dose-response line of each toxin material was not significant at the 5 percent level of probability. The common slope, $\overline{b}$, was calculated from the following equation:

$$\Sigma Sxy/\Sigma Sxx = -247.11/109.74 = -2.252$$

Since the logarithm to base 2 was used in the analyses, the figure is to be divided by 0.301 to express it in a common logarithm.

$$-2.252/0/301 = -7.48$$

The common variance, s^2, was calculated to be 1.05.

Estimation of the intraperitoneal LD$_{50}$ from the results of the intravenous injections.—The intraperitoneal LD$_{50}$ was calculated for each material from the results shown in table 4 by the equation given below:

$$\overline{y} = \overline{y} + \overline{b}\,(x - \overline{x})$$

where *y* is 3.65, the mean score obtained from the injection of 5,000 intraperitoneal LD$_{50}$ of toxin No. 7, $\overline{y}$ the mean score of the sample, *x* the log dose of

Table 4.—Examples of titration of type E toxin by the proposed parallel-line-assay method

Toxin Number	Dilution	log $\bar{x}$	Scores					$\bar{y}$
1	1:2 1:4 1:8 1:16	−1.749	0 0 1 1 5 3 3 3 4 4 3 4 5 6 6 8 8 8 8 8					4.40
2	1:4 1:8 1:16	−1.903	1 1 1 1 2 3 3 4 5 5 6 6 6 8 8					4.00
3	1:4 1:8 1:16	−1.903	1 1 2 3 3 5 5 5 6 8 6 8 8 8 8					5.13
4	1:1 1:2 1:4 1:8	−1.460	0 1 1 1 1 1 3 3 4 5 5 5 5 6 5 6 6 6 8					3.79
5	1:1 1:2 1:4	−1.301	0 0 0 0 1 1 1 1 2 3 3 4 4 5 6					2.07
6	1:100 1:200 1:400	−3.301	0 1 1 2 2 3 3 3 4 4 5 6 6 8 8					3.73
7	1:32.5 1:65 1:130	−2.813	1 2 2 2 2 5 5 5 6 6 5 6 6 8 8					4.60
8	1:4 1:8 1:16	−1.903	1 1 2 2 2 2 3 3 4 4 3 5 6 6 8					3.40

Table 5.—Statistical analyses of the results shown in table 4

Nature of variation	Degree of freedom	Sum of squares	Mean squares
Preparations	7	363.12	51.87
Regression	1	556.44	556.44
Parallelism	7	13.26	1.89
Lineality	10	17.11	1.71
Between doses	25	949.93	37.99
Error	103	107.95	1.05
Total	128	1,057.88	---------------

the sample which would give a score of 3.65 when injected, x the mean log dose of the sample in the assay, and $\bar{b}-7.48$, the common slope. The results are shown in table 6 in comparison with the intraperitoneal LD_{50} values actually determined.

The following is an example of calculation with toxin No. 1:

$$3.65 = 4.40 + (-7.48)\{x - (-1.749)\}$$
$$x = -1.649 = \bar{2}.351 \qquad (0.0224)$$

This indicates that if 0.0224 ml. portions of toxin No. 1 are injected, a mean score of 3.65 would be obtained. In other words, 0.0224 ml. of this material should contain approximately 5,000 intraperitoneal LD_{50}. Therefore, intraperitoneal LD_{50}/ml. can be estimated by the following equation:

$$5,000 \times 1/0.0224 \ 1/0.224 = 223,000$$

As shown in table 6, the ratios of the intraperitoneal LD_{50}/ml. estimated from the intravenous method and those actually determined are close to 1 with undissociated and dissociated trypsin-activated toxins; while, those with undissociated and dissociated unactivated toxins are close to 10.

Table 6.—Comparison of intraperitoneal LD_{50} estimated from the intravenous injections and that actually determined

Toxin Number	Intraperitoneal LD_{50}/ml		Ratio
	Determined	Estimated	
1	18,000	223,000	12.39
2	30,200	360,000	11.92
3	25,900	255,000	9.85
4	11,200	130,000	11.61
5	13,500	165,000	12.22
6	13,200,000	9,750,000	0.74
7	2,860,000	2,450,000	0.86
8	372,000	430,000	1.16

The method proposed for titrating type E toxins by intravenous injection.—It is desirable to determine the toxicity of any toxin in relation to that of a reference toxin, rather than determining a mere "animal unit" such as MLD or LD_{50}, because it is extremely difficult to control every condition under which bioassays are performed. The parallel-line-assay method should be accurate and reproducible enough for this purpose. The principle of the parallel-line-assay method proposed for titrating *C. botulinum* type E toxin is as follows:

A test sample is activated with trypsin and the graded doses are injected intravenously into mice of one group and a reference toxin also in graded doses into another group. The time from challenge to death of each mouse is recorded. The time is converted into the corresponding score such as the one in table 2. The relative toxicity (M) of the sample is calculated by the following equation:

$$M = \bar{x}_s - \bar{x}_t - (\bar{y}_s - \bar{y}_t)\bar{b}$$

where $\bar{x}_s$ and $\bar{x}_t$ represent the mean log doses of the reference toxin and the toxin sample, respectively, $\bar{y}_s$ and $\bar{y}_t$ the mean scores of the reference toxin and the toxin sample, repectively, and $\bar{b}$ the common slope.

Table 7 shows the relative toxicities with the fiducial limits of two other toxin samples titrated against the arbitrary reference toxin, No. 6.

Discussion

Ipsen (*4, 5*) proposed a score system for bioassay of tetanus toxoid. Kondo et al. (*8*) reported a bioassay method for diphtheria toxin by intracerebral injection

Table 7.—Relative toxicities of the activated toxins against toxin No. 6 as a temporary reference and their fiducial limits

Toxin Number	Logarithm relative toxicity (M)	Fiducial limits[1]	
6	0		
7	−0.604	−0.706	−0.502
8	−1.355	−1.457	−1.252

[1] $M \pm t \sqrt{V(M)} : V(M) = s^2/\bar{b}^{-2} \left\{ \dfrac{1}{N_s} + \dfrac{1}{N_t} + (M - \bar{x}_s + \bar{x}_t)^2/Sxx \right\}$

into mice. The method was based upon the principles of scoring and the parallel-line-assay method.

Botulinus toxin is assayed by diluting serially and injecting each dilution into mice, intraperitoneally, in order to yield the LD_{50} or MLD in four days. A rapid method was studied in which the time from intraperitoneal injection to death was taken as a measure of the toxicity (11). The method was applicable to type A toxin containing 200 to 200,000 LD_{50}/ml., but the precision was reported to be about ±40 percent when 50 mice were used for one assay. Boroff and Fleck (1) described a similar rapid method in which toxin is injected intravenously into mice.

It seems unsatisfactory to express the toxicity of botulinus toxin merely in such an "animal unit" as MLD or LD_{50}, if one wants to compare, strictly, the toxin potency of one sample to that of another in the same or different laboratories, because the conditions under which bioassays are performed may be quite variable. For higher reproducibility of bioassay of botulinus toxins of any type, the parallel-line-assay method should be introduced. The assay method proposed for type E toxin was based on scoring the time from intravenous injection to death and on the parallel-line-assay method. The toxicities of several samples can be assayed in 1 or 2 hours. The precision of about ±27 percent is expected when 15 mice for each sample (five mice for each of three dilutions) and the same number of mice for the reference toxin are used. For the same level of precision, about 10 mice must be injected with each dilution of at least six graded doses by the usual intraperitoneal method (11).

It was very interesting to find that the unactivated and the activated toxins cannot be assayed by the same scoring system. The unactivated toxin killed the mice significantly more quickly than the activated toxin containing the same intraperitoneal LD_{50}/ml. It seems impractical to establish an independent scoring system for assaying unactivated toxin, because type E toxin in natural circumstances, especially in the presence of various contaminating organisms, may represent a mixture of the unactivated and activated toxins at an unknown proportion (9). The present

method, therefore, is applicable only to the toxin samples that have been activated with trypsin. The discrepancy found between the unactivated toxins in intraperitoneal and intravenous injections needs further study to be given a satisfactory explanation.

The proposed method is applicable to assaying type E activated toxins containing about 1,000 intraperitoneal LD_{50}/0.1 ml. or higher toxicities. The method is rapid to perform and of satisfactorily high precision. It is very useful for assaying samples at steps of purification of type E toxin (7).

Food samples, however, may contain lower toxicities. By setting up an independent scoring system covering longer death times, the extract of food could be assayed by the same method. The linear relationship between the log dose of type E toxin and the log death time has been demonstrated to hold down to 200 intraperitoneal LD_{50}/0.1 ml. However, the precision of the method will be lower when used to assay toxins of lower toxicities. The incriminated food, izushi, has been demonstrated to contain different toxicities; some were shown to contain 20,000 intraperitoneal LD_{50}/g. or higher toxicity after tryptic activation (2, 3). With such highly toxic food, quantitative determination of type E toxin can be made very rapidly by applying this method. Even if a food sample contains lower toxicity than the lowest detectable level of the present method, the inoculated mice should die within a few hours. Therefore, it would be worth performing the present method by injecting, intravenously, the food extract into the mice, both unprotected and protected with type-specific antitoxins, and also injecting the heat-treated extract into unprotected mice in order to detect and identify the toxin in foods.

References

(1) BOROFF, D. A., and U. FLECK. 1966. Statistical analysis of a rapid *in vivo* method for the titration of the toxin of *Clostridium botulinum*. J. Bacteriol. *92*: 1580–1581.

(2) IIDA, H., Y. NAKAMURA, I. NAKAGAWA, and T. KARASHIMADA. 1958. Additional type E botulism outbeaks in Hokkaido, Japan. Japan. J. Med. Sci. Biol. *11*: 215–222.

(3) IIDA, H., K. KANZAWA, Y. NAKAMURA, T. KARASHIMADA, T. ONO, and T. SAITO. 1964. Botulism outbreaks encountered in Hokkaido in 1962; with special reference to the therapeutic value of the specific antitoxin. Hokkaido Inst. Publ. Health, Rep. *14*: 6–18.

(4) IPSEN, J. 1952. The effect of environmental temperature on the immune response of mice to tetanus toxoid. J. Immunol. *69*: 273–283.

(5) IPSEN, J. 1955. Appropriate scores in bioassays using death-times and survivor symptoms. Biometrics *11*: 465–480.

(6) KITAMURA, M., S. SAKAGUCHI, and G. SAKA-GUCHI. 1967. Dissociation of *Clostridium botulinum* type

E. toxin. Biochem. Biophys. Res. Commun. *29:* 892–897.

(*7*) KITAMURA, M., S. SAKAGUCHI, and G. SAKAGUCHI. 1968. Purification and some properties of *Clostridium botulinum* type E toxin. Biochem. Biophys. Acta *in press*.

(*8*) KONDO, H., S. KONDO, S. HIROSE, M. KUROKAWA, S. ISHIDA, and Y. FUJISAKI. 1959. The assay of diphtheria toxin using mouse. Japan. J. Med. Sci. Biol. *12:* 331–342.

(*9*) SAKAGUCHI, G., Y. TOHYAMA, S. SAITO, S. FUJISAWA, and A. WADA. 1954. An outbreak of type E botulism in Akita prefecture due to gilthead-izushi. Japan. J. Med. Sci. Biol. *7:* 539–546.

(*10*) SAKAGUCHI, G., S. SAKAGUCHI, and N. IMAI. 1964. Comparative gel filtration of toxin precursor and trypsin-activated toxin of *Clostridium botulinum* type E. J. Bacteriol. *87:* 401–407.

(*11*) SCHANTZ, E. J. 1964. Purification and characterization of *Clostridium botulinum* toxins. *In* Botulism (K. H. Lewis and K. Cassel, Jr., eds.), pp. 91–103. U.S. Department of Health, Education, and Welfare, Public Health Service.

ACTIVATION OF *CLOSTRIDIUM BOTULINUM* TOXIN BY TRYPSIN

by HIROO IIDA
Hokkaido Institute of Public Health, Sapporo, Japan

Summary

The turbidity and pH of culture fluids and the process of toxin production were examined with *C. botulinum* types A, B, C, D, E, and F.

In the case of the proteolytic group, the turbidity of culture fluids increased at the beginning of incubation and then rapidly decreased. The pH fell to the acid side and then approached the neutral point. In the case of the nonproteolytic group, on the contrary, the turbidity increased at the beginning and maintained the initial level. The pH fell rapidly to the acid side and did not rise again. This seemed to be due to the difference in the biological (proteolytic and saccharolytic) activities of the two groups.

As for the process of toxin production, however, these two groups were each further subdivided into two subgroups. In the proteolytic group, the activation of toxin by trypsin was observed only at the early period of incubation in type A, strain 190 and type F, strain Denmark, while it was clearly observed during the later period of incubation in type B, strain Lamanna. In the nonproteolytic group, the activation was clearly observed in type E, strains VH and Iwanai, type B, strain QC and type F, strain OSU, while in type C, strains 468 and Stockholm and type E, strain 1873, the activation phenomenon was not observed from the early period of incubation. Thus, the simple scheme that toxin molecules are produced as precursors of low toxicity and then activated by proteolytic enzymes elaborated by the organisms seems to be not always applicable to all types of *C. botulinum*.

Introduction

It is generally accepted that toxin of *C. botulinum* type E is first produced as a precursor or prototoxin of low toxicity and then activated into toxin by some kind of enzymes produced by the organisms.

Sakaguchi and Tohyama (*10*) isolated a strain of anaerobe from "izushi" which had caused an outbreak of type E botulism and reported that the culture filtrate of this organism increased the toxicity of type E culture which had been isolated from the same izushi.

Duff, Wright, and Yarinsky (*5*) reported that trypsin activated type E toxin and that the optimum pH for the activation was around pH 6. Dolman (*2*) reported on the phase variation of *C. botulinum* type E and demonstrated that proteolytic mutants of type E have a conspicuous ability to activate type E toxin. Dolman (*3*) also reported findings which suggest that the activation takes place *in vivo*. The present author (*8*) also reported that the toxicity of type E toxin contained in izushi which had caused an outbreak in Hokkaido was increased more than a hundredfold by trypsin, thus suggesting that *in vivo* activation should play an important role in the pathogenesis of type E botulism.

As described above, the phenomenon of the activation of botulinus toxin has been chiefly investigated on type E and the possible mechanisms of the activation have been studied by Gerwing, Dolman, and Ko (*6*) and Sakaguchi and Sakaguchi (*11*). This phenomenon, however, was observed, not only with type E but also with types A and B toxins. For example, Bonventre and Kempe (*1*) reported that activation by trypsin was demonstrable with young cultures of types A and B and presumed that, in case of these proteolytic strains, proteinases produced by the organisms activated the toxin very rapidly, whereas in case of nonproteolytic strains such as type E, the production of proteinases was so limited that most toxin molecules remained as precursor molecules.

It is well known that *C. botulinum* is divided into two groups by their proteolytic activity. The proteolytic group was formerly named *C. parabotulinum* and the nonproteolytic group was named *C. botulinum*. This nomenclature, however, was abandoned and now they are called *C. botulinum* types A, B, C (Cα and Cβ), D, E, and F, according to the antigenic difference of their toxins. All type A, most type B and a few of type F strains belong to the proteolytic group while types C, D, E and a few of types B and F strains belong to the nonproteolytic group.

The present study was carried out in order to investigate the process of toxin production with all types of *C. botulinum*. Also, the changes in turbidity and in pH of the culture and the proteolytic activity of the strains were examined.

Materials and Methods

Strains.—The following strains were used in the present study:

Proteolytic group: *C. botulinum* type A, strain 190; type B, strain Lamanna; type F, strain Denmark.

Nonproteolytic group: *C. botulinum* type B, strain QC; type C, strains 468 and Stockholm; type D, strain 1873; type E, strains VH and Iwanai; type F, strain OSU.

Culture medium.—Thioglycollate (TGC) medium consisting of the following formula was employed.

Yeast extract, 5.0 g.; casein peptone, 15.0 g.; L-cystine, 0.5 g.; sodium chloride, 0.5 g.; glucose, 5.5 g.; sodium thioglycollate, 0.5 g.; agar, 0.75 g.; resazurin, 0.001 g. and distilled water, 1,000 ml., pH 7.0±0.1.

Cultivation.—Each *Cl. botulinum* strain was inoculated into 60 ml. of TGC medium and incubated at 30° C. Samples of 10 ml. each were removed immediately and at the intervals of 1, 3, 5, and 7 days after the inoculation. These samples were stored at −20° C. until use.

pH measurements.—The pH of each culture was estimated by the pH meter (Horiba Co.).

Turbidity.—The turbidity of each culture was determined by the photoelectric colorimeter (Klett-Summerson Co.) using a filter of 620–680 mμ.

Proteolytic activity.—Each sample was diluted by serial two-fold dilutions with phosphate buffer, pH 7.0. An equal volume of 10 percent gelatin solution was added to each tube, kept at 37° C. for 1 hour and removed to 4° C. to examine for the liquefaction of gelatin. The highest dilution of the sample which liquefied gelatin was expressed as a gelatin unit (GU).

Trypsin treatment.—Trypsin (Difco 1:250) was dissolved to 1 percent in M.10 phosphate buffer, pH 6.0. Equal volumes of each sample and the trypsin suspension were mixed and kept at 37° C. for 2 hours. As a control, each sample was kept at 37° C. for 2 hours, after mixing with an equal volume of the phosphate buffer, pH 6.0.

Toxicity test.—After incubation at 37° C. for 2 hours with 1 percent trypsin or with the phosphate buffer, each sample was diluted by serial tenfold dilutions with M/10 phosphate buffer of pH 6.0 added with 0.2 percent gelatin. Each dilution was injected intraperitoneally in the amount of 0.4 ml. into each of five mice, weighing 15 to 25 gr. The LD$_{50}$ value of each sample was calculated by Behrens-Kärber's method.

Results

Turbidity.—The changes of turbidity of culture fluids observed with five types of *C. botulinum* are shown

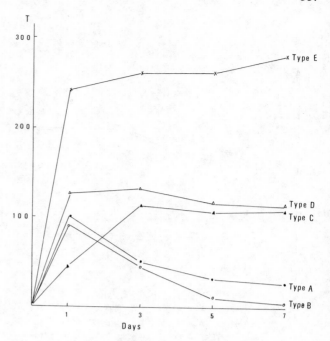

Figure 1.—Turbidity of cultures.

in figure 1. In case of type A strain 190 and type B strain Lamanna, both belonging to the proteolytic group, the turbidity of the culture fluids increased at the beginning, then decreased rapidly. A similar curve was observed with type F, strain Denmark.

On the other hand, in the cases of types C, D, and E which belong to the nonproteolytic group, the turbidity increased from the beginning without the subsequent fall. Similar results were also obtained with type B, strain QC and type F, strain OSU. Thus a conspicuous autolysis was observed with strains belonging to the proteolytic group while in strains belonging to the nonproteolytic group, this phenomenon was not observed.

pH during cultivation.—The changes of pH of TGC culture fluids inoculated with five types of *C. botulinum* are shown in figure 2. An obvious difference was observed between the proteolytic and the nonproteolytic groups. In the former group, the pH of culture fluids fell at the beginning but then rose upward. In the latter group, however, the pH fell to the acid side and never rose again.

Toxin production.—*C. botulinum* type A strain 190: The toxicity of the culture fluid was followed at intervals by injecting each sample into mice before and after the trypsin treatment. As indicated in figure 3, activation by trypsin was observed to some extent at the beginning of the cultivation, but thereafter, the toxin seemed to have been destroyed by trypsin. A similar phenomenon was observed with type F strain Denmark.

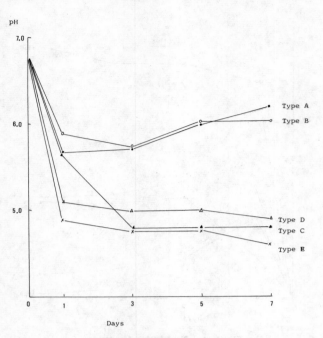

Figure 2.—pH of cultures.

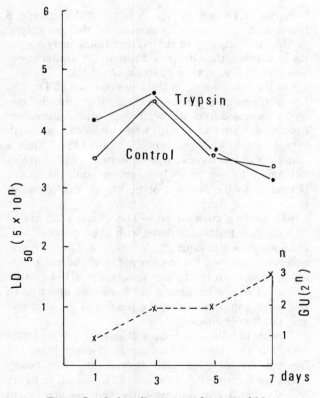

Figure 3.—*C. botulinum* type A, strain 190.

C. botulinum type B, strain Lamanna: Although this strain also belongs to the proteolytic group, activation

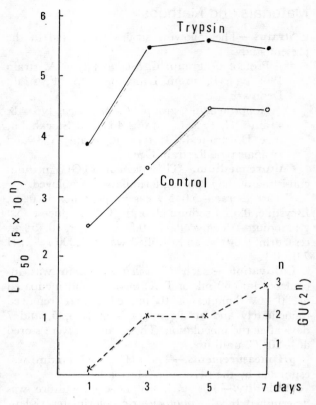

Figure 4.—*C. botulinum* type B, strain Lamanna.

by trypsin was clearly observed even at the end of the incubation period. As indicated in figure 4, more than 90 percent of toxin remained as precursors even at the seventh day of incubation.

C. botulinum type C strain 468: Figure 5 shows the results obtained with this nonproteolytic strain. As indicated in the figure, the activation of toxin by trypsin was hardly observed. A similar result was obtained with type C strain Stockholm.

C. botulinum type D strain 1873: As is evident in figure 6, no activation of toxin was demonstrated by trypsin with this nonproteolytic strain.

C. botulinum type E strain VH: It is a well known fact that type E toxin is activated by trypsin (5) and as indicated in figure 7, the toxicity of the culture fluid of type E, strain VH, was increased by trypsin more than a hundredfold through the course of the incubation. A similar phenomenon was observed with type E, strain Iwanai, and to a lesser extent, with type B, strain QC and type F, strain OSU, both nonproteolytic.

Discussion

These results apparently indicate that *C. botulinum* can be classified into two groups; the proteolytic and

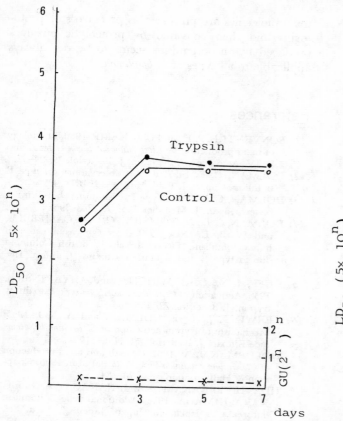

Figure 5.—*C. botulinum* type C, strain 468.

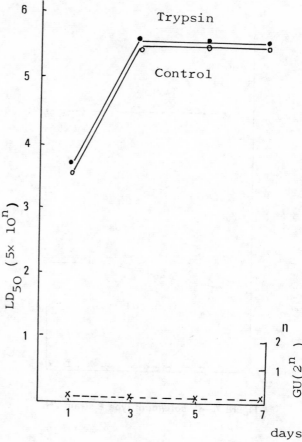

Figure 6.—*C. botulinum* type D, strain 1873.

nonproteolytic groups. In the former group, the turbidity of culture fluids increases at the beginning of incubation, then decreases rapidly; the pH falls to the acid side and then approaches to the neutral point. In the latter group, on the contrary, the turbidity does not decrease after the initial increase and the pH does not rise after the initial fall. This seems to be due to the fact that organisms belonging to the former group show a considerable proteolytic activity whereas those belonging to the latter group exhibit a conspicuous saccharolytic activity.

In the process of toxin production, however, there is a marked difference between type A strain 190 and type B strain Lamanna, both belonging to the proteolytic group. In the case of type A strain 190 (and also type F strain Denmark), the activation of toxin by trypsin is observed only at the early period of incubation, which suggests the rapid activation of toxin by some enzymes produced by the organisms. For example, Bonventre and Kempe (1) reported that proteolytic enzymes elaborated by types A and B activated the toxin precursor and Inukai (9) also reported that type A toxin was activated by proteolytic enzymes produced by the same organisms. In

proteolytic type B, strain Lamanna, however, toxin in the culture fluid is activated by trypsin even at the later period of incubation. The similar phenomenon was also observed by Skulberg (13) and by Schmidt (12). This suggests that proteolytic enzymes produced by the organisms do not always exert activating influences upon the toxin precursor.

In the nonproteolytic group, there also seem to be two different patterns of toxin production. In case of nonproteolytic organisms, such as types E (strains VH and Iwanai), B (strain QC) and F (strain OSU), activation by trypsin is clearly demonstrated whereas in case of nonproteolytic organisms, such as types C (strains 468 and Stockholm) and D (strain 1873), activation by trypsin is scarcely observed even in the early period of incubation. In the former, toxin molecules will be produced as precursors of low toxicity or prototoxins and then activated to highly toxic molecules. A considerable amount of research has been published on the activation of type E toxin (2, 5, 6, 10, 11). As for nonproteolytic type B, Dolman et al. (4) reported that the toxin was activated by trypsin and

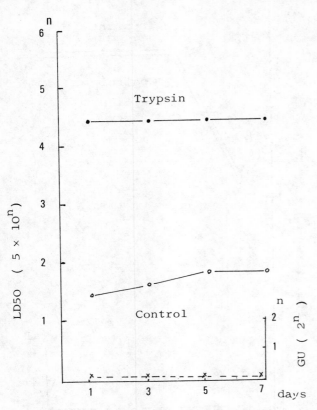

Figure 7.—C. botulinum type E strain VH.

toxin molecules are produced as precursors or proto-toxins and then activated by proteolytic enzymes produced by the organisms seems to be not always applicable to all types of *C. botulinum*.

References

(1) BONVENTRE, P. F., and L. L. KEMP. 1960. Physiology of toxin production by *Clostridium botulinum* types A and B. IV. Activation of the toxin. J. Bacteriol. *79:* 24–32.

(2) DOLMAN, C. E. 1957. Recent observations on type E botulism. Canad. J. Publ. Health. *48:* 187–198.

(3) DOLMAN, C. E. 1957. Type E. (fish-borne) botulism: A review. Japan. J. Med. Sci. Biol. *10:* 383–395.

(4) DOLMAN, C. E., M. TOMSICK, C. C. R. CAMPBELL, and W. B. LAING. 1960. Fish eggs as a cause of human botulism. Two outbreaks in British Columbia due to type E and B botulinus toxins. J. Infect. Dis. *106:* 5–19.

(5) DUFF, J. Y., G. G. WRIGHT, and A. YARINSKY. 1956. Activation of *Clostridium botulinum* type E toxin by trypsin. J. Bacteriol. *72:* 455–460.

(6) GERWING, J., C. E. DOLMAN, and A. KO. 1965. Mechanism of trypsin activation of *Clostridium botulinum* type E toxin. J. Bacteriol. *89:* 1176–1179.

(7) HOLDEMAN, L. V. 1967. Growth and toxin production of *Clostridium botulinum* type F. *In* Botulism 1966. Chapman & Hall, London. pp. 176–184.

(8) IIDA, H., Y. NAKAMURA, I. NAKAGAWA, and T. KARASHIMADA. 1958. Additional type E botulism outbreaks in Hokkaido, Japan. Japan. J. Med. Sci. Biol. *11:* 215–222.

(9) INUKAI, Y. 1963. Activation of the toxin in the culture of *Clostridium botulinum* type A. Japan. J. Vet. Res. *11:* 87–93.

(10) SAKAGUCHI, G. and Y. TOHYAMA. 1955. Studies on the toxin production of *Clostridium botulinum* type E. I and II. Japan. J. Med. Sci. Biol. *8:* 247–262.

(11) SAKAGUCHI, G., and S. SAKAGUCHI. 1967. Some observations of activation of *Clostridium botulinum* type E toxin by trypsin. *In* Botulism 1966. Chapman & Hall, London, pp. 266–277.

(12) SCHMIDT, C. F. 1966. Personal communication.

(13) SKULBERG, A. 1961. "Studies on the formation of toxin by *Clostridium botulinum*." A/S Kaare Gryttig, Orkanger, Oslo, Norway.

Holdeman (7) reported on the activation of type F (both proteolytic and nonproteolytic) toxin.

Alternative hypotheses may be proposed for types C and D; whether toxin molecules are produced as highly active forms or some enzymes are produced which can activate toxin precursors immediately after they are produced. In the latter case, these enzymes should not be proteolytic ones.

The process of toxin production in *C. botulinum* seems to be complicated and the simple scheme that

PURIFICATION AND MOLECULAR DISSOCIATION OF *CLOSTRIDIUM BOTULINUM* TYPE E TOXIN

by GENJI SAKAGUCHI
Department of Food Research, National Institute of Health, Tokyo

Summary

The precursor of *Clostridium botulinum* type E toxin, which can be extracted from the bacterial cells as a ribonucleoprotein, has been purified by percolation through a column of CM-Sephadex, followed by digestion with RNase, rechromatography on CM-Sephadex and finally gel filtration on Sephadex G–200. The highly purified materials contained a toxicity of 1 to 8 x 10^5LD$_{50}$/mg. N, which was increased to 5 to 10 x 10^7 LD$_{50}$/mg. N by tryptic activation. The materials behaved as homogeneous protein in ultracentrifugation, electrophoresis and chromatography at pH below 6 with an S$_{20,w}$ of approximately 11.5.

Electrophoresis at pH above 7 and agar-gel-diffusion tests, however, demonstrated two distinct components. The materials, whether unactivated or activated, were demonstrated to consist of toxigenic Eα and nontoxigenic Eβ components with the same S$_{20,w}$ of 7.3 The antigenic and some of the other properties of either component of the precursor were identical to the corresponding component of the trypsin-activated toxin.

Introduction

We reported a marked enhancement of the toxicity of *C. botulinum* type-E toxin in mixed cultures, seeded together with a contaminant strain of nontoxigenic anaerobic bacteria, orginating from an incriminated "izushi" (*11*). Having investigated this peculiar phenomenon further, we concluded that type E toxin is produced in the form of virtually nontoxic precursor which is activated by a proteinase produced by the contaminant strain to become the fully active toxin (*12, 13*). Duff, Wright and Yarinsky (*3*) substantiated our finding by reporting activation of type E toxin by trypsin in a similar mode. The activation appeared to be directly associated with pathogenesis of type E botulism and has led to much interest from medical, biological and chemical viewpoints. To elucidate the mechanisms of the activation, purification of the type-E toxin of low toxicity, or the "precursor," was the

first step to be undertaken. Although the materials purified previously (*17*) appeared to be homogeneous in ultracentrifugation, heterogeneity was demonstrated later by agar-gel diffusion and disk electrophoresis.

In this paper, the improved procedures for purification (*7*) and the molecular dissociation of the precursor (*6*) and also of the trypsin-activated type E toxin will be described.

Materials and Methods

Bacterial strain.—A spore suspension of *C. botulinum* type E strain 35396 (*5*) in 0.05 M acetate buffer, pH 5.0, kept at −20° C. was used as the inoculum.

Culture medium.—The medium was composed of 1 percent glucose, 0.5 percent yeast extract, 2 per cent peptone and 0.025 percent sodium thioglycolate with the pH adjusted to 6.3. About 3,000 viable spores were inoculated into every 5 liters of the medium. The inoculated medium was incubated at 30° C. for 4 days.

Determination of protein content.—Protein content was determined by the method of Lowry et al. (*8*). The whole culture, culture supernatant and cell suspension were extracted with cold and then hot 5 percent trichloroacetic acid. The residual precipitate was determined for protein content.

Determination of RNA content.—RNA content was determined by the method of Mejbaum (*9*) on the cold trichloroacetic acid precipitate. Yeast RNA was used as the standard.

Tryptic activation of the precursor.—Crystalline trypsin was added to a sample solution of pH 6.0 to a concentration of 100 or 200 μg./ml. regardless of the substrate concentration. The mixture was incubated at 37° C. for 30 minutes. The toxicity resulting from the tryptic activation will be referred to as "potential toxicity."

Determination of toxin potency.—A sample was diluted twofold serially in 0.05 M phosphate buffer, pH 6.0, containing gelatin at 0.2 percent and merthiolate at 0.01 percent. Each dilution was injected intraperitoneally into at least four mice at a dose of

0.5 ml. to calculate LD_{50} by the method of Reed and Muench (10).

The toxin potency after tryptic activation was determined also by intravenous injection into mice and measuring the time, in minutes, from injection to death (1). This method will be reported in a separate paper.

Agar-gel-double-diffusion test.—On a glass plate of 5 x 5 cm., about 4 ml. of 1 percent agar gel in 0.05 M acetate buffer, pH 6.0, was spread. Wells of 2 mm. in diameter were cut at a distance of 7 mm. between every two wells. Horse immune sera prepared against crude preparations of precursor or activated toxin were used with or without dilution. The agar plates were incubated at 4° C. for 2 days.

Results

Purification of the precursor.—Botulinum toxins are generally defined as true exotoxins, but often more of type E toxin is associated with the bacterial cells than with the supernatant. When type E organisms were grown in the medium with an initial pH of 6.3, the pH dropped to about 4.8 and 80 percent or more of the precursor was recovered from the centrifugal precipitate. The precipitate was washed with 0.05 M acetate buffer, pH 5.0, and used for the starting material for isolation of the precursor. The precursor was extracted with 0.2 M phosphate buffer, pH 6.0, which had been shown to extract the highest specific toxicity among the phosphate buffers of different pH values and molal concentrations. The suspension was incubated at 37° C. for 2 hours and then centrifuged. The extraction was repeated twice. It was found that the incubation of 37° C. was not essential, but the precursor was extracted almost instantaneously even at 0° C. The precursor thus extracted was precipitated at half saturation of ammonium sulfate.

The precursor at this stage was an RNA-protein complex (14). The digestion of the precursor with RNase removed the RNA nearly completely and yet the toxicity remained unchanged. The undigested precursor did not absorb onto a column of CM-cellulose or CM-Sephadex equilibrated to pH 6, whereas the RNase-digested precursor did absorb (15). We found it advantageous to subject the undigested precursor to chromatography on CM-Sephadex in order to remove a protein fraction absorbed onto the column, which was eluted at an NaCl concentration of approximately 0.075 M. This protein fraction represented an antigenic protein having a molecular size similar to the precursor and would require much effort to eliminate by other methods (fig. 1, top).

The percolate fractions containing most activity of the precursor were digested with RNase and then

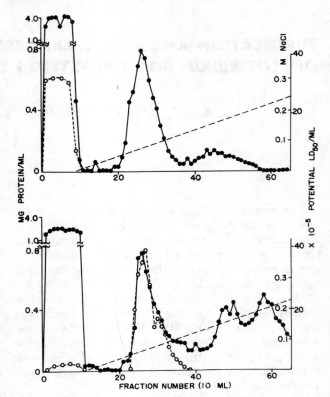

Figure 1.—Chromatography of "cell extract" (730 mg.) (top) and "RNase digest" (530 mg.) (bottom) on CM-Sephadex (1 x 10.5 cm.). ●————●, protein content; ○————○, potential toxicity; ○————○, NaCL concentration.

subjected to chromatography again under similar conditions (fig. 1, bottom). The precursor was absorbed onto the column, which was eluted at an NaCl concentration of approximately 0.07 M. Without the first CM-Sephadex chromatography, the precursor and the nontoxigenic protein would have overlapped.

When subjected to gel filtration on a column of Sephadex G—200, the precursor was eluted at the front, but later than Blue Dextran 2,000 (MW = 2,000,000), as shown in figure 2. The specific potential toxicities were on the same level throughout the peak. Small molecular-sized substances originating from the bacterial cells were separated in the trailing fractions.

Through the procedures shown in figure 3, namely extraction of the bacterial cells, chromatography on CM-Sephadex, RNase-digestion of the percolate, rechromatography of the RNase-digested precursor on CM-Sephadex under similar conditions, and finally gel filtration on Sephadex G—200, a highly purified precursor material was obtained (table 1). An overall purification of about sixtyfold was accomplished from the washed cells as the starting material.

To obtain the trypsin-activated toxin in the pure

Table 1.—Purification of the precursor of *Clostridium botulinum* type E toxin from 120—L culture

Step	Protein content (milligrams)	RNA content (milligrams)	RNA / Protein	LD$_{50}$ (x 10^{-5}) Before activation	After activation	LD$_{50}$/mg. N(x 10^{-3})[1] Before activation	After activation	Activation ratio[2]
1 Whole culture	42,000(111)	17,300(199)	0.4	220(79)	61,000(122)	3.3(0.7)	910(1.1)	280
Washed cells	37,900(100)	8,680(100)	.2	280(100)	50,000(100)	4.6(1.0)	830(1.0)	180
2 Cell extract	3,890(10.3)	2,270(26)	.6	76(27)	31,000(62)	12(2.6)	5,000(6.0)	410
3 CM–1 percolate	2,550(6.7)	2,270(26)	.9	110(39)	37,000(74)	27(5.9)	9,100(11)	340
4 RNase digest	1,800(4.7)	(3)	(3)	90(32)	38,000(76)	31(6.7)	13,000(16)	420
5 CM–2 adsorbate	341(0.9)	(3)	(3)	82(29)	30,000(60)	150(33)	55,000(66)	370
6 G–200 filtrate	221(0.6)	(3)	(3)	32(11)	17,000(34)	91(20)	48,000(58)	530

[1] LD$_{50}$/mg. N protein x 6.25.
[2] LD$_{50}$ after activation per LD$_{50}$ before activation.
[3] Not determined.

NOTE.—The figures in parentheses are the relative values when the values for the washed cells are taken as 100 or 1.0.

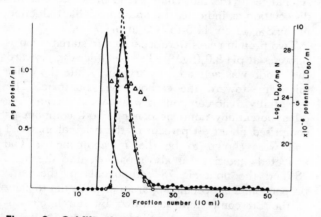

Figure 2.—Gel filtration of precursor (40 mg.) on Sephadex G–200 (2.5 x 91 cm.) with 0.02 M acetate buffer, pH 6.0, as eluant. ●————●, protein content; ○————○, potential toxicity; ●————●, elution pattern of Blue Dextran 2,000; △, potential toxicity per milligram N.

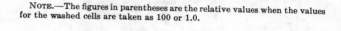
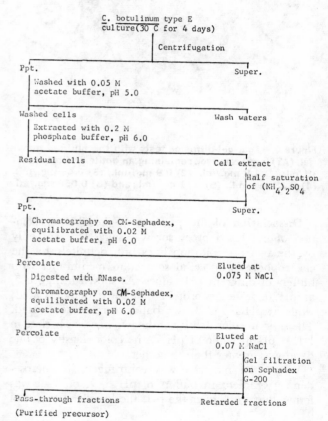

Figure 3.—Procedures for purification of the precursor of *C. botulinum* type E toxin.

form, the precursor was activated with trypsin and passed through a column of Sephadex G–200. The toxin was eluted at the same position as the precursor; the trypsin and its degraded products were retarded on the column (*17*).

Examinations for the purity.—The purified precursor materials contained a toxity of 1 to 8 x 10^5 LD$_{50}$/mg. N, which was increased to 5 to 10 x 10^7 LD$_{50}$/mg. N when treated with trypsin. This was an increase of about 200 to 500 times in toxicity. In rechromatography on CM-Sephadex under the same conditions as before, except for a much more gradual gradient increase in NaCl concentration in the eluant, the precursor was eluted in a single and symmetric peak with specific potential toxicities on the same level throughout the peak. In ultracentrifugal analysis, a single symmetrical boundary with an S$_{20,w}$ of 11.6 (11.1 to 12.3) was obtained with both the precursor and the trypsin-activated toxin in buffers of pH 4.5

or PH 6.0. In disk electrophoresis in polyacrylamide gel at pH 4, the material gave a single band.

Although the material appeared to be homogeneous at pH 6 or below, it gave two distinct precipitation lines at any dilution of the antigen in agar-gel-diffusion test with anti-crude precursor horse immune serum (fig. 4).

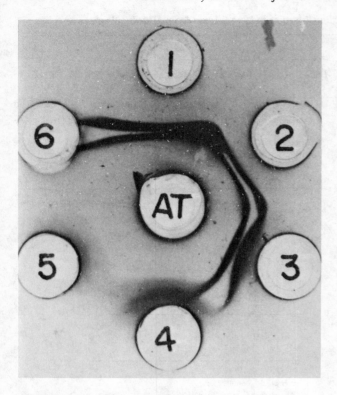

Figure 4.—Agar-gel-diffusion tests with the purified material. (AT), antiprecursor containing an antitoxin titer of 970 IU/ml; (1) 1.8 mg./ml., (2) 0.9 mg./ml., (3) 0.45 mg./ml., (4) 0.23 mg./ml., (5) 0.11 mg./ml. and (6) 0.056 mg./ml.

Dissociation of the precursor.—Possible dissociation of the 11.5S precursor was suggested, not only by the two precipitation lines but, definitely by the electrophoreses on cellulose acetate membranes with buffers of different pH values. As shown in figure 5, at pH 6, a single protein band was demonstrated; while at pH 7 and 8, two bands were demonstrated. The ratio in color density of the two bands was close to 1:1 at pH 8; while at pH 7, the color density of one band was greater than the other.

When the material was centrifuged in sucrose-density gradient in buffers of pH 6, 7, or 8, it was found that the higher the pH, the lesser the extent of

sedimentation of the material (fig. 6). By comparing with the sedimentation of a preparation of 7S serum globulin and 3.5S egg albumin, the S value of the precursor at pH 8 was estimated to be about 7. The sedimentation pattern at pH 9 was essentially the same as that at pH8. The sedimentation patterns with the trypsin-activated material were exactly the same as those with the precursor.

The precursor sedimented in a single boundary with an $S_{20,w}$ of 12.3 in 0.05M acetate buffer, pH 6.0; in two boundaries, the major one with an $S_{20,w}$ of 10.3 and the minor one of 6.9 in 0.05 M phosphate buffer, pH 7.0; in a single boundary with an $S_{20,w}$ of 7.3 in 0.05 M vernoal buffer, pH 8.0 (fig. 7a, b, c, respectively). The 11.5S precursor and the activated toxin dissociate into 7S components at pH 8 or above. A change in the molecular shape must precede the dissociation as indicated by an appreciable reduction in the $S_{20,w}$ from 11.5 to 10.3 at pH 7.

Two protein peaks were separated in starch electrophoreses at pH 8.0 (fig. 8). The one migrating toward the anode was activated by trypsin; while the other migrating toward the cathode was nontoxic. The potentially toxic component was named Eα and the other potentially nontoxic one Eβ. Both components comprised about 50 percent of the original material and were shown to be the 7S components. The activated material was also separated into the toxic 7S and the nontoxic 7S components in the same proportion. The specific apparent or potential toxicity of the Eα component separated by starch electro-

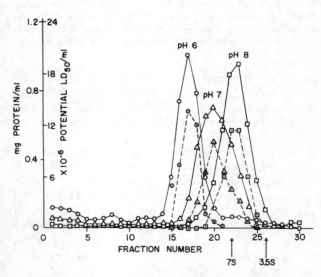

Figure 6.—Separation of the purified material (400 μg.) in sucrose-density gradient of 5 to 20 percent at pH 6, 7, or 8. Centrifugation, at 39,000 r.p.m. for 7 hours at 5°C. in an SW 39 rotor in a Beckman ultracentrifuge model L₂; fractionation, 12 drops per tube. ————, protein content; — — — —, potential toxicity.

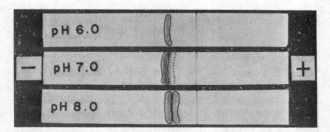

Figure 5.—Electrophoreses of the purified material on cellulose acetate membrane at pH 6, 7, or 8.

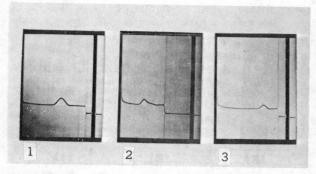

Figure 7.—Sedimentation of the purified precursor. (1) in 0.05 M acetate buffer, pH 6.0, (2) in 0.05 M phosphate buffer, pH 7.0, and (3) in 0.05 M veronal buffer, pH 8.0. Revolution at 56,100 r.p.m. and 20°C. Time after reaching the highest speed, 24 minutes.

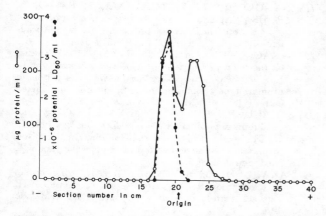

Figure 8.—Starch electrophoresis of the precursor at pH 8. Sample, 4 mg.; trough size, 2 x 1.5 x 40 cm.; buffer, 0.05 M veronal, pH 8.0; electrophoresis, at 6 mA, 200 V for 24 hours at 6 C; extraction, each 1-cm. segment with 1.0 ml. of 0.05 M veronal buffer, pH 8.0.

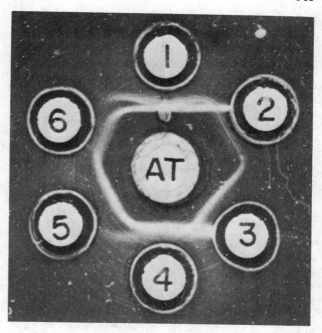

Figure 9.—Agar-gel-diffusion tests with the 12S toxins and Eα and Eβ components. (A), antiprecursor (485 IU/ml.), (1) 12S precursor, (2) Eα of the precursor, (3) Eα of the activated toxin, (4) 12S activated toxin, (5) Eβ of the precursor, and (6) Eβ of the activated toxin.

phoresis was on the same level as the starting 11.5S materials.

Agar-gel-diffusion tests demonstrated that the precipitation line of the α component from either the precursor or the activated toxin and the one nearer to the antigen of the 11.5S precursor or the activated toxin fused; the precipitation line of the β component from either material and the one nearer to the antibody of either of the 11.5S material fused equally (fig. 9).

Discussion

C. botulinum type-E toxin is available in the form of a precursor, which is mainly associated with the bacterial cells when grown in a medium of pH 6.3. The ease with which the precursor is extracted may be an indication that the precursor is located on or near the surface of the bacterial cells. The precursor in the cell extract is in the form of ribonucleoprotein. We took advantage of this property for purification by introducing a step of percolation of the cell extract through CM-Sephadex. The RNA-precursor complex was not adsorbed onto the column; while some nontoxic protein possessing a molecular size similar to the precursor was adsorbed. Thus, we succeeded in eliminating a distinct antigenic fraction, which was difficult to eliminate by other procedures. The RNA-precursor in the percolate was digested with RNase. The precursor, free from RNA, was adsorbed under the same conditions onto CM-Sephadex, which was eluted at the NaCl concentration similar to that for eluting the nontoxigenic protein. Smaller molecular-sized substances originating from the bacterial cells were removed by gel filtration on Sephadex G—200.

The material purified by these procedures appeared to be physicochemically homogeneous at pH below 6 with an $S_{20,w}$ of about 11.5, but this formed two distinct precipitation lines in agar-gel-diffusion tests.

The molecular dissociation of the 11.5S precursor and the activated toxin, into 7S components at pH above 8, was demonstrated. Before dissociation, a change in the molecular shape may take place, by which the sedimentation constant is reduced appreciably, from 11.5 to 10.3 One of the 7S components was either potentially or apparently toxic; while the other nontoxic. Crystalline type-A toxin has also been shown to consist of 7S toxic and the 13S nontoxic components, the latter being associated with hemagglutinin (*19. 2*). It is interesting that the active components of type E and type A toxins are essentially of the same molecular size. The Eβ component, however, contained no hemagglutinating activity against avian or mammalian red blood cells.

Thus, type E 11.5S toxin, both in the precursor and the activated forms, represents a complex consisting of one molecule of Eα and one molecule of Eβ. It is, however, not an artifact resulting from aggregation during the purification as suggested by Gerwing, Dolman, and Ko (*4*). In such natural circumstances as in "izushi" (*16*) or in spent cultures (*18*), botulinus toxin of type E, or any other types, is present in the stable, macromolecular state.

Trypsinization of the 11.5S precursor at pH 6 is not associated with any change in molecular size, amino acid composition, electrophoretic pattern, antigenic property, or in any other physicochemical properties so far examined. From these and some enzymological indications, the hypothesis was advanced that tryptic activation may not involve breakage of any peptide bond in the precursor molecule (*17*). The main obstacle in providing direct evidence for this hypothesis was the large molecular size as 11.5S possessed by our preparations. The isolation of the 7S precursor encourages us a great deal to provide direct proof for explaining the mechanism of the tryptic activation.

Acknowledgment

This investigation was supported in part by U.S. Public Health Service Research Grant No. UI–00123 from the National Center of Urban and Industrial Health.

References

(*1*) BOROFF, D. A., and U. FLECK. 1966. Statistical analysis of a rapid *in vivo* method for the titration of the toxin of *Clostridium botulinum*. J. Bacteriol., *92*: 1580–1581.

(*2*) DASGUPTA, B. R., D. A. BOROFF, and E. ROTHSTEIN. 1966. Chromatographic fractionation of the crystalline toxin of *Clostridium botulinum* type A. Biochem. Biophys. Res. Commun. *22*: 750–756.

(*3*) DUFF, J. T., G. G. WRIGHT, and A. YARINSKY. 1956. Activation of *Clostridium botulinum* type E toxin by trypsin. J. Bacteriol. *72*: 455–460.

(*4*) GERWING, J., C. E. DOLMAN, and A. KO. 1965. Mechanism of tryptic activation of *Clostridium botulinum* type E toxin. J. Bacteriol. *89*: 1176–1179.

(*5*) HAZEN, E. L. 1937. A strain of *B. botulinus* not classified as type A, B, or C. J. Inf. Dis. *60*: 260–264.

(*6*) KITAMURA, M., S. SAKAGUCHI, and G. SAKAGUCHI. 1967. Dissociation of *Clostridium botulinum* type E toxin. Biochem. Biophys. Res. Commun. *29*: 892–897.

(*7*) KITAMURA, M., S. SAKAGUCHI, and G. SAKAGUCHI. 1968. Purification and some properties of *Clostridium botulinum* type E toxin. Biochem. Biophys. Acta. In press.

(*8*) LOWRY, O. H., N. J. ROSEBROUGH, A. L. FARR, and R. J. RANDALL. 1951. Protein measurement with the Folin phenol reagent. J. Biol. Chem. *193*: 265–275.

(*9*) MEJBAUM, W. 1939. Uber die Bestimmung Kleiner Pentosemengen, insbesondere in Derivaten der Adenylsaure. Z. Physiol. Chem. *258*: 117–120.

(*10*) REED, L. J., and H. MUENCH. 1938. A simple method of estimating 50 percent end points. Am. J. Hyg. *27*: 493–497.

(*11*) SAKAGUCHI, G., Y. TOHYAMA, S. SAITO, S. FUJISAWA, and A. WADA. 1954. An outbreak of type E botulism in Akita prefecture due to giltheadizushi. Japan. J. Med. Sci. Biol. *7*: 539–546.

(*12*) SAKAGUCHI, G., and Y. TOHYAMA. 1955. Studies on the toxin production of *Clostridium botulinum* type E. I. A strain of genus *Clostridium* having the action to promote type E botulinal toxin production in a mixed culture. Japan. J. Med. Sci. Biol. *8*: 247–253.

(*13*) SAKAGUCHI, G., and Y. TOHYAMA. 1955. Studies on the toxin production of *Clostridium botulinum* type E. II. The mode of action of the contaminant organisms to promote production of type E organisms. Japan. J. Med. Sci. Biol. *8*: 255–262.

(*14*) SAKAGUCHI, G., and S. SAKAGUCHI. 1959. Studies on toxin production of *Clostridium botulinum* type E. III. Characterization of toxin precursor. J. Bacteriol. *78*: 1–9.

(*15*) SAKAGUCHI, G., S. SAKAGUCHI, and N. IMAI. 1964. Comparative gel filtration of toxin precursor and trypsin-activated toxin of *Clostridium botulinum* type E. J. Bacteriol. *87*: 401–407.

(*16*) SAKAGUCHI, G., S. SAKAGUCHI, and T. KARASHIMADA. 1966. Molecular size of *Clostridium botulinum* type E toxin in "izushi". Japan. J. Med. Sci. Biol. *19*: 201–207.

(*17*) SAKAGUCHI, G., and S. SAKAGUCHI. 1967. Some observations on activation of *C. botulinum* type E toxin by trypsin. *In* Botulism 1966, M. Ingram and T. A. Roberts, eds. Chapman & Hall, London, pp. 266–277.

(*18*) SCHANTZ, E. J., and L. SPERO, 1967. Molecular size of *Cl. botulinum* toxins. *In* Botulism 1966, M. Ingram and T. A. Roberts, eds. Chapman & Hall, London, pp. 296–301.

(*19*) WAGMAN, J. 1954. Isolation and sedimentation study of low-molecular weight forms of type A botulinus toxin. Arch. Biochem. Biophys. *50*: 104–112.

Addendum

After presentation of this paper, some important questions concerning nomenclature of toxic and nontoxic components of *C. botulinum* type E toxin were raised by Dr. C. Lamanna.

According to him, the true toxin should be such molecular species that contain the highest specific activities, namely "the Eα component" in this case. The other dissociation product of type E toxin is not toxic, so it should not be given the name "Eβ", which might imply toxicity. Furthermore, the Greek alphabet has been used in the past to designate similar toxins with different immunological specificities, as in the case of Cα and Cβ toxins. Therefore, it would be confusing if the names "Eα" and "Eβ" are used to differentiate the dissociation products of type E toxin on some other basis than specificity in toxin neutralization. These questions remain and should be resolved.

STUDIES ON BOTULINUS TOXIN

by S. I. ZACKS *and* M. F. SHEFF*
The Ayer Clinical Laboratory and Neurochemistry Department,
Pennsylvania Hospital, Philadelphia, Pa.

For more than 60 years, bacterial exotoxins have attracted the interest of investigators because of their extreme toxicity in terms of amount needed to produce lethality. In more recent years, their ability to produce highly specific changes in the nervous system has lead to their reinvestigation using modern methods in the hope that they would help to unravel some of the problems of neurophysiology. An excellent review that I would recommend to all interested in the subject is that of Drs. Lamanna and Carr which appeared in "Clinical Pharmacology and Therapeutics," vol. 8. This discussion will be devoted to botulinum toxin though in few instances we will contrast data from our studies on tetanal neurotoxin.

As to the toxin itself, six immunologically distinct varieties have been labelled A, B, C, D, E, and F. The mechanism of poisoning appears the same although the proteins differ in several respects. At present, purification to at least a 90 percent level is available for four of these toxins and the A toxin has been crystallized. The toxin itself has proved to be rather difficult to work with in chemical terms due to its tendency to dissociate and to denature. We have found that conditions of agitation, absorption on to glass and other factors must be carefully controlled if reproducible results are to be obtained. Usually, a gelatin solution in phosphate buffer pH 6.2 to 6.8 or in our hands, human serum albumen, is used to minimize this instability. The toxin is stable for months in 0.5 M phosphate buffer or 0.1 M NaCl at ph 7.2. Early attempts to purify the toxin employed salting out methods and more recently DEAE cellulose columns have been used.

A major problem of the toxin concerns the minimum toxic unit. The crystalline type A toxin has a molecular weight of approximately 900,000 and behaves as a homogeneous preparation in some systems but not in others. For example, it sediments as a single component yet it tends to come apart in electrophoretic measurements. In solubility and boundary spreading tests it behaves as if multiple components were present. Furthermore, there are no serological quantitative precipitin reactions. On gel electrophoresis, two bands were seen followed by a

smear of protein staining material as was observed on cellulose acetate electrophoretic preparations. In the latter, elution of protein from the area of apparent low concentration showed toxic activity throughout the entire length. In our experiments with labelled and unlabelled crystalline A toxin using the celite column method we obtained two precipitin lines in Ouchterlony plates. This appeared with whole or intentionally dissociated toxin. However, the plates revealed that the immunologic properties were the same. Experiments where the toxin was dissociated in solutions ranging from 7 to 9.2 pH and ionic strengths 0.02 to 1 M, yielded two principle and multiple secondary components. When the dissociated fractions were allowed to stand for a period of time, one could then repeat the electrophoretic pattern of two major bands followed by a long smear of secondary material. This suggests to us that the toxin exists in an equilibrim mixture of greater or less well associated toxic units depending upon the conditions. Other workers using several techniques have described three classes of subunit sizes ranging from 150,000 to as little as 3,800. This latter figure seems very small to bear enough amino acid residues to convey toxicity. It has been pointed out, that an unknown quantity of a probably separate protein with hemo-agglutinin properties is associated with crystalline toxin but this material cannot account for the secondary dissociation that has been observed. Lamanna and Carr point out that on a milligram nitrogen basis, the smaller units tend to be less toxic. Indeed, these authors raise the question whether the low molecular weight fractions claimed to be active may actually be contaminated by larger toxin fragments present in very small amounts. This problem is acute because very few molecules are needed to produce toxicity.

The problem of dissociation of the toxin remains controversial. A reasonable hypothesis is that the 900,000 weight molecular crystalline toxin contains both hemagglutinin and neurotoxin and that the neurotoxic protein is probably made up of subunits possibly as small as 150,000 to 15,000 MW.

Amino acid analyses of the various toxins have been performed. Type A for example, contains 19 amino acids with particularly striking quantities of aspartic, glutamic and tyrosine residues. However, although

---

*Not read at the conference.

tyrosine has been thought significant in toxicity, it is absent in B toxin.

An additional controversial issue is the problem of entry of the toxin. The natural route of intoxication is oral, yet it was early recognized that large proteins are not normally absorbed through the intestine in adult animals and data obtained by several investigators show that the enzymes in gastric and intestinal contents can destroy the toxin. The whole subject has been greatly confused by the fact that different investigators have used various animals which have varying susceptibilities to the toxin. It must be stressed that the few molecules necessary to produce toxicity may enter as if by accident in that the number which do enter are very small compared to the great number of molecules which are not absorbed or destroyed. As far as the animal is concerned, absorption of a few molecules constituting a toxin dose is sufficient.

We have labeled toxin and antitoxin with various fluorescent and electron dense labels. In studies using fluorescein-labeled botulinum toxin or indirect methods in which fluorescein-labeled botulinum antitoxin were used, the distribution of toxin following instillation of the toxin into the oropharynx, stomach and intestinal areas was traced in frozen sections subsequently examined in the ultraviolet microscope. After small amounts of toxin were placed in the oropharynx, fluorescein-labeled material was found within submucosal lymphatics whereas after gastric instillation, toxin could not be found. Again, when toxin was placed in intestinal loops, fluorescein-labeled material was found *between* epithelial cells and submucosal vessels, probably lymphatics. We also observed that attempts to instill the toxin into the stomach by conventional gastric intubation produced significant regurgitation into the oropharynx. In additional experiments in which minute quantities of saline (0.2μl,) containing large doses of toxin (0.5 μg.) were placed directly in the oropharynx, the survival times observed suggested that significant absorption occurred in this region. For example, 5 μg. of toxin in an 0.5 ml. drop placed on the tongue proved as toxic as 50 μg. instilled by stomach tube. We found that we could place large amounts of toxin in small volumes directly into the stomach without producing lethality.

The extreme toxicity of this material suggests a possible explanation. A remarkably small number of molecules is sufficient to produce paralysis and death in large animals. Even "accidental leakage" into oropharyngeal epithelium is sufficient. Part of the explanation for this seems to be the highly specific binding of botulinum toxin by neuromuscular junctions. Studies using ferritin-labeled botulinum A or B toxin showed localization within the subneural apparatus of the neuromuscular junctions. When fresh frozen sections of tissues from intoxicated mice were stained with fluorescein-labeled botulinum antitoxin, the only site of toxin binding occurred in the neuromuscular junctions. Unlike tetanal intoxication in which the skeletal muscle and central nervous system binds toxin, these tissues were entirely negative under the conditions used. These observations also help to explain why an estimated human parenteral lethal dose is approximately equal to only seven mouse lethal doses. It is clear that the toxicity is not related to the mass of the animal but probably to the mass of its motor endplates. Since most muscles contain one neuromuscular junction per myofiber in both mice and men, the greater muscle mass of man is largely due to greater myofiber size than number of myofibers, it follows that the ratio of human endplates to mouse endplates will be less than about 1 to 2 orders of magnitude than the ratio of their body weights. Instead of a ratio of 3500:1 (20 gm. mouse versus 70 kg. man) the factor is more of the order of 10 to 100x. Estimated in this way, a minimum oral dose in man would be about 5×10^{-9} to 5×10^{-8} gms. If only 0.01 percent is absorbed, a dose in range of 0.5 to 5.0 μgm. should be lethal, a figure that approximates the one cited by Lamanna and Carr. Stated in another way, mouse motor endplates are not very much smaller than human neuromuscular junctions; but once paralyzed, human neuromuscular junctions can paralyze a much greater volume of muscle fibers. Explanation for the variation of toxicity between different animal species and the ages of the individual animals raise several additional problems which cannot be discussed for lack of space.

Originally, it was thought that the toxin acted on the central nervous system but by 1923 several investigators had collected evidence pointing to a peripheral site of action. It is soon recognized that the toxin could slow the heart by blocking the vagus nerve, inhibit salivary secretion by inhibiting the chorda tympani nerve and interfere with bladder contraction and pupillary constriction. However, muscle contractility and nerve conduction were unaffected. As we have seen, this localizes the site of toxin action to the neuromuscular junction and pre- and post-ganglionic synapses.

Interest in the central nervous system has now been revived in some work by Simpson et al. who have shown electrical changes during intoxication. Tyler has reported that H reflexes could be elicited from a patient with botulism which he interpreted as evidence of central release or failure of inhibitory control in spinal relex arcs. There is too little data to evaluate these findings at present.

It seems likely that the toxin prevents the release of acetylcholine (Ach). When isolated neuromuscular preparations are stimulated in a bath, less Ach was released following stimulation of intoxicated muscle than in controls. Some investigators have claimed that presynaptic terminals have increased Ach content. Possible toxin inhibition of choline acetylase of Ach-ase has been disputed by several investigators. Since the poisoned muscle still responds to Ach or electrical stimuli with a contraction, the mode of action of the toxin is unlike curare but more like hemicholinium which blocks the synthesis of Ach. With microelectrode studies, poisoned endplates show a gradual reduction of MEPP's which may also be consistent with this idea.

As we have said, ferritin-labeled toxin is found in the subneural apparatus and indirect labeling with fluorescein-labeled antitoxin also shows binding in the subneural apparatus and/or terminal axons.

It has been shown that the toxin remains bound to the motor endplates for long periods of time. However, restoration of neuromuscular function can be accelerated by reinnervation of the muscle. If the motor nerve is crushed, allowed to degenerate and then regenerate, it will reinnervate the muscle and function is restored. The toxin apparently has no effect on the rate of reinnervation. This experiment emphasizes that the toxin acts on the presynaptic element in view of the fact that there is no prolonged delay in reinnervation, the old axons probably return to the old subneural apparatuses rather than form new endplates.

If it is accepted that the muscle is flaccid because of lack of Ach release from the nerve terminal, several interesting observations raise questions about the interrelationship between nerve and muscle in this region. Several investigators have shown that acutely intoxicated muscle shows no fine structure abnormalities in the neuromuscular junction although one investigator has reported chronic changes in muscle similar to denervation in light microscopic studies. However, in our hands, working with mice with chronic intoxication of up to 20 days, we have not been able to find muscle atrophy. The only changes occurring in the mitochondria are nonspecific. It is interesting that no muscle atrophy occurs in chronic botulinus intoxication as contrasted with the situation of crush or sectioning of the nerve where atrophy is a prominent consequence. It seems that what we may call "chemical denervation" differs from actual physical denervation where degeneration of the nerve occurs. This raises questions about the "trophic activity" of the nerve with respect to maintenance of the muscle. It has also been shown that the toxin prevents the normally occurring rejection of secondary innervating nerve fibers, a result similar to that observed when the endplate area is isolated from the remainder of the muscle.

As to the molecular mode of action, we can only speculate. The best evidence suggests that there is block of release of Ach. We do have evidence the toxin lies in the subneural apparatus. The ferritin labeling experiments do not permit assessment of binding to synaptic vesicles, the supposed site of Ach release, since this tracer does not penetrate cells. It may be possible to use the new horseradish peroxidase labeling technique to investigate this aspect of the problem.

Other data of interest concerning the toxin include the lack of temperature dependence in homothermic animals such as occurs with tetanus neurotoxin. Poikilothermic animals are not intoxicated until the temperature is raised to approximately 23° C.

We have also observed local botulinism in mice similar to the syndrome of tetanus. Reversible paralysis of muscle occurs when minute quantities of botulinum toxin are injected directly into the muscle.

Another interesting observation is the production of deformed chick embryos with severe muscle atrophy and contractures by means of injection of the toxin into embryonated eggs. It is not clear at the moment whether this is a specific effect or results only as a consequence of severe muscle weakness.

Another interesting aspect is the resistance to botulinum A intoxication that occurs in a small number (approximately 5 percent) of randomly bred Swiss white mice. This appears to be a genetic characteristic and in some breeding experiments that we have performed, we were able to distribute the gene rather than concentrate it. However, this observation may lead to additional studies to explain the basis of natural resistance.

THE ABSORPTION OF *CLOSTRIDIUM BOTULINUM* TYPE E TOXIN FROM THE ALIMENTARY TRACT

by Teiji Ono, Takashi Karashimada, *and* Hiroo Iida*
Hokkaido Institute of Public Health, Sapporo, Japan

Introduction

We have previously reported that specific antitoxic serum has a considerable therapeutic value in human type E botulism (2, 5). This led us to the further investigation concerning serum therapy of type E botulism in experimental animals. Of several conclusions obtained from the experiments with mice (6), the following have been of particular interest.

When toxin is injected subcutaneously and antitoxin is immediately injected subcutaneously, the ratio of the amount of toxin to that of antitoxin required to bring about 50 percent neutralization is roughly 1:1. When however, toxin is given orally and antitoxin subcutaneously, the quantitative relationship between toxin and antitoxin, at the 50 percent neutralization, changes remarkably; thus 7.5 times more toxin is required and about 1,300 times more antitoxin is required to neutralize it.

In order to ascertain if the same phenomenon occurs in another species of experimental animals, a similar experiment was carried out with guinea pigs.

Materials and Methods

Toxin.—*C. botulinum* type E, strain Iwanai, was used for the preparation of toxin. The method described by Sakaguchi and Sakaguchi (11) for the partial purification of toxin was employed. The salient data concerning the toxicity of the toxin preparation are shown in table 1. In consideration of the practical conditions of human botulism, toxin without trypsin-treatment was used for the oral administration. Trypsin-treated toxin was used for the subcutaneous injection.

Antitoxin.—Type E antitoxic horse serum used in the experiment was prepared by the National Institute of Health, Tokyo, containing 840 International Units (IU) of antitoxin per milliliter.

Results and Discussions

As is indicated in table 1, activation of toxin by trypsin was clearly demonstrated by the subcutaneous route but not by the oral route, both in mice and guinea pigs, in keeping with the results of Duff, Wright, and Yarinsky (3). This seems to suggest that toxin precursors should be activated in the alimentary tract before being absorbed.

Neutralization tests with guinea pigs were carried out as follows. A known amount of toxin was injected under the skin of the back of the animals. A known dilution of antitoxin was then immediately injected subcutaneously on the other side of the back of these animals. As shown in figure 1, the ratio of the increase in the amount of antitoxin to that of toxin is roughly 1:1, resembling the results obtained with mice.

Then, neutralization tests were carried out with toxin administered *per os* and antitoxin injected immediately subcutaneously. As clearly shown in

Table 1.—Toxicity of type E toxin preparation

Toxin	Oral	Subcutaneous	Intraperitoneal
Toxicity for mice (LD_{50}/N mg.):			
Before trypsin treatment	2.1×10^3	3.7×10^4	1.3×10^5
After trypsin treatment	1.9×10^3	4.8×10^6	2.5×10^7
Activated/Unactivated	0.91	128	
Toxicity for guinea pigs (LD_{50}/N mg.):			
Before trypsin treatment	1.3×10^2	4.3×10^2	
After trypsin treatment	9.5×10^1	2.4×10^4	1.0×10^6
Activated/Unactivated	0.71	55	
Ratio of guinea pig LD_{50} to mouse LD_{50}:			
Before trypsin treatment	15.5	86.2	
After trypsin treatment	20.3	200	

*Paper read by H. Iida.

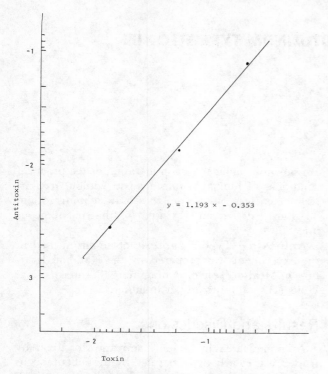

Figure 1.—Neutralization of toxin injected subcutaneously.

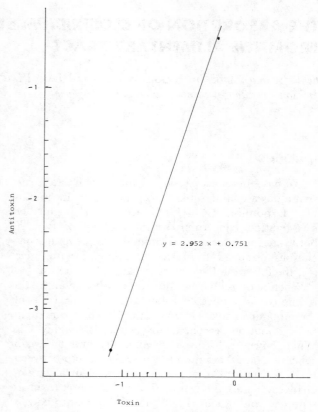

Figure 2.—Neutralization of toxin given orally.

figure 2, the amounts of antitoxin required to neutralize increased amounts of toxin are much larger when the latter are given orally than when given subcutaneously. This also coincides with the results obtained with mice.

Figures 3 and 4 show the results of the neutralization tests with mice and guinea pigs on the same graphs.

What is the reason for the fact that a considerably larger amount of antitoxin is required against toxin given orally as compared with toxin given subcutaneously? It was conceived that if the amount of toxin given orally was increased, the amount of toxin absorbed from the alimentary tract into the blood stream would be markedly increased. Therefore, an experiment was devised to determine the amount of toxin absorbed after oral administration of various doses of toxin.

Rabbits were used for the experiment because of the facility of treatment. The rabbits were divided into four groups and each of four different dilutions of toxin was given once into the stomach of the animals of each group through a vinyl tube. The animals had been deprived of food for 16 to 18 hours before the administration of toxin and were fed on clover after the administration. Samples of the blood were obtained from the auricular veins at intervals of one hour. Heparin was added to the blood and the plasma obtained was diluted and injected intraperi-

toneally into mice in order to estimate the amount of toxin per milliliter of plasma.

Group I was given eight rabbit *per os* LD_{50} (144,000 mouse intraperitoneal LD_{50}) of toxin. The results are shown in Figure 5. The average death time of the four rabbits was 6.8 hours. The toxin appeared in the blood within 1 hour after the administration and reached the maximum titer after 4 hours. The maximum toxin titer in the blood was approximately 2,000 mouse LD_{50}/ml.

Group II was given four rabbit *per os* LD_{50} of toxin. As shown in figure 6, the average death time of the four rabbits was 10.4 hours. The appearance of the toxin in the blood stream was slightly delayed and the maximum titer was 128 mouse LD_{50}/ml.

Group III was given two rabbit *per os* LD_{50} of toxin. As shown in figure 7, the average death time of the four rabbits was 11.9 hours. The toxin appeared in the blood 2 hours after the administration and the maximum titer as approximately 64 mouse LD_{50}/ml.

Group IV was given 1 rabbit *per os* LD_{50} of toxin. As shown in figure 8, only two out of five rabbits died and the remaining three survived. In the former, toxin was definitely demonstrated in the blood, while in the latter, the presence of toxin was barely proved

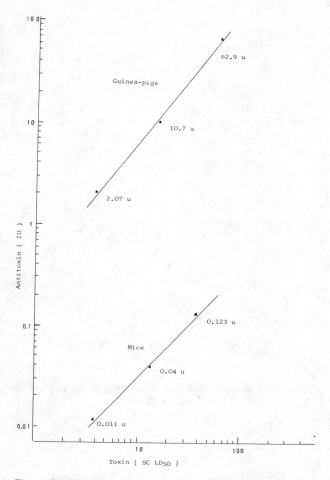

Figure 3.—Neutralization of toxin injected subcutaneously.

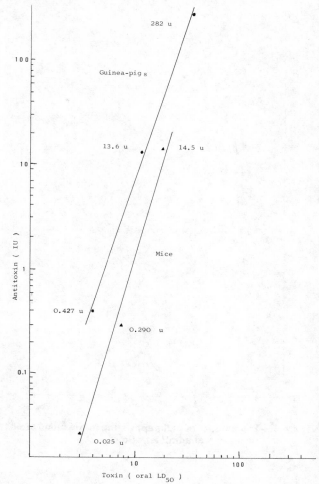

Figure 4.—Neutralization of toxin given orally.

by the symptoms of mice receiving the blood samples.

It was obvious from these results that the more toxin administered, the shorter the incubation period and the death time of the animals.

The amount of toxin in the blood collected immediately after death was plotted against the amount of toxin administered *per os* and the curve obtained indicated a straight line relationship as shown in figure 9. This means that the amounts of toxin absorbed from the alimentary tract markedly increased when the amounts of toxin administered *per os* increased. A considerably large amount of antitoxin would be required to neutralize such a large amount of toxin in the blood. Thus, the results obtained by the experiments on the absorption of toxin seem to support the results of neutralization tests carried out with toxin given orally and antitoxin given subcutaneously.

Type E toxin given *per os* first appeared in the lymphatic system, collected in Ductus thoracicus and then removed into the blood stream. This is in agree-

ment with the early work by May and Whaler (*9*) with type A toxin.

The molecular size of the toxin in the blood is now under study. The molecular size is assumed to be more than 100,000 as estimated by ultracentrifugation and gel-filtration with Sephadex G100 and G200. (figs. 10 and 11).

The mechanism of the absorption of toxin molecules is not clear. Recently it was reported that some proteinases are absorbed from the intestinal canal of rabbits as active high-molecular enzymes (*10*). This is surmised to occur through pinocytosis and a similar mechanism might be postulated in the absorption of the toxin. An alternative view is that the toxin might be absorbed as smaller units, for example as active peptides described by Gerwing et al. (*4*), and then become larger molecules in the blood.

One of the most interesting findings obtained in the present experiments is that unexpectedly large

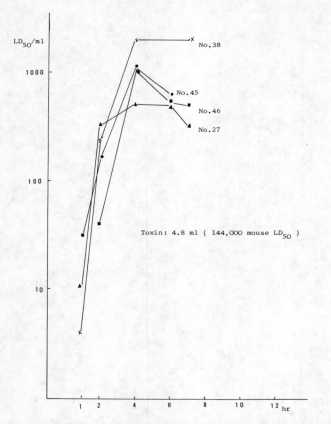

Figure 5.—The amount of toxin appearing in the blood after oral administration.

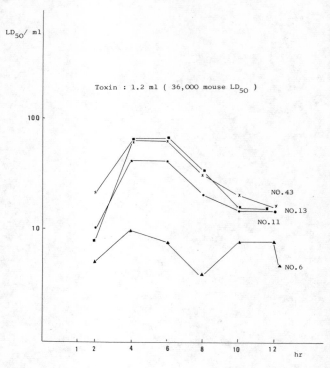

Figure 7.—The amount of toxin appearing in the blood after oral administration.

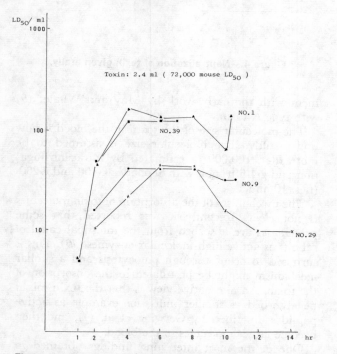

Figure 6.—The amount of toxin appearing in the blood after oral administration.

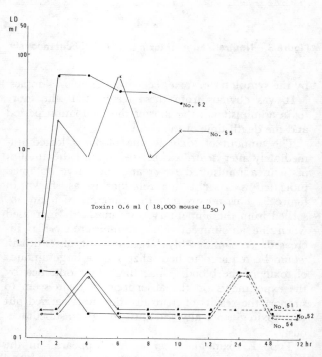

Figure 8.—The amount of toxin appearing in the blood after oral administration.

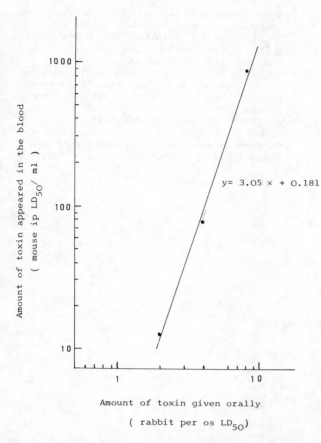

Figure 9.—Relationship between the amount of toxin given orally and the amount of toxin appearing in the blood.

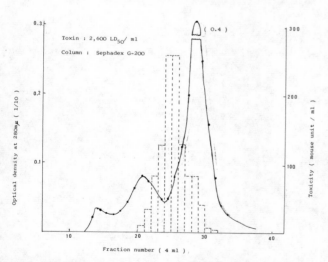

Figure 10.—Gel-filtration of toxin in the serum at pH 6.0.

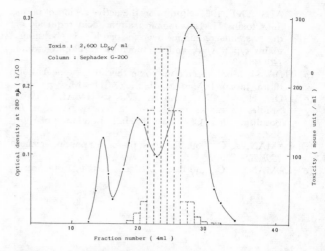

Figure 11.—Gel-filtration of toxin in the serum at pH 8.0.

If calculated on the assumption that the body weight of rabbits was 3 kg. and the amount of the blood was one-thirteenth of body weight, the total amount of toxin in the blood amounts to 470,000 mouse LD_{50}. This means that the toxin administered (144,000 mouse LD_{50}) was activated *in vivo* and a considerable part of it was absorbed. This finding is quite distinct from the results of previous papers on type A toxin (*1, 7, 9*) which reported that an extremely small quantity of toxin is absorbed from the alimentary tract.

One of the reasons for this discrepancy might be the difference in the stability to digestive enzymes of type A and type E toxin preparations. Also the genetic line of experimental animals, the kind of feeds used (*8*) and the time of feeding (*9*) will all be related to the absorption of toxin from the alimentary tract. Further studies into these problems are necessary.

Acknowledgment

We wish to express our thanks to Messrs. K. Kameyama and M. I. Yamaguchi in our laboratory for much assistance. This investigation was supported by Research Grant No. CC 00173 from the National Communicable Disease Center, Atlanta, Ga., U.S.A.

References

(*1*) DACK, G. M., and W. L. WOOD. 1927. Impermeability of the small intestine of rabbits to botulinum toxin. J. Infect. Dis. *40:* 585–587.

(*2*) DOLMAN, C. E., and H. IIDA. 1963. Type E botulism: Its epidemiology, prevention and specific treatment. Canad. J. Publ. Health *54:* 293–308.

(*3*) DUFF, J. T., G. G. WRIGHT, and A. YARINSKY. 1956. Activation of *Clostridium botulinum* type E toxin by trypsin. J. Bacteriol. *72:* 455–460.

(*4*) GERWING, J., B. MITCHELL, and D. VAN

amount of toxin was absorbed from the alimentary tract into the blood stream. For instance, the maximum toxin titer in the blood of the rabbits belonging to group I was approximately 2,000 mouse LD_{50}/ml.

ALSTYNE. 1967. Studies on the active region of botulinus toxins II. Isolation and amino acid sequence of the cysteine-containing tryptic peptide in botulinus toxins types A, B, and E. Biochim. et Biophys. Acta *140:* 363–365.

(5) IIDA, H. 1963. Specific antitoxin therapy in type E botulism. Japan. J. Med. Sci. Biol. *16:* 311–313.

(6) IIDA, H., T. ONO, and T. KARASHIMADA. 1967. Studies on the serum therapy of type E botulism. *In* Botulism 1966. Chapman & Hall, London, pp. 346–362.

(7) LAMANNA, C. 1959. The most poisonous poison. Science *130:* 763–772.

(8) LAMANNA, C., and C. E. MEYERS. 1960. Influence of ingested foods on the oral toxicity in mice of crystalline botulinal type A toxin. J. Bacteriol. *79:* 406–410.

(9) MAY, A. J., and B. C. WHALER. 1958. The absorption of *Clostridium botulinum* type A toxin from the alimentary canal. Brit. J. Exper. Pathol. *39:* 307–316.

(10) MURACHI, T. 1967. The absorption of proteinases from the intestinal canal. Proceedings of the 17th Congress of Japan Medical Association pp. 341–342. (text in Japanese).

(11) SAKAGUCHI, G., and S. SAKAGUCHI. 1961. A simple method for purification of type E botulinal toxin from the precursor extract of the bacterial cells. Japan. J. Med. Sci. Biol. *14:* 243–248.

EPIDEMIOLOGICAL AND CLINICAL OBSERVATIONS OF BOTULISM OUTBREAKS IN JAPAN

by Hiroo Iida

Hokkaido Institute of Public Health, South 2, West 15, Sapporo, Japan

Summary

The following two epidemiological features of botulism in Japan are mentioned and discussed:

(1) Almost all of the human botulism outbreaks in Japan have been of type E and this seems to be due to the fact that type E spores are distributed widely and in high frequency in the soil of Tohoku and Hokkaido districts, two main endemic areas of botulism in Japan.

(2) Most of these type E outbreaks have been caused by a special fermented food called izushi. The reasons seem to be that raw fish used in izushi are often contaminated with type E spores in coastal sand and river side mud, that the spores easily germinate, multiply and produce toxin in fish as the degree of freshness of fish decreases, and that izushi thus prepared is consumed without cooking.

The clinical symptoms of type E botulism are similar to those of types A and B except that excessive dryness of the mouth, due to the dysfunction of salivary secretion, and retention of urine have been frequently observed in type E cases.

The case fatality rate of type E botulism in Hokkaido has decreased from 28.5 to 4.3 percent since specific antitoxin has been distributed and used.

Epidemiology

Two outstanding features are observed in the epidemiology of botulism outbreaks in Japan (*4*, *6*, *14*); one is that most of them have been of type E and the other is that they have been all caused by a foodstuff called "izushi", except for a few episodes.

A total of 57 outbreaks of human botulism have been reported in Japan since 1951 when the authors reported the first outbreak in Hokkaido (*13*). Except for one episode due to type B (*12*) and a few unexamined outbreaks, all of these outbreaks were caused by *C. botulinum* type E. The number of cases amounts to 321, of which 85 died (table 1 and fig. 1.).

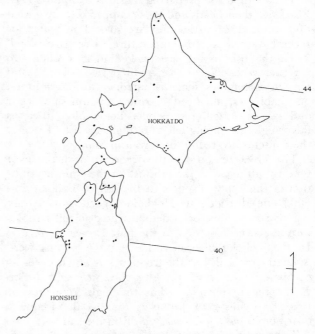

Figure 1.—Botulism outbreaks in Japan (1951–67).

Table 1.—Botulism outbreaks in Japan (1951–67)

Place	Number of outbreaks	Persons at risk	Cases	Deaths	Food incriminated
Hokkaido	35	483	231	43	Izushi, kirikomi, trout eggs.
Akita Prefecture	13	75	60	24	Izushi.
Aomori Prefecture	6	32	19	10	Do.
Iwate Prefecture	2	16	8	5	Do.
Yamagata Prefecture	1	3	3	3	Canned mackerel.
Total	57	609	321	85	

NOTES.—Morbidity rate:—52.7 percent;—Mortality rate:—26.5 percent.

Foods incriminated in the majority of outbreaks were izushi made of raw fish. Izushi is a kind of fermented food preferably prepared by the fishermen living in Tohoku and Hokkaido districts of Japan. It is usually prepared only in the cold winter season, but since the facilities for preserving raw fish are lacking in small fishing villages, izushi often is the only way for preserving raw fish caught in great numbers at a time. From the data on the past outbreaks, it is evident that izushi prepared in spring or autumn seasons has caused botulism most frequently.

Many kinds of fish, raw or frozen, are used to prepare izushi. Most often used are "hata-hata" (*Arctoscopus japonicus*), herring, sole, and salmon, but others such as Lockington, trout, cod, sardine, mackerel, "sanma" (*Cololabis saira*) and "yamabe" (a sort of dace) are also used in homemade izushi. Izushi made of these kinds of fish have been reported to have caused human type E botulism.

The method for preparing izushi is as follows (*14*). Fish have their heads and tails chopped off, are gutted and made into patties and are soaked in water for several days at room temperature to remove blood. Then the fish patties are packed in a wooden tub together with cooked rice, malted rice ("koji") and various vegetables such as carrots, garden radishes, and cabbages, all diced. A small amount of vinegar and salt is added, red pepper being often used as flavoring. After being left to ferment for 3 to 4 weeks, the contents are ready for consumption.

The chief reason for the frequent occurrence of type E outbreaks in Japan must be the wide distribution of this type as spores in the soil of Tohoku and Hokkaido districts. In Hokkaido, particularly, only type E spores have been demonstrated in soil samples through several surveys in the past 15 years (*10, 15*). In the Tohoku district, a few type A strains were isolated from soil, but the frequency is much lower as compared with type E. Therefore, it seems to be reasonable to postulate that the high frequency of type E botulism in Japan is due to the frequent distribution of *C. botulinum* type E in the soil.

The reasons for the frequent occurrence of type E botulism due to izushi seem to be as follows. Fish used as an ingredient of izushi will have many chances of being contaminated with type E spores. This view is sustained by the results of several surveys on the coastal and inland soil samples in Hokkaido, which always have shown the high frequency of type E. Fish seem to be contaminated with type E spores both before and after the death.

C. botulinum type E spores readily germinate, proliferate and produce toxin in fish flesh as the degree of freshness of fish decreases. In general, the redox potential is high in fresh fish, which prevents type E spores from germinating. As the degree of freshness falls, however, the redox potential also decreases by the autolysis of fish flesh and by the proliferation of various micro-organisms indigenous to them, which enables type E spores to germinate and the organisms to proliferate. It is well known that type E spores injected into fish can germinate, multiply and produce toxin in 2 or 3 days at room temperature (*3, 5*). It has also been reported by us (*1*) that a remarkable decrease in redox-potential is observed in fish flesh at the early period of putrefaction. Therefore, it is reasonable to presume that the decrease of the redox-potential in fish during the "soaking" period will bring about the germination, proliferation and toxin production of type E spores. This process may also take place during the fermentation period, but as the pH of fish falls due to the fermentation of malted rice, the outgrowth of type E organisms will be inhibited to some extent.

The chief reason why sliced raw fish ("sashimi"), which is very often eaten by the Japanese people, has not yet caused botulism seems to be the extremely high degree of freshness of the fish used.

The fact that izushi is usually consumed without cooking also seems to make this food the commonest vehicle of botulism. As the toxin of *C. botulinum* is a protein which is easily destroyed by heating at 70° to 80° C. for several minutes, foods which are heated and cooked before consumption cannot cause botulism. As the heat-resistance of type E spores is much lower as compared with that of types A and B spores (*9*), type E outbreaks due to canned foods have been relatively rare.

Clinical Observations

The clinical features of type E botulism encountered in Hokkaido are summarized as follows (*6, 14*).

After the incubation period, between several hours to a few days, almost all of the patients complained of dizziness, malaise, nausea, and vomiting. Then the characteristic neurological symptoms appeared. These consisted of ocular symptoms such as blurring of vision, diplopia, ptosis, mydriasis and loss or tardiness of reflex to light; pharyngeal symptoms, such as difficulties in swallowing and speaking; gastro-intestinal symptoms such as constipation and expansion of the abdomen. In serious cases, paralysis of the limbs and dyspnea due to paralysis of the respiratory muscles appeared.

The symptoms characteristic of type E outbreaks are extreme dryness of the mouth due to the dysfunction of salivary secretion and retention of urine. These symptoms have not been reported as frequently in types A and B human botulism.

The above described signs and symptoms of type E botulism encountered in Hokkaido, Japan, are in

Table 2.—Effect of type E antitoxin therapy (Hokkaido, Japan)

Antitoxin	Number of outbreaks	Persons at risk	Cases	Deaths	Morbidity rate (percent)	Mortality rate (percent)
Not used_____	20	282	137	39	48.5	28.5
Used_____	15	201	94	[1]4	46.8	4.3
Total_____	35	483	231	43	47.8	18.7

[1]2 died before antitoxin could be administered.

accord with those of type E episodes recently reported in the United States (11).

In Hokkaido, a case was operated upon due to a misdiagnosis of ileus because of the expansion of the abdomen. A case was complicated by a parotitis resulting from disturbances of salivation, accompanied by a retropharyngeal abscess and this patient died about a month after the onset of his illness.

As for the therapeutic value of specific antitoxin, we have observed a considerable effect, at least in type E botulism (7, 8). Table 2 shows the remarkable efficacy of antitoxin therapy in type E outbreaks in Hokkaido. The case fatality rate was only 4.3 percent in 94 patients receiving antitoxin in 15 recent outbreaks, compared with a rate of 28.5 percent in 137 untreated cases in 20 previous outbreaks. Moreover, of four deaths in the treated series, two occurred before antitoxin was administered.

The therapeutic value of specific antitoxin in type E botulism has been reported not only in Japan but also in Canada (4) and the United States (11). The results of the experimental studies on this problem is presented in another report. Recently, guanidine, an accelerator of the release of acetylcholine from the nerve endings, was reported to have been effective in treating a case of botulism (2), so the combination of guanidine and specific antitoxin will be of great value in the treatment of the disease.

Acknowledgments

The author wishes to express his gratitude to Prof. C. E. Dolman, Department of Microbiology, University of British Columbia, for his invaluable advice and encouragement. The author is also indebted to the staff of the laboratory of the National Institute of Health, Tokyo, for helpful discussions and to his colleagues for their assistance throughout this work.

References

(1) ANDO, Y., K. INOUE, and H. IIDA. 1958. Experimental studies on the prevention of type E botulism due to izushi P. I. Rep. Hokkaido Inst. Pub. Health. 9: 39–57 (in Japanese).

(2) CHERINGTON, M., and D. W. RYAN. 1968. Botulism and guanidine. New England J. Med. 278: 931–933.

(3) DOLMAN, C. E., H. CHANG, D. E. KERR, and A. S. SHEARER. 1950. Fish-borne and type E botulism: Two cases due to home-pickled herring. Canad. J. Pub. Health. 41: 215–229.

(4) DOLMAN, C. E., and H. IIDA. 1963. Type E botulism: Its epidemiology, prevention and specific treatment. Canad. J. Pub. Health. 54: 293–308.

(5) IIDA, H., K. KANZAWA, and Y. NAKAMURA. 1956. Experimental studies on the toxin production by Cl. botulinum type E in fish. Rep. Hokkaido Inst. Pub. Health. Special Report 5: 10–16 (in Japanese).

(6) IIDA, H., Y. NAKAMURA, I. NAKAGAWA, and T. KARASHIMADA. 1958. Additional type E botulism outbreaks in Hokkaido, Japan. Med. Sci. Biol. 11: 215–222.

(7) IIDA, H. 1963. Specific antitoxin therapy in type E botulism. Japan. J. Med. Sci. Biol. 16: 311–313.

(8) IIDA, H., K. KANZAWA, Y. NAKAMURA, T. KARASHIMADA, T. ONO, and T. SAITO. 1964. Botulism outbreaks encountered in Hokkaido in 1962; With special reference to the therapeutic value of antitoxic serum. Rep. Hokkaido Inst. Pub. Health. 14: 6–18 (in Japanese).

(9) KANZAWA, K. 1956. Heat-resistance of spores of Cl. botulinum type E. Rep. Hokkaido Inst. Pub. Health Special Report 5: 24–27 (in Japanese).

(10) KANZAWA, K. 1960. Ecological studies on Cl. botulinum type E. Rep. Hokkaido Inst. Public Health. 11: 161–172 (in Japanese).

(11) KOENIG, M. G., A. SPICKARD, M. A. CARDELLA, and D. E. ROGERS. 1964. Clinical and laboratory observations on type E botulism in man. Medicine. 43: 517–545.

(12) NAKAMURA, G., M. TAKEYA, H. KUDO, C. IZUMIYAMA, K. YAMAMOTO, H. ASANO, and M. TAKEYAMA. 1963. Ein Fall von Typus B Botulismus. Hirosaki Med. J. 14: 123–127.

(13) NAKAMURA, Y., H. IIDA, and R. NAKAO. 1951. An outbreak of food poisoning suspicious of botulism. Rep. Hokkaido Inst. Pub. Health. 2: 29–34 (in Japanese).

(14) NAKAMURA, Y., H. IIDA, K. SAEKI, K. KANZAWA, and T. KARASHIMADA. 1956. Type E botulism in Hokkaido, Japan. Japan. J. Med. Sci. Biol. 9: 45–58.

(15) ONO, T., T. KARASHIMADA, K. KAMEYAMA, A. SATO, K. KANZAWA, and H. IIDA. 1967. Studies on the distribution of Cl. botulinum type E in Hokkaido, Japan. Rep. Hokkaido Inst. Pub. Health. 17: 1–12 (in Japanese).

CLINICAL AND EPIDEMIOLOGICAL ASPECTS OF BOTULISM IN THE UNITED STATES

by V. R. Dowell, Jr., E. J. Gangarosa, *and* R. W. Armstrong,*
National Communicable Disease Center,
Health Services and Mental Health Administration,
Department of Health, Education, and Welfare, Atlanta, Ga. 30333

Summary

From 1899 to 1967, 640 outbreaks (1,669 cases) of botulism were reported in the United States with 948 deaths. In cases where the toxin type was identified, type A was most common, followed by types B, E, mixed types A and B, and F. Home processed vegetables were most commonly incriminated. Out of 53 suspected outbreaks of botulism investigated by the NCDC from 1964 to 1967, only 18 were found to be botulism. Reported signs and symptoms from 145 cases of botulism were reviewed, revealing that intestinal symptoms, dizziness, and vertigo are more common in types E and B botulism than in other types. Other signs and symptoms were equally common to all types. Gastrointestinal symptoms and signs in botulism may mislead clinicians to other diagnoses.

Introduction

Interest in botulism and the causative organism was greatly stimulated in 1963 when four outbreaks in humans were traced to commercially processed foodstuffs (8). This was the first year since 1924 that commercially prepared foods were responsible for more cases of botulism in the United States than foods processed in the home (7). Since 1963, the volume of research on problems related to botulism has vastly increased particularly in relation to *Clostridium botulinum* type E (4, 5). Interest was further stimulated in 1966 when an outbreak of type F botulism occurred in California, the second recorded outbreak of this type in the world (1, 2). This report reviews the reported outbreaks of botulism in the United States from 1899 through 1967 and discusses current concepts in diagnosis and treatment.

The statistical information from 1899 to 1949 was derived from the excellent review by Meyer and Eddie (7). Data after 1950 were based on outbreaks reported to the National Communicable Disease Center (NCDC), Atlanta, Ga., and recently summarized by Armstrong and Gangarosa (9). In recent

years, Epidemic Intelligence Service Officers of the Epidemiology Program, NCDC, participated in the investigation of a number of outbreaks, and laboratory support was provided when needed by the Anaerobic Bacteriology laboratory, Laboratory Program, NCDC. Methods employed for the detection of botulinum toxins and *C. botulinum* are described in detail in the U.S. Public Health Service publication, *Laboratory Methods in Anaerobic Bacteriology* (3).

Epidemiology

Figure 1 lists outbreaks by State. From 1899 to 1967, 640 outbreaks were reported resulting in 1,669 cases and 948 deaths, an overall case fatality rate of 56.9 percent. There were 463 cases of type A, 121 cases of type B, 57 cases of type E (34 occurring after 1960), three cases of type F, six cases involving both type A and type B toxins and 1,019 cases (57 percent of the total number) in which the toxin type was not determined (table 1).

The number of outbreaks attributed to commercially processed and home processed foods and the outbreaks in which the food involved was not determined are listed in table 2. Although home processed foods were involved in the majority of the outbreaks, after 1949 their number decreased significantly whereas outbreaks in which the food responsible was not determined increased.

Vegetables of various types were the foods most commonly incriminated in outbreaks, followed by fruits and fish products (table 3). Meats, excluding fish and poultry, were responsible for only eight of the recorded outbreaks. The type A outbreaks in which meats were involved included two from pork, two from beef, and one from mutton. Only two outbreaks of type B botulism involving meats were reported; one due to the ingestion of beef and one from the ingestion of pork. The single type F outbreak, with three cases, was associated with the ingestion of home prepared venison jerky (1). Miscellaneous "foods" listed in table 3 included products such as tomato relish, chile peppers, salad dressing, corn, and chicken mash (9).

---

*Present address at Stanford University Hospital, Palo Alto, Calif.

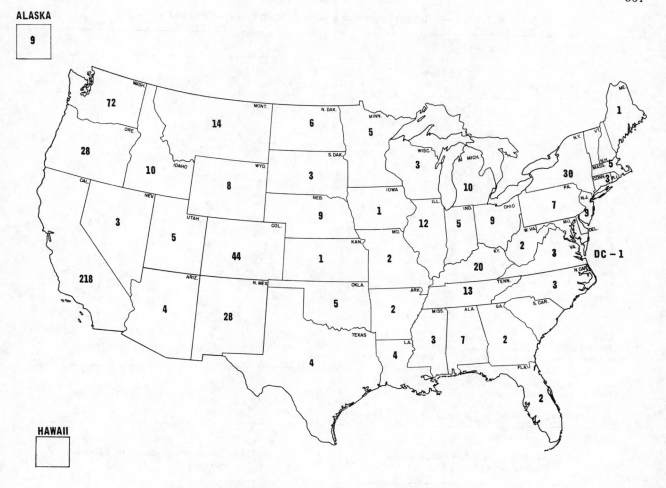

Figure 1.—Outbreaks of botulism, 1899–1967.

Diagnosis

During 1964–1967, the NCDC investigated 53 suspected outbreaks of botulism (table 4). Only 18 of the 53 were actually botulism. The remainder of the outbreaks were due to a variety of causes, including staphylococcal foodborne disease, chemical food poisoning, Guillain-Barré syndrome and carbon monoxide poisoning. As these data indicate, many illnesses can be confused with botulism.

Tables 5 and 6 summarize the symptoms and signs observed in 145 cases of botulism reported to the NCDC from 1953–67. Gastrointestinal symptoms, dizziness, and vertigo were found in cases caused by all toxin types but were more common in types B and E cases. Signs and symptoms were otherwise equally common in cases caused by all botulinum toxin types (9).

The following cardinal features of botulism may help exclude other diagnoses (9):

(1) *Fever is absent* early in the disease, but may develop later from pneumonia or other complications.

(2) *Mental processes are clear*. The patient may be anxious or agitated for obvious reasons or drowsy but most patients are responsive.

(3) Pulse is normal or slow, but may accelerate after hypotension develops.

(4) Although *vision* may be impaired and *hearing* distorted, there is *no numbness* or decreased perception or touch, and no paresthesia or other sensory disturbances.

(5) All neurological manifestations are symmetrical (9).

The first manifestations of illness in most patients with type E botulism are gastrointestinal, which may include nausea or vomiting, substernal burning or pain, abdominal distention, decreased bowel sounds, and dilated loops of small bowel on radiologic examination. Some patients have initial transitory diarrhea but later become constipated. Gastrointestinal symptoms may also be present in cases of types B and A

Table 1.—Botulism cases and deaths by toxin types, 1899–1967

Toxin type	Years							
	1899 to 1909	1910–19	1920–29	1930–39	1940–49	1950–59	1960–67	Total
Type A:								
Cases	0	44	156	94	110	39	20	463
Deaths	0	31	94	69	62	18	4	278
Fatality rate (percent)		70.5	60.3	73.4	56.4	46.2	20.0	60.0
Type B:								
Cases	0	10	33	33	22	4	19	121
Deaths	0	7	20	16	12	2	2	59
Fatality rate (percent)		70.0	60.6	48.5	54.5	50.0	10.5	48.7
Type E:								
Cases	0	0	0	6	3	14	34	57
Deaths	0	0	0	2	1	7	15	25
Fatality rate (percent)				33.3	33.3	50.0	44.1	43.9
Type F:								
Cases	0	0	0	0	0	0	3	3
Deaths	0	0	0	0	0	0	0	0
Fatality rate (percent)							0	0
Mixed types A and B:								
Cases	0	0	1	5	0	0	0	6
Deaths	0	0	1	1	0	0	0	2
Fatality rate (percent)			100.0	20.0				33.3
Type undetermined:								
Cases	11	189	138	245	181	176	79	1,019
Deaths	6	135	92	162	119	58	12	584
Fatality rate (percent)	55.0	71.4	66.7	66.1	65.7	33.0	15.2	57.3
Total:								
Cases	11	243	328	383	316	233	155	1,669
Deaths	6	173	207	250	194	85	33	948
Fatality rate (percent)	55.0	71.2	63.1	65.3	61.4	36.5	21.2	56.8

Table 2.—Foods involved in outbreaks of botulism, 1899–1967

Interval	Home processed	Commercially processed	Unknown
1899–1909	2	1	0
1910–19	48	14	8
1920–29	77	26	13
1930–39	135	6	13
1940–49	120	1	13
1950–59	50	3	50
1960–67	31	9	20
Total	463	60	117

Table 3.—Foods involved in botulism outbreaks, 1899–1967

Food	Toxin type				
	A	B	E	F	A and B
Vegetables	90	21	1	0	2
Fruits	22	4	0	0	0
Meats	5	2	0	1	0
Poultry	0	1	0	0	0
Fish and fish products	5	2	16	0	0
Milk and milk products	2	2	0	0	0
Miscellaneous	15	2	0	0	0
Total	139	34	17	1	2

botulism. The gastrointestinal symptoms and signs may be so prominent in botulism that clinicians are misled to a diagnosis of appendicitis, bowel obstruction, or diaphragmatic myocardial infarction (6, 9).

Laboratory confirmation

The most effective way to confirm a diagnosis of botulism in the laboratory is to identify the specific botulinum toxin in the patient's blood by performing toxin neutralization tests in mice with the patient's serum and specific botulinum antitoxins (3). For

this reason, in all cases where botulism is suspected, 10 ml. or more of the patient's serum should be collected prior to antitoxin treatment for toxin detection, and at intervals during the acute and convalescent stages of the illness. Acute and convalescent serum samples should also be frozen and held for further studies in case the illness is not botulism.

An indirect laboratory diagnosis of botulism can be made by demonstrating botulinum toxin in ex-

Table 4.—Suspected outbreaks of botulism investigated by NCDC, 1964–67

Diagnosis	Number of outbreaks	Diagnosis	Number of outbreaks
Botulism	18	Hyperventilation syndrome	1
Staphylococcal food poisoning	9	Neuropsychiatric disorder	1
Chemical food poisoning	3	*C. perfringens* gangrene	1
Carbon monoxide poisoning	3	No illness	4
Guillain-Barré	3	No final diagnosis	7
CVA	2	Total investigations	53
Shigella or Salmonella	1		

Table 5.—Symptoms observed in 145 cases of botulism reported to NCDC from 1953 to 1967

Symptoms	Number of Patients	Symptoms	Number of Patients
Blurred vision, diplopia or photophobia	50	Abdominal pain, cramps, fullness	9
Dysphagia	34	Diarrhea	5
Dysphonia	26	Constipation	2
Generalized weakness	23	Difficult urination	2
Nausea and/or vomiting	30	Paresthesias	1
Dizziness or vertigo	13		

Table 6.—Signs observed in 145 cases of botulism reported to NCDC from 1953 to 1967

Signs	Number of patients
Respiratory impairment	29
Eye muscle involvement, including ptosis	10
Dilated, fixed pupils	7
Specific muscle weakness or paralysis	8
Dry throat, mouth, or tongue	7
Ataxia	7
Somnolence	1
Nystagmus	1
Postural hypotension	1

tracts of the suspect food by performing mouse protection tests with specific botulinum antitoxins. The tests should always be performed with trypsinized extract as well as untrypsinized extract to allow the detection of the toxins of nonproteolytic strains of *C. botulinum* (type E, some strains of types B and F) which may require activation for toxin activity. It is also helpful to isolate the causative organism from the food and confirm the type by identification of the toxin produced by the culture (3).

Therapy

Recent studies substantiate the efficacy of the use of therapeutic antitoxins, particularly in type E botulism, if the antitoxin is administered early in the disease (6, 9). Equally important is prompt symptomatic treatment of patients under close supervision. Early tracheostomy should be performed in patients with significant respiratory impairment. The use of cathartics, high enemas, gastric lavage, and systemic penicillin is advocated by some to prevent the theoretical possibility of further elaboration of toxin by *C. botulinum* in the bowel (9).

At present there are two therapeutic botulinum antitoxins (both of equine origin) licensed for use in the United States: monovalent E (Connaught) distributed by the NCDC and bivalent AB (Lederle) available from the manufacturer and also from the NCDC. In addition, the Connaught Laboratories have recently prepared a trivalent ABE preparation which is expected to be licensed in the near future for distribution by the NCDC. It is recommended (until the trivalent preparation is available) that both the types E and AB antitoxins be given in cases of botulism when the toxin type is unknown regardless of the food history (9). A polyvalent ABEF preparation (Serum Institute, Copenhagen) is also stocked at the NCDC but it is reserved for known type F outbreaks. Because of the serious risk of anaphylaxis and serum sickness when horse serum is administered, the decision to give an asymptomatic individual equine botulinum antitoxin should be weighed very carefully.

References

(1) CONDIT, P. K., and H. A. RENTELN. 1966. Botulism—California. Morbidity and Mortality Weekly Reports, U.S.P.H.S., National Communicable Disease Center. *15* (41): 349.

(2) CONDIT, P. K., and H. A. RENTELN. 1966. Botulism type F—California. Morbidity and Mortality Weekly Reports, U.S.P.H.S., National Communicable Disease Center. *15* (42): 359.

(3) DOWELL, V. R., JR., and T. M. HAWKINS. 1968. Laboratory methods in anaerobic bacteriology. U.S.

Public Health Service Publication No. 1803, U.S. Government Printing Office, Washington, D.C.

(4) FOSTER, E. M., and H. SUGIYAMA. 1967. Recent developments in botulism research. Health Lab. Sci. *4:* 193–198.

(5) INGRAM, M., and T. A. ROBERTS. 1967. *In* Botulism 1966. Proc. of the Fifth International Symposium on Food Microbiology, Moscow, July 1966, Chapman & Hall, London.

(6) KOENIG, M. G., A. SPICKARD, M. A. CARDELLA, and D. E. ROGERS. 1964. Clinical and laboratory observations on type E botulism in man. Medicine *43:* 517–545.

(7) MEYER, K. F., and B. EDDIE. 1965. Sixty-five years of human botulism in the United States and Canada. George Williams Hooper Foundation, San Francisco Medical Center, University of California, San Francisco, Calif.

(8) Morbidity and Mortality Weekly Reports. U.S. Public Health Service, National Communicable Disease Center, Atlanta, Ga.: Botulism Surveillance Issue, Jan. 10, 1964.

(9) National Communicable Disease Center, Atlanta, Ga. Publication: A review of botulism from 1899–1967 and a working manual for clinicians, epidemiologists, and laboratory workers. In press.

ANTIGENICITY OF THE FORMOL TOXOIDS DERIVED FROM THE PRECURSOR AND THE TRYPSIN-ACTIVATED TOXIN OF CLOSTRIDIUM BOTULINUM TYPE E

by Hisashi Kondo, Satoru Kondo, Ryosuke Murata, and Genji Sakaguchi*

Second Department of the Bacteriology and the Department of Food Research,
National Institute of Health, Tokyo

Summary

The tryptic activation of the precursor of *Clostridium botulinum* type E toxin increased the lethal toxicity up to several hundredfold, but no appreciable increase in the antitoxin-combining power resulted. The antigenicities of the formol toxoids derived from the precursor and the trypsin-activated toxin were identical in quality, but the precursor toxoid stimulated the formation of a larger amount of antitoxin in guinea pigs and rabbits. The precursor toxoid stimulated the formation of the antitoxin to satisfactorily high levels in human volunteers without causing any unfavorable reactions.

Introduction

C. botulinum type E toxin is produced in the form of precursor, which is activated by trypsin, producing up to several hundredfold increase in the toxicity (5). Gordon et al. (6) observed that the toxoid derived from the unactivated toxin showed lower immunogenicity than that from the activated toxin. Sakaguchi and Sakaguchi (14) failed to show any changes in the physicochemical properties of the precursor, caused by tryptic activation.

We attempted to compare the antigenicities of partially purified preparations of the precursor and the trypsin-activated toxin, qualitatively and quantitatively, with the hope that the results could throw light on explaining the mechanism of the activation. Also, it has become a matter of considerable interest to protect, by active immunization, the inhabitants of the districts where izushi-borne type E botulism has been prevalent. A type E toxoid for human use was prepared from the precursor rather than the activated toxin. The toxoid was injected into human volunteers. The results will be described in the present report.

---

*Paper read by G. Sakaguchi.

Materials and Methods

The precursor and the trypsin-activated toxin.—Partially purified precursor materials were obtained by the method of Sakaguchi, Sakaguchi, and Imai (13). Precursor materials were activated with trypsin at pH 6 and the activated materials passed through Sephadex G–200 to remove the trypsin (13). Both materials proved to be homogeneous in ultracentrifugation with the same $S_{20,w}$ of 11.5 (14), but contained at least three distinct antigenic substances (8).

Toxoids.—Both the precursor and the activated toxin were detoxified at pH near 6 with 0.2 to 0.4 percent formalin at 33° C. The loss of toxicity was determined by injecting mice intraperitoneally with 0.5 ml. doses. The toxoid was absorbed onto either aluminum hydroxide or aluminum phosphate. Some properties of the toxids used in the present investigation are shown in table 1.

Table 1.—Some properties of the type E toxoids used in the present investigation

Lot No.	Origin	$LD_{50}/$ mg. N before toxoiding	N $\mu g./$ ml.	pH	Adjuvant	Al $\mu g./$ ml.
1	Activated toxin	8.8×10^7	41	6.0	$Al(OH)_3$	675
2	Precursor	1.2×10^5	22	6.0	$AlPO_4$	675
3	do	1.2×10^5	22	5.6	$AlPO_4$	675
4	do	1.4×10^5	11.3	6.05	$AlPO_4$	710
5	Activated toxin	4.6×10^7	11.5	6.10	$AlPO_4$	710

Determination of protein and nitrogen contents.—Protein content was determined by the method of Lowry et al. (9) with bovine serum albumin as the standard. Protein nitrogen (N) was calculated by dividing the protein value by a factor of 6.25.

Determination of toxicity.—The material to be tested was diluted 1.4-fold serially in 0.05 M phosphate-buffered saline, pH 6.3, containing gelatin at

0.2 percent. Doses of 0.5 ml. of each dilution were injected intraperitoneally into four mice weighing 14 to 18 g. After 2 days' observation the LD_{50} was calculated by the method of Reed and Muench (*11*).

Standard antitoxin.—The standard antitoxin was prepared by hyperimmunizing horses with formalinized and later untreated trypsin-activated toxin. The antitoxin titers were standardized against the International Standard for type E antitoxin (WHO, 1963, 1964).

Titration of antitoxin.—To each tube containing one test dose of the test-toxin solution was added the same volume of each graded dose of a serum sample. The mixture was allowed to stand at room temperature for 60 minutes and injected intraperitoneally into four mice in 0.5 ml. doses. The mice were observed for 2 days for deaths. The antitoxin titers relative to that of the standard antitoxin, titrated at each determination, were calculated.

One test dose of the test toxin utilized in the present investigation was that amount which, when mixed with 0.01 IU of the standard antitoxin and injected intraperitoneally into mice, would kill one-half the group within 2 days.

Results

Antitoxin-combining powers of the precursor and the activated toxin.—The ratios of the L+ doses of the precursor to that of the activated toxin at different levels ranged from 1.1 to 4.0 (table 2). In spite of the 250-fold increase in the toxicity, very little increase in the antitoxin-combining power resulted from the tryptic activation.

Toxoiding the precursor and the activated toxin.—Materials in 0.05 M acetate buffer, pH 6.0, were added with formalin to 0.2 percent (v/v) and incubated at 33° C. (fig. 1). The precursor became nontoxic in 7 days; on the eighth day, additional formalin at 0.1 percent was added to the activated toxin, which became nontoxic in 17 days.

Immunogenic efficiencies of toxoids derived from the precursor and the activated toxin.—

(*A*) *Immune response of mice to a single dose.* A

Table 2.—Antitoxin-combining powers of precursor and activated toxin

Level of test	Precursor (milliliters)	Activated toxin (milliliters)	Ratio
L+/100___	1.4×10^{-4}	5.6×10^{-4}	4.0
L+/32____	5.6×10^{-3}	1.4×10^{-4}	2.5
L+/10____	1.4×10^{-3}	2.8×10^{-3}	2.0
L+/3.2____	5.6×10^{-2}	6.3×10^{-2}	1.1
L+_____	1.4×10^{-2}	2.8×10^{-2}	2.0
LD_{50} ------	4.0×10^{-4}	1.0×10^{-7}	250

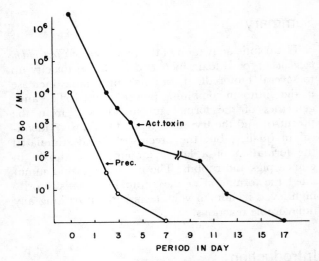

Figure 1.—Time course of detoxification of precursor (271 µg. protein per milliliter) and activated toxin (269 µg. protein per milliliter) with formalin (0.2 per cent) at 33°C.

toxoid derived from the precursor (Prec. Td.) (lot 3) or one derived from the activated toxin (Act. Td.) (lot 1) was injected once subcutaneously into mice in a 0.2-ml. dose. The mice immunized with either toxoid survived the challenge made 4 weeks later with multiples of the lethal dose of either the precursor or the activated toxin (table 3).

(*B*) *Immune response of guinea pigs to a single dose.* Prec. Td. or Act. Td., both containing 16 µg.N/ml., pH 5.4, was injected once subcutaneously

Table 3.—Immune response of mice to a single dose of toxoid

Protected with—	\multicolumn{10}{c}{Challenged with LD_{50}/inoculum}

	Precursor				Activated toxin				
	320	100	32	10	10,000	3,200	1,000	320	100
Prec. Td. (lot 3)_____	1/12	7/12	9/11	11/12	5/8	8/11	7/11	9/12	4/4
Act. Td. (lot 1)_____	3/10	6/12	11/12	11/12	4/7	5/10	6/12	10/12	4/4

NOTE.—Each mouse was injected subcutaneously with 0.2 ml. of either toxoid and challenged by intraperitoneal injection 4 weeks later. Fractional numbers represent: number survived per mice tested.

at a dose of 0.5 ml. into 14 guinea pigs. Blood samples were taken after 4 weeks and, on the next day, the animals were challenged by subcutaneous injection with an activated toxin of 10,000 mouse LD_{50} corresponding to about 100 to 300 guinea pig MLD.

The antitoxin contents of all guinea pigs were below 0.01 IU/ml., the lowest detectable level; however, all but two of those having received Prec. Td. survived the challenge (table 4).

Table 4.—Immune response of guinea pigs to a single dose of toxoid

Protected with—	Challenged with 10,000 mouse LD_{50} Number survived/ number tested	Circulating antitoxin titer (IU/ml.)
Prec. Td.	12/14	<0.01
Act. Td.	14/14	<0.01

NOTE.—Both toxoids contained 1.0 mg. Al/ml. and N at 16 μg.N/ml. (pH 5.4).

(C) *Immune response of guinea pigs to two doses.* The challenge method did not quantitate the antigenicity of a toxoid nor did a single dose stimulate the formation of antitoxin to a detectable level. Two doses, therefore, were injected into guinea pigs to quantitate the antigenicities of Prec. Td. and Act. Td.

Forty guinea pigs in four groups of equal numbers received two doses by subcutaneous injection at a 4-week interval. The first group received 0.2 ml. Prec. Td. (lot 1); the second 0.2 ml. Act. Td. (lot 2); the third 0.5 ml. Prec. Td.; the fourth 0.5 ml. Act. Td. All the animals were bled 2 weeks after the second injection. The antitoxin contents are shown in table 5. The mean antitoxin titers were: 22.2 IU/ml. for the third group; 13.8 IU/ml. for the first group; 4.22 IU/ml. for the fourth group; 2.02 IU/ml. for the second group.

Similar experiments were performed with another lot of Prec. Td. (lot 3) and the same Act. Td. (lot 1) (table 6).

The results given in tables 5 and 6 are illustrated in figure 2. The antitoxin titer is shown by the ordinate and the dose of toxoid by the abcissa. Statistical analyses showed that the dose-response curves were parallel from one to another.

Comparison of the antigenic efficiencies of the toxoids derived from the precursor and the activated toxin.—The Prec. Td. and Act. Td. of the same lot (lot 4), which were toxoided and adsorbed onto $AlPO_4$, under the same conditions, were used.

Immune response of guinea pigs to two doses.— A total of 32 guinea pigs were injected subcutaneously with two doses of either toxoid at a 4-week interval.

Table 5.—Immune response of guinea pigs to 2 doses of toxoid

Immunized with—	0.2 ml. x 2		0.5 ml. x 2	
	IU/ml.	Mean	IU/ml.	Mean
Prec. Td. (lot 2)	10–30	13.8	3–10	22.4
	10–30		30	
	3–10		30–100	
	10–30		3–10	
	10		3–10	
	3–10		30–100	
	10		10–100	
	10–30		30	
	30–100		30–100	
	--------		30–100	
Act. Td. (lot 1)	0.3–1	2.02	1–3	4.22
	1–3		1–3	
	3–10		3–10	
	0.3–1		3–10	
	1–3		1–3	
	1–3		10–30	
	1–3		3–10	
	3–10		3–10	
	3–10		1–3	
	--------		10	

NOTE.—The 1st injection—(4 weeks)—the 2d injection—(2 weeks)—bleeding.

Table 6.—Immune response of guinea pigs to 2 doses of toxoid

Immunized with—	0.2 ml. x 2		0.5 ml. x 2	
	IU/ml.	Mean	IU/ml.	Mean
Prec. Td. (lot 3)	10–30	56	30–100	115
	100		30–100	
	30–100		100–300	
	100		30–100	
	30–100		100–300	
	30–100		100–300	
	30–100		100–300	
	30–100		100–300	
	30–100		--------	
Act. Td. (lot 1)	1–3	5.0	10	12
	10–30		10	
	1–3		3–10	
	3–10		10–30	
	3–10		10–30	
	1–3		3–10	
	3–10		10–30	
	3–10		30	
	10		3–10	
	10		10–30	

NOTE.—The 1st injection—(4 weeks)—the 2d injection—(2 weeks)—bleeding.

The first group was injected with 0.2 ml. of Prec. Td.; the second with 0.2 ml. Act. Td.; the third with 0.5 ml. Prec. Td.; the fourth with 0.5 ml. Act. Td. Two weeks after the second injection, blood samples were taken to measure the level of antitoxin. The results are shown in table 7.

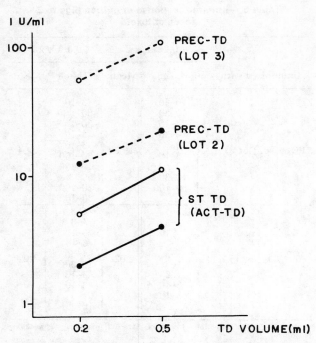

Figure 2.—Dose-response curves of toxoid derived from precursor (lots 2 and 3) and activated toxin (lot 1).

Table 7.—Immune response of guinea pigs to 2 doses of toxoid

Immunized with—	0.2 ml. x 2[1]		0.5 ml. x 2	
	IU/ml.	Mean	IU/ml.	Mean
Prec. Td. (lot 4)	0.3–1 1–3 10 3–10 3–10 3–10 3–10 -------	3.6	30 10–30 3–10 10–30 10–30 10 3–10 10–30	13.3
Act. Td. (lot 4)	0.3–1 0.1 0.1 0.1 0.1 1–3 0.1 ------- -------	(2)	0.1–0.3 0.1–0.3 0.1 0.1 0.1–0.3 0.1–0.3 0.1–0.3 0.1 0.1–0.3	(2)

[1]The 1st injection—(4 weeks)—the 2d injection—(2 weeks)—bleeding.
[2]Means were too low for calculation.

The animals injected with Prec. Td. yielded antitoxin titers higher than those injected with Act. Td.

Immune response of rabbits to multiple doses.— The toxoids (lot 4) were injected into rabbits. For the primary immunization, three 0.2-ml. doses were injected subcutaneously every other day. After a 4-week rest, two 0.4-ml. doses were injected at an interval of 3 days. After another 3-week rest, additional three 0.5-ml. doses were injected at intervals of 10 and 14 days. Blood samples were taken before each injection. The antitoxin titers are illustrated in figure 3.

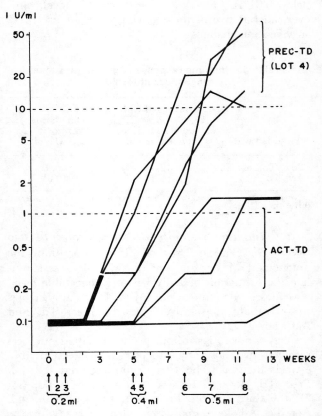

Figure 3.—Immune response of rabbits to multiple doses of toxoid derived from precursor (lot 4) and activated toxin (lot 4).

The animals receiving Prec. Td. developed antitoxin in an earlier stage and the subsequent increase in the titer was steeper than the group receiving Act. Td. In 11 weeks, the antitoxin contents of the rabbits receiving Prec. Td. reached 10, 14, 50, and 70 IU/ml., respectively. Thus, a higher immunogenic those receiving Act. Td. were only 0.14, 1.4, and 1.4 IU/ml., respectively. Thus, a higher immunogenic efficiency of the Prec. Td. was also demonstrated in rabbits.

Immunization of human volunteers with Prec. Td.—The Prec. Td. (lot 4) passed the sterility, safety, and detoxification tests performed in accordance with the procedures for the diphtheria toxoid as required in the Minimum Requirements for the Biological Products (Ministry of Health and Welfare).

Four 0.5-ml. doses of the toxoid were injected subcutaneously into 18 volunteers at intervals of 4, 2, and 12 weeks. Blood samples were taken six times, immediately before each injection, 2 weeks after the third and 3 weeks after the fourth injections. The antitoxin titers before the first and the second injections were all below 0.01 IU/ml. Two weeks after the third injection, two subjects had antitoxin titers below 0.01 IU/ml.; the remaining 14 between 0.01 to 0.1 IU/ml. The fourth injection stimulated a marked increase in the titer by about thirtyfold to hundredfold. The majority showed antitoxin titers between 0.33 to 10 IU/ml. 3 weeks after the fourth injection (table 8).

During the whole period, no one complained of such general symptoms as fever, feeling of languor, exanthema or arthralgia, although very mild local symptoms such as pain or induration at the injection site were reported by a few of the volunteers.

Discussion

Tryptic activation of the precursor of *C. botulinum* type E toxin results in up to several hundredfold increase in the lethal potency. We failed, however, to differentiate the precursor from the activated-toxin by the following procedures: (*a*) CM-Sephadex chromatography, (*b*) gel filtration on Sephadex G–200, (*c*) ultracentrifugal analysis ($S_{20,w}$ of 11.5 for both), (*d*) sucrose-density-gradient centrifugation, (*e*) amino acid analyses, (*f*) destruction curves by urea, γ-ray irradiation and heating, (*g*) ninhydrin values, (*h*) ultraviolet absorption spectra, and (*i*) fluorescence reaction spectra (*14, 10, 12*).

A very little difference was found between the precursor and the trypsin-activated toxin in the antitoxin-combining power. Dolman (*4*) was of the same opinion as our finding, but no data supporting his opinion were presented. Gordon et al. (*6*) showed that tryptic activation decreased the combining power as determined from the Lf values. Flocculation with impure materials, however, may not reflect the true picture of the combining powers.

The mice immunized with Prec. Td. or Act. Td. resisted the challenge with either the precursor or the activated toxin. The dose-response curves obtained with the Prec. Td. and those with the Act. Td. were linear and parallel from one to another (fig. 2). It would appear, therefore, that the antigenicities of the precursor and the activated toxin are identical in the quality. This may indicate that the toxic and the antigenic sites are not the same, and activation is concerned only with the toxic site. Boroff and Das-

Table 8.—Immune response of human volunteers to 4 doses of type E toxoid derived from precursor (lot 4)

Subject	Bleedings					
	I[1]	II	III	IV	V	VI
1. H. K.	[2]0	0	0.01–0.03	0.03	0.01–0.03	1
2. S. K.	0	0	0	0.01	0.03	3–10
3. R. M.	0	0	0.01–0.03	[3]n.d.	0.01–0.03	1–3
4. T. S.	0	0	0	0.01	0	0.1–0.3
5. A. O.	0	0	0	0.01–0.03	0.01–0.03	0.3–1
6. S. S.	0	0	0.01	0.03	0.01–0.03	0.3–1
7. S. Y.	0	0	0	0.03–0.1	0.03–0.1	0.3–1
8. K. H.	0	0	0	0.03–0.1	0.03–0.1	1–3
9. S. K.	0	0	0	n.d.	n.d.	n.d.
10. S. T.	0	0	0	0.01	n.d.	n.d.
11. A. I.	0	0	0.01–0.03	0.03–0.1	0.03	3–10
12. S. Y.	0	0	0.1	0.3	n.d.	n.d.
13. S. K.	0	0	0	0.1	0.01–0.03	1
14. S. S.	0	0	0	0.03–0.1	0	0.3–1
15. T. N.	0	0	0.01–0.03	0.03–0.1	0.1	3
16. G. S.	0	0	0	0	0.01	0.1–0.3
17. K. A.	0	0	0	0	0.01–0.03	0.1–0.3
18. T. T.	0	0	0	0.03–0.1	0.1	1–3

Antitoxin level (IU/ml.)	Number of volunteers/total, showing indicated antitoxin levels					
<0.01	18/18	18/18	9/18	2/16	2/15	0/15
[4]0.01	0/18	0/18	4/18	3/16	1/15	0/15
>0.01	0/18	0/18	5/18	11/16	12/15	15/15

[1]Order of procedures: Bleeding I, 1st injection, 4-week lapse; bleeding II, 2d injection, 2-week lapse; bleeding III, 3d injection, 2-week lapse; bleeding IV, 10-week lapse; bleeding V, 4th injection, 3-week lapse; bleeding VI.

[2]0 means lower than 0.01 IU/ml.
[3]n.d.= no data.
[4]Approximation.

gupta (2) ascribed the toxicity and the antigenicity of type A toxin to one and the same site.

From the results shown in table 7 and figure 3, it is apparent that the immunogenic efficiency of the Prec. Td. is much higher than that of the Act. Td. It might be possible that the formalinization impaired the antigenicity of the activated toxin more than the precursor. Comparison of the physicochemical properties of Prec. Td. and the Act. Td. may be needed. A reverse relationship was observed by Gordon et al. (6) with type E toxin and Batty and Glenny (1) with C. welchii epsilon toxin. In one of the four experiments made by the former authors, however, the immunogenicity of the nonactivated toxoid was greater than the activated toxoid. We concluded that tryptic activation may not affect the antigenic site of the precursor, but it may change either the susceptibility of the molecule to formalin or to some unknown *in vivo* factors.

Antitoxin therapy has been employed in botulism cases, although there have been arguments for and against the effectiveness. In Hokkaido, the case fatality rate of type E botulism had been 28.9 percent before type E antitoxin became available in 1959; whereas since 1959, the rate dropped to only 3.4 percent (7). In spite of this dramatic achievement, it may still hold true that the use of antitoxin is limited because the effect cannot be expected if administration is delayed and the repeated use of antitoxins may cause serum diseases. Therefore, active immunization may be desirable for those who are in contact with botulinus toxin in laboratories or who habitually eat izushi, especially those who have received antitoxin.

Since our results demonstrated higher immunogenic efficiency of the Prec. Td. than the Act. Td. in animals, we used the Prec. Td. for immunizing human volunteers. We tried to keep the protein content of the Prec. Td. lower than that of the commercial diphtheria toxoid. If a diphtheria toxoid containing 50 Lf/ml. is prepared from the crystalline toxin, it should contain about 15 μg. N/ml. Our toxoid contained 11.3 μg. N/ml.

The toxoid stimulated production of antitoxin to satisfactorily high levels, comparable to those attained by Cardella (3). To improve the time schedule for vaccination, the toxoid was injected into an additional 16 volunteers in the Hokkaido area by Dr. H. Iida and his associates of Hokkaido Institute of Public Health, Sapporo. Three injections were given at 4- and 9-week intervals. The antitoxin titers 9 weeks after the second injection were lower than 0.01 IU/ml. in five persons, 0.01 IU/ml. in another nine persons, and higher than 0.1 IU/ml. in another one. Those determined 2 weeks after the third injection were 0.01 to 0.1 IU/ml. in 4 persons, 0.01 to 1

IU/ml. in another nine, and 1 IU/ml. or higher in the other three persons. Thus, more satisfactory immunization was accomplished by prolonging the interval between the second and the third injections.

To guarantee complete protection against the hazard of botulism, we must know how high the antitoxin titer should be. We demonstrated that the monkey containing an antitoxin titer of at least 2 IU/ml. attained by vaccination resisted the intraperitoneal challenge with the activated toxin of 1,000 monkey MLD, corresponding to 800,000 mouse LD$_{50}$. From these results, the antitoxin titers attained by the volunteers may be high enough to protect them from intoxication by ingestion of a botulinogenic food.

Acknowledgments

This investigation was supported partly by U.S. Public Health Service Research Grant EF 00361 and UI 00123 from the Division of Environmental Engineering and Food Protection and National Center for Urban and Industrial Health.

References

(1) BATTY, I., and A. T. GLENNY. 1948. The antigenic efficiency Clostridium welchii epsilon toxin and toxoid after treatment with trypsin. Brit. J. Exp. Pathol. 29: 141–148.

(2) BOROFF, D. A., and B. R. DASGUPTA. 1966. Study of the toxin of Clostridium botulinum. Effects of 2-hydroxy-5-nitrobenzyl bromide on the biological activity of botulinum toxin. Biochem. Biophys. Acta. 117: 289–296.

(3) CARDELLA, M.A. 1964. Botulinum toxoids. In Botulism, K. H. Lewis and K. Cassel, Jr., eds., U.S. Department of Health, Education, and Welfare, Public Health Service, pp. 113–130.

(4) DOLMAN, C. E. 1957. Recent observations on type E botulism. Can. J. Publ. Health, 48: 187–198.

(5) DUFF, J. T., G. G. WRIGHT, and A. YARINSKY. 1956. Activation of Clostridium botulinum type E toxin by trypsin. J. Bacteriol. 72: 455–460.

(6) GORDON, M., M. A. FIOCK, A. YARINSKY, and J. T. DUFF. 1957. Studies on immunity to toxins of Clostridium botulinum. III. Preparation, purification and detoxification of type E toxin. J. Bacteriol. 74: 533–538.

(7) IIDA, H., K. KANZAWA, Y. NAKAMURA, T. KARASHIMADA, T. ONO, and T. SAITO. 1964. Botulism outbreaks encountered in Hokkaido in 1962; with special reference to therapeutic value of specific antitoxin. Rep. Hokkaido Inst. Publ. Health 14: 6–18 (in Japanese).

(8) KITAMURA, M., S. SAKAGUCHI, and G. SAKAGUCHI. 1967. Dissociation of Clostridium botulinum type-E toxin. Biochem. Biophys. Res. Commun. 29: 892–897.

(9) LOWRY, O. H., N. J. ROSEBROUGH, A. L. FARR, and R. J. RANDALL. 1951. Protein measurement with the Folin phenol reagent. J. Biol. Chem. 193: 265–275.

(10) MIURA, T., S. SAKAGUCHI, G. SAKAGUCHI, and K. MIYAKI. 1967. Radiosensitivity of type E botu-

linus toxin and its protection by protein, nucleic acids and some related substances. *In* Microbiological Problems in Food Preservation by Irradiation. pp. 45–54. International Atomic Energy Agency, Vienna.

(*11*) REED, L. J. and H. MUENCH. 1938. A simple method of estimating fifty percent endpoints. Am. J. Hyg. *27: 493–497.*

(*12*) SAKAGUCHI, G. 1968. *Clostridium botulinum* type-E toxin. Japan. J. Bacteriol. *23:* 155–164 (in Japanese).

(*13*) SAKAGUCHI, G., S. SAKAGUCHI, and N. IMAI. 1964. Comparative gel filtration of toxin precursor and trypsin-activated toxin of *Clostridium botulinum* type E. J. Bacteriol. *87:* 401–407.

(*14*) SAKAGUCHI, G. and S. SAKAGUCHI. 1967. Some observation on activation of *Cl. botulinum* type E toxin by trypsin. *In* Botulism 1966. M. Ingram and T. A. Roberts, eds. 1963. pp. 266–267. Chapman & Hall, London.

(*15*) EXPERT COMMITTEE ON BIOLOGICAL STANDARDIZATION. 1963. *Clostridium botulinum* (types A, B, C, D, E) antitoxins. World Health Organ., Tech. Rept. Ser. No. 259, p. 25.

(*16*) EXPERT COMMITTEE ON BIOLOGICAL STANDARDIZATION. 1964. *Clostridium botulinum* (types A, B, C, D, E, and F) antitoxins. World Health Organ., Tech. Rept. Ser. No. 274, p. 20.

THE EFFECT OF MALATHION ON THE SUSCEPTIBILITY OF THE MALLARD DUCK (ANAS PLATYRHYNCHOS) TO CLOSTRIDIUM BOTULINUM TYPE C TOXIN

by WAYNE I. JENSEN *and* JAMES M. MICUDA
Bureau of Sport Fisheries and Wildlife, Bear River Research Station, Brigham City, Utah 84302

Summary

Malathion [S-(1, 2-dicarbethoxyethyl)-0, 0-dimethyl phosphorodithioate], given orally or intraperitoneally in doses of about 112 to 280 mg. to mallards prior to oral or intraperitoneal administration of 1 to 2 MLD of type C toxin, delayed the development of paralysis and decreased the death rate from botulism.

Preliminary experiments to explain the antitoxic activity of the pesticide have been carried out, but no conclusions have been reached.

Introduction

In several published reports (*2, 3, 7, 8, 9*), investigators have presented evidence that type E botulism was responsible for the death of several thousand herring gulls, ring-billed gulls, common loons, and other aquatic birds on Lake Michigan in 1963 and 1964. Jensen and Gritman (*6*), however, were unable to induce intoxication in mallard ducks and California gulls with large oral doses of the VH strain of type E toxin. Among the possible explanations offered for this finding were: (*a*) That these two species were less susceptible to type E botulism than were those on Lake Michigan, or (*b*) that other agents in the Lake Michigan birds' environment (a pesticide or another toxin, for example) somehow influenced their susceptibility to intoxication.

Further studies (*9, 12*) showed that both mallards and California gulls were susceptible to at least one strain of *C. botulinum* type E toxin (026–080X; isolated from Lake Michigan whitefish chubs by Food and Drug Administration personnel). Although type C toxin apparently did not affect the birds' resistance to intoxication with the VH strain, the converse was true; the addition of VH to type C cultures before oral administration increased the birds susceptibility to type C intoxication (*6*).

The study reported here is a continuation of our effort to identify agents, both manmade and naturally occurring, that may modify the susceptibility of aquatic birds to any type of botulism in their natural habitats.

Malathion [S-(1, 2-dicarbethoxyethyl)-0, 0-dimethyl phosphorodithioate] was selected as the first pesticide for investigation because of its widespread use in insect control and its anticholinesterase activity. There is little evidence in the published literature to support a belief that cholinesterase inhibitors favorably influence the course of botulism in mammals, but the pharmacological action of botulinum toxins in birds is poorly understood. Our first step in this study was to find whether the administration of malathion to ducks influenced their response to subsequent doses of type C. This was done in a series of small exploratory experiments in which both the pesticide and the toxin were given at several dosage levels by two routes. The results are given here, but an explanation of our findings must await the completion of work now in progress.

Materials and Methods

Malathion formulations.—For the first experiments, technical grade emulsifiable malathion (55.7 percent in xylene) was obtained from the Box Elder County (Utah) Mosquito Abatement District Office. To minimize the possibility of emulsifying agents, diluents, or other substances being responsible for the observed effects on the birds' response to type C toxin, we repeated these experiments with an improved technical grade malathion of 95 percent purity.

Before administration to ducks, 55.7 percent malathion was diluted 1:10 in distilled water. The 95 percent pure compound was diluted in 95 percent ethyl alcohol to the same final concentration. For convenience in reporting, both formulations are hereafter considered to contain 56 mg. of malathion per milliliter.

Production and assay of toxin.—The X220B2 strain of type C (isolated in northern Utah) was used throughout the investigation. In the first experiments, type C cultures were mixed with the VH strain of type

E (provided by Dr. E. C. Dolman) before administration to experimental birds. The VH was added as a part of another study, and its presence in this study is incidental. Although it enhanced the toxicity of type C for ducks, the doses of type E contained in the mixtures were never as much as one-third of those found earlier to be nontoxic for mallards (6).

Both types were grown in a lactalysate-yeast autolysate medium (6) by using the cellophane bag technique described by Sterne and Wentzel (11). Cultures were harvested after 5 days of incubation at 37° C. for type C and 30° C. for type E.

Toxin assays were performed by injecting mice intraperitoneally with cultures suitably diluted in gelatin-phosphate buffer at pH 6.2. Median lethal doses (LD_{50}) were calculated by the method of Reed and Muench (10).

Administration of malathion and toxin.—In all experiments reported here, malathion was given to one group of mallards (group A) in repeated 1.0-ml. doses (ranging from a total of 112 to 280 mg.) over a period of 1 to 2 days. Within 2½ to 5 hours after the last dose of malathion, group A and a comparable untreated group (group B) received a single dose of toxin.

In preliminary trials, both the malathion and the toxin were administered by releasing a measured volume of fluid from a pipette inserted into the esophagus. Because of the possibility of chemical inactivation of toxin in the bird's digestive tract by malathion (or another ingredient of the technical formulations), we gave the pesticide by the intraperitoneal route thereafter but continued to give the toxin by the oral route. Finally, in the most recent trials we gave the toxin as well as the malathion by intraperitoneal injection. This was done after consultation with Dr. B. C. Whaler (personal communication), who suggested that parasympathetic stimulation by anticholinesterases might accelerate the passage of food through the gut, thereby decreasing the time for absorption of toxin.

The oral doses of type C toxin ranged from 28,800 to 72,000 mouse LD_{50}; the intraperitoneal doses ranged from 2,250 to 5,000 mouse LD_{50}. On the basis of earlier titrations, these were calculated to be one (or, in two cases, two) mallard MLD. However, mallards differ greatly in their susceptibility to type C toxin by both routes, not only among individuals, but among different lots of commercially produced birds. Ambient temperatures during the period of a bird's exposure to toxin also appear to influence its response, but the importance of this factor has not been evaluated experimentally. For these reasons, the doses were sometimes lower or, judging from the rapid development of paralysis, higher than calculated.

Experimental animals.—White mice of the Rocky Mountain Laboratory (Hamilton, Mont.) strain were used for toxin assays of *C. botulinum* cultures.

A commercial breeder in Illinois supplied the mallards, which ranged in age from 8 weeks to adulthood (6 months or more) during the period of the investigation. All birds used in any particular experiment were approximately the same age. In most experiments, equal numbers of males and females were used. They were held in outdoor cages during the course of the experiments, which were performed from October to May. Food (mixed, dry small grains) was withheld for 24 hours before oral dosing with toxin.

Results

This is a summary of the results of 14 small experiments designed to define the optimum conditions for demonstrating the effects of malathion on subsequent botulinal intoxications in mallards. By design or necessity, then, each trial differed from all others with respect to dosage levels or route of administration of malathion and toxin, age of the birds, or environmental temperature.

No single experiment was large enough to give statistically meaningful results in itself. By inspection, however, it appeared that the trend was the same in all cases, regardless of the particular experimental conditions, in groups of birds treated with malathion before the administration of toxin there was a delay in the development of signs of intoxication and an appreciably, but not remarkably, lowered death rate. For this reason, we have pooled the results of the 14 experiments and summarized them in table 1.

Table 1.—The effect of malathion on the response of mallard ducks to oral or intraperitoneal doses of type C toxin

			Clinical signs at 16 to 18 hr. (number of birds)			
Treatment	Number of birds	Slight[1]	Intermediate[2]	Severe[3]	Deaths Number	Percent
Group A (112–280 mg. Malathion plus toxin)	[4]78	23	46	9	51	65.4
Group B (Control: Toxin alone)	80	6	38	36	74	92.5

[1]Slight means normal or with leg weakness that can be detected only by careful observation.
[2]Intermediate means from slight but obvious leg weakness to inability to walk and difficulty in holding the head erect.
[3]Severe means prostration or death. A bird was considered to be prostrate when it could not move legs, wings, or neck. Commonly a careful examination was necessary to determine whether or not death had occurred.
[4]2 birds died, apparently from malathion poisoning, before toxin was administered.

In our laboratory records, we place birds' reactions into 11 categories according to the degree and anatomical location of the signs of paralysis. Obviously they sometimes overlap, and fine lines cannot be drawn between adjacent categories. For the purpose of this tabulation, therefore, we have divided the birds into three broader classes (table 1). For a comparison of the rate of development of paralysis in group A (malathion treated) and group B (control) birds, the clinical signs exhibited at the first observation on the day after administration of toxin are used, usually a period of 16 to 18 hours.

As the tabulation shows, the number of mildly affected birds in group A was nearly four times that in group B at 16 to 18 hours. By contrast, there were only one-fourth as many prostrate or dead birds in group A. By the time the experiments were terminated, usually after 1 week of observation, the mortality rate was about 27 percent higher in the control group.

Discussion

In assessing the antitoxic activity of malathion, we should keep in mind that cholinesterase inhibitors themselves are toxic. However, the toxicity of malathion for mallards, as judged by clinical signs only, varies even more among individuals than does that of type C toxin. Two birds were excluded from the results summarized in table 1 because they died after receiving only two and three intraperitoneal doses (112 and 168 mg., respectively). Others, included in the results, showed various degrees of trembling and leg weakness from malathion before the toxin was administered. In another study (unpublished data), 12 mallards were given repeated intraperitoneal doses of malathion to determine their tolerance to the pesticide alone. Five birds died after cumulative doses of 196, 224, 336 (two birds), and 504 mg., respectively. Seven birds survived doses of 336 (three birds), 420 (two birds), and 560 mg. (two birds) without apparent ill effects. This broad range in susceptibility to malathion has also been noted in other species. Garner (4), for example, lists the acute LD_{50} for male rats as 200 to 5,000 mg. per kg body weight.

Group A mallards, therefore, were combating two poisons, both of which were quite variable in their toxicity, but one of which, either directly or indirectly, was somewhat antagonistic toward the other. Judging from the observations on birds injected with malathion alone, we are probably safe in assuming that some of the clinical signs and mortality in this group were, in part, attributable to cholinesterase inhibition. Once the toxin was administered, however, it was difficult to distinguish clearly between the effects of the two poisons.

We do not yet have enough information to explain the protective action of malathion. Brooks (1) states that "Normal postsynaptic ACh sensitivity after botulinum block precludes relief by action of anticholinesterases." Huges and Whaler (5) showed that eserine and tetraethyl pyrophosphate (TEPP), both anticholinesterases, accelerated the rate of paralysis of a rat phrenic nerve-diaphragm preparation by type A toxin. The findings of other workers have been similar. Although we have little reason, therefore, to believe that the effect of malathion was related to its anticholinesterase activity, the studies of these workers have been concerned largely with mammals and amphibians, and we cannot yet conclude that the mode of action of botulinum toxins in birds is precisely the same.

If we assume that some cases of botulism result from toxin produced within the body of the bird, we may hypothesize that the malathion inhibits this production. In our experience with avian botulism, we have found no real evidence that type C toxin is formed in the digestive tract or, particularly, in the parenteral tissues of living ducks. We have carried out a few preliminary experiments, however, to learn whether malathion inhibits the growth of *C. botulinum* type C *in vitro*. Ten parts per million of the technical grade formulation in lactalysate yeast autolysate broth prevented growth, when a spore inoculum was used. When the medium was inoculated with an actively growing culture, growth occurred, but some inhibition was noted.

Our current studies will ultimately show whether malathion detoxifies toxin within the body of a bird. All we know at this point is that, in the test tube, 400-mouse MLD of type C toxin incubated for 30 minutes with 10 mg. of malathion in a total volume of 10 ml. is just as toxic for mice as the same dose of toxin alone.

We do not now anticipate any practical application for the antitoxic activity of malathion in the control of avian botulism. Even the minimum effective dose (which we have not yet determined with certainty) would probably be toxic to some ducks and might be even more so to other wildlife species. We shall continue these studies, however, to learn how the pesticide mitigates the effects of the toxin and this information, perhaps, will make possible the selection of less toxic, more effective agents that could be safely used in the field for control of the disease.

References

(1) BROOKS, V. B. 1964. The pharmacological action of botulinum toxin, pp. 105–111. *In* K. H. Lewis and K. Cassel, Jr. (ed.), Botulism. Public Health Service Publication No. 999–FP–1.

(2) FAY, L. D. 1966. Type E botulism in Great Lakes

waterbirds. Trans. Thirty-first North Amer. Wildlife and Nat. Res. Conf. 139–149.

(3) FAY, L. D., O. W. KAUFMAN, and L. A. RYEL. 1965. Mass mortality of waterbirds in Lake Michigan 1963–64. Univ. Mich., Great Lakes Res. Div. Publ. No. *13:* 36–46.

(4) GARNER, R. J. 1961. Insecticides, pp. 226–260. *In* R. J. Garner, Veterinary Toxicology. Williams & Wilkins, Baltimore.

(5) HUGHES, R., and B. C. WHALER. 1962. Influence of nerve-ending activity and of drugs on the rate of paralysis of rat diaphragm preparations by *Cl. botulinum* type A Toxin.

(6) JENSEN, W. I., and R. B. GRITMAN. 1967. An adjuvant effect between *Cl. Botulinum* types type C and E toxins in the mallard duck (*Anas platyrhynchos*), pp. 407–413. *In* Botulism 1966. M. Ingram and T. A. Roberts, eds. Chapman & Hall, Ltd., London.

(7) KAUFMANN, O. W., and L. D. FAY. 1964. *Clostridium botulinum* type E toxin in tissues of dead loons and gulls. Mich. State Univ. Agri. Exp. Sta. Quart. Bull. *47:* 236–242.

(8) KAUFMANN, O. W., H. M. SOLOMON, and R. H. MONHEIMER. 1967. Experimentally induced type E botulism in gulls hatched under natural field conditions and reared in captivity. *In* Botulism 1966. and T. A. ROBERTS (ed.), pp. 400–405. Chapman & Hall, Ltd., London.

(9) MONHEIMER, R. H. 1968. The relationship of Lake Michigan waterbird mortalities to naturally occurring *Clostridium botulinum* type E toxin. Bull. Wildlife Disease Assoc. *4*(3): 81–85.

(10) REED, L. J., and H. MUENCH. 1938. A simple method of estimating fifty percent end points. Amer. J. Hygiene. *27*(3): 493–497.

(11) STERNE, M., and L. M. WENTZEL. 1950. A new method for large-scale production of high-titre botulinum formol-toxoid types C and D. J. Immunol. *65*(2): 175–183.

(12) WILDLIFE DISEASES AND PARASITES. 1967. Pp. 67–71. *In* Wildlife Research Problems Programs Progress, 1966. U.S. Dept. of the Interior, Fish and Wildlife Service, Bureau of Sport Fisheries and Wildlife. Resource Publication 43.

OUTBREAKS OF BOTULISM AMONG MINKS IN HOKKAIDO

by Takashi Karashimada, Teiji Ono, Hiroo Iida, Yoshiaki Ando, Genji Sakaguchi,* Sumiko Sakaguchi and Katsumoto Kagota
Hokkaido Institute of Public Health, Sapporo,
National Institute of Health, Shinagawa-ku, Tokyo, and
Hokkaido Livestock Experiment Station, Takikawa, Hokkaido

Summary

Natural outbreaks of botulism among captive minks occurring in April 1961, at Yoichi and Otaru, and in June 1964, in Asahikawa, Hokkaido, were investigated. The feed ingredient incriminated for the earlier outbreak was the meat of a sperm whale (*Physter catodon* Linne) caught off the coast of Kiritappu, Hokkaido, and for the latter outbreak the meat of a horse which had died with colic-like signs. Type $C\beta$ botulinus toxin was detected in the remains of the sperm whale meat and the horse meat. The earlier outbreak was the first proven to be due to other than type E toxin and the first natural outbreak of botulism in livestock in this country.

A high susceptibility of the mink to type C toxin by oral and parenteral administration was demonstrated. The susceptibility of the mink to types A, B, and E toxins was moderate, it was lower to type F and the mink was highly resistant to type D toxin.

These outbreaks emphasize the necessity of active immunization of minks with botulinus toxoid and the necessity for sanitary handling and processing of the raw meats used for feeding minks in order to protect them from botulinic hazard.

Introduction

Since 1951, a number of outbreaks of human type E botulism due to izushi have been reported in Hokkaido and in the northern part of Honshu. Extensive surveys for spores of *C. botulinum* made in this country detected type E spores in high frequency in samples of soil, lakeshore mud, fish, etc. Types A and B organisms were very rarely found (*4, 6*). No report has been published on animal botulism or on the isolation of *C. botulinum* other than types A, B, or E in Japan.

Recently, mink raising has developed in Hokkaido for the production of fur for export. It was observed at times that a number of minks died suddenly and these outbreaks were suspected to be botulism.

We had the opportunity to carry out bacteriological examinations of the feedstuffs incriminated in the sudden deaths of minks which had occurred at Yoichi and Otaru and later in Asahikawa, Hokkaido. We demonstrated the presence of type $C\beta$ toxin in the meat of a sperm whale (*Physter catodon*, Linne) and in the horse meat. This paper deals with the features of the two independent outbreaks of botulism among captive minks, with the laboratory examinations of the incriminated feedstuffs, and with the susceptibility of the mink to botulinus toxins of different types.

Features of the Outbreaks

The first outbreak occurred in April 1961. Approximately 200 minks on three different fur farms, one at Otaru and the other two at Yoichi, died suddenly. The feedstuff common to all the farms was raw meat from the same whale which had been caught off the coast of Kiritappu, Hokkaido, in October 1960, and kept in frozen state at Otaru. The whale meat was mixed with other foodstuff, such as grain and vegetables, and fed to the minks in the evening. During the next morning, the minks became ill and died within 1 to 2 days. The symptoms recorded were cyanosis of the lips, bleeding from the nares, diarrhea with greenish excreta, salivation and paralyses. Just before death, they either squatted down in the corner of the cage or were frenzied.

Another outbreak occurred in June 1964. A total of 1,249 (55 percent) out of 2,274 minks on a fur farm in Asahikawa, Hokkaido, died during a period of 5 days with such symptoms as general weakness, paralysis of lower extremities and difficulty in breathing. The minks had been fed with the meat from a horse which had died after suffering for 2 days from colic-like signs. The signs recorded were similar to those reported by Quartrup and Holt (*7*), Dinter and Kull (*2*), Scheibner (*10*) and Avery et al. (*1*).

Laboratory Findings

In the earlier outbreak, carcasses of two minks and the remaining whale meat and, in the later outbreak, the remaining horse meat were sent to the Hokkaido

---

*Paper read by G. Sakaguchi.

Institute of Public Health. The postmortem examinations of the mink carcasses revealed no particular pathological changes except for a slight congestion of the lungs and inflammation of the intestinal mucosa. No significant aerobic pathogens were detected in the whale meat, the horse meat or in the main organs of the mink carcasses with such culture media as selenite broth, DCLS agar, McConkey agar and blood agar.

The whale meat was macerated by adding with an equal amount of saline and centrifuged at 3,000 r.p.m. for 15 minutes. A half ml. of the supernatant fluid, injected intraperitoneally, killed a mouse in a few hours with the signs of botulism. One gram of the whale meat contained approximately 320 mouse intraperitoneal LD_{50}. The same extract, when heated for 10 minutes at 90° C., did not cause any signs. Antitoxins of type A, B, D, E, or F failed to protect the mice from the challenge with the whale meat extract; only type C antitoxin neutralized the toxicity. A mixture of a dilution of the International Standard Antitoxin containing 0.032 IU/ml. and the same amount of toxin solution containing 25 LD_{50}/ml. of each of four different type Cβ strains and also of the whale meat was not toxic. The same amount of the antitoxin failed to neutralize the same dose of a type Cα toxin (table 1). Therefore, the toxin in the whale meat appeared to be type Cβ rather than Cα.

The remnant of the horse meat contained a toxicity of 320 intraperitoneal MLD/g. and a sample from the frozen meat contained approximately 40 MLD/g.

The toxin was identified in the same manner as type Cβ.

Although there were considerable difficulties, cultures of C. botulinum type C were isolated from the whale meat and the horse meat on soy-yeast extract-sulfite agar (13) plates streaked with the young cultures in cooked liver broth.

Susceptibilities of the Mink to the Botulinus Toxins of Different Types

Botulinus toxins of types A, B, C (α and β), D, E, and F cause essentially the same signs in laboratory animals. The minimum lethal doses of the toxins of different types are different from one species to another. It is generally accepted that the mink is most highly susceptible to type C toxin.

We reexamined the susceptibility of the minks to types A, B, C, D, E, and F toxins at Hokkaido Livestock Experiment Station at Takikawa, Hokkaido in December 1962 and 1963, just before taking the furs.

All the toxic materials, except type E, were prepared from culture filtrate by repeated precipitations with 50 percent saturation of ammonium sulfate. The third ammonium sulfate precipitate was dialyzed against distilled water and lyophilized. Type E toxin was partially purified from the trypsinized cell extract according to the method of Sakaguchi and Sakaguchi (9) and kept in frozen state. The specific toxicities of the materials are shown in table 2.

Table 1.--Neutralization tests with international standard antitoxins types C and D

	Antitoxin type	IU per milliliter				
Toxin 25 LD_{50}/ml.	C	4.0	0.8	0.16	0.032	0
	D	4.0	1.3	0.44	0.15	
Cα, strain	C	0/2	0/2	0/2	2/2	2/2
Cα^1	D	2/2	2/2	2/2	2/2	
Cβ, strain	C	0/2	0/2	0/2	0/2	2/2
Stockholm[2]	D	2/2	2/2	2/2	2/2	
Cβ, strain	C	0/2	0/2	0/2	0/2	2/2
571[3]	D	2/2	2/2	2/2	2/2	
Cβ, strain	C	0/2	0/2	0/2	0/2	2/2
1259[3]	D	2/2	2/2	2/2	2/2	
Cβ, strain	C	0/2	0/2	0/2	0/2	2/2
D 468[1]	D	2/2	2/2	2/2	2/2	
D, strain	C	2/2	2/2	2/2	2/2	2/2
1873[3]	D	0/2	0/2	0/2	0/2	
Whale meat	C	0/2	0/2	0/2	0/2	2/2
Extract	D	2/2	2/2	2/2	2/2	

[1]Given by Dr. C. E. Dolman, University of British Columbia, Vancouver.
[2]Given by Dr. J. Muller, State Veterinary Serum Laboratory, Copenhagen.
[3]Given by Dr. A. R. Prevót, l'Institute de Pasteur, Paris.
NOTE.—Equal volumes of toxin and antitoxin were mixed. 2 mice were injected intraperitoneally. The fractional numbers indicate $\frac{\text{Mice died}}{\text{Number injected}}$.

Table 2.—Specific toxicities of the toxins administered to minks

Type of toxin	Strain used	Mouse ip LD_{50}/mg.N
A	Type A, 97[1]	4.03×10^6
B	Type B, NIH[2]	1.81×10^4
Cα	Type C, α	8.44×10^4
Cβ	Type C, 571	1.65×10^6
Cβ	Type C, D468	6.48×10^5
D	Type D, 1873	2.27×10^7
E	Type E, VH[3]	2.01×10^7
F	Type F, Langeland[4]	3.08×10^5

[1]Given by the Institute for Infectious Diseases, Tokyo.
[2]Given by the National Institutes of Health, Bethesda.
[3]Given by Dr. C. E. Dolman, University of British Columbia, Vancouver.
[4]Given by Dr. V. Møller, Statens Seruminstitut, Copenhagen.

The materials were dissolved in 0.05 M phosphate buffer, pH 6.0, and all the toxin solutions were diluted tenfold serially in the same buffer so that 1.0 ml. portions should contain from 1×10^8 to 1×10^0 mouse intraperitoneal LD_{50}. Two minks were injected with toxin intraperitoneally and another two were administered the toxin orally at a dose of 1.0 ml. of each dilution. The minks were observed for 7 days. When one or both minks died within 7 days with the

Table 3.—Susceptibilities of the mink to botulinus toxins of different types injected intraperitoneally

| | Dose in terms of mouse intraperitoneal LD_{50} | | | | | | | | |
Toxin type	10^8	10^7	10^6	10^5	10^4	10^3	10^2	10^1	10^0
A			2/2	2/2	2/2	2/2			
B			2/2	2/2	1/2	0/2			
Cα			2/2	2/2	2/2	2/2	0/2		
Cβ (C 571)						2/2	2/2	0/2	0/2
Cβ (D 468)					2/2	2/2	2/2	0/2	0/2
D	2/2	2/2	0/2	0/2					
E			2/2	2/2	2/2	0/2	0/2		
F			2/2	0/2	0/2	0/2			

NOTE.—The fractional numbers indicate $\dfrac{\text{Mink died}}{\text{Number injected}}$.

Table 4.—Susceptibilities of the mink to botulinus toxins of different types administered orally

| | Dose in terms of mouse intraperitoneal LD_{50} | | | | | | |
Toxin type	10^8	10^7	10^6	10^5	10^4	10^3	10^2
A		2/2	0/2	0/2			
B			0/2	0/2			
Cα			2/2	2/2	0/2		
Cβ (C 571)				2/2	1/2	0/2	0/2
Cβ (D 468)				2/2	2/2	0/2	0/2
D	0/2	0/2	0/2				
E		1/2	0/2	0/2	0/2		
F			0/2	0/2	0/2		

NOTE.—The fractional numbers indicate $\dfrac{\text{Mink died}}{\text{Number administered}}$.

signs of botulism the mouse intraperitoneal LD_{50} contained in the inoculum was regarded as a minimum lethal dose for the mink. The results of the susceptibility tests are shown in tables 3 and 4.

Minimum lethal doses for the mink by intraperitoneal injection, in terms of mouse intraperitoneal LD_{50}, were 10^3 or less for type A, 10^4 for type B, 10^3 for type Cα, 10^2 for type Cβ, 10^7 for type D, 10^4 for type E, and 10^6 for type F; those by oral administration were 10^7 for type A, 10^7 or larger for type B, 10^5 for type Cα, 10^4 for type Cβ, 10^9 or larger for type D, 10^7 for type E, and 10^7 or larger for type F.

It was reconfirmed that the mink is most susceptible to type Cβ toxin both by intraperitoneal and peroral administration. The mink seemed to be slightly less susceptible to Cα toxin. The susceptibility of the mink to the toxins of types A, B, and E seemed to be essentially the same, that to type F seemed to be lower than types A, B, or E, and that to type D the lowest by either route.

Discussion

Outbreaks of botulism among animals had not been reported in Japan before 1961. Until that time

only type E human botulism due to izushi or similar kinds of foodstuffs had been reported. Isolates from soil and other materials collected in this country detected mostly type E organisms; very few type A and B isolations have been reported (4, 6).

Type Cβ toxin was demonstrated from the sperm whale meat and the horse meat incriminated in the outbreaks of botulism among minks, and cultures of *C. botulinum* type C were isolated. The facts indicate that *C. botulinum* type Cβ may also be distributed in Japan.

The whale, caught off the coast of Kiritappu, Hokkaido, was not intended for human consumption, since sperm whale meat has a very bad odor. The carcass of the horse which died from colic-like signs should have been condemned. In recent years, however, mink raising has become very popular in Hokkaido and such hitherto condemned materials are utilized for feeding them. It is not known whether the whale and the horse had originally carried *C. botulinum* type Cβ. It is likely that the carcasses of the whale and the horse were dressed under unsanitary conditions and that a long time elapsed before they were frozen. No matter whether the whale and the horse originally carried type C organisms or were contaminated during the dressing, it seems that there was sufficient time to allow the organisms to grow and develop the lethal toxin in the meat.

Quortrup and Gorham (8), Moll and Brandly (5), Wagenaar, Dack, and Mayer (12), Dinter and Kull (3) and Scheibner (10) pointed out that the mink is more highly susceptible to type C toxin than to types A, B, D, or E toxins. The ratio of the mink lethal dose by oral administration of type A toxin to that of type C toxin was found to be 250:1 by Quortrup and Gorham (8) and 400:1 by Dinter and Kull (3). The corresponding ratio found in the present investigation was 100:1 with respect to type Cα toxin and 1,000:1 with type Cβ toxin. Quortrup and Gorham (8) and Moll and Brandly (5) reported that minks are more highly susceptible to type B toxin than to type A toxin whereas in the present investigation such was not the case. The former authors reported that the mink is very highly resistant to type E toxin whereas our data show that it is as susceptible to type E as to types A and B. Scheibner (10) reported that the mink's susceptibility to type D toxin is the second highest whereas the present results show that it is more resistant to type D toxin than to any other types.

Minks must be fed on raw animal or fish meat in order to keep the fur in good condition. If the meat is contaminated with type C organisms, the chance of botulism occurring is very high. The possibility of contamination of meat with type C toxin through fly larvae was suggested by Wagenaar, Dack, and Mayer (12). Insanitary handling of raw fish and raw meat for mink feed would be very dangerous.

Thus, to prevent botulism in minks, sanitary handling and processing of raw fish and meat seem to be essential. Vaccination of minks with botulinus toxoid must also be done immediately in this country. In European and North American countries, vaccination of minks with type C monovalent or types A, B, and C trivalent toxoid is practiced. Eighty-five percent of the mink population in this country is located in Hokkaido, where type E spore distribution is very heavy. Since type E mink botulism was reported in Norway (11) and a considerably high susceptibility of the mink to type E toxin was demonstrated, it may be worth adding type E to the toxoid employed for immunization of minks.

Acknowledgment

The authors are grateful to Dr. Y. Nakamura, the former director of the Hokkaido Institute of Public Health, Dr. M. Yamamoto, the former director, and Dr. T. Takahashi, Director of the Hokkaido Livestock Experiments Station, for having made it possible to carry out the present investigation. Thanks are also due to Dr. K. Kanzawa, Hokkaido Institute of Public Health, for his helpful assistance.

References

(1) AVERY, R. J., C. E. DOLMAN, P. L. STOVELL, and A. J. WOOD; 1959. A natural outbreak of *Clostridium botulinum* type C intoxication in ranch mink arising from pork liver. Can. J. Comp. Med. *23:* 203–209.

(2) DINTER, Z., and K. E. KULL. 1951. Erganzende Untersuchungen uber den Botulismus beim Nerz. Nord. Vet. Med. *3:* 297–311.

(3) DINTER, Z., and K. E. KULL. 1955. Uber die Emfanglichkeit des Nerzes fur die Botulinus Toxine A und C. Nord. Vet. Med. *7:* 549–563.

(4) KODAMA, E., S. FUJISAWA, T. SAKAMOTO, H. ASANO, and J. ETO. 1963. Uber den *Cl. botulinum* Typus A der in der Akita Prafektur Gefunden Wurde. Hirosaki Med. J. *14:* 156–164.

(5) MOLL, T., and C. A. BRANDLY. 1951. Botulism in the mouse, mink and ferret with special reference to susceptibility and pathological alternations. Am. J. Vet. Res. *12:* 355–363.

(6) NAKAMURA, G., M. TAKEYA, H. KUDO, C. IZUMIYAMA, K. YAMAMOTO, H. ASANO, and M. TAKEYAMA; 1963. Ein Fall von Typus B-Botulismus. Hirosaki Med. J. *14:* 123–127

(7) QUOTRUP, E. R., and A. L. HOLT. 1940. Case report on botulism type C in minks. J. Am. Vet. Med. Assoc. *96:* 167–168.

(8) QUORTRUP, E. R., and J. R. GORHAM. 1949. Susceptibility of fur-bearing animals to the toxins of *Clostridium botulinum* type A, B, C, and E. Am. J. Vet. Res. *10:* 268–271.

(9) SAKAGUCHI, G., and S. SAKAGUCHI. 1961. A simple method for purification of type E botulinal toxin from the precursor extract of the bacterial cells. Japan. J. Med. Sci. Biol. *14:* 243–248.

(10) SCHEIBNER, G. 1955. Zum Botulismus beim Nerz in Deutschland. Monatschr. Tierheilkunde *7:* 195–203.

(11) SKULBERG, A. 1961. Botulism in mink caused by *Clostridium botulinum* type E. Nord. Vet. Med. *13:* 87–95.

(12) WAGENAAR, R. O., G. M. DACK, and D. P. MAYER. 1953. Studies on mink food experimentally inoculated with toxin-free spores of *Clostridium botulinum* types A, B, D, and E. Am. J. Vet. Res. *14:* 479–483.

(13) SAKAZAKI, R., S. NAMIOKA, and S. WATANABE. 1955. SYS medium. Japan. J. Bacteriol. *10:* 835–837.

SENSITIVITY AND IMMUNE RESPONSE OF FRESH-WATER FISHES TO *CLOSTRIDIUM BOTULINUM* TYPE E TOXIN

by Hikokichi Hiroki
Department of Bacteriology, Nihon Dental College, Tokyo

Summary

All of the 15 species of fresh water fish tested were susceptible to *Clostridium botulinum* type E toxin. No particular differences in the susceptibility were observed among the different species of fish. Characteristic histopathological changes, especially edematic degeneration of the respiratory epithelium, were noted in the morbid fish. The administration of type E antitoxin to the fish that had been inoculated with type E toxin protected them from intoxication if the antitoxin was administered sufficiently early. The administration of type E toxoid in two doses induced a specific immunity in the fish.

Introduction

The botulism outbreaks that occurred in northern parts of Japan (in Hokkaido and in Akita, Yamagata, Aomori, and Iwate Prefectures) were principally caused by "izushi". The main ingredient of izushi was either sea or fresh water fish caught in the particular district. Fifteen species of sea water fish and eight species of fresh water fish have been involved in the incriminated izushi. The fish were caught in rivers, marshes, lakes, or seas of the districts involved.

During the 16 years from 1951 to 1967, there were 35 proved outbreaks in Hokkaido involving 231 cases and 43 deaths. The mortality rate was 18.7 percent. In this area, 13 species of fish were used to prepare the izushi. Among these 13 species, karei was involved in 12 outbreaks (34.3 percent) and hatahata in 10 outbreaks (28.6 percent). Outbreaks caused by the other species occurred at lower frequencies.

Fish undoubtedly played an important role in the outbreaks of type E botulism in Japan by izushi, a particular type of food, as a vector. It is not known, however, whether fish are susceptible to botulinus toxin, whether the susceptibility, if any, is different from one species to another, or whether fish show an immune response to the toxin. The author attempted to answer these questions. The results will be described in this paper.

Materials and Methods

Fresh water fish.—For the present investigation, mainly koi and kingyo were used. Carps (*Cyprinus carpiol*) were of Japanese origin (kinkabutokoi and magoi), aged 6 to 7 months and weighing about 70 to 80 g. Goldfish (*Carassius carassium auratus Line*) used were also of Japanese origin (Wakin), weighing 50 to 60 g.

Eleven additional species of fresh water fish were used for part of the investigation. These had been caught at Lake Kasumigaura, Ibaragi Prefecture. The majority were young fish. They were kept in a tank at 15° to 17° C. for a week in the laboratory and only healthy fish were subjected to the experiments.

Bacterial strains and toxins.—*C. botulinum* type A strain 97 and type E strains Iwanai and 35396 were provided by the National Institute of Health, Tokyo. Each strain was grown in cooked-liver broth for 5 days at 30° C. The culture was then centrifuged at 8,000 r.p.m. for 20 minutes. The supernatant fluid was used as the crude toxin material. A highly purified type E activated toxin was provided by Dr. G. Sakaguchi of the National Institute of Health, Tokyo. The material contained 1.3×10^8 LD_{50}/mg. nitrogen and gave a single boundary in ultracentrifugal analysis with an $S_{20,w}$ of approximately 11.5.

Antitoxin.—A lyophilized preparation of type E antitoxin, lot 4, containing 8,400 IU per vial prepared by the National Institute of Health, Tokyo, was provided by the courtesy of Dr. H. Kondo of the Institute.

Toxoid.—Botulinum toxoid type E for human use, aluminum-phosphate precipitated, lot 3, was provided by Dr. Kondo.

Results and Discussions

Susceptibility of fresh water fishes to type E toxin.—Young fish of 12 different species were used for the tests. Crude type E toxin was diluted tenfold serially in sterile saline and 0.1 or 0.2 ml. of each dilution was injected intraperitoneally into the fish. The inoculated fish were observed for 6 days. The results are shown in table 1. All the inoculated fish died in 1 to 5 days, showing that fish are highly

Table 1.—Susceptibility of various species of fresh water fish to *Clostridium botulinum* type-E toxin

Species	Cumulative dead per inoculated on days postinoculation				
	1	2	3	4	5
Cyprinus carpiol _____	3/5	5/5			
Carassius carassius curieri. _____	2/5	4/5	5/5		
Carassius carassius auratus. _____	5/5				
Sarcocheilichthys variegatus. _____	5/5				
Hypophthalmichthys molitrix. _____	5/5				
Pseudoras bora parva _____	5/5				
Gnathopogen elongatus elongatus.____	2/5	4/5	5/5		
Tridentiger obscurus _____	5/5				
Abbottina rivularis _____	4/5	5/5			
Pseudoras bora parva _____	5/5				
Pseudoperilampus typus. _____	5/5				
Acheilognathus lanceolata. _____	5/5				
Hemibarbus barbus _____	1/5	4/5	5/5		
Misgurnus anguillicaudautus _____	5/5				
Anguilla japoeica _____	0/5	1/5	3/5	4/5	5/5

NOTE.—All fish received 0.1 ml., intraperitoneally, of culture filtrate of type E strain 35396 except for *A. japoeica* which received 0.2 ml.

susceptible to type E botulinus toxin. No appreciable difference in the susceptibility was found among the 15 species of fish.

The objective signs and the histopathological changes of the fish (carps) inoculated with type-E toxin.—The carps inoculated with type E toxin developed the following objective signs. From about an an hour after the innoculation, the rate of branchial respiration increased gradually until the 4th or 5th hour, after which it decreased. From about 2 to 3 hours after the inoculation, secretion of slime was noted on the surface of the scales. The amount of slime increased gradually. Sometimes, the slime formed a membranous coat and a part of the coat came off. The swimming activity decreased gradually. Sometimes, the fish did not swim at all. When the disease was very severe, the fish turned laterally and the branchial respiration stopped before death.

The fish inoculated intraperitoneally with the crude

or the purified type E toxin were killed on the fifth to the seventh day when the signs were most severe. Specimens were taken, fixed in 10 percent formalin solution, sectioned, and stained with hematoxylin-eosin for microscopic examinations.

In the carp inoculated with type E toxin, the branchi and kidneys showed the greatest pathological changes. No apparent changes were noted in the liver, the pancreas, or the spleen.

Histopathological changes.—The most marked histopathological changes in the carp were edematic degeneration of the respiratory epithelium. Degeneration of the capillary blood vessels and cell infiltration were also observed. A marked atrophy of the slime cells was observed. These cells had enlarged nuclei, which were heavily stained with hematoxylin. No particular secreted substances were found.

Histopathological observations of the nervous system were not made.

Passive immunization of fresh water fishes (kingyo, koi and *Misgurnus anguillicaudaupus*) with type E antitoxin.

Passive immunization of goldfish.—For this experiment, 23 goldfish (wakin), weighing 50 to 60 g. were injected intraperitoneally with 0.1 ml. of the crude type E toxin, containing at least 800 mouse lethal doses. At intervals of 1, 3, 5, 10, 12, or 24 hours later, each of three fish received 0.3 ml. of the antitoxin containing an antitoxic potency of 840 IU/ml. by intraperitoneal injection in the side opposite the site of the toxin injection. The fish were observed for 7 days. The five fish of the control group received the toxin only.

As seen in table 2, those fish which received the antitoxin 1, 3, or 5 hours after the toxin injection developed no symptoms. Deaths occurred among the fish that received the antitoxin at the eighth hour or later after the toxin injection. All the fish of the control group that had received no antitoxin died within 24 hours. The results show that if antitoxin is administered within 5 hours after injection with toxin

Table 2.—Effect of botulinum antitoxin type E in *Carassius carassius auratus*

Time in hours between toxin[1] and antitoxin[2] injections	Cumulative deaths per inoculated on days postinoculation of toxin								
	1	2	3	4	5	6	7	8	14
1 _____	0/3								
3 _____	0/3								
5 _____	0/3								
10 _____	3/3								
12 _____	1/3	1/3	1/3	1/3	1/3	1/3	1/3	2/3	2/3
24 _____	2/3	2/3	2/3	3/3					
No antitoxin _____	3/3								

[1]Toxin: All fish received 0.1 ml., intraperitoneally, of filtrate of a culture of type E, strain 35396.

[2]Antitoxin: Botulinus antitoxin, type E, 252 IU/0.3 ml., intraperitoneally.

of a considerably high potency, the fish are protected from development of botulism.

Passive immunization of carp.—A total of 20 carp (magoi) weighing 70 to 80 g. were used. The fish were injected with 0.2 ml. of 1 to 5 dilution of the crude toxin, followed by 0.5 ml. of the antitoxin, injected intraperitoneally, at intervals of 1, 3, 8, or 10 hours. The fish were observed for 14 days. The results are shown in table 3. All 15 of the carp that

Table 3.—Effect of botulinus antitoxin type E in Cyprinus carpiol

Time in hours between toxin[1] and antitoxin[2] injections	Deaths per total
1	0/3
3	0/3
5	0/3
8	0/3
10	[3]1/3
No antitoxin	[4]5/5

[1]Toxin: All fish received 0.2 ml., intraperitoneally, of a 1:5 dilution of a filtrate of a culture of type E, strain 35396.
[2]Antitoxin: Botulinus antitoxin, type E 420 IU/0.5 ml., intraperitoneally, observation period, 14 days after toxin administration.
[3]The death occurred in the 13th day of observation.
[4]4 deaths occurred within 1 day and the 5th death in the 2nd day, posttoxin, of observation.

received the antitoxin survived, while all five fish of the control group died in 1 or 2 days.

Passive immunization of Misgurnus anguillicaudaupus.—Mis. anguillicaudaupus, weighing 20 g. were injected with 0.1 ml. of a 1 to 20 dilution of the crude toxin followed by 0.3 ml. of the antitoxin, intraperitoneally at 1, 3, 5, 8, 10, 12, 24, or 48 hours after the toxin injection. The fish were observed for 14 days. The results are shown in table 4.

The fish that received the antitoxin 1, 3, or 5 hours after the toxin injection did not develop any signs.

Table 4.—Effect of botulinum antitoxin type E in Misgurnus anguillicaudautus

Time in hours between toxin[1] and antitoxin[2] injections	Period in days after injection of antitoxin, cumulative deaths per total on days posttoxin					
	1	2	3	4	5	14
1	0/3	0/3	0/3	0/3	0/3	0/3
3	0/3	0/3	0/3	0/3	0/3	0/3
5	0/3	0/3	0/3	0/3	0/3	0/3
8	0/3	0/3	0/3	1/3	1/3	1/3
10	0/3	0/3	0/3	1/3	1/3	1/3
12	0/3	1/3	2/3	3/3	3/3	3/3
24	0/3	2/3	3/3	3/3	3/3	3/3
48	0/3	0/3	1/3	3/3	3/3	3/3
No antitoxin	2/10	5/10	10/10	10/10	10/10	10/10

[1]Toxin: All fish received 0.1 ml., intraperitoneally, of a 1:20 dilution of a filtrate of a culture of type E, strain 35396.
[2]Antitoxin: Botulinus type E, 252 IU/0.3 ml., intraperitoneally.

Those that received the antitoxin 8 or 10 hours after the toxin injection, developed signs. Two of three in each group recovered in a few days but the remaining one in each group showed more severe signs and died. All the fish that received the antitoxin 12 hours or later after the challenge with the toxin died in 1 to 5 days. All of the control group died in 1 to 3 days after the toxin inoculation.

From the foregoing experiments, it is apparent that passive immunization against type E botulinus toxin is bestowed upon fish (kingyo, koi, and Mis. anguillicaudaupus) just as it is upon warmblooded animals.

Active immunization of fish against type E toxin.

Active immunization of carp with type E toxoid.—Eight carp weighing 50 to 60 g. were injected intraperitoneally with type E toxoid, lot 3, in two doses, 0.2 and 0.3 ml., at a 7-day interval. Some 38 days later, the carps were challenged by intraperitoneal injection with 0.2 ml. of 1 to 50 dilution of the purified toxin. The challenged fish were observed for 14 days.

No objective abnormalities nor deaths were found in any of the eight carp during the 14 days, while all five carp of the control group died within 1 day after the challenge with the toxin. The results proved that fish (carp) respond to the botulinus toxoid in the

Table 5.—Specificity of the immunity acquired by immunization of Cyprinus carpiol with type E toxoid

Immunization	Toxin challenge	Cumulative dead per inoculated during 7-day observation period
Survivors, after immunization with type E toxoid and subsequent challenge with type E toxin.[1]	Type E, crude toxin, 1:3 dilution, 0.2 ml., intraperitoneally.	0/4
	Type A, crude toxin, 1:50 dilution, 0.2 ml., intraperitoneally.	[2]4/4
None	Type E, crude toxin, 1:3 dilution, 0.2 ml., intraperitoneally.	[2]3/3
Do	Type A, crude toxin, 1:50 dilution, 0.2 ml., intraperitoneally.	[2]3/3

[1]These fish received 2 inoculations of type E toxoid, 0.2 and 0.3 ml., 7 days apart. They survived subsequent challenge with purified type E toxin (5SA15–G–d), 1:50 dilution, 0.2 ml., intraperitoneally administered 38 days after immunization.
[2]All deaths within 3 days.

same way as warmblooded animals, producing active immunity.

Specifiicity of the immune response of the fish (carp) to type E toxoid.—The eight carp immunized with the type E toxoid and surviving the challenge with type E toxin in the preceding experiment were divided into two groups of four each, A and B. The A group fish were challenged again with a 1 to 3 dilution of type E crude toxin and the B group with a 1 to 50 dilution of type A crude toxin. The A group developed no symptoms; all of the B group died after the challenge with type A toxin. (table 5). The results confirmed that the active immunization established in the fish was a specific one.

BOTULISM: POTENTIAL HAZARDS OF FOOD PRESERVATION

by KEITH H. LEWIS *and* HERBERT E. HALL
U.S. Department of Health, Education, and Welfare,
Consumer Protection and Environmental Health Service, Cincinnati, Ohio

Botulism as a disease has probably been known for centuries, but as an entity associated with food poisoning and identified bacteriologically, its history is less than a hundred years old. Dr. Charles S. Petty (9), writing on this disease, remarked that since Van Ermengem described it and isolated the causative organisms in the 1890's, nearly 6,000 cases have been recorded throughout the world and more than 1,700 of these died. This is a relatively small number of fatalities in a 70-year period, yet there have been more than 1,500 publications on the subject—nearly one for every fatal case—which is a good indication of the high level of interest the disease has aroused throughout the world. For information on incidence and types involved, reviews by Matveev in 1959 (7), Lewis and Cassel in 1964 (6), Meyer and Eddie in 1965 (8), and Ingram and Roberts in 1966 (3) may be consulted. The vast majority of cases are related to the ingestion of food containing preformed toxin, and human botulism is nearly always caused by types A, B, or E. Petty (9) noted, however, that the other types have been observed on rare occasions. Some workers are convinced that many cases of botulism should be considered toxinfections that result not only from the effects of preformed toxin, but from additional amounts of toxin produced by growth of the organisms in the intestinal tract (9). In a few instances, symptoms have been produced by wound infections or by the inhalation of an aerosol containing the toxin (9). Such cases are admittedly rather rare, but they represent potential hazards associated with laboratory manipulation of the toxins against which workers should guard themselves.

Botulism has been traditionally associated with improper home preservation of foods by canning or curing. The data reported by Meyer and Eddie (8) indicate that homemade foods account for roughly 90 percent of the outbreaks and 85 percent of the cases occurring in the United States and Canada. Government agencies continue to urge home processors to use safe processes, and the serving of home-preserved foods in public eating places is generally prohibited. There is, however, even greater concern about the safe processing of commercial products, which, if toxic, could affect very large numbers of consumers. With this thought in mind, the remainder of the discussion will be devoted entirely to the botulinal hazards of commercial food processing and distribution.

The interest in botulism in relation to food production and preservation increases and declines in direct proportion to the reported incidence during a particular period of time. In the early part of this century, a high level of interest was aroused in the United States by the occurrences of botulism related to commercially canned foods such as clam juice, pork and beans, string beans, olives, tunafish, and other products. The research engendered by this interest produced the information that has made American canned foods the safest commodity on the grocers' shelves.

To demonstrate the changes in trends of botulism associated with commercially produced foods, table 1 shows the foods that were involved in outbreaks from 1921 to 1940 in the United States. Of 24 such outbreaks recorded in this 20-year period, all were from commerically canned foods, and included spinach, olives, sardines, potted meat, milk, salmon, sprats, and tuna. A total of 110 cases occurred, and there were 45 deaths (40.9 percent). Of these outbreaks, 15 occurred in the 1920's and nine in the 1930's, thus indicating a gradual decline in prevalence.

Table 2 summarizes the occurrence of botulism-associated foods processed commercially in the United

Table 1.—Botulism associated with commercially prepared foods in the United States, 1921–40

Year	Food	Commercial pack	Outbreak	Cases	Deaths
1921	Spinach, olives	Canned	5	42	10
1922	Spinach	do	2	11	6
1924	Olives	do	3	22	8
1925	Sardines, spinach, potted meat	do	4	13	9
1929	Shallot (Italy)	do	1	2	1
1931	Milk, antipasto, sardines	do	3	6	2
1932	Salmon	do	1	3	1
1933	Crab, salmon	do	2	2	1
1934	Sprats	do	1	3	1
1936	Clams (Japan)	do	1	4	4
1938	Tuna	do	1	2	2
	Total		24	110	45

Table 2.—Botulism associated with commercially prepared foods in the United States, 1941–67

Year	Food	Commercial pack	Outbreak	Cases	Deaths
1941	Mushroom sauce	Canned	1	3	1
1951	Cheese		1	1	1
1954	Pork barbecue		1	2	0
1960	Ciscoes	Vacuum packed	1	2	2
1963	Tuna	Canned	1	3	2
1963	Whitefish	Smoked	1	2	2
1963	Whitefish chub	Vacuum packed	1	18	5
1963	Liver paste	Canned	1	2	0
1965	Pork and beans or olives?	do	1	6	0
1965	Luncheon meat?		1	3	0
	Total		10	42	13

States during the 26-year period from 1941 to 1967. Only 10 outbreaks, involving 42 cases and 13 deaths (31 percent), were recorded. Commercially canned foods were implicated in four outbreaks, but one of these is somewhat doubtful because toxicity of the pork and beans or olives was not proven by laboratory tests. In contrast with the preceding 20 years, commercial products processed by means other than canning were incriminated in at least three outbreaks. The lower death rate probably reflects a more efficient use of antitoxin therapy, plus the occurrence of more type E botulism.

In discussing the relation of botulism to food preservation, we might first turn to the conventional methods. The canning industry, using the information provided by the research carried out in the 1920's and 1930's, has adopted the "12 D" process for treating low-acid foods so that the probability of C. botulinum spores surviving is very remote. The spores of C. botulinum are not the most heat-resistant known, and other sporeforming organisms, such as PA 3679, are frequently used in time-temperature studies; however, in the interest of safety, canning processes must be of such lethality that the likelihood of C. botulinum spores surviving is negligible in the practical sense. The concentration of organisms in a food product is very important because bacteria are killed by heat at a rate that is, in general, proportional to the number of organisms present (12). Consequently, the "12 D" process is designed to reduce a bacterial load of a billion spores in each of a thousand cans to one spore in a thousand cans. These processes are now standardized and controlled to the point that only through recontamination after heating is it likely that a significant degree of spoilage or hazard from C. botulinum could occur. An additional safety factor is provided by proper sanitary control, which tends to

reduce the original bacterial load. Recontamination may occasionally occur from postprocessing can-handling operations due to faulty seams, or the presence of bacterial contamination in the cooling water or on wet runways, or poor operation or adjustment of the filled can-handling equipment (10). In fact, all outbreaks of botulism from U.S. canned food in the recent past have been the result of technical errors and not of the process itself. This segment of the food-processing industry need have little concern about botulism from heat-processed canned foods as long as the manufacturers consistently apply the sanitation principles and technological knowledge available to them.

Drying and smoking as methods of food production received much adverse publicity in 1963 when the outbreaks of type E botulism from smoked fish occurred in the United States. Examination of the fish processing plants and the results of research stimulated by this catastrophe have revealed a great need for better sanitation practices (11) and more rigidly controlled heating and smoking procedures. Conventional dried foods such as fruits have not, to our knowledge, presented a problem as far as botulism is concerned.

The knowledge concerning the effects of chemicals, such as salt, nitrite, and organic acids, on the germination and outgrowth of C. botulinum spores has been utilized by the meat-curing industry to produce safe and acceptable products without subjecting them to the "12 D" process. Ham, bacon, sausages, and similar foods have not appeared on the lists of commercially produced foods associated with botulism in the United States in recent years. In 1965, a luncheon meat was suspected, but detailed studies failed to confirm this suspicion and the incident must go into the records as questionable.

Some of the newer methods of food processing are still in the stage of development where trouble spots could occur, even though their safety record to date is excellent. Presumably, there will be a continued increase in the production of frozen, freeze-dehydrated, vacuum-packaged, and possibly irradiated foods. In the United States, the so-called convenience foods cover a wide variety of partially or completely prepared items, ranging from single vegetables to complete meals. They are usually maintained in a frozen or dried state until used, and in all probability, are quite safe when prepared and used as directed. That they may contain C. botulinum is shown by the occurrence of two cases of botulism after the ingestion of chicken potpies. The pies were cooked as directed in a home oven, but two members of the family did not attend the evening meal and their pies were left in the turned off oven overnight. The pies were removed in the morning and taken to be eaten cold for lunch. Such severe mishandling could not be anticipated by the producer, but the fact remains that *C. botulinum* spores were present in the food. It should be noted, however, that the incidence of *C. botulinum* spores in such foods is extremely low in the United States. Taclindo et al. (*13*) found one positive sample of luncheon meat among 73 specimens examined, and Insalata et al. (*4*) found one positive in 400 samples of "boil-in-the-bag," vacuum-packaged, pressurized, and dehydrated foods. The point of consideration here is that very many of these convenience and other frozen foods do not receive any treatment in their production that would eliminate the spores of *C. botulinum*. It is, therefore, essential that a very high level of sanitation be maintained during production to reduce the bacterial contamination as much as possible, including contamination with *C. botulinum*. Under such conditions, with proper direction for storage and use, these foods should pose little hazard of botulism.

The preservation of food by drying, or smoking and drying, goes back beyond recorded history. One can picture a cave wife hanging a haunch of venison high in the cave out of the reach of the half-wild dogs and later discovering that it had been preserved and even improved by the exposure to heat and smoke. Modern commercial drying processes are a far cry from the crude smoking-drying combinations of the past that were sometimes responsible for botulism. Freeze-dehydration as well as conventional air drying are commercially attractive because of increased shelf life, weight reduction, and packaging ease. Some type of pretreatment is usually required so that rapid freezing and dehydration can occur. For example, chicken is cooked, removed from the bone, and diced. This and other like operations might allow considerable contamination of the products before drying unless a very high level of sanitation is maintained. Drying is not a reliable means of destroying micro-organisms, and freeze-drying is an effective method of preserving not only bacterial spores but vegetative cells as well. As in the case of frozen foods, dried foods, if reconstituted and used immediately, offer little hazard. Severe mishandling after reconstitution might, however, render them dangerous.

The type E, *C. botulinum*, has been so frequently associated with sea water, mud, and fish (*3*) that products from a marine environment are readily suspected. Other types, including A and B are, in fact, also rather universally distributed in nature and may be present in almost any environment from which foods are produced and prepared for dehydration or other types of processing.

Vacuum packaging offers its own special hazards in that when foods with sufficient moisture content to allow growth of bacteria are placed in a gaseous environment that will discourage growth of spoilage organisms on the surface, it is conducive to the growth of anaerobes. Smoked fish, for example, will support growth of *C. botulinum* in a normal gaseous environment (*1, 2, 5*), but such growth and toxin production are enhanced by vacuum packaging (*1, 5*). Concomitant growth of facultative organisms may well be an enhancing factor to the outgrowth of anaerobic species. Such growth uses up trace amounts of oxygen in the substrate, reduces the Eh, and provides growth-promoting substances. On the other hand, heavy overgrowth by aerobes may prevent the germination and outgrowth of anaerobic species due to toxic metabolites. In vacuum-packaged foods, growth of aerobic organisms is considerably curtailed, and the shelf life appears, therefore, to be extended because visible spoilage has not occurred. This additional time may be sufficient for anaerobes, such as *C. botulinum*, to grow and produce toxin. Furthermore, the well-preserved appearance of vacuum-packaged foods may lead the consumer to take risks that he would not consider if the food were exposed to air. Since it is now known that type E, *C. botulinum*, can grow and produce toxin at refrigerator temperatures, this longer storage time may constitute a significant hazard. The level and percentage of *C. botulinum* contamination have been shown to be very low in many types of vacuum-packaged foods, smoked fish perhaps being an exception. It appears, however, that the hazard is always present, unless, as is the case of many types of meats, chemical substances are present to prevent germination and outgrowth. With vacuum-packaged foods, as with so many others, every attempt must be made to establish high levels of sanitation in the processing plant so that contamination levels will be held to a minimum.

The radiation preservation of foods has been subjected to intensive study in recent years. If the radiation were at a level that produced a sterile product there would, of course, be no hazard from botulism. Processes designed to pasteurize, however, would have little or no effect upon the spores of *C. botulinum*, which are very resistant to radiation damage. The extended shelf life obtained by radiation might allow outgrowth and toxin production. Although other contributors will discuss radiation preservation in detail, we should like, at this point, to raise some questions about the effects of such treatment on the microflora as a whole and on *C. botulinum* in particular. Will such treatment give rise to radiation-resistant mutants? Will radiation affect the amount and type of toxin produced by surviving spores if they germinate and grow to sizable populations? Will changes in microbial ecology enhance the danger from *C. botulinum* or reduce it? Considering the many factors involved, it seems reasonable to assume that the same high levels of sanitation must be maintained with foods to be treated by radiation as are advocated in other types of food preservation.

Considering all of these newer methods of food production and preservation together, we might almost think of them as being in the stage of development that canning was 40 years ago. Only the continued application of the best information on sanitation and processing technology can make them safe and keep them free of hazards from botulism. Education of the consumer to minimize abuse of the products is also essential.

We should also be looking toward the future. Just as the last 20 years have shown marked changes in the food-processing field, so will coming decades introduce new technologies, methods, and products. These new advances must be investigated and evaluated for safety from the hazard of botulism as carefully as any we know today. It seems reasonable to suppose, for example, that in the future mass feeding of large numbers of people from centrally located automated kitchens will become a reality. We can anticipate that the massive centralization of populations in urban areas will eventually lead to the construction of large complexes designed to provide living space, utilities, entertainment, recreation facilities, and food. In such complexes the conventional home kitchen will be obsolete; rather the housewife will "dial-a-meal," which will be centrally prepared in a matter of minutes and delivered by conveyor, hot and ready to eat, to the living unit. Such complexes will require food-preservation processes much more complex than any we have today, but the essential hazards may still be the same. The only factor that will be eliminated will be consumer error, and it may well be replaced by automation breakdown.

In addition to new and novel methods of food preparation and serving, we can look forward to the use of new substances as foods. With increased pressure on the already overburdened agricultural potentials of the world, there will come the production of food supplements in the form of protein and other materials not now accepted as food components. Protein and fat from vegetable sources are, in fact, already being manufactured into synthetic foods that resemble meat, fish, poultry, and dairy products. Fish flour, soy protein, yeast and algal protein, and other food supplements will be produced by novel extraction and fermentation processes. These new substances and processes will require alert attention to their pos-

sible botulinal contamination for other foods or even as sources of the toxins themselves. We foresee no possibility of eradicating *C. botulinum* from the raw-product environment.

References

(1) ABRAHAMSSON, K., N. N. DE SILVA, and N. MOLIN. 1965. Toxin production by *Clostridium botulinum* type E in vacuum-packed, irradiated fresh fish in relation to changes of the associated microflora. Canad. J. Microbiol. *11*: 523–529.

(2) ANDO, Y., and K. INOUE. 1957. Studies on growth and toxin production of *Clostridium botulinum* type E in fish products. I. On the growth in relation to the oxydation-reduction potential in the fish flesh. Bull. Japan. Soc. Sci. Fish. *23*: 458–462.

(3) INGRAM, M., and T. A. ROBERTS. 1966. *Botulism 1966.* Proceedings of the Fifth International Symposium on Food Microbiology: Moscow, July 1966. Chapman & Hall, Ltd., London.

(4) INSALATA, N. F., S. J. WITZEMAN, J. H. BERMAN, and G. J. FREDERICKS. 1968. Incidence study of the spores of *C. botulinum* in convenience foods. Bacteriol. Proc., p. 10.

(5) KAUTTER, D. A. 1964. *Clostridium botulinum* type E in smoked fish. J. Food Sci. *29*: 843–849.

(6) LEWIS, K. H., and K. CASSEL, JR. *Botulism.* Public Health Service Publication No. 999-FP-1. Cincinnati, Ohio, 1964.

(7) MATVEEV, K. I. 1959. *Botulism.* State Medical Publishers (in Russian).

(8) MEYER, K. F., and B. EDDIE. 1965. *Sixty-five years of human botulism in the United States and Canada.* George Williams Hooper Foundation, Univ. Calif. Med. Center, San Francisco, Calif.

(9) PETTY, C. S. 1965. Botulism: The disease and the toxin. Am. J. Med. Sci. *249*: 345–359.

(10) PFLUG, I. J., and W. B. ESSELEN. 1967. Food processing by heat sterilization. *In* Fundamentals of Food Processing Operation Ingredients, Methods and Packaging. Hied, J. L., and M. A. Josly, eds. The Ani Publishing Co., Inc., Westport, Conn.

(11) PUBLIC HEALTH SERVICE PUBLICATION NO. 1587, Part I, Fish Smoking Establishment 1967 Recommendations, Sanitation Standards for Smoked-Fish Processing. A joint publication of the U.S. Departments of Interior, and Health, Education, and Welfare, U.S. Government Printing Office, Washington, D.C. 20201. 1967.

(12) SCHMIDT, C. F. 1957. Thermal resistance of microorganisms. *In* Antiseptics, Disinfectants, Fungicides, and Commercial and Physical Sterilization. G. F. Reddish, ed., 2d ed., Lea and Febiger, Philadelphia, Pa.

(13) TACLINDO, C., JR., T. MIDURA, C. S. NYGAARD, and H. L. BODILY. 1967. Examination of prepared food in plastic packages for *Clostridium botulinum.* Appl. Microbiol. *15*: 426–430.

ON THE REALITY OF "IZUSHI," THE CAUSAL FOOD OF BOTULISM, AND ON ITS FOLKLORIC MEANING

by Wataru Nakano *and* Eiichiro Kodama
The Iwate Institute of Public Health, Morioka, and
The Akita Institute of Public Health, Akita, Japan

From 1951 until the present there have been 57 outbreaks of botulinal poisoning in Japan, comprising a total of 319 patients and including 83 deaths. In most cases the toxigenic food was so-called "izushi" of fish but a few cases were due to related products. Four cases were ascribed to "kirikomi" (a raw herring product), one case to "kayuzushi" of some fish, and one case to "sujiko" (salted fish egg). One other case was caused by canned fish (mackerel). The kirikomi and the kayuzushi of fish both are very similar in composition to izushi. Therefore, an understanding of the employment of izushi as a food is a most important aspect of the problem.

If we can prevent the present use of izushi as food, the incidence of botulism in Japan should decrease greatly. Hitherto, whenever botulinal food-poisoning occurred in Japan, the danger of eating izushi was reported and the public was cautioned in the newspapers and on radio and television. Notwithstanding such information, izushi is even at present made and eaten. This shows that izushi must be felt to be necessary, at any cost, to the people in spite of a possible danger to life.

What is Izushi?

Izushi is a type of fermented food made of boiled rice and raw fish meat. The first letter "i" of the word izushi represents "ii." The term "ii" or "meshi" means boiled rice and "zushi" or "sushi" means a sour food, composed of boiled rice and fish meat or vegetables. However, among the so-called izushi preparations there is one kind which does not contain fish meat and there is another kind of sushi which lacks the fermentation procedure. Food-poisoning has not occurred from the latter kinds of izushi. It is during the course of the fermentation that the contaminating clostridial spores or vegetative bacteria may multiply and produce the toxin.

The materials employed in the processing of izushi are boiled rice, koji (rice malt), raw fish meat, vegetables, condiments. A brief description of the process follows:

Step 1.—Any fish will do. When the fish is large, the head and viscera must be removed and then cut into pieces of moderate size. The pieces of fish are placed in water, for 1 to 7 days, in order to extract the blood. The water is changed once or twice a day. The fish meat is then taken out of the water and the water is discarded.

Step 2.—Minced vegetables (carrot, cabbage, radish, ginger, turnip, eggplant, etc.) and condiments (salt, vinegar, sake, sugar, mirin, etc.) are mixed.

Step 3.—Rice is boiled and when cooled to body temperature it is mixed with koji.

Step 4.—The fish portion, rice portion and the vegetable portions are piled alternately, in layers of 1 to 3 cm. thickness in a tub.

Step 5.—When the layering operation is finished, bamboo grass leaves are placed on the surface. Often a straw bundle is coiled around the inner surface of the tub. Next, the tub is covered with a lid and a heavy stone, about 3 to 5 kg., is placed on it in order to press the contents.

The so-called maturing of izushi takes anywhere from 5 days to 2 months. During maturation, some water appears on the lid, and is removed from time to time. When the maturing process is complete, izushi is approximately half solids and the fish meat and vegetables retain their original form.

Observations on Izushi from the Standpoint of History and Folklore

Izushi is made not only by the people in Hokkaido and in the northeastern districts of Honshu, but it is also made in many other districts of Japan. However, botulinal izushi-poisonings have occurred only in Hokkaido and in the northeastern part of Japan.

Why this geographical distribution? At first we considered that the cause lay in the processing method employed in those areas. If so, when did such a dangerous method, which then became a tradition inherited by the people in the northeastern part of the country, develop? Therefore, we sought to find the initial description of izushi in the ancient Japanese literature.

The many characters, which are used now for writing in Japan, were introduced from China in ancient times. Chinese characters were hieroglyphs, but in Japan they were used to write the Japanese language. A single Chinese character may have one or several meanings. In order to express the sounds of the Japanese language, Chinese characters were used, having no relation to the Chinese meanings. The ancient Japanese wanted letters to be able to express the sound of Japanese language, not ideographs. There are several characters which we must read as having the meaning of sushi.

In the ancient Japanese book, "Taiho-Ritsuryo" written in 701, we find a Chinese character meaning sushi for the first time. In 898–901, a bonze (a buddhist priest) named Shoju-Hoshi, published a book entitled "Shinsenji-Kyo." This book was a kind of dictionary in which the author pointed out a Chinese character to read sushi and also several other characters which could be read with the same meaning. In a book named "Engi-shiki" written in 905–930 we can find two characters which mean sushi and we know that at that time three kinds of sushi were made in various areas of Japan and presented to the Emperor. The kinds of sushi and the specific areas of their production are shown in table 1 and figure 1.

The materials comprising sushi in those ancient times were varied but can be divided into three basic types. One type was fish (salmon, crucian carp, halfbreak, carp), the second type was fish egg, and the third kind was animal meat (deer and wild boar). The preparation of sushi depended on the availability of raw materials in each area, that is, fish was employed in the areas near sea or lake and animal meat was used in the mountainous areas.

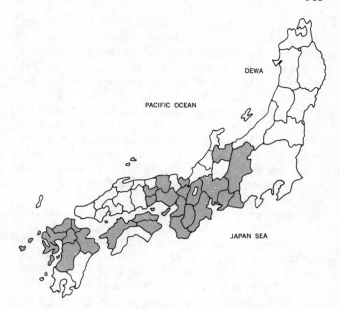

Figure 1.—The countries or areas from where sushi were presented to the court.

Whether the sushi made at that time was the same as the sushi which now is made in Hokkaido or in northeastern Honshu is not clear, but it appears that the ancient sushi did not use as much rice. The lesser proportion of rice can be estimated from an ancient formula recorded as follows, "The material for making 10 *koku* (unit of volume) of 'zako-sushi': salted fish *6 to* (unit of volume = 1/10 koku), shofu 16 *dan* (unit of length), shinano-asa 6 *kin* (unit of weight), white rice 1 *koku*, salt 1 *koku* 6 *to*." And also another ancient

Table 1.—The kinds of sushi presented to the Court of Japan and the areas of their origin (from an ancient book, "Engi-Shiki")

Kind of sushi	Area of origin	Kind of sushi	Area of origin
		Chapter of Accountant	
Sweetfish	Mino, Harima, Awa, Chikugo, Higo, Buzen, Bungo.	Ear shell	Awa, Iyo, Chikuzen, Hizen, 5-Kinai.
Crucian carp	5-Kinai, Mino, Chikuzen, Chikugo, Dazaifu.	Ear shell (light salted)	Wakasa, 5-Kinai.
Salmon	Ecchu.	*Mytilus coruscus*	Mikawa, Iyo, 5-Kinai.
Trout	Ohmi.	*Mytilus* and sea squirt mixed	Wakasa, 5-Kinai.
Miscellaneous (fish)	Ise, Owari, Bizen, Awa, 5-Kinai.	Wild boar	Kii, Buzen, Kai.
Miscellaneous	Shima, Wakasa, Awaji.	Deer	Kii, Chikuzen, Buzen, Bungo.
Sushi (material unknown)	Sanuki.		
		Chapter of Provision	
Sweetfish	Yamato, Iga, Ise, Tamba, Tajima, Harima, Kii, Mimasaka, Mino.	Egg of fish	Dazaifu.
		Miscellaneous	Kawachi.
		Crucian carp	Ohmi.

formula, "As material, salted fish 20 *koku* 6 *to*, 'shofu' 16 *dan*, 'shinanoasa' 100 *kin*, salt 2 *koku*."

Among the above-mentioned materials, shofu and shinanoasa are not food, perhaps they were used for other purposes during the processing. We find an unexpected aspect when we consider the volumetric relationships among the materials, that is, too much salt (about 10 percent) and too little rice as compared to contemporary formulae. The fish prepared under such conditions ought to be called salt-preserved fish. Some rice was used, but it is not comparable to the present izushi, yet the people at that time might have expected an acid fermentation.

At least we can now presume that sushi was present as food in the ancient time of the Heian-Era (781–1198). We also can find the letter or character meaning sushi in two books: "Wamyosho" by Minamoto no Shitagau, written in 931, and "Tosa Nikki" by K. Tsurayuki, written in 936. A book "Shasekishu" written by a bonze, named Muju-Hoshi in 1278–88, describes the sushi of sweetfish in Dewa, a district of northeastern Japan. A famous series of documents "Oyudono no Ue no Nikki" (1477–1687), written by many court ladies in succession, contain the word "sumoji" which means sushi. In this period sushi made from rice and vegetables were presented to the Emperor. In a book named "Ninagawa Motochika Nikki" (1473–86), we find the word "namanare" which means the "fermentation is not complete," and the word "ichiya-zushi" which means "made in one night."

In the book "Kebuki-guse" written in 1645 by Matsue Shigeyori, which is a kind of saiji-ki, a reference work for Haikai (Japanese sonnet), we note the presence of "hatahata-sushi" in the Dewa district and that "tsurube-zushi" and "suzume-zushi" were made in the Kinki district. Tsurube-zushi was a kind of instant zushi and suzume-zushi was a kind of "namanare-zushi." From this book we also find that sushi was made in every season. At this period three styles in sushi were distinguished, "narezushi," "namanare," and "ichya-zushi." For the processing of "narezushi" a long period was needed for completion, for "namanare-zushi" less time was required and "ichya-zushi," as the designation shows, was made in one night. The izushi, which is the causal food for botulism in Hokkaido or in Tohku districts at present, is a kind of nare-zushi or "namanare-zushi." The three styles of sushi were described in "Honcho Shokukan," by On Hichidai (1695).

When we compare the methods for making izushi in the Kinki district and in Hokkaido and in the northeastern districts of Honshu, we do not find great differences. One difference between them is the initial processing of the fish meat. As already mentioned, in Hokkaido and in northeastern Honshu the manipulation called "chidashi" is used in order to rid fish meat of blood. This is done by extraction with water but in Kinki this procedure is not used. Instead, the manipulation is to salt the fish meat for a long period (about 1 month). However, we do not know whether or not *Clostridium botulinum* or its spores is killed by such a salting. There are many districts where narezushi or namanare-zushi is made and eaten but botulism has not been reported as occurring in these areas.

At present, "kirikomi" of fish is made and sold at market in Hokkaido and three outbreaks of botulism have been reported. In Akita Prefecture izushi of salmon is made and sold at market but botulism has not occurred. However, we have isolated one strain of *C. botulinum* type E out of 19 samples from the market. The operation of dipping fish meat into vinegar or salt is not always safe; because, notwithstanding such manipulation, several cases have occurred in Hokkaido.

The Present Status of Izushi in Akita Prefecture

In 1962 we made a survey of the present status of izushi manufacture among the population in Akita Prefecture. This program was carried out with the aid of 13 health educators in the prefecture (4). Thirteen towns or villages out of 72 were selected for inquiry. They were spread uniformly from north to south in the prefecture.

Out of 6,739 households, 3,372 households (50 percent) made izushi and 4,039 households ate it (63.5 percent). As regards the season of processing, 2,451 households (60.6 percent) replied that they make it in December; the next most frequent time was in November (19.9 percent), followed by January (4 percent). Processing during February, April, and May was reported by 2.8 percent for each month and in March by 1.8 percent. Very few reported processing during the rest of the year (June through September). It is noteworthy that izushi is made even in the warmer season by some people. (Table 2.)

The next inquiry concerned the kinds of fish which were processed. Usually fish of moderate size are selected but small fish are also utilized without removing heads or viscera. The kinds of fish are listed in table 3. The utilization rate of hatahata was highest of all followed by mackerel and herring. Flatfish was only employed in 2.9 percent of preparations but in the 57 outbreaks in Japan the flatfish izushi was the causal food highest in the frequency. The kinds and frequency of utilization of vegetables are shown in table 4. About one half of 5,502 households use carrot, probably for color. Radish and turnip were used in about 19.0 percent of recipes.

Table 2.—The month for processing izushi

Month	Number of households	Rate (percent)
April	113	2.8
May	112	2.8
June	36	.9
July	26	.6
August	13	.3
September	26	.6
October	118	2.9
November	805	19.9
December	2,451	60.6
January	163	4.0
February	113	2.8
March	67	1.8
Total	6,739	100.0

Table 3.—The kinds of fish for the processing of izushi

Kind of fish	Number of households	Rate (percent)
Hatahata	3,217	69.4
Saury	539	11.6
Herring	210	4.5
Salmon, light salted	171	3.7
Flatfish	136	2.9
Salmon	103	2.2
Trout	49	1.2
Goby	40	.9
Mackerel	38	.8
Crucian carp	21	.5
Carp	11	.2
Kanagi	11	.2
Others	88	1.9
Total	6,739	100.0

Table 4.—The vegetables used in processing izushi

Kinds of vegetables used	Number of households	Rate (percent)
Carrot	2,524	45.9
Radish	1,047	19.0
Turnip	1,046	19.0
Chinese cabbage	428	7.8
Seaweeds (kombu, wakame)	303	5.5
Others	154	2.8
Total	5,502	100.0

Inquiry as to the usage of "koji" (rice malt) revealed that koji was used by 2,197 households (83.6 percent). Therefore, the majority used koji and in the southern part of the prefecture the rate was a little higher than the northern.

"Shoku-su" (vinegar) is used as the condiment for sour taste. Its prime component is acetic acid and its pH is generally 2.4. Shoku-su was used by 2,686 households (39.8 percent) and the rest of them did not employ it. Most households (99.1 percent) used salt but the quantity was of course small.

The periods reported for chidashi (water soaking of fish meat) are shown in table 5. In the course of chidashi, autolysis may occur in the fish meat as well as denaturation of protein and hemolysis of fish blood. It is not clear whether this manipulation has an effect on the taste of izushi. Inquiry as to the size of the fish resulted in 1,868 households (29.5 percent) replying that they cut it in two or three pieces when the fish were big. The number of households which replied they cut off the head and viscera from fish was 1,819 (28.6 percent), but 984 households (15.4 percent) replied they preserved the whole fish. These operations are of course related to the size of the fish, for when the fish are too small, it is difficult to cut off the head or remove viscera.

The times used for the completion of maturation are shown in table 6. About one third of the house-

Table 5.—The soaking interval of fish meat in water preliminary to making izushi (chidashi)

Interval in days	Number of households	Rate (percent)
1 to 2	875	32.0
2 to 3	665	24.3
3 to 4	538	19.7
4 to 5	227	8.3
5 to 6	97	3.5
6 to 7	123	4.5
7 to 8	69	2.5
8 to 9	5	.3
9 to 10	39	1.4
10 to 11	26	1.0
11 +	69	2.5
Total	2,733	100.0

Table 6.—The time for maturation of izushi

Time (days)	Number of households	Percent
1	2	
2	10	0.3
3	20	.6
4 to 7	57	1.6
7 to 10	223	6.4
10 to 15	410	11.8
15 to 20	889	25.7
20 to 30	1,158	33.4
30 to 40	512	14.8
40 or more	145	4.2
Unknown	36	1.1
Total	3,462	99.9

holds waited 20 to 30 days, one fourth waited 15 to 20 days and about 10 percent of households required only 10 to 15 days for the maturation of izushi.

Inquiry concerning the acquisition of the habit of making izushi revealed that 1,479 households (41.2 percent) replied that the habit was continued from their ancestors; 1,271 households (35.4 percent) replied that the habit was inherited from their parent generation; and those who had initiated the practice themselves numbered 642 households (17.9 percent). As the data show, the habit of making and eating izushi is deeply rooted in folk custom.

Inquiry as to the purpose of making izushi revealed (table 7) that 2,237 (47.4 percent) enjoyed its taste, and 1,137 households (24.1 percent) felt that izushi was convenient during the busy farming period. Households constituting 10.3 percent of the total gave reasons of economy and 18.2 percent answered, "merely because of habit."

Conclusion

Japanese botulinal food-poisoning has occurred due to ingestion of so-called izushi, composed of raw fish meat and boiled rice. If we can militate against the habit of making and eating izushi, botulinal poisonings should decrease greatly.

Table 7.—Reasons for making izushi

Reasons given	Number of households	Rate (percent)
Good taste	2,237	47.4
Economy	487	10.3
Convenience	1,137	24.1
Habit	862	18.2
Total	4,623	100.0

Sushi, especially izushi, are fermented foods and their manufacture is not proper from the standpoint of bacteriology and hygiene, because such foods are eaten without disinfection. In order to avoid poisoning, either a change is needed in the method of its preparation or the people must be induced to abandon the folk habit of eating it.

References

(1) "ENGI-SHI". The Complete Work Series, 1–6. 1929.
(2) TANGAKU NO HITSUDAI, "Honcho Shokukan." Genroku 8.
(3) SHINIDA, OSAMU, 1966. "Book of Sushi."
(4) SHOHKO, KOJI. On the realities of izushi. 1962. Rept. Akita Pref. Inst. Public Health. 6: 58.

CHARACTERIZATION OF *CLOSTRIDIUM BOTULINUM* TYPE E TOXIN IN "IZUSHI"

by Genji Sakaguchi, Sumiko Sakaguchi, *and* Takashi Karashimada
Department of Food Research, National Institute of Health, Tokyo,
and Hokkaido Institute of Public Health, Sapporo, Hokkaido

Summary

We prepared a type E botulinogenic "izushi". The molecular size, the stability and other properties of the toxin in the izushi were examined. The flounder slices inoculated with type E spores were soaked in water for 3 days, during which period the potential toxicity of the fish meat reached 64,000 LD_{50}/g. The potency was quadrupled in the first 10 days after the initiation of fermentation, attaining 250,000 LD_{50}/g. The toxin in the izushi was very stable. After 20 months of storage, the fish meat in the izushi still contained a potential toxicity of 52,000 LD_{50}/g. The toxin in the izushi was mostly in the form of the precursor, but the activation ratio gradually decreased.

The toxin in the izushi possessed a molecular size of about 11.5S, which was not reduced by the tryptic activation. The much higher stability shown with the purified 11.5S toxin than the 7S toxin at a pH of izushi may well explain the high stability of the toxin in izushi.

Introduction

Inconsistent molecular sizes of the *Clostridium botulinum* toxins have been reported. A partially purified trypsin-activated type E toxin showed a main peak with an $S_{20,w}$ of 12.5 in ultracentrifugal analysis (3). The precursor and the trypsin-activated type E toxin purified by us possessed the same $S_{20,w}$ of about 11.5 (13, 7). On the other hand, the toxin purified by Gerwing et al. (4), possessed an $S_{20,w}$ of 1.70 and a molecular weight of 18,600. They suggested that the large molecular sized toxins are the artifacts formed by aggregation during the purification procedures and stated that the true molecular weight of toxin should approximate the smallest figure (6).

The type A toxin obtained by Gerwing, Dolman, and Bains (5) possessed a molecular weight of 12,000, but much smaller toxic peptides with a molecular weight of about 3,800 were demonstrated by Wagman (15) by peptic digestion of the dissociated toxin originating from the crystalline toxin with the molecular weight of 900,000. One would rather hesitate, however, to regard the smallest figure, 3,800, as the true molecular weight of type A toxin.

Before attempting to obtain the smallest possible figure of the molecular weight, one must answer a fundamental question: What is the true molecular size of botulinus toxin normally produced by the organisms in foods or in cultures? Schantz and Spero (14) answered it for some cases. They found the sedimentation constants of the toxins in the spent cultures, without any purification steps, to be about 19S for type A, 16S for type B, and 14S for the other four types.

We attempted to answer the question (12) in regard to the molecular size of type E toxin in izushi, the foodstuff involved in most outbreaks of human botulism in Japan. In this investigation, an izushi was prepared with flounders inoculated with the spores of *C. botulinum* type E. The developed toxin was examined for the form and the molecular size by gel filtration and sucrose-density-gradient separation and for the stability in the izushi kept under refrigeration for 20 months. Attempts were also made to explain why the toxin in izushi is so stable.

Materials and Methods

Preparation of the izushi.—Fresh flounders, after the heads and viscera had been removed, were sliced. About 250,000 spores of *C. botulinum* type E strain Iwanai were injected into each slice. The fish slices were soaked in water in a plastic container at 20° to 23° C. for 3 days, during which time the water was changed twice a day. The soaked fish slices, cooked rice, "koji" (malted rice), and cut-up radish and carrot were placed into a plastic container. The contents were compressed tightly and kept standing at room temperature to allow fermentation for 10 days. After that, the izushi was kept under refrigeration at about 4° C.

Preparation of toxin materials.—The turbid fluid, with a pH of 4.20 to 4.28, deposited on the izushi was removed. A portion of a fish slice was emulsified in an equal amount of 0.1 M phosphate buffer, pH 6.0.

The exudate and the fish emulsion were centrifuged at 12,000 x g. for 20 minutes. The clear supernatant fluids served as the toxin materials. Partially purified preparations of the precursor with an $S_{20,w}$ of 11.5 were prepared by the method described by Sakaguchi, Sakaguchi and Imai (*11*). The 7S toxin, one of the dissociation products of the 11.5S toxin (*7*), was prepared chromatographically on DEAE-Sephadex at pH 8 (Kitamura, Sakaguchi, unpublished work).

Gel filtration.—A column of Sephadex G–100 (2.5 x 30 cm.) equilibrated with 0.05 M acetate buffer, pH 6.0, was loaded with 5.0 ml. of the exudate or the fish extract prepared on the 10th day of fermentation. Elution was carried out at room temperature with the same buffer. Ten-ml. fractions were collected. The protein content of each fraction was determined; the toxicities of the combined fractions of every three tubes were determined before and after tryptic activation.

Sucrose-density-gradient separation.—The fish extract prepared on the 10th day of fermentation before and after tryptic activation was examined. Density gradient of 20 to 5 percent sucrose was prepared by mixing two solutions of 0.05 M phosphate buffer, pH 6.0, containing sucrose at 20 percent and 5 percent, respectively. Two-tenths milliliter of each material was placed on top of the gradient. The tubes were centrifuged in an Hitachi swinging bucket rotor, model PRS 40, at 40,000 r.p.m. (105,000 x g.) for 5 hours. The fractionation was accomplished by inserting a hypodermic needle into the tube's bottom and controlling the outflow of solution by water pressure. Fractions of 20 drops each were collected. The toxic potency of each fraction of the nonactivated fish extract and the purified precursor material was determined after tryptic activation.

Other methods.—The tryptic activation, toxin assay and protein determination were performed as described by Sakaguchi et al. (*11*). Toxin potencies after tryptic activation were also determined by the mouse intravenous injection method (*1*) (Sakaguchi, Sakaguchi and Kondo, unpublished work).

Results

Development of the toxin in the fish slices and the izushi and the stability of the toxin.—One of the fish slices, inoculated with the spores and soaked in water for 3 days, contained toxic potencies of 320 and 64,000 $LD_{50}/g.$ before and after activation, respectively. Such toxigenic fish slices and other ingredients were packed together in the container to make izushi by fermentation.

The pH values, the toxin potencies before and after tryptic activation, and also the survival of the spores determined at times during the 20 months' storage

under refrigeration are shown in table 1. The pH of the izushi was 4.20 on the 4th day and it no longer changed appreciably during the following 20 months. The highest toxin potency of the fish meat was shown on the 10th day. The toxic potency of the izushi did not decrease rapidly. Twenty months later, the fish slice still contained a potential toxicity of 52,000 $LD_{50}/g.$ and a fairly large number of the viable organisms.

Table 1.—Storage stability of *Clostridium botulinum* type E toxin and spores in fish meat in izushi

| Period of storage | pH of exudate | Toxin potencies ($LD_{50}/g.$) | | Activation ratio | Spore survival |
		Before activation	After activation		
0 day		320	64,000	200	
4 days	4.20				
10 days	4.28	4,100	250,000	61	
77 days		6,400	210,000	33	
10 months		2,500	100,000	40	+
20 months	4.25	3,300	52,000	16	+

NOTE.—During the first 10 days, the izushi was allowed to ferment at room temperature; after that period, it was kept at about 4° C.

The molecular size of the toxin in the izushi: Gel filtration on Sephadex G–100.—The elution patterns of the exudate and the fish extract are shown in figure 1. The majority of the toxic activities of both samples were eluted in the void volume (fraction A), being accompanied by a very small amount of protein; no significant amount of toxic activity was detected in the retarded fractions (fractions B, C, D, and E). A large part of the proteinaceous substances were eluted in the retarded fractions.

Sucrose-density-gradient separation.—The patterns of the sucrose-density-gradient separation of the fish extract before and after tryptic activation and of the 11.5S material are shown in figure 2. The toxins in the nontreated and the trypsin-activated extracts sedimented to the same relative position; the precursor to a lesser extent. The position of the peak of the toxic activity and that of the protein were the same with the precursor; most proteinaceous substances in the fish extract were separated from the toxin.

Since the toxic potency of the fish extract was much lower than that of the 11.5S material, having possibly caused the higher extent of sedimentation of the former, the toxin in the extract was concentrated by ammonium sulfate precipitation at 50 percent saturation. The precipitate, dissolved in a smaller amount of 0.1 M phosphate buffer, pH 6.0, contained sixfold higher toxicity than the original fish extract.

Sucrose-density-gradient separations were made in

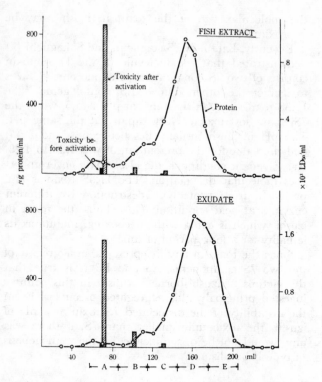

Figure 1.—Elution patterns of type E botulinus toxin in the exudate of izushi and in the extract of the fish from a column of Sephadex G–100 (2.5 x 30 cm.).

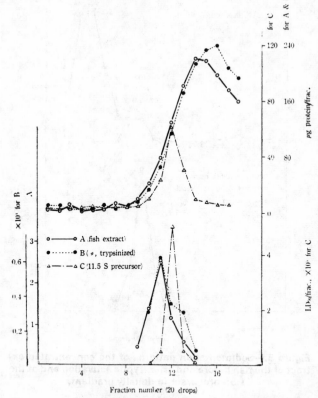

Figure 2.—Sedimentation patterns of type E botulinus toxin in the extract of the fish before and after tryptic activation and of the 11.5S precursor in sucrose density gradient.

the same way as before. As seen in figure 3, the toxic activities of the three materials sedimented to the same relative position.

Stability of the 11.5S and 7S toxins at pH 4.4.— Figure 4 shows the destruction curves of the precursor (11.5S) and the dissociated precursor (7S) at pH 4.4 and 33° C. No decrease in the potential toxicity was noted with the 11.5S material; the 7S material lost the toxicity very rapidly.

Discussion

The flounder slice supported the toxin production by *C. botulinum* type E to the same extent as a good laboratory medium (*3*). The toxin production took place mostly before and immediately after the initiation of fermentation. This fact may justify the warnings issued by Kanzawa and Iida (*8*) that izushi making should be limited only to the cold seasons using very fresh fish. The soaking of the fish must be done in the water at 5° C., or lower temperature, and acetic acid should preferably be added to the soaking water.

The greater part of the toxin in izushi was found to be in the form of precursor. The activation ratio, however, gradually decreased, possibly by partial

activation with trypsin-like enzyme produced by contaminating organisms (*9*).

Type E botulism has often been caused by acidic preserved foods, such as izushi, vinegared fish, etc. Although multiplication and toxin production of *C. botulinum* type E in herring at pH 4.0 to 4.2 were reported (*2*), no growth was demonstrated in a culture medium at pH 5.5 or lower in two days at 30° C. (*10*). In the present investigation, the toxin potency in the fish meat apparently increased during the first 10 days after the initiation of fermentation. It seems, however, that the increase had taken place before the pH of the fish meat dropped to a certain level. It is noteworthy that the toxin once produced in izushi retains the toxicity for a long time.

The gel-filtration experiments demonstrated that the toxin in izushi is for the most part of a large molecular size. The sucrose-density-gradient separation demonstrated that the toxin, whether untreated or treated with trypsin, possessed a molecular size of at least 11.5S. Since the toxin in the fish extract concentrated with ammonium sulfate sedimented to the same relative position as the purified precursor,

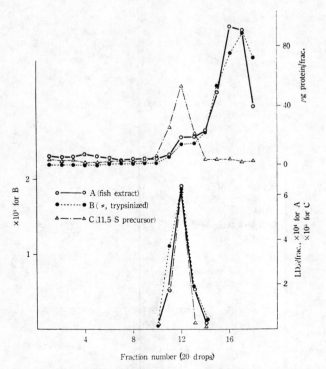

Figure 3.—Sedimentation patterns of the concentrated extract of the fish before and after tryptic activation and of the 11.5S precursor in density gradient.

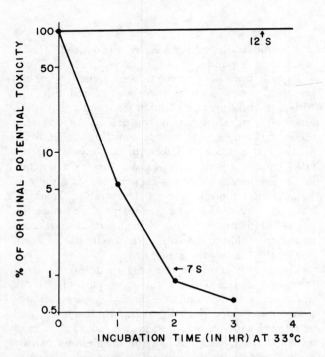

Figure 4.—Destruction of the precursor (11.5S) and the dissociated precursor (7S) at pH 4.4 and 33° C.

the molecular size of the toxin in izushi may be approximately 11.5.S

Recently, Kitamura, Sakaguchi, and Sakaguchi (7) demonstrated that the molecule of the 11.5S toxin consists of two 7S components. The one named $E\alpha$ is toxigenic; the other named $E\beta$ nontoxigenic. The 11.5S toxins were fairly stable at pH 4 to 5, while the 7S toxins lost toxicity very rapidly at the same pH. The pH of izushi usually lies between 4 and 5 (8) and the value for the present izushi was 4.20 to 4.28. At such acidic conditions, the 11.5S toxin never undergoes molecular dissociation. The 11.5S toxin is also protected from proteolytic destruction by different enzymes at acid conditions (13). Thus, the toxin in izushi, which is eaten without cooking, maintains its lethality for a long period of time.

Since the toxin in izushi represents an aggregate of the two 7S components, $E\alpha$ and $E\beta$ it is true that the victims of izushi-borne botulism in this country ingested principally this aggregated precursor. From the instability of the dissociated 7S toxin at a pH of izushi, the toxic unit smaller than 7S, if there was any, would not be of significance in the pathogenesis of type E botulism.

Acknowledgment

This investigation was supported in part by U.S. Public Health Service Research Grant EF–00361 from the Division of Environmental Engineering and Food Protection.

References

(1) BOROFF, D. A., and U. FLECK. 1966. Statistical analysis of a rapid *in vivo* method for the titration of the toxin of *Clostridium botulinum*. J. Bacteriol. *92:* 1580–1581.

(2) DOLMAN, C. E., and H. IIDA. 1962. Recent occurrences of type E botulism in Canada and Japan: Successful antitoxin therapy. Canad. J. Publ. Health *53:* 39–40.

(3) FIOCK, M. A., A. YARINSKY, and J. T. DUFF. 1961. Studies on immunity to toxins of *Clostridium botulinum*. VII. Purification and detoxification of trypsin-activated type E toxin. J. Bacteriol. *82:* 66–71.

(4) GERWING, J., C. E. DOLMAN, M. E. REICHMANN, and H. S. BAINS. 1964. Purification and molecular weight determination of *Clostridium botulinum* type E toxin. J. Bacteriol. *88:* 216–219.

(5) GERWING, J., C. E. DOLMAN, and H. S. BAINS. 1965. Isolation and characterization of a toxic moiety of low molecular weight from *Clostridium botulinum* type A toxin. J. Bacteriol. *89:* 1383–1386.

(6) GERWING, J., C. E. DOLMAN, and A. KO. 1965. Mechanism of tryptic activation of *Clostridium botulinum* type E toxin. J. Bacteriol. *89:* 1176–1179.

(7) KITAMURA, M., S. SAKAGUCHI, and G. SAKAGUCHI. 1967. Dissociation of *Clostridium botulinum* type E toxin. Biochem. Biophys. Res. Commun. *29:* 892–897

(8) KANZAWA, K., and H. IIDA. 1957. Studies on prevention of toxin production by *Clostridium botulinum* type E in "izushi", Report 2. Rep. Hokkaido Inst. Publ. Health *8:* 33–38. (In Japanese)

(9) SAKAGUCHI, G., Y. TOHYAMA, S. SAITO, S. FUJISAWA, and A. WADA. 1954. An outbreak of type E botulism in Akita prefecture due to gilthead-izushi. Japan. J. Med. Sci. Biol. *7:* 539–546.

(10) SAKAGUCHI, G., S. SAKAGUCHI, T. KAWABATA, Y. NAKAMURA, T. AKANO, and K. SHIROMIZU. 1960. Influence of oxytetracycline upon the toxin production of type E *Cl. botulinum*. Japan. J. Med. Sci. Biol. *13:* 13–22.

(11) SAKAGUCHI, G., S. SAKAGUCHI, and N. IMAI. 1964. Comparative gel filtration of toxin precursor and trypsin-activated toxin of *Clostridium botulinum* type E. J.

Bacteriol. *87:* 401–407.

(12) SAKAGUCHI, G., S. SAKAGUCHI, and T. KARASHIMADA. 1966. Molecular size of *Clostridium botulinum* type E toxin of "izushi". Japan. J. Med. Sci. Biol. *19:* 201–207.

(13) SAKAGUCHI, G., and S. SAKAGUCHI. 1967. Some observations on activation of *Cl. botulinum* type E toxin by trypsin. *In* Botulism 1966 M. Ingram and T. A. Roberts (eds.), Chapman & Hall, London, pp. 266–277.

(14) SCHANTZ, E. J., and L. SPERO. 1967. Molecular size of *Cl. botulinum* toxins. *In* Botulism 1966, M. Ingram and T. A. Roberts (eds.), Chapman & Hall, London, pp. 296–301.

(15) WAGMAN, J. 1963. Low molecular weight forms of type A botulinum toxin. II. Action of pepsin on intact and dissociated toxin. Arch. Biochem. Biophys. *100:* 414–421.

U.S. REGULATORY ADMINISTRATION FOR CONTROL OF MICROBIOLOGICAL HEALTH HAZARDS IN FOODS

by Joseph C. Olson, Jr.
Division of Microbiology, Food and Drug Administration,
Department of Health, Education, and Welfare, Washington, D.C. 20204

In the United States the common objective of government programs for the sanitary control of food production, processing, and distribution is to provide safe and wholesome foods to consumers—including, of course, foods free from microbiological health hazards such as food-borne pathogens and their toxins.

For the purpose of this discussion I wish to emphasize at the outset that sanitation as it relates to safe and wholesome foods is considered inseparable from microbiological health hazards, and is recognized as one of the paramount approaches to wholesomeness and microbiological safety of foods.

The basis for Government regulatory programs to protect the public health, including all aspects of food protection, is the law, or as one frequently hears or sees expressed—the "public health law." The term public health law merely expresses the application of legal principles to the practice of public health, and thus does not embody principles different from those applied to other professions or interests.

The public health regulatory mechanisms in the United States that pertain to food protection and more specifically to control of food-borne disease—including botulism—are complex and often confusing to our visitors from foreign lands and frequently to ourselves as well. To understand these mechanisms some orientation is necessary to the types of law to which we are subjected and to our governmental organization which provides for the sources of law. Hamlin (*6*) has presented a most useful discussion of the interrelationship of law and public health administration. Accordingly, I have drawn heavily from pertinent portions of his treatment of the subject.

We shall then consider first the types of law. Although the types of law may be described in many ways, for our immediate purposes they may be referred to as constitutional law, statute law, and administrative law.

Briefly, constitutional law is concerned with government organization, extent of jurisdiction of sovereignty, and the principles that underlie the interrelationships between the government and the people. A constitution is a written document that enumerates these principles.

Statute law is law created by enactment of legislative or lawmaking bodies. These are called statutes, ordinances, codes, or bylaws depending upon the level of government within which the legislative body functions. (We shall return to this later for further clarification.) Thus, there is clear distinction between a constitution and statutes. A constitution is the organic or basic law of a State or the nation which provides for the political organization; statutes are made by legislative bodies established and acting under the authority granted them by the constitution.

Administrative law is that which is created or enacted by various government subdivisions (i.e., the U.S. Food and Drug Administration) acting under the authority provided them by the appropriate legislative body. These enactments are commonly called rules, regulations, and orders. They prescribe in detail the procedure and content of programs and activities of the government subdivisions; they have the effect of law.

We shall turn now to government organization in the United States through which the sources of law are provided. A brief description of both vertical and horizontal organization of government is pertinent.

Vertically, our government is organized in the following descending order in size, but not necessarily in respective power or authority:

(1) Federal or National;
(2) Regional (a grouping of several States);
(3) State;
(4) Regional (county, city-county, township); and
(5) Local (municipalities; i.e., cities, villages).

For purposes of this discussion this descending order may be simplified to the three levels—Federal, State, and local.

Historically the Federal Government has only those powers originally granted by the States and embodied in the Federal Constitution—all other powers are retained by the States. Likewise, the powers or authorities of local governments (cities, villages) are only those delegated to them by the States through the respective State constitutions and statutes enacted by State legislative bodies.

At each of the three vertical levels of government

just described, there are three horizontal branches—legislative, executive, and judicial. The legislative body enacts laws; e.g., statutes, ordinances, etc. At the Federal level this is the Congress, consisting of the U.S. Senate and the U.S. House of Representatives; at the State level, the respective State legislatures; and at the local level, it is generally known as the city council. The judicial body judges the application of laws to particular cases, their constitutionality, etc. At the Federal level this is the Supreme Court and its lower courts; at the State level, the State supreme court and its lower courts; and at the local level it is the local courts. The executive body administers the law or supervises enforcement of the law. At the Federal level the executive branch of Government consists of the President and officials subordinate to him; at the State level, the Governor, his subordinates and other elected officials having executive power; and at the local level, the Mayor, his subordinates and others with executive authority.

The principal U.S. Federal organization charged with responsibility for the health of the Nation (including food protection) is the Deparment of Health, Education, and Welfare (DHEW). The source of its legal responsibility stems from its position as a part of the executive branch of the Government. Generally, health agencies whether at the Federal, State, or local level have the following legal powers:

(1) Quasi-legislative; i.e., authority to enact rules and regulations;
(2) Quasi-judicial; i.e., hold hearings; grant, suspend or revoke licenses and permits, etc.;
(3) Plan, develop, and operate programs;
(4) Make inspections, conduct surveys; and
(5) Undertake pertinent general educational and personnel training programs.

These powers are not inherent in health agencies. The general authority for each activity of the agency must have been previously granted by the legislative body. Consequently, they are concerned largely with administrative law, as authorized by the appropriate legislative body.

Administrative responsibility for food protection and other environmental health matters is further delegated to a subordinate unit of the department known as the Consumer Protection and Environmental Health Services (CPEHS). This administrative organization consists of three large operational agencies: The Food and Drug Administration (FDA), the Environmental Control Administration (ECA), and the Air Pollution Control Administration (APCA). Specific responsibility for food protection rests with the FDA, although there are other Federal agencies having similar but more limited responsibilities. These will be referred to later.

The principal activity of the Food and Drug Administration is concerned with the enforcement of the Federal Food, Drug, and Cosmetic Act (3, 4). This act is a regulatory act designed for public protection. It is a broad act with broad aims, and in enforcement operations the FDA gages the levels of practical, reasonable compliance by a concept of what is or is not "good commercial practice."

Briefly the act prohibits adulterated foods from interstate commerce. Three parts of one section of the act specifically cover the microbiological bases for considering a food adulterated. Section 402(a)(1) states a food is adulterated "if it bears or contains any poisonous or deleterious substances which may render it injurious to health." The presence in food of specific infectious bacteria such as salmonellae, the enterotoxins of staphylococci or the toxins of *Cl. botulinum* is considered adulteration under this provision of the Act. No other supporting evidence is needed.

Section 402(a)(3) of the act states that a food is adulterated "if it consists in whole or in part of any filthy, putrid, or decomposed substance or if it is otherwise unfit for food." It is under this provision of the act that a food may be considered adulterated with filth if it contains *Esherichia coli*, excessive coliform bacteria or excessive numbers of bacteria in general. It is necessary to establish, however, that such findings actually constitute filth. Experience has shown that the best and most reliable way of establishing that a product is adulterated with filth is the finding of the filth in the product supplemented by factory evidence of observed insanitary conditions, thus demonstrating that the product has been handled in an insanitary, filthy manner which resulted in the presence of excessive bacteria.

This brings us to a third pertinent part of the section of the act covering adulterated food. Section 402(a)(4) states that a food is adulterated "if it has been prepared, packed, or held under insanitary conditions whereby it may have become contaminated with filth or whereby it may have been rendered injurious to health." Thus, establishment inspection evidence alone showing insanitary practices may constitute basis for legal action.

The definitions of "filth," "putrid," "decomposition" are used and applied by enforcement officials in their common, everyday meanings. Repeated legal decisions have substantiated this everyday meaning. Without detracting from benefits to be gained from comfortable, beautiful surroundings, it is essential to differentiate between the factors that contribute to these conditions and those that assure basic sanitation.

The terms "sanitary" and "sanitation" in the narrow sense, carry connotations pertaining to health or danger to health. Modern usage does not restrict such terms to conditions affecting health only. And in the light of the language of paragraph 402 (a) (4) of the Food, Drug, and Cosmetic Act, the terms must be interpreted broadly. The sanitary aspect of food handling, therefore, encompasses the broad field of food plant sanitation and includes not only conditions that lead to contamination of food with micro-organisms or other elements dangerous to health, but also filth and other extraneous matter that have no place in food (5). Also included are considerations of other aspects of food handling not necessarily encompassed in, but often related to, food plant sanitation. The use of unfit raw materials or failure to provide for the elimination of filthy or decomposed raw materials not infrequently leads to violations of paragraph 402(a)(3) and may contribute to insanitary conditions in violation of paragraph 402(a)(4). Failure to process adequately or expeditiously and consequent decomposition of foods by micro-organisms is another important aspect of the problem.

Innumerable inquiries are received by the Food and Drug Administration as to permitted variations from complete cleanliness or soundness in foods. The act does not authorize "tolerances" for filth or decomposition in foods. This may be illustrated by the language of the Act, that a food is adulterated if it is produced under insanitary conditions whereby it may have become contaminated with unclean foreign matter.

This does not mean that a food is necessarily condemned because of the presence of foreign matter in amounts below the irreducible minimum after all precautions humanly possible have been taken to prevent contamination. In some instances the Food and Drug Administration has informally advised producers of the basis upon which actions are taken against foods which may have been subjected to attack by insect pests or subjected to deterioration due to climatic conditions. As commercial practices improve or an insect infestation is brought under control, the basis of action may be lowered.

Recognition has long been given to the principle that the public is entitled to protection from illness and death caused by consumption of impure foods. Initial regulatory efforts were directed mainly toward protection of food from contamination with pathogenic organisms or with other substances harmful to the health of the consumer. There also has developed a public consciousness, reflected by regulatory agencies, that in addition to protection of his health the consumer has the right to protection against practices violating hygienic decency—practices that are offenses only to his esthetic sense. Often the line of demarcation between a harmful and a filthy food is exceedingly narrow. But since many of the sources of filth in food products are potential sources of disease organism (e.g., rodents, flies, insects), they carry implications of

danger to health although the specific agents of disease may be difficult or impossible to demonstrate.

Some mention should be made of the section of the Food, Drug, and Cosmetic Act that covers the use of food additives. Certain important microbiological considerations are involved. The term "Food additive" for the purpose of the Act means any substance with certain specified exceptions, the intended use of which may result in its becoming a component, either directly or indirectly, of a food, or result in its otherwise affecting the characteristics of a food if such substance is not generally recognized as safe. The definition specifically includes any substance intended for use in producing, manufacturing, packing, processing, preparing, treating, packaging, transporting, or holding food; and including any source of radiation intended for any such use. Hence, it is under this section of the law that the Food and Drug Administration has an interest and responsiblity in the radiation treatment of food. The same general procedures are involved in the development of radiation regulations as are followed in the development of regulations for other types of food additives such as preservatives, emulsifiers, and stabilizers (2). In the case of any food additive, FDA's primary responsibility is to determine that the additive or the process to be regulated is safe, including freedom from a microbial health hazard, and that it does accomplish the intended effect. Therefore, proposals submitted to the FDA for use of "food additives" must be supported by data adequate to establish these facts. Various facets of radiation processing of foods will be covered extensively later in this program.

As previously indicated the separate States operate their intrastate affairs with considerable autonomy. Similarly, municipalities exercise independence in governing their internal affairs within, however, the broad legal authority granted to them by their respective States. There is, therefore, need and desire among the 50 States and the many thousand municipalities for uniformity in many aspects of State and municipal government activity. Federal agencies and various national organizations have provided effective leadership in this regard. Several examples will serve to illustrate.

The Public Health Service, one of the agencies of the U.S. Department of Health, Education, and Welfare, has since the turn of this century included among its functions research, education and regulatory public health control activities relative to milkborne disease. In the interest of effective and uniform programs among the several States for prevention of milkborne disease, the Public Health Service, in 1924, developed a model ordinance or regulation, the grade "A" Pasteurized Milk Ordinance, now in its 13th revision (8). An indication of its impact on State and local milk sanitation legislation may be gained from the fact that as of December 1964, the ordinance was the basis of the milk sanitation legislation in 35 States, 1,435 municipalities and 512 counties located in 40 States. It is recognized by the public health agencies, the milk industry, and many others as a national standard for milk sanitation.

In the broad aspects of Food and Drug legislation, the Association of Food and Drug Officials of the United States (AFDOUS) has been most active. This organization developed a "model" act known as the Uniform State Food, Drug, and Cosmetic Act. Shortly after the Congress of the United States passed the Federal Food, Drug, and Cosmetic Act in 1938, AFDOUS submitted the model law to the Council of State Governments for consideration. Subsequently, it was included among the Council's recommendations for uniform State legislation. The model act has served a most useful purpose in this regard. At the present time about 35 States have food and drug laws based substantially on the provisions of the Uniform State Food, Drug, and Cosmetic Act. The Food and Drug Administration has actively supported efforts directed toward uniformity of legislation of this nature and has continuously worked through the AFDOUS toward improving and updating the model law.

The U. S. Department of Agriculture has broad responsibility (7) beginning with the law that established the USDA in 1862, "the general designs and duties of which shall be to acquire and to diffuse among the people of the United States useful information on subjects connected with agriculture in the most general and comprehensive sense of the word. . . ." Over the years educational, research and regulatory food protection programs of great magnitude and significance have evolved.

These include administrative and financial support for research and education in the State Agricultural Experiment Stations; the administration of animal health regulations designed to prevent the spread of disease from a foreign country to the United States or from State to State; authority for meat and poultry inspection and for restricting the use of contaminated meat, poultry, and meat and poultry products; and authority for inspection and grading of dairy products.

The U. S. Department of the Interior (USDI), through its Bureau of Commercial Fisheries, operates a voluntary fishery products inspection and grading service. The overall objective is to promote the orderly marketing of wholesome fishery products of high quality. Through this program, the Bureau provides an impartial, national inspection and certification service for all types of processed fishery products— fresh, frozen, canned, and cured. The program is voluntary, meaning that a processor must request and pay for the service. In addition, grading services

are provided for 15 frozen products for which official U.S. grade standards have been established. Last year over 260 million pounds of fishery products were inspected representing 22 percent of our domestic consumption.

Two types of service are provided, lot and continuous. Once a processor subscribes to continuous inspection, he must comply with rigid regulations regarding plant construction, sanitation practices, product quality, and labeling. Should he fail to comply, he is denied the benefits of the inspection service and the use of the Packed Under Continuous Inspection shield of the U.S. Department of the Interior. Subscribers to lot inspection services are issued a certificate describing the conditions of the lot, but they may not apply inspection marks to packages of their product.

Recognizing the unique problems surrounding the inspection of smoked fish, and the fact that the Food and Drug Administration has published recommendations for smoked chub processing, the Bureau has set up special requirements for those requesting to smoke fish under USDI inspection. These requirements are, in essence, that the fish smoker must meet the provisions of the FDA recommendations in addition to the USDI requirements for all plants operating under the continuous inspection program.

While the above-mentioned agencies provide major impetus toward control of microbiological health hazards in the interest of the consuming public at large, several other Federal agencies contribute importantly but through more limited programs. For example, the Department of Defense has responsibility for the health of its personnel including responsibility for safety of their food; likewise, the Treasury Department has similar responsibility for the U.S. Coast Guard; and the National Space Administration has important food protection responsibility in support of manned space exploration programs.

In deference to time and avoidance of redundancy, examples that could be cited of food protection activity by other agencies will be omitted.

Since *Clostridium botulinum* and botulism collectively comprise one of the major subjects of this conference, perhaps a brief description of regulatory control of this microbiological hazard exercised at each of the three levels of U.S. Government structure will suffice to bring this discussion to a close. This description will be confined to the regulation of the smoked fish industry.

Following the U.S. outbreaks of botulism in 1963 due to smoked fish, research on the nature, ecology and control of *Clostridium botulinum*, type E accelerated. Results of these studies provided the basis for legislation and regulation specifically affecting the smoked fish industry. The Food and Drug Administration began a stepped up program of surveillance invoking the provisions previously mentioned of section 402 of the Food, Drug, and Cosmetic Act. Similarly, several States and municipalities under authority of general provisions of their laws and regulations governing the sanitary operation of food processing plants increased their surveillance of the industry.

The city of Milwaukee, Wis., was one of the first to enact specific legislation, when in 1964 the City Council enacted an ordinance licensing and regulating smoked fish processors, haulers, and distributors offering smoked fish for sale in the city of Milwaukee (1). Included in the ordinance are requirements governing the sanitary condition of plant premises and buildings; the safety of water supplies and adequacy of sewage disposal; the sanitary design, treatment and care of fish processing and handling equipment; hygienic practices of personnel; plant processing procedures; refrigeration; a dating provision limiting period of sale; and a penalty provision for noncompliance with the ordinance. Specific processing requirements include: (a) Smoking, whereby every portion of every fish shall be heated to at least 180° F. for a minimum period of 30 minutes, (b) packaging at place of processing, (c) cooling and packaging within 2 hours after smoking, (d) refrigeration immediately after packaging and maintenance of refrigeration throughout storage, transportation, and retail display, and (e) a labeling requirement limiting sale to a period not to exceed 7 days after smoking.

In the same year, 1964, the Wisconsin State Department of Agriculture promulgated specific regulations (administrative law) governing operations of the smoked fish industry (9). Requirements similar to those of the city of Milwaukee are included. The labeling requirement, however, limits the period of sale to not more than 14 days after smoking, and a salt (sodium chloride) content of not less than 5 percent in the water phase of the loin muscle is an additional requirement.

At the federal level the Food and Drug Administration continues its surveillance of the industry as previously indicated; however, in 1967 the FDA published "recommendations" in the form of "Good Manufacturing Practice Guidelines" primarily for use by its inspectors but which were disseminated to the industry. These were based upon studies conducted by the Bureau of Commercial Fisheries, U.S. Department of the Interior, which indicated that 180° F. for 30 minutes during processing should destroy most type E spores, and if brining is accomplished in such manner as to result in a salt content in excess of 3 percent in the aqueous phase of the loin muscle, and if the fish are held at 38° F. or less, the surviving spores will be prevented from growing out in the fish.

Accordingly, the recommended "Guidelines" include the temperature-time for processing (180° F.—30 minutes), general sanitation practices, proper refrigeration, and not less than 3 percent salt in the aqueous phase of the loin muscle.

As noted previously the Bureau of Commercial Fisheries through its operation of the voluntary fishery products inspection and grading service requires that the fish smoker must meet the provisions of the FDA recommendations in addition to the USDI requirements for all plants operating under the continuous inspection program.

Admittedly there have been problems relative to compliance especially with the heat treatment of 180° F. for 30 minutes specified in recommendations, ordinances or regulations. Adverse effect of the heat treatment on the quality of the fish is a common complaint. For this and other reasons the Bureau of Commercial Fisheries and others have carried out extensive studies on the use of sodium nitrite in the brining procedure, whereby less severe heat treatments may be used, thus minimizing heat damage to fish quality. These studies will be reviewed later in this program and will not be discussed further at this point. Commercial use of this compound at present is questionable because the problem of possible formation of dimethyl-nistrosamine, a carcinogen, in the smoked fish has not been resolved.

The account just given of the "tri-level" system of governmental regulatory activity directed toward the control of the smoked fish industry is only one of many examples that could be given. Much remains to be accomplished in establishing throughout the U.S. uniform and effective regulatory programs for consumer protection from microbiological hazards in foods. Increasing efforts, however, are being made to bring State and Federal programs in many areas into common agreement. Progress may, to some, seem slow and cumbersome; nevertheless, we are fortunate that the very nature of our Government organizational structure and operation is conducive to considered judgment in the interest of the common good.

The author wishes to acknowledge and express his appreciation to the following individuals for their assistance in the preparation of this manuscript: Mr. L. L. Ramsey, Bureau of Science, FDA, for his critical review and guidance to source materials; Mr. R. A. Tucker, Office of Legislative and Governmental Services, FDA, for his help with the section on the Uniform State Food, Drug, and Cosmetic Act; Mr. L. R. Shelton, Division of Microbiology, FDA, for his helpful comments and suggestions; and Mr. H. B. Allen, Bureau of Commercial Fisheries, USDI, for a summary of the Bureau's inspection and grading program.

References

(*1*) CITY OF MILWAUKEE, an Ordinance No. 735, pt. 1, sec. 70–55 through 70–71 of the Milwaukee Code: Smoked Fish and Smoked Fish Products. Mar. 17, 1964. City Hall, Milwaukee, Wis. 53201.

(*2*) FOOD AND DRUG ADMINISTRATION. Preparation and processing of food additive petitions: Radiation application to food. Proc. Bureau of Science Staff Seminar, May 1967. U.S. Department of Health, Education, and Welfare. Washington, D.C. 20204.

(*3*) FOOD AND DRUG ADMINISTRATION. Federal Food, Drug, and Cosmetic Act as amended. Reprinted March 1968. U.S. Department of Health, Education, and Welfare. Washington, D.C. 20204.

(*4*) FOOD AND DRUG ADMINISTRATION. Requirements of the U.S. Food, Drug, and Cosmetic Act. Publication No. 2, revised September 1967. (This publication places emphasis on those aspects of special interest to foreign manufacturers and importers.) U.S. Department of Health, Education, and Welfare. Washington, D.C. 20204.

(*5*) FOOD AND DRUG ADMINISTRATION. General principles of food sanitation. Technical Bulletin No. 1, FDA Publication No. 16, reprinted January 1968. U.S. Department of Health, Education, and Welfare. Washington, D.C. 20204.

(*6*) HAMLIN, R. H. 1961. Public Health law or the interrelationship of law and public health administration. Am. J. Public Health, 51: 1733–1737.

(*7*) SAULMON, E. E. (Chairman). 1967. Activities and programs of the U.S. Department of Agriculture pertaining to Salmonella. Rept. of the USDA Salmonella Working Group to the NAS-NRC Salmonella Study Committee. Agricultural Research Service, U.S. Department of Agriculture, Washington, D.C. 20250.

(*8*) U.S. PUBLIC HEALTH SERVICE. Grade "A" Pasteurized Milk Ordinance—1965 Recommendations of the Public Health Service. Public Health Service Publication No. 229. Department of Health, Education, and Welfare, Washington, D. C. 20204.

(*9*) WISCONSIN ADMINISTRATIVE CODE. Smoked Fish Processing Plants. Rules of the State of Wisconsin Department of Agriculture. Sec. Ag 46, par. 46.01–46.11. March 1964. Madison, Wis. 53702.

THE HEAT RESISTANCE OF *CLOSTRIDIUM BOTULINUM* TYPE E IN FOOD

by ROBERT ANGELOTTI

Environmental Control Adminsitration, Consumer Protection and Environmental Health Service,
U.S. Department of Health, Education, and Welfare, Cincinnati, Ohio 45202

Though outbreaks of botulism attributable to *Clostridium botulinum* type E have occurred with considerable frequency and some regularity since 1932 when the first outbreak was reported, relatively little information concerning the heat resistance of this organism has thus far been accumulated.

Type E spores were recognized early as being less heat resistant than the other known botulinal types. Early workers such as Kushnir et al. (*9*) and Hazen (*8*) found it necessary to omit the traditional practice of heating samples to 80° C. for 30 minutes or more to obtain positive results. Though Hazen (*8*) orginally described the thermal resistance of type E spores as approximately 10 minutes at 80° C., the first definitive statement of the heat resistance of this group was published by Gunnison and her coworkers (*7*) who reported that in pH 7.4 buffer solution, 5 million spores per milliliter were destroyed in 2 minutes at 100° C., and in 6 minutes at 80° C., whereas 50 million spores per milliliter were destroyed in 5 and 40 minutes, respectively, at these same temperatures.

Not until 1953, however, did Dolman and Chang (*5*) make the point, in discussing the epidemiology and pathogenesis of type E fishborne botulism, that type E spores, with rare exception, are heat-labile but may vary widely in their heat resistance.

Since that time, a number of workers have reported on the thermal resistance of spores of this organism. The first precise description of type E thermal resistance is that of Ohye and Scott (*11*). These workers heated spores of strains 103 and 108 in M/15 phosphate buffer pH 7.0 and enumerated survivors after various periods of exposure at 70°, 75°, and 80° C. The D values for strain 103 were 36, 10, and 3.3 minutes, and for strain 108, 7.8, 3.1, and 0.4 minutes, respectively.

At the Symposium on Botulism held in Cincinnati in 1964, Schmidt (*17*) presented data on the thermal resistance of the Minneapolis strain of type E spores. In separate trials in which two different suspensions were heated in trypticase-peptone-glucose (TPG) medium, the strain was characterized by a D_{176} (80° C.) of 1.9 and a z of 16 in the first trial, and a D_{176} (80° C.) of 1.8 and a z of 14 in the second trial. The second suspension was also tested in M/15 phosphate buffer at pH 7.0 and under these conditions, the D_{176} (80° C.) value was 2.3 minutes with a z of 15.

Roberts and Ingram (*15*) measured the heat resistance of several strains of type E spores in water by the open-tube, sealed-ampoule, and sealed-capillary-tube methods. Their results characterized the organism with a D_{176} in the range of 0.6 to 1.25 and a z of approximately 10. More recently, Bohrer (*3*) and his coworkers at the National Canners Association laboratories in Washington, D.C., determined that the D_{176} (80° C.) value for four strains of type E spores in M/15 phosphate buffer ranged from 1.2 to 1.5 with z values between approximately 13 and 15. Table 1 presents a compilation of the data accumulated to date on the heat resistance of type E spores, and the findings of these various authors are in good agreement.

It is obvious from table 1 that type E spores are much less resistant than types A and B, and it is apparent that the D_{176} (80° C.) value for various strains of type E spores is in the range of 0.3 to 3.3 when heated in aqueous solutions and under circumstances that guarantee maintenance of wet heat conditions throughout the thermal process. The z values for these spore types range between a low of 7.4 for strain 8E, as determined by Roberts and Ingram, and a high of 17 for strain 103, as reported by Ohye and Scott (*11*). There is some question, however, as to the validity of the low z values reported by Roberts and Ingram because these values are based on only two points.

These data indicate that type E spores are relatively heat sensitive and display heat resistance intermediate between vegetative cells and heat resistant spores. Though these data reveal the adequacy of thermal processes based on temperatures of 80° C. or above, there remains a questioning attitude on the part of some because a few published reports have noted survival times much in excess of those observed by the workers listed in table 1. Graikoski and Kempe (*6*) reported that survivors existed after heating spores in phosphate buffer in open tubes for 120 minutes at 85° C. and for 60 minutes at 90° C. These authors used both open tubes and sealed ampoules, and the "tailing" effect was observed with both systems.

Table 1.—The wet-heat resistance of *C. botulinum* type E spores

Strain	Exposure temperature °C.	Sealed TDT tubes, ampoules, or capillary tubes containing—	Z	D_{176} (80° C.)	Reference
103	70, 75, 80	M/15 PO₄ buffer pH 7.0.	17.0	3.30	Ohye and Scott, 1957.
108			14.0	.40	
Minneapolis	70, 75, 80	TPG	14.0	1.78	Schmidt, 1964.
Do		M/15 PO₄ buffer pH 7.0.	15.0	2.30	
Alaska			10.5	.60	
Beluga			9.5	.75	
Iwanai			10.0	1.00	
Minneapolis			10.5	0.87	
8E	70, 80	Water	7.4	0.80	Roberts and Ingram, 1965.
1957/61			10.8	1.25	
1537/62			10.7	.83	
16/63			9.0	.33	
4318/63			10.0	.66	
Saratoga			12.8	1.17	
Beluga	70, 75, 80	M/15 PO₄ buffer pH 7.0.	15.0	1.10	Bohrer et al., 1966.
Alaska			14.0	1.35	
1304 E			14.5	1.45	

Though an explanation offered by Roberts and Ingram may be applied to the extended survival times noted in open tubes in their own work as well as that of Graikoski and Kempe, no such explanation suffices for the limited sealed-tube data of the latter workers. Roberts and Ingram (*15*) state: "the most plausible explanation of the discrepancy between the results using open tubes and capillary tubes for estimating heat resistance is that the former gave erroneously high values because a few cells were incompletely heated. This might have been due to the formation of microdrops in the atmosphere of the tube, though macroscopic splashing was avoided."

"An alternative explanation is that drying of microdrops occurred even in the comparatively short-heating time, and that a few spores were, in fact, heated in the dry state, when their heat resistance might reasonably be expected to be considerably greater than in aqueous suspension."

The fishborne outbreaks of botulism in 1963 that occurred in the United States prompted the U.S. Public Health Service, as well as other Federal agencies, to review the adequacy of smoked fish processes that are used in the United States. Under the supervision of Dr. F. D. Crisley, we undertook, in our Cincinnati laboratories, a study of the thermal resistance of type E spores in fish. Beluga, Alaska, Iwanai, Tenno, and 8E strains of type E spores were used. Whole frozen Great Lakes chubs were ground and the resulting fish paste was sterilized by autoclaving. The sterile fish paste was inoculated with 1×10^6 heat resistant spores per gram. The count for heat resistant spores was determined by enumerating the number of spores per milliliter in the inoculum that survived an exposure of 15 minutes at 60° C. Thermal death time (TDT) tubes were filled with 1.0 g. of inoculated fish paste and flame sealed. Heat resistance

studies were performed at 165 (73.9° C.), 170 (76.7° C.), 175 (79.4° C.), and 185° F. (85° C.) by complete submersion of the sealed tubes in a water bath. Ten tubes per exposure time interval were examined for survivors by subculture of the tube contents in Noyes' veal broth medium containing 0.2 percent soluble starch and 0.5 percent glucose (*1*). The recovery cultures were incubated at 30° C. and examined for growth and gas production periodically for 168 hours. The cultures were then incubated at room temperature for an additional 6 months to allow for delayed germination. Tubes in which growth had occurred were tested for specific type E toxicity by means of the mouse protection test and specific type E antitoxin.

End points or F values were determined for each strain and exposure temperature. The F values for temperatures of 175° F., 180° F., and 185° F., and their corresponding 95 percent confidence limits are presented in table 2. Particular note should be taken that with the most resistant strain studied (Alaska), 17 minutes exposure at 180° F. were required to destroy 1×10^6 spores. To compare these data to those presented in table 1, it is necessary to convert from F to D values. By means of the interconversion equation of Schmidt (*16*) for calculating D from F values ($D = \dfrac{F}{\log A + 2}$ where A is the number of spores in the inoculum), the D_{176} values presented in table 3 are obtained. Note again that the D_{176} values are all small and are in good agreement with those presented in table 1 for aqueous solutions.

Ito and Denny (private communications) of the National Canners Association laboratories have independently conducted limited studies of the thermal resistance of type E spores in food substrates. Denny inoculated the liquid from commercially canned whole kernel corn with 12 million spores per milliliter

Table 2.—Thermal death time of C. botulinum type E[1] spores in sterile fish paste

Strain	175° F. (79.4° C.)		180° F. (82.2° C.)		185° F. (85° C.)	
	°F	95 percent C.I.	°F	95 percent C.I.	°F	95 percent C.I.
Alaska	40.7	28.7–57.7	17.0	10.5–27.4	7.1	3.8–13.1
Beluga	20.3	17.2–23.9	8.6	6.9–10.5	3.6	2.8– 4.7
8E	17.2	10.4–28.4	5.7	2.9–10.7	1.8	0.8– 4.1
Iwanai	14.8	12.3–18.0	6.4	4.9– 8.2	2.7	2.0– 3.8
Tenno	15.8	11.5–21.6	6.5	4.1–10.3	2.7	1.5– 5.0

[1] Inoculum = 1 x 10⁶ spores per gram.

Table 3.—Thermal resistance of C. botulinum type E spores in sterile fish paste

Strain	D_{176} (80° C.)	z_D[2]
Alaska	4.3	13.2
Beluga	2.1	13.3
8E	1.8	10.3
Iwanai	1.6	13.6
Tenno	1.6	13.1

[1] Inoculum = 1 x 10⁶ spores per gram.
[2] z_F = z_D using the conversion factor of Schmidt and assuming $\log_{10}$ A is constant in all experiments.

of the suspension of the Saratoga strain used by Bohrer and shown in table 1. The reaction of the liquid was pH 6.2. One milliliter of the inoculated liquid was dispensed into TDT tubes, and the tubes were flame sealed and heated by complete immersion. Thermal death time determinations were performed using 10 tubes per interval. By means of the interconversion formula, the D_{176} value for this system was calculated to be 1.28 as compared with 1.17 for the same strain heated in M/15 phosphate buffer.

Ito also conducted thermal resistance studies on the Saratoga strain in yellowfin tuna. The tests were conducted using six replicate TDT cans. Thirteen grams of rendered tuna were placed in a TDT can. Each container was then inoculated with 1 x 10⁶ spores. The containers were immersed in a constant temperature water bath, removed at the appropriate time intervals, cooled, and then incubated at 30° C. Each container that swelled was tested for toxicity to

confirm the presence of type E organisms. The tests were run twice. The organism on both occasions survived 5 minutes but was destroyed in 8 minutes at 180°F. The D_{180} of the two runs was 0.74 minutes.

Data on the thermal resistance of type E spores in various substrates, independently collected and reported by different investigators, are compiled in table 4. This table and those presented previously clearly indicate that type E spores are readily destroyed by wet heat provided that carefully controlled conditions are applied throughout the heating cycle to ensure the maintenance of wet heat conditions. Based on the findings to date and assuming logarithmic destruction, a wet heat process of 180° F. for 30 minutes should destroy approximately 10⁷ spores of the more resistant of the strains studied thus far.

That viable type E spores do survive a commercial smoking process in which the internal temperature of the loin muscle of fish is heated to 180° F. and held continuously for no less than 30 minutes was first reported by Pace et al. (12, 13, 14) who demonstrated that 1 percent of such fish were contaminated after processing. Shortly thereafter, Christiansen et al. (4) reported on experiments in which they injected 1 x 10⁶ type E spores into the loin muscle of Great Lakes Chubs and smoked them to an internal temperature of 180° F. for 30 minutes. Viable type E spores were found in practically all the fish so processed. In view of the data presented in this review thus far, the observations of Pace et al. and Christiansen et al. pose a fascinating question. Namely, by what mecha-

Table 4.—Thermal resistance of C. botulinum type E spores in various substrates

Heated in sealed TDT tubes containing—	Investigators	Number of different strains studied by all investigators	D_{176}	D_{180}
Water, buffer solution, or culture medium.	Ohye and Scott, 1957 Schmidt, 1964 Roberts and Ingram, 1965 Bohrer et al., 1966	13	0.3–3.3	
Fish or corn liquor.	Ito, 1968 Denny, 1968 Crisley and Angelotti, 1968.	6	1.3–4.3	[1]0.74

[1] Duplicate experiments, single investigation, Saratoga strain in yellowfin tuna.

nism do type E spores associated with fish survive a thermal process of 180° F. for 30 minutes? Christiansen et al. (4) stated that the intramuscular injection of spores resulted in some spore leakage back onto the skin of the fish. They demonstrated that the skin moisture level of fish is reduced early in the smoking process and suggested that spores located on the dry skin were surviving the process because dry heat is known to be less effective than wet heat. In an attempt to experimentally test this hypothesis, they inoculated fish in the loin muscle with 1 x 10⁶ spores and heated the fish in sealed plastic pouches. A horizontal midline seal with a gap of 2 inches gave two interconnected compartments within the pouch. The fish were located in the upper compartment, and 50 ml. of TPG-yeast extract broth were contained in the bottom compartment. The pouches were sealed above the fish and heated to an internal fish temperature of 180° F. for 30 minutes. Viable spores were present in 68 percent of the fish so processed. In view of these data, it is difficult to accept surface drying as the answer to the puzzle. On the other hand, Pace et al. (personal communication) have attempted to establish whether a time-temperature-relative-humidity relationship is contributing to spore survival in smoked fish. They employed "cured" fish in these studies. Cured fish are those that have been smoked to an internal temperature of 135° F. to 155° F. for approximately 2 hours. This process is employed commercially in Milwaukee to "set the color" of the fish and is followed by an additional heating to 180° F. for 30 minutes. By means of an electronically controlled environmental chamber, the effects of relative humidity and temperature on the survival of type E spores inoculated intramuscularly and onto the surface of cured chubs has been determined. Temperature-relative humidity combinations in the range of 140° F. (60° C.) to 190.4° F. (88° C.) and 20 through 90 percent relative humidity have been employed. The data collected to date indicate that 70 percent relative humidity is the minimum environmental chamber humidity that will consistently free fish of viable type E spores when an internal fish temperature of 179.6° F. (82° C.) for 30 minutes is used. Combinations of lower internal fish temperatures and lower environmental chamber relative humidities consistently yielded viable spores. Conversely, lower environmental chamber relative humidity but higher internal fish temperature for 30 minutes consistently yielded fish free of survivors. At an environmental chamber relative humidity of 50 percent and an internal fish temperature of 190.4° F. (88° C.) for 30 minutes, fish were consistently rendered free of viable type E spores. Some of these data are summarized in tables 5 and 6.

It is difficult, at this point, to reconcile the data of

Table 5.—Effect of heating chamber relative humidity on the survival of *C. botulinum* type E spores located in or on fish heated to an internal temperature of 179.6° F. (82° C.) for 30 minutes

Inoculum location	Spore load per fish	Total time in chamber		Chamber RH	Number of fish producing toxic cultures/ number fish examined
		Hour	Minutes		
Surface	304	1	55	63	5/5
	468	1	35	70	0/5
	578	1	10	82	0/5
	1.2 x 10⁵	1	22	61	2/5
	6 x 10⁵	1	20	70	0/5
	6.3 x 10⁵	1	15	80	0/5
Intra-muscular	1.7 x 10⁵	1	40	61	2/5
	1.6 x 10⁴	1	35	70	0/5
	4.1 x 10⁴	1	35	80	0/5

Table 6.—Effect of heating chamber relative humidity on the survival of *C. botulinum* type E spores located in or on fish heated to an internal temperature of 190.4° F. (88° C.) for 30 minutes

Inoculum location	Spore load per fish	Total time in chamber		Chamber RH	Number of fish producing toxic cultures/ number fish examined
		Hour	Minutes		
Surface	6.1 x 10⁵	1	30	30	5/5
	1.2 x 10⁵	1	33	39	5/5
	1.6 x 10⁵	1	26	50	0/5
	2.5 x 10⁵	1	32	61	0/5
Intra-muscular	4.1 x 10⁴	1	40	31	5/5
	5.9 x 10⁴	2	2	40	1/5
	2.2 x 10⁴	1	40	51	0/5
	4.6 x 10⁴	1	43	61	0/5

Christiansen and Pace. Pace achieved consistent kill of type E spores in or on fish heated to an internal temperature of 179.6° F. for 30 minutes with an environmental relative humidity of 70 percent, whereas Christiansen, at a slightly higher temperature and an assumed even higher relative humidity, possibly a saturated environment, found survivors in 68 percent of the samples. To add further intrigue to the puzzle are the recent data collected at the Food Research Institute of the University of Wisconsin. Upon request, Dr. Sugiyama graciously supplied me with data from his laboratory that, as yet, have not been published. In separate experiments, sterile jars, some empty and some containing TPG broth, were placed in a smoke chamber immediately below fish that had been inoculated intramuscularly with 1 x 10⁶ spores. The drippings from these fish were collected in the jars for 10 minutes. The jars were removed from beneath the fish and placed in another area of the smoking chamber. Heat was then introduced, and the fish were processed to an internal temperature of 180° F. for 30 minutes. Following the process, TPG was added to the jars that had not contained the broth, and tests for viable type E spores were applied to all the jars after appropriate incubation. Fourteen of 16 jars in which drippings had been collected and that were heated without broth were shown to contain viable type E spores. None of the 16 jars in which drippings had been collected and heated in TPG broth contained viable type E spores. These data indicate that survival of spores occurs in a smokehouse and that, after processing, fish may become recontaminated with dried spores that are present in the smokehouse. These experiments may offer an explanation for the observed contamination rate of commercially processed fish. In other experiments, Sugiyama inoculated fish intramuscularly or on the surface with one million spores and hung them in 2-quart jars containing 200 ml. TPG broth. The jars were covered with screw capped lids with a small hole in the center of the lid and the fish were heated to an internal temperature of 180° F. for 30 minutes. Viable type E spores were found in 35 of 36 fish inoculated intramuscularly but in only three of 25 fish inoculated on the surface. If, as demonstrated by Pace, high humidity enhances spore inactivation, why were not the spores located internally killed in these experiments of Sugiyama? If one accepts that both types of inoculated fish were heated under comparable conditions of moisture and temperature, one concludes that the location of the spore inoculum influences heat resistance and the question may now be asked, "Are spores in the muscle of fish more resistant than those located on the surface and, if so, why?"

In a recent publication concerning the influence of spore moisture content on dry-heat resistance, Angelotti et al. (2) defined a wet or moist-heat sterilization cycle as one in which the organism is in contact with an environment having a water activity of 1.0 or a water saturated atmosphere. These conditions are met only when the organism is heated in contact with pure water or saturated steam. This definition of wet heat implies that there are varying degrees of dry heat and that the latter is not a specific condition but is a range of conditions that may be influenced by the moisture content of the spore before and during heating, the water vapor pressure and the flow rate of the gaseous atmosphere in contact with the spore, and the chemical hydration and water vapor sorption characteristics of the material in or on which the spore is located. We corroborated the findings of Murrell and Scott (10) that spores are most resistant

to dry heat when adjusted to a water activity in the range of 0.2 to 0.4 and heated at an equilibrium relative humidity of 20 to 40 percent. In addition, we independently demonstrated that the dry-heat resistance of Bacillus subtilis var. niger spores is influenced by the initial spore moisture content, by the rate at which spores dry out during heating, and, lastly, by the equilibrium relative humidity of the system at temperature.

In reviewing the thermal inactivation studies of type E spores in smoked fish, it becomes apparent that, in no case, is wet heat being applied as defined above. Thus, the smoking of fish is performed within that rather wide range of conditions know as dry heat. The brining of fish will affect the water activity of the spores located in and on fish. The initial fish moisture content as well as the water vapor pressure and the flow rate of gas within the chamber will affect the rate at which the fish dry during heating. This latter rate, in turn, will affect the rate and the degree of change in spore moisture content during processing. Murrell and Scott (10) reported that of the several species of bacterial spores they studied, C. botulinum type E showed the greatest response to the water activity of the heating medium. A 100,000-fold greater heat resistance was noted at a water activity of 0.2 to 0.3 than at 1.0. Herein may lie the answer to the apparent anomalies in the data collected by Christiansen, Pace, and Sugiyama. Brining, heat coagulation of fish protein, and fish desiccation all result in some change in water activity of the fish flesh during processing. A reduction in water activity to that range at which type E spores are maximally resistant could easily occur. Assuming that such changes do occur, then the controlling factors that influence survival of spores located in fish would be the initial water activity of the spores that develops as a result of the equilibrium reaction between the spores and the fish flesh and the rate of change of this water activity during processing. The rate of change in water activity would be influenced, in turn, by the amount of moisture in the gas and the flow rate of the gas. In pursuing this hypothesis further, it appears reasonable that the factor that influences survival of spores located on fish may be the moisture content of the gaseous processing environment. A dry environment permits rapid drying of fish surfaces with a consequent reduction in spore moisture contents to levels that enhance thermal resistance. Wet or high humidity environments prevent desiccation of spores located on fish surfaces and the water activity of spores heated under such conditions remains high and within the range described by Murrell and Scott as that at which type E spores are thermally labile.

Data presently available demonstrate, unequivocally, that C. botulinum type E spores are not particularly resistant to wet heat. Little more of value appears to be gained by additional studies of the wet-heat resistance of this organism. The survival of type E spores in smoked fish that have experienced conditions that superficially appear to be those of wet heat suggests that food scientists may be well advised to turn their attention to the study of the dry-heat resistance of this organism and to the identification of those physiochemical environmental factors that cause dry-heat conditions to develop within a food in spite of the presence of moisture in the hot environment.

References

(1) ANGELOTTI, R., H. E. HALL, M. J. FOTER, and K. H. LEWIS. 1962. Quantitation of *Clostridium perfringens* in foods. Appl. Microbiol. *10:* 193–199.

(2) ANGELOTTI, R., J. H. MARYANSKI, T. F. BUTLER, J. T. PEELER, and J. E. CAMPBELL. 1968. Influence of spore moisture content on the dry-heat resistance of *Bacillus subtilis* var. *niger*. Appl. Microbiol. *16:* 735–745.

(3) BOHRER, W. C. 1966. Unpublished data. Presented before the Interagency Botulism Research Coordinating Committee, March 31, 1966. Cincinnati, Ohio.

(4) CHRISTIANSEN, L. N., J. DAFNER, E. M. FOSTER, and H. SUGIYAMA. 1968. Survival and outgrowth of *Clostridium botulinum* type E spores in smoked fish. Appl. Microbiol. *16:* 133–137.

(5) DOLMAN, C. E., and HELEN CHANG. 1953. The epidemiology and pathogenesis of type E and fishborne botulism. Canad. J. Public Health *44:* 231–244.

(6) GRAIKOSKI, J. T., and L. L. KEMPE. 1964. Heat resistance of *Clostridium botulinum* type E spores. Bacteriol. Proc., p. 3.

(7) GUNNISON, J. B., J. R. CUMMINGS, and K. F. MYER. 1936. *Clostridium botulinum* Type E. Proc. Soc. Exptl. Biol. Med. *35:* 278–280.

(8) HAZEN, E. L. 1937. A strain of *B. botulinus* not classified as A, B, or C. J. Infect. Diseases *60:* 260–264.

(9) KUSHNIR, E. D., T. M. BRUN, and S. S. PAIKANA. 1937. The sources of *Bacillus botulinus* infection in sturgeons. Zhur. Mikrobiol., Epidemiol. Immunobiol. *19:* 80–85.

(10) MURRELL, W. G., and W. J. SCOTT. 1966. The heat resistance of bacterial spores at various water activities. J. Gen. Microbiol. *43:* 411–425.

(11) OHYE, D. F., and W. J. SCOTT. 1957. Studies in the physiology of *Clostridium botulinum* Type E. Australian J. Biol. Sci. *10:* 85–94.

(12) PACE, P. J., E. R. KRUMBIEGEL, R. ANGELOTTI, and H. J. WISNIEWSKI. 1966. Isolation of *Clostridium botulinum* in smoked fish processing. Bacteriol. Proc., p. 10.

(13) PACE, P. J., E. R. KRUMBIEGEL, R. ANGELOTTI, and H. J. WISNIEWSKI. 1967. Demonstration and isolation of *Clostridium botulinum* types from whitefish chubs collected at fish smoking plants of the Milwaukee area. Appl. Microbiol. *15:* 877–884.

(14) PACE, P. J., E. R. KRUMBIEGEL, H. J. WISNIEWSKI, and R. ANGELOTTI. 1967. The distribution of *Cl. botulinum* types in fish processed by smoking plants of the Milwaukee area, pp. 40–48. *In* Botulism 1966. Proc. Intern. Symp. Food Microbiol., 5th, Moscow. M. Ingram and T. A. Roberts, Eds. Chapman & Hall, Ltd., London.

(15) ROBERTS, T. A., and M. INGRAM. 1965. The resistance of spores of *Clostridium botulinum* type E to heat and radiation. J. Appl. Bacteriol. *20:* 125–138.

(16) SCHMIDT, C. F. 1957. Thermal resistance of microorganisms. *In* Antiseptics, disinfectants, fungicides, and chemical and physical sterilization, 2d ed. Edited by G. F. Reddish. Lea and Febiger, Philadelphia, Pa.

(17) SCHMIDT, C. F. 1964. Spores of *C. botulinum:* Formation, resistance, germination, pp. 69–81. *In* Botulism, Proceedings of a Symposium. Edited by K. H. Lewis and K. Cassel, Jr. Public Health Service Pub. No. 99–FP–1, U.S. Dept. Health, Education, and Welfare.

THE THERMAL AND GERMICIDAL RESISTANCE OF
CLOSTRIDIUM BOTULINUM TYPES A, B, AND E SPORES

by K. A. Ito, Marcia L. Seeger, C. W. Bohrer, C. B. Denny, *and* Mary K. Bruch*
National Canners Association Western Research Laboratory, Berkeley, Calif.,
National Canners Association Research Laboratory, Washington, D.C.

The thermal resistance of *Clostridium botulinum* type A and B spores has been the subject of many reports. Van Ermengem was one of the earliest to report the thermal resistance of *C. botulinum*. He concluded, erroneously, that a process of 1 hour at 80° C. (176° F.) would effectively destroy *C. botulinum* spores (*30*). Unfortunately, the results of these heat resistance experiments were widely accepted and were even the basis for a bulletin on home canning of vegetables (*1*).

After conducting epidemiological studies upon several incidents of food poisoning, Dickson (*5*) began to question the safety of the "cold-pack" method of home canning. He inoculated quart jars of peas and corn and cooked them for the recommended times. He found that they soon became toxic.

In view of the previous findings Dickson, Burke, and Ward (*6*) thought it advisable to carry out a thorough study on the thermal resistance of *C. botulinum* spores and also to investigate the efficacy of the various recommended methods of home canning being utilized at the time. They found that *C. botulinum* spores were able to survive 2 hours in boiling water. They found that the addition of 5 percent lemon juice markedly reduced the thermal death point. As a result of these experiments they concluded that a number of environmental factors, which were not previously considered, markedly influenced the resistance of *C. botulinum* spores. This in turn cast doubts upon the recommended home canning methods of the time.

Burke (*2*) continued the investigation of the adequacy of the home canning methods of the period. She conducted thermal resistance studies on 10 *C. botulinum* strains. She heated individual strains in test tubes in brain medium and found survival after 4 hours at 100° C. She concluded that the recommended home canning methods were inadequate. Her studies also indicated that of the methods advocated at the time, pressure canning was the only safe method.

Weiss (*31*) heated 16 strains in sheep brain medium and found considerable variation in thermal resistance. The most resistant suspension tested was destroyed within 5 hours at 100° C. Weiss also studied the thermal death point of *C. botulinum* spores in the juice from 36 varieties of canned food (*32*). He found the spore resistance to vary with the pH, consistency and syrup concentration. Spores inoculated into the juice from succotash and lima beans were the most resistant, surviving 150 minutes, but not 180 minutes at 100° C. Spores in juice from spinach and sweet corn survived 120 minutes, but not 150 minutes at 100° C.

In 1922, the now classic study by Esty and Meyer on *C. botulinum* heat resistance was reported (*9*). They examined 109 different type A and B strains at each of five heating temperatures between 100° and 120° C. They observed that the death rate of these suspensions were logarithmic between 100° and 120° C., that the heat resistance was a function of spore concentration, that the pH affected the thermal resistance and that variations in resistance occurred depending upon growth medium, strain, and heating menstruum. In an attempt to obtain reproducible results most of their heating tests were conducted in M/15 Sorensen's phosphate buffer, pH 7.0. Because they used this heating medium, the thermal resistance of other *C. botulinum* spore suspensions can still be related to their experimental values. This is of great value in determining the suitability of new spore suspensions for use in TDT (thermal death time) tests in food for which commercial heat processes are to be calculated.

Their thermal destruction values for 60 billion spores were 4 minutes at 120° C., 33 minutes at 110° C. and 330 minutes at 100° C. This resistance was many times that reported by Van Ermengem. Townsend, Esty, and Baselt (*28*) in 1938 substantiated the work of Esty and Meyer. They applied a correction for the heating lag and obtained a corrected value of 2.45 minutes at 121.1° C. (250° F).

The available experimental data on the thermal resistance of type E spores are quite meager compared to that available for types A and B spores. Gunnison, Cummings, and Meyer (*11*) noted in 1936 that the thermal resistance of type E was quite low. They heated 5 million spores per milliliter in pH 7.4 buffer,

*Present address: Clean Assembly and Sterilization Laboratory, Goddard Space Flight Center, Greenbelt, Md.

and found them to be destroyed after heating at 100° C. for 2 minutes or 80° C. for 6 minutes. Dolman and Chang (7) have reported wide variability in the heat-resistance of type E. spores. They reported that some spores were able to withstand as long as 30 minutes at 100° C., while others could not withstand 5 minutes at 100° C. Nakamura et al. (18), after testing eight type E strains, were able to report relatively low resistance with 80° C. for 20 minutes or 90° C. for 5 minutes destroying all spores. The relatively low thermal resistance of type E spores has also been reported by several other investigators. (12, 20, 21, 22).

Several methods have been used in determining the thermal resistance values. Dickson et al. (6) used 10 ml. of material in a thin glass test tube immersed in a water bath. Heated material was removed at appropriate intervals, then subcultured. Esty and Meyer (9) used narrow glass tubes, 7 mm. in diameter by 250 mm. long, inoculated with 2 ml. of suspension and flame sealed. The tubes were then immersed in an electrically heated oil bath. At appropriate time intervals, tubes were removed from the bath, opened and then subcultured. Townsend, Esty, and Baselt (28) placed 13 ml. of food sample in TDT cans, size 208 x 006 (2½ inches by three-eighths of an inch). The containers were heated in a battery of small retorts. This apparatus was designed by A. C. Richardson to enable more accurate TDT determinations.

Other TDT devices which have been used are the "tank" method of Williams, Merrill, and Cameron (33) and the Thermoresistometer method of Stumbo (24). The Thermoresistometer has been used most often at high temperatures where very short heating times prevail.

Much of the current data on the thermal resistance are expressed in terms of D values, the time in minutes at constant temperature required to destroy 90 percent of the original population. On this basis Esty and Meyer's data as corrected by Townsend et al., give a $D_{121.1} = 0.204$ minutes. Schmidt (22) has obtained an extrapolated $D_{121.1} = 0.200$ minutes in phosphate buffer and Tsuji and Perkins (29) have obtained an extrapolated $D_{121.1} = 0.21$ minutes in phosphate buffer. Knock and Lambrecht (14), using a type B strain, isolated from South African soil, have obtained an extrapolated $D_{121.1} = 0.36$ minutes in phosphate buffer. The phosphate data of Esty and Meyer have, therefore, been substantiated by other investigators.

No maximum phosphate working value similar to Esty and Meyer's value for type A and B spores has yet been obtained for type E spores. Table 1 gives D values we have obtained using 1 x 10^7 spores per milliliter TDT tubes in a constant temperature bath.

These values are similar to those of Schmidt (22),

Table 1.—Thermal resistance of *C. botulinum* type E

[M/15 phosphate buffer, pH 7.0]

Strain	z (°F.)	D values			
		158° F. (70° C.)	163° F. (72.8° C.)	167° F. (75° C.)	176° F. (80° C.)
Saratoga	13	33.8	13.1	8.2	1.4
Beluga	14	29.3	8.0	5.1	1.4
Alaska	14	37.5	11.8	5.3	1.6
1304 E	15	29.6	10.6	5.6	1.8

who found the Minneapolis strain had a $D_{80} = 2.3$ minutes; Roberts and Ingram (21), who heated nine strains and found a D_{80} range of less than 0.33 to 1.25 minutes; and Ohye and Scott (20), who obtained a D_{80} of 3.3 and 0.4 minutes.

The thermal resistance of *C. botulinum* is markedly affected by environmental conditions. Weiss (32) noted that the thermal death point varied with the hydrogen-ion concentration of a particular food. The more acid foods, such as canned fruits required a maximum of 50 minutes at 100° C. to destroy their spore inoculum, while the less acid foods, such as vegetable products, required as long as 180 minutes at 100° C. to destroy their spore inoculum. Esty and Meyer (9) found *C. botulinum* had maximum resistance between pH 6.3 and 6.9. They indicated a marked influence on the heat resistance by the hydrogen-ion concentration at pH values below 5.0 and above 10.0. Lang (15) in his investigations found no apparent correlation between pH and heat resistance between pH 5.4 to 6.8. However, he noted a marked reduction in resistance at pH 4.9. Sognefest, Hays, Wheaton, and Benjamin (23) concluded that the lower the pH of a raw vegetable within the range of pH 4.9 to 9.0, the lower the sterilizing value required to insure a commercially sterile product. Xezones and Hutchings (34) found the D values to increase with an increase in pH. They found the pH effect to be greatest at lower temperatures, between 110° and 115.6° C.

Salt has been found by some workers to affect the thermal resistance. Weiss (31) found the resistance reduced by the presence of 3 percent salt. Esty and Meyer (9) noted an enhancement in resistance with 0.5 to 1.0 percent, no decrease from 1 to 6 percent and a larger decrease with more than 8 percent. Yesair and Cameron (35) noted a reduction with 3.5 percent salt at temperatures below 110° C. but no appreciable effect at 110° to 112.8° C.

Sugiyama noted an increase in thermal resistance with an increase in sucrose concentration (25). He also noted (26) that spores grown in media supplemented with fatty acids had increased thermal resistance. In general, he found that the longer the fatty acid chain, the greater the increase in heat tolerance. Lang (15) observed an increased resistance when spores were trapped in oil. Murrell and Scott (17) have indicated that *C. botulinum* type B spores have increased resistance at lower water activity, the maximum occurring between $a_w = 0.2$ to 0.4. This is affirmation of the accepted fact that spores heated under dry conditions are more resistant than those heated under moist conditions.

Table 2 indicates some resistance values which have been obtained for *C. botulinum* type A and/or B spores in foods. The extent to which each environmental factor, such as the type of food, pH and the amount of fat influences the thermal resistance is not always clearly predictable.

Today, many canned foods are convenience foods; foods which are packaged in such a manner as to enable the housewife to prepare a meal with a minimum of effort. As a result many commodities are packed in exotic sauces, different styles and combinations of ingredients, each component of which will affect the thermal resistance and the ultimate process which the product will receive.

Thermal resistance data in food substrates alone are not sufficient information upon which to base a process. However, when such data are combined with the rate at which a product heats, a process may be calculated for the product. Under some conditions it is recommended that the calculated process be confirmed by use of an inoculated pack.

Much of the research effort of the National Canners Association (NCA) and the container and equipment manufacturers on the heat resistance of *C. botulinum* types A and B has been in specific products. New information concerning thermal death times, heat penetration, and design of commercial canning equipment are periodically reviewed by the Processing Committee of NCA. This group consists of thermal processing specialists from container manufacturing companies, manufacturers of processing equipment and NCA staff members. This group periodically revises processing bulletins such as the Bulletin 26–L, Processes for Low-Acid Canned Foods in Metal Containers and the Bulletin 30–L, Processes for Low-Acid Canned Foods in Glass Containers.

The term "processed" as used in NCA Bulletin 26–L means the application of heat to sealed containers for a definite time and at a definite temperature under specific conditions. The purpose of processing is to produce a commercially sterile product. Commercial sterility for low-acid foods may be defined as that condition in which all *C. botulinum* spores and all other pathogenic bacteria have been destroyed, as well as the more heat resistant organisms which, if present, could produce spoilage under normal conditions of storage and distribution. Since, in the case of heat processing, the typical spoilage types are much more heat resistant than *C. botulinum*, processes for spoilage control carry a considerable margin of safety.

The margin of safety in thermally processed foods can be increased further by reducing the number of viable organisms on the raw product and by preventing the recontamination of the product after the process. The use of germicidal solutions can be of great use in these areas of application.

Although germicides have been effectively used for the destruction of micro-organisms for many years, their effectiveness against anaerobic spore formers, and in particular *C. botulinum* spores, has received only slight attention. This lack of definitive information on the germicidal resistance of *C. botulinum* spores was emphasized by the case in which a commercially canned food, known to be properly sterilized, became toxic. It is presumed that viable *C. botulinum* spores were able to invade the containers through defective seams, possibly during water-cooling of the containers. Since chlorine is the principal germicide used in the canning plant considerable interest developed in the effectiveness of chlorine as a chemical disinfectant against *C. botulinum* spores.

Table 2.—Resistance of *C. botulinum* types A and B in foods

Product	Nature of substrate	Extrapolated pH	$D_{121.1}$[1]	z (°F.)	Reference
Asparagus	Pureed	5.5	0.10	16.7	Getchell et al. (10).
Corn	Cream style	6.3	.24	19.3	NCA (19).
Do	Chopped		.16	18.5	Kaplan et al. (13).
Peas	Pureed	6.0	.14	17.0	NCA (19).
Spinach	Chopped		.15	18.5	Kaplan et al. (13).
Do	Creamed	5.8	.34		NCA (19).
Sweet potatoes	Chopped with added syrup	5.5	.12	17.7	Collier (4).
Tuna	Pureed	5.9	.34	25.0	NCA (19).
Rock lobster	Liquor	6.6	.30	19.0	Knock and Lambrecht (14).

[1]Not corrected for classic phosphate resistance.

Germicidal resistance studies have been conducted utilizing an adaptation of the Chamber's (3) method of evaluating bactericidal agents (12). Ninety-nine milliliters of test solution were placed in a 250 ml. narrow-mouthed Erlenmeyer flask capped with a rubber serum-type stopper. The flask was placed inverted upon a mechanical wrist action shaker and continuously agitated. One milliliter of spore suspension, containing 10^6 spores, was inoculated into the test solution using a hypodermic syringe and needle. The test solution was neutralized with sterile sodium thiosulfate after the appropriate time intervals. The germicidal solutions were used in water solutions and in buffer solutions. Phosphate buffer, pH 6.5, was used as the standard buffer mixture. The concentration of the chlorine or iodine present was determined by amperometric titration. The number of viable spores remaining after a given time interval was determined by culturing appropriate dilutions of the neutralized test solutions in triplicate, in pork-pea infusion agar in Prickett tubes. The colonies were counted after 20 to 72 hours' incubation at 30° C.

There are a large number of commercially available germicides which are used in cannery sanitation. Several of these germicidal compounds were tested to determine their efficacy as sporicidal agents for types A, B, and E spores. Representative results of these tests, shown in table 3, indicate that under the test conditions of constant pH, temperature, spore concentration and germicide concentration, calcium hypochlorite, sodium hypochlorite, and gas chlorinated water have equal effectiveness as sporicidal agents for *C. botulinum* types A, B, and E spores. The two detergent-chlorine compounds tested were not as efficient as sporicides. The iodophor which was tested was also not as effective as the hypochlorite solutions or the gas chlorinated water.

Chlorine has been shown to have an effective spori-cidal action against *C. botulinum* types A, B, and E spores (12). Two type A, two type B, and four type E strains were tested in calcium hypochlorite solution at 4.5 p.p.m. free available chlorine, in pH 6.5 phosphate buffer at 25° C. A sigmoid-shaped survivor curve was constructed based upon the number of viable spores present after a given time interval. The time to reduce the number of survivors to 99.99 percent of the original number was 3 and 8 minutes for the two type B strains and 6 and 8 minutes for the two type A strains. The four type E strains required 4 to 6 minutes in order to obtain a similar reduction. Tonney, Greer, and Liebig (27) obtained destruction of one type A culture in 15 to 30 seconds at 15 p.p.m. and four type B cultures in 15 to 30 seconds at 17.5 p.p.m. In contrast, Dozier (8) used sodium hypochlorite of 4,500 to 5,000 p.p.m. and found it ineffective after 1 hour.

In order to determine the effect of pH on the germicidal property of chlorine, buffers at pH 3.5 and 5.0 were prepared from a mixture of disodium hydrogen phosphate and acetic acid. Buffers at pH 6.5 to 8.0 were prepared using disodium hydrogen phosphate and potassium dihydrogen phosphate. Buffer components were used in the concentration of 0.1 M or less.

Table 4 shows the chlorine resistance of types A, B, and E spores exposed to buffered solutions of calcium hypochlorite. As the pH increased from 3.5 to 8.0, there was also an increase in the time required to reduce the spore population to 99.99 percent of the original number. Of particular interest is the marked increase in time required for reduction when the pH increased from 7.0 to 8.0. When 10 p.p.m. sodium hypochlorite is placed in tap water, the pH is increased to over 8.0. Thus when used in cannery sanitation, increased exposure time may be required to

Table 3.—Resistance of *C. botulinum* types A, B, and E to germicidal compounds

[1 x 10^4 spores/ml. pH 6.5 phosphate buffer, 25°C]

Germicide	Type A		Type B		Type E	
	Concentration (p.p.m.)	Minutes	Concentration (p.p.m.)	Minutes	Concentration (p.p.m.)	Minutes
Calcium hypochlorite_____	4.5	8.0	4.5	7.4	4.5	4.0
Sodium hypochlorite_____			4.5	8.0	4.5	3.8
Gas chlorinated water_____	4.5	8.2	4.5	8.0	4.5	4.6
Dichloro(s) triazinetrione_____	10.0	15.0	20.0	>15.0	10.0	7.2
Trichloro cyanuric acid_____	4.5	17.0	[1]500.0	40.0	5.0	9.0
Butoxy polypropoxy poly-ethoxy ethanol-iodine complex_____	[2]100.0	>25.0				

[1]pH 10.8—unbuffered solution.
[2]pH 2.8—unbuffered solution.

Table 4.—Chlorine resistance of C. botulinum types A, B, and E at various pH levels

[4.5 p.p.m. free available chlorine, 1 x 10⁴ spores per milliliter, 25° C.]

pH	Time (in minutes) to destroy 99.99 percent		
	12885A	213B	Saratoga E
3.5	2.1	3.7	1.0
5.0	4.3	6.2	2.8
6.5	7.8	7.8	4.0
7.0	8.5	8.7	5.0
7.5	10.6	11.2	7.6
8.0	24.0	26.6	17.0

overcome the loss of effectiveness due to the increase in pH.

Water used in cannery sanitation varies in temperature. The effect of temperature upon the sporicidal properties of chlorine solutions was investigated using water-jacketed, 250 ml. Erlenmeyer flasks as the test vessels. Water from a circulating cooling bath was used to cool the test solution. The test solution was maintained within ±0.5° C. of the desired temperature. Table 5 shows the effect of temperature upon the sporicidal properties of calcium hypochlorite solutions.

Table 5.—Effect of temperature upon sporicidal properties of calcium hypochlorite solutions

[1 x 10⁴ spores per milliliter, pH 6.5 phosphate buffer, 4.5 p.p.m. free available chlorine]

Organism	Time (in minutes) to destroy 99.99 percent		
	25° C.	15° C.	5° C.
62A	6.0	15	35
213B	6.0	20	40
Saratoga E	4.0	10	24

A decrease in temperature necessitated an increase in exposure time in order to achieve comparable reduction in spore numbers. The reduction time approximately doubled for each 10° C. decrease in temperature. Mercer and Somers (16) have noted that usage of the increased germicidal activity of chlorine solutions at elevated temperatures will depend upon the type of chlorine compound from which the solution is prepared as well as the intended use of the solution.

When used in the cannery, chlorine solutions often cannot be used under the ideal conditions which are employed in experimental studies. The organic substances which are often present combine with chlorine and reduce its effectiveness. The effect of organic

material upon the sporicidal properties of chlorine is shown in table 6.

Table 6.—Effect of organic material on the chlorine resistance of C. botulinum 12885A, 213B, and saratoga E

[1 x 10⁴ spores per milliliter, 25° C.]

Type of organic material	Time to destroy 99.99 percent					
	12885A		213B		Saratoga E	
	Time[1]	Concentration[2]	Time[1]	Concentration[2]	Time[1]	Concentration[2]
None	8.0	4.5	7.4	4.5	4.0	4.5
Oil (0.1 percent)	6.0	4.5	10.0	4.5	6.0	4.5
Peptone (0.001 percent)	8.0	5.8	7.0	8.0	4.5	8.0

[1]Minutes.
[2]Parts per million.

The time required to cause a 99.99 percent reduction in the number of oil-coated spores is longer than for uncoated spores at the same chlorine concentration. Organic debris, such as peptone, combines with the free available chlorine, causing the chlorine solution to be ineffective. Enough chlorine must be added to obtain a free residual adequate in concentration to be germicidal.

The ability of germicides, particularly chlorine, to effectively act as a sporicide is greatly influenced by the method and environment in which it is used. When used with care, with consideration for pH, water temperature, and assurance of a sufficient free residual concentration, hypochlorite or other germicidal solutions can effectively be used to reduce C. botulinum spore populations as they have been used to reduce other harmful bacterial populations.

Acknowledgments

The authors gratefully acknowledge the technical assistance of Donna L. Seslar and Jacqueline R. Whitney. We wish to thank Mr. Walter A. Mercer for his helpful suggestions during the preparation of this report. We also wish to thank Dr. K. F. Meyer, G. W. Hooper Foundation for Medical Research, University of California Medical Center, for his support and encouragement during the course of this investigation.

This study was supported in part by the U.S. Department of the Interior, Fish and Wildlife Service, Bureau of Commercial Fisheries, under contract No. 14–17–007–259.

References

(1) BREAZEALE, J. F. 1909. Canning vegetables in the home. U.S. Dept. Agr. Farmers Bull. 359. 16 pp.

(2) BURKE, G. S. 1919. The effect of heat on the spores of *Bacillus botulinus:* Its bearing on home canning methods: Part I. J. Amer. Med. Assoc. *72:* 88.

(3) CHAMBERS, C. W. 1956. A procedure for evaluating the efficiency of bactericidal agents. J. Milk Food Tech. *19*, 183.

(4) COLLIER, C. P. 1952. Thermal death time tests on Sirup pack sweet potatoes. NCA Research Report No. 14907–A.

(5) DICKSON, E. C. 1917. Botulism. The danger of poisoning from vegetables canned by the cold-pack method. J. Amer. Med. Assoc. *69:* 966.

(6) DICKSON, E. C., G. S. BURKE, and E. S. WARD. 1919. A study of the resistance of the spores of *Bacillus botulinus* to various sterilizing agencies which are commonly employed in the canning of fruits and vegetables. Arch. Intern. Med. *24:* 581.

(7) DOLMAN, C. E., and H. CHANG. 1953. The epidemiology and pathogenesis of type E and fish-borne botulism. Can. J. Publ. Hlth. *44:* 231.

(8) DOZIER, C. C. 1924. Resistances of spores of *B. botulinus* to disinfectants. XVIII. J. Infect. Dis. *35:* 156.

(9) ESTY, J. R., and K. F. MEYER. 1922. The heat resistance of the spores of *Bacillus botulinus* and allied anaerobes. XI. J. Infect. Dis. *31:* 650.

(10) GETCHELL, R. N., J. E. W. McCONNELL, and C. T. TOWNSEND. 1957. Processing studies on asparagus. NCA Research Report No. 57 p. 4.

(11) GUNNISON, J. B., J. R. CUMMINGS, and K. F. MEYER. 1936. *Clostridium botulinum* type E. Proc. Soc. Exp. Biol., N.Y. *35:* 278.

(12) ITO, K. A., D. J. SESLAR, W. A. MERCER, and K. F. MEYER. 1967. The thermal and chlorine resistance of *Cl. botulinum* types A, B, and E spores. p. 108. *In* Botulism 1966. M. Ingram and T. A. Roberts, eds. Proc. Intern Symp. Food Microbiol., 5th, Moscow. Chapman and Hall, Ltd., London.

(13) KAPLAN, A. M., H. REYNOLDS and H. LICHTENSTEIN. 1954. Significance of variations in observed slopes of thermal death time curves for putrefactive anaerobes. Food Research *19:* 173.

(14) G. G. KNOCK, and M. S. J. LAMBRECHTS. 1956. A note on the heat resistance of a South African Strain of *Clostridium botulinum* type B. J. Sci. Food Agr. *7:* 244.

(15) LANG, O. W. 1935. Thermal processes for canned marine products. Univ. Calif. Publ. in Publ. Hlth. *2:* (1) 1-182.

(16) MERCER, W. A., and I. I. SOMERS. 1957. Chlorine in food plant sanitation. Adv. Food Research *7:* 129.

(17) MURRELL, W. G., and W. J. SCOTT. 1966. The heat resistance of bacterial spores at various water activities. J. Gen. Microbiol. *43:* 411.

(18) NAKAMURA, Y., H. IIDA, K. SAEKI, K. KANZAWA, and T. KARASHENIADA. 1956. Type E botulism in Hokkaido, Japan. Japan J. Med. Sci. Biol. *9:* 45.

(19) NATIONAL CANNERS ASSOCIATION. Unpublished data.

(20) OHYE, D. F., and W. J. SCOTT. 1957. Studies in the physiology of *Clostridium botulinum* type E. Aust. J. Biol. Sci. *10:* 85.

(21) ROBERTS, T. A., and M. INGRAM. 1965. The resistance of spores of *Clostridium botulinum* type E to heat and radiation. J. Appl. Bact. *28:* 125.

(22) SCHMIDT, C. F. 1964. Spores of *Clostridium botulinum:* Formation, Resistance, Germination. p. 257. *In* Botulism Proc. Symp., Cincinnati, Ohio, Jan. 1964. Lewis, K. H. and Cassel, K. Jr. (ed.), P.H.S. Publ. No. 999–FP–1. U.S. Publ. Hlth. Serv. Cincinnati, Ohio, Dec. 1964.

(23) SOGNEFEST, P., G. L. HAYS, E. WHEATON and H. A. BENJAMIN. 1948. Effect of pH on thermal process requirements of canned foods. Food Research *13:* 400.

(24) STUMBO, C . R. 1948. A technique for studying resistance of bacterial spores to temperatures in the higher range. Food Technol., Champaign *4:* 321.

(25) SUGIYAMA, H. 1951. Studies on factors affecting the heat resistance of spores of *Clostridium botulinum*. J. Bacteriol. *62:* 81.

(26) SUGIYAMA, H. 1952. Effect of fatty acids on the heat resistance of *Clostridium botulinum* spores. Bacteriol. Rev. *16:* 125.

(27) TONNEY, F. O., F. E. GREER and G. F. LIEBIG, Jr. 1930. The minimal "chlorine death points" of bacteria. II. Vegetative forms. III. Spore-bearing organisms. Amer. J. Publ. Hlth. *20:* 503.

(28) TOWNSEND, C. T., J. R. ESTY, and F. C. BASELT. 1938. Heat-resistance studies on spores of putrefactive anaerobes in relation to determination of safe processes for canned foods. Food Research. *3:* 323.

(29) TSUJI, K., and W. E. PERKINS. 1962. Sporulation of *Clostridium botulinum*. I. Selection of an aparticulate sporulation medium. J. Bacteriol. *84:* 81.

(30) VAN ERMENGEM, E. 1912. Der *Bacillus botulinus* und der Botulismus. *In* "Handbuch der pathogenen Mikroorganismen," 2d ed., W. Kolle and A. Von Wasserman, eds., G. Fisher, Jena. *4:* 909.

(31) WEISS, H. 1921. The heat resistance of spores with special reference to the spores of *B. botulinus*. J. Infect. Dis. *28:* 70.

(32) WEISS, H. 1921. The thermal death point of the spores of *Bacillus botulinum* in canned foods. J. Infect. Dis. *29:* 362.

(33) WILLIAMS, C. C., C. M. MERRILL, and E. J. CAMERON. 1937. Apparatus for determination of spore-destruction rates. Food Research. *2:* 369.

(34) XEZONES, H., and I. J. HUTCHINGS. 1965. Thermal resistance of *Clostridium botulinum* (62A) spores as affected by fundamental food constituents. I. Effect of pH. Food Technol., Champaign *19:* 1004.

(35) YESAIR, J. and E. J. CAMERON. 1942. Inhibitive effect of curing agents on anaerobic spores. Canner *94:* 89.

IDENTIFICATION OF THE VOLATILE ACID ODORS PRODUCED BY *CLOSTRIDIUM BOTULINUM*

by Yoshiaki Ando *and* Takashi Karashimada
Hokkaido Institute of Public Health, Sapporo, Japan

Summary

In order to establish the chemical nature of the volatile acid odors produced by *Clostridium botulinum* during growth, volatile fatty acids were determined by gas chromatography in cultures of Cooked Meat Broth inoculated with each strain of the six toxin types.

Acetic, propionic, n-butyric, isobutyric, n-valeric, isovaleric (and/or active α-methyl-butyric), and isocaproic acids were identified in the cultures of the proteolytic strains of types A, B, and F. The branched-chain acids except isocaproic acid were deduced to be metabolic products derived from certain amino acids by Stickland reaction.

Propionic acid, in higher proportion than acetic and n-butyric acids, was identified in the cultures of types Cβ and D.

N-butyric acid, in considerable higher proportion than acetic and propionic acids, was identified in the cultures of the nonproteolytic strains of types B, E, and F. Furthermore, the chemical nature of the off-odors which developed in some incriminated foods was examined. An abnormally high proportion of n-butyric acid, being responsible for the "butyric acid-like odor," was found in the homemade izushi of raw fish, which had caused an episode of human type E botulism. Also, a high proportion of propionic acid as well as n-butyric acid were found in the raw whale meat, which had caused an outbreak of type Cβ botulism in minks.

Experiments were also made, for the detection of volatile fatty acids in irradiated fish, in relation to the growth and toxin production of *C. botulinum* type E. When plaice homogenates were irradiated and stored at room temperature, a high proportion of n-butyric acid was found in the inoculated samples, while no detectable amount of the acid was found in the uninoculated samples.

Introduction

It is a noticeable fact that, in many cases of outbreaks of botulism, the causative foods were considered to have been abnormal in physical appearances.

In fact, it has been reported by many investigators (*2*) that certain foods had an off-odor such as rancid, butyric acid-like, or cheese-like, as a result of growth of *C. botulinum*. Besides off-odor, the appearance of spoilage due to the proteolytic ablility of the strains of *C. botulinum* (types A or B) might have suggested that the foods should have been thrown away as being unfit for consumption.

In outbreaks of human botulism in Japan, most cases have proved to be of type E and caused by homemade izushi of raw fish. Because of their nonproteolytic abilities, type E organisms give less evidence of spoilage to foods. Moreover, like other fermented foods, izushi has an excellent odor of its own, being somewhat like pickled fish, which would make it difficult to distinguish an odor of decomposition due to other species with proteolytic ability. Nevertheless, according to the evidence available in the past outbreaks, most of the incriminated izushi had the specific butyric acid-like odor, while other normal izushi had little or no off-odor. Although it is impossible to rely only on physical appearances of foods as a criterion of a safety margin against botulism, the judgment of this kind of off-odor would appear to be useful in protecting against outbreaks of botulism.

The present study was, therefore, initiated to determine the chemical nature of the volatile acid odors produced by *C. botulinum* during growth. Volatile fatty acids, being responsible for the odors, were analyzed by gas chromatography in the cultures of the different types of *C. botulinum* as well as of two other *Clostridia*. Also, detection of volatile fatty acids in some incriminated foods or irradiated fish was carried out to determine the relationship between toxic foods and the off-odors developed in them.

Materials and Methods

Organisms.—The following types and strains of *Clostridium botulinum* were used: Type A 190 and AK 38; type B Lamanna and QC (nonproteolytic strain); type Cβ 468, Asahigawa, and Yoichi; type D 1873; type E Iwanai, VH, and Morai (nontoxic strain); type F Denmark and OSU (nonproteolytic strain).

C. sporogenes and *C. perfringens* were compared with *C. botulinum*.

Culture medium and cultural conditions.—The organisms were grown in Cooked Meat Broth (Eiken), unless otherwise stated. Cultures for fatty acid analysis were obtained by two successive transfers in the Cooked Meat Broth followed by a final transfer into 100 ml. of the same medium. All cultures were incubated at 30° C. for 10 days.

Preparation of samples for gas chromatography.—To each culture (100 ml.) or 30 g. of food sample were added 30 ml. and 40 ml. of $N/1\text{-}H_2SO_4$, respectively. The acidified material was mixed thoroughly and then steam distilled. Approximately 500 ml. of distillate was collected. The distillates were neutralized with a dilute solution of NaOH and then concentrated to a small volume. The concentrated solution was acidified to pH 1.0 by drop-wise addition of 10 percent H_2SO_4, and the free acids were extracted with several portions of ethyl ether. The extracts were combined, then freed from water by addition of anhydrous Na_2SO_4, and the solvent was evaporated at room temperature in a stream of nitrogen. The residue was used immediately for gas chromatography analysis.

Gas chromatography analysis.—The free acids prepared as described above were analyzed by use of a "Yanagimoto GCG–2" gas chromatograph. The U-shaped copper columns (5 mm. ID an 3 m. long) were packed with 10 percent polyethylene glycol adipate coated on Diasolid L (80 to 100 mesh). Operating parameters of the instrument were: Column temperature, 130.5° 5, C.; carrier gas, helium; gas flow rate, 26 ml. per minute; recorder sensitivity, 4 mV.

A mixture of known composition, containing both the n-types and the isotypes of the authentic fatty acids, was chromatographed to obtain relative retention data. Table 1 lists the data obtained from the gas chromatogram of a mixture of the eight fatty acids as shown in figure 1. Peak areas were determined by the method of "Height x width at half-height." The percentage of each acid was calculated from the ratio of the area of its peak to the total area of all peaks and the weight of acid corresponded to its peak area.

Results and Discussions

Volatile fatty acids produced by *C. botulinum*.—Representative gas chromatograms of the volatile fatty acids produced by the strains of different types of *C. botulinum* and other two *Clostridia* are illustrated in figures 2–16. Quantitative composition of the percentages of the fatty acids (table 2) obtained from the gas chromatographic profiles permitted these

Table 1.—Relative retention times and quantities of the authentic fatty acids

Peak number	Fatty acid	Relative retention time	Peak area of 1 g. acid (cm.²)	Relative quantity of acid
1	acetic	1.00	5.14	1.00
2	propionic	1.39	5.44	1.05
3	isobutyric	1.56	5.90	1.14
4	n-butyric	2.07	5.22	1.01
5	isovaleric	2.48	5.19	1.00
6	n-valeric	3.36	4.98	.96
7	isocaproic	4.50	4.77	.92
8	n-caproic	5.33	4.33	.84

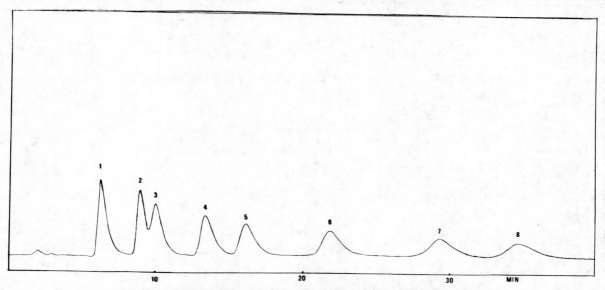

Figure 1.—Gas chromatogram of a mixture of the eight authentic fatty acids.

Table 2.—Analysis of composition of the volatile fatty acids produced by *Clostridium botulinum* and other clostridia

Organism	Ratio of individual acids (weight percent)						
	Acetic	Propionic	Isobutyric	n-butyric	Isovaleric[1]	n-valeric	Isocaproic
C. botulinum:							
A 190	15.2	2.2	8.5	31.2	33.7	0	8.3
A AK 38	6.8	.1	14.3	33.8	36.5	0	7.4
B Lamanna	21.8	1.7	10.0	19.2	22.4	2.6	22.0
B QC	10.1	6.2	-----------	83.6	-----------	-----------	-----------
Cβ 468	5.3	57.1	-----------	37.5	-----------	-----------	-----------
Cβ Yoichi	22.8	54.9	-----------	22.1	-----------	-----------	-----------
Cβ Asahigawa	9.9	53.5	-----------	36.5	-----------	-----------	-----------
D 1873	8.9	51.1	-----------	39.9	-----------	-----------	-----------
E Iwanai	29.4	.6	-----------	69.9	-----------	-----------	-----------
E VH	12.9	5.9	-----------	81.1	-----------	-----------	-----------
E Morai	7.9	5.2	-----------	86.8	-----------	-----------	-----------
F Denmark	16.9	2.1	9.1	32.6	28.2	0	10.8
F OSU	7.8	6.1	-----------	86.0	-----------	-----------	-----------
C. sporogenes	20.7	4.2	10.5	23.8	27.8	2	10.5
C. perfringens	68.0	6.1	-----------	25.8	-----------	-----------	-----------

[1]And/or α-methyl-butyric acid.

organisms to be differentiated into three groups. Each group had certain distinguishing components of fatty acids. Group I had both straight- and branched-chained acids. Acetic, propionic, n-butyric, isobutyric, n-valeric, isovaleric (and/or active α-methyl-butyric), and isocaproic acids were identified. This group contains proteolytic strains of types A (190, Ak 38), B (Lamanna), and F (Denmark) of *C. botulinum*, as well as *C. sporogenes*. It has been well known that almost all the species of proteolytic *Clostridia* obtain their energy by means of the Stickland reaction (*4*), coupled deamination between two amino acids. The following

fatty acids are recognized as normal end products of this reaction:

Alanine ➡ Acetic acid.
Glycine ➡ Acetic acid.
Valine ➡ Isobutyric acid.
Leucine ➡ Isovaleric acid.
Isoleucine ➡ Valeric acid, active α-methyl-butyric acid.

The fact that the organisms comprising group I produced all the volatile fatty acids listed above except isocaproic acid gives evidence of occurrence of the Stickland reaction.

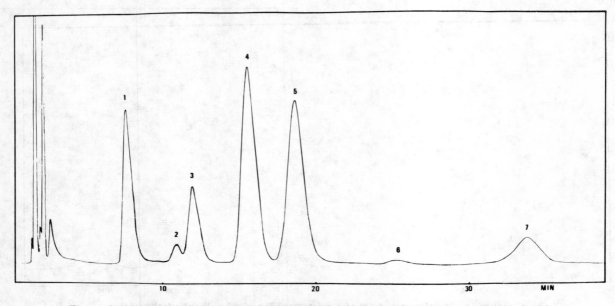

Figure 2.—Gas chromatogram of the volatile fatty acids produced by *C. botulinum* type A 190.

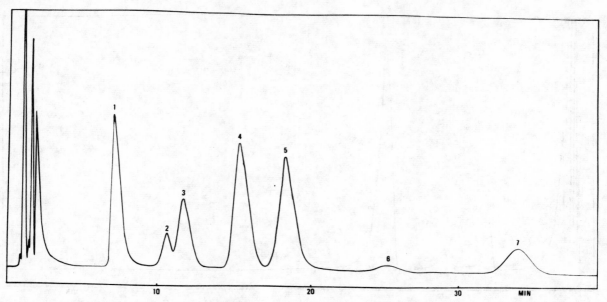

Figure 3.—Gas chromatogram of the volatile fatty acids produced by *C. botulinum* type A AK 38.

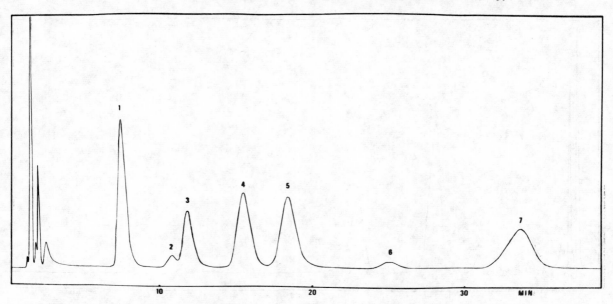

Figure 4.—Gas chromatogram of the volatile fatty acids produced by *C. botulinum* type B Lamanna.

As for the existence of isocaproic acid, its source is as yet uncertain in the literature. An attempt was made to determine whether this fatty acid would be produced also in a synthetic medium consisting of all the amino acids essential for the growth of *C. botulinum*. Fatty acids were analyzed after the growth of type B (Lamanna) in the synthetic medium (*3*). As can be seen in figure 17, acetic, propionic, isobutyric, and isovaleric (and/or active α-methyl-butyric) acids were identified, but no evidence of isocaproic acid was obtained at all in this experiment. Therefore, it is

conceivable that isocaproic acid may not be a characteristic product of Stickland reaction, but is probably formed from some materials other than amino acids present in the Cooked Meat Broth.

Group II had only such straight-chained fatty acids as acetic, propionic, or n-butyric acids, and was distinguished from other groups by the presence of a higher proportion of propionic acid. This group contains strains of types Cβ and D of *C. botulinum*. It seems probable that these organisms may obtain their energy by a propionic acid fermentation rather than

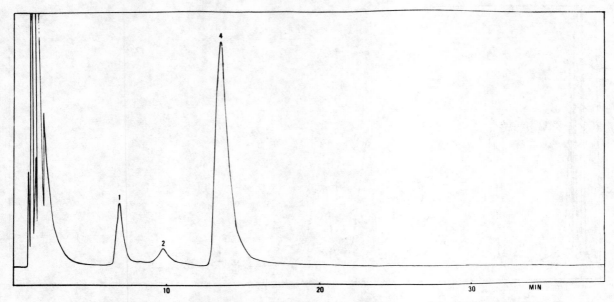

Figure 5.—Gas chromatogram of the volatile fatty acids produced by *C. botulinum* type B QC.

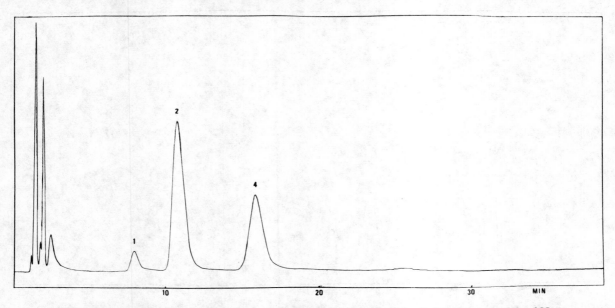

Figure 6.—Gas chromatogram of the volatile fatty acids produced by *C. botulinum* type Cβ 468.

by way of the Stickland reaction. *C. propionicum* (5) ferments alanine and other amino acids without the presence of any added hydrogen acceptor. However, we do not have sufficient data on the metabolic pathway of the organisms comprising group II to establish this as a fact.

Group III also had only straight-chained fatty acids, but differed from group II by having n-butyric acid in large percentages. This group contains nonproteolytic strains of types B (QC), E (Iwanai, VH, and Morai), and F (OSU) of *C. botulinum*, as well as *C.*

perfringens.

In order to clarify whether or not *C. botulinum* type E can utilize certain amino acids by means of the Stickland reaction, experiments on the oxidation of alanine or glucose, as determined by ammonia production in the presence of glycine or proline, were carried out. The results are presented in table 3. The amino acids used were not attacked with washed cells of *C. botulinum* type E, showing no production of ammonia. On the contrary, *C. sporogenes* which can effect a Stickland reaction attacked these amino acids

Table 3.—Ammonia production during the oxidation of amino acids by washed cells of *Clostridium botulinum* type E and *C. sporogenes*

M/10 substrate (milliliters)		Bacterial suspension (milliliters)	Phosphate buffer pH 7.0 ml.	Water (milliliters)	Ammonia produced N-mg. percent	
H-donor	H-acceptor				*C. botulinum* type E	*C. sporogenes*
1-Alanine 1	Glycine 1	1	2	2	0	2.1
Do	Glycine 0	1	2	1	0	.2
1-Alanine 0	Glycine 1	1	2	1	0	.4
Do	Glycine 0	1	2	0	0	.1
1-Alanine 1	1-Proline 1	1	2	0	0	.7
1-Alanine 0	do	1	2	1	0	.1
Glucose 1	Glycine 1	1	2	0	0	1.0
Do	Glycine 0	1	2	1	0	.1

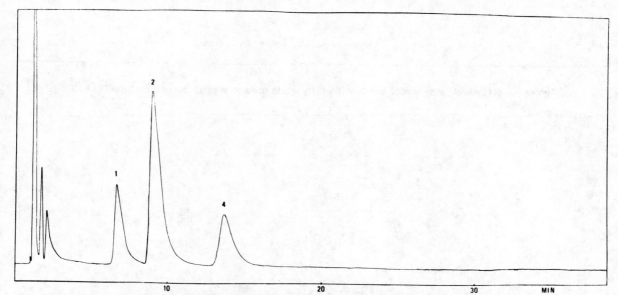

Figure 7.—Gas chromatogram of the volatile fatty acids produced by *C. botulinum* type Cβ Yoichi.

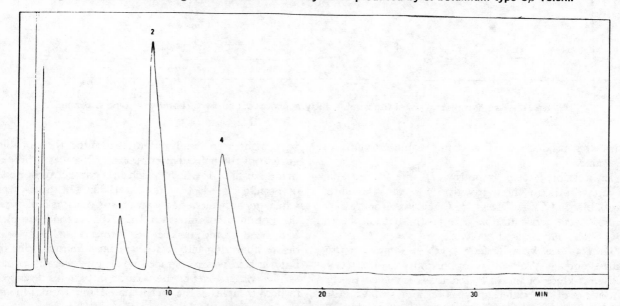

Figure 8.—Gas chromatogram of the volatile fatty acids produced by *C. botulinum* type Cβ Asahigawa.

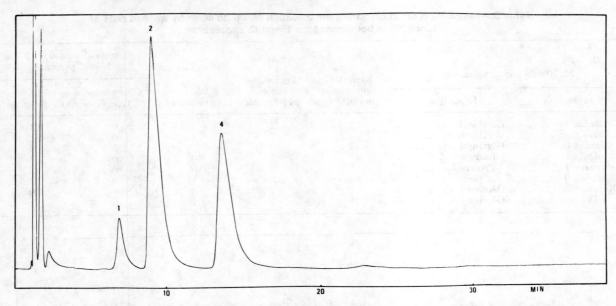

Figure 9.—Gas chromatogram of the volatile fatty acids produced by *C. botulinum* type D 1873.

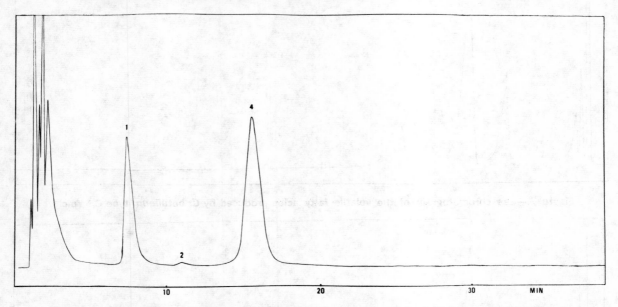

Figure 10.—Gas chromatogram of the volatile fatty acids produced by *C. botulinum* type E Iwanai.

with the production of a considerable amount of ammonia.

In addition, type E organisms require fermentable carbohydrates in their growth. It seems, therefore, probable that *C. botulinum* type E obtains its energy by butyric acid fermentation similar to that displayed by certain butyric acid bacteria.

Detection of volatile fatty acids in some incriminated foods.— We had the opportunity to obtain two different kinds of incriminated foods involved in the outbreaks of two different types of botulism. Volatile fatty acids were analyzed to determine the possible growth of the causative organisms. One was a home-made izushi of raw fish which had caused an episode of human type-E botulism in 1965. The other was whale meat which had caused an outbreak of type Cβ botulism in minks in 1961. These food samples had been stored in the deep freezer at −20° C. before analyzing fatty acids, and an offensive odor of butyric acid was recognized when they were thawed.

The components of the volatile fatty acids detected in both samples of the incriminated and normal foods are presented in table 4. A considerable difference was observed between the two samples in both the nature and amounts of the fatty acids present. An abnormally high proportion of n-butyric acid was found in the incriminated izushi, whereas it was absent in the normal izushi. Also, a relatively high proportion of propionic acid was found in the incriminated whale meat, as compared with that in the normal one.

Accordingly, the gas chromatographic profiles of the volatile fatty acids characterizing each type of *C. botulinum* seem to be reflected in those foods contami-

Table 4.—Analysis of composition of the volatile fatty acids in samples of the foods contaminated with or without botulinal toxins

Name of sample	Type of toxin	Ratio of individual acids (weight percent)		
		Acetic	Propionic	n-Butyric
Izushi (hata-hata)__E_____		60.6	3.6	35.7
Do_____None____		100.0	-------------------	-------------------
Izushi (salmon)_____do____		100.0	-------------------	-------------------
Whale meat_____Cβ_____		44.8	41.2	13.9
Do_____None____		80.0	10.4	9.6

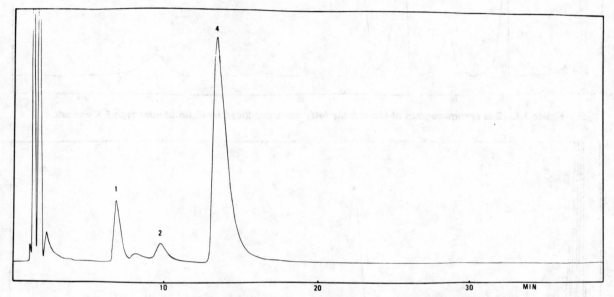

Figure 11.—Gas chromatogram of the volatile fatty acids produced by *C. botulinum* type E VH.

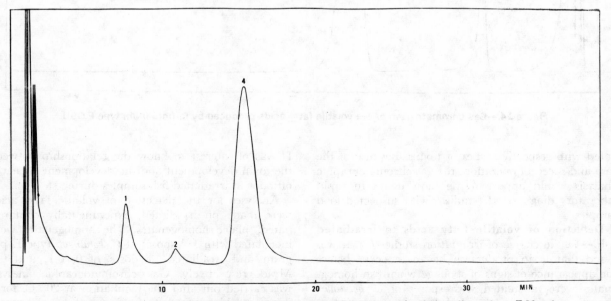

Figure 12.—Gas chromatogram of the volatile fatty acids produced by *C. botulinum* type E Morai.

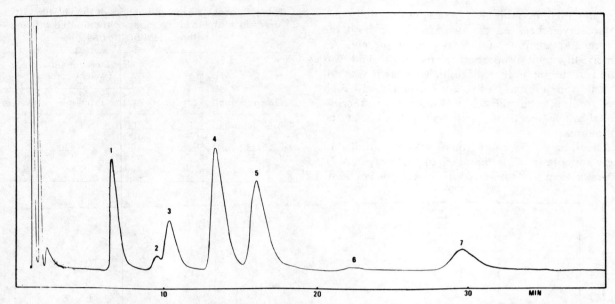

Figure 13.—Gas chromatogram of the volatile fatty acids produced by *C. botulinum* type F Denmark.

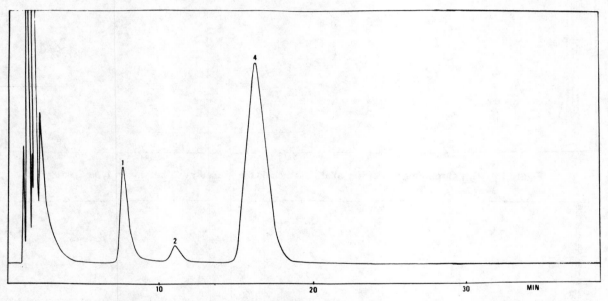

Figure 14.—Gas chromatogram of the volatile fatty acids produced by *C. botulinum* type F OSU.

nated with respective types of toxins. Because of the ease and speed of operation, the gas chromatographic analysis would appear to be most useful in rapid laboratory diagnosis of botulism with suspected food samples.

Detection of volatile fatty acids in irradiated fish.—In the course of irradiation studies (*1*), it was found that toxin production began to occur before the appearance of signs of spoilage when fish homogenates were inoculated with spores of *C. botulinum* type E, irradiated and stored at room temperature.

It was of interest to know the relationship between the toxin development and the development of acidic off odor in irradiated fish samples during storage.

Analyses for the detection of volatile fatty acids were made on irradiated, experimentally contaminated, plaice homogenates. The homogenates were inoculated with 10^4 spores of *C. botulinum* type E per gram and irradiated at doses of 0, 0.1, and 0.3 Mrad, respectively. Gas chromatographic analysis was carried out after the incubation at 20° C. for 3 days, at which time all of the samples had become toxic. As controls, uninoculated homogenates, irradiated at the same levels and held at 20° C. for 3 days, were examined.

The components of the volatile fatty acids detected in both samples of the irradiated fish homogenates are shown in table 5. It is clear that n-butyric acid was present in all samples of the inoculated homogenates regardless of irradiation doses, while a relatively small or undetectable amount of the acid was found in the uninoculated samples. Since irradiation of fish results in the marked reduction of the normal spoilage microflora, there is a definite possibility that the type E spores surviving irradiation germinate and

Table 5.—Analysis of composition of the volatile fatty acids in both inoculated and noninoculated samples of the irradiated plaice homogenates

Sample	Irradi-ation dose (Mrad)	Ratio of individual acids (weight percent)				
		Ace-tic	Pro-pionic	Iso-bu-tyric	n-bu-tyric	Iso-val-eric
Inoculated	0	15.4	9.2	------	75.3	------
Do	.1	15.6	6.3	------	77.7	------
Do	.3	18.8	1.8	------	79.2	------
Noninoculated	0	58.0	14.3	5.8	7.4	14.3
Do	.1	------------------------------------				
Do	.3	------------------------------------				

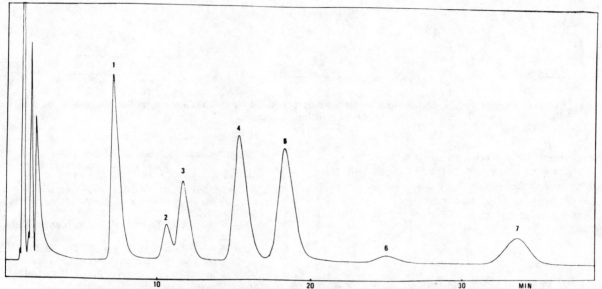

Figure 15.—Gas chromatogram of the volatile fatty acids produced by *C. sporogenes.*

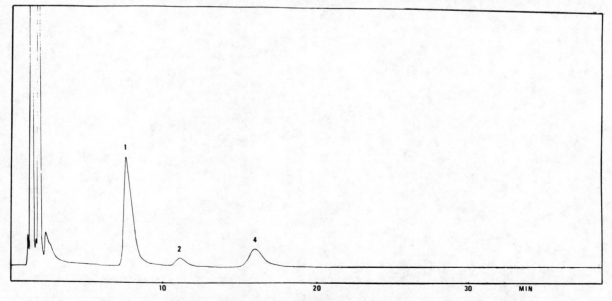

Figure 16.—Gas chromatogram of the volatile fatty acids produced by *C. perfringens.*

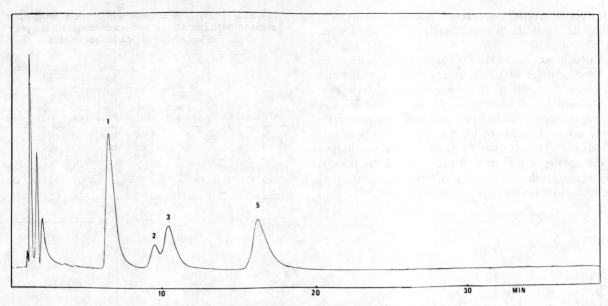

Figure 17.—Gas chromatogram of the volatile fatty acids produced by *C. botulinum* type B Lamanna in the cultures of the synthetic medium.

produce toxin before obvious signs of spoilage occur during storage. Therefore, detection of volatile fatty acids by gas chromatography would also be valuable for predicting the possible occurrence of the growth and toxin production of *C. botulinum* type E in irradiated fish samples.

References

(*1*) ANDO, Y., T. KARASHIMADA, T. ONO, and H. IIDA. 1968. Toxin production by *Clostridium botulinum* Type E in radiation pasteurized fish. These proceedings.

(*2*) DACK, G. M. 1956. *Food Poisoning*, pp. 62–66. The University of Chicago Press, Chicago, Ill.

(*3*) MAGER, J., and H. KINDLER. 1954. Nutritional studies with *Clostridium parabotulinum* Type A. J. Gen. Microbiol. *10:* 130–141.

(*4*) NISMAN, B. 1954. The Stickland Reaction. Bacteriol. Rev. *18:* 16–42.

(*5*) STADMAN, E. R., and P. R. VAGELOS. 1958. *In* "Proceedings of the International Symposium of Enzyme Chemistry, Tokyo-Kyoto", K. Ichihara, ed., p. 86, Academic Press.

INDUCIBLE BACTERIOPHAGES IN *CLOSTRIDIUM BOTULINUM*

by KATSUHIRO INOUE *and* HIROO IIDA
Hokkaido Institute of Public Health, Sapporo, Japan

Summary

Studies on the lysogenicity in *C. botulinum* were carried out. Some strains of *C. botulinum* (types A–F) were found to be lysogenic and were able to produce temperate phages when treated with ultraviolet light or mitomycin C. These phages consisted of complete or incomplete particles and were classified into three groups. The lysates containing these particles agglutinated and lysed some strains of *C. botulinum*, *C. sporogenes*, and other clostridial species although the lytic agents seemed to be unable to multiply in the sensitive bacteria. The lytic activity in the lysates was completely lost by heating at 60° C. for 10 minutes. The active agents were not dialyzable and were not destroyed by trypsin.

Introduction

Although studies on lysogenicity have been carried out with a great number of bacteria (*3, 8, 10*), few reports have been published on *C. botulinum* (*5, 11*). The present paper deals with lysogenicity observed in several strains of *C. botulinum* and some characteristics of the temperate phages produced by them.

Materials and Methods

Bacterial strains.—Bacterial strains used in the experiments are listed in table 1. These strains were passaged in cooked meat medium, checked for purity, and kept in the refrigerator until used.

Culture medium.—Trypticase-yeast extract-glucose (TYG) medium consisting of the following ingredients was employed. Trypticase (BBL), 3 percent; yeast extract (Difco), 2 percent; glucose, 1 percent; sodium thioglycollate 0.1 percent. The pH of the medium was adjusted to 7.2 with 10 percent sodium carbonate solution.

Induction.—Each bacterial strain was inoculated into TYG medium, kept at 30° or 37° C. overnight and 2.5 ml. of each culture was transferred to two tubes containing 50 ml. of TYG medium. After incubation for 4 to 6 hours, one tube of each culture was irradiated in a petri dish by ultraviolet light (National Co., model GX-590G, 15 w.) at a distance of 50 cm.

Table 1.—Bacterial strains used in this study

Species	Strain	Number of strains	Number of lysogenic strains
C. botulinum:			
Type A	190 / AK–38	2	1
Type B	Lamanna / QC	2	1
Type C	Stockholm / 468	2	1
Type D	1873	1	1
Type E	Kamiyama / Others	58	6
Type F	OSU / Others	3	1
C. sporogenes	NAC 1 / NAC 2	2	....
Clostridial species	No. 1, No. 204	204	....

for 45 seconds. Mitomycin C (1µ g./ml.; Kyowa Hakko Kogyo Co.) was added to the other tube of each culture, incubated for 10 minutes and centrifuged. The supernatant was discarded and the sedimented cells were resuspended with fresh TYG medium. All tubes were incubated for an additional 4 to 6 hours, until lysis was complete.

Preparation of lysate.—Each culture fluid obtained as above was centrifuged to remove bacterial cells and debris, sterilized by filtration through Millipore filter and kept in the refrigerator until used.

Estimation of lytic activity.—The activity of bacteriophages or bacteriocins are usually demonstrated by plaque- or lacuna-formation employing the double-layer method (*1*). These techniques, however, were found to be unsuccessful in the present experiment and the following method was employed to estimate the lytic activity of the lysates. To 1 ml. of logarithmic-phase culture fluid of each sensitive strain was added 1 ml. of each lysate. Two ml. of fresh TYG medium was added to each mixture and all tubes were incubated at 30° or 37° C. The turbidity of each culture fluid was estimated by the photoelectric colorimeter using a 610 mµ filter.

Electron microscopy.—The lysate obtained was clarified by centrifugation at 4,000 x g. for 20 minutes. The pellet was discarded and the supernatant fluid was centrifuged at 60,000 x g. for 60 minutes in a No. RP 40 rotor of a Hitachi model 40P ultracentrifuge. The pellet from 50 ml. of each clarified lysate was resuspended in 0.5 ml. of 0.1 M ammonium acetate solution, pH 6.8. The resulting suspension was examined in an electron microscope (model JEM 7A: Japan Electron Optical Laboratory Co.) by use of the negative staining technique with 2 percent phosphotungstic acid.

Results

Induction of lysis.—Growing bacterial cells of a total of 67 strains of *C. botulinum* (types A-F) were treated by ultraviolet light or mitomycin C. As shown in table 1 and fig. 1, 11 strains showed a marked lysis by one or both of the two treatments. Lysis was observed in all types of *C. botulinum*.

Search for sensitive bacterial strains.—The lytic phenomenon observed above is similar to lysogeny or bacteriocinogeny reported in various species of bacteria. In order to demonstrate lysogeny or bacteriocinogeny in *C. botulinum*, experiments were carried out whereby each lysate was tested with 67 strains of

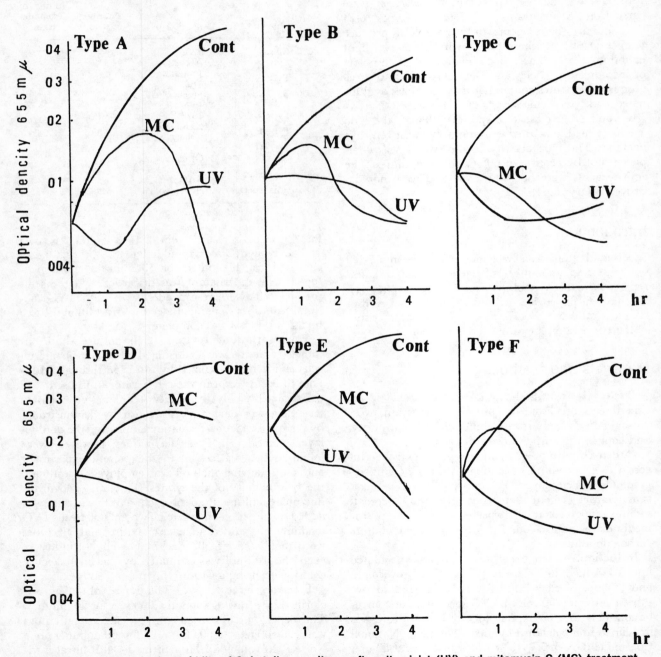

Figure 1.—Changes in the turbidity of *C. botulinum* cultures after ultraviolet (UV) and mitomycin C (MC) treatment.

C. botulinum, two strains of *C. sporogenes* and 204 strains of clostridial species isolated from soil samples.

The results are summarized in table 2. As indicated in the table, lysis of various clostridia was observed to occur with lysates of *C. botulinum* types B, C, E, and F and growing cells of *C. botulinum* types B and E, *C. sporogenes,* and a few strains of other clostridial species. However, with lysates of *C. botulinum* types A and D, none of the bacterial strains used showed sensitivity.

Table 2.—Activity spectrum of lytic substances produced by *C. botulinum*

Host strain, *C. botulinum*	Sensitive strain
Type A 190 _ _ _ _ _ _ _ _ _	None.
Type B QC _ _ _ _ _ _ _ _ _	*C. botulinum* type E F30–11, Iwanai, Pitt, F30–5, AK–10, and AK–12.
Type C Stockholm _ _ _ _	*C. botulinum* type E AK–11, type B QC. *C. sporogenes* NAC 2, Clostridial sp. No. 165, No. 166.
Type D 1873 _ _ _ _ _ _ _ _	None.
Type E Kamiyama _ _ _	*C. botulinum* type E Iwanai, Saroma, F305, Otaru, Y1–5, AK–10, AK–12, 685, 801, and 1304. *C. botulinum* type B QC, Clostridial sp. No. 137, No. 202, No. 204.
Type F OSU _ _ _ _ _ _ _	*C. botulinum* type E Iwanai, Pitt, F30–11, 760, 667, AK–10, and AK–12. *C. botulinum* type QC, Clostridial sp. No. 137, No. 202, No. 204.

Action of lysate on sensitive bacteria.—The induced lysates of *C. botulinum* showed a lytic effect on several strains of *C. botulinum, C. sporogenes,* and *Clostridium* species. An example of the kinetics of the lytic reaction is shown in figure 2. The sensitive cells were agglutinated in 60 minutes after being mixed with the lysate and then lysed gradually. By continuing the incubation of the mixture, a luxuriant growth was observed in most cases due to the appearance of resistant mutants. These resistant cells were insensitive to the action of the lysate. The lytic activity of the supernatant of the mixture did not increase after lysis was completed, which suggested that no multiplication of the lytic agent occurred (5).

Characteristics of lytic substances in lysate.—Beerens (2) reported that bacteriocin-like substances are produced by *C. botulinum* types A, B, and C and Kautter (7) reported that a similar substance (boticin) is produced by organisms resembling *C. botulinum* type E. As shown in table 3, the lytic agents obtained by the present experiment seem to be different from these bacteriocins in terms of dialysis and heat resistance.

Electron-microscopic studies on phage particles.—The lysates were centrifuged at 60,000x g. for

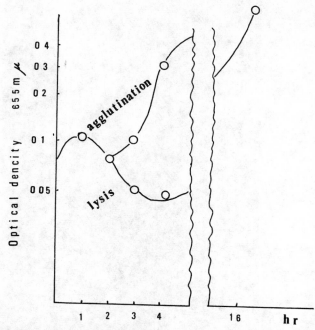

Figure 2.—Action of a lytic substance on growing cells of a sensitive strain. Lytic substance: *C. botulinum* type E Kamiyama. Sensitive cell: *C. botulinum* type E AK–10.

Table 3.—Properties of bacteriolytic or bactericidal agents produced by *C. botulinum*

Agents	Heat stability	Dialyzability
Lysate of *C. botulinum* type E strain Kamiyama.	Heat labile. Inactivate to heating for 10 min. at 60° C.	Nondialyzable.
Bacteriocins[1] of *C. botulinum* types A, B, and C.	Heat stable. Resistant to heating for 30 min. at 70° C.	
Botocin E[2] _ _ _ _ _ _ _ _	Heat stable. Resistant to heating for 60 min. at 100° C.	Dialyzable.

[1] By Beerens, H., and Tahon, M.
[2] By Kautter, D. A., et al.

60 minutes and the pellets obtained were examined in an electron microscope. Phage particles were observed as shown in fig. 3. As summarized in table 4, these phages are classified into three groups. The first group consists of type A phage, which exhibited mainly empty hexagonal heads, 80 mμ in diameter. The sheath of the tail appeared to be contracted to a length of 50 mμ, and tail tubes were clearly visible in almost all of the phage. The second group consists of types C and D phages. These phages exhibited hexagonal heads, 120 mμ in diameter, and long, flexible tails which consisted of a tail tube, 350 to 450 mμ long

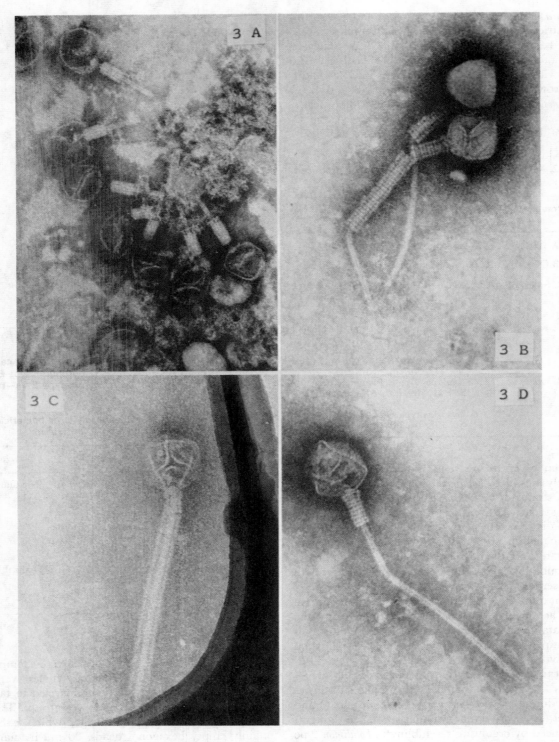

Figure 3.—Bacteriophages from lysates of *C. botulinum*. 150,000 ×. (3A) type A, strain 190; (3B) type C, strain Stockholm; (3C) type C, strain Stockholm; (3D) type D, strain 1873.

Figure 3 (continued).—Bacteriophages from lysates of *C. botulinum.* 150,000 ×. (3E) type B, strain QC; (3F) type E, strain Kamiyama; (3G) type F, strain OSU; (3H) type F, strain OSU.

Table 4.—Morphology of phage particles produced by C. botulinum

Host strain, C. botulinum	Group	Head diameter (mμ)	Tail length (mμ)	Basic morphology
Type A 190_____I		80	50___	Empty hexagonal head, tail with contracted sheath.
Type C Stockholm_____II		120	350, 450	Hexagonal head, long flexible tail with contracted or noncontracted sheath.
Type D 1873_____II		120	350___	Hexagonal head, long tail with contracted sheath.
Type B QC_____III			120, 150	Tail with sheath.
Type E Kamiyama_____III			120, 150	Tail with sheath.
Type F OSU_____III		85	120___	Hexagonal head, tail with noncontracted sheath.

and 15 mμ in diameter, surrounded by a sheath, 30 to 35 mμ in diameter. The third group consists of types B, E, and F phages. In most of the specimens of this group, only tail-like rods, 120 to 150 mμ long and 15 to 20 mμ wide, were found, suggesting the abnormal and excessive production of tail component due to some genetic defects. Complete phages were observed with type F on rare occasions.

Discussion

In some strains of *C. botulinum* (types A–F), a marked lysis was observed after treating their growing cells by ultraviolet light or mitomycin C. Electron microscope studies on these lysates revealed phage particles, complete or incomplete (5). The lysates containing these particles agglutinated and lysed some strains of *C. botulinum*, *C. sporogenes*, and *clostridial* species isolated from soil samples. These particles, however, seemed to be unable to multiply in the sensitive bacteria.

Lysogenic strains with genetic defects are known in various kinds of bacteria and the temperate phages obtained from these strains sometimes show an incomplete morphology (9). It has also been reported

that colicin-15 (4) is morphologically identical to a bacteriophage and pyocin (6) has the structure resembling a phage tail.

Bacteriophages found by us in *C. botulinum* are classified into three groups by their morphological characters and also by the biological properties of their host organisms. Some of them seem to be complete phage particles and some to be incomplete.

These findings are of interest in relation to the recent concerns on defective phages and bacteriocins.

Acknowledgment

We thank Prof. C. E. Dolman, University of British Columbia, Canada, for constant encouragement and criticism. We are deeply indebted to Prof. R. Yanagawa, Department of Veterinary Science, Hokkaido University, and Dr. H. Yotsumoto and Dr. T. Matsuo, Japan Electron Optical Laboratory, for the preparation of electron micrographs. We also thank Dr. G. Sakaguchi, National Institute of Health, Tokyo, for sending us some of the bacterial strains used in this study.

References

(1) ADAMS, M. H. 1959. *Bacteriophages*. Interscience Publishers Inc., New York.

(2) BEERENS, H., and M. TAHON. 1967. Production of bacteriocins by different types of *C. botulinum*. *In* Botulism 1966, Chapman & Hall, London, pp. 424–427.

(3) BOREK, E. 1952. Factors controlling aptitude and phage development in a lysogenic *Escherichia coli* K–12. Biochim. Biophys. Acta *8*: 211–215.

(4) ENDO, H., K. AYABE, K. AMAKO, and K. TAKEYA. 1965. Inducible phage of *Escherichia coli* 15. Virol. *25*: 469–471.

(5) INOUE, K., and H. IIDA. 1968. Bacteriophages of *Clostridium botulinum*. J. Virol. *2*: 537–540.

(6) ISHII, Y., Y. NISHI, and F. EGAMI. 1965. The fine structure of pyocin. J. Molec. Biol. *13*: 428–431.

(7) KAUTTER, D. A., S. M. HARMON, R. K. LYNT, and T. LILLY. 1966. Antagonistic effect on *Cl. botulinum* type E by organisms resembling it. Appl. Microbiol. *14*: 616–622.

(8) PRESCOTT, L. M., and R. A. ALTENBERN. 1967. Inducible lysis in *Clostridium tetani*. J. Bacteriol. *93*: 1220–1226.

(9) SEAMAN, E., E. TARMY, and J. MARMUR. 1964. Inducible phages of *B. subtilis*. Biochem. *3*: 607–612.

(10) SIMINOVITCH, L., and S. PAPKINE. 1952. Biochemical modification in lysogenic *B. megatherium* 899 (1) after induction with ultraviolet light. Biochim. Biophy. Acta. *9*: 478–487.

(11) VINET, G., L. BERTHIAUME et V. FREDETTE. 1968. Un bacteriophage dans une culture de *Cl. botulinum* C. Rev. Canad. Biol. *27*: 73–74.

IN VITRO DETECTION OF *CLOSTRIDIUM BOTULINUM*

by A. W. Anderson *and* G. J. Niedermeyer

Department of Microbiology, Oregon State University, Corvallis, Oreg.

Summary

Electrophoresis of samples containing types A or B botulinal toxins on acrylamide gell separated the toxin molecules from hemagglutinins which are responsible for cross reactions obtained with commercially available antitoxins.

Immunoprecipitin reactions could be used on an experimental basis to identify *C. botulinum* types A, B, E, and F in complex media. A test of the procedure to identify types A and B toxins in a series of "unknowns" composed of various strains of types A, B, E, and F resulted in 100 percent accuracy. Time lapse from innoculation of "unknown" cultures into complex medium to positive identification was 40 hours. Types A and B were correctly separated from other types present after 30 hours' incubation by an immunoprecipitin screening test. Experiments to determine quantitative recovery data for *C. botulinum* types A and B toxins and the sensitivity of the system are needed.

Examination of culture substrates for proteases, lecithinases, and lipases reveal multiple forms of extracellular enzymes which may be of value for the identification of clostridial types. Other extracellular enzymes are also being investigated.

Introduction

Antitoxin prepared against botulinum types A, B, C, D, E, and F are effective in protecting animals against the lethal nature of the toxin, and under suitable *in vitro* conditions immunoprecipitates are formed. However, the fact that commercially available antitoxin prepared against types A and B toxins contain common antigens which cross-react presents a major obstacle which must be solved before an immunoprecipitin test can be used with confidence.

The protein, a hemagglutinin synthesized in close association with the toxin, is difficult to remove by presently used purification procedures. The hemagglutinins produced by types A and B are reciprocally precipitated by the available A and B antitoxins. The lack of identity of hemagglutinating activity with toxicity of the type A botulinal organism was first established by Lamanna and Lowenthal in 1951 (*4, 6*). Initially, Lamanna reported that toxin of type A

and its specific antitoxin form two precipitation bands in an Oudin serum-agar system, whereas the type A toxin formed only one band with type B antitoxin. After repeated exposure to red blood cells the toxins were freed from hemagglutinating activity, and yield only a single band of precipitate with type A antitoxin and no precipitate with type B antitoxin.

Obviously, to arrive at any degree of confidence in an immunoprecipitin test, the cross-reacting hemagglutinins must be separated from the toxins. A procedure for separating the toxins of types A and B from their cross-reacting hemagglutinins followed by identification of the specific toxins is described. Also, described is a simple and rapid method for the determination of extracellular enzymes by electrophoretic purification and concentration.

Materials and Methods

Cultures.—*C. botulinum* type A strains 33A and 5A and type B strain 115B were obtained from the Quartermaster Food and Developement Command for the Armed Forces, Natick, Mass. *C. botulinum* type A strains 64–89, 73A and 78A and type B strains 32B, 113B, and 213B were obtained from the National Canners Association, Washington, D.C.

Robertson cooked meat broth was used to keep stock cultures. For toxin production a liquid medium, consisting of 2 percent yeast extract (Difco), 2 percent peptone (Difco), 1 percent glucose, and distilled water to 1,000 ml., pH 7.0, was used. Each 500 ml. batch of medium in 750 ml. Erlenmeyer flasks was heated to 100°C., shock-cooled in ice water, and charged with a 10 percent inoculum from an 18 hours culture and incubated anaerobically at 30° C. for 72 hours. Cultures were checked for contaminants by gram staining and by plating on blood agar.

Following incubation, the cells were removed from the medium by centrifugation at 10,000 x g. for 20 minutes at 4° C. and remaining cells removed by filtration through an HA Millipore filter. The filtrates were concentrated from 500 to 12 to 15 ml. by dialyzing in cellulose tubing against polyethylene glycol-4,000 at 5° C.

Concentration and purification.—In order to purify and further concentrate the toxins and enzymes, several synthetic polyacrylamide gel methods have been developed in our laboratory. The first method consists of a column of 4 layers supported in a 175 mm. x 15 mm. section of pyrex glass tubing (fig. 1): (*a*) A 3¾ percent large pore gel, pH 6.7, containing the sample concentrated as described above, in which electrophoretic partial purification of the sample is initiated; (*b*) a 3¾ percent large pore spacer gel, pH 6.7, in which electrophoretic partial purification of the sample takes place; (*c*) a liquid buffer, pH 8.9, prepared by the same method as the standard separating gel described by B. J. Davis (*3*) from which the acrylamide and ammonium persulfate are omitted and to which sucrose is added to a concentration of 20 percent. This buffered sucrose solution received the sample ions which exist in the 3¾ percent gels; (*d*) a 30 percent small pore gel, pH 8.9, which receive molecular weights less than 10,000.

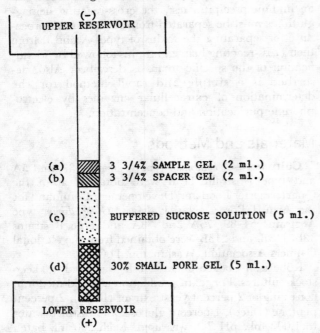

Figure 1.—Schematic design of gel unit used for partial purification of toxin.

One to four columns are mounted in a unit (not described) constructed in our laboratory with each column enclosed by a cooling jacket through which ice water is circulated. Electrophoresis is performed in a vertical position, the gel containers are attached to an upper buffer reservoir and the lower ends are submerged in the buffer solution of a lower reservoir. Both reservoirs hold 500 ml. Tris-glycine buffer, pH 8.9, with a trace of bromphenol blue in the upper reservoir as a tracking dye. Current is applied at 20 m.a./column and polarity is set so that the sample molecules migrate toward the 30 percent gel. Electrophoresis is completed when the tracking dye enters

the 30 percent small pore gel (90 to 120 minutes). The buffered sucrose solution containing the desired sample fraction can then be drawn into a 10 ml. syringe via a needle inserted through the 30 percent gel layers.

In the second method, the concentrated dialysate was electrophoresed directly. The dialysate was diluted onefold with upper buffer diluted 1:5 containing 40 percent sucrose. One to two ml. of either concentrate was then subjected to electrophoresis on polyacrylamide gel prepared by the method of Ornstein (*7*) and Davis (*3*). Following electrophoresis the protein laden gels were sliced into sections (flat gel instrument developed in our laboratory) and treated as follows: (*a*) Stained with Coomassie blue as described by Chramback, Reisfeld, Wyckoff, and Zaccari (*1*); (*b*) analyzed for extracellular enzymes, and (*c*) analyzed for immunoprecipitates. The samples could also be immediately frozen and stored at −20° C. for future analysis of toxic products.

Identification of bands.—Corresponding bands in the stained gels were identified by comparing them with the enzyme reacting band or the immunoprecipitin bands. The toxic bands were identified by elution of the portion of the frozen and thawed acrylamide gel corresponding to a reacting band, followed by intraperitoneal injection into 20 to 25 g. male, white mice. The eluates were prepared by cutting out desired sections of the gel and macerating them in a conical centrifuge tube with 10 times their volume of 0.05 molar phosphate-buffered saline (0.85 percent) at pH 6.8. Elution was completed by storage overnight at 5° C.

Hemagglutinating activity was determined macroscopically with sheep red blood cells as described by Lamanna (*5*).

Agar gel-diffusions were performed on clear microscope slides coated with 0.2 percent Oxoid "Ionagar" No. 2 in distilled water as described by Crowle (*2*). Ionagar No. 2 was dissolved to 1.0 percent in 0.05 M phosphate buffer at pH 7.1 containing merthiolate (1:10,000). Four milliliter of 1 percent agar was applied to each coated slide and allowed to gel. All precipitin tests were performed on these slides with various templates being utilized. Immunoprecipitates were allowed to develop at 20° C. in a moist chamber for periods of 8 hours to 48 hours. When precipitin formation appeared maximum, the slides were irrigated with physiological saline to remove nonprecipitated protein from the agar (usually 24 hours), followed by treating with 2.5 percent trichloroacetic acid (TCA) for approximately 5 minutes and then staining with 0.5 percent light green SF in 5 percent TCA for 1 hour. Stained slides were stored in 5 percent TCA and photographed when convenient.

All the extracellular enzymes were detected by layering a 1-inch slice of electrophoresed gel on a microscope slide and then flooding with 1.5 ml. of the proper substrate imbedded in agar gel. The slides were then incubated in moist chamber for 10 to 15 minutes at 37° C. and then observed either directly or following proper treatment.

Proteases.—5 ml. of 10 percent sterilized reconstituted skim milk was added to 8 ml. of a 1.5 percent ion agar No. 2 prepared in physiological saline. The preparation was added to the slide at a temperature of 45° ± 3° C.

Gelatinase.—0.8 g. gelatin and 0.8 g. agar was dissolved in 100 ml. of physiological saline. The mixture was heated to dissolve the agar and applied to the slide when cooled (45° ± 3° C). Following incubation, the slide was developed by immersion in a solution of mercury chloride prepared as follows: 1.5 g. of HgCl, 2 ml. of concentrated HCl and 10 ml. of water. The bands appear as clear areas on a milky background.

Lipase.—0.8 g. agar dissolved in 30 ml. of physiological saline; to the above solution add 1.3 ml. of thymol-sulfonphtalein (3mg./ml.) and 2 ml. of tributyrin. Following incubation, bands appear as yellow areas against a light blue background.

Lecithinase.—Dilute egg yolk (1:1) with physiological saline solution. Add 5 percent of the above solution to a 1.5 percent agar solution (45° ± 5° C). Following incubation, the bands appear as opaque yellow areas against a translucent yellow background.

Results and Discussion

Strain 33A and strain 115B were used as representative type strains for the production of types A and B toxins respectively. After 24 hours incubation, culture media supporting growth of types A and B gave positive precipitin reactions with B antitoxin. Type A toxins gave single precipitin bands, whereas type B toxins shows two or more bands of precipitation (fig. 2).

The similar rate at which the various proteins migrate makes it difficult to separate multiple precipitin lines, some of which may be either superimposed or too close to each other to separate distinctly. The logical approach to a solution of this problem was either to remove interfering proteins leaving only that one which is characteristic of the strain's toxin, or to separate the proteins in such a manner that the various precipitin lines were more easily observed. The latter approach was investigated.

If the media supporting growth of types A and B was electrophoresed using the techniques described above, type B showed 18 to 21 protein bands while that of type A gave a similar number, not all of which corresponded to the bands produced by type B (fig. 3). These bands consist of protein of the medium

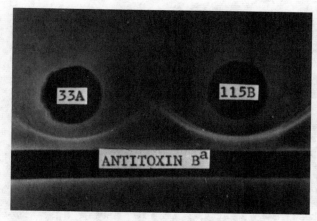

Figure 2.—The immunoprecipitin reaction of antisera prepared for *Clostridium botulinum* type B cross-reacting with type A.

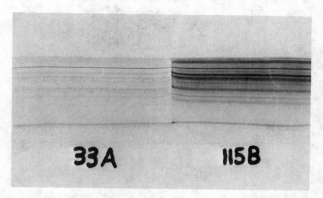

Figure 3.—Electrophoresis of toxic medium resulting from growth of types A and B showing differences in bands. (Comparable concentration.)

which may vary depending upon its composition; they also consist of proteins specific for or common to each type. By separating the proteins electrophoretically one can identify them as extracellular enzymes common to both types, type specific toxins, or unidentifiable migrating components of the cells.

When an excised strip of electrophoresed protein of type B was subjected to a double diffusion precipitin reaction with type B antitoxin, two or more bands resulted (fig. 4). Type A toxin containing medium gave one band corresponding to the lower band of type B (fig. 5).

Subsequent elution of bands from corresponding frozen gel halves demonstrated that the upper band of the type B gel was highly toxic to mice and that the lower band occurring in both type A and B was nontoxic. Hemagglutinating activity was present in the lower band of type A and B but not in the upper band of the type B column (hemagglutinin tests were qualitative). The additional precipitin bands shown in figure 4 did not always occur. There may be multiples of a basic molecule, of which the smallest fraction represents the basic molecule. These bands have not been assayed for toxicity. The apparent distribution of toxins and hemagglutinins is shown in figure 6.

A series of 25 tubes, each containing 15 ml. of yeast liquid medium, were inoculated with organisms of types A, B, E, and F. After 18 hours incubation at 30° C., a screening test by double diffusion of the

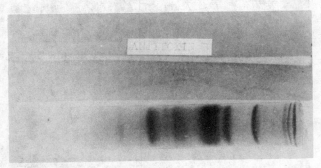

Figure 4.—Electrophoresis of toxic type B medium preparation forming multiple-precipitin bands with type B antisera.

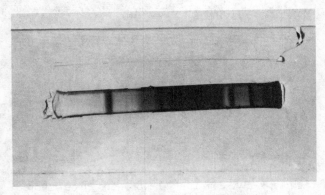

Figure 5.—The precipitin reaction resulting when type B antisera is used against type B electrophoresed toxic medium. Precipitin band corresponds to the hemagglutinin band of type B.

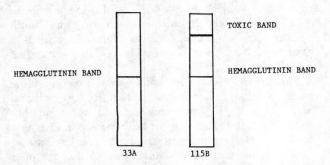

Figure 6.—Schematic representation of apparent distribution of toxins and hemagglutinins in type B.

unconcentrated media against type B antitoxin separated the A and B strains (positive reactions) from the E and F strains (negative reactions). Cultures giving positive reactions in the above test were cleared of cells and concentrated by dialysis as described. Following dialysis the samples were electrophoresed and the protein laden polyacrylamide gels tested for toxin by double-diffusion against type B antisera. At the end of 8 hours one or two immunoprecipitins were detectable. Results indicated that at the end of 18 hours incubation the screening test had detected all the A and B cultures. The types E and F had been eliminated. Comparison of code numbers with the preparation chart showed that the results of both tests were 100 percent accurate.

Although preliminary data presented here are quite promising, there remains much work to be done in refining the system. The comparison of sensitivity obtained with this system with the presently used mouse protection tests remains to be accomplished as does a quantitative determination of the recovery of toxin. Sensitivity would appear to be quite high considering that little toxin is present in the media at 18 hours incubation.

Preliminary data from identical experiments with *C. botulinum* types E and F have shown equally promising results, and comparison with nontoxic strains is presently being conducted.

The low quality of type A antitoxin in our possession precludes its use in the immunoprecipitin techniques and necessitates the indirect identification of type A toxin by formation of one rather than two precipitin bands with type B antitoxin.

The proposed system to be tested for identification of botulinal toxins in food products is as follows: (*a*) Concentration of the liquor from the sample by dialysis, (*b*) the separation of the toxin from nontoxic materials in the preparatory gels, (*c*) concentration of collected toxin by dialysis, and an immunoprecipitin screening test, (*d*) further concentration and purification of the toxin by electrophoresis in polyacrylamide gels, and (*e*) typing of the toxin by immunoprecipitin techniques. Total time lapse for identification of toxin with this system could be held to a maximum of 48 hours.

The electrophoretic separation of the toxins from the hemagglutinin also provides means of preparing specific, non-cross-reacting antitoxins for toxins produced by strains of types A and B *C. botulinum*.

Purifying and concentrating the extracellular enzymes by gel electrophoreses permits their detection in a few minutes rather than hours as formerly done by the plating technique. It is also possible to assay for many different enzymes as well as detecting those proteins which form immunoprecipitates, thus combining several forms of information on the same gel,

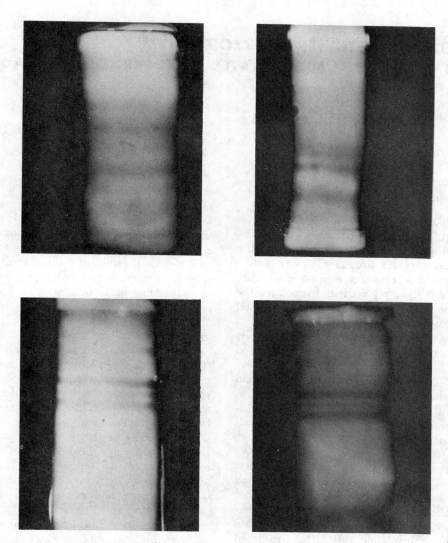

Figure 7.—Upper left and upper right shows extracellular proteolytic enzyme patterns of type A on gelatin and milk, respectively; while lower left and lower right shows similar reactions for type B.

reinforcing identification. Minutes after electrophoresis, one can separate the proteolytic from the nonproteolytic, the lipolytic from the nonlipolytic. Preliminary evidence would indicate that there are differences in the numbers of isozymes as well as in their migrational rate.

In figure 7 the effect of proteolytic enzymes of types A and B on a milk substrate and on a gelatin substrate is shown. By employing similar procedures, one can assay for lipases, and lecithinases.

References

(1) CHRAMBACH, A., R. A. REISFELD, M. WYCKOFF, and J. ZACCARI. 1967. A procedure for rapid and sensitive staining of protein fractionated by polyacrylamide gel electrophoresis. Analyt. Biochem. 20: 150.

(2) CROWLE, A. J. 1958. A simplified micro double-diffusion agar precipitin technique. J. Lab. Clin. Med. 52: 784–787.

(3) DAVIS, B. J. 1964. Disc Electrophoresis II. Methods and application to human serum proteins. Ann. New York Acad. Sci. 121: 404–427.

(4) LAMANNA, C. 1948. Hemagglutination by botulinal toxin. Proc. Soc. Exp. Biol. Med. 69: 332–336.

(5) LAMANNA, C., and J. P. LOWENTHAL. 1951. The lack of identity between hemagglutinin and the toxin of type A botulinal organism. J. Bacteriol. 61: 751–752.

(6) LOWENTHAL, J. P., and C. LAMANNA. 1951. Factors affecting the botulinal hemagglutination reaction, and the relationship between hemagglutinating activity and toxicity of toxin preparations. Amer. J. Hyg. 54: 342–353.

(7) ORNSTEIN, L. 1964. Disc Electrophoresis I. Background and theory. Ann. New York Acad. Sci. 121: 321–349.

(8) OUCHTERLONY, O. 1958. Diffusion-in-gel methods for immunological analysis. Prog. Allergy 5: 1.

INOCULATED PACK STUDIES ON *CLOSTRIDIUM BOTULINUM* TYPE E IN UNIRRADIATED AND IRRADIATED HADDOCK

by W. P. SEGNER *and* C. F. SCHMIDT
Metal Division Research and Development,
Continental Can Co., Inc., Chicago, Ill. 60620

Summary

Inoculated packs were initiated to assess the public health aspect of *Clostridium botulinum* type E in radurized and unirradiated haddock. Estimates of the maximal expected product storage life were determined by an untrained consumer-type panel. Values of storage life are designated as X and represent the time for unanimous product rejection by this panel. Triplicate samples per variable were inoculated with 10^6, 10^4, or 10^2 of the Beluga strain per gram. Samples were given 0.1 and 0.2 Mrad doses and incubated along with inoculated unirradiated controls at intervals from 50° F. (10° C.) to 40° F. (4.4° C.). Toxin assays were conducted at fractions and multiples of X. At 40° and 42° F. incubation, control, and irradiated samples inoculated with 10^6 and 10^4 levels showed no toxin up to 2X. At 46° F. incubation, samples inoculated with 10^6 spores and given 0.1 Mrad irradiation showed toxin at X, but not earlier; controls remained nontoxic through 2X. Control and 0.1 Mrad samples with a 10^4 inoculum showed no toxin development up to 2X. With 0.2 Mrad irradiation, toxin was detected at ½X for both inoculum levels. At 50° F., control and 0.1 Mrad irradiated samples were nontoxic up to X with 10^4 and 10^2 inoculum levels. However, 0.2 Mrad samples showed detectable toxin at ½X and ¾X with 10^4 and 10^2 inoculum levels. The results with 0.1 Mrad appear encouraging, but the data with 0.2 Mrad irradiation are less favorable.

Introduction

The commercial distribution of fresh seafood on the mainland of the United States is limited primarily to those coastal areas where seafood is caught, because of its extremely high perishability. The U.S. Atomic Energy Commission has proposed the possible exploitation of low doses of ionizing radiation, or so-called radurization doses (4), to extend the refrigerated storage life of certain marine food products.

Radurization doses of 0.1 and 0.2 Mrad when combined with adequate refrigeration cause a considerable extension of storage life for many seafoods. However, a marked extension of their storage life might create a health hazard problem due to *C. botulinum* type E. Three facts support this statement. First, ecological surveys in the United States and elsewhere have definitely established the ubiquity of *C. botulinum* type E in a marine environment. Second, radiation doses of the magnitude being considered have no major destructive effect on spores of this organism (7, 8). Third, it possesses the ability to grow and to produce toxin as low as 38° F. or 3.3° C. (6).

Since haddock (*Melanogramus aeglefinus*) and cod (*Gadus callarius*) are being considered by the AEC for possible commercial irradiation, inoculated pack studies were undertaken to assess the health hazard risk of *C. botulinum* type E. This paper presents the inoculated pack data on haddock.

The concept of the inoculated pack to determine the margin of public health safety of radurized marine food products was discussed by Slavin, Ronsivalli, and Connors (10). Briefly, the rationale for such packs is an attempt to show that low-dose irradiated seafoods pose no more health hazard than comparable unirradiated product. This involves the determination of the maximal expected product storage life and the earliest time of type E toxin production. The estimates of maximal product storage life are obtained by scientists at the Bureau of Commercial Fisheries Gloucester laboratory using an untrained consumer-type panel. The storage life values for unirradiated and irradiated product are designated as X and represent the time for unanimous rejection of a sample by this panel. Acceptance or rejection of a sample is based mainly on odor. The occurrence of unquestionable spoilage as recognized by the consumer appreciably ahead of the earliest time of possible type E toxin production would suggest a considerable margin of public health safety for radurized marine food products.

Materials and Methods

Preparation and standardization of type E spore suspensions.—Spores of the Beluga type E strain were produced in TPG medium with incubation at 85° F. (30° C.) as described by Schmidt et al. (*7*). A low-temperature spore suspension was produced in TPG medium with 1 percent added yeast extract (Difco) and incubation at 50° F. (10° C.). The suspensions were standardized by a replicated deep-tube technique using 5 percent Peptone (Difco) agar medium and incubation at 85° F. Sodium thioglycollate at a concentration of 0.1 percent was employed for sporulation and in the standardization medium.

Inoculated packs.—Freshly caught haddock were filleted, packed in ice, and shipped by air freight to Chicago by Gloucester BCF personnel. The fillets were about 24 hours old when each experiment was started. Wide-mouth, 2-ounce screwcap jars were subjected to 250° F. (121° C.) for 5 minutes to destroy the nonheat resistant microflora. Circular plugs of fish were cut out with a stainless steel die attached to a ¼-inch drill press. The die was sanitized before use, and the fillets were handled with rubber gloves to avoid any additional contamination. Each sample consisted of two plugs of fish having a total weight of about 40 g. Triplicate samples were inoculated for each experimental variable. The inoculum (0.5 ml.) was injected with a sterile syringe and needle at multiple sites to give 10^6, 10^4, or 10^2 spores per gram. The 10^6 inoculum was preheated at 140° F. (60° C.) for 15 minutes to reduce possible toxin carryover. Unless stated otherwise, the 10^4 and 10^2 levels were not preheated.

Irradiation source.—Samples were given 0.1 and 0.2 Mrad doses with a cobalt-60 source located at the Illinois Institute of Technology Research Institute. The source contained about 5,200 curies of cobalt-60 and delivered a dose rate of 6.24×10^4 rads per hour. The samples were irradiated at 40° F. (4.4° C.) to 42° F. (5.6° C.) in a temperature controlled chamber. Midway through the irradiation, the sample was rotated 180° to equalize the dose. The samples were transported at wet ice temperatures prior to and after irradiation. The irradiated and inoculated unirradiated control samples were incubated at 50° F. (10° C.), 46° F. (7.8° C.), 42° F. (5.6° C.), or 40° F. (4.4° C.).

Sampling and toxin assays.—At each designated sampling period, triplicate samples per variable were examined for odor, pH, and the presence of type E botulinum toxin. Each sample was blended with 80 ml. of prechilled, sterile, distilled water to give a 1:3 blend. A portion of the blend was pipetted with a sterile cotton-plugged large-bore pipette into a 20 x 150 mm. screw-cap tube and frozen. The pH of the sample was determined on a second portion of the blend; in some cases, a total aerobic plate count was made with TPY agar (*5*). Finally, the sample was assayed for type E toxin using a sodium acetate buffer.

The acetate buffer toxin assay procedure involved pipetting 2 ml. of a blend into 2 ml. of 0.5 M acetate buffer (pH 5.0) in a sterile 16 x 125 mm. screw-cap tube. The buffered samples were mixed on a Vortex Mixer and held about 16 to 20 hours at 38° F. (3.3° C.). The buffer gave a final pH in the range 5.2 to 5.5. For digestion, 0.2 ml. of freshly prepared trypsin (10 percent, Difco 1:250) was added. The sample was incubated at 98° F. (37° C.) for 3 hours. Duplicate mice were each injected intraperitoneally with 0.5 ml. of the digest. In many instances, a simultaneous protection test was run; in others, the sample was assayed for toxin without antitoxin protection and toxin verified in a repeat test. The antitoxin used was obtained from the Pasteur Institute.

Blends assayed for type E toxin without trypsin digestion were diluted 1:2 with 0.5 M acetate buffer and held from 16 to 20 hours at 38° F. (3.3° C.) before being injected into mice. The lowest level of toxin theoretically detectable without or with trypsin digestion was 12 MLD/g. Nonspecific mouse deaths occurred with both unirradiated and 0.1 Mrad irradiated samples. To avoid nonspecific reactions, the antibiotics chloramphenicol and oxytetracycline were employed (*9*). Each mouse was given two intraperitoneal injections of the antibiotics, one approximately 20 hours before injection of the fish sample and the other when the sample was administered. Each antibiotic injection consisted of 0.1 ml. volume containing 5.0 mg. of Chloromycetin and 0.625 mg. of Terramycin. The antibiotics were not used with 0.2 Mrad irradiated samples, since these samples failed to produce nonspecific toxicities.

Results

Before the experiments on inoculated pack of haddock were started, a study was made to determine the sensitivity of the acetate toxin assay procedure. Frozen haddock and cod fillets were thawed, finely ground, and packed in 20 x 150 mm. screw-cap tubes. These were inoculated with spores of the Beluga strain, subjected to 0.1 and 0.2 Mrad doses, vaspar sealed, and incubated at 40° F. (4.4° C.). Periodically during incubation, the samples were assayed for type E toxin. Assays were made without trypsin digestion by the acetate buffer procedure and with trypsin digestion by both the phosphate buffer and acetate buffer procedures. The comparative toxin assay results are shown in table 1. Since the samples were incubated anaerobically, a gram-positive bacterial flora predominated, that caused a gradual reduction from pH 6.6 to about 6.0. Sodium acetate buffer at pH 5.5 was used for the undigested samples and for the samples to be trypsin digested. The results showed no

Table 1.—Comparative toxin assay results on irradiated fish samples incubated at 40° F. (4.4° C.)[1]

Substrate	Mrad	U[2]	AC[3]	PB[4]
		Fraction of samples toxic		
Haddock	0.1	7/7	7/7	6/7
	0.2	8/9	9/9	4/9
Cod	0.1	7/12	9/12	0/12
	0.2	2/12	5/12	0/12
Totals		24/40	30/40	10/40

[1]Ground unsteamed product inoculated with 10^6 spores per 10 to 12 g. sample.
[2]Assayed undigested by the acetate buffer procedure.
[3]Trypsin assayed by the acetate buffer procedure.
[4]Trypsin assayed by the conventional phosphate buffer procedure.

advantage in testing for toxin by the phosphate buffer, trypsin digestion procedure, but rather strongly suggested the desirability of toxin assaying using the acetate buffer technique. The acetate procedure was adopted in the inoculated pack studies.

Table 2 shows the inoculated pack results on fresh haddock with inoculum levels of 10^4 and 10^2 spores per gram and incubation at 50° F. (10° C.). The table is arranged to show the irradiation dose, the length of incubation, the fraction or multiple of X, and the number of toxic samples recovered. In all cases, samples reported as being nontoxic failed to show type E toxin without and with trypsin digestion. The inoculated unirradiated controls showed no detectable type E toxin at either inoculum level up to 2X. Samples inoculated with 10^4 spores and given 0.1 Mrad irradiation showed no toxin through 2X; however, similar irradiated samples inoculated with 10^2 spores showed toxin at 2X in one out of three replicates, but no toxin at earlier incubation times.

Table 2.—Toxin assay results on haddock incubated at 50° F. (10° C.)

Mrad	Incubation time (days)	X value[1]	10^4 Inoculation	10^2 Inoculation
			Fraction of samples toxic[2]	
0	4	½	0/3	0/3
	8	1	0/3	0/3
	16	2	0/3	0/3
0.1	6	½	0/3	0/3
	12	1	0/3	0/3
	24	2	0/3	1/3
0.2	10	½	0/3	0/3
	20	1	3/3	2/3
	40	2	2/3	2/3

[1]BCF tentative estimates of maximal product storage life under aerobic conditions.
[2]Number of samples containing type E toxin per number of samples assayed.

Samples given 0.2 Mrad were definitely toxic at X and 2X with both inoculum levels, although comparable samples were nontoxic at ½X.

Not shown in table 2 or in the tables to follow are the total aerobic counts, pH data, and our spoilage rejection determinations. Samples incubated at temperature intervals in the range 50° F. (10° C.) to 40° F. (4.4° C.) showed rapidly increasing total counts often reaching 10^8 bacteria or higher at storage times equal to ½X in many instances. Every sample showed a rapidly increasing pH, reaching pH 7.6 and, in some cases, as high as pH 8.4. Spoilage was characterized by the development of strong putrid odors in both unirradiated and irradiated samples. The unirradiated samples invariably showed slime during spoilage, while the irradiated samples frequently showed mold growth in addition to slime growth. In general, our spoilage rejection times tended to coincide with the tentative values reported by the BCF laboratory consumer panel.

The 46° F.(7.8° C.) assay results with 10^6 and 10^4 inoculum levels are shown in table 3. The control and 0.1 Mrad samples showed no toxin at incubation times corresponding to ½X, X, and 2X. Samples inoculated with 10^4 spores and given 0.2 Mrad irradiation also were nontoxic at comparable values of X. But with a 10^6 inoculum level, 0.2 Mrad irradiated samples showed the presence of toxin at X and 2X in one out of three supposedly replicate samples.

Table 3.—Toxin assay results on haddock incubated at 46° F. (7.8° C.)

Mrad	Incubation time (days)	X value	10^6 Inoculation	10^4 Inoculation
			Fraction of samples toxic[1]	
0	6	½	0/3	0/3
	12	1	0/3	0/3
	24	2	0/3	0/3
0.1	6	½	0/3	0/3
	13	1	0/3	0/3
	26	2	0/3	0/3
0.2	12	½	0/3	0/3
	24	1	1/3	0/3
	50	2	1/3	0/3

[1]Number of samples containing type E toxin per number of samples assayed.

The inoculated pack results shown in tables 2 and 3 are based on spores produced at 85° F. (30° C.). Work in ground fish substrates at 40° F. (4.4° C.) and 42° F. (5.6° C.) suggested that spores of the Beluga strain produced at 50° F. (10° C.) possessed somewhat faster outgrowth ability at low incubation temperatures than spores produced at 85° F. An experiment was conducted in fresh haddock with incubation at 42° and 40° F. to compare the outgrowth ability of spores produced at 50° F. to that of spores formed at 85° F. The comparative results are shown in table 4. None of the unirradiated or the irradiated samples produced toxin up to 2X. Toxin assays conducted at ¾X, X, and 1½X also were negative. From these results, there appears to be no reason to expect faster spore outgrowth or growth at any lower temperature from spores produced at suboptimal temperatures.

Table 4.—Toxin assay results on haddock incubated at 42° F. (5.6° C.) and 40° F. (4.4° C.)

Temperature degrees F.	Experiment[1]	Mrad	Incubation time (days)[2]	10⁶ Inoculation	10⁴ Inoculation
42	1	0	29	0/3	0/3
		0.1	60	0/3	0/3
		0.2	82	0/3	0/3
	2	0	30	0/3	0/3
		0.1	60	0/3	0/3
		0.2	72	0/3	0/3
40	1	0	34	0/3	0/3
		0.1	82	0/3	0/3
		0.2	82	0/3	0/3
	2	0	34	0/3	0/3
		0.1	80	0/3	0/3
		0.2	80	0/3	0/3

[1]Experiment 1 conducted with Beluga spores produced at 85° F. and experiment 2 with spores produced at 50° F.
[2]Incubation times represent 2X values.
[3]Number of samples containing type E toxin per number of samples assayed.

To confirm the inoculated pack data on haddock incubated at 50° F. (10° C.) and 46° F. (7.8° C.), a second experiment was run. A new spore suspension of the Beluga strain was produced at 85° F. (30° C.) and used. All of the inoculum levels tested were preheated at 140° F. (60° C.) for 15 minutes. Unirradiated and irradiated samples were toxin assayed at ½X, ¾X, X, 1½X, and 2X. The toxicity results are shown in tables 5 and 6. As compared to the first experiment, unirradiated controls inoculated with 10⁴ spores and incubated at 50° F showed toxin at 1½X and 2X. In general, the results of the two experiments are comparable, although toxin was detected somewhat earlier with 0.2 Mrad irradiation in the second experiment. Table 7 summarizes the toxicity data of the second haddock experiment in terms of the earliest time for type E toxin production at 50° and 46° F.

Discussion

Detection of low levels of type E toxin is complicated by the fact that the toxin is bound intracellu-

Table 5.—Toxin assay results for 50° F. (10° C.) incubated haddock (Experiment 2)

Mrad	Incubation time (days)	X value	10⁴ Inoculation U[1]	10⁴ Inoculation TD[2]	10² Inoculation U	10² Inoculation TD
0	4	½	0/3	0/3	0/3	0/3
	6	¾	0/3	0/3	0/3	0/3
	8	1	0/3	0/3	0/3	0/3
	12	1½	0/3	1/3	0/3	0/3
	16	2	2/3	2/3	0/3	0/3
0.1	6	½	0/3	0/3	0/3	0/3
	9	¾	0/3	0/3	0/3	0/3
	12	1	0/3	0/3	0/3	0/3
	18	1½	0/3	0/3	0/3	1/3
	24	2	0/3	0/3	0/3	0/3
0.2	10	½	0/3	2/3	0/3	0/3
	15	¾	0/3	3/3	0/3	1/3
	20	1	0/3	0/3	2/3	2/3
	30	1½	2/3	2/3	1/3	0/3
	40	2	2/3	2/3	1/3	1/3

[1]Undigested.
[2]Trypsin digested.

Table 6.—Toxin assay results for 46° F. (7.8° C.) incubated haddock (Experiment 2)

Mrad	Incubation time (days)	X value	10⁶ Inoculation U[1]	10⁶ Inoculation TD[2]	10⁴ Inoculation U	10⁴ Inoculation TD
0	6	½	0/3	0/3	0/3	0/3
	9	¾	0/3	0/3	0/3	0/3
	12	1	0/3	0/3	0/3	0/3
	18	1½	0/3	0/3	0/3	0/3
	24	2	0/3	0/3	0/3	0/3
0.1	6	½	0/3	0/3	0/3	0/3
	9	¾	0/3	0/3	0/3	0/3
	13	1	0/3	3/3	0/3	0/3
	18	1½	0/3	0/3	0/3	0/3
	24	2	2/3	2/3	0/3	0/3
0.2	12	½	0/3	3/3	0/3	1/3
	18	¾	0/3	2/3	0/3	1/3
	24	1	0/3	1/3	0/3	0/3
	36	1½	0/3	1/3	0/3	0/3
	48	2	1/3	1/3	0/3	0/3

[1]Undigested.
[2]Trypsin digested.

larly and released primarily by vegetative cell lysis. It seems that type E cells do not lyse as readily when grown at low temperatures as they do at temperatures near the optimum for growth. Thus, a significant amount of toxin may pass undetected unless some means is used extract the toxin from the cells or cause them to lyse.

The role of sodium acetate in the detection of low

Table 7.—Summary of toxin assay results on haddock with incubation at 50° F. (10° C.) and 46° F. (7.8° C.) (Experiment 2)

Temperature degrees F.	Inoculation	Mrad	Incubation time (days)	
			No toxin[1]	Toxin[1]
50	10⁴	0	8 (1)	12 (1½)
		.1	24 (2)	----------
		.2	----------	10 (½)
	10²	0	16 (2)	----------
		.1	12 (1)	18 (1½)
		.2	10 (½)	15 (¾)
46	10⁶	0	24 (2)	----------
		.1	9 (¾)	13 (1)
		.2	----------	12 (½)
	10⁴	0	24 (2)	----------
		.1	24 (2)	----------
		.2	----------	12 (½)

[1]Values in parenthesis show fraction or multiple of X.

levels of type E toxin in fish samples is not clear. It may cause an extraction of toxin from intact cells, cause a release of possible adsorbed toxin on fish tissue, or simply establish a more favorable pH for toxin activation. In any event, it provides a convenient means of adjusting the sample pH for trypsin digestion. In the conventional phosphate buffer trypsin digestion assay procedure, as described by Duff, Wright, and Yarinsky (3), digestion is conducted with 0.067 M phosphate buffer at pH 6.0 to 6.2. This buffer is suitable for use with assays of broth cultures; however, it is a poor buffer for assays of food products showing high pH values. Haddock fillets incubated aerobically or under partially aerobic conditions show a marked increase in pH. Unless the precaution is taken to adjust the pH for trypsin digestion, a significant amount of type E toxin may be destroyed. Use of the acetate buffer eliminates the necessity of making manual pH adjustments.

There appears to be little advantage in toxin assaying simultaneously with and without trypsin digestion. In the second experiment on haddock at 50° F. (10° C.) and 46° F. (7.8° C.), 180 samples were assayed both ways. With trypsin digestion, 32 samples showed detectable toxin versus 13 without digestion. In only two instances, toxin was detected without digestion from samples that failed to show toxin with digestion. These results suggest the desirability of first assaying with digestion and then retesting all apparently nontoxic samples without digestion.

The inoculated pack data on haddock with 0.1 and 0.2 Mrad irradiation at 42° F. (5.6° C.) and 40° F. (4.4° C.) suggest no type E hazard, provided the product is distributed and stored at 42° F. or below. This conclusion is supported by inoculum levels of 10⁶ and 10⁴ spores per gram and spores produced at optimal and suboptimal temperatures. At 50° F. (10° C.) and 46° F. (7.8° C.) incubation, the inoculated pack results with 0.1 Mrad irradiation appear favorable, since no toxin was detected up to twice the expected storage life with a 10⁴ inoculum level. At 46° F., toxin was detected at X with a 10⁶ inoculum level, but not at earlier sampling periods. We believe that negative toxin assay results with 10⁴ spores per gram for twice the maximal expected storage life would be ample evidence of the absence of a type E hazard, even though occasional toxin production might be detected earlier with a challenge dose of 10⁶ spores per gram.

The results with 0.2 Mrad irradiation and incubation at 46° and 50° F. are less favorable than those without irradiation or with 0.1 Mrad irradiation. Samples inoculated with 10⁶ and 10⁴ spores and given 0.2 Mrad irradiation showed type E toxin production at ½X with 46° F. incubation. With 50° F. incubation, samples inoculated with 10⁴ and 10² spores were toxic at ½X and ¾X, respectively.

Cann et al. (2) reported that vacuum packed herring, cod, and haddock given 0.3 Mrad irradiation and stored at 50° F. (10° C.) showed little differences in the time of type E toxin production from similar unirradiated fish. However, Ajmal (1) found that aerobically packed herring and cod subjected to 0.65 Mrad irradiation and incubated at 50° F. were appreciably more susceptible to type E toxin development than comparable unirradiated product. Our toxicity results on unirradiated and irradiated haddock in most cases are not based on equivalent incubation times. However, 0.1 and 0.2 Mrad irradiated haddock samples appeared to show toxin production somewhat earlier at 50° and 46° F. than corresponding unirradiated samples. When compared on the basis of equivalent X values, 0.2 Mrad irradiated samples definitely showed toxin formation earlier than either 0.1 Mrad irradiated samples or unirradiated controls.

The reason for this apparent increased susceptibility of radurized fish to type E toxin production is unknown. Perhaps it is attributable to the reduction in the competitive microflora as Ajmal (1) suggests. However, it might be due to some favorable changes produced in the substrate by irradiation that stimulate faster outgrowth of type E spores. Another possibility is that low dose irradiation causes spore activation comparable to the heat activation effect observed with certain bacterial spores.

There were two instances in the inoculated pack experiments at 50° F. (10° C.) where type E toxin was detected with a 10² inoculum level in one out of three replicate samples, but none was detected at a comparable time period with a 10⁴ inoculum. Both cases occurred with 0.1 Mrad irradiation. Such results suggest that if additional replicates had been run with a 10^4 inoculum some samples might have shown toxin. The results illustrate the necessity of extensive replication to secure meaningful toxicity data.

The inoculated pack protocol followed for haddock will be extended to assess the public health safety of other marine food products of interest in the AEC program. Inoculated packs appear to be the best approach for determining the possible risk of growth and toxin production of *C. botulinum* type E in radurized refrigerated seafoods.

Acknowledgments

This investigation was conducted under contract AT(11–1) 1183 with the Division of Biology and Medicine of the U.S. Atomic Energy Commission. The cooperative efforts of Louis J. Ronsivalli and Vincent Ampola of the Bureau of Commercial Fisheries Laboratory at Gloucester in supplying the fish fillets are gratefully acknowledged. The excellent technical assistance of Jerald K. Boltz of our laboratory is appreciated.

References

(1) AJMAL, M. 1968. *Clostridium botulinum* type E: Growth and toxin production in food. J. Appl. Bact. *31*: 124–132.

(2) CANN, D. C., B. B. WILSON, J. M. SHEWAN, T. A. ROBERTS, and D. N. RHODES. 1966. A comparison of toxin production by *Clostridium botulinum* type E in irradiated and unirradiated vacuum packed fish. J. Appl. Bact. *29*: 540–548.

(3) DUFF, J. T., G. G. WRIGHT, and A. YARINSKY. 1956. Activation of *Clostridium botulinum* type E toxin by trypsin. J. Bacteriol. *72*: 455–460.

(4) GORESLINE, H. E., M. INGRAM, P. MACUCH, G. MACQUOT, D. A. A. MOSSEL, C. F. NIVEN, and F. S. THATCHER. 1964. Tentative classification of food irradiation processes with microbiological objectives. Nature *204*: 237–238.

(5) PELROY, G. A., and M. W. EKLUND. 1966. Changes in the microflora of vacuum-packaged, irradiated petrale sole (*Eopsetta jordani*) fillets stored at 0.5° C. Appl. Microbiol. *14*: 921–927.

(6) SCHMIDT, C. F., R. V. LECHOWICH, and J. F. FOLINAZZO. 1961. Growth and toxin production by type E *Clostridium botulinum* below 40° F. J. Food Sci. *26*: 626–630.

(7) SCHMIDT, C. F., W. K. NANK, and R. V. LECHOWICH. 1962. Radiation sterilization of food. II. Some aspects of the growth, sporulation, and radiation resistance of spores of *Clostridium botulinum* type E. J. Food Sci. *27*: 77–84.

(8) SEGNER, W. P., and C. F. SCHMIDT. 1966. Radiation resistance of spores of *Clostridium botulinum* type E. Proc. Intern. Symposium on food irradiation. Karlsruhe, Federal Republic of Germany. Intern. Atomic Energy Agency, Vienna, 287–298.

(9) SEGNER, W. P., and C. F. SCHMIDT. 1968. Nonspecific toxicities in the mouse assay test for botulinum toxin. Appl. Microbiol. *16*: In press.

(10) SLAVIN, J. W., L. J. RONSIVALLI, and T. J. CONNORS. 1966. Status of research and developmental studies on radiation pasteurization of fish and shellfish in the United States. Proc. Intern. Symposium on food irradiation. Karlsruhe, Federal Republic of Germany. Intern. Atomic Energy Agency, Vienna, 509–533.

TOXIN PRODUCTION BY *CLOSTRIDIUM BOTULINUM* TYPE E IN RADIATION-PASTEURIZED FISH

by Yoshiaki Ando, Takashi Karashimada, Teiji Ono, *and* Hiroo Iida
Hokkaido Institute of Public Health, Sapporo, Japan

Summary

Herring homogenates were inoculated with 10^5 spores of *Clostridium botulinum* type E per gram, irradiated at 0, 0.1, and 0.3 Mrads and then stored at 20° or 10° C. Total volatile base, total bacterial counts, and oxidation-reduction potential were periodically assayed and the relation between these indices in irradiated samples was compared with that in unirradiated ones. Toxin production in unirradiated samples occurred so rapidly that there seem to be no significant difference between the time for development of toxin and the spoilage time; whereas, toxin production in irradiated samples began to occur before the appearance of signs of spoilage. More toxin was produced in irradiated samples than in unirradiated ones.

The fact that radiation pasteurization apparently enhances the growth and toxin production of *C. botulinum* type E in herring homogenates is discussed form the viewpoint of the oxidation-reduction potential.

Introduction

The purpose of the present investigation is to clarify the microbiological safety of the radiation pasteurized fish, with special regard to the possible occurrence of the *C. botulinum* type E hazard.

It is generally recognized that radiation pasteurization in the low-dose levels (0.1 to 0.5 Mrads) followed by preservation at chilling temperatures, offers many advantages to irradiation preservation of fish. At such low doses, however, it is conceivable that a considerable number of spores of *C. botulinum* type E in the contaminated fish survive irradiation and thus the possibility of development of toxin exists whenever suitable conditions for their outgrowth occur. One of the grounds for accepting this assumption is the data on radiation resistance of type E spores. Reports by several workers show that the radiation resistance of spores of *C. botulinum* type E is generally considered to be lower than that of types A or B. Schmidt et al. (8) determined D values of spores of six type-E strains suspended in a beef stew by using the partial spoilage method and obtained a mean D value of 0.132 Mrad.

Roberts and Ingram (6) reported that the D values of spores of nine type-E strains in aqueous suspension, calculated from the exponential part of survivor curves, ranged from 0.065 to 0.16 Mrads and the shoulder, followed by exponential part, extended to about 0.4 Mrad. The resistance values of spores of 14 type E strains isolated in Hokkaido are summarized in table 1.

Table 1.—D and L values of spores of various strains of *Clostridium botulinum* type E in aqueous suspension

Strain	D value (Mrad)	L value (Mrad)
Iwanai	0.156	0.161
Mashike	.145	.137
Abashiri	.174	.141
Zenigamesawa	.127	.136
Saroma	.153	.156
Morai[1]	.160	.058
Memanbetsu[1]	.145	.015
K–20	.103	.184
T–27–3	.139	.132
S–29–1	.141	.087
R–1–3	.120	.197
N–6–4	.116	.177
M–2	.128	.159
K–4	.144	.061

[1]Nontoxic strain.

Nevertheless, pasteurization doses of irradiation would not eliminate type E spores as stated by Schmidt et al. Cann et al. (3, 4) also suggested the possibility of the radiation pasteurized fish becoming botulogenic, by confirming that the spores surviving irradiation germinated and produced toxin more rapidly than an equivalent number of the spores in unirradiated fish.

Generally speaking, radiation pasteurized fish must be stored at temperatures as low as possible, because *C. botulinum* type E can grow even at chilling temperature in the region of 40° F. (7). However, it is not uncommon for fish or fish products, even if irradiated, to be stored at undesirable temperatures before consumption. For example, in recent outbreaks in this country, it has been pointed out that most of the incriminated fish were processed at the relatively high temperature during warm seasons.

The present work was undertaken in order to determine the time required for the development of toxin in irradiated and unirradiated fish homogenates in relation to the spoilage time when homogenates were stored at room temperature (20° C.) or below (10° C.).

Materials and Methods

Preparation of irradiation samples.—Homogenates were employed throughout these experiments. To prepare homogenates, fresh muscle of herring was blended with an equal weight of distilled water in an homogenizer. The homogenates were distributed in 10-gram quantities in test tubes (18 x 150 mm.), plugged with cotton. The tubed homogenates were inoculated with spores of *C. botulinum* type E, strain Iwanai, to a level of 10^5 spores per gram of homogenate. The inoculated tubes were held at 0° C. until needed for irradiation.

Irradiation.—On the following day, the inoculated tubes were irradiated with either a dose of 0.1 or of 0.3 Mrads at ambient temperature (4° to 10° C.). Immediately after being irradiated, the samples were divided into groups and incubated at either 10° or 20° C. together with unirradiated controls.

Preparation of assay samples.—At each sampling interval, the contents of both irradiated and unirradiated samples were transferred into separate sterilized tubes, rinsed thoroughly with 20 ml. of cold, sterilized saline containing 0.1 percent of peptone. The samples were mixed thoroughly with aid of mixing equipment, "Thermomixer," before assay.

Toxin assay.—After centrifugation at 2,000 r.p.m. for 5 minutes, the supernatant fluid was incubated at 37° C. for 1 hour with an equal volume of 0.1 M phosphate buffer (pH 6.0) containing 0.2 percent of trypsin. Appropriate dilutions were made with gelatin-phosphate buffer (pH 6.0) and portions of 0.5 ml. of the dilutions were injected intraperitoneally into two mice. The mice were observed for typical symptoms of botulism for 2 days.

Total bacterial count.—Four plates were prepared in duplicate using TPN agar of Corlett et al. (5). The plates were incubated at 25° C. for 48 hours prior to counting total colony numbers.

Total volatile base (TVB).—TVB was determined by means of Conway's microdiffusion analysis.

Oxidation-reduction potential (Eh).—The arrangement of the apparatus for measuring Eh of the irradiated or unirradiated samples is illustrated in figure 1. The platinum electrode was cleaned in chromic-sulphuric acid, rinsed thoroughly in distilled water, and flamed in a methanolic flame just prior to set up. Both the electrode and the small glass tube for the KCl-agar bridge were suspended firmly by a cotton plug in a test tube of the same diameter as irradiation tube and autoclaved. Then the KCl-agar bridge was filled aseptically and the cotton plug with the electrode and KCl-agar bridge was bodily set over into the tube containing herring homogenate. The electrode was inserted as deeply as possible. The tubes were subsequently irradiated and incubated.

Eh was measured potentiometrically by use of a pH meter, "Hitachi-Horiba's M-5," with attachment of automatic recording equipment. Care was taken not to disturb the electrode-homogenate system during measurement of Eh.

Results

Bacterial counts.—The total bacterial counts in the herring homogenates irradiated at 0, 0.1 and 0.3 Mrads and stored at either 10° or 20° C. are illustrated in figure 2. Irradiation at 0.1 and 0.3 Mrads reduced the initial counts by about 82.0 and 97.2 percent, respectively. With storage at 20° C., the counts of the unirradiated samples increased rapidly to a maximum level after 2 days, whereas those of the irradiated samples increased more slowly to their maxima after 4 to 5 days. With storage at 10° C., the changes in bacterial counts showed trends similar to those observed at 20° C.; however, the counts at 10° C. in all required an approximately fourfold longer period to reach their respective maxima as compared with storage at 20° C.

Changes in total volatile base.—As shown in figure 3, the TVB values of the unirradiated samples increased almost steadily over the storage periods, while those of the irradiated samples increased very slowly after some lag periods.

When the TVB value exceeded 30 mg. percent, a significant degree of spoilage, as based on putrefactive odors, was observed in all the samples. The storage times in which the TVB values of the irradiated and unirradiated samples exceeded 30 mg. percent are as follows: Unirradiated samples, 2 to 4 days and 1 day at 10° and 20° C., respectively; samples irradiated at 0.1 Mrad, 8 to 10 days and 3 days at 10° and 20° C., respectively; samples irradiated at 0.3 Mrad, 12 to 14 days and 5 days at 10° and 20° C., respectively.

Eh changes.—The changes of the Eh values measured during storage are shown as potential-time curves in figure 4. Measurements of initial potential were made in the unirradiated samples after being kept at 0° C. for at least 12 hours, because fish homogenates, poised poorly in the presence of air, showed some irregular drifts in the initial potential, owing to unstable equilibria developed in the homogenates themselves. On the contrary, measurements were made in the irradiated samples immediately after irradiation.

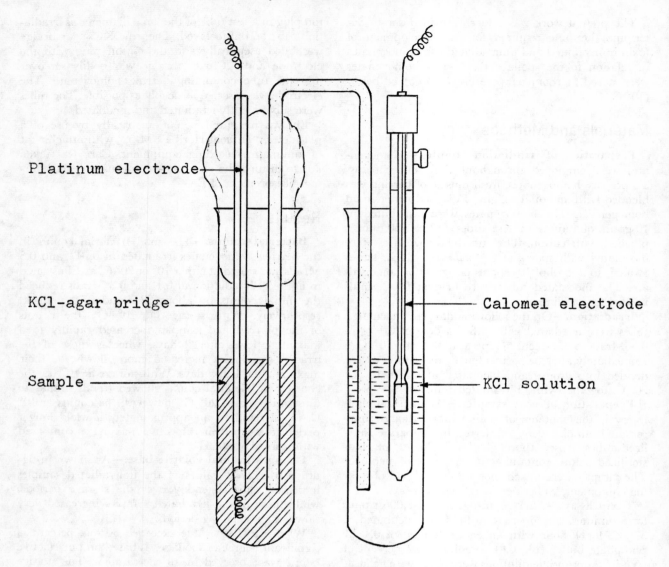

Figure 1.—Apparatus for measurement of Eh in fish homogenates.

With the unirradiated samples stored at 10° C., the potential fell gradually from its initial value of —0.03 volt to the minimum value of —0.33 volt after 6 days and then rose gradually to the final value of —0.20 volt after 15 days.

Remarkably it was found that all the irradiated samples were poised heavily in the reducing potentials, indicating much lower level of negative values than that of the unirradiated samples. The initial Eh values of the irradiated samples stored at 10° C. were —0.25 and —0.34 volts at 0.1 and 0.3 Mrads, respectively. These potentials proceeded through some undulating drifts toward their final Eh values, —0.20 and —0.31 volts at 0.1 and 0.3 Mrads, respectively.

With the unirradiated samples stored at 20° C., the potential fell rapidly to the minimum value of —0.35 volt after 36 hours and subsequently rose to the final value of —0.20 volt. The initial Eh values of the irradiated samples stored at 20° C. were —0.19 and —0.27 volts at 0.1 and 0.3 Mrads, respectively. These potentials rose gradually toward the same final Eh value of —0.11 volt. As can be seen in figure 4, none of these potentials ever proceeded upward to positive values during the whole storage period.

Toxicity changes.—The changes of the toxin production in the irradiated and unirradiated samples during storage at either 10° or 20° C. are shown in figure 5. With the storage temperature of 10° C., no detectable amount of toxin was found in all the samples after 4 days. More toxin was demonstrated after 8 days; the highest level of toxin was detected in the samples irradiated at 0.1 Mrad, the

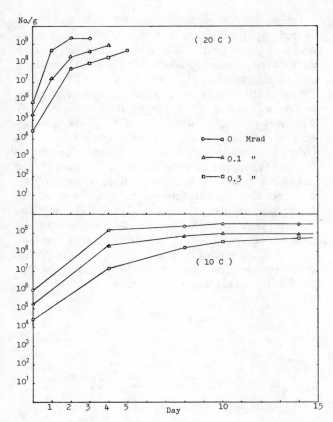

Figure 2.—Changes in total bacterial counts of irradiated and unirradiated herring homogenates during storage at 10° or 20° C.

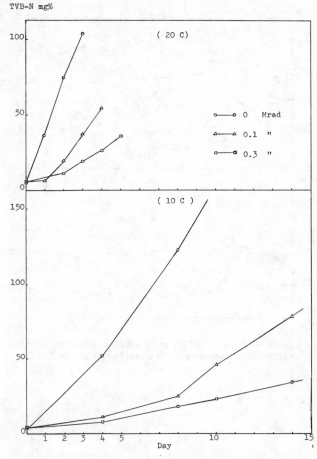

Figure 3.—Changes in TVB–N of irradiated and unirradiated herring homogenates during storage at 10° or 20° C.

lowest being detected in the samples irradiated at 0.3 Mrad. More toxin was detected in both of the irradiated than in the unirradiated samples after 14 to 20 days.

With the storage temperature of 20° C., the unirradiated samples became toxic after only 1 day and reached to the maximum titre of toxin after 3 days. Both of the irradiated samples became toxic after 2 days and reached to the same maximum titre after 3 and 4 days at 0.1 and 0.3 Mrads, respectively. Production of toxin proved to be more conspicuous in its rate and quantity in the samples stored at 20° C. than in those stored at 10° C., regardless of irradiation doses.

Discussion

When the change of total bacterial counts was compared with those of TVB and Eh, the relation between these indices in the irradiated samples was somewhat different from that in the unirradiated samples. With the unirradiated samples, the bacterial counts increased in parallel with the linear increase

of TVB and the drop of Eh value during early period of storage.

On the contrary, with the irradiated samples, neither the changes of TVB nor of Eh coincided with the change in bacterial counts. The rate of the TVB production was relatively slow, so that no linear increase was observed until the bacterial counts exceeded the order of 10^7 per gram of homogenate. In addition, these changes were not always reflected in the potential-time curves. These discrepancies may have resulted from the marked reduction of the organisms responsible for development of volatile base.

Previously, one of the authors (2) reported that sterilized fish homogenates were found to be suitable media for the growth of *C. botulinum* type E because of their low initial potentials, and that the growth and toxin production were observed also in nonsterilized fish homogenates as a result of rapid fall in Eh values due to spoilage occurring during storage.

In the present experiments, particular attention

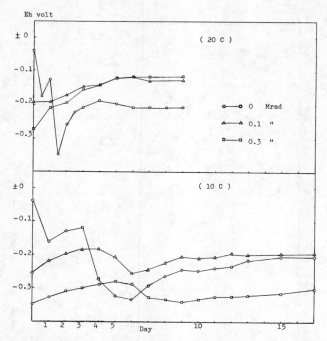

Figure 4.—Changes in Eh of irradiated and unirradiated herring homogenates during storage at 10° or 20° C.

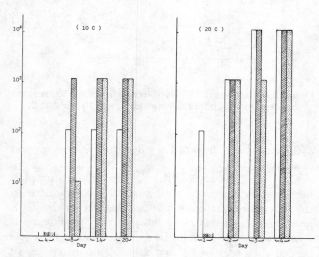

Figure 5.—Changes in toxicity of irradiated and unirradiated herring homogenates during storage at 10° or 20° C. Blanc area, O Mrad; hatched area, 0.1 Mrad; dotted area, 0.3 Mrad.

was paid to the following two points with regard to the Eh involved in irradiation of fish:

(1) Would aerobic or anaerobic conditions be brought about in fish homogenates by irradiation at pasteurization dose of 0.1 or 0.3 Mrads?

(2) Would measurements of Eh potential in irradiated fish serve as one of the criteria for the growth of *C. botulinum* type E during storage?

Preliminary experiments showed that irradiation caused rapid reduction of dissolved oxygen in some aerobic culture media, as well as in some fish homogenates. For examples, when TPG medium, without sodium thioglycollate, was irradiated at 0.3 Mrad, the Eh value fell rapidly from its initial value of 0.11 volt to a negative value of −0.25 volt, as shown in figure 6. This was probably due to the effect of oxygen-consuming reaction caused by ionizing radiation. The reducing condition created by irradiation proved to be able to support outgrowth of type E spores. When the TPG medium, without sodium thioglycollate, was inoculated with the spores, irradiated at 0.3 Mrad, and incubated at 20° C., gas production and turbidity were observed within 48 hours, whereas no change was observed in the unirradiated medium even after 2 weeks of incubation. The rapid fall of Eh value during irradiation was also demonstrated in the fish homogenates as shown in figure 7.

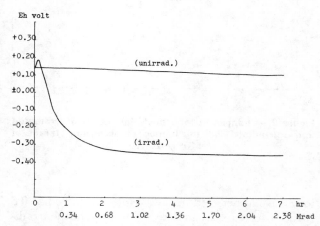

Figure 6.—Changes in Eh of TPG medium during irradiation.

It is evident from our data that the herring homogenates which had received irradiation at either dose, 0.1 or 0.3 Mrads, were found to show considerably negative levels of Eh value, so that the spores of *C. botulinum* type E surviving irradiation could grow sufficiently to produce toxin. Also, unirradiated homogenates showed a rapid fall of Eh to value as low as those of irradiated samples, thus permitting the growth and toxin production of *C. botulinum* type E. This may, however, mainly have been due to the oxygen-scavenging activity of aerobic microflora normally present in fish. Consequently, there exists the possibility of development of type E toxin in fish during storage, whether irradiated or not.

Several factors influence the toxin production by *C. botulinum* type E in irradiated fish. Such factors as inoculation level of the spores, irradiation dose, and

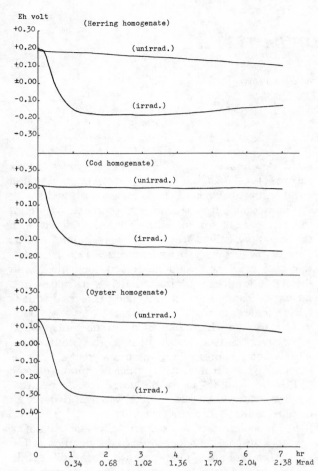

Figure 7.—**Changes in Eh of the fish homogenates during irradiation.**

incubation temperature are mainly among those concerned.

Abrahamsson et al. (*1*) reported that the irradiated (0.3 Mrad) packs of herring filet which were inoculated with the spores of *C. botulinum* type E at a level of 2 x 10⁶ per gram of muscle, became toxic within 64 hours incubation at 20° C. They also observed that a significantly higher concentration of toxin was observed in the vacuum-packed than in the non-vacuum-packed samples. Toxin formation in vacuum-packed and irradiated herring, stored at 10° C., was also reported by Cann et al. (*3, 4*), who stated that more toxin was produced by 10⁵ spores per 100 g. of fish in an irradiated sample than by a comparable number of spores in an unirradiated sample, and that the rate of toxin formation in the former was about twice that in the latter. Similar results, observed in our data, indicated that

higher titre of toxin was detected in irradiated than in unirradiated samples, despite fewer spores in the former than in the latter, owing to the killing effect of ionizating radiation.

On the basis of these observations, it seems more likely that irradiation at a pasteurization dose enhances the trend of the toxin production of *C. botulinum* type E in herring, at least under certain conditions. An anaerobic circumstance created by irradiation is likely to be one of the causes of such enhancement, but there seem to be other reasons still unknown. Further experiments will be carried out to know whether the same results can be obtained even in species of fish other than herring.

Acknowledgment

This study was supported in part by the Research Grant No. 315R/B from the International Atomic Energy Agency in Vienna, Austria.

References

(*1*) ABRAHAMSSON, K., N. N. DESILVA, and N. MOLIN. 1965. Toxin production by *Clostridium botulinum* type E, in vacuum-packed, irradiated fresh fish in relation to changes of the associated microflora. Canad. J. Microbiol. *11*: 523–529.

(*2*) ANDO, Y., and K. INOUE. 1957. Studies on growth and toxin production of *Clostridium botulinum* type E in fish products. I. On the growth in relation to the oxidation-reduction potential in the fish flesh. Bull. Japan. Soc. Sci. Fisheries *23*: 458–462.

(*3*) CANN, D. C., B. B. WILSON, G. HOBBS, and J. M. SHEWAN. 1965. The growth and toxin production of *Clostridium botulinum* type E in certain vacuum packed fish. J. Appl. Bacteriol. *28*: 431–436.

(*4*) CANN, D. C., B. B. WILSON, J. M. SHEWAN, T. A. ROBERTS, and D. N. RHODES. 1966. A comparison of toxin production by *Clostridium botulinum* type E in irradiated and unirradiated vacuum packed fish. J. Appl. Bacteriol. *29*: 540–548.

(*5*) CORLETT, D. A. JR., J. S. LEE, and R. O. SINN-HUBER. 1965. Application of replica plating and computer analysis for rapid identification of bacteria in some foods. I. Identification scheme. Appl. Microbiol. *13*: 808–817.

(*6*) ROBERTS, T. A., and M. INGRAM. 1965. The resistance of spores of *Clostridium botulinum* type E to heat and radiation. J. Appl. Bacteriol. *28*: 125–141.

(*7*) SCHMIDT, C. F., R. V. LECHOWICH, and J. F. FOLINAZZO. 1961. Growth and toxin production by type E *Clostridium botulinum* below 40 F. J. Food Sci. *26*: 626–630.

(*8*) SCHMIDT, C. F., W. K. NANK, and R. V. LECHOWICH. 1962. Radiation sterilization of food. II. Some aspects of the growth, sporulation, and radiation resistance of spores of *Clostridium botulinum* type E. J. Food Sci. *27*: 77–84.

OUTGROWTH OF *CLOSTRIDIUM BOTULINUM* TYPE E IN RADIATION-PASTEURIZED FISH

by J. T. GRAIKOSKI
U.S. Bureau of Commercial Fisheries, Ann Arbor, Mich. 48107

Introduction

The proper evaluation of the potential botulinum hazard in foods, is to study the growth characteristics and toxin producing ability of the organisms in the particular food under question, and under the specific conditions of processing. In case of the radiation process currently under study to extend the storage life of fish at refrigeration temperatures, consideration must be given to *Clostridium botulinum* type E; the type commonly associated with fish and seafoods. Of primary importance is the ability of type E to grow and produce toxin at lower temperatures of incubation than types A and B (*1, 2, 3, 4*).

Low doses of ionizing radiation, in the 0 to 300 kilorad range, have been shown to be effective in prolonging the storage life of fresh fish twofold to threefold when subsequently held at refrigeration temperatures. The effectiveness of the radiation treatment in prolonging the storage life of fish is to decrease the number of micro-organisms on the fish which are primarily responsible for spoilage.

The irradiation doses employed for pasteurization not only reduces the number of micro-organisms, but is also selective, in that the most predominant bacterial species causing fish spoilage (*Pseudomonas sp.*) are essentially eliminated because of their greater degree of sensitivity to irradiation. The result is a change in the typical spoilage pattern of irradiated fish. It has been long recognized that the potential botulism hazard in foods can be enhanced by an alteration of the so-called "normal spoilage pattern" of a particular food. The amount of irradiation treatment proposed for pasteurization of fresh fish is not effective in destroying type E spores. The problem, therefore, is to determine the outgrowth of the botulinum spores and toxin production in various fish species, in order to assess the safety of the fish when held at refrigeration temperatures.

The following presentation will be concerned with growth and toxin production of several type E strains in fish fillets and a fish substrate.

Materials and Methods

In the first experiment, the rate of growth and toxin development in haddock homogenates by six strains of *C. botulinum* type E at seven incubation temperatures between 0° to 37° C. was studied.

The haddock homogenate was prepared by blending one part of frozen Atlantic haddock fillets with two parts of distilled water in a Sorvall Omni-Mixer. Part of the tissue pulp was dispensed into 20 x 150 mm. (25 ml.) screw cap tubes and then filled with filtrate. The tubes were immediately sterilized with 3 megarads of gamma radiation. The pH of the haddock homogenate was 7.2.

The six type E strains used in this study were: Vancouver, Seattle Forks, Beluga, E–74, Nanaimo, and Iwanai. Spores of the organisms to be used for inocula were grown in trypticase-peptone-glucose (TPG) broth at 33° C. for 36 hours. The spores were washed six times in cold distilled water and stored in distilled water under refrigeration.

For inoculation of the culture tubes, an aliquot of the stock suspension was heated and detoxified at 65° C. for 15 minutes. The suspension was diluted in sterile distilled water to produce a final concentration of 10^6 spores per milliliter. One milliliter of the spore suspension was used to inoculate tubes of haddock homogenates. Immediately after inoculation, all tubes were layered with 3 percent agar containing 0.4 percent sodium thioglycollate. During the procedure of inoculation, all tubes were kept cold in an ice water bath. The culture tubes were incubated at the following temperatures: 37.5°, 33.0°, 18.0°, 8.3°, 5.4°, 3.3°, 0.0°, and ±0.5° C.

Growth was ascertained by the observation of gas bubbles collecting beneath the agar layers, by the development of off-odors, and by clearance of the opalescence of the homogenates. Confirmation of growth was established by the presence of toxin. Samples which gave low or no toxin titres on the initial assay were treated with 0.1 percent trypsin at 37° C. for 1 hour at pH 5.8 to 6.0 and again tested for toxin in mice.

In the second experiment, the objective was to determine outgrowth of type E in radiation pasteurized Atlantic cod fillets. The Beluga type E strain was employed in this study. The preparation of spore suspension used as inocula was described in the first experiment.

For irradiation, portions of three individual cod fillets were contained in a small cylindrical carton. The middle fillet was inoculated with 0.1 ml. of the spore suspension of the desired concentration. Spore concentrations employed were 10^6, 10^4, and 10^2 per gram of fish.

After inoculation, samples were immediately irradiated at ice temperature. For irradiation, a cobalt-60 source was employed. For these experiments the fish received a total dose of 100 and 200 kilorads at a dose rate of 50,000 rads per hour.

After irradiation, samples were placed in storage at the desired temperatures. The temperatures of storage employed in the experiment were 10°, 7°, and 3° C.

Outgrowth of the spores in the fillets during storage was determined by testing three inoculated fillets for toxin. Samplings were performed at 3- or 4-day intervals for samples stored at 10° C. and at weekly intervals for those stored at 7° and 3° C. An 1:1 extract was prepared with sterile phosphate buffer from the fillets to be tested for the presence of toxin. After centrifugation, 0.3 ml. of the supernatant was injected into each of three mice. Supernatants negative for toxicity were treated with 0.2 percent trypsin at 37° C. for 1 hour. Samples which did give questionable botulism symptoms in mice were neutralized with type E antitoxin to confirm the presence of toxin.

Results

The results of the growth experiment in haddock homogenates is presented in table 1. At the incubation temperatures of 37.5° and 33° C., cultures developed gas readily within 2 days, and 3 to 4 days at 19° C. All of the strains, with the exception of the Iwanai strain, produced cultures at 8.3° C. within 9 to 12 days. Gas bubbles were observed in the Iwanai cultures at 38 days of incubation at this temperature. Two strains, Iwanai and Vancouver herring, did not

develop gas in haddock homogenates after 290 days of incubation at 5.4° C.; the other four strains developed gas within 15 days at this incubation temperature. At 3.3° C., no gas formation was observed in any of the cultures, with one exception; one out of four tubes of homogenate inoculated with spores of the E-74 strain contained definite gas bubbles. At 0° C., no gas formation was evident in any of the tubes after 290 days of incubation, at which time the experiment was terminated.

The results of the toxin assays performed on the cultures developed in haddock homogenates are summarized in figure 1. Except with strain E-74, no

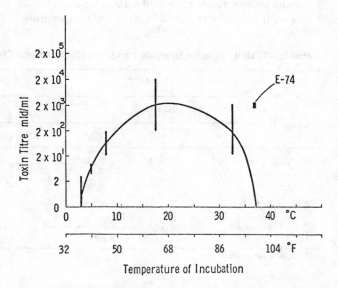

Figure 1.—Toxin titres for six strains of *C. botulinum* type E cultures developed in haddock homogenates at various temperatures.

toxin was detected in the haddock homogenates after 2 days of incubation at 37.5° C. Maximum titres of toxin occurred at 18° C., being of the order of 200 to 20,000 MLD's per milliliter without activation. At 5° C., low titres (2 MLD) of toxin were obtained when checked at 38 days of incubation. The titres were increased to 8 to 16 MLD by activation with trypsin. At 3.3° C., toxin was detected in strain E-74 with activation by trypsin at 38 days of incubation; a low titre (4 MLD) was obtained. At 0° C., no toxin was detected in the culture tubes when tested at 80 days of incubation.

After 250 days of incubation the samples, which were incubated at 3° and 0° C., were again checked for the presence of toxin and viable spores in the culture tubes. No toxin, with or without trypsinization, was detected in any of the tubes tested. The small amount of toxin detected in tubes incubated at

Table 1.—Time for gas formation by *C. botulinum* type E in haddock homogenates

Type E strain	Days for gas formation— Incubation temperatures						
	37.5 °C.	33.0 °C.	18.0 °C.	8.3 °C.	5.4° C.	3.3° C.	0° C.
Nanaimo	2	-----	3	10	12	>290	>290
Vancouver herring	2	2	3	12	>290	>290	>290
Forks	2	2	4	12	15	>290	>290
Beluga	2	2	3	10	15	>290	>290
Iwanai	2	2	3	38	>290	>290	>290
E-74	2	2	3	9	11	[1]12	>290

[1] 1 tube out of 4 contained gas bubbles.

3° C. (after 38 days of incubation), was no longer detectable at this time. When cultures which had been incubated at 3° and 0° C. for 250 days were transferred to 33° C., growth with toxin formation readily occurred within 48 hours, showing that the spores of the various strains remained viable in the haddock homogenates during this period of incubation.

The toxicity results of the two experiments with Atlantic cod are presented in tables 2 and 3. The results are expressed as number of fish containing toxin per number of fillets tested.

In the first experiment (table 2—fillets inoculated with 10^6 spores), results show that toxin was detected in the irradiated fillets both at the 100 and 200 kilorad levels within 5 days at the 10° C. storage temperature.

At the 7° C. storage temperature, toxin was detected only in the sample irradiated to 200 kilorads and at the 15th day of storage. Also, at 26 days of incubation, toxin was detected in two out of three fillets in the nonirradiated control at the 7° C. storage temperature. No toxin was detected in any of the samples stored at 3° C. up to 34 days of storage in this experiment.

The second experiment (table 3) was designed to test the effect of inoculum size on toxic outgrowth in the cod fillets. A different lot of fish was employed in this study. At the storage temperature of 10° C., toxic outgrowth occurred at the 10^6 spore inoculum level in 10 days, and within 17 days at the 10^2 spore level for the nonirradiated samples. None of the fillets became toxic at the 10^4 spore level. No explanation

Table 2.—Toxicity date for irradiated and nonirradiated cod fillets inoculated with spores[1] of *C. botulinum* type E (Beluga)

| Storage time (days) | 10° C. (50° F.) | | | 7° C. (44.6° F.) | | | 3° C. (37.4° F.) | | |
| | Kilorad | | | Kilorad | | | Kilorad | | |
	0	100	200	0	100	200	0	100	200
5	[2]0/3	3/3	3/3						
8	0/3	3/3	3/3	0/3	0/3	0/3	0/3	0/3	0/3
12	0/3	3/3	3/3						
15				0/3	0/3	1/3	0/3	0/3	0/3
22				0/3	0/3	3/3	0/3	0/3	0/3
26				2/3	0/3	1/3			
28							0/3	0/3	0/3
34							0/3	0/3	0/3

[1] 10^6 spores per gram of fish.

[2] Number fillets toxic / Number fillets tested

Table 3.—Toxicity data for irradiated and nonirradiated cod fillets inoculated with spores of *C. botulinum* type E (Beluga)

Storage time (days)	10° C. (50° F.)								
	0 kilorad			100 kilorad			200 kilorad		
	Spores per gram of fish								
	10^6	10^4	10^2	10^6	10^4	10^2	10^6	10^4	10^2
3	[1]0/3	0/3		1/3	0/3		0/3	0/3	
6	0/3	0/3		1/3	0/3		3/3	1/3	
10	1/3	0/3	0/3	2/3	1/3	0/3	3/3	3/3	1/3
13			0/3			1/3			1/3
17			2/3			1/3			1/3
20						2/3			3/3
	7° C. (44.6° F.)								
6	0/3	0/3		0/3	0/3		0/3	0/3	
13	0/3	0/3		0/3	0/3		0/3	0/3	
20	0/3	1/3		0/3	0/3		0/3	0/3	
27	0/3	0/3		0/3	0/3		0/3	0/3	

[1] Number fillets toxic / Number fillets tested

could be made for this discrepancy. The results on the fish fillets, which received the irradiation treatment (100 and 200 kilorads) and 10^6 spore inoculum, are similar to the previous experiment. Toxic outgrowth by the spores was observed in 3 to 6 days at 10° C. storage in this experiment.

Toxic outgrowth was observed also in the irradiated fish stored at 10° C. which had received a spore inoculum of 10^4 and 10^2. There was a delay in time for toxin appearance in fish inoculated at the 10^2 spore level, as compared to those inoculated at the 10^4 spore level. Similarly, a comparison of toxin appearance at the 10^6 inoculum level shows a shorter outgrowth time for the spores under these conditions. This is logical since the time for germination, outgrowth, and subsequent toxin production would depend on the size of the original inoculum injected into the fish fillets.

In this experiment, storage at 7° C. resulted in only one fillet containing toxin; this was in the nonirradiated control after 20 days of storage.

The results of these two experiments would indicate that outgrowth and toxin production at 7° C. is sporadic. This would be an indication that this temperature is near minimal in reference to outgrowth of the type E spores in the cod fillets under the experimental conditions employed.

Discussion

In haddock homogenates, four out of the six type E strains tested, readily produced gas at 5.4° C. within 2 weeks. The Vancouver herring and Iwanai strains did not grow out at this temperature. The cultures which were produced at 5.4° C. contained low levels of toxin. At 3.3° C., only one tube out of four inoculated with the E–74 strain showed definite gas production. After trypsinization, toxin was detected in these cultures. An incubation temperature of 3° C. would be minimal for outgrowth of spores from the E–74 strain as determined from the results of this study. For the other strains, a temperature between 3° and 5° C. would be the limiting growth temperature.

In cod fillets, outgrowth of the spore was variable at 7° C., which would indicate that this is near the limiting temperature for type E outgrowth under the conditions of the experiment. The results on outgrowth of type E obtained in fish homogenates is

similar to that observed in fillets in this study. Therefore, use of fish homogenates would be of some practical advantage in additional studies of this type.

Estimates of spoilage by odor evaluation of the cod fillets stored at 10° C. in the two experiments, would indicate that toxin formation could possibly occur at the high spore inoculum level before the fish were rejected as spoiled. At the 7° C. storage temperature, fish were generally considered spoiled before toxin was detected. In the sample at 7° C., where fish fillets received 10^6 spores and 200 kilorad radiation treatment, the fish contained toxin and were considered on the borderline of spoilage. At 3° C., no toxin was detected before definite spoilage occurred.

From a practical consideration, the employment of large spore inocula in assessing the potential hazard of radiation processed fish may be unrealistic. However, until some practical estimation of incidence of the botulinum organism is obtained on fish as natural contaminants, outgrowth studies employing various spore concentrations need to be employed.

Although much emphasis has been placed on type E in low temperature outgrowth studies in the evaluation of the radiation process, consideration must also be given to other types. Nonproteolytic types B and F have been demonstrated in the commercial fisheries environment and have the ability to grow at low temperatures of incubation.

Acknowledgment

This study was supported in part by the U.S. Atomic Energy Commission, Division of Biology and Medicine, under Contract No. AT(49)–113006.

References

(1) ABRAHAMSSON, K., B. GULLMAR, and N. MOLIN. 1966. The effect of temperature on toxin formation and toxin stability of *Clostridium botulinum* type E, in different environments. Canad. J. Microbiol. *12:* 385–394.
(2) DOLMAN, C. E., H. CHANG, D. E. KERR, and A. R. SHEARER. 1950. Fishborne and type E botulism: Two cases due to home-pickled herring. Canad. J. Public Health *41:* 215.
(3) OHYE, D. F., and W. J. SCOTT. 1957. Studies in the physiology of *Clostridium botulinum* type E. Australian J. Biol. Sci. *10:* 85.
(4) SCHMIDT, C. F., R. V. LECHOWICH, and J. F. FOLINAZZO. 1961. Growth and toxin production by type E *Clostridium botulinum* below 40° F. J. Food Sci. *26:* 626–630.

RADIOSENSITIVITY OF TYPE E BOTULINUM TOXIN AND ITS PROTECTION BY PROTEINS, NUCLEIC ACIDS, AND SOME RELATED SUBSTANCES

by Toshiyuki Miura, Sumiko Sakaguchi, Genji Sakaguchi, *and* Komei Miyaki
Department of Food Research, National Institute of Health, Tokyo

Summary

Three preparations of different purities of type E botulinus toxin containing toxicity or potential toxicity of about 50,000 LD_{50} per milliliter were irradiated with cobalt-60 in 0.05 M acetate or 0.2 M phosphate buffer, pH 6.0. The D values were about 2.1 Mrad for the cell suspension, about 0.21 Mrad for the cell extract and about 0.04 Mrad for the purified preparation. Tryptic activation did not change the radiosensitivity of the toxin except for the cell suspension.

Serum albumin, casein, deoxyribonucleic acid and ribonucleic acid protected the purified and activated toxin against radiation detoxification; sugars or ascorbic acid showed little or no protection.

The same extent of protection was afforded by sulfur-containing, aromatic or some heterocyclic amino acids and also by purines.

Preirradiation of amino acid solutions with 7.7 Mrad did not appreciably change the protecting effect on type E toxin, except for the irradiated lysine which was shown to be protective in some experiments. Some amino acid derivatives, methionine sulfoxide, aminoethyl mercaptan, and cadaverine, were shown to be protective to different extents.

Introduction

Much work has been performed on destruction of spores of *Clostridium botulinum* by ionizing radiation but only scant information has been available on the radiosensitivity of botulinus toxins. The present investigation was directed to explain why such a large dose as several megarads (Mrad) is required to inactivate botulinus toxins in foods (*3, 5, 6, 7*). Attempts were made to analyze the radiation destruction of type E toxin and the protection afforded by proteins, nucleic acids and some related substances.

Materials and Methods

Toxin materials.—Three preparations of type E toxin of different purities, with and without tryptic activation, were used: (*a*) A suspension of washed cells of *C. botulinum* type E, strain 35396, the German

canned sprats strain isolated by Hazen (*2*); (*b*) a cell extract in which the precursor was in the form of ribonucleoprotein; and (*c*) a material partially purified by the methods described elsewhere (*4*). The material described under (*c*) possessed a sedimentation constant ($S_{20,w}$) of approximately 11.5 before and after tryptic activation. Each material was diluted in 0.05 M acetate or 0.2 M phosphate buffer, pH 6.0, so as to contain approximately 50,000 mouse LD_{50}/ml. Protein concentrations of the materials were: 152 μg./ml. for (*a*); 140 μg./ml. for (*b*); and 21 μg./ml. for (*c*).

Irradiation.—Two milliliter samples in glass dishes (3.1 x 1.6 cm.) were irradiated from a 260 curie and later a 550 curie cobalt-60 source with a dose rate of 0.023 Mrad per hour and 0.025 Mrad per hour, respectively. All irradiations were performed in air at ambient temperature (4° to 28° C.) and atmospheric pressure.

Titration of toxin potency.—All the materials were diluted twofold serially with 0.05 M phosphate buffer, pH 6.0 containing 0.2 percent gelatin. Four or more mice were injected intraperitoneally with each dilution.

Results

Radiosensitivity of type E toxin of different purities.—The inactivation curves of type E toxin of different purities at pH 6.0 are illustrated in figure 1. The purer the material, the smaller the D value. About 1.7 Mrad was required to inactivate 90 percent of the potential toxicity of the cell suspension, about 0.21 Mrad for the cell extract, and only about 0.04 Mrad for the purified precursor.

Tryptic activation of the cell suspension increased the sensitivity, but did not change the sensitivity of the cell extract or the purified precursor.

Influence of various substances on the radiosensitivity of the purified toxin.—The small radiation dosage needed for inactivation of the purified precursor or toxin indicated the possible protection afforded by various constituents in the cruder materials. In order to analyze the protection, each of such

substances as proteins, nucleic acids, sugars, etc., at different concentrations was added to a solution of trypsin-activated toxin and the mixture irradiated with 0.1 Mrad. The toxin potencies were determined and compared with those before and after irradiation without the added substance (table 1).

Serum albumin, mild casein, yeast ribonucleic acid, and herring-sperm deoxyribonucleic acid showed a marked protection; while sugar such as ribose, glucose, sucrose or starch, showed little or no protection.

Influence of amino acids, purines and pyrimidines on the radiosensitivity of the purified toxin.— The purines, adenine and guanine, at a concentration of 500 μg./ml. showed a marked protection; whereas the pyrimidines, uracil and thymine, showed little protection (table 2).

Each of 19 amino acids at a final concentration of 10^{-3} M was added to the toxin solution to test for protection. Seven amino acids, histidine, phenylalanine, tyrosine, tryptophan, cysteine, cystine, and methonine showed a marked protection of type E toxin against radiation detoxification; leucine and isoleucine a little protection; and the other 10 amino acids little or no protection (table 3).

The D value of the purified toxin solution, approximately 0.04 Mrad, increased roughly 10 times to 0.35 Mrad by adding albumin at 600 μg./ml. or cysteine at 1.3×10^{-3} M (fig. 2). The concentration of cysteine corresponded to 4 times that of cysteine-cystine residues in the albumin solution.

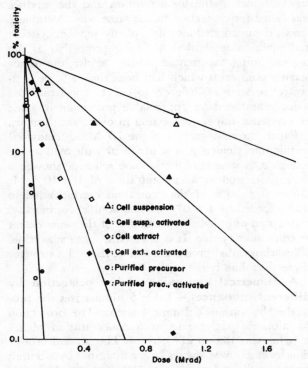

Figure 1.—Detoxification of precursor and the trypsin-activated toxin of different purities of *C. botulinum* type E by irradiation with ^{60}Co γ-rays.

Table 1.—Protection of type E botulinus toxin (21 μg./ml., pH 6.0) against detoxification by 0.1 Mrad of γ-ray

Substance	Concentration (mg./ml.)	LD₅₀/ml.		
		I	C	T
Albumin	2.4	25,800–55,000	10–1,810	10,200–32,400
Casein	2.4	32,700–55,000	10–1,810	41,400–68,200
RNA	1.0	34,400–46,000	<10–20	6,960–12,100
DNA	1.0	34,400–46,000	<10–10	12,600–14,200
Glucose	1.0	81,900	29	1,080
Ribose	1.0	81,900	29	1,520
Sucrose	1.0	81,900	29	828
Starch	1.0	81,900	29	20

NOTE.—I = initial; C = without the substance; T = with the substance.

Table 2.—Protection of type E botulinus toxin (21 μg./ml., pH 6.0) against detoxification by 0.1 Mrad of γ-ray

Substance	Concentration (μg./ml.)	LD₅₀/ml.		
		I	C	T
Adenine	500	34,400	20–40	14,200–25,800
Guanine	500	47,800	40	12,000
Uracil	500	34,400	20	368
Thymine	500	34,400	40	970

NOTE.—I = initial; C = without the substance; T = with the substance.

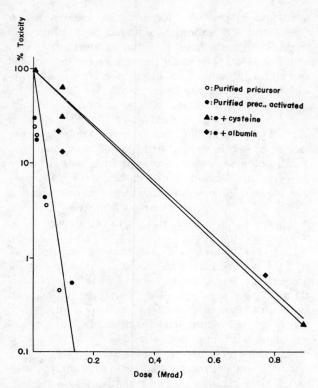

Figure 2.—Protection of type E botulinus toxin (21 µg./ml.) by albumin (600 µg./ml.) or cysteine (1.3 x 10⁻³M) against γ-ray irradiation.

Influence of preirradiated amino acids and some amino acid derivatives upon radiosensitivity of the purified toxin.—Aqueous solutions of some amino acids at a concentration of 1×10^{-2} M were

preirradiated with a dose of 7.7 Mrad. One volume of each irradiated amino acid solution was added to nine volumes of the toxin solution and the mixture was tested for protection in the same way. As table 4 shows, the irradiated histidine, phenylalanine, cysteine and methionine showed a similar protection as the corresponding nontreated amino acids; the other seven amino acids which had been shown to be nonprotective were of little or no effect. The irradiated lysine manifested an appreciable protection in some experiments, but no protection in other experiments.

Paper chromatography of the 7.7 Mrad-irradiated methionine yielded a spot identical with methionine sulfoxide. A sample of methionine sulfoxide showed a little protection at a concentration of 1×10^{-3} M; but at 5×10^{-3} M the protection corresponded to that afforded by 1×10^{-3} M methionine. Aminoethyl mercaptan afforded the protection of the same extent as equimolar cystine. It is of interest that cadaverine, a decarboxylated product of lysine, showed a stronger protection than lysine.

A numerical expression of the protection by different substances.—Table 5 summarizes the protection by various substances tested. The protection by albumin and casein at a concentration of 2.4 mg./ml. was 18.6 to 214 percent. The percent protection by casein was always larger than that by albumin and sometimes larger than 100 percent. This fact suggests that the irradiation with a dose of 0.1 Mrad in the presence of casein potentiated the toxicity.

Protein molecules were not indispensable for the protection, and certain amino acids substituted for the proteins. The protection by the seven amino acids, histidine, phenylalanine, tyrosine, tryptophan, cys-

Table 3.—Protection of type E botulinus toxin (21 µg./ml., pH 6.0) against detoxification by 0.1 Mrad of γ-ray

Substance	Concentration	LD₅₀/ml.		
		I	C	T
Arginine	$1 \times 10^{-3}M$	58,000	320	2,560
Histidine	$1 \times 10^{-3}M$	58,000–67,500	320–2,560	14,500–29,000
Lysine	$1 \times 10^{-3}M$	67,500–81,900	21–2,560	189– 3,220
Aspartic acid	$1 \times 10^{-3}M$	81,900	21	25
Glutamic acid	$1 \times 10^{-3}M$	81,900	21	57
Phenylalanine	$1 \times 10^{-3}M$	81,900	21– 107	8,250–24,200
Tyrosine	$1 \times 10^{-3}M$	57,800	20	17,700
Oxyproline	$1 \times 10^{-3}M$	58,000	320	742
Tryptophan	$1 \times 10^{-3}M$	51,400	20	14,500
Cysteine	$1 \times 10^{-3}M$	51,400–67,500	20–2,560	15,000–57,700
Cystine	$1 \times 10^{-3}M$	51,400	20	14,500
Methionine	$1 \times 10^{-3}M$	53,000–58,000	20– 422	17,100–25,700
Serine	$1 \times 10^{-3}M$	57,800	20	21
Threonine	$1 \times 10^{-3}M$	57,800	20	21
Leucine	$1 \times 10^{-3}M$	57,800	20	1,280
Isoleucine	$1 \times 10^{-3}M$	57,800	20	1,810
Valine	$1 \times 10^{-3}M$	81,900	21	124
Alanine	$1 \times 10^{-3}M$	58,000	320	874
Glycine	$1 \times 10^{-3}M$	58,000	320	494

NOTE.—I = initial; C = without the substance; T = with the substance.

Table 4.—Protection of type E botulus toxin (21 μg./ml., pH 6.0) with 7.7 Mrad-irradiated amino acids (10⁻³M) and other related substances against detoxification by 0.1 Mrad of γ-ray

Substance	Concentration	LD_{50}/ml.		
		I	C	T
Arginine	$1 \times 10^{-3}M$	56,400	26	1,640
Histidine	$1 \times 10^{-3}M$	67,500	2,560	32,400
Lysine	$1 \times 10^{-3}M$	55,000–67,500	<10–23	506– 5,120
Glutamic acid	$1 \times 10^{-3}M$	56,400	26	226
Phenylalanine	$1 \times 10^{-3}M$	81,900	107	35,400
Oxyproline	$1 \times 10^{-3}M$	56,400	20	160
Cysteine	$1 \times 10^{-3}M$	67,500	2,560	32,400
Methionine	$1 \times 10^{-3}M$	53,000	422	16,200
Serine	$1 \times 10^{-3}M$	56,400	20	454
Threonine	$1 \times 10^{-3}M$	56,400	20	80
Glycine	$1 \times 10^{-3}M$	56,400	26	80
Methionine sulphoxide	$5 \times 10^{-3}M$	56,400	20	17,200
Aminoethyl mercaptan	$1.4 \times 10^{-3}M$	34,400	254	15,500
Cadaverine	$1 \times 10^{-3}M$	34,400–47,800	40	4,560–10,100

NOTE.—I = initial; C = without the substance; T = with the substance.

Table 5.—Protection of type E botulinus toxin (21 μg./ml., pH 6.0) against detoxification by 0.1 Mrad of γ-ray

Protector	Concentration	Percent protection[1]
Albumin	2.4 mg./ml.	18.6–99.0
Casein	2.4 mg./ml.	75.3–214
RNA	1.0 mg./ml.	20.2–26.3
DNA	1.0 mg./ml.	27.4–41.2
Ribose, glucose, sucrose, starch	1.0 mg./ml.	−0.52– 1.82
Histidine	$10^{-3}M$	24.6–40.7
Phenylalanine	$10^{-3}M$	10.4–29.5
Tyrosine	$10^{-3}M$	30.6
Tryptophan	$10^{-3}M$	28.2
Cysteine	$10^{-3}M$	29.2–84.9
Cystine	$10^{-3}M$	28.2
Methionine	$10^{-3}M$	31.7–44.0
Other amino acids	$10^{-3}M$	0.0– 3.9
Adenine, guanine	0.5 mg./ml.	25.0–75.0
Uracil, thymine	0.5 mg./ml.	1.0– 2.7
Methionine sulphoxide	$5 \times 10^{-3}M$	30.5
Aminoethyl mercaptan	$1.4 \times 10^{-3}M$	44.7
Cadaverine	$10^{-3}M$	13.2–21.1
Ascorbic acid	10 mg./ml.	−0.7–−0.72

[1]Percent protection = C − T/C x 100 where C and T are the percent decrease in LD_{50}/ml. in the absence and presence of the protective agent.

teine, cystine, and methionine, ranged from 10.4 to 84.9 percent; while that by the other 12 amino acids ranged from 0.0 to 3.9 percent. This difference appears to be significant.

Free purines, but not pyrimidines, substituted for ribonucleic acid and deoxyribonucleic acid in protecting type E toxin. The protection by sugars ranged from −0.52 to 1.82 percent thus being insignificant.

Methionine sulfoxide, amino-ethyl mercaptan and cadaverine showed protection of 30.5, 44.7, and 13.2 to 21.1 percent, respectively.

Ascorbic acid at a concentration of 10 mg./ml. gave protection of −0.7 percent, indicating an accelerated destruction of toxin.

Discussion

The D values of botulinus toxins by γ-ray radiation were reported to be about 1.8 to 4.2 Mrad for type A or B (5) and 2.1 Mrad for type E (3). These values were obtained with crude materials of toxin or crystalline type A toxin added to foods. Wagenaar, Dack, and Murrell (6) and Wagenaar and Dack (7) obtained a D value of about 0.003 to 0.015 Mrad for crystalline type A toxin in 0.05 M phosphate buffer, pH 7.5. The cell suspension, the crudest material in the present investigation, gave a D value of about 1.7 Mrad and the purest material about 0.04 Mrad. The latter was approximately 50 times more sensitive than the former.

Roberts, Ingram, and Skulbert (3) presumed that the D value of botulinus toxin is dependent upon its polymerization, although Wagenaar, Dack and Murrell (6) obtained a similar range of D values for the intact crystalline type A toxin and the two dissociated fragments of the toxin. The precursor and the trypsin-activated toxin used in the present experiments had a sedimentation constant ($S_{20,w}$) of approximately 11.5. Gerwing, Dolman, and Ko (1) ascribed the large molecular size of our materials to the aggregation formed by artifact during the purification steps. We have demonstrated, however, that most of type E toxin in "izushi" has the same sedimentation constant as the purified material (Sakaguchi, Sakaguchi, and Karashimada, to be published). At any rate, the present results may indicate that the resistance of the toxin against ionizing radiation is dependent more largely on the properties and the amount of concomitant substances rather than on polymerization of the toxin molecules. A marked protection was demonstrated with proteins and nucleic acids but not with sugars. The proteins were replaceable by the amino acids containing sulfur, an aromatic ring or a heterocyclic ring; nucleic acids by purines but not by pyrimidines.

In any case, we conclude that type E botulinus toxin molecule itself is as sensitive to γ-ray radiation as type A toxin molecules; nevertheless complete destruction of the toxin in foods by irradiation cannot be expected with practical doses because of the protection afforded by proteins, nucleic acids and some of the constituents of these macromolecules.

The mechanism of inactivation of botulinus toxin by ionizing radiation is still obscure, therefore the mechanism of protection could only be speculated upon. It is of interest to find whether or not the spectrum of protectors for botulinus toxin aginst ionizing radiation is the same as that against other destructive agents, including ultraviolet light and heat, and whether or not the same holds for other biologically active proteins.

References

(1) GERWING, J., C. E. DOLMAN and A. KO. 1965. Mechanism of tryptic activation of *Clostridium botulinum* type E toxin. J. Bacteriol. *89:* 1176–1179.

(2) HAZEN, E. L. 1937. A strain of B. botulinus not classified as type A, B, or C. J. Infect. Dis. *60:* 260–264.

(3) ROBERTS, T. A., M. INGRAM, and A. SKULBERG. 1965. The resistance of spores of *Clostridium botulinum* type E to heat and radiation, with an addendum on the radiation resistance of *Clostridium botulinum* type E toxin. J. Appl. Bacteriol. *28:* 125–141.

(4) SAKAGUCHI, G., S. SAKAGUCHI, and N. IMAI. 1964. Comparative gel filtration of toxin precursor and trypsin-activated toxin *Clostridium botulinum* type E. J. Bacteriol. *87:* 401–407.

(5) WAGENAAR, R. O., and G. M. DACK. 1956. Effect in surface ripened cheese of irradiation on spores and toxin of *Clostridium botulinum* type A and B. Food Res. *21:* 226–234.

(6) WAGENAAR, R. O., G. M. DACK, and C. B. MURRELL. 1959. Studies on purified type A *Clostridium botulinum* toxin subjected to ultracentrifugation and irradiation. Food Res. *24:* 57–61.

(7) WAGENAAR, R. O., and G. M. DACK. 1960. Studies on the inactivation of type A *Clostridium botulinum* toxin by irradiation with cobalt 60. Food Res. *25:* 279–284.

RESISTANCE OF *CLOSTRIDIUM BOTULINUM* SPORES TO IONIZING RADIATION AS RELATED TO RADAPPERTIZATION OF FOODS

by D. B. ROWLEY, H. M. EL-BISI,* A. ANELLIS, *and* O. P. SNYDER
Microbiology Division, Food Laboratory, U.S. Army Natick Laboratories Natick, Mass.

Summary

The U.S. Army's research program designed to obtain data to support the microbiological safety of radappertized meats is discussed. Major emphasis is placed on: (1) Selection of appropriate test strains of *Clostridium botulinum* spores as the microbial index of safety; (2) determination of the most radiation resistant strain(s) in a specific food by the screening inoculated pack studies; and (3) the clearance inoculated pack studies designed to provide an experimental sterilizing dose (ESD) and data for the computation of a minimal radiation dose (MRD).

Progress in pertinent research areas is presented: (1) NaCl decreased the germination rate of *C. botulinum* 62A spores but not total germination. The rate of outgrowth of unirradiated spores was decreased by 2.5 percent NaCl but all spores developed macrocolonies in the presence of up to 4.0 percent NaCl. Irradiation did not alter the normal germination pattern of spores or enhance the inhibitory effect of NaCl on the rate of germination. NaCl in the irradiated suspension did not sensitize spores to irradiation but NaCl in the recovery medium reduced the number of radiation survivors. (2) The D value (dose for 90 percent reduction) for *C. botulinum* 53B spores increased from 0.268 to 0.350 Mrad and 0.400 Mrad when the temperature of irradiation was lowered from 20° to −80° and −196° C., respectively. (3) There was a slight increase in radiation survivors of *C. botulinum* 53B spores as the pressure during irradiation was lowered from 760 to 200 mm. Hg. As the pressure was further lowered to 25 mm. Hg. there was a marked increase in survivors.

A program designed to evaluate the present 12D concept of microbiological safety of radappertized meats is briefly outlined.

Introduction

The processing of food with ionizing radiation (radaprocess) results in a reduction in the numbers of viable bacteria with a consequent increase in the storage life of food without refrigeration and in a reduction in the health hazards accompanying the ingestion of foods contaminated with disease-producing microbes. Based on the microbiological objective, radaprocessing has been classified into three major categories (*15*):

Radappertization.—The radaprocess destroys all potential pathogens and spoilage microbes. Foods thus processed would be preserved indefinitely. The U.S. Army's food irradiation program is presently concerned primarily with the development of radappertization, with the major emphasis on meat products.

Radicidation.—The radaprocess destroys all non-spore-forming microbial pathogens.

Radurization.—The radaprocess reduces or eliminates the dominant spoilage microflora, with the consequent increase in the products' shelf life.

The Minimal Radiation Dose (MRD)

Assuming first-order kinetics for the killing of bacterial spores by ionizing radiation, the minimal radiation dose (MRD) is the dose computed to effect a reduction in a botulinal spore population, determined to be of the highest radiation resistance, in a specific food under simulated process conditions by a factor of 10^{12}. Accepting "D" as the appropriate death rate constant expressing the dose for decimal reduction (90 percent destruction) in the index botulinal spore population, the MRD has been conventionally prescribed as equivalent to 12D (*13, 30*). We are of the opinion that such a concept of safety (12D) has been arbitrarily adopted without a scientifically sound foundation (*10*). While we have complied with this MRD standard, we are developing evidence leading to a scientifically based safety concept.

Clostridium botulinum as the Microbial Index

Generally, bacterial species may be arranged in an order of ascending radiation resistance as follows: pseudomonads, coliforms, staphylococci and salmonellae, streptococcal species, nonbotulinal sporeformers, *C. botulinum* type A (*34*) and *Micrococcus radiodurans* (*1*). Of the common foodborne pathogenic and spoil-

---

*Paper read by H. M. El-Bisi.

age micro-organisms, *C. botulinum* spores, types A and B are the most resistant (*12, 25, 26, 34*). Generally, among the clostridia *C. botulinum* type A spores appear to be the most resistant (*5, 32*). They are more resistant than those of type E (*12, 32*) and are generally more resistant than *C. sporogenes* (PA 3679) which is an appropriate indicator of safety for the production of thermally processed foods (*5, 22, 25*). Since *C. botulinum* spores are the most radiation resistant among the bacteria of public health concern they have been selected as the microbial index for determining the MRD requirement for radappertized foods.

To decide which test strains of *C. botulinum* should be used as the microbial index the radiation resistance of 102 strains from numerous sources was determined (*5*). Expecting a change in relative resistances in different foods we selected from the 102 surveyed strains 10 representative cultures—five of the highest (33A, 36A, 40B, 41B, and 53B), four of the intermediate (62A, 77A, 12885A, and 9B), and one of the lowest (51B) relative radiation resistant groups (table 1). These 10 strains have been used in obtaining the specific microbiological data for computing the MRD of each prototype irradiated food.

Table 1.—Comparative radiation resistance of representative strains of *C. botulinum* types A and B[1]

Type	Strain Number	Mean D value (Mrad)
A	33	0.334
A	36	.336
B	40	.317
B	41	.318
B	53	.329
A	62	.224
A	77	.253
A	[2]12885	.241
B	9	.227
B	51	.129

[1]Spores suspended in 0.067 M phosphate buffer (pH 7) were heated at 80° C. for 10 min., and diluted with chilled buffer to 10⁴ spores per milliliter. 1-ml. amounts of the suspension were distributed into sterile 10 x 75 mm. pyrex tubes which were stoppered with sterile cotton plugs. 10 replicate tubes were inserted in a polystyrene holder contained in a No. 2 can. The cans were sealed in the presence of nitrogen and irradiated at successive doses of 0.1 Mrad from 0 to 2.0 Mrad at the High Level Gamma Irradiation Facility of the Argonne National Laboratory. To detect surviving spores double-strength Wynne's medium (*36*) without the agar was added to each tube, and, after sealing in an oxygas flame, the tubes were incubated at 30° C. for 6 weeks. Survivors and D values were determined as described by Anellis et al. (*3*).
[2]Toxigenic variant.

Specific Microbiological Evidence

The screening inoculated pack study.—The inoculated pack studies were designed to select the botulinal spore population of the greatest radiation resistance in a specific food product. For each inoculated

pack study, the comparative radiation resistance of the 10 selected cultures was determined in the prototype food under simulated process conditions. The food was given a mild heat treatment (bringing the internal temperature up to a minimum of 70° to 80° C.) prior to inoculation and radiation. The heat treatment which was primarily intended to inactivate the indigenous food enzymes, thus preventing autolysis during prolonged postirradiation storage without refrigeration, also had the function of destroying food contaminants such as viruses and nonsporogenic bacteria; e.g., *Micrococcus radiodurans* (unpublished data from our laboratory, and the Food Protection Laboratories of the National Center of Urban and Industrial Health, Cincinnati, Ohio). This screening pack consisted of 20 inoculated (10⁶ spores per can) replicate cans per radiation dose. The inoculated cans were irradiated with doses from 0 to 4.0 Mrad, or higher, in increasing steps of either 0.25 or 0.5 Mrad, in order to provide partial spoilage data, an experimental sterilizing dose (ESD) and data for computing an MRD. The irradiated pack was then incubated at 30° C. for 3 months; the cans were observed for swelling at weekly periods for the first month, and monthly thereafter. At the end of the incubation period, cans were opened and examined for botulinal toxin and viable *C. botulinum* as described elsewhere (*2*). The examination of cans for toxic spoilage and viable *C. botulinum* began at the highest dose yielding 100 percent swollen cans and included all swollen and flat cans at all higher doses. Radiation D values, the index of resistance, were computed for each of the 10 strains for the three criteria of spoilage: swelling, toxicity, and viable *C. botulinum*. The strain(s) exhibiting the highest radiation resistance in the specific food product was then used for the final clearance pack study.

The clearance inoculated pack study.—An extensive study of the resistance of the selected strain(s) was then undertaken to determine the ESD and to provide data for the computation of the MRD for the prototype product and process in question. Such a study comprised the use of 100 replicate inoculated (10⁶ spores per can) cans per dose with the doses increasing in 0.5 Mrad increments. The dose range selected was dependent upon the outcome of the screening pack partial spoilage data, the ESD and the computed MRD for the most resistant strain(s). The irradiated cans were incubated at 30° C. for 6 months and examined as in the preliminary screening pack. Again, D values were calculated from the partial spoilage data and converted to an MRD.

We have recently published the detailed experimental evidence for the radappertization of bacon (*4*) and of ham (*2*). We have also submitted a paper for publication dealing with statistical methods available for the computation of the MRD (*7*). We are dissatisfied with the Schmidt-Nank conventional method (*31*) since it has given us questionable results in our inoculated pack studies.

Current research objectives and progress.—Three major objectives motivated our current research activities:

(1) Establish conditions that would reduce the inherent radiation resistance of *C. botulinum* spores or abort their postradiation toxigenic activities in the product.

(2) Investigate conditions which would result in an irradiated product of good organoleptic quality with retention of a high rate of destruction of *C. botulinum* spores.

(3) Establish a sound safety concept for radappertized foods.

We shall summarize our progress to date toward these major objectives.

The MRD is currently computed on the basis of spore survival regardless of their incapability to outgrow or intoxicate the product. Meat products have provided a differential of 0.5 to 1.5 Mrad between the MRD for swelling or toxicity and that for survival. In thermally processed cured meats the consumer experience of over 40 years justified the acceptance of a markedly underprocessed product, of the order of F_o of 0.1 to 0.5 instead of the standard botulinal cook of F_o of 2.78 (*17*). In the absence of such experience in the case of radappertized cured meat it is obligatory to establish the laboratory evidence that may justify an analogous reduction in dose. We have, therefore, geared our research effort over the past 2 years toward the acquisition of such evidence.

There is considerable evidence for the suppressive properties of curing salts in irradiated meats for spores of *C. botulinum* (*2, 17, 23*). Without curing ingredients doses as high as 3.0 Mrad were ineffective in preventing cans of ground round steak inoculated with *C. botulinum* spores (10^6/g.) from undergoing spoilage (*23*). Unirradiated cans of round steak with 2.5 percent NaCl and 1,000 p.p.m. $NaNO_3$ also underwent spoilage; similar cans irradiated with a dose of 2.0 Mrad did not spoil. Nitrite was not as effective as nitrate because when nitrite (200 p.p.m.) was substituted for nitrate (1,000 p.p.m.) the product required a dose of 2.5 Mrad rather than 2.0 Mrad to prevent spoilage. Spoilage data (*17*) indicated that the radiation resistance of *C. botulinum* spores in cured ham was considerably below that reported for uncured meats. Also, it has been observed that spores of *C. botulinum* (33A, 36A, 12885A, 9B, 41B, and 53B) irradiated in mildly heated cured bacon exhibited smaller D values (*4*) than when irradiated in phosphate buffer, pH 7.0 (*5*). None of these studies determined whether the curing ingredients sensitized the

C. botulinum spores to irradiation or whether the surviving spores were unable to undergo germination and/or postgerminative development in their presence. The radiation resistance of *C. sporogenes* and *C. oedematiens* type C spores in aqueous suspension was unaffected by the presence of NaCl (3 and 6 percent w./v.) during irradiation (*28*). However, radiation survivors were more sensitive to NaCl in the recovery medium than were uniradiated spores. An important factor in the stability of an irradiated cured product may be radiation injury of the spores (*17*). Sublethal injury of spores by heat treatment was shown to be an important component of the stability system of canned comminuted cured meats (*33*).

A model system was developed in our laboratories which would enable us to determine the effect of curing salts and irradiation on the germination and postgerminative development of *C. botulinum* 62A spores (*29*).

Materials and Methods

Spore preparation.—Spores of *C. botulinum* 62A were produced at 37° C. in a medium (pH 7.5) containing 5 percent trypticase (BBL), 0.5 percent peptone (BBL), 0.5 percent yeast extract (BBL), and 0.125 percent K_2HPO_4. A vegetative-cell inoculum was used (*6*). After harvesting, the spores were cleaned by centrifugation and by the lysozyme-trypsin enzyme treatment described by Anellis and Rowley (*6*). Spores, freed of vegetative debris, were resuspended in distilled water (2.6 x 10^9/ml.) and stored at 4° C.

Medium for germination and postgerminative development.—The medium used for studies of germinative and postgerminative development (model system) contained 3 percent thiotone (BBL), 0.1 percent sodium bicarbonate and 0.05 percent sodium thioglycollate. This medium was buffered at pH 7.0, with 0.1 M TES [N-tris (hydroxymethyl)-methyl-2-aminoethanesulfonic acid,] (*14*) and contained 0.07 percent NaCl. The filter-sterilized medium minus sodium bicarbonate was added to standardized colorimeter tubes and steamed for 20 minutes to remove oxygen. Sodium bicarbonate was added to the medium at 37° C., followed by spores previously heat-shocked at 80° C. for 10 minutes in an aqueous suspension. The tubes containing a final volume of 10 ml. (7 x 10^7 spores/ml.) were plugged with serum stoppers and the head space flushed with purified nitrogen (99.997 percent) for 2 minutes.

Estimation of germination.—The germination of 62A spores was estimated by measuring the percentage of spores staining with 0.5 percent aqueous methylene blue and by measuring the loss in optical density of spore suspensions (Klett-Summerson colorimeter, No. 62 filter).

Exposure to radiation.—Suspensions (1.5–2.0 ml.) of *C. botulinum* spores were exposed to gamma radiation from the U.S. Army Natick Laboratories 1.0 Mc[60] Co source, which emitted 39 Krads per minute. The temperature of irradiation was controlled with liquid N_2.

Recovery.—After irradiation, the spore suspensions were diluted with distilled water. Colony counts were made in 12 x 200 mm. tubes with thiotone agar with or without NaCl: 3.0 percent BBL thiotone, 0.05 percent sodium thioglycolate, 0.85 percent Oxoid ionagar No. 2, pH 7.0; 0.3 ml. of 5 percent Millipore-filtered NaHCO$_3$ was added to each culture tube prior to the appropriate dilution of the spore suspension. Thiotone agar (13 ml.) was added, allowed to solidify, capped with 2 cm. of the same medium and tubes were incubated at 37° C. for 72 hours.

Results and Discussions

Spores underwent germination and postgerminative development when incubated at 37° C. (fig. 1). In 2 hours about 83 percent of the spores became stainable. Emerged and elongated cells first appeared at 2 hours; cell division was first evident at 3 hours and about 79 percent of the population had undergone division by 6 hours.

The addition of increasing levels of NaCl to the thiotone medium progressively decreased the germination rate as measured by loss in optical density over a 3-hour period (Fig. 2) but did not prevent germination of spores which were incubated for more extended periods. In the presence of 4 percent NaCl only 24 percent of the spores were stainable within 3 hours, but by 24 hours about 80 percent were stainable. At the end of 12 days of incubation vegetative cells and toxin had developed in all cultures. Mundt, Mayhew, and Stewart (*27*) demonstrated that germination of *C. sporogenes* c spores in spleen infusion broth was not materially reduced by the addition of 8 percent NaCl; after 24 hours there were 99 percent heat-sensitive cells in the absence of NaCl as compared to 89 percent in the presence of 8 percent NaCl. However, vegetative development did not occur in the presence of 8 percent NaCl. Gould (*16*) demonstrated that 5–7 percent NaCl prevented outgrowth but not germination of *Bacillus* spores.

To test the influence of NaCl on postgerminative development of *C. botulinum*, spores were allowed to undergo germination for 2 hours at which time water

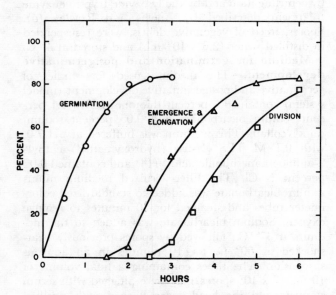

Figure 1.—Germination and postgerminative development of *Clostridium botulinum* 62 A spores (about 7 x 10⁷ spores per millimeter), incubated (37° C.) in theotone medium containing 3 percent thiotone, 0.1 percent NaHCO₃, 0.05 percent sodium thioglycollate; buffered at pH 7.0 with TES. Smears prepared periodically were examined microscopically to determine percent germination (stainable with 0.5 percent methylene blue), emergence and elongation, and dividing cells.

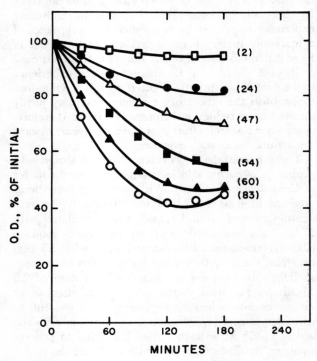

Figure 2.—Effect of increasing levels of sodium chloride on the germination of *C. botulinum* spores in thiotone medium. Spores were suspended in thiotone medium (control) (0); control +1.0 percent (w./v.) NaCl (▲); control +2.5 percent (w./v.) NaCl (■); control +3.0 percent (w./v.) NaCl (△); control +4 percent (w./v.) NaCl (●); control +8.5 percent (w./v.) NaCl (□). Numbers in parentheses represent the percent of stainable spores after 180 minutes incubation at 37° C.

or NaCl was added. Postgerminative development occurred in the presence of 2.5 percent NaCl but was slower than in its absence (fig. 3). Furthermore, when an aqueous spore suspension was cultured in thiotone agar tubes and counts made after 24 and 72 hours at 37° C. there was some lag in colony formation but no reduction in the final counts with the incorporation of up to 4 percent NaCl. Thus, up to 4 percent NaCl did not permanently inhibit the spores from undergoing germination and development to the point of forming macrocolonies. Duncan and Foster (9) showed that in the presence of 3–6 percent NaCl most of the spores of PA 3679 germinated and formed vegetative cells.

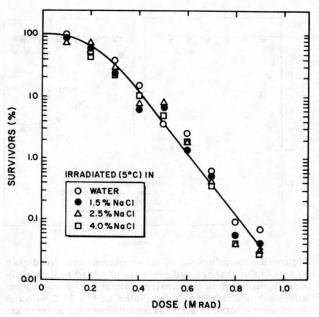

Figure 4.—Effect of sodium chloride on the resistance of *C. botulinum* spores to gamma radiation. Spores were suspended (about 4 x 10⁷ spores per milliliter) in water (0); 1.5 percent (w./v.) NaCl (●); 2.5 percent (w./v.) NaCl (△); or in 4.0 percent (w./v.) NaCl (□) and irradiated at 5°±2° C in a ⁶⁰Co source. Thereafter, the suspensions were diluted with water and colony counts made.

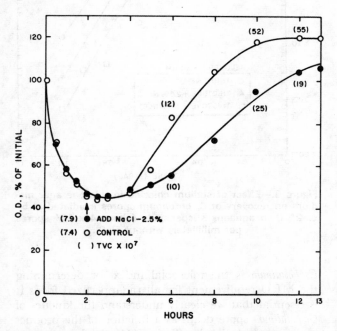

Figure 3.—Effect of 2.5 percent (w./v.) sodium chloride on the postgerminative development of *C. botulinum* spores. Spores were germinated in thiotone medium for 2 hours (80 percent germination), at which time water (0); or NaCl (●) was added. Germination and postgerminative development were followed by optical density measurements and the number of viable cells (represented by numbers in parentheses) in samples, appropriately diluted in 0.1 percent peptone plus 0.1 percent sodium thioglycollate was determined at intervals after addition of water or NaCl.

Although NaCl lowered the germination rate of *C. botulinum* 62A spores and caused a lag in outgrowth of the germinated spores it did not sensitize spores to gamma irradiation (fig 4). Spores irradiated in the presence 1.5, 2.5, or 4.0 percent NaCl, diluted and cultured in the absence of added NaCl appeared to have essentially the same radiation resistance as those irradiated in the absence of NaCl. The inability of salt to sensitize spores to radiation kill has also been reported for *C. sporogenes* and *C. oedematiens* (28).

Several investigators have demonstrated that nonsterilizing doses of radiation resulted in spore survivors (*C. botulinum*) which were not capable of developing and producing toxin in cured meats (2, 4, 17). Also, it has been reported for aqueous suspensions of both aerobic and anaerobic spores that levels of irradiation capable of destroying the ability of spores to undergo postgerminative development do not influence the rate or extent of spore germination (8, 24). Irradiation of aqueous *C. botulinum* spore suspensions with 0.9 Mrad, a dose reducing the spores capable of forming macrocolonies by > 99.9 percent did not appear to alter spore permeability as the irradiated spores suspended in 0.1 M TES buffer (plus 0.1 percent sodium bicarbonate and 0.05 percent sodium thioglycollate) without thiotone, showed no decrease in optical density or increase in stainability when incubated (37° C.) for 3 hours (fig. 5). Furthermore, exposure to 0.9 Mrad did not alter the germination pattern of *C. botulinum* spores in thiotone or enhance the inhibitory effect of 2.5 percent NaCl on the rate of germination. However, the ability of some of the spores surviving irradiation to form macrocolonies was decreased by the addition of NaCl to the thiotone agar recovery medium (fig. 6). The decrease in colony count of irradiated spores was greater as the salt concentration in the recovery

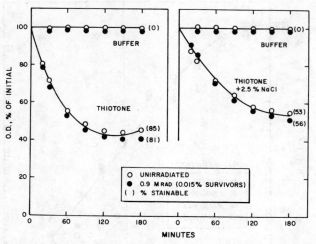

Figure 5.—Germination of unirradiated and irradiated spores in the absence and presence of added sodium chloride. Aqueous spore suspensions (about 3 x 10^8 spores per milliliter) unirradiated or irradiated at 5°±2° C with 0.9 Mrad were diluted in 0.1 M TES containing 0.1 percent sodium bicarbonate and 0.05 percent sodium thioglycollate (buffer); buffer with 3 percent thiotone (thiotone); or thiotone plus 2.5 percent (w./v.) NaCl. Rate of germination was followed by loss in optical density. The percentage of stainable spores after 3 hours incubation at 37° C is indicated in parentheses.

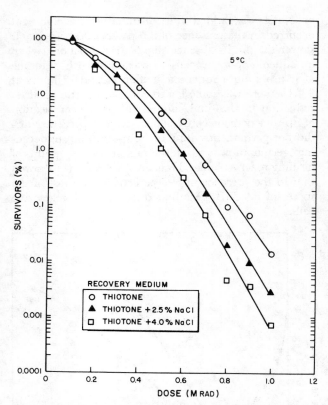

Figure 6.—Effect of sodium chloride in thiotone agar medium on recovery of *C. botulinum* spores irradiated at 5° ± 2° C in aqueous suspensions (about 4 x 10^7 spores per millilieter) without NaCl.

medium was increased from 2.5 to 4.0 percent. The presence of up to 4.0 percent NaCl in the medium caused no reduction in the recovery of unirradiated spores. Apparently, radiation-injured spores were unable to grow out in the presence of NaCl; thus as with *C. sporogenes* and *C. oedematiens* (*28*) irradiation sensitizes *C. botulinum* 62A spores to organoleptically acceptable levels of salt. Furthermore, this sensitization at an irradiation temperature of 5° ±2° C. also took place at irradiation temperatures of −30°±10° C. and −80°± 10° C. (data not shown). The organoleptic quality of ham irradiated at −80° C. is better than that irradiated at 5° C. (*21*). It is conceivable that combinations of curing salts (NaCl, NaNO$_2$, and NaNO$_3$) together with radiation may have greater inhibitory qualities than NaCl alone. In the absence of NaCl, filter sterilized NaNO$_2$ (200 p.p.m.) or NaNO$_3$ (1,000 p.p.m.) had no apparent effect on germination or outgrowth of irradiated or unirradiated *C. botulinum* 62A spores (data not shown).

Cryogenic Temperature.—Meats irradiated in the frozen state underwent less deleterious organoleptic changes than when irradiated in the unfrozen state (*19, 21, 35*). Low temperature (−30° ± 10°C.) irradiation was a basic requirement for producing acceptable shrimp and beef (*21*). The organoleptic qualities of foods (ham, chicken, and pork) were better when the temperature of irradiation was lowered (*21, 35*). Since

C. botulinum is the microbial index for determining the MRD requirement for all radappertized foods it is essential that we clearly understand the kinetics of *C. botulinum* spore death as a function of the product temperature during irradiation (*11*). As the temperature of irradiation was decreased from 20° to −196°C. an increase in D values from 0.268 to 0.400 Mrad was observed (fig. 7). Most of this increase occurred between 20° and −80° C. (D=0.350). These data, together with data on the irradiation of meats at cryogenic temperatures (*21, 35*), suggest that the differential between spore death rate and quality deterioration rate widens as the temperature of irradiation is decreased, thus offering a definite technological advantage (*11*).

Vacuum levels.—To test the influence of atmospheric pressure on the radiation resistance of *C. botulinum* 53B spores, beef cubes were inoculated with 3 x 10^6 spores; tubes were sealed at pressures varying from 25 to 760 mm. Hg. and samples were irradiated (*11*). The radiation resistance of *C. botulinum* 53B spores at all radiation levels and temperatures examined increased only slightly with a decrease in atmospheric pressure from 760 to 200 mm. Hg. (fig. 8). At

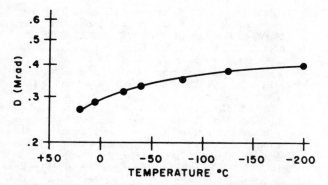

Figure 7.—Effect of temperature of irradiation on the dose required for 90 percent reduction (D value) of spores of *C. botulinum* 53B. Slices of beef (0.5 g.) were inoculated with spores ($10^6/0.5$ g.), sealed in 10 x 150 mm. tubes at 200 mm. Hg. and irradiated. Samples were appropriately diluted in water and total viable cells were determined after 72 hours' incubation (32° C.) in 12 x 200 mm. tubes containing: 0.3 ml. of 5 percent $NaHCO_3$ and 15–20 ml. TPY agar (5 percent trypticase, 0.5 percent yeast extract, 0.5 percent peptone, 0.1 percent soluble starch, 0.01 percent glucose, 0.125 percent K_2HPO_4, 0.05 percent sodium thioglycollate, 0.85 percent deionized agar, pH 7).

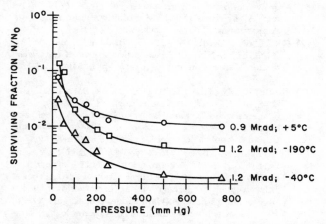

Figure 8.—Effect of atmospheric pressure on the radiation resistance of *C. botulinum* 53B spores irradiated at 5° C; —40° and —190° C. Beef cubes (1 g./tube) were inoculated with 3 x 10^6 spores, sealed at varying pressures at 22°–25° C and irradiated. Colony counts were made as in Figure 7.

a processing pressure of about 200 mm. Hg. (21 inches of vacuum) there was little difference in kill at a given temperature with sealing the inoculated meat at atmospheric pressure. Fortunately this amount of vacuum is commonly used commercially and it yields a very satisfactory irradiated product. However, as the pressure was further decreased to 25 mm. Hg. there was a definite increase in spore survival. Such data suggest that sealing pressures used in packaging foods for radappertization should be carefully monitored.

The present safety concept, borrowed from the older and analogous canning technology requires that the MRD be equivalent to a computed 12D for a most radiation resistant *C. botulinum* spore population in the prototype food. As regards acid foods and cured foods, the present 12D concept appears inapplicable or requires change (20). Moreover, we emphasize the need for specific evidence, both theoretical and experimental, that would adequately support the present 12D concept.

We are developing a program, aimed toward a comprehensive critical evaluation of the present 12D concept, which hopefully will generate the evidence, both theoretical and experimental, that would provide the grounds for a duly adopted alternative (10).

The program encompasses the following: (a) Establish through extensive surveys the incidence, levels and resistance of *C. botulinum* spores in raw meats; (b) Reexamine the order of spore death—its experimental and statistical validity. Also, evaluate all methods advanced for its computation; (c) Establish the probability of spore survival; interpretation of survival probability beyond the experimental data; i.e., extrapolation to the negative region of the survival curve; (d) Establish the toxigenic and outgrowth potential of dormant radiation survivors; (e) Survey and evaluate analogous safety concepts such as those prevailing in the production of vaccines.

The above program is underway as evidenced by recent results:

(a) *Incidence.*—Greenberg et al. (18) made an extensive survey for putrefactive anaerobic spores including *C. botulinum* in raw beef, chicken, and pork. From 2,358 meat samples they isolated 19,727 clostridial colonies with an average of 2.8 spores per grams of meat. The highest ratio of botulinal spores to putrefactive anaerobe spores was about 1:20,000; one was characterized as *C. botulinum* type C. Recently, Anellis et al. (2) summarized the findings of the known information on the incidence of clostridial spores in meat and meat products. The data clearly showed that indigenous mesophilic anaerobic spores occurred in very small numbers, and, that the presence of *C. botulinum* was a relatively rare event.

Data accumulated by studies on incidence and level of *C. botulinum* spores in raw meat would serve in the effort to establish a more realistic and more scientifically grounded principle behind the concepts of microbiological safety of radappertized foods.

(b) *Estimation of D values.*—The Schmidt-Nank conventional method (31) for determining radiation D values has been found to give anomalous results in our ham and pork inoculated pack studies. Use of the equation with partial spoilage data from the scientific literature confirmed this inconsistency. Hence, we applied an entirely different principle to estimate D values (7). Since partial spoilage data represent statistically a quantal response, LD_{50} values can be computed by statistically accepted methods of various degrees of rigorousness. The LD_{50} can be converted to a D value by this relationship: $D = LD_{50}/\log N_0 - \log 0.69$. Ten different calculation methods were compared with the Schmidt-Nank estimate. The comparative resistance of botulinal strains varied with the method of computation. One procedure, the Weibull distribution, yielded a 12D equivalent or any n-D without resorting to the D value. It also determines the type of death response occurring in an inoculated pack without the need for assumptions.

Acknowledgments

We thank Florence Feeherry and Daniel Berkowitz for technical assistance, and H. S. Levinson and E. S. Josephson for critical reviews of the manuscript.

This paper reports research undertaken at the U.S. Army Natick (Mass.) Laboratories and has been assigned No. TP–565 in the series of papers approved for publication. The findings in this report are not to be construed as an official Department of the Army position.

References

(1) ANDERSON, A. W., H. C. NORDAN, R. F. CAIN, G. PARRISH, and D. DUGGAN. 1956. Studies on a radio-resistant micrococcus. I. Isolation, morphology, cultural characteristics and resistance to gamma radiation. Food Tech. *10:* 575–578.

(2) ANELLIS, A., D. BERKOWITZ, C. JARBOE, and H. M. EL-BISI. 1967. Radiation sterilization of prototype military foods. II. Cured ham. Appl. Microbiol. *15:* 166–177.

(3) ANELLIS, A., C. J. CICHON, and M. M. RAYMAN. 1960. Resistance of *Bacillus coagulans* spores to gamma rays. Application of the multiple tube probability method. Food Research *25:* 285–295.

(4) ANELLIS, A., N. GRECZ, D. A. HUBER, D. BERKOWITZ, M. D. SCHNEIDER, and M. SIMON. 1965. Radiation sterilization of bacon for military feeding. Appl. Microbiol. *13:* 37–42.

(5) ANELLIS, A., and R. B. KOCH. 1962. Comparative resistance of strains of *Clostridium botulinum* to gamma rays. Appl. Microbiol. *10:* 326–330.

(6) ANELLIS, A., and D. B. ROWLEY. 1968. Production of *Clostridium botulinum* spores types A and B. This conference.

(7) ANELLIS, A., and S. WERKOWSKI. 1968. The estimation of radiation resistance values of microorganisms in food products. Appl. Microbiol. In press.

(8) COSTILOW, R. N. 1962. Fermentative activities of control and radiation-"killed" spores of *Clostridium botulinum*. J. Bacteriol. *84:* 1268–1273.

(9) DUNCAN, C. L., and E. M. FOSTER. 1968. Effect of sodium nitrite, sodium chloride, and sodium nitrate on germination and outgrowth of anaerobic spores. Appl. Microbiol. *16:* 406–411.

(10) EL-BISI, H. M. 1965. Principles of microbiological safety and stability of radiation-sterilized foods. Natl. Acad. Sci.-Natl. Res. Council Publ. 1273, pp. 223–232.

(11) EL-BISI, H. M., O. P. SNYDER, and R. E. LEVIN. 1967. Radiation death kinetics of *Cl. botulinum* spores at cryogenic temperatures, pp. 89–107. *In* Botulism 1966. M. Ingram and T. A. Roberts (eds.), Chapman & Hall, Ltd., London.

(12) ERDMAN, I. E., F. S. THATCHER, and K. F. MAcQUEEN. 1961. Studies on the irradiation of microorganisms in relation to food preservation. I. The comparative sensitivities of specific bacteria of public health significance. Can. J. Microbiol. *7:* 199–205.

(13) FAO/IAEA/WHO. The technical basis for legislation on irradiated food. Pp. 29–30. Report of a Joint FAO/IAEA/WHO Expert Committee, Rome, April 21–28, 1964. Food and Agriculture Organization of the United Nations, Rome.

(14) GOOD, N. E., G. D. WINGET, W. WINTER, T. N. CONNOLLY, S. IZAWA, and R. M. M. SINGH. 1966. Hydrogen ion buffers for biological research. Biochem. *5:* 467–477.

(15) GORESLINE, H. E., M. INGRAM, P. MACUCH, G. MOCQUOT, D. A. A. MOSSEL, C. F. NIVEN, and F. S. THATCHER. 1964. Tentative classification of food irradiation processes with microbiological objectives. Nature *204:* 237–238.

(16) GOULD, G. W. 1964. Effect of food preservatives on the growth of bacteria from spores, pp. 17–24. *In* N. Molin and A. Erichsen (eds.), Microbial inhibitors in food. Almqvist and Wiksell, Stockholm.

(17) GREENBERG, R. A., B. O. BLADEL, and W. J. ZINGELMANN. 1965. Radiation injury of *Clostridium botulinum* spores in cured meat. Appl. Microbiol. *13:* 743–748.

(18) GREENBERG, R. A., R. B. TOMPKIN, B. O. BLADEL, R. S. KITTAKA, and A. ANELLIS. 1966. Incidence of mesophilic *Clostridium* spores in raw pork, beef, and chicken in processing plants in the United States and Canada. Appl. Microbiol. *14:* 789–793.

(19) INGRAM, M., B. COLEBY, M. J. THORNLEY, and G. M. WILSON. Advantages of irradiating pork and beef in the frozen state for sterilization. P. 161. Proc. of International Conference on the preservation of foods by ionizing radiations, Cambridge, Mass., July 27–30, 1959. Massachusetts Institute of Technology, Cambridge.

(20) INGRAM, M., and T. A. ROBERTS. Microbiological principles in food irradiation. P. 267. "Food Irradiation," Proceedings of a Symposium, Karlsruhe, June 6–10, 1966. International Atomic Energy Agency, Vienna.

(21) JOSEPHSON, E. S., A. BRYNJOLFSSON, and E. WIERBICKI. 1968. Engineering and economics of food irradiation. Trans. New York Acad. of Sci. *30:* 600–614.

(22) KEMPE, L. L., J. T. GRAIKOSKI, and R. A. GILLIES. 1954. Gamma ray sterilization of canned meat previously inoculated with anaerobic bacterial spores. Appl. Microbiol. *2:* 330–332.

(23) KRABBENHOFT, K. L., D. A. CORLETT, Jr., A. W. ANDERSON, and P. R. ELLIKER. 1964. Chemical sensitization of *Clostridium botulinum* spores to radiation in meat. Appl. Microbiol. *12:* 424–427.

(24) LEVINSON, H. S., and M. T. HYATT. 1960. Some effects of heat and ionizing radiation on spores of *Bacillus megaterium*. J. Bacteriol. *80:* 441–451.

(25) MORGAN, B. H., and C. W. BOHRER. 1953. N. C. A.

Information Letter No. 1426. National Canners Association, Washington.

(26) MORGAN, B. H., and J. M. REED. 1954. Resistance of bacterial spores to gamma irradiation. Food Res. *19:* 357–366.

(27) MUNDT, J. O., C. J. MAYHEW, and G. STEWART. 1954. Germination of spores in meats during cure. Food Technol. *8:* 435–436.

(28) ROBERTS, T. A., P. J. DITCHETT, and M. INGRAM. 1965. The effect of sodium chloride on radiation resistance and recovery of irradiated anaerobic spores. J. Appl. Bacteriol. *28:* 336–348.

(29) ROWLEY, D. B., F. FEEHERRY, and H. M. EL-BISI. 1968. Effect of sodium chloride and irradiation on the germination and outgrowth of spores of *Clostridium botulinum* 62A. Bacteriol. Proc. p. 35.

(30) SCHMIDT, C. F. 1963. App. II. Dose requirements for the radiation sterilization of food. Internatl. J. App. Rad. Isotopes. *14:* 19–26.

(31) SCHMIDT, C. F., and W. K. NANK. 1960. Radiation sterilization of Food. I. Procedures for the evaluation of the radiation resistance of spores of *Clostridium botulinum* in food products. Food Res. *25:* 321–327.

(32) SCHMIDT, C. F., W. K. NANK, and R. V. LECHOWICH. 1962. Radiation sterilization of food. II. Some aspects of the growth, sporulation and radiation resistance of spores of *Clostridium botulinum* Type E. J. Food Science *27:* 77–84.

(33) SILLIKER, J. H., R. A. GREENBERG, and W. R. SCHACK. 1958. Effect of individual curing ingredients on the shelf stability of canned comminuted meats. Food Technol. *12:* 551–554.

(34) THORNLEY, M. J. 1963. Radiation resistance among bacteria. J. Appl. Bacteriol. *26:* 334–345.

(35) WADSWORTH, C. K., and G. W. SHULTS. 1966. Low temperature irradiation of meat. U. S. Army Natick Laboratories Publ. Activities Report *18:* 13–17.

(36) WYNNE, E. S., W. R. SCHMIEDING, and G. T. DAYE, JR. 1955. A simplified medium for counting *Clostridium* spores. Food Res. *20:* 9–12.

THE EFFECTS OF CHEMICALS UPON THE GROWTH OF *CLOSTRIDIUM BOTULINUM**

by R. V. LECHOWICH
Department of Food Science, Michigan State University, East Lansing, Mich. 48823

Summary

Many chemical substances which are permitted for use in foods or in food processing are inhibitory to the outgrowth of spores of *Clostridium botulinum*. Approximately 8.2 to 10.5 percent sodium chloride (NaCl) has been reported to inhibit outgrowth of types A and B *C. botulinum* while only 5.0 percent NaCl has inhibited the outgrowth of type E spores. Sucrose concentrations of 30 to 55 percent inhibit the outgrowth of types A, B, and E *C. botulinum*. The effect of the antibiotics subtilin, nisin, and tylosin on the outgrowth of *C. botulinum* spores are presented. As little as 0.5 to 5.0 p.p.m. of tylosin lactate has inhibited outgrowth of the serotypes A, B, and E. The pH limits for outgrowth of type E *C. botulinum* spores show that outgrowth at a specific pH is temperature dependent and outgrowth (but not germination) at optimum conditions is inhibited at pH 5.0. Inhibition of spore outgrowth of *C. botulinum* by sodium nitrite, sodium nitrate, sodium benzoate, sodium parahydroxy benzoate, and disodium ethylenediaminetetraacetic acid have been reported. Chlorine in the form of gaseous chlorine or calcium hypochlorite were effective sporicides at a concentration of 7.5 p.p.m. of free chlorine at pH 6.5. Solute concentration affects the water activity (a_w) of microbial substances. The limiting a_w values for types A and B spores have been reported as ranging between 0.94 to 0.96 a_w. Type E spores are inhibited by lower a_w and values of 0.97 to 0.98 a_w have been reported by three different laboratories. The inhibitory a_w for type E *C. botulinum* spores at 30° C. at the following concentrations (w/w) of solutes in the medium was: 5 percent NaCl (a_w 0.975), 6.0 percent KCl (a_w 0.974), 5.5 percent NaCOOH (a_w 0.971), 22.5 percent glucose (a_w 0.970), and 35.0 percent sucrose (a_w 0.977).

Introduction

Some of the resistance characteristics of the spores of *C. botulinum* were presented by Smith (*24*). He stated that "The spores of *C. botulinum* are quite resistant to chemical agents. Exposure of the spores to 5

---

*Michigan Agricultural Experiment Station Journal, article No. 4522.

percent phenol or 'Lysol' did not inactivate the spores within 7 days. Severe treatments such as exposure to 10 percent hydrochloric acid destroys the spores within 1 hour. Commercial formalin diluted with an equal volume of hot water and exposing the organism for at least 24 hours was recommended for the disinfection of material which cannot be heated or treated with hydrochloric acid. Quaternary ammonium compounds are probably rather ineffective."

The study of chemical inhibition of the growth of *C. botulinum* is somewhat complicated due to the nature of the organism itself. The various serotypes of the micro-organisms comprising *C. botulinum* can be grouped into two physiological groups: those which are proteolytic and those which are saccharolytic. Although the types A, B, and F are generally regarded as proteolytic and the types C, D, and E as saccharolytic, saccharolytic types B and F also do occur. It would be expected that micro-organisms with greatly different schemes for obtaining energy would be quite different with respect to their resistances to adverse conditions such as heat, cold, chemicals, and radiation. This is indeed what has been reported.

The types A and B *C. botulinum* have been more widely studied with regard to the effects of chemicals upon their growth, most probably due to their greater heat and radiation resistances and therefore of greater importance to the food industry. In addition, the relatively recent discoveries of type E and especially type F, coupled with the relative rarity of type F, would result in a decreased amount of data on chemical inhibition being available for these serotypes.

Limited data are available on the effects of chemicals upon the growth of types C and D as well. More recent studies have been principally concerned with determining inhibitory agents effective against the outgrowth of type E *C. botulinum*. These studies have also included the concept of the effects of solutes upon the equilibrium relative humidity (ERH) or water activity (a_w) of solutions and this important concept will be discussed in further detail in the last section of this presentation.

Besides the physiological differences of *C. botulinum* which determine their resistances to chemicals, there are many experimental variables which can affect resistance such as inoculum size, cell type, physiological condition of the cells, temperature, composition of the suspending medium or substrate, pH, and oxidation-reduction potential. Thus, resistance experiments of any sort must be designed so that all other variables with the exception of the test variable are optimal for the growth of the micro-organism.

A further comment on the type of inoculum used in resistance studies is warranted. Either vegetative cells or spores may be used as inocula, and it would be desirable to include both cell types. Data also indicate that spore germination can occur within a narrower range of environmental conditions than does vegetative cell growth. Although spore germination is an important index, most food microbiologists are more concerned about the outgrowth of the germinated spore into an actively growing vegetative cell population. It is this actively growing, toxin-producing vegetative cell population that we are trying to control in food protection studies.

Sodium chloride and sucrose.—Historically, two commonly accepted, widely used, and generally recognized as safe food chemicals are NaCl and sucrose. These have been added to foods in salting or syruping procedures for centuries. Table 1 presents a partial summary of inhibitory concentrations of NaCl and sucrose which have historical significance as food preservation agents.

Table 1.—Inhibitory levels of NaCl and sucrose required to inhibit Clostridium botulinum under optimum conditions

Type of C. botulinum	Inhibitory substance	Inhibitory concentration percent (w/w)	Inhibits
A and B	NaCl	8.5–10.5	Growth of vegetative and spore inocula.
Do	NaCl	6.25 in aqueous phase of ham.	Proteolysis and putrefaction—not toxin formation.
Do	NaCl	9.0	Toxin formation.
Do	NaCl	8.2	Growth of vegetative inocula.
E	NaCl	5.0	Spore outgrowth.
E	NaCl	5.8	Growth of vegetative cells.
E	NaCl	6.5 (>4.8)	Do.
E	NaCl	4.9	Spore outgrowth.
A and B	Sucrose	50–55	Growth of vegetative cells.
B	do	30	Do.
B	do	31	Spore germination.
E	do	38.5	Spore outgrowth.

It is apparent from the data in table 1 that the studies reported by Tanner and Evans (25) concerning NaCl inhibition of types A and B have remained valid since there are no major differences between their studies and those of Baird-Parker and Freame

(1). The range of NaCl concentration inhibiting growth of types A and B is between 8.2 to 10.5 percent based upon use of different strains. It should be noted that proteolysis and putrefactive changes of pasteurized ham produced by a 10-strain mixture of types A and B C. botulinum were inhibited at concentrations of 6.25 to 8.95 percent NaCl (10). However, toxin was produced in 14 out of 104 samples containing an average NaCl concentration of 7.12 percent in the water phase of the ham. No toxic samples were detected in the above group when the average salt content of the water phase was 8.95 percent.

The inhibitory NaCl level for type E outgrowth is considerably lower than that reported for types A and B and is reported as between 4.9 and 5.8 percent (1, 6, 17, 20). Baird-Parker and Freame (1) reported growth in the presence of 4.8 percent NaCl, but not in 6.5 percent.

Sucrose is another solute which has been employed in confections, canned breads, and bakery products to control spore outgrowth, including C. botulinum. There is a substantial difference between the inhibitory sucrose concentration of 50 to 55 percent reported by Bever and Halvorson (3) and the 30 to 31 percent sucrose inhibition of type B as noted by Beers (2). However, both types A and B strains were used in the earlier study while Beers reported data only for type B.

Studies performed in our laboratory (7) indicate that the inhibitory level of sucrose for four strains of type E C. botulinum is comparable to that reported by Beers for type B, since our reported inhibitory concentration was 38.5 percent as determined at 30° C.

Antibiotics.—Due to the criteria imposed by the U.S. Food and Drug Administration on the use of antibiotics in foods, little commercial interest has been shown in this area. Prior to 1966, substantial work had been done. Kaufmann et al. (13) examined nine antibiotics for their effectiveness in inhibiting the outgrowth of type B C. botulinum. These antibiotics included neomycin, celiomycin, streptin, circulin, and five experimental antibiotics. None was effective in inhibiting outgrowth of the type B strain.

The polypeptide antibiotic subtilin gave promising results when 4 μg./ml. of substrate was reported to be inhibitory for type 62A C. botulinum. However, Campbell and Winiarski (4) showed that type 62A would develop a resistance to subtilin, and they reported that a mutant strain of 62A gave good growth in 100 μg. of subtilin per milliliter. Control of both the parent and mutant strain was accomplished by the use of 30 μg. of nisin per milliliter. It appears that the polypeptide antibiotic nisin is at least as effective as subtilin. Unfortunately, nisin is not effective in non-acid foods at or near pH 7.0.

Tylosin or tylosin lactate has appeared to have some applications as an additive to minimize economic spoilage of canned foods. Data presented by Denny et al. (5) and by Greenberg and Silliker (9) showed that members of the genus *Clostridium* are highly susceptible to tylosin. Most researchers have stipulated that tylosin and other food processing adjuvants should not be considered as a means of reducing thermal processes below a "minimum botulinum cook" which is defined as equivalent to 2.8 minutes of heating at 121° C. As little as 5 p.p.m. of tylosin lactate was found to be inhibitory to types A and B spore outgrowth when added to six different canned foods containing meat. Tylosin was found to inhibit outgrowth of the germinated spore while germination was unaffected.

One product type in which the use of another inhibitory ingredient appears warranted is that of the partially preserved or semipreserved fish products. There are several species of hot smoked (70° to 82° C.) and cold smoked (30° to 37° C.) fishery products which depend solely upon their NaCl content and use of low temperatures (2° to 4° C.) to prevent the outgrowth of type E spores which can be present in an appreciable percentage of fish samples in certain sections of the world. It was for this reason that Sheneman (22) examined the use of 100 p.p.m. of tylosin lactate in the brining procedure used for whitefish "chubs." After smoking at approximately 55° or 65° C. for 30 minutes, residual tylosin ranged from about 0.5 to 5 p.p.m. This tylosin residual remained relatively constant in the product for at least 30 days at 6° C. Fish containing tylosin did not support the growth of type E *C. botulinum* during 14 days of incubation at ambient conditions. Further studies and commercial trials with this additive appear warranted when the regulatory position on the use of antibiotics in foods changes.

In contrast to U.S. Food and Drug Administration regulations, Japan permits the use of several antibiotics in fishery products. Kawabata et al. (14) summarized the use of these antibiotics in fishery products. They reported that chlortetracycline is approved for use in Japan for preserving raw fish for fish paste products such as "Kamaboko" and for canned or salted salmon. Furylfuramide, or 2-(2-furyl)-3-(5-nitro-2-furyl) acrylamide, has been permitted for use in Japan since 1965 and has been substituted for nitrofurazone and nitrofuryl acrylamide. Furylfuramide is a widespectrum antibiotic, is fairly stable to heat and is recommended for use at 20 p.p.m. in fish sausage and 2.5 p.p.m. in semipreserved food products such as Kamaboko.

Tylosin has not yet been approved for use in Japan but many trials have been performed there evaluating its efficacy in semipreserved foods such as fish sausage

and bean-curd cake as well as in certain canned foods. These studies have demonstrated that the effectiveness of tylosin against gram-positive organisms coupled with tylosin's low toxicity appear to render this antibiotic a useful food additive.

Other inhibitors.—pH. It is generally agreed that the limiting pH for the growth of spore inocula of *C. botulinum* types A and B is pH 4.6 to 5.0 (11). Table 2 presents these data and that reported for the inhibition of type E spores which is generally considered to occur at pH 5.0 under optimal conditions. The study of Segner et al. (21) showed that the limiting pH for growth of type E strains in laboratory media depended upon the initial number of spores in the inoculum, the amount of reducing agent present, and the incubation temperature. They reported a limiting pH of 5.03 for growth in the best medium inoculated with about 1×10^6 heat shocked spores per milliliter at 30° C. while at 8° C. the limiting pH was 5.9 and was even higher for unheated spores. In liver broth the limiting pH for vegetative cell growth from spore inocula was pH 5.22 but germination did occur at pH 5.01.

Table 2.—pH limits for outgrowth of *Clostridium botulinum*

Type of *C. botulinum*	Inoculum	Lowest pH permitting	
		Germination	Outgrowth
A and B	Spores		4.6–5.0
A	do	5.3	5.3
	Vegetative cells		5.0
B	Spores (30° C.)	5.0	5.0
	(20° C.)	5.0	(1)
	Vegetative cells		5.3
E	Spores	5.0	5.3
	Vegetative cells		5.3
E	Spores in TPG (30° C.)		5.03
	(8° C.)		5.90
	Spores in liver broth	5.01	5.22
E	Spores at 15.6° C.		5.2
	10.0° C.		5.4
	7.2° C.		5.6
	5.0° C.		6.0

[1]No growth.

Baird-Parker and Freame (1) reported similar findings for the Beluga strain of *C. botulinum* type E with germination but no outgrowth at pH 5.0 while outgrowth from vegetative or spore inocula was obtained at pH 5.3. Spores of the type A strain germinated at pH 5.3, and vegetative cell inocula produced growth at pH 5.0 when incubated at 30° C. but not at 20° C. The type B spores germinated at 20° C. at pH 5.0 but could not grow further, while germination and outgrowth took place at 30° C. at pH 5.0.

Emodi and Lechowich (6) reported that the pH

limits for outgrowth of five type E strains in a laboratory medium were also temperature dependent. Outgrowth from spore inocula occurred at pH 5.2 at 15.6° C., while at 5.0° C. pH 6.0 was the lowest pH that permitted outgrowth.

Sodium nitrite and sodium nitrate.—Sodium nitrite and sodium nitrate have received wide use as meat curing agents for a long time. It was believed that concentrations in excess of 0.2 to 0.5 percent retarded both the rate of death and the outgrowth of anaerobic spores in canned ham. Tarr (27) believed that the inhibitory action of nitrate was due to inhibition of catalase by hydroxylamine formed during nitrate reduction which permitted hydrogen peroxide to accumulate in the medium. *Clostridial* spores are quite sensitive to hydrogen peroxide.

Nitrite at approximately 200 p.p.m. was effective against microbial spores only when the pH was below 7.0 and was more effective when the pH was less than 6.5.

Yesair and Cameron (29) found a 70 percent decrease in the spore count of *C. botulinum by* the addition of 0.1 percent sodium nitrate, 0.005 percent sodium nitrite, or 2 percent NaCl to a meat infusion agar. Nitrites have also been reported to have a considerable inhibitory influence on the spores of *C. botulinum* and those of other clostridia (23). The effect of approximately 80 p.p.m. of nitrite has been reported to be comparable in inhibiton to that of 3.5 percent of NaCl in the aqueous phase of canned cured meat. Silliker et al. (23) have shown that a combination of 78 p.p.m. of sodium nitrite, 3.5 percent NaCl in the aqueous phase of a meat product, and slight heat injury resulted in sufficient damage to clostridial spores to prevent subsequent growth in the product. The use of nitrate appeared to be of little value against anaerobic spores. Tarr (26) reported that a range of from 25 to 500 p.p.m. of nitrite inhibited type A *C. botulinum* spores for more than 1 month at optimum temperatures and at a pH range of 5.9 to 7.6.

Pivnick and Barnett (18) reported that toxin production in ham was considerably delayed but not prevented when the nitrite concentration was increased while the sodium chloride concentration was kept constant. Their data for types A and B spores inoculated into ham and incubated at several temperatures are reported in table 3. As the nitrite concentration increased, toxinogenesis was delayed. A decrease in temperature from 30° to 20° C. delayed toxinogenesis for an additional 13 days even when nitrite was omitted.

Segner, et al. (20) reported that outgrowth of the Beluga strain of type E was inhibited in haddock homogenate by the addition of sodium nitrite. Table 4 shows the effect of nitrite addition at 8° C. incuba-

Table 3.—Effect of nitrite concentration and temperature on toxinogenesis by types A and B *Clostridium botulinum* in cooked sliced ham[1]

Nitrite added (parts per million)	Nitrite recovered after cooking (parts per million)	Temperature (°C.)	Nitrite recovered after 1 week (parts per million)	Days to become toxic
0	0	30	0	2
		25	0	3
		20	0	15
50	37	30	9	3
		25	9	4
		20	23	25
300	160	30	15	8
		25	42	25
		20	130	60

[1]Ham was sliced, vacuum packed in air-impermeable pouches, and was inoculated with 10,000 spores per gram prior to cooking to 70° C. Postprocessing sodium chloride concentration in the aqueous phase was 4.1 percent.

Table 4.—The effect of sodium nitrite on spore outgrowth of *Clostridium botulinum* type E Beluga at 8° C. in haddock homogenate

Nitrite concentration (parts per million)	Average outgrowth time in days
0	8
50	10
100	11
150	11
200	16

tion. In the presence of 200 p.p.m. of nitrite outgrowth was not prevented, but the outgrowth time was doubled. It required 500 p.p.m. of nitrite to completely inhibit type E outgrowth at 6° C. A concentration of 500 p.p.m. of sodium nitrate in haddock homogenate did not prevent outgrowth of four type E strains at either 6° or 8° C.

Graikoski (8) has reported that smoked whitefish chubs containing more than 3 percent NaCl in the aqueous phase and about 100 p.p.m. of sodium nitrite were incapable of supporting the outgrowth of type E spores when 1 x 10^6 spores were inoculated into the loin muscle of each fish after heat processing.

Sodium benzoate.—Table 5 presents a comparison of the effects of sodium benzoate or sodium parahydroxy benzoate (PHB) on spore outgrowth of the Beluga type E strain at 8° C. incubation (20). The PHB form appeared to be a better inhibitor of spore outgrowth, since outgrowth time was somewhat increased at the 100-p.p.m. level and was substantially increased over the control and benzoate variables at the 500-p.p.m. level.

Table 5.—The effect of sodium benzoate or sodium-para-hydroxy benzoate on spore outgrowth *Clostridium botulinum* type E Beluga at 8° C. in haddock homogenate

Additive concentration (parts per million)	Average outgrowth time in days	
	Na benzoate	Na parahydroxy benzoate
0	8	8
100	8	11
500	14	24

Ethylenediaminetetraacetic acid (EDTA).— The effects of the disodium salt of EDTA upon the outgrowth of heat shocked spores of four type E strains in haddock homogenate incubated at various temperatures was also reported by Segner, et al. (20). Table 6 presents the data obtained for incubation temperatures between 6° and 30° C. The concentration required for inhibition increased with temperatures between 6° and 21° C. but decreased at 30° C.

Although the mechanism of inhibition of type E outgrowth by nitrite and the benzoates is not perfectly clear, Segner, et al. (20) proposed that EDTA functions to chelate essential cations which are necessary for spore outgrowth. They confirmed the previous results using much higher concentrations (1,000 to 5,000 p.p.m.) of sodium tripolyphosphate which is a much less effective chelator of cations than EDTA.

Table 6.—The effect of temperature on the inhibitory concentration of disodium EDTA upon four type E *Clostridium botulinum* strains in haddock homogenate

Incubation temperature (°C.)	Inhibitory concentration (parts per million)
6	150
8	200
10	250
16	300
21	350
30	200

Chlorine.—Studies performed at the National Canner's Association of the United States have indicated that chlorine is an effective sporicidal agent against *C. botulinum* (12). The studies they have been performing are designed to obtain better methods of sanitation and inplant control of *C. botulinum* in food processing plants. These studies determined the chlorine resistance of two type A, two type B, and four type E strains in phosphate buffered calcium hypochlorite solutions at pH 6.5. A 99.99-percent reduction in spore count in the presence of 7.5 p.p.m. of free chlorine was obtained in 4 to 6 minutes for the type

E strains and in 3 to 8 minutes for the types A and B strains. One strain each of types A, B, and E spores was exposed to calcium hypochlorite solutions at various pH. The time required to destroy 99.99 percent of the botulinum spores increased as the pH increased from 3.5 to 8.0.

One strain of types A, B, and E spores was exposed to organic debris such as fish oil, peptone, and fish material. Under these conditions, the chlorine dosage must be adequate to satisfy the chlorine demand and provide a free chlorine residual before any germicidal advantages of chlorine could be shown

Results for one type E strain indicated that the time required to destroy 99.99 percent of the population decreased as the concentration of available chlorine increased. Studies with this type E strain indicated that the time required to destroy 99.99 percent of the population approximately doubled for each 10° C. rise in temperature. One type E *C. botulinum* strain was exposed to various sporicidal compounds in pH 6.5 phosphate buffer. Calcium hypochlorite and water chlorinated with gaseous chlorine were the most effective sporicides of the compounds tested.

Solutes and Their Effect on Water Activity

Recent studies on the effects of solutes upon the growth of *C. botulinum* have included the concept of water activity (a_w) of the solute-solvent system as an index of the availability of the water for microbial growth. Scott (19) defined a_w as a fundamental property of aqueous solutions that is equal to $\frac{p}{p_0} = \frac{n_2}{n_1 + n_2}$; where p is the vapor pressure of the solution and p_0 is the vapor pressure of the solvent, and n_1 and n_2 refer to the number of moles of solute and solvent in the solution. Scott showed that the inhibitory effect of different carbohydrates and salts on certain bacteria could be explained by their effect on a_w. Scott (19) examined the relationship of the a_w concept to canned ham and showed that the a_w of canned ham was largely due to the brine concentration of the ham. However, the salt concentration and the a_w do not always correspond for all cured meat products. Scott (19) reported that the a_w of canned ham varied between 0.95 and 0.97. This compares with the reported data that *C. botulinum* type B would grow in 50 percent sucrose (a_w 0.935) but not in 55 percent sucrose (a_w 0.917). However, Beers (2) reported that germination was prevented by 31 percent sucrose (a_w 0.975) and growth was prevented by 30 percent sucrose (a_w 0.976). Williams and Purnell (28) reported that germination of *C. botulinum* spores would occur in liver powder adjusted to various a_w levels even when the a_w was somewhat less than 0.90, but vegetative cell development was reduced at 0.94 to 0.96 a_w and generally was prevented at 0.95 to 0.90 a_w. Scott (*19*) believed that the a_w measurements reported in these earlier studies were not accurate and indicated that the minimum a_w permitting development of spores into vegetative cells in media containing various solutes was about 0.95 a_w.

Ohye and Christian (*16*) studied the effects of a_w and pH on the ability of spores of *C. botulinum* types A, B, and E to initiate growth at temperatures between 0° and 50° C. using a mixture of salts to adjust the a_w. Between the optimum conditions of 30° to 40° C. and pH 7.0, growth was inhibited at a_w levels of 0.95 for type A, 0.94 for type B and 0.97 for type E. When the temperature was reduced from the optimum to 20° C. for types A and B, the limiting a_w values became 0.97 for both types. Type E was inhibited by 0.97 a_w at both 30° C. and 20° C., but only 0.99 a_w became inhibitory for type E at 10° C. Not only does temperature affect the minimum a_w limiting growth of *C. botulinum*, a change in pH from the optimum also served to increase the minimum a_w at which vegetative cell growth was prevented. It appeared that there was an interaction between pH and temperature for the type E spores which was less pronounced with the types A and B spores.

Ohye et al. (*17*) studied the effect of a_w on the growth of *C. botulinum* from spore and vegetative cell inocula and the effect of temperature on the limiting a_w. They found that the growth of *C. botulinum* type E from vegetative cell inocula was limited at almost the same a_w whether NaCl alone or a mixture of NaCl, KCl, and Na_2SO_4 were used to adjust the a_w of the growth medium. However, the data presented in table 7 show that the salt mixture was slightly less inhibitory than NaCl alone.

The most salt tolerant strain they encountered was the 103 strain which grew at a minimum a_w of 0.965 when incubated at 25° or 30° C. Strain 103 grew in 0.970 a_w at 20° C. and at 0.975 a_w at 15° C. They found that the optimum a_w for growth was 0.995, and any reduction in a_w affected the growth

rate of the strains at any of the four temperatures they studied.

Baird-Parker and Freame (*1*) also investigated the a_w relationships of one strain each of types A, B, and E *C. botulinum* under a variety of environmental conditions. These workers evaluated the effects of various concentrations of NaCl and glycerol on the germination and growth over a wide range of pH and temperature.

The water activity measurements were confirmed experimentally on all variables after preparation. Baird-Parker and Freame devised an electrical dewpoint measuring apparatus with a reported accuracy of ±0.002 a_w. Unfortunately, this instrument is not commercially available. Table 8 summarizes a portion of their study and presents only the results obtained at pH 6.0 and 7.0 and at 20° and 30° C. incubation.

There is reasonably close agreement between the results of Ohye and Christian (*16*) who reported limiting a_w values of 0.95, 0.94, and 0.97 for types A, B, and E, respectively, and the limiting a_w values reported by Baird-Parker and Freame (*1*) of 0.96, 0.96, and 0.98 a_w for types A, B, and E, respectively. However, lower limiting values were reported when glycerol was present in the medium.

We examined the effect of a wider range of solutes upon the outgrowth of type E *C. botulinum* covering a large portion of the growth temperature range for type E (*7*). Both electrolytes and nonelectrolytes were used in this study and the a_w of a trypticase-peptone-sucrose-yeast extract medium was adjusted to different a_w levels by the addition of NaCl, KCl, NaCOOH, glucose or sucrose. The graphical interpolation method of Landrock and Proctor (*15*) was used to measure a_w. The a_w variables ranged from 0.988 to 0.969 a_w and incubation temperatures included 7.2°, 10°, 15.6°, 21.1°, and 30° C. The incubation period was for 180 days at each temperature. The results for four type E strains are presented in table 9.

The inhibitory levels of a_w at 30° C. were obtained at the following concentrations (w/w) of solutes in

Table 7.—Growth of four strains of type E *Clostridium botulinum* at low a_w levels in a laboratory medium

Temperature	15° C.				20° C.				25° C.				30° C.			
a_w	0.975		0.970		0.970		0.965		0.970		0.965		0.970		0.965	
Solutes added	NaCl	S.M.[1]	NaCl	S.M.	NaCl	S.M.	NaCl	S.M.	NaCl	S.M.	NaCl	S.M.	NaCl	S.M.	NaCl	S.M.
Strain:																
102	+[2]	+	−	−	−	+	−	−	+	−	−	+	+	−	−	−
103	+	+	−	−	+	+	−	−	+	+	−	+	+	+	−	+
104	+	+	−	−	−	−	−	−	−	−	−	−	−	−	−	−
160	+	+	−	−	−	−	−	−	−	−	−	−	−	−	−	−

[1]Salts mixture of NaCl, KCl, and Na_2SO_4. [2]+ = growth, − = no growth.

Table 8.—Minimum water activity permitting growth of *Clostridium botulinum* types A, B, and E from vegetative cell inocula at pH 6.0 and pH 7.0

	Minimum a_w permitting growth in media at —					
	pH 7.0 containing			pH 6.0 containing		
C. botulinum type	Glycerol at 30° C.	NaCl at— 20° C.	NaCl at— 30° C.	Glycerol at 30° C.	NaCl at— 20° C.	NaCl at— 30° C.
A	0.93	0.97	0.96	0.94	0.98	0.97
B	.93	.97	.96	.94	.97	.96
E	.95	.98	.98	.95	.98	.98

Table 9.—Water activity limits for outgrowth of spore inocula of 4 type E *Clostridium botulinum* strains in laboratory medium containing various solutes

Solute added to medium	Incubation temperature				
	30° C.	21.1° C.	15.6° C.	10° C.	7.2° C.
NaCl	0.975	$(^1)$	0.975	0.975	0.975
KCl	.974	0.976	.974	.980	.980
NaCOOH	.971	.971	.971	.979	.976
Glucose	.970	.970	.970	.972	.970
Sucrose	.977	.976	.977	.977	.977

[1]Not tested.

the medium: 5.0% NaCl (a_w 0.975), 6.0% KCl (a_w 0.974), 5.5% NaCOOH (a_w 0.971), 22.5% glucose (a_w 0.970), and 35.0% sucrose (a_w 0.977).

The ability of the different strains to germinate and produce outgrowth in the different solute-containing media was quite constant at 30° C., but varied widely (from 2 to 86 days) at 15.6° C. and below. The ability of the strains to produce outgrowth at almost identical a_w levels was only slightly different. The Vancouver Herring strain required somewhat more time to produce outgrowth at the three lower temperatures, but it and the Seattle Forks strain possessed somewhat greater tolerance to increased solute concentration.

The morphology of the cultures producing outgrowth at the lowest a_w levels was examined. The cells appeared normal and sporulation was detected in the media containg glucose and sucrose. The salt-controlled media produced long filamentous vegetative cells, long chains of cells, some curved rods, and a few normal cells. Sporulation was not observed in the media containing salt. Thus, normal growth of *C. botulinum* is affected by electrolytes even though the water activity limits are the same as those produced by the sugars that are not electrolytes.

The finding that glycerol appears to act upon *C. botulinum* cells in a different fashion thus producing an increased tolerance to a_w was confirmed in our

laboratory. Outgrowth took place when the a_w of the medium containing glycerol was less than 0.95. Thus, another factor besides a_w may be affecting the outgrowth of *C. botulinum* in the presence of high concentrations of polyhydric alcohols.

In conclusion, the botulism hazard of foods appears to be considerably reduced when several inhibitory conditions are simultaneously imposed upon a food product. The interrelationships of reduced temperature, pH, presence of antibiotics, presence of inhibitors, or reduced a_w remain subjects for additional study.

References

(1) BAIRD-PARKER, A. C., and B. FREAME. 1967. Combined effect of water activity, pH, and temperature on the growth of *Clostridium botulinum* from spore and vegetative cell inocula. J. Appl. Bacteriol. *30:* 420–429.

(2) BEERS, R. J. 1957. Effect of moisture activity on germination. *In* H. O. Halvorson (ed.), "Spores" p. 45–55. A.I.B.S., Washington, D.C.

(3) BEVER, J. S., and H. O. HALVORSON. 1948. Rep. Hormel Inst. Univ. Minn. 1947–48. (*In* Scott, 1955, reference 19.)

(4) CAMPBELL, L. L., and W. WINIARSKI. 1959. Isolation and properties of a subtilin resistant strain of *Clostridium botulinum*. Appl. Microbiol. *7:* 285–288.

(5) DENNY, C. B., L. E. SHARPE, and C. W. BOHRER. 1961. Effects of tylosin and nisin on canned food spoilage bacteria. Appl. Microbiol. *9:* 108–110.

(6) EMODI, A. S., and R. V. LECHOWICH. 1968a. Low temperature growth of type E *Clostridium botulinum* spores. I. Effect of sodium chloride, sodium nitrite, and pH. J. Food Sci. *33:* in press.

(7) EMODI, A. S., and R. V. LECHOWICH. 1968b. Low temperature growth of type E *Clostridium botulinum* spores. II. Effects of solutes and incubation temperature. J. Food Sci. *33:* in press.

(8) GRAIKOSKI, J. T. 1968. Personal communication.

(9) GREENBERG, R. A., and J. H. SILLIKER. 1964. Spoilage patterns in *Clostridium botulinum*—inoculated canned foods treated with tylosin, 4th Intl. Symp. on Food Microbiol. SIK, Gothenberg, Sweden.

(10) GREENBERG, R. A., J. H. SILLIKER, and L. D. FATTA. 1959. The influence of sodium chloride on toxin production and organoleptic breakdown in perishable cured meat inoculated with *Clostridium botulinum*. Food Technol. *13:* 509–511.

(11) INGRAM, M., and R. H. M. ROBINSON. 1951. A discussion of the literature on botulism in relations to acid food. Proc. Soc. Appl. Bacteriol. *14:* 73–84.

(12) ITO, K. 1968. Personal communication.

(13) KAUFMANN, O. W., Z. J. ORDAL, and H. M. EL-BISI. 1954. The effect of several antibiotics on certain sporeforming organisms involved in food spoilage. Food Res. *19:* 483–487.

(14) KAWABATA, T., T. KOZIMA, N. SHIMURA, and E. YOSHIMURA. 1968. Factors affecting the stability of chlortetracycline, tylosin, and furylfuramide against low level of ionizing radiation. J. Food Sci. *33:* 110–113.

(15) LANDROCK, A. H., and B. E. PROCTOR. 1951. A new graphical interpolation method for obtaining equilibrium relative humidity data, with special reference to its role in food packaging studies. Food Technol. *5:* 332–337

(16) OHYE, D. F., and J. H. B. CHRISTIAN. 1967. Combined effects of temperature, pH and water activity on growth and toxin production by *Clostridium botulinum* types A, B, and E. *In* Botulism 1966 M. Ingram and T. A. Roberts, (eds.), pp. 217–223. Chapman & Hall, Ltd., London.

(17) OHYE, D. F., J. H. B. CHRISTIAN, and W. J. SCOTT. 1967. Influence of temperature on the water relations of growth of *Clostridium botulinum* type E. *In* Botulism 1966. M. Ingram and T. A. Roberts, (eds.) pp. 136–143. Chapman & Hall, Ltd., London.

(18) PIVNICK, H., and H. BARNETT. 1965. Effect of salt and temperature on toxinogenesis by *Clostridium botulinum* in perishable cooked meats vacuum-packed in air-impermeable plastic pouches. Food Technol. *19:* 140–143.

(19) SCOTT, W. J. 1955. Factors in canned ham controlling *Clostridium botulinum* and *Staphylococcus aureus*. Ann. Inst. Pasteur Lille *7:* 68–74.

(20) SEGNER, W. P., C. F. SCHMIDT, and J. K. BOLTZ. 1966. The interaction of selected chemical additives with low doses of ionizing radiation against *Clostridium botulinum* type E spores. Institute of Food Technologists, Portland, Ore., p. 146.

(21) SEGNER, W. P., C. F. SCHMIDT, and J. K. BOLTZ. 1966. Effect of sodium chloride and pH on the outgrowth of spores of type E *Clostridium botulinum* at optimal and suboptimal temperatures. Appl. Microbiol. *14:* 49–54.

(22) SHENEMAN, J. M. 1965. Prevention of type E *Clostridium botulinum* toxin formation in smoked whitefish chubs with tylosin lactate. J. Food Sci. *30:* 337–343.

(23) SILLIKER, J. H., R. A. GREENBERG, and W. R. SCHACK. 1958. Effect of individual curing ingredients on the shelf stability of canned comminuted meats. Food Technol. *12:* 551–554.

(24) SMITH, L. D. S. 1955. Introduction to the pathogenic anaerobes. 253 p. Univ. Chicago Press, Chicago.

(25) TANNER, F. W., and F. L. EVANS. 1933. Effect of meat-curing solutions on anaerobic bacteria. I. Sodium chloride. Centbl. Bakt., 2 Abt. *88:* 44–54.

(26) TARR, H. L. A. 1953. The action of hydroxylamine on bacteria. J. Fish. Res. Bd. Canada *10:* 69–75.

(27) TARR, H. L. A. 1962. Microbial inhibitors. *In* J. C. Ayres, A. A. Kraft, H. E. Snyder, H. W. Walker (ed.) "Chemical and biological hazards in food," pp. 202–223. Iowa State University Press, Ames.

(28) WILLIAMS, O. B., and H. G. PURNELL. 1953. Spore germination, growth, and spore formation by *Clostridium botulinum* in relation to the water content of the substrate. Food Res. *18:* 35–39.

(29) YESAIR, J., and E. J. CAMERON. 1942. Inhibitive effect of curing agents on anaerobic spores. Canner *94:* 89–92.

CLOSING PLENARY

• • •

CLOSING REMARKS

by DR. CHESTER R. BENJAMIN
Panel Chairman

There is an old saying in the United States that all good things must come to an end. This is the case for the present conference. Although my knowledge of what transpired in the botulism sessions is limited, I understand that these sessions were generally thought quite good, with active and valuable discussion. I know firsthand that the mycotoxin sessions were uniformly excellent.

You may be interested in the joint communique that we have prepared to be released by the press tomorrow. It is as follows: (read joint communique, see page 482).

This, then, reflects some of the results of the Conference. In terms of the five objectives that I identified in the opening plenary session, I feel that most, or perhaps all, of them may have been attained or will be effected by publication of our proceedings volume.

Before closing, let me make the observation that I have been tremendously impressed with the high spirit of cooperation that has been obvious throughout our deliberations and with the quality of scientific input by the participants from both Japan and the United States. Also, the organized effort of those of you from Japan to maximize your participation in both the formal presentations and the discussions has contributed greatly to the worth of the programs and is much appreciated.

I should like again to thank you all—participants, committees, session chairmen, interpreters, and others—for your united efforts to make the Conference so fruitful.

Special mention should be made of the efforts of Drs. Amano, Aibara, and Sakaguchi, who made exceptional contributions to our conference, and to Dr. Slater, our chairman, who has assisted us immeasurably all along the way. To all of you thank you. I trust that you all have safe and pleasant return trips home and I look forward to renewing our new and old friendships at another place and time in the not-so-distant future.

CLOSING REMARKS

by Dr. Kageaki Amano
Acting Panel Chairman

I am extremely happy to have this opportunity to thank you all, on behalf of Dr. Miyaki and the Japanese panel members and participants.

During the past 4 days of the sessions, we have read and discussed a number of papers presented by very enthusiastic scientists from the two countries. These papers all contain most valuable information on the important subjects of our common interest.

And participants, particularly from my country, will no doubt say that they have gained much more than they had expected.

I would like to extend sincerest thanks to Dr. Slater, Dr. Benjamin, and his associate panel members, and Dr. Bell, for their assistance during the Conference.

I also wish to extend my hearty thanks to Dr. Herzberg, who has helped a majority of our participants in reviewing our papers for the Proceedings.

Mrs. Lejins and her translator colleagues have contributed a great deal in this Conference by helping us to understand the presentations spoken in English.

I believe, that our people will make wonderful advances in their future work by absorbing the many suggestions given by the Conference.

Again, I do thank you all for your hospitality.

CLOSING REMARKS

by Dr. James A. Slater, *Conference Chairman*

Dr. Amano, Dr. Benjamin, and Distinguished Delegates:

Again, I am privileged to serve as your chairman,— this time to close officially the United States–Japan Conference on Toxic Micro-Organisms. We can close the door on this historic Conference, but we shall never close it on the accomplishments of the past 4 days.

There is no question that we fulfilled our minimum objectives: To compare, gather, and exchange information. This was done through the presentation of the 68 detailed scientific papers that you so thoroughly prepared and ably presented. Just as fruitful were the question-and-answer sessions which were an integral part of our Conference. Even as a complete layman, I was overwhelmed with the depth and comprehensiveness of your discussions. You have indeed set an impressive precedent for the other UJNR panels to follow.

Another important objective that we attained was the establishment of close personal and professional relationships with our Japanese and United States colleagues. Much of this was accomplished through informal, "side-hall" discussions. As a result, we are much better acquainted with the scientists and with their important areas of research. These contacts will prove invaluable for future followup on this Conference.

In our opening plenary session, I indicated that the maximum outcome of the conference would result in identifying and solving serious problems of mutual concern. Again, I feel that we have succeeded, at least in identifying many of the problems. As a matter of fact, our discussions pinpointed a staggering number of problems—ranging from research methodology, to effects on health, to establishment of standards, to techniques of control, and to many other areas. As someone once said, "half the problem is identifying the problem." It will be some time yet before we fully comprehend everything we covered during the last 4 days.

All this work has advanced scientific knowledge toward our ultimate objective of solving serious problems. How rapidly they are solved depends on our application of the knowledge gained here to the benefit of our domestic activities and programs. I encourage each of you to maximize this application as we now return to our respective laboratories and administrative positions.

Before formally closing this final plenary session, I would like to express again my deep and sincere appreciation to each of you who has contributed so significantly to the success of this Conference. In particular, I would like to single out our Japanese colleagues whose extensive preparations and willingness to travel such a long distance to this meeting are symbols of our joint conviction that mutual cooperation in science not only greatly advances our technical knowledge but also creates conditions so vital to world peace. Indeed, President Johnson has termed the search for world peace "the assignment of the century."

On behalf of all Conference participants, I want to express our deep appreciation to the Japanese and United States members of the UJNR Joint Panel on Toxic Micro-Organisms for their superb planning and organization of the Conference. With no discriminating intent, I would like to extend special thanks to Drs. Keith Lewis and Chet Benjamin. I am sure that none of us fully realizes the detailed preparations these two men, over the last 3½ years, have put into the staging of this meeting.

Finally, I want to thank Mrs. Lejins and her very competent (and I might add, patient), staff of interpreters and Dr. Bell, Dr. Herzberg, Mr. Barber, and the University staff for their very willing and able assistance before and during the Conference. Their outstanding efforts have made Honolulu and the East-West Center just like home to us. To show our gratitude for all these efforts, may I suggest we give a rising vote of thanks.

And now, before we adjourn, does anyone wish to comment further? If not, the first UJNR Conference on Toxic Micro-Organisms is hereby closed. Again, many thanks, and Aloha.

JOINT COMMUNIQUE
UJNR CONFERENCE ON TOXIC MICRO-ORGANISMS

October 10, 1968*

United States and Japanese scientists met at the East-West Center, University of Hawaii, during October 7–10 in a joint study of mycotoxins and botulism. This was the first major conference bringing together Japanese and United States governmental scientists working in these vital areas of research dealing with food poisons and harmful organisms. It was also the first large-scale conference held under auspices of the United States–Japan Cooperative Program in Natural Resources (UJNR), which was established in 1964 by the Cabinet-level Joint United States–Japan Committee on Trade and Economic Affairs. The current cooperative program consists of 11 panels of experts; the panel on toxic micro-organisms planned and organized the Hawaiian Conference.

The 4-day meeting was called to order by its Chairman, Dr. James A. Slater, U.S. coordinator for the UJNR. Remarks and welcoming addresses were given by Lt. Gov. Thomas Gill, State of Hawaii; Japanese Consul-General to Hawaii Akira Yoshioka; Vice President Richard S. Takasaki, University of Hawaii; Dr. Keishi Amano, acting Japanese panel chairman; and Dr. Chester R. Benjamin, U.S. panel chairman. Telegrams of greetings and best wishes for a successful conference were received from Dr. Donald Hornig on behalf of President Lyndon Johnson, from Secretary of the Interior Stewart Udall (cabinet coordinator for the UJNR), and from the Secretary of Agriculture Orville Freeman.

After the opening plenary meeting, the 75 scientists were organized into two concurrent sessions—one on mycotoxins and the other on botulism. A few of the salient findings and conclusions were:

Mycotoxins:

(1) Important research results were reported for 23 different mycotoxins produced by 21 fungal species.
(2) The toxic compounds produced by the fungal genus *Fusarium* are of serious concern in the production of rice. Japanese scientists reported a broad series of studies on the chemistry and pathology of these toxins.

(3) Some success was shown in the U.S. attempts to minimize aflatoxin formation under field conditions for the important crops of peanuts, cotton, and soybeans.
(4) Advances were reported in the isolation, identification, chemistry, biosynthesis, destruction, pharmacology, pathology, and other aspects of toxins and on our understanding of the fungi that produce them.
(5) Mycotoxins represent serious potential hazards in certain crops and commercial foods, but so far have not been demonstrated in commercially fermented foods.

Botulism:

(1) Production of antitoxin in humans was suggested to replace equine antiserum for treatment of botulism in order to avoid serum sickness.
(2) Basic scientific information which makes practical the development of a hexavalent toxoid was an important accomplishment.
(3) Outbreaks of type E intoxication, including those caused by ingestion of fish, were reviewed for both countries.
(4) Future cooperation on common problems was recognized to be important.

In summary, many fruitful exchanges of information, data, and research findings were made at the United States–Japan Conference on Toxic Micro-Organisms. The sessions were of great value in facilitating the meeting of many scientists from both countries for direct exchange of ideas and discussion of research in progress. Basic and practical research were intermeshed with an outstanding degree of success. Japanese scientists were particularly pleased, for example, to learn how such practical work as assay methods and large-scale feeding tests on large animals are important to protect man from the hazards of mycotoxins.

The results of the Conference will benefit domestic programs and research work throughout the world. It is through such efforts that man might someday control many of the harmful organisms that have plagued him through the ages.

---

*Issued by Joint Panel on Toxic Micro-Organisms, UJNR, at the final meeting of the Conference.

UJNR JOINT PANELS ON TOXIC MICRO-ORGANISMS

Japanese Panel

DR. KOMEI MIYAKI, *Chairman*
Ministry of Health and Welfare
DR. KEISHI AMANO, *Alternate Chairman*
Ministry of Agriculture and Forestry
DR. KAGEAKI AIBARA
Ministry of Health and Welfare
MR. MITSUO KANBAYASHI
Ministry of Health and Welfare
DR. HIROSHI KURATA
Ministry of Health and Welfare
DR. GENJI SAKAGUCHI
Ministry of Health and Welfare
DR. SHINJI MATSUURA
Ministry of Agriculture and Forestry
DR. TOMOTARO SATO
Ministry of Agriculture and Forestry

U.S. Panel

DR. CHESTER R. BENJAMIN, *Chairman*
Department of Agriculture
DR. JOHN T. GRAIKOSKI
Department of the Interior
DR. CLIFFORD W. HESSELTINE, *Alternate Chairman*
Department of Agriculture
DR. CARL LAMANNA
Department of the Army
DR. KEITH H. LEWIS
Department of Health, Education, and Welfare
DR. JOSEPH C. OLSON
Department of Health, Education, and Welfare
DR. HARRY W. SCHROEDER
Department of Agriculture
DR. EUGENE M. SPORN
Department of the Army

UJNR PROGRAM COORDINATORS

Japan

MR. HIROSHI ANDO
Chief, International Affairs Section, Promotion Bureau, Science and Technology Agency

United States

DR. JAMES A. SLATER,
International Activities Assistant
Office of the Under Secretary
U.S. Department of the Interior

UNIVERSITY OF HAWAII
COMMITTEE FOR LOCAL ARRANGEMENTS

THEODORE BELL, Ph.D., School of Public Health, *Chairman of Committee*
RICHARD BARBER, *Associate Program Officer*, East-West Center
MENDEL HERZBERG, Ph.D., Department of Microbiology, *Editor of the Proceedings*
KINGSTON WILCOX, Ph.D., State Health Department
ROBERT WORTH, M.D., Ph.D., School of Public Health

UJNR CONFERENCE ON TOXIC MICRO-ORGANISMS

LIST OF PARTICIPANTS

Dr. K. Aibara
Department of Food Research
National Institute of Health
10–35, 2-chome Kamiosaki
Shinagawa-ku, Tokyo, Japan

Dr. K. Amano
Tokai Regional Fisheries Research Laboratory
5–5 Kachidoki, Chuo-ku
Tokyo, Japan

Dr. A. W. Anderson
Department of Microbiology
Oregon State University
Corvallis, Oreg. 97331

Dr. Y. Ando
Hokkaido Institute of Public Health
South 2, West 15, Sapporo, Japan

Mr. A. Anellis
Food Division
U.S. Army Natick Laboratories
Natick, Mass. 01762

Dr. R. Angelotti
National Center for Urban and Industrial Health
222 E. Central Parkway
Cincinnati, Ohio 45202

Dr. C. R. Benjamin
Crops Research Division, ARS, USDA
Plant Industry Station
Beltsville, Maryland 20705

Dr. R. F. Brown
Microbiology Division
Food and Drug Administration
Washington, D.C. 20204

Dr. A. D. Campbell
Food and Drug Administration
200 "C" St. S.W.
Washington, D.C. 20204

Dr. W. W. Carlton
Department of Veterinary Medicine
Lynn Hall, Purdue University
Lafayette, Ind. 47907

Dr. N. Davis
Department of Botany
and Plant Pathology
Agricultural Experiment Station
Auburn University
Auburn, Ala. 36830

Dr. V. R. Dowell, Jr.
National Communicable Disease Center
Atlanta, Georgia 30333

Dr. M. W. Eklund
18727 35th Street, N.E.
Seattle, Washington 98155

Dr. H. El-Bisi
Food Division
U.S. Army Natick Laboratories
Natick, Massachusetts 01762

Dr. L. A. Goldblatt
Oilseed Crops Laboratory
Southern Utilization Research & Development
   Division, ARS, USDA
1100 Robert E. Lee Boulevard
New Orleans, Louisiana 70119

Dr. J. T. Graikoski
Bureau of Commercial Fisheries
1451 Green Road, Box 640
Ann Arbor, Mich. 48107

Dr. C. W. Hesseltine
Fermentation Laboratory
Northern Utilization Research & Development
   Division, ARS, USDA
1815 North University Street,
Peoria, Ill. 61604

Dr. H. Hiroki
Department of Bacteriology
Nihon Dental College
9–20, 1-chome Fujimi-cho
Chiyoda-ku, Tokyo, Japan

Dr. L. V. Holdeman
Department of Veterinary Science
Virginia Polytechnic Institute
Blacksburg, Va. 24061

484

Dr. R. W. Howell
  Oilseed and Industrial Crops
    Research Branch
  Crops Research Division, ARS, USDA
  Plant Industry Station
  Beltsville, Md.   20705

Dr. M. Ichinoe
  National Institute of Hygienic Sciences
  203, 2-chome Tamagawa-yoga
  Setagaya-ku, Tokyo, Japan

Dr. H. Iida
  Hokkaido Institute of Public Health
  South 2, West 15
  Sapporo, Japan

Dr. K. Inoue
  Hokkaido Institute of Public Health
  South 2, West 15
  Sapporo, Japan

Dr. G. W. Irving, Jr.
  Agricultural Research Service, Building A
    U.S. Department of Agriculture
  Washington, D.C. 20250

Mr. K. Ito
  National Canners Association
  1950 Sixth St.
  Berkeley, Calif. 94710

Dr. W. I. Jensen
  Bear River Research Station
  P.O. Box 459
  Brigham City, Utah 84302

Dr. H. M. Johnson
  Food Protection Research Laboratory
  National Center for Urban and Industrial Health
  4676 Columbia Parkway
  Cincinnati, Ohio 45226

Dr. K. Kanota
  National Institute of Hygienic Sciences
  203, 2-chome Tamagawa-yoga
  Setagaya-ku, Tokyo, Japan

Dr. D. A. Kautter
  Division of Microbiology
  Food and Drug Administration
  Washington, D.C. 20204

Dr. A. C. Keyl
  Western Utilization Research and Development
  Division, ARS, USDA
  600 Buchanan Street
  Albany, Calif. 94706

Dr. E. Kodama
  Akita Prefectural Institute of Hygienic Sciences
  1–40 Chiaki Meitoku-cho
  Akita-shi, Japan

Dr. H. Kurata
  National Institute of Hygienic Sciences
  203, 2-chome Tamagawa-yoga
  Setagaya-ku, Tokyo, Japan

Dr. C. Lamanna
  Army Research Office
  3045 Columbia Pike
  Arlington, Va. 22204

Dr. R. V. Lechowich
  Department of Food Science
  Michigan State University
  East Lansing, Michigan 48823

Dr. K. H. Lewis
  National Center for Urban and Industrial Health
  222 East Central Parkway
  Cincinnati, Ohio 45202

Dr. S. Matsuura
  Food Research Institute
  Ministry of Agriculture and Forestry
  2-Hamazono-cho, Fukagawa-ku
  Tokyo, Japan

Dr. G. M. Milne, Jr.
  Department of Chemistry
  MIT 2-315
  Cambridge, Mass. 02139

Dr. T. Miura
  Department of Food Research
  National Institute of Health
  10–35, 2-chome, Kamiosaki
  Shinagawa-ku, Tokyo, Japan

Dr. S. Morooka
  National Institute of Health
  Department of Food Research
  10–35, 2-chome Kamiosaki
  Shinagawa-ku, Tokyo, Japan

Dr. H. Murakami
  Research Institute of Brewing
  Tax Administration Agency
  2–6 Takinogawa, Kita-ku
  Tokyo, Japan

Dr. W. Nakano
  Iwate Institute of Public Health
  1–15 Kaminohshi-cho
  Morioka, Japan

Dr. K. Okubo
Nippon Veterinary and Zootechnical College
1–7–1, Kyonan-Cho
Musashino-City
Tokyo, Japan

Dr. J. C. Olson
Division of Microbiology
Food and Drug Administration
Washington, D.C. 20204

Dr. M. Saito
Institute of Medical Science
Tokyo University
Shiba Shrokenedai-machi
Minato-ku, Tokyo, Japan

Dr. G. Sakaguchi
Department of Food Research
National Institute of Health
10–35, 2-chome Kamiosaki
Shinagawa-ku, Tokyo, Japan

Dr. M. Sasaki
Central Research Institute of Kikkoman Shoyu
Co. Ltd.
399 Noda, Noda-shi
Chiba-ken, Japan

Dr. H. W. Schroeder
Field Crops and Animal Products Branch
Market Quality Research Division, ARS, USDA
P.O. Box ED
College Station, Tex. 77840

Dr. W. P. Segner
Continental Can Co., Inc.
1350 West 76th Street
Chicago, Ill. 60620

Dr. G. Semeniuk
Plant Pathology Department
South Dakota State University
Brookings, S. Dak. 57006

Dr. J. A. Slater
Office of the Under Secretary
U.S. Department of the Interior
Washington, D.C. 20204

Dr. E. B. Smalley
Department of Plant Pathology
University of Wisconsin
1450 Linden Drive
Madison, Wis. 53706

Dr. E. M. Sporn
Army Research Office
3045 Columbia Pike
Arlington, Virginia 22204

Dr. H. Sugiyama
Food Research Institute
119 Bacteriology
University of Wisconsin
Madison, Wis. 53706

Dr. K. Terao
Chiba University
Izuni-cho, Narashino-shi
Chiba-ken, Japan

Dr. H. Tsunoda
Food Research Institute
Ministry of Agriculture and Forestry
2-Hamazono-cho, Fukagawa-ku
Tokyo, Japan

Dr. S. Udagawa
National Institute of Hygienic Sciences
203, 2-chome Tamagawa-yoga
Setagaya-ku, Tokyo, Japan

Dr. Y. Ueno
Science University of Tokyo
12 Funagawara-cho
Ichigaya, Shinjuku-ku
Tokyo, Japan

Dr. B. Q. Ward
Institute of Marine Sciences
10 Rickenbacker Causeway
Miami, Fla. 33149

Dr. K. Yamamoto
Department of Bacteriology,
Hirosaki University
Hirosaki-shi, Aomori-ken
Tokyo, Japan

Dr. T. Yokotsuka
Central Research Institute of Kikkoman Shoyu Co.,
Ltd.
399 Noda, Noda-shi
Chiba-ken, Japan

LIST OF AUTHORS NOT PARTICIPATING

Dr. R. W. Armstrong
Stanford University Hospital
Palo Alto, Calif.

Dr. T. Asahi
Institute for Biochemistry
Faculty of Agriculture
Nagoya University
Chikusa-ku
Nagoya, Japan

Dr. H. Asano
Department of Bacteriology
Faculty of Medicine of the Hirosaki University
Hirosaki, Japan

Dr. Y. Asao
Central Research Institute of Kikkoman Shoyu
    Co., Ltd.
399 Noda, Noda-shi
Chiba-ken, Japan

Dr. J. R. Bamberg
University of Wisconsin
Madison, Wis. 53706

Dr. M. Biollaz
Department of Chemistry
Massachusetts Institute of Technology
Cambridge, Mass. 02139

Dr. C. W. Bohrer
National Canners Association
Research Laboratory
Washington, D.C.

Dr. A. N. Booth
Western Regional Research Laboratory
Agricultural Research Service
U.S. Department of Agriculture
Albany, Calif. 94710

Dr. T. L. Bott
University of Wisconsin
Madison, Wis. 53706

Dr. E. W. Bowman
U.S. Bureau of Commercial Fisheries
Ann Arbor, Mich. 48107

Dr. K. Brenner
Department of Health, Education and Welfare
U.S. Public Health Service
National Center for Urban and Industrial Health
Environmental Sanitation Program
Cincinnati, Ohio 45202

Dr. J. B. Brooks
National Communicable Disease Center
Atlanta, Ga.

Dr. M. K. Bruch
National Canners Association
Research Laboratory
Washington, D.C.

Dr. G. Buchi
Department of Chemistry
Massachusetts Institute of Technology
Cambridge, Mass. 02139

Dr. C. W. Carlson
South Dakota State University
Brookings, S. Dak. 57006

Dr. C. B. Denny
National Canners Association
Research Laboratory
Washington, D.C.

Dr. L. Diener
Botany and Plant Pathology Department
Auburn University Agricultural Experiment Station
Auburn, Ala.

Dr. J. J. Ellis
Northern Regional Research Laboratory
ARS, USDA
Peoria, Ill. 61604

Dr. E. M. Foster
University of Wisconsin
Madison, Wis. 53706

Dr. W. E. Gagne
Syntex Laboratories
Palo Alto, Calif.

Dr. E. J. Gangarosa
National Communicable Disease Center
Atlanta, Ga. 30333

Dr. M. R. Gumbmann
Western Regional Research Laboratory
Agricultural Research Service
U.S. Department of Agriculture
Albany, Calif. 94710

Dr. H. E. Hall
Department of Health, Education and Welfare
U.S. Public Health Service
National Center for Urban and Industrial Health,
    Environmental Sanitation Program
Cincinnati, Ohio 45202

Dr. S. M. Harmon
Division of Microbiology
Food and Drug Administration
Washington, D.C. 20204

Dr. G. S. Harshfield
South Dakota State University
Brookings, S. Dak. 57006

Dr. Y. Horiuchi
Department of Bacteriology
Faculty of Medicine of the Hirosaki University
Hirosaki, Japan

Dr. M. Hosoya
Microbial Chemistry, Faculty of Pharmaceutical
    Sciences
Science University of Tokyo
Ichigaya, Tokyo, Japan

Dr. K. Kagota
Hokkaido Livestock
Experiments Station
Takikawa, Hokkaido, Japan

Dr. K. Kanzawa
Hokkaido Institute of Public Health
South 2, West 15, Sapporo
Hokkaido, Japan

Dr. T. Karashimada
Hokkaido Institute of Public Health
South 2, West 15, Sapporo
Hokkaido, Japan

Dr. K. Kasai
Department of Bacteriology,
Faculty of Medicine of the Hirosaki University
Hirosaki, Japan

Dr. R. A. Koch
U.S. Bureau of Commercial Fisheries
Ann Arbor, Mich. 48107

Dr. H. Kondo
National Institute of Health
Department of Microbiology II
10–35, 2-chome, Kamiosaki
Shinagawa-ku, Tokyo, Japan

Dr. S. Kondo
Department of Bacteriology II
National Institute of Health
Shinagawa-ku, Tokyo, Japan

Dr. T. Koshida
Department of Bacteriology
Faculty of Medicine of the Hirosaki University
Hirosaki, Japan

Dr. N. R. Kosuri
University of Wisconsin
Madison, Wis. 53706

Dr. H. Kudo
Department of Bacteriology
Faculty of Medicine of the Hirosaki University
Hirosaki, Japan

Dr. W. F. Kwolek
Northern Regional Research Laboratory
ARS, USDA
Peoria, Ill. 61604

Dr. T. Lilly, Jr.
Division of Microbiology
Food and Drug Administration
Washington, D.C. 20204

Dr. R. K. Lynt, Jr.
Division of Microbiology
Food and Drug Administration
Washington, D.C. 20204

Dr. R. Majima
Institute for Biochemical Regulation and Labora-
    tory of Biochemistry
Faculty of Agriculture
Nagoya University, Chikusa-ku
Nagoya, Japan

Dr. M. Manabe
Food Research Institute
Ministry of Agriculture and Forestry
2-Hamazono-cho, Fukagawa-ku
Tokyo, Japan

Dr. W. F. O. Marasas
University of Wisconsin
Madison, Wis. 53706

Dr. M. S. Masri
Western Regional Research Laboratory
Agricultural Research Service
U.S. Department of Agriculture
Albany, Calif. 94710

Dr. J. M. Micuda
Bureau of Sport Fisheries and Wildlife
Bear River Research Station
Brigham City, Utah 84302

Dr. P. Mislivec
Department of Botany and Plant Pathology
School of Agriculture
Purdue University
Lafayette, Ind. 47907

Dr. K. Miyaki
National Institute of Health
10–35, 2-chome, Kamiosaki
Shinagawa-ku, Tokyo, Japan

Dr. Z. Mori
  Institute for Biochemical
  Regulation and Laboratory of Biochemistry
  Faculty of Agriculture
  Nagoya University, Chikusa-ku
  Nagoya, Japan

Dr. R. Murata
  Department of Bacteriology II
  National Institute of Health
  10–35, 2-chome Kamiosaki
  Shinagawa-ku, Tokyo, Japan

Dr. S. Nabeya
  Department of Bacteriology
  Faculty of Medicine of the Hirosaki University
  Hirosaki, Japan

Dr. R. E. Nichols
  Department of Veterinary Science
  College of Agriculture
  University of Wisconsin
  Madison, Wis. 53706

Dr. G. J. Niedermeyer
  Oregon State University
  Department of Microbiology
  Corvallis, Oreg. 97331

Dr. T. Ono
  Hokkaido Institute of Public Health
  South 2, West 15, Sapporo, Japan

Dr. K. Oshita
  Central Research Institute of Kikkoman Shoyu
    Co., Ltd.
  399 Noda, Noda-shi
  Chiba-ken, Japan

Mr. F. T. Poysky
  U.S. Bureau of Commercial Fisheries
  Technological Laboratory
  Seattle, Wash. 98102

Dr. R. A. Robohm
  U.S. Bureau of Commercial Fisheries
  Ann Arbor, Mich. 48107

Dr. D. B. Rowley
  Microbiology Division Food Laboratory
  U.S. Army
  Natick, Laboratories
  Natick, Mass. 01760

Dr. S. Sakaguchi
  Department of Food Research
  National Institute of Health
  Shinagawa-ku, Tokyo, Japan

Dr. Tomataro Sato
  Food Research Institute
  Ministry of Agriculture and Forestry
  1–4, Shiohama, Koto-ku
  Tokyo, Japan

Dr. Tsutomu Sato
  Department of Bacteriology
  Faculty of Medicine Hirosaki University
  Hirosaki, Japan

Dr. C. F. Schmidt
  Metal Division Research and Development
  Continental Can Co., Inc.
  Chicago, Ill. 60620

Dr. M. L. Seeger
  National Canners Association
  Western Research Laboratory
  Berkeley, Calif.

Dr. G. Shannon
  Northern Regional Research Laboratory
  ARS, USDA
  Peoria, Ill. 61604

Dr. M. F. Sheff
  The Ayer Clinical Laboratory and Neurochemistry
    Department
  Pennsylvania Hospital
  Philadelphia, Pa.

Dr. L. Shotwell
  Northern Regional Research Laboratory
  ARS, USDA
  Peoria, Ill. 61604

Dr. B. G. Smith
  Department of Health, Education and Welfare
  U.S. Public Health Service
  National Center for Urban and Industrial Health
  Environmental Sanitation Program
  Cincinnati, Ohio 45202

Dr. M. Smith
  Northern Regional Research Laboratory
  ARS, USDA
  Peoria, Ill. 61604

Dr. O. P. Snyder
  Microbiology Division Food Laboratory
  U.S. Army
  Natick Laboratories
  Natick, Mass.

Dr. H. M. Solomon
  Division of Microbiology
  Food and Drug Administration
  Washington, D.C. 20204

Dr. F. M. Strong
Department of Biochemistry
University of Wisconsin
Madison, Wis. 53706

Dr. M. Suzuki
Research Institute of Brewing
Tax Administration Agency
2–6 Takinogawa, Kita-ku
Tokyo, Japan

Dr. T. Suzuki
National Institute of Hygienic Sciences
Kamiyoga 1-chome
Setagaya, Tokyo, Japan

Dr. H. Tanabe
National Institute of Hygienic Sciences
203, 2-chome Tamagawa-yoga
Setagaya-ku, Tokyo, Japan

Dr. T. Tatsuno
Institute of Physical and Chemical Research
Yamato-Machi
Saitama-ken, Japan

Dr. J. Tuite
Department of Botany and Plant Pathology
School of Agriculture
Purdue University
Lafayette, Ind. 47907

Dr. I. Uritani
Department of Agricultural Chemistry
Faculty of Agriculture
Chikusa, Nagoya, Japan

Dr. E. Vandergraft
ARS, USDA
Northern Regional Research Laboratory
Peoria, Ill. 61604

Dr. S. Yamagishi
National Institute of Health and University of Chiba
Chiba-ken, Japan

Dr. H. Yoshikura
Department of Food Research and Department of Pathology
National Institute of Health
Tokyo, Japan

Dr. S. I. Zacks
Pennsylvania Hospital
Eighth and Spruce Street
Philadelphia, Pa. 19139